At the time of his death in 1928, Alexander A. Maximow left an unfinished manuscript of a Textbook of Histology. This was completed and edited by William Bloom with the help of some of his colleagues, especially the late C. Judson Herrick.

Extensively revised editions appeared in 1934, 1938, 1942, 1948, 1952, 1957, and 1962. There have been several translations of the work, principally four in Spanish.

All of the editions profited by criticisms and contributions of material by many histologists. With the passing years, most of the original work and early changes have been modified or eliminated in successive revisions as points of view changed and new discoveries were made. However, unchanged are some parts of the material contributed by George W. Bartelmez on the female reproductive system, Clayton G. Loosli on the lung, J. Walter Wilson on the liver, Edward A. Boyden on the gallbladder and biliary ducts, and W. H. Taliafero on the spleen.

In the eighth edition, Don W. Fawcett joined William Bloom as coauthor of the book and has contributed a progressively larger share of the work as it is presented herewith in its ninth edition.

A Textbook of

HISTOLOGY

WILLIAM BLOOM, M.D.
CHARLES H. SWIFT DISTINGUISHED SERVICE PROFESSOR
EMERITUS OF ANATOMY, THE UNIVERSITY OF CHICAGO

DON W. FAWCETT, M.D.
HERSEY PROFESSOR OF ANATOMY,
HARVARD MEDICAL SCHOOL

Ninth Edition

W. B. SAUNDERS COMPANY

Philadelphia — London — Toronto

W. B. Saunders Company: West Washington Square
Philadelphia, Pa. 19105

12 Dyott Street
London W.C.1

1835 Yonge Street
Toronto 7, Ontario

Reprinted May, 1968

A Textbook of Histology

Preface

The ninth edition of our Textbook of Histology follows the eighth after five years of rapid progress in the continuing exploration of the structure and function of the tissues and organs. The authors acknowledge that the privilege of teaching, the fascination of research and the burden of administration may have left too little time to keep abreast with the rising tide of scientific literature in all areas of microscopic anatomy. However, in this edition changes have been more extensive than in revisions of the recent past, and we believe that very substantial progress has been made in updating the text by incorporating many new discoveries that have been accorded general acceptance. In the present revision, a number of chapters have been completely rewritten to improve coherence and clarity. In others, errors and outmoded interpretations have been eliminated and new material incorporated short of complete revision.

The material of the first chapter of earlier editions has been expanded and divided into two chapters. The first presents a brief account of the principal methods now used for the analysis of biological structure, and the second is devoted to a description of the cell and its organelles, together with a consideration of cell division. A separate chapter on Adipose Tissue has been included in recognition of the large volume of recent work emphasizing the continual activity and importance of this tissue in metabolism. The chapter on Muscular Tissue has been completely rewritten to encompass the rapid advances in our understanding of the fine structural components of muscle and of the mechanism of its contraction and excitation-contraction coupling. The section on the Liver has been extensively revised to include new information on the function of its organelles, particularly the role of the smooth surfaced endoplasmic reticulum in cholesterol synthesis, hydroxylation of steroids, and metabolism of drugs. The chapter on Glands and Secretion has been brought up to date by inclusion of new findings from morphology and biochemistry bearing upon the structural basis for protein synthesis and upon the intracellular pathways and the mechanisms of release of the secretory products. As a result of the recent widespread realization that lymphocytes can turn into other cell types that play important roles in the local and generalized defense mechanisms of the body, the chapters on Blood, Blood Cell Formation, and Thymus have been partially rewritten to describe some of the new experimental evidence and interpretations in this rapidly changing field of research. The Male Reproductive System was redone with more detailed treatment of the structure of the spermatozoon, and of spermatogenesis, including the contributions of electron microscopic studies and the recent description of the stages of the cycle of the seminiferous epithelium of man. In the several chapters on the endocrine glands, the current concepts of their histophysiology have been included, and new evidence is presented relating the hormones to specific cell types.

Many changes in this edition have been effected through extensive contributions of colleagues. We are greatly indebted to Dr. Jay Angevine for rewriting the chapter on the Nervous System. The extensive revision of the chapter on the Ear is, in large measure, the work of Dr. David Hamilton. Dr. George Szabo made a major contribution to the writing of the chaper on the Skin. Dr. Douglas Kelly wrote most of the chapter on the Pineal Gland, and Dr. Franklin McLean furnished much of the new material for the chapter on Bone, which has been largely rewritten.

In a textbook of histology, illustrations of good quality can be as valuable a resource for learning as the text. In the present edition, many unsatisfactory old figures have been eliminated and 380 new figures have been added, bringing the total number of illustrations to 820. In selecting the illustrative material we have tried to maintain a reasonable balance between light and electron microscopy. It is evident that many of the major advances in histology and histopathology in the coming decade will be made with the electron microscope. Future scientists and physicians must therefore have some experience as students in the interpretation of electron micrographs if they are to be able, in later years, to read the literature of biology and medicine with understanding and discrimination. At the same time we are sensitive to the opinion of many experienced teachers that the number of electron micrographs in the book should not be increased to the neglect of light microscopy, which continues to be the dominant concern of courses in histology. Accordingly, 156 of the new figures are photomicrographs, 159 are electron micrographs, and 65 are drawings or diagrams. It was not always practical to place figures in juxtaposition to the pertinent text, but we have used frequent references to figures to achieve a better integration of the illustrations with the text. Wherever possible in the labeling of the figures, abbreviations have been eliminated and the identifying terms have been spelled out on the figure. We believe this change will provide a welcome saving of the time and inconvenience involved in repeatedly referring from the picture to the legend to find the abbreviations defined. The nearly 1600 selected references at the ends of the chapters may be helpful to teachers and graduate students who wish to pursue particular subjects in greater depth.

In earlier editions, the subsections on histogenesis, blood supply, innervation of the organs, and other matters not of primary concern to beginning students, were set in smaller type. Where such sections have been retained in this edition, they have been set in the same type as the rest of the text. This change has contributed to the increased length of the book and may be criticized, but there were offsetting advantages in discontinuation of the second size of type.

Although this text has never attempted to be encyclopedic, it has striven to cover the subject in some depth. It is our hope that there will continue to be a demand for such a book, although we recognize that even a modest increase in its length is not in keeping with the current trend represented in the development of core curricula in the medical schools of this country.

All books of broad scope depend in many particulars upon the special knowledge, suggestions and help of interested teachers and associates. We have had advice and helpful criticism from Dr. Matthew Block on the blood and myeloid tissue, from Dr. J. Walter Wilson on the liver, and from Dr. E. W. Taylor on the cell and mitosis. Dr. E. P. Geiduschek inserted a few changes in his discussion on the chemical composition of protoplasm. Dr. H. S. Kaplan revised his remarks on the thymus and leukemia. Dr. R. B. Uretz made several changes in the section on principles of microscopic analysis which he contributed to the previous edition. Dr. Ian Monie and Dr. Steven Wissig kindly made available to us the excellent set of histological slides loaned to students at the University of California, San Francisco. This material was the source of a number of the photomicrographs. The many investigators in this country and abroad who have generously given permission to reproduce illustrations are credited in the legends. We are indebted to Mrs. Sylvia Colard Keene for most of the new drawings and diagrams and to Mrs. Esther Bohlman Patterson for redrawing two of the old figures. We are particularly appreciative of the patience and skill of Miss Judith Drummond and Miss Helen Deacon who typed most of the manuscript. And finally, we express our sincere appreciation to the staff of the W. B. Saunders Company for their interest in providing fine reproduction of the illustrations and for their generosity and cooperation in all other aspects of production of the book.

We look forward now to the tenth edition and hope that in the meantime we will continue to receive the constructive criticism of students and teachers, so that the book will be further improved in accuracy and clarity of exposition.

WILLIAM BLOOM

DON W. FAWCETT

Contents

CHAPTER ONE

Methods of Histology and Cytology

Anatomy is the branch of science that is concerned with the external form and internal organization of plants and animals. It has as its major aims a thorough understanding of the underlying architectural principles on which living organisms are constructed, the discovery of the structural basis for the functioning of the various parts, and a comprehension of the mechanisms responsible for the development of their complex structure. It is customary to subdivide the broad field of anatomy into several parts based upon the method by which the structures are revealed or the size of the subunits studied. Thus *gross anatomy* encompasses all those features accessible to dissection and direct inspection, and *microscopic anatomy* or *histology* includes those minute parts beyond the reach of the naked eye.

The systematic study of the gross structure of the body is the oldest of the sciences basic to medicine, extending back at least to the second century. The investigation of its infinitely small components had to await the development of optical methods and is of relatively recent origin. Significant microscopic observations were recorded by Leeuwenhoek, Hooke, and others in the seventeenth century, but histology did not acquire the status of a separate branch of science until the accumulated observations of the eighteenth and nineteenth centuries led to the enunciation by Schleiden and Schwann of the *cell theory*—the most important generalization in the science of morphology. It held that cells are potentially independent organisms and that entire plants and animals are aggregations of these living units arranged according to definite laws. To this basic generalization was soon added the concept that all cells originate from pre-existing cells by a process of division in which the nucleus divides into two that are precise replicas of the original nucleus. These principles are the foundations upon which much of modern biology and medicine has been built.

The progress of any branch of science is seldom uniform. Introduction of a new instrument or a new technique initiates a period of rapid advance. Then after a phase of vigorous exploitation, progress slows as the application of existing methods gradually comes to yield diminishing returns of new information. A new period of rapid advance must often await the discovery of a novel approach or the development of a new instrument. Such has been the history of microscopic anatomy. The grinding of improved lenses by Amici in 1827 led directly to the development of the well corrected compound microscopes that made possible the recognition of the cell as the basic unit of living matter. The ensuing classical period of descriptive *histology* and *cytology* established the normal structure of tissues and cells and provided information essential to the development of the allied field of *histopathology*, which had its origins in Virchow's enunciation of the concept that the fundamental changes in human disease can be traced to alterations in cells. Few discoveries have had such a far-reaching influence on the development of scientific medicine, but in time, the pace of

1

new discovery in both histology and pathology slackened. A little over a hundred years after the perfection of the compound microscope, the first electron microscope was built in 1932 by Knoll and Ruska. The modern instruments constructed on the same principle have extended the limits of resolvable tissue structure more than a hundredfold and have opened up for the microscopist a vast area of biological structure that was previously inaccessible. As a consequence, histology is again in a period of rapid advance. The numerous discoveries are leading to entirely new concepts of the structural organization and function of cells and subcellular components.

Important as the microscope is in this branch of science, it is but one of the means by which knowledge is gained. With each major forward step in optical instrumentation, numerous ancillary techniques have been developed that extend the range of its usefulness, sharpen its resolution, and offer the possibility of more accurate and penetrating analysis of biological structure. The student can scarcely hope to acquire a useful knowledge of the substantive content of histology and cytology without an understanding of the principles of microscopic analysis (p. 20) and the other instrumental, observational, and experimental methods by which new information is obtained in this field. This chapter is therefore presented early in the book, so that the student of histology will have some understanding of the principles underlying the various methods that will be referred to again and again throughout the remainder of the book.

METHODS FOR DIRECT OBSERVATION OF LIVING TISSUES AND CELLS

Much of histology is, of necessity, based upon the examination of samples of tissues that have been killed and preserved, but the primary objective of their study is to discover structural relationships that will contribute to an understanding of the vital processes of the *living* organism. It is one of the paradoxes of biology that we often destroy at the outset the very property we most desire to understand. Someone has aptly phrased the problem in a simile: "the quality of being *alive* is like the snowflake on the window pane that vanishes at the warm touch of an inquisitive child."

There is, however, a growing list of methods for the study of living tissues—some rela-

tively crude, others quite refined, but all of them yielding information of a kind that cannot be obtained from dead tissues alone.

EXTERIORIZATION AND TRANSILLUMINA-TION OF ORGANS. Some organs have a long vascular pedicle and are sufficiently mobile that they can be brought out of the body cavity of the anesthetized animal and can be maintained in a moist chamber under conditions that permit their transillumination and direct microscopic examination at relatively low power. The smallest laboratory animals have naturally been most useful for this approach because their thinner tissues lend themselves better to transillumination. By this simple procedure valuable observations have been made on the dynamics of the circulation of various organs (Knisely). The release of secretory material from the pancreatic cells under the influence of various pharmacological agents has been observed (Covell), and the ovaries of rats have been brought out into a perfusion chamber and the process of ovulation

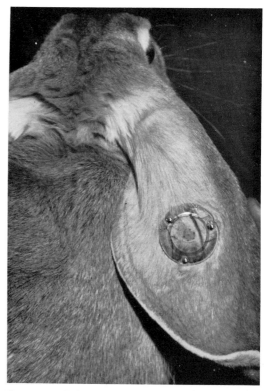

Figure 1-1. Rabbit with a transparent chamber in its ear. This strain of rabbits has unusually large ears that are especially favorable for this purpose. (Courtesy of J. Irwin.)

and passage of the ova into the oviduct have been recorded cinematographically (Blandau).

In the applications of this approach, the investigator is usually severely limited in the duration of observation and in the magnification that can be employed. There have been numerous efforts, therefore, to create indwelling windows or chambers that will permit prolonged and repeated observations of tissues over a period of days or even months.

TRANSPARENT CHAMBER METHODS. One of the most successful means of studying living tissues has involved the installation of chambers of metal and glass in the long flexible ears of rabbits (Figs. 1-1 and 1-2). The tissue to be studied is transplanted between the windows of the thin chamber, where it acquires a blood supply from the neighboring connective tissue and survives for long periods. For periodic examination, the rabbit is trained to rest quietly on the bench beside the microscope with its ear secured to the mechanical stage in such a way that the transparent chamber is centered over the condenser. With such chambers, important observations have been made on the growth of capillaries and nerves (Clark); the emigration of leukocytes from the blood vessels (Florey); the development of adipose cells, and many other histophysiological and developmental processes.

The anterior chamber of the eye is a naturally occurring transparent chamber. Small fragments of autologous tissue transplanted into the anterior chamber of the eye acquire a blood supply by ingrowth of capillaries from the corneoirideal angle. They are bathed in a physiological fluid, the aqueous humor, and can be observed with a microscope through the transparent cornea. Transplantation of tissue to the anterior chamber of the eye permits the investigator to assess the functional or developmental potentialities of a tissue when removed from its nerve supply and from the influence of neighboring tissues in its normal environment. It has been possible, for example, to transplant fertilized mouse ova to the anterior chamber and to demonstrate their capacity for growth and limited differentiation, independent of the specialized nutritional environment normally provided by the uterus (Fig. 1-4). Similarly, small pieces of the lining of the monkey uterus have been successfully transplanted to the monkey's eye for extended observation of cyclic changes. At the time of the

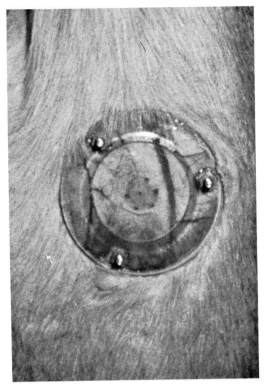

Figure 1-2. A close view of the ear chamber, with the vascular pattern showing through the transparent window. The three threaded studs on the rim are used to hold the chamber onto the stage of the microscope (Courtesy of J. Irwin.)

reproductive cycle when the female host was menstruating, the transplants of endometrium in her eye underwent similar changes and bled in the anterior chamber. Thus it was demonstrated by this experimental device that menstruation is under hormonal rather than nervous control. The transplants also permitted direct microscopic visualization of some of the vascular changes involved (Markee).

CELL AND ORGAN CULTURE. Tissue culture as an experimental procedure had its inception in the demonstration by Ross Harrison in 1907 that nerve fibers would grow out from fragments of frog spinal cord isolated in clotted lymph. Methods were later developed by Carrel, Warren Lewis and others for serial propagation of various kinds of cells in vitro. In the classical procedure, an explanted fragment of tissue is embedded in a coagulum of blood plasma containing embryo juice as a growth stimulant. Upon incubation the cells migrate radially from the explant and pro-

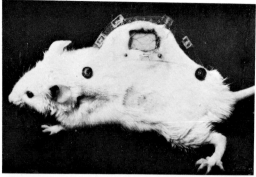

Figure 1-3. An economical transparent chamber for use in mice. A fold of loose dorsal skin and subcutaneous tissue is held in a plastic frame. For observation, the mouse is confined in a brass cylinder on the stage of the microscope (*lower*). The fin-like chamber projects through a slit in the cylinder and is centered over the condenser of the microscope. (After G. H. Algire and F. Y. Legallais, J. Nat. Cancer Inst., *10:*225, 1949.)

liferate in the zone of outgrowth to form a colony, which, in a few days, may be several times the diameter of the original fragment (Fig. 1–5). This may then be subdivided and used to initiate new colonies. The specialized structural features of the original organ are lost in the outgrowth in culture, and there is a simplification of cell form and organization such that the population tends to be reduced to one of three basic patterns of growth: isolated ameboid cells, sheets of flattened polygonal cells, or networks of stellate or fusiform cells. Using these classical methods of tissue culture, Carrel kept a line of cells derived from chick embryo heart in continuous cultivation for long periods. During the early period of experimentation with cultures, much was learned about the characteristics of isolated populations of living cells, but it is only recently

that rapid advances in technical methods have made it possible to realize the potential of isolated cell systems for experimental investigations of morphogenesis, malignant transformation, cytogenetic variation, cell-virus relations, cell nutrition, cell interactions, and a host of other interesting problems (Harris).

The classical clot-embedded explant procedures are now of historical interest only. Simplified and chemically defined culture media have now been developed (Parker). Methods have been devised for dissociation of organs to yield cell suspensions for the initiation of cultures in which the cells form a monolayer on the floor of the culture vessel. Some mammalian cells can now be grown in suspension in fluid medium (Gey; Earle). Procedures have been developed for isolation of clones from single cells, so that uniform populations of identical cells are available for experiment (Puck and Marcus). Cell populations can be preserved in the frozen state for long periods and retain their viability. These newer methods now make it possible to handle vertebrate somatic cells in much the same way as cultures of microorganisms. The earlier belief that the arrangement of cells in the pattern typical of the tissue of origin is essential for the expression of the specialized physiological capabilities of cells has now been found to be erroneous. Dispersed cultures of cartilage cells continue to elaborate matrix components, and similar cultures of adrenal cells continue to produce their hormones in vitro and respond to stimulation by tropic hormones. The availability of such systems opens the way to correlated structural and biochemical studies of biosynthetic pathways, metabolic control mechanisms, and the mechanism of action of hormones.

The short-term cultures of the white cells of the blood have come into widespread use as the simplest means of studying human chromosomes. Modified chromosomal types or departures from the normal number have been correlated with Mongolian idiocy and several other congenital disorders.

By altering the conditions of cultivation so as to discourage migration and dispersion of the cells, the original organ architecture can be retained. This method is called *organ culture*, and its principal value is that it provides a means of isolating an embryonic organ rudiment for the purpose of assessing its inherent capacity for growth and differentiation in the absence of the external influences that act upon it in the complex environment of the intact organism. An organ primordium from an embryo, when placed upon the surface of a plasma clot in a moist chamber, will often continue to grow for days or even weeks if transferred frequently to a fresh plasma substrate. Among the earliest contributions of this experimental approach was the demonstration that bone rudiments from early embryos would grow in length and undergo calcification outside of the body (Fell and Robison; Maximow). A recent improvement in the procedure involves placement of the primordium on a piece of lens paper floating on a liquid medium.

A

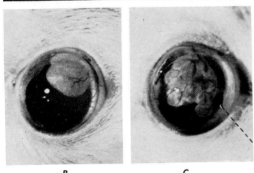

B   C

Figure 1-4. *A,* Photograph of a mouse that received a fertilized mouse ovum in the eight cell stage in the anterior chamber of the right eye 12 days earlier. The early stages of implantation and development in the corneo-iridial angle could be observed directly through the transparent cornea. (After D. W. Fawcett et al., Am. J. Anat., *81:*413, 1947.) *B,* Photograph of a rat ovary transplanted to the anterior chamber 10 days earlier. No follicles are visible yet. The vascular connections can be seen on the surface of the graft. × 5. *C,* Same animal 21 days after implantation. Many follicles are now present. One, indicated by the dotted line, is hemorrhagic. (After L. Goodman, Anat. Rec., *59:*223, 1934.)

There have been many ingenious applications of this and other modifications of organ culture, which enable the experimenter to control the composition of the environment and thus to influence or even to change the direction of differentiation of embryonic tissues. For example, organ cultures of embryonic chick skin, which normally differentiate feather buds, can be made to develop instead into mucus secreting cells by adding an excess of vitamin A to the culture medium.

Organized populations of neurons and their supporting glial cells from several regions of the brain have been maintained for months in vitro under conditions that permit experimental manipulation and direct visual evaluation of the results on the living cells (Murray). By the use of such simplified model systems it has been shown that blood serum from patients with multiple sclerosis, added to the culture medium, will produce structural and functional changes in vitro that stimulate the pathological changes characteristic of the disease in vivo (Bornstein).

Cell and tissue culture "affords an ethically acceptable means of experimentation on human tissues and provides an opportunity to isolate living units from the complex environment of the body and to expose them directly to various agents whose effects in vivo might be obscured or confused by irrelevant systemic responses" (Murray).

MECHANICAL MICROMANIPULATION. The exploration of living cells by microsurgery presents a number of intriguing technical problems. Cells are so small that they must be magnified 100 to 1000 times for the relevant structures to be clearly seen, and at the same time they must be maintained in a physiological environment. Cultures provide cells free of connective tissue and spread out on a glass surface, so that they are accessible to microsurgical procedures. By working glass in a microforge, extremely minute instruments are devised—microneedles, micropipettes, and microhooks. These are positioned within an operating chamber on the stage of the compound microscope by highly precise mechanical micromanipulators capable of achieving controlled movements in various planes (Chambers; Kopac).

Micromanipulation has been applied to a variety of fundamental problems in cell biol-

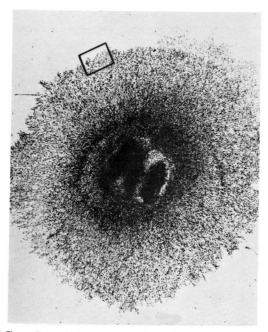

Figure 1-5. A photomicrograph of a tissue culture colony of fibroblasts from mouse subcutaneous tissue. The dense area in the center is the original explant and the broad halo around it represents the zone of outgrowth that has developed in four days of cultivation. × 14. The area indicated is shown at higher magnification in Figure 1-6.

ogy. Studies have been made of the elasticity and viscosity of protoplasm. The dependence of cell function upon the nucleus has been demonstrated by removal of the nucleus from an ameba. In the absence of the nucleus, synthetic activities were greatly impaired and locomotion ceased, but the anucleate ameba remained viable. Insertion of a nucleus into it restored its motility and other vital activities. This approach has also been used to demonstrate that materials pass from the nucleus into the cytoplasm. The nucleus of an ameba that had incorporated radioactive isotopes into its nucleoplasm was transferred to the cytoplasm of a normal ameba. By autoradiography it was shown that radioactivity introduced in the transplanted nucleus was later found in the surrounding cytoplasm. It is now possible to inject minute amounts of substances directly into the cytoplasm of fertilized mammalian eggs and to assess their effect upon subsequent development (Fig. 1-8). Microinjectors have been developed to handle volumes as small as 1 $\mu\mu$l (1/50,000,000 of a drop). Such ingenious and skillfully contrived mechanical devices for microsurgery are no longer the only means available for manipulating cell components.

USE OF RADIATION PROBES. The development of microbeams of protons and beams of ultraviolet light a few microns in diameter have made possible the selective irradiation of small areas of living cells. By the use of suitable microapertures, it is possible to get 80 per cent of the protons emitted to fall within a circle 2.5 μ in diameter (Zirkle and Bloom). With ultraviolet beams (Uretz), the smallest area is about a micron in diameter (Fig. 1-9). With the recent development of inexpensive lasers, microbeams of extremely intense, focused visible light are now available.

A probe of a very few microns in diameter is therefore small enough to irradiate parts of individual nuclei or segments of their chromosomes. This method has been used to study the dynamics of cell division. Localized irradiation of a small area of cytoplasm with protons caused no observable abnormality, but a similar irradiation with ultraviolet caused disappearance of spindle elements and disorder of the chromosomes. Segments of chromosomes in the path of the beam become distinctly paler (Figs. 1-10 and 1-11). By irradiating the region of attachment of spindle filaments to a single chromosome, it was shown that this chromosome lost all capacity for directed movements and simply drifted as a micronucleus. Thus, by irradiation it is possible to achieve the selective destruction of specific cell organelles and to assess its effect upon the cell as a whole (see review by Zirkle).

VITAL AND SUPRAVITAL STAINING. When certain dyes of relatively low toxicity are injected into living animals (*vital staining*) or applied to surviving cells and tissues removed from the body (*supravital staining*), they are taken up selectively by some cells, subcellular organelles, or extracellular components. The localization of the dye may either aid in identification of the stained component or provide insight into its function.

Alizarin, used as a vital dye, is taken up selectively by the calcifying matrix of bone that is being deposited at the time of administration of the dye. The newly deposited bone is colored red. This classical labeling procedure contributed greatly to our understanding of the mechanism of growth in length and girth of long bones.

Particulate vital dyes, such as trypan blue or lithium carmine, have been widely used to study the phenomenon of *phagocytosis,* a process whereby certain cell types are able to engulf particles from their environment and concentrate them in vacuoles within their cytoplasm. The method is useful for distinguishing certain cell types that are difficult to identify from morphological criteria alone.

The supravital dyes *neutral red* and *Janus green* have been widely used either singly or in combination in the study of blood leukocytes. Janus green selectively stains the mitochondria, while neutral red is concentrated in the specific granules of leukocytes, staining the granules of neutrophils light pink, those of eosinophils yellow, and basophilic granules brick red. Janus green has also proved useful in distinguishing mitochondria from other particles isolated from cell homogenates by differential centrifugation. Neutral red is now often used for the identification of lysosomes. Particularly useful in the study of the nervous system has been the ability to stain nerve cells

and their processes supravitally with methylene blue under certain conditions.

ISOLATION OF COMPONENTS OF LIVING CELLS BY DIFFERENTIAL CENTRIFUGATION

The function of the various cell organelles can seldom be deduced from morphological observations alone, and their significance was purely conjectural until it became possible to isolate them in bulk and in sufficient purity to permit their biochemical analysis. Although *differential centrifugation* has become one of the most valuable and widely used methods in biological chemistry, the method was first developed by the cytologists Bensley and Hoerr in 1934 to separate mitochondria from liver, and in 1937 Bensley made the first chemical analysis of mitochondria. The method was further developed some years later by Claude and by Hogeboom, Schneider and Palade.

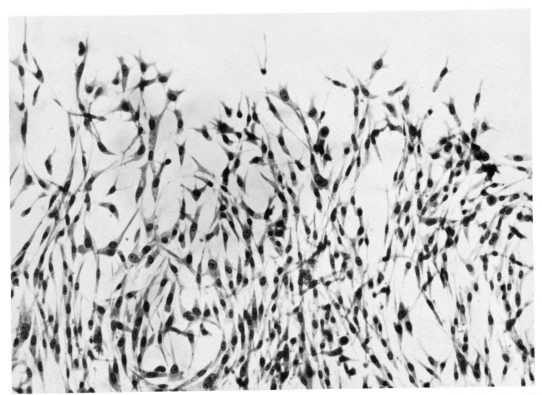

Figure 1-6. Photomicrograph of the edge of the zone of outgrowth of a colony of mouse fibroblasts (see Fig. 1-5). The cells in such a region are free of connective tissue fibers and favorable for observation in the living state, or in fixed and stained preparations such as this. Harris hematoxylin stain. × 260.

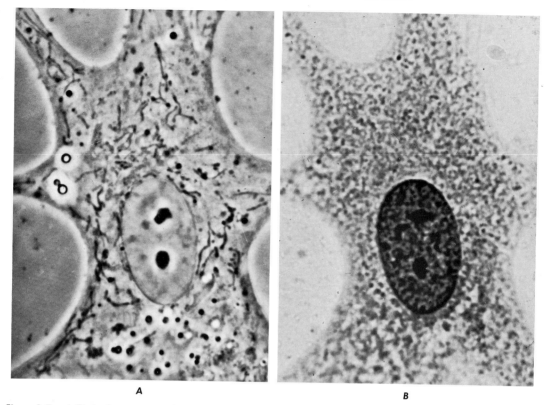

A   **B**

Figure 1-7. *A,* Dark phase contrast photomicrograph of a living fibroblast from a cell culture. Threadlike mitochondria and spherical lipid droplets are clearly visible in the cytoplasm. The cytoplasmic matrix shows little structure and the nucleoplasm is homogeneous except for two prominent nucleoli and a few small karyosomes. *B,* The same cell after fixation in alcohol and staining. The fixation has produced a coarse granular precipitation of the proteins of the cytoplasm and nucleus, and the organelles are no longer visible.

The cells are mechanically disrupted by grinding in glass homogenizers. The resulting homogenate, consisting of a highly heterogeneous suspension of the various cell organelles and inclusions, is layered onto a viscous solution of sucrose and centrifuged at high speed while being maintained at temperatures just above freezing. The heaviest particles are sedimented first, and particles of lower specific densities can be brought down by successive centrifugations at progressively higher speeds (Fig. 1-12). In the case of nuclei and mitochondria, a satisfactory identification and estimate of purity of the fraction can be obtained by examination of the sedimented material with the phase contrast microscope. In the case of microsomes and smaller particles, it is necessary to examine thin sections of the pellets with the electron microscope for morphological identification. Because certain compounds or enzymes have been found to be restricted to a single organelle, these characteristic substances

or activities can be used as biochemical markers for identification of centrifugal fractions. Thus deoxyribonucleic acid (DNA) is often used as the identifying marker for a nuclear fraction; succinoxidase or cytochrome oxidase for mitochondria; glucose-6-phosphatase for microsomes; acid phosphatase for lysosomes; and so on.

The newer method of *density gradient centrifugation* is now being widely used because of the improved resolving power of the method and the greater purity of the fractions obtained. The homogenate is layered on top of a stabilized gradient. Prolonged high speed centrifugation causes the particles to sediment only so far as their density permits. They come to rest when they reach a position in the gradient corresponding to their own density.

Centrifugal methods have made it possible to isolate reasonably pure fractions of nuclei, nucleoli, mitochondria, lysosomes, microsomes, ribosomes, pigment granules, and several types of secretory granules (Fig. 1-13). Much of what we know of the chemical composition and enzymatic activities of these cell components is the result of the application of these valuable methods.

PREPARATION AND EXAMINATION OF KILLED TISSUE

Although the histologist seeks to describe and to understand the structure of *living cells* and tissues, the usefulness of direct examination in the living condition is limited by the natural transparency of the tissues, which does not permit easy differentiation of their components, and by their considerable thickness, which interferes with their transillumination and results in a confusing superimposition of parts. It is usually necessary, therefore, to work with killed, chemically preserved tissues that have been cut into thin slices called *histological sections*. These lend themselves to study by transmitted light and can be stained with various dyes to increase the contrast of the tissue components, so that they can be more easily resolved and recognized with the light microscope. The ideal histological method would be one that would result in minimum deviation from the condition in the living state and yet permit maximum resolution of the various components. This goal is difficult to attain, and countless methods of preparing tissues have been developed that claim to approach this ideal more closely in one way or another.

Fixation

The first requirement for preservation of protoplasmic structure is to interrupt the dynamic processes of the cell as promptly as possible and to stabilize the structure with a minimum of change. The essence of the process of *fixation* is to render the structural components of cells insoluble, and this is accomplished by the use of various chemicals that precipitate the proteins and certain other classes of compounds. It should be borne in mind that in this process structures may be formed that had no precise counterpart in the cell before fixation. Gross distortions that have no basis in the structure of the living cell are referred to as *fixation artifacts*. The best fixatives are those that produce very finely grained precipitates.

In general, the more acid the fixative, the more coarsely clumped will be the nuclear material. Because this clumping results in a prominent pattern of chromatin after staining, fixatives producing this result because of their content of picric, acetic, or trichloracetic acid were formerly regarded as "good fixatives." This criterion is no longer accepted. Actually, preparations fixed with solutions containing neutral formalin, osmic acid, and mercuric chloride, singly or in combination, are among the best available for study with the optical microscope. These fixatives produce relatively little clumping of nuclear material and preserve an appearance very close to that of living cells viewed with the phase contrast microscope (Figs. 1-14 and 1-15).

To obtain histological sections that are sufficiently thin for satisfactory examination, it is necessary to infiltrate the tissue after fixation with a solution of gelatin, paraffin, celloidin, or other plastic material, which is later

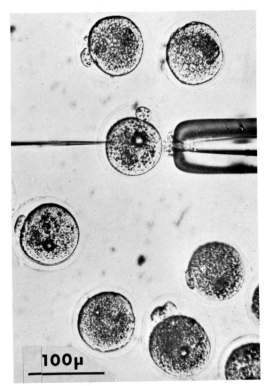

100μ

Figure 1-8. Photomicrograph of micromanipulation of mouse ova. The pipette at the right is used to hold the ovum while it is pierced by the micropipette at the left, from which a chemical agent is injected into the cytoplasm. (After T. P. Lin, Science, *151*:333, 1966.)

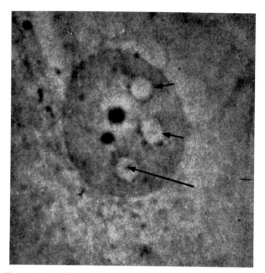

Figure 1-9.   Illustration of the potentialities of microbeam irradiation. Living mesothelial cell nucleus of Amblystoma in interphase. It was irradiated three times by the 3 μ beam of heterochromatic ultraviolet light with a Uretz microbeam. All three areas paled (arrows). In the lowest site of irradiation a bit of chromatin (long arrow) had not paled at the time the cell was photographed. The two dark central bodies are nucleoli.

solidified, so that the tissue and the embedding matrix may be sectioned together. The use of paraffin or celloidin requires that the tissue be dehydrated in organic solvents such as ethanol, which remove most of the lipids. Tissues embedded in paraffin may be sectioned rapidly, with a microtome, and may be cut at a thickness of 3 or 4 μ. Embedding with celloidin, which is used at room temperature, disturbs the arrangement of the cells less and causes less shrinkage than does the paraffin method, which exposes the tissues to the higher temperatures necessary to keep the wax molten during infiltration. However, infiltration with celloidin is a rather slow process, and sections cannot be cut as thin as those prepared by paraffin embedding.

To avoid the extraction of lipid and other constituents in the process of dehydration, sections of fresh or fixed tissue may also be cut with a freezing microtome after embedding in gelatin or without use of any embedding medium. The *frozen section* method has the additional advantage of great speed, and it is widely used for surgical biopsies to determine the benign or malignant nature of a lesion while the patient is still on the operating table. In the *freeze-drying method,* the tissue is frozen and then dehydrated at low temperature in a high

vacuum. If freezing is carried out with sufficient rapidity to minimize distortions due to ice crystal formation, many structural differences are observable between frozen-dried preparations and those treated with liquid fixatives. This method of dehydration does not render the proteins insoluble, so that additional reagents are required if specimens are to remain "fixed" in aqueous solutions. In the modification of this method, called *freeze-substitution,* the replacement of ice by alcohol or other solvents is carried out at very low temperatures.

Staining

The sections obtained by one of these preparative methods may then be stained by any of a great variety of combinations of dyes that color various tissue constituents more or less selectively. The study of fixed, sectioned, and stained tissue has long been the principal method of histological investigation, and to it we owe most of what we know now of the microscopic organization of the tissues and organs.

Because living cells are colorless and translucent or transparent, little of their inner structure can be seen without applying one or more biological stains or resorting to phase contrast microscopy (p. 22). The staining methods now in general use were, for the most part, developed empirically, on the basis of their capacity to increase the contrast of the tissue constituents and thus to enable the microscopist to resolve fine structural details. The colors were seldom meaningful as indicators of the chemical nature of the substances stained.

With the most commonly used staining method, *hematoxylin and eosin,* the nuclear structures are stained dark purple or blue, and practically all cytoplasmic structures and intercellular substances are stained varying shades of pink. Actually little else but the character of the nucleus and the extent of the cytoplasm can be seen with this method. To demonstrate other constituents of fixed cells, such as mitochondria, centrioles, and Golgi apparatus, special cytological staining methods must be used. A single staining method does not suffice to reveal all of the functionally significant components of cells that can be preserved by use of appropriate fixatives. Some of the striking differences in the effects of a few of the commonly used fixing and staining agents are shown in Figure 1-14, of cells from the small intestine of the guinea pig. It is seen that the nuclei appear to have a clearly defined membrane, a prominent body called the nucleolus, and darkly staining granules (chromatin) embedded in a pale ground substance. The cells fixed in neutral formalin and Zenker-formol show much the same structures, although the latter reveals more chromatin material. After treatment with absolute alcohol and two distinctly acid fixatives (Bouin and Zenker-acetic), nuclei have heavily clumped, prominent chromatin. This figure also shows the differences in the effect of these fixatives on mitochondria. These cellular constituents are seen with difficulty in the living cell viewed with bright field microscopy, but are obvious as blue rods and granules after supravital staining with Janus green. They are black in the cells stained with Heidenhain's iron-hematoxylin after fixation with neutral formalin or Zenker-formol, but are not visible with this stain after Bouin or Zenker-acetic fixation because the mitochondria are destroyed by these highly acid mixtures. Neither are they visible in cells stained with hematoxylin and eosin (H and E) after use of any of these fixatives.

At the extreme right of Figure 1-14 are three cells from the epithelium of guinea pig

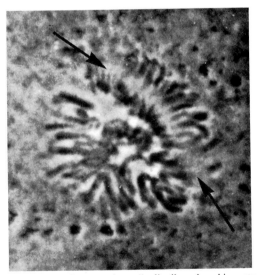

Figure 1-10. Arrows point to "paling" produced in metaphase chromosomes in a living mesothelium cell of Amblystoma by a 3 μ stripe of ultraviolet light from the Uretz microbeam. Such "paled" areas are Feulgen-negative. Phase contrast photomicrograph of living cell. × 880. (After Bloom and Özarslan Proc. Nat. Acad. Sci., *53:* 1294, 1965.)

small intestine, which was dehydrated in the frozen state and sectioned. The sections were then treated with alcohol and stained by the periodate-leukofuchsin method (periodic acid–Schiff or PAS reaction) for insoluble *carbohydrates* and by hematoxylin and eosin to reveal general cell structure. Inasmuch as the cells of the intestine change their shape greatly with the extensive movements of this organ, differences in the size and shape of these cells as shown in Figure 1-14 are not to be ascribed to the influence of the various fixing agents used. However, the impression that the cells and their nuclei are larger when living than after histological preparation is correct.

Some of the features to be seen in unfixed and fixed liver cells with special staining reactions are illustrated in Figure 1-15. Here the usual appearance in hematoxylin and eosin preparations after Zenker-formol fixation is shown. By addition of azure II, additional basophilic regions of nucleus and cytoplasm are revealed. The two cells stained with hematoxylin-eosin-azure II, one after Zenker-formol fixation and the other a frozen-dried preparation treated with alcohol, should be compared, since the other cells shown in the figure were fixed by the latter method. Toluidine blue is frequently substituted for hematoxylin-eosin-azure II to demonstrate basophilic components. This dye stains both deoxyribo- and ribonucleoprotein. To distinguish staining attributable to one or the other of these, the section can be digested with the enzyme ribonuclease prior to staining. Because the ribonuclease solution may have solvent action other than that due to the enzyme, a better comparison may be made with a section treated with buffer solution. After selective removal of ribonucleoprotein, the areas still stained with toluidine blue can be identified as deoxyribonucleoprotein. Components containing deoxyribonucleoprotein can also be identified by their specific staining with the Feulgen reaction. The glycogen and other carbohydrates in such cells are shown by the periodate-leukofuchsin (PAS) reaction. The effect of prior treatment with saliva on such preparations is also shown. The loss of red staining being due to removal of glycogen by amylase in the saliva, fatty components can be demonstrated if fat solvents are avoided in fixation and dehydration; they are colored with Sudan black and Nile blue. In the cell stained with Nile blue sulfate the blue component is nonspecific, but the salmon-pink staining occurs in fat droplets.

By use of various methods of fixation and staining, many structures can be demonstrated within the cell. These are artificial to the extent that the structures in fixed material are not the same as those in the living cell, nor are all the structures of the living cell still present in any given preparation. However, with the same fixation and staining methods, the factors of artificiality are constant and the appearance of the cells is reproducible. With improved optical methods for studying living cells, evidence has been found for the presence in the living cell of most of the important structures that had been described on the basis of fixed and stained preparations. The comparison of their form in living and in fixed cells is facilitated by use of phase microscopy and by supravital staining.

THE CHEMICAL BASIS OF HISTOLOGICAL STAINING

In general the mechanism of the binding of dyes to tissue components is not known, but experiments with model systems (Singer) suggest that it is not too great an oversimplification to assume that in some examples of staining, anionic and cationic dyes form electrostatic (salt) linkages with ionizable radicals of proteins, glycoproteins, and lipoproteins in the tissue section. These constituents of protoplasm

are *amphoteric*; that is, they can ionize either as bases or as acids depending upon the pH and certain other conditions in their environment. Whether a protein behaves as an acid or as a base depends upon its net charge—the algebraic sum of its positive and negative charges at the pH at which the staining is carried out. For each kind of protein there is a pH at which the number of positive charges equals the number of negative charges. This is called its *isoelectric point*. At this pH it stains poorly, but above its isoelectric point, ionization of its anionic groups is favored and it will bind basic (cationic) dyes such as *methylene blue* or *basic fuchsin*. Below its isoelectric point the same protein will have a net positive charge and will combine with acidic (anionic) dyes such as *eosin, orange G*, or *light green*.

Proteins of the tissues differ greatly in the relative abundance of their constituent amino acids and therefore have very different isoelectric points. Thus at the pH ordinarily used for

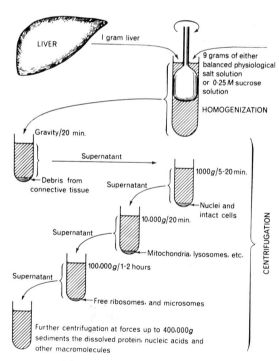

Figure 1-12. A diagram showing the successive stages in fractionation of cell components. The cells are disrupted by the shearing forces created in the homogenizer. Connective tissue fibers and other debris sediment on standing. The supernatant is then centrifuged at a series of increasing speeds and pellets of the various organelles are recovered as indicated. (Modified after K. B. Roberts, *in* G. H. Haggis et al., Introduction to Molecular Biology, New York, John Wiley & Sons, Inc., 1964.)

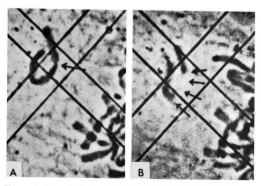

Figure 1-11. Effect of localized ultraviolet irradiation of a portion of a metaphase chromosome of Amblystoma. *A*, Before irradiation, during metaphase (kinetochore at arrow). *B*, Immediately after irradiation, the irradiated segment became "pale" as indicated by the arrows. Phase contrast microscopy. Prints from 16 mm. motion picture film. Each print represents an area $30 \times 40 \ \mu$. (After Uretz, Bloom, and Zirkle, Science, *120*:197, 1954.)

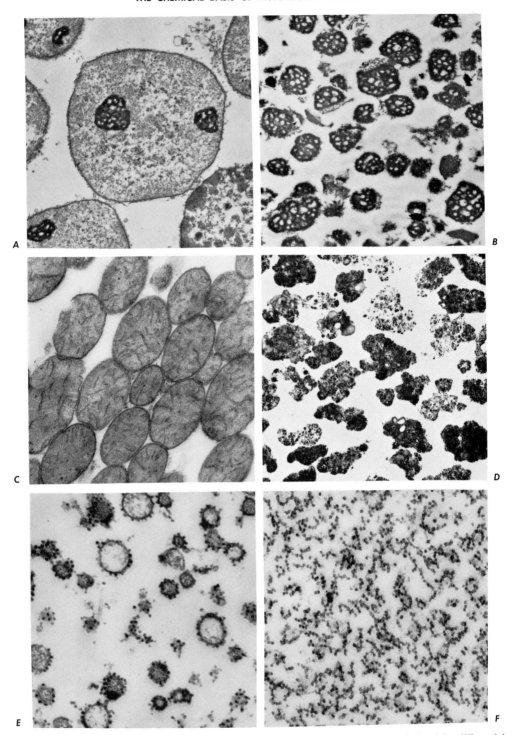

Figure 1-13. Electron micrographs of the pellets of various fractions of cell homogenates isolated by differential centrifugation. *A,* Liver cell nuclei. × 5000. (After R. Maggio, P. Siekevitz, and G. E. Palade, J. Cell Biol., *18:*267, 293, 1963.) *B,* Liver cell nucleoli. × 16,000. (After R. Maggio, P. Siekevitz, and G. E. Palade, J. Cell Biol., *18:*267, 293, 1963.) *C,* Liver mitochondria. (Courtesy of S. Malamed.) *D,* Lipofuscin pigment granules from cardiac muscle. (Courtesy of S. Björkerud.) *E,* Microsomes from pancreas. (Courtesy of G. E. Palade.) *F,* Ribosomes from pancreas. (Courtesy of G. E. Palade.)

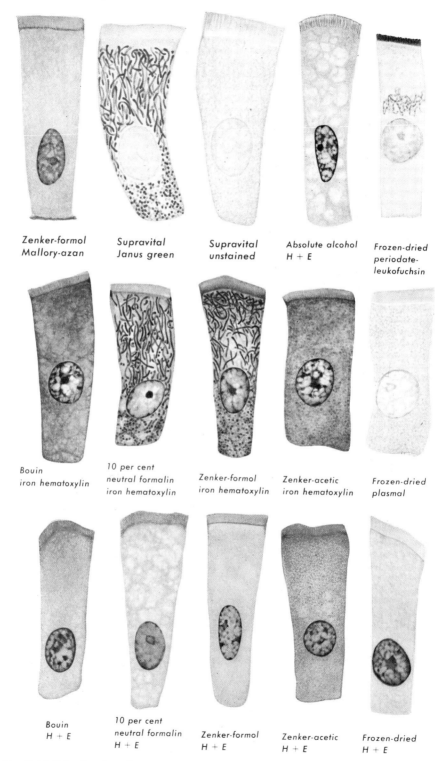

Zenker-formol
Mallory-azan

Supravital
Janus green

Supravital
unstained

Absolute alcohol
H + E

Frozen-dried
periodate-
leukofuchsin

Bouin
iron hematoxylin

10 per cent
neutral formalin
iron hematoxylin

Zenker-formol
iron hematoxylin

Zenker-acetic
iron hematoxylin

Frozen-dried
plasmal

Bouin
H + E

10 per cent
neutral formalin
H + E

Zenker-formol
H + E

Zenker-acetic
H + E

Frozen-dried
H + E

Figure 1-14. Epithelial cells of small intestine of guinea pig fixed and stained in a variety of ways to emphasize the extreme importance of choice of method for the preservation, demonstration, and study of cytoplasmic and nuclear structures. For explanation, see text. × 1620.

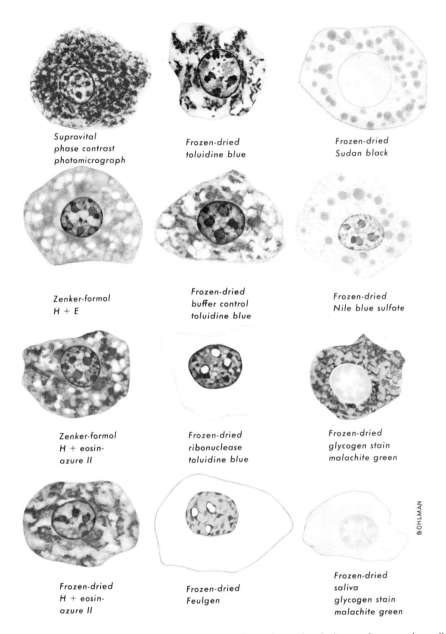

Figure 1-15. Mouse liver cells fixed and stained by a variety of cytochemical procedures to show distribution of deoxyribonucleic acid, ribonucleic acid, and lipid droplets. As these tests were all done on material fixed by freezing and drying, some of the sections are compared with similarly stained sections fixed by Zenker-formol. For further orientation, the fixed cell stained by hematoxylin and eosin and the unfixed cell photographed by phase contrast are also shown. × 1500. (Courtesy of I. Gersh.)

histological staining, some components stain more readily with basic dyes and are said to be *basophilic*, while others, at the same pH, take up acidic dyes and are said to be *acidophilic*. For example, red blood cells, the granules of eosinophilic leukocytes, and the cytoplasm of parietal cells in the stomach all stain with acid dyes at pH 6, while the chromatin of cell nuclei, the ergastoplasm of the cytoplasm in glandular cells and neurons, and the hyaline matrix of cartilage all bind basic dyes. The histologist is therefore able, in a general way, to categorize tissue components on the basis of their affinities for acid or basic dyes under specified staining conditions.

It is important to realize, however, that only a limited number of staining methods involve electrostatic linkages between the dye and the tissue. Hematoxylin, for example, stains chromatin under many conditions and does not behave simply as a basic dye. Some of the most widely used staining methods, such as Mallory's trichrome, Masson's stain, and Heidenhain's azan, combine two or three acid dyes, and the mechanism by which they stain various tissue components differentially is not known. Although these methods provide no insight into the chemical nature of the components stained, they are nevertheless extremely useful to the histologist in providing the contrast necessary for visualization of various components that otherwise would not be distinguishable.

HISTOCHEMICAL METHODS

Desiring to get away from the purely empirical use of dyestuffs for improvement of contrast, and to go beyond the description of structure without regard for function, histologists have developed a large number of so-called histochemical methods. *Histochemistry* can be defined as the application to histological preparations of methods of physical and chemical analysis that permit identification of chemical substances in their normal sites in tissues. It differs from biochemistry in its greater emphasis upon the localization of chemical events to particular cellular or subcellular components, and it often provides valuable information that cannot be obtained by the analysis of tissue homogenates. It includes a group of *chemical methods* that permit (1) identification of lipids by their uptake of certain fat soluble dyes; (2) the staining of carbohydrates by means of a reagent that produces a colored compound with the products of their oxidation; (3) the demonstration of deoxyribonucleoprotein by staining of a specific aldehyde group made available by mild hydrolysis; and (4) the localization of numerous enzymes. These methods depend upon incubation of tissue sections with substrates that yield insoluble hydrolytic products that are either already colored or capable of being detected by subsequent conversion to a colored compound.

A group of *physical methods* takes advantage of (1) absorption of ultraviolet light at specific wavelengths to identify and localize nucleoproteins (ultraviolet spectrophotometry); (2) absorption of x-rays of selected wavelengths by calcium and other elements (historadiography); (3) emission of x-rays of specific wavelengths by elements bombarded by an electron beam (electron microprobe analysis); and (4) emission of ionizing particles from unstable isotopes incorporated in tissue components (radioautography).

Chemical Methods

The requirements for an ideal histochemical procedure that depends upon chemical reactions are the following: (1) the preparation of the tissue section should be carried out without alteration of the position of the chemical constituent being studied; (2) the reaction should be specific for this substance; and (3) the reaction product should be intensely colored, so that it can be readily visualized with the microscope. In practice, few methods completely satisfy all of these requirements, but many approach them closely enough to be useful. One of the most widely used of this category of staining methods is a group reaction for the identification of carbohydrates, called the periodic acid–Schiff reaction (PAS reaction). In this test the section is exposed to periodic acid, which oxidizes hydroxyl groups on adjacent carbon atoms or adjacent hydroxyl and amino groups to produce aldehydes. The section is then stained with the Schiff reagent, fuchsin-sulfurous acid, which forms an addition product with aldehydes to produce a red or magenta reaction product. This widely used method stains glycogen, epithelial mucins, neutral polysaccharides, and glycoproteins. A positive staining reaction in one section that can be abolished by digestion of a parallel section with the enzyme diastase identifies the substance staining as glycogen (Fig. 1-16).

A similar principle is involved in the Feulgen reaction, a highly specific histochemical method for deoxyribonucleoprotein (DNA). The tissue is subjected to mild hydrolysis to remove the purine group of DNA and make available the aldehyde group of deoxyribose. Subsequent treatment with the Schiff reagent results in staining of the DNA of the nuclear chromatin. The Feulgen reaction is perhaps the most specific of the histochemical staining reactions; it owes its specificity to the presence of an aldehyde in deoxyribose and to the fact that no naturally occurring substance other than DNA will yield an aldehyde group under the conditions of gentle hydrolysis employed in this method.

Representative of the methods for enzymes is the classical Gomori-Takamatsu procedure for alkaline phosphatase. A tissue section is incubated in a buffered solution containing the substrate, glycerophosphate, and calcium ions. As hydrolysis of the substrate releases phosphoric acid, it combines with calcium and precipitates as calcium phosphate. This colorless precipitate is converted to brown cobalt sulfide, which is readily visualized with the microscope. It is to be noted that, in methods for enzymes based upon this principle, it is not the enzyme itself that is stained but the product of the enzyme-catalyzed reaction. Diffusion of the reaction product may therefore result in false localization, but methods have been devised for minimizing artifacts of this kind. Methods are now available for localizing a great many enzymes (Figs. 1-17 and 1-18).

Physical Methods

Several useful methods in this category depend upon selective absorption at particular wavelengths in the spectrum of electromagnetic radiation (Fig. 1-25).

ULTRAVIOLET MICROSPECTROPHOTOMETRY. Nucleic acids have the property of absorbing ultraviolet light at a wavelength of 2600 Å. Thus, if intact cells or histological sections being transilluminated with ultraviolet at this wavelength are photographed, the dark

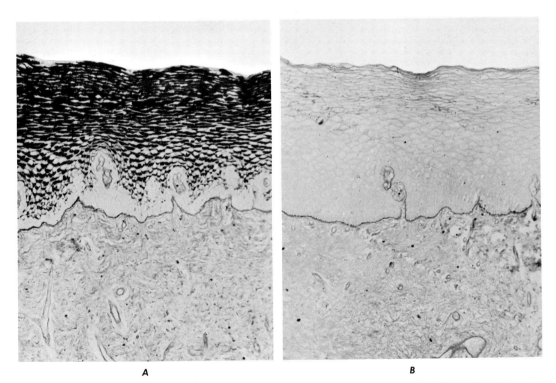

A   B

Figure 1-16. *A,* Photomicrograph of human vaginal epithelium stained with the periodic-acid Schiff (PAS) reaction for carbohydrates. *B,* An adjacent section stained in the same way after digestion with salivary amylase. The abolition of the intense staining of the epithelium by enzymatic digestion demonstrates that the material responsible was glycogen. The faint residual staining is due to protein-polysaccharides of the connective tissue ground substance.

areas in the resulting image will represent the sites of highest concentration of nucleic acids (Fig. 1-19). To ascertain whether nucleic acid absorption in a particular area is due to the presence of ribonucleoprotein or to deoxyribonucleoprotein, the preparation can be photographed before and after digestion with the enzymes ribonuclease or deoxyribonuclease. Areas of absorption removed by a specific enzyme can then be attributed to the corresponding substrate.

HISTORADIOGRAPHY. Absorption of soft x-rays can be related to particular elements in a tissue sample. A thin section of bone, for example, is placed in contact with a fine grained photographic emulsion and exposed to a beam of x-rays at a critical absorption wavelength for calcium. The light areas in the resulting histo180radiogram represent areas of specific absorption and reflect the distribution of the bone mineral in the section (Fig. 1-20). By densitometric comparison with suitable standards, it is possible to determine the quantity of calcium per unit area with a fairly high degree of accuracy.

It should be pointed out that, as is the case with ultraviolet light, it is the *contrast* afforded by differences in x-ray absorption (in this case, of individual atoms) that is utilized in such techniques as *contact historadiography* and *projection x-ray microscopy*. In these techniques, resolution is not particularly high.

ELECTRON MICROPROBE ANALYSIS. An approach not yet in general use but showing promise of fruitful biological application is the electron probe microanalyzer. In this complex instrument a slender electron beam of low accelerating potential strikes the tissue section, exciting the emission of long wavelength x-rays from a small area of the specimen. An analyzer set for the wavelength characteristic of the element of interest measures the emission in a proportional counter. At the same time, the distribution of the element in the specimen can be recorded in an image in which the pattern of light areas reflects the location and relative abundance of the emitting element (Fig. 1-21). By changing the setting of the analyzer to a new wavelength, the topographical abundance of another element can be recorded from the same specimen. The instrument has the capability of quantitative analysis for all elements heavier than beryllium with an accuracy of a few per cent and a limit of detection as low as fifty parts per million. Its limitations for

biological application reside in considerable beam damage to the specimen and in the relatively poor resolution, which at present is probably no better than 5 μ. There appears to be no insuperable technical obstacle, however, to the development of the smaller beams that would provide the resolution needed for regional analysis within cells of ordinary size.

RADIOAUTOGRAPHY (AUTORADIOGRAPHY). A method of extraordinary importance for the tracing of specific substances in the body and for the localization of metabolic events in cells and tissues is radioautography. When a substance containing a radioactive isotope is injected into an animal, subsequent preparation of radioautographs makes it possible to detect and establish the location of the labeled compound in the tissues. A histological section con-

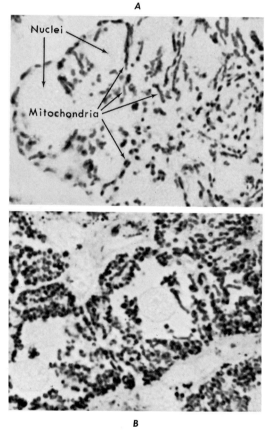

Figure 1-17. Histochemical reaction for an enzyme, showing exceptionally precise localization. *A*, Section of pancreas stained for succinic dehydrogenase. The nuclei and cytoplasm are unstained, but the mitochondria exhibit a strong reaction for the enzyme. *B*, Section of liver, showing a similar localization of the enzyme. (After D. G. Walker and A. Seligman. J. Cell Biol., *16:*455, 1963.)

taining radioactive material is coated with a photographic emulsion in the dark and put away in a light-tight box to "expose" for a period of days or weeks. The ionizing particles emitted in radioactive decay of the isotope within the tissue strike silver bromide crystals in the overlying emulsion, producing a "latent image" that is subsequently "developed" with photographic developer and appears as black dots over the section when the preparation is examined under the microscope. The black spots produced in the emulsion betray the location of the radioactive substance in the underlying tissue section, and it is possible in this way to localize the label with a resolution of 1 to 2 μ using the light microscope. With the thinner layers of emulsion and the ultrathin sections employed for electron microscopy, the resolution of the method is about 0.2 μ. Radioautography at the electron microscope level therefore has sufficient precision to make it a valuable technique for localization of substances *within* cells.

It can only reveal compounds that are taken up and incorporated into tissue components at sites that are metabolically active during the brief period between injection of the radioactive ("labeled") material and its excretion from the body. This limitation, in a sense, makes the method more valuable than methods for simple identification of stable substances already present in the tissues, because it means that injection of labeled precursors and their subsequent localization in cell products by autoradiography makes it possible to study the dynamics of metabolic processes. This approach has been employed to study the sequential participation of the various cell organelles in the synthesis and release of various secretions (see Chapter 4).

Another kind of application of radioautography employs the principle of bird banding and enables the investigator to tag the nuclei of cells, so that the marked cells can be traced in the course of their morphogenetic migrations during early development. Tritium labeled thymidine injected into an embryo is incorporated into the deoxyribonucleic acid (DNA) of the nucleus in all of those cells that are preparing for cell division at the time of the injection. The nuclei of these cells and their daughter cells will then be labeled, while those cells that are in other stages of interphase or are not dividing at all will remain unlabeled. Thus such complex problems as the

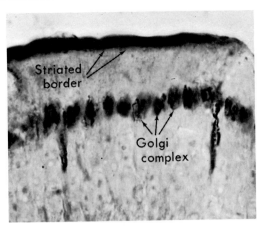

Figure 1-18. A further example of selective histochemical localization of enzymatic activity. A section of epithelium from rat duodenum incubated in the substrate thiamine pyrophosphate for 10 minutes at 37° C., showing localization of phosphatase in the Golgi complex and the striated border. (After A. B. Novikoff et al., *in* R. J. C. Harris, ed., The Interpretation of Ultrastructure. New York, Academic Press, 1962.)

histogenesis of the brain of experimental animals can be approached by preparing radioautographs of embryos at successive times after administration of labeled thymidine. The path taken by the labeled cells can then be plotted from their site of origin to their ultimate destination in the cerebral cortex. This is proving to be one of the most valuable of the modern morphological methods for studying certain functional and developmental processes.

Immunohistochemical Methods

A highly sensitive method for localization of specific proteins or polysaccharides in tissues is the fluorescent antibody technique. This takes advantage of the fact that the body recognize foreign protein substances, *antigens*, and makes specific macromolecules called *antibodies* that combine with and inactivate the antigens. The discovery that fluorescent dye molecules could be chemically linked to antibody molecules without interfering with their capacity to react specifically with antigen has opened up a new approach to histochemical localization (Coons). For example, if it is desired to localize the muscle protein, myosin, in mouse tissue, purified myosin from mouse muscle can be injected into a rabbit. In due course the rabbit's blood serum contains antibodies produced against the antigenic mouse

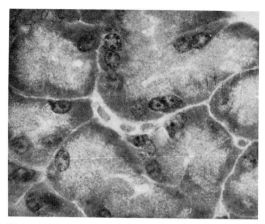

Figure 1-19. Ultraviolet photomicrograph of an un-stained section of rabbit pancreas, illustrating the marked absorption by nuclear and cytoplasmic nucleotides that results in an appearance very similar to that found after staining with basic dyes. The absorbing material can be removed by ribo- and deoxyribonuclease. (After T. O. Caspersson, Cell Growth and Cell Function. New York, W. W. Norton Co., 1950.)

myosin. These are precipitated from blood serum, purified, and conjugated in vitro with the fluorescent dye *fluorescein*. This product is then used as a staining reagent. When flooded onto a histological section, the fluorescent antimyosin antibody combines specifically with myosin. When the excess is washed off and the preparation is examined in ultraviolet light under the microscope, the sites of the antigen-antibody complex appear as bright yellow luminescent areas against a dark background (Fig. 1-24). The method has been successfully used to establish the cell of origin of protein hormones, the intracellular location of various enzymes, and the sites of synthesis of serum albumin (Fig. 1-24C), as well as in many other problems.

Instead of being coupled to the specific antibody, the fluorochrome can be coupled to an antibody against globulins of the species originally reacting to antigen. By this indirect method, the site of antibody production has been localized in the plasma cells. (Fig. 6-21).

PRINCIPLES OF MICROSCOPIC ANALYSIS

The principal instrument in histology and cytology is, of course, the *compound microscope.* This basic instrument has been modified in various ways, so that in addition to the common light or optical microscope, we now have

available the *phase contrast microscope*, the *interference microscope*, the *polarizing microscope*, the fluorescence microscope, and the ultraviolet microscope. Each has its own advantages for special purposes and its limitations. These will be considered below after a preliminary discussion of the general principles of microscopic analysis. *Throughout this book unless otherwise indicated, "microscope" refers to the optical microscope using visible light.*

Beams of different wavelengths from different segments of the spectrum of electromagnetic radiation can be thought of as optical probes of varying degrees of coarseness or fineness. The prime considerations in the microscopic analysis of minute structure are that (1) the probe being utilized must not be appreciably larger than the detail to be seen; (2) the probe and the object being investigated must interact; and (3) it must be possible to observe and to interpret this interaction. In no case does the image formed in a microscope ever correspond exactly with the object from which it originates. Certain general rules and considerations governing the relation between object and image are applicable to quite diverse, and at first glance unrelated, methods of microscopic analysis.

To begin with, the terms *resolution* and *magnification,* which are used to characterize the performance of a microscope, must be carefully distinguished. Of the two, resolution, or resolving power, is by far the more important criterion. The resolving power of an analytic system is a measure, generally in terms of linear distance, of the smallest separation at which two details can still be distinguished from each other. Magnification, which is the ratio of image size to object size, simply gives us the scale by which we relate object dimensions to image dimensions. Magnification is a useful criterion for ensuring that the image is brought to sufficient size that all of the resolved detail may be easily viewed. Clearly, any image is capable of indefinite magnification (a photographic transparency may be projected on as large a screen as we care to choose), but once an image is large enough that all of the resolved detail it contains may be viewed comfortably, any further enlargement becomes empty rather than useful magnification.

THE LIGHT (OR OPTICAL) MICROSCOPE. Historically, the most used and familiar histological probe has been visible light, observed and analyzed in the classical light microscope in its interactions with biological objects. The probe size to be associated with this light is roughly that of its wavelength, or about 0.5 μ. Resolution in the microscope is further determined by the *numerical apertures* of the objective and condenser lenses. Numerical aperture is a measure of the size or angle of the cone of light delivered by the illuminating condenser lens to the object plane and of the cone of light emerging from the object that is collected by the objective lens. Light coming through fine details of the object is diffracted into directions different from that of its original propagation, and the finer the detail involved, the wider the angle over which this light is diffracted. This is analogous to the diffraction and spreading of light coming through small pinholes. Numerical aperture, then, is a measure of the ability of the microscope to collect diffracted light from fine details in the object. The overall resolving power of a well constructed light microscope of high numerical aperture approaches the theoretical limit and is approximately 0.25 μ.

The capacity of the *compound microscope* to reveal structural detail depends upon differences in *absorption* of light by the parts to be differentiated. We commented earlier upon the fact that tissue components are largely transparent. The usefulness of this instrument in biology and medicine depends largely upon the fact that differences in absorption (opacity) can be created by histological staining, and this makes it possible to distinguish components that would otherwise escape detection.

However, even for highly transparent objects, information is available in the image in the form of phase differences, and the methods of *phase* and *interference microscopy* (see pp. 22 and 23) can be used to convert these phase differences into contrasting intensity differences.

Understanding the concept of *index of refraction* and its underlying molecular basis is essential to an understanding of the phase, interference, and polarizing microscopes. Index of refraction is a measure of the rate of propagation of a light wave, or other electromagnetic impulse, through a given medium, and is defined as the ratio of the velocity of light in vacuo to its velocity in the medium. Even for a highly transparent, nonabsorbing medium, there can be a considerable interaction between the medium and a passing light wave or other electromagnetic disturbance. The electrons associated with the atoms and molecules of the medium can oscillate in

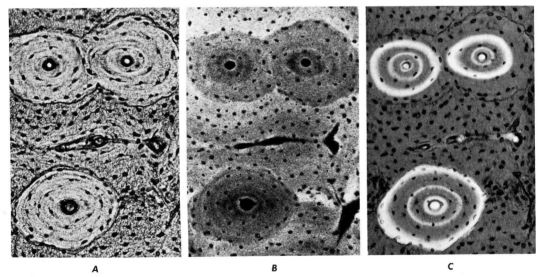

A B C

Figure 1-20. Photomicrographs of bone, illustrating applications of historadiography and fluorescence microscopy. A ground section of bone from a young dog that had received two courses of treatment with a fluorescent tetracycline compound 19 days apart. *A,* Ordinary microscopy. Three newly formed haversian systems are seen. *B,* In a historadiogram of the same section, the differing shades from black to white reflect the differing concentrations of calcium. In the haversian canals there has been no absorption of the x-rays and the film is therefore black. The areas containing the greatest concentration of calcium are white and regions of intermediate degrees of calcification exhibit shades of gray. *C,* Fluorescence microscopy detects, as two concentric bright rings, the fluorescent tetracycline compound incorporated into the bone during the two periods of treatment. (Courtesy of R. Amprino and R. Marotti.)

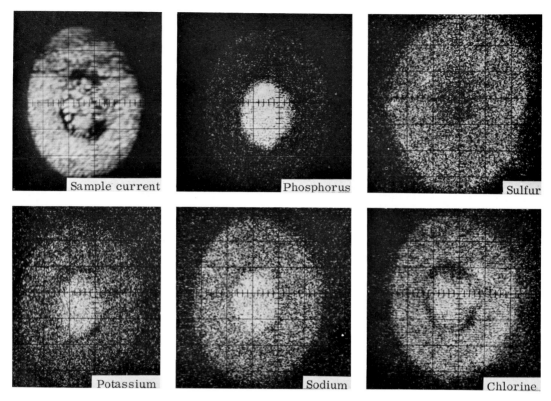

Figure 1-21. Images of nucleated erythrocytes of the amphibian, *Amphiuma,* made with the electron probe micro-analyzer. At the upper left is a sample current image for orientation. The remaining represent analyses for the element indicated. The light areas represent regions of high concentration of the element. (Courtesy of J. P. Revel and C. A. Anderson.)

response to the alternating electric field associated with the passing light. In so doing, these moving electrons act as miniature antennas and radiate secondary energy. This secondary radiation interacts with the primary light coming through. In general, the net result is a retardation in the phase of the oscillating electric field at any point in comparison with what it would have been had the secondary radiation not been present. This leads to a lowering of the velocity of propagation of the light through the medium. The intensity of this secondary radiation, and, hence, the velocity of propagation through the medium, depends on the freedom of the electrons to respond to the field and will be determined by the wavelength of the light and by the nature of the structure being traversed.

Light coming through an object of higher refractive index will be retarded with respect to light passing through a surrounding medium of lower refractive index; that is, the alternating electromagnetic field of the light wave will be displaced in time relative to the light coming through the surrounding medium. The total retardation of the light wave will be a function of both the index of refraction and the thickness of the object.

THE PHASE CONTRAST MICROSCOPE. This is essentially an optical device for converting small differences in refractive index that cannot be appreciated by the eye into differences in *intensity* that can be seen. It therefore renders visible certain components of living cells that can ordinarily be seen only in killed stained material (Fig. 1-7). In the image plane of the light microscope, areas corresponding to transparent regions of the specimen with an index of refraction different from that of their surroundings will have their light arriving out of phase with the surrounding light. However, the ordinary light microscope is not sensitive to such phase differences and will therefore show no difference in intensity between these various regions, and hence no contrast. The phase contrast microscope is equipped with special apertures and with absorbing and phase-shifting plates. These serve (1) to partially separate from the background illumination the diffracted light scattered at wide angles from small transparent specimen details, and (2) to shift the phase and intensity of these two components of the light in such a way that they interact in the image plane to produce intensity differences and contrast where only phase differences had been present before.

The phase contrast microscope suffers several major defects: (1) there are halos around the images because of incomplete separation of the background light from the diffracted light; (2) only phase differences from small objects or from border regions of rapidly changing retardation are converted into intensity differences; and (3) in the commonly used phase microscopes, each phase contrast objective is designed to work optimally for only a limited range of retardations.

THE INTERFERENCE MICROSCOPE. The interference microscope is designed for looking at the same kind of refractile detail in specimens as is the phase microscope, but it utilizes the more straightforward principle of sending two separate beams of light through the specimen. These two beams are then recombined with each other in the image plane. One beam is focused through the detail under observation and the other, a comparison beam, is focused in a neutral area, beside or above or below the observed detail. This instrument allows the direct quantitative measurement of retardation and of the related quantities of index of refraction and thickness, without the presence of halos and with independence of detail size. Such measurements of retardation can be used to measure dry mass per unit area of specimens and to do contour mapping of small objects.

The interference microscope is a more versatile instrument than the phase microscope and the only one of the two to be considered for quantitative measurements. However, it is a more expensive and more cumbersome instrument and, for many types of qualitative observation, the phase microscope is to be preferred. A recent development is differential interference (Nomarski) optics, which are designed to detect localized gradients in refractive index and, in many cases, give most excellent results in the detection of fine transparent detail.

THE POLARIZING MICROSCOPE. Constituents of cells and tissues that are crystalline or fibrous show a high degree of molecular orientation. When a ray of plane polarized light strikes such an object, it acts as if it were split into two rays polarized in planes perpendicular to one another. These two rays have different velocities. Such an object is said to be birefringent. Another way of looking at it is that objects with a high degree of molecular orientation have a different refractive index depending upon the plane of vibration of the ray of polarized light with respect to the orientation of the molecules. This occurs when the cloud of electrons associated with the atoms and molecules of the structure is not free to move equally in all directions under the influence of an external electromagnetic field, or if

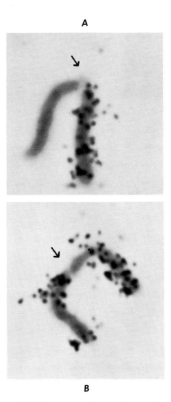

Figure 1-22. Radioautography can be used at the light microscope level to study the distribution of tritium labeled DNA in chromosomes during meiotic division. The dyads shown here are from cells that incorporated labeled thymidine one cell cycle before premeiotic interphase. The arrows indicate the terminal centromeres. In *A*, the silver grains are over one chromatid only and there are no visible exchanges. In *B*, there have been reciprocal exchanges of labeled and unlabeled segments of sister chromatids. (After J. H. Taylor, J. Cell Biol., *25*:57, 1965.)

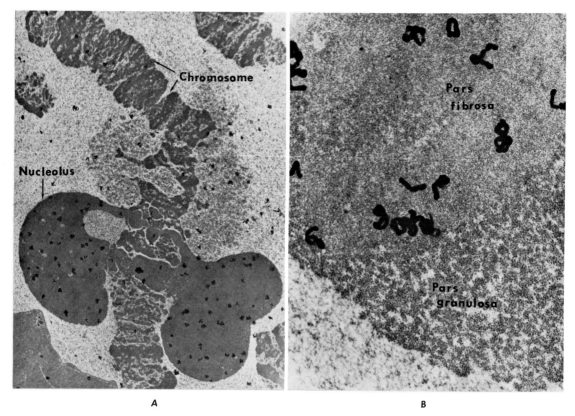

A   **B**

Figure 1-23. *A,* Electron microscopic radioautograph of a longitudinal section through chromosome IV of *Chironomus thummi* with its attached nucleolus and an adjacent Balbiani ring. Fingerlike nucleolar processes extend into the chromosome. At this time interval, 27 hours after injection of tritiated uridine, silver grains are distributed over the entire nucleolus and somewhat less abundantly over the Balbiani ring, indicating incorporation into RNA in these sites. (After B. von Gaudecker, Zeitschr. f. Zellforsch., 1967.) *B,* Higher magnification radioautograph showing silver grains over the pars fibrosa but not the pars granulosa of the nucleolus 13 minutes after injection of ^{3}H-uridine. At 46 hours after the injection (not shown here), most of the label is over the pars granulosa. Thus the resolution of radioautography at the electron microscope level is good enough to demonstrate that RNA in the fibrous region of the nucleolus subsequently moves into the granular region. (After B. von Gaudecker, Zeitschr. f. Zellforsch., 1967.)

some other ordering or layering of the structure is present on a scale smaller than the wavelength of the light used. Such ordered structures possessing more than one index of refraction can be studied in the polarizing microscope, which restricts the probing light to preferred directions and orientations and makes it possible to detect the presence of orderly arrangements of fibrous proteins or other arrays of long molecules, even though the molecules are not visible. It is, then, a device that can indirectly provide information about structural arrangement at the molecular level, and it can be applied to the living cell.

THE FLUORESCENCE MICROSCOPE. Another form of visible light microscopy that is coming into rapidly increasing use is fluorescence microscopy. In this technique light of one wavelength is used to illuminate the specimen. The image seen is due to emission from molecules that have absorbed the primary exciting light and then re-emitted light of longer wavelength and lower energy. Suitable filters are placed both below the condenser and above the objective to ensure that only the desired secondary emission from the specimen will contribute to the observed image. Under these conditions, the specimen behaves as if it were "self-luminous." The secondary emission may be from naturally occurring "fluorochromes" in the specimens, or from introduced fluorescent dyes bound to certain specific components of the specimen, or from fluorescent dyes coupled to specific antibodies. Owing to the great contrast and specificity inherent in the fluorescent image, this microscopic technique is one with great promise and importance for the future.

THE ULTRAVIOLET MICROSCOPE. In order to obtain resolution greater than that of the visible light microscope, we must find finer probes. One step in this direction is to use ultraviolet light, with the aid of quartz or reflecting lenses, instead of visible light. Its wavelength of approximately 0.25 μ allows, in principle, a gain of a factor of two in the smallest spacings that can be resolved. However, in practice the ultraviolet microscope has been used more for the natural contrast it provides, owing to the absorption of nucleic acids and proteins in the ultraviolet region, than for any small increase in resolution.

THE ELECTRON MICROSCOPE. A system analogous to that of the visible light microscope, but utilizing very much smaller probes, is that of the electron microscope. In this system, the ordinary light source is replaced by electrons emitted by a tungsten filament, their effective wavelength being determined by the voltage by which they are accelerated; shaped magnetic or electric fields take the place of glass lenses, and a fluorescent screen replaces the human eye for direct viewing. In practice, the requirements of a vacuum-enclosed system, high voltage, and mechanical stability, plus the special treatment and preparation of samples, make for a highly complex and costly microscope system. But it is one well worth the expense and trouble in view of the results obtained to date and anticipated in the future.

The problem of resolution in the electron microscope is, in practice, somewhat different from that of the light microscope. At the voltages used, the wavelengths to be associated with the electrons are very short, of the order of 0.05 Å. However, the shaped electric or magnetic lens fields that serve to focus the beam of electrons, being as yet quite crude and imperfect, have numerical apertures of 0.01 to 0.001, rather than the 1.3 to 1.4 associated with a good visible light objective lens. Therefore, the overall limit of resolution of the electron microscope has been about 5 Å, at least until recently, and the usual limit for biological preparations has been about 15 Å. Unlike the ordinary visible light microscope, the best

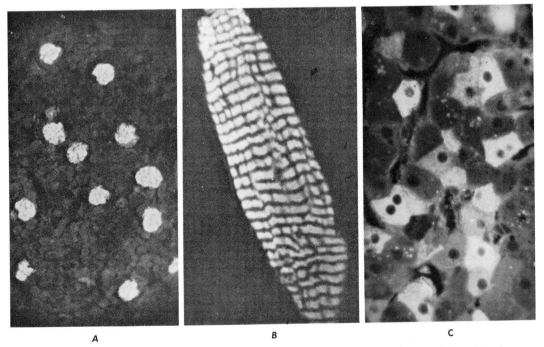

| A | B | C |

Figure 1-24. Examples of the use of the immunohistochemical method. *A,* Kidney from rat injected six days previously with rabbit antiserum against rat kidney. The section was stained with fluorescent antibody against rabbit globulin. (After L. G. Ortega and R. Mellors, J. Exper. Med., *104:*151, 1956.) *B,* Chicken muscle stained with antibody against chicken myosin. The fluorescent antibody localizes myosin in the A bands. × 1300. (After H. Finck, H. Holtzer, and J. M. Marshall, J. Biophys. & Biochem. Cytol., Suppl. *2:*175, 1956.) *C,* Human liver section stained with fluorescent antihuman serum albumin, which localizes serum albumin in certain liver cells and not in others. (After Y. Hamashima, J. G. Harter, and A. J. Coons, J. Cell Biol., *20:*271, 1964.)

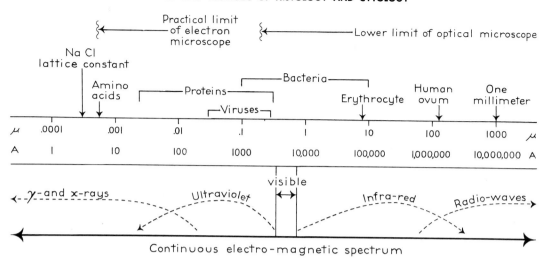

Figure 1-25. Comparison of dimensions of molecules and cells with wavelengths of the electromagnetic spectrum. Logarithmic scale. The different names given to overlapping regions of the spectrum do not represent different kinds of radiation. These names were determined historically by the range of sensitivity of the human eye and the varying approaches of investigation and instrumentation centering around different regions of what is actually a single continuous spectrum. (From data supplied by A. B. Hastings, T. F. Young, R. Uretz, and P. Geiduschek.)

electron microscope, despite its great accomplishments, is very far from approaching the theoretical limits for its performance.

Current developmental advances involving improved lens design and greatly increased voltages promise both increased resolution and the prospect of working with hydrated objects.

Specimen Preparation for Electron Microscopy. Because electrons will form a coherent beam only when traveling in a high vacuum, it is impossible, at least in current conventional electron microscopes, to introduce living cells into the column of the microscope. Therefore, with this instrument, only material that has been killed and dehydrated can be examined. The old and difficult problem of preserving tissue in a lifelike condition has been greatly compounded by the greater resolution of the electron microscope. The majority of the fixatives that are deemed satisfactory for light microscopy produce a precipitation of proteins that is intolerably coarse when viewed with the electron microscope. Of the traditional fixatives, only formalin osmium tetroxide and osmium-dichromate mixtures have been successfully adapted for use in electron microscopy. To these have recently been added acrolein and glutaraldehyde. With any of these killing agents, it has been found important to maintain the pH of the fixative in the range 7.2 to 7.8 by addition of buffers.

The most widely used fixative is a 1 or 2 per cent buffered solution of osmium tetroxide. This acts not only to preserve the tissue but also stains many of its constituents. "Staining" for the electron microscope does not consist of combination with colored dyes, because registration of color is not possible with an electron optical system. However, reduced osmium from the fixative is bound by the lipoprotein membranes and other components of cells, and because of its high atomic number increases their electron scattering and therefore enhances the contrast of the electron microscopic image. Glutaraldehyde as a fixative does not simultaneously stain the tissue, and it is common practice to expose the tissue to osmium afterward for further fixation and, particularly, to take advantage of the osmium staining. The tissues are dehydrated in increasing concentrations of ethanol or acetone and imbedded in acrylic plastic or epoxy resins.

Because an electron beam of the conventional electron microscope has very little penetrating power, the sections of tissue must be extremely thin, 50 to 100 mμ as compared to 5 to 10 μ for the light microscope. The most challenging part of specimen preparation for electron microscopy, and the most frequent obstacle to success, is the cutting of such exquisitely thin sections, free of compression, scratches and other distortions. This is accomplished on an ultramicrotome using a knife of fractured plate glass or of cleaved and polished diamond.

To gain additional contrast it is now common practice to restain the tissue by floating the ultrathin sections briefly on a solution of uranyl acetate or lead citrate or both in sequence. This additional staining procedure makes it possible to obtain sufficient contrast even in very thin sections.

X-RAY DIFFRACTION

As we proceed farther along the electromagnetic spectrum in the direction of shorter wavelengths and higher energies, we come first to an ultraviolet region known as the vacuum ultraviolet, where almost everything, including the intervening air, absorbs heavily, and then to the regions of low-energy "soft" x-rays, high-energy "hard" x-rays, and finally gamma rays. It must be emphasized that all of these regions are part of a single continuous electromagnetic spectrum, and that the name associated with a particular wavelength of radiation in a region of overlapping nomenclature usually depends on the source used to produce the radiation in a particular instance (Fig. 1-25).

One would expect that the very short wavelengths associated with x-rays would make them ideal as probes for microscopic analysis, with the ability to resolve interatomic distances accurately. Unfortunately no lenses are available to take full advantage of these short wavelengths by focusing and utilizing them for high resolution studies with a microscope system analogous to those used with visible light. Alternatively, then, one uses mathematical analysis in lieu of real lenses. In this technique of x-ray diffraction, one allows a narrow beam of x-rays to impinge upon a specimen. Depending upon the fine detail present,

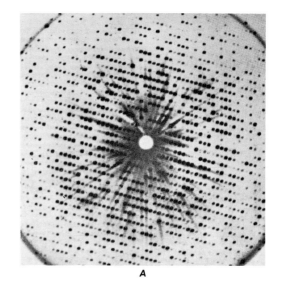

A

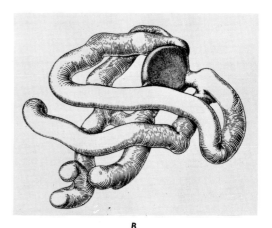

B

Figure 1-26. *A,* X-ray diffraction pattern of myoglobin. (Courtesy of J. C. Kendrew. Copyright 1963 by the American Association for the Advancement of Science.) *B,* Drawing of an early model of the myoglobin molecule constructed from an x-ray diffraction analysis with a relatively low resolution (6 Å). (Redrawn after J. C. Kendrew, Nature, *181:* 662, 1958.) *C,* Depiction of the myoglobin molecule as revealed by a higher resolution x-ray diffraction analysis (2Å). (Painted by I. Geis. From J. C. Kendrew: The three-dimensional structure of a protein molecule. Scientific American, *205:* 96 (Dec.) 1961. Reproduced with permission. Copyright © 1961 by Scientific American, Inc. All rights reserved.)

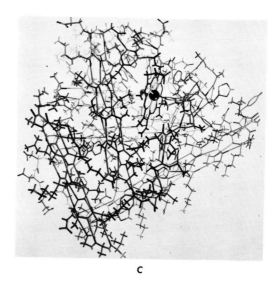

C

these x-rays will be diffracted and scattered by the specimen. In the absence of an objective lens analogous to that used in visible light microscopy, this scattered energy is observed directly, usually by means of a photographic film. Unfortunately, this means that we are restricted to the observation of highly ordered structures, crystalline or semicrystalline in nature, for which x-rays are diffracted in discrete directions and give patterns that are amenable to mathematical analysis. Further, because the diffracted x-ray energy is collected on a photographic film rather than refocused onto an image plane by means of a lens, the information contained in the phase relationships between the secondary x-ray beams diffracted in various directions is lost. This means that the x-ray diffraction pattern obtained is not uniquely and simply related to the object that gave rise to it, but that a series of approximations and trial solutions are necessary in order to decide on the structure that most probably corresponds to the observed pattern. It should be emphasized, also, that in x-ray diffraction, unlike visible light microscopy, we do not see focused individual elements of structure but only the averaged properties of repetitive ordered structures, all elements of which contribute to the observed x-ray diffraction pattern.

For a given wavelength of x-rays, the finer the detail observed, the larger the angle over which the x-rays will be diffracted. This has led to two distinct areas of x-ray diffraction analysis, in which the details of experimental technique are somewhat different: *Large-angle x-ray diffraction,* in which the small distances between individual atoms are studied, and *small-angle x-ray diffraction,* in which more widely spaced repetitions of entire groups of atoms are studied.

In recent years application of x-ray diffraction analysis has led to the determination by Kendrew and Perutz of the secondary and a large part of the primary structure of the molecule of *myoglobin,* a muscle protein involved in oxygen transport, and of *hemoglobin.* It has also made an important contribution to the analysis of the structure of DNA by Wilkins and by Crick and Watson.

In practice a crystal of the protein being analyzed is rotated in the path of a slender beam of monochromatic x-rays. The regularly spaced planes of high electron density within the crystal are thus successively brought to the correct angle to the incident beam. On a pho-

tographic plate placed some distance behind the crystal, a pattern of spots is produced, from which the scattering angles and spacing of the scattering centers in the crystal can be calculated. The size and shape of the *unit cell* or repeating group can thus be determined. For a protein, the main regions of high electron density are the backbone of the peptide chain and any atoms of high atomic number that may be present. In a relatively low resolution study, these are the only regions localized. In high resolution x-ray diffraction studies, the high density regions are localized more precisely and the less electron dense regions of the unit cell are also studied. Three dimensional contour maps of the electron density within the unit cell of the crystal are produced, and from these, models are constructed showing further detail.

REFERENCES

Transillumination of Exteriorized Organs

Knisely, M. H.: Fused quartz rod technique. *In* Cowdry, E. V., ed.: Microscopic Technique in Biology and Medicine. Baltimore, Williams & Wilkins Co., 1948.

Transparent Chamber Methods

Algire, G. H.: An adaptation of the transparent chamber technique to the mouse. J. Nat. Cancer Inst., *4:*1, 1943.
Algire, G. H., and F. Y. Legallais: Recent developments in the transparent chamber technique as adapted to the mouse. J. Nat. Cancer Inst., *10:*225, 1949.
Fawcett, D. W., G. B. Wislocki, and C. M. Waldo: The development of mouse ova in the anterior chamber of the eye and in the abdominal cavity. Am. J. Anat., *81:*413, 1947.
Goodman, L.: Observations on transplanted immature ovaries in the eyes of adult male and female rats. Anat. Rec., *59:*223, 1934.
Lutz, B. R., and G. P. Fulton: The use of the hamster cheek pouch for the study of vascular changes at the microscopic level. Anat. Rec., *120:*293, 1954.
Runner, M.: The development of mouse ova in oculo. Anat. Rec., *98:*1, 1947.
Sandison, J. C.: The transparent chamber of the rabbit's ear, giving a complete description of improved techniques of construction and introduction and general account of growth and behavior of living cells and tissues as seen with the microscope. Am. J. Anat., *41:*447, 1928.
Sewell, I. A.: Studies of the microcirculation using transparent tissue observation chambers inserted in the hamster cheek pouch. J. Anat. (Lond.), *100:*839, 1966.

Cell and Organ Culture

Carrel, A.: On the permanent life of tissues outside of the organism. J. Exper. Med., *15:*516, 1912.
Earle, W. R., F. C. Bryant, E. L. Schilling, and V. J. Evans: Growth of cell suspensions in tissue culture. Ann N.Y. Acad. Sci., *63:*666, 1956.
Fell, H. B., and J. Robison: The growth, development and phosphatase activity of embryonic avian femora and limb-buds cultivated *in vitro.* Biochem. J., *23:*767, 1929.
Harris, M.: Cell Culture and Somatic Variation. New York, Holt, Rinehart & Winston, 1964.
Harrison, R. G.: Observations on the living developing nerve fiber. Proc. Soc. Exper. Biol. & Med., *4:*140, 1907.
Maximow, A. A.: Tissue-cultures of young mammalian embryos. Carnegie Contributions to Embryol., *16:*47, 1925.

Moscona, A. A., and H. Moscona: The dissociation and aggregation of cells from organ rudiments of the early chick embryo. J. Anat. (Lond.), *86:*287, 1952.

Parker, R. C.: Methods of Tissue Culture. 3rd ed. New York, Hoeber Medical Division, Harper & Row, 1961.

Puck, T. T., and P. I. Marcus: A rapid method for viable cell titration and clone production with HeLa cells in tissue culture. The use of x-irradiated cells to supply conditioning factors. Proc. Nat. Acad. Sci., *41:*432, 1955.

Puck, T. T., P. I. Marcus, and S. J. Cieciura: Clonal growth of mammalian cells *in vitro*. Growth characteristics of colonies from single HeLa cells with and without a feeder layer. J. Exper. Med., *103:*273, 1956.

Scherer, W. F., and A. C. Hoogasian: Preservation at subzero temperatures of mouse fibroblasts (strain L) and human epithelial cells (strain HeLa). Proc. Soc. Exper. Biol. & Med., *87:*480, 1954.

White, P. R.: The cell as organism, tissue culture, cellular autonomy, and cellular interrelations. *In* Brachet, J., and A. E. Mirsky, eds.: The Cell. Vol. I, New York, Academic Press, 1960.

Micromanipulation

Chambers, R.: Micrurgial studies on protoplasm. Biol. Rev., *24:*246, 1949.

Chambers, R., and M. J. Kopac: Micrurgical technique for the study of cellular phenomena. *In* Jones, R. M., ed.: McClung's Handbook of Microscopical Technique. 3rd ed. New York, Paul B. Hoeber, Inc., 1950.

deFonbrune, P.: Technique de Micromanipulation. Paris, Masson, 1949.

Kopac, M. J.: Cytochemical micrurgy. Int. Rev. Cytol., *4:*1, 1955.

Kopac, M. J.: Micrurgical studies on living cells. *In* Brachet, J., and A. E. Mirsky, eds.: The Cell. Vol. I, New York, Academic Press, 1960.

Radiation Probes

Bloom, W., and R. V. Leider: Optical and electron microscopic changes in ultraviolet irradiated chromosome segments. J. Cell Biol., *13:*269, 1962.

Bloom, W., and S. Özarslan: Electron microscopy of ultraviolet-irradiated parts of chromosomes. Proc. Nat. Acad. Sci., *53:*1294, 1965.

Bloom, W., R. E. Zirkle, and R. B. Uretz: Irradiation of parts of individual cells. III. Effects of chromosomal and extrachromosomal irradiation on chromosome movements. Ann. N.Y. Acad. Sci., *59:*503, 1955.

Uretz, R. B., W. Bloom, and R. E. Zirkle: Irradiation of parts of living cells. II. Effects of ultraviolet microbeam focused on parts of chromosomes. Science, *120:*197, 1954.

Zirkle, R. E.: Partial cell irradiation. Advances in Biological and Medical Physics. Vol. 5, New York, Academic Press, 1957.

Zirkle, R. E. and W. Bloom: Irradiation of parts of individual cells. Science, *117:*481, 1953.

Isolation of Cell Components by Differential Centrifugation

Allfrey, V.: The isolation of subcellular components. *In* Brachet, J., and A. E. Mirsky, eds.: The Cell. Vol. I. New York, Academic Press, 1960.

Bensley, R. R.: On the fat distribution in mitochondria of the guinea pig liver. Anat. Rec., *69:*341, 1937.

Bensley, R. R., and N. L. Hoerr: Studies on cell structure by the freezing-drying method. VI. The preparation and properties of mitochondria. Anat. Rec., *60:*449, 1934.

Claude, A.: Fractionation of mammalian liver cells by differential centrifugation. J. Exper. Med., *84:*51, 1946.

Hogeboom, G. H., W. C. Schneider, and G. H. Palade: Isolation of intact mitochondria from rat liver; some biochemical properties of mitochondria and submicroscopic particulate material. J. Biol. Chem., *172:*619, 1948.

General Histological Methods

Baker, J. R.: Principles of Biological Microtechnique. New York, John Wiley & Sons, 1958.

Conn, H. J.: Biological Stains. 7th ed. Geneva and New York, Biochemical Publications, 1961.

Jones, R. M., ed.: McClung's Handbook of Microscopical Technique. 3rd ed. New York, Paul B. Hoeber, Inc., 1950.

Histochemical Methods

Barka, T., and P. J. Anderson: Histochemistry—Theory, Practice, and Bibliography. New York, Hoeber Medical Division, Harper & Row, 1963.

Boyd, G. A.: Autoradiography in Biology and Medicine. New York, Academic Press, 1955.

Caro, L. G.: High resolution autoradiography. *In* Prescott, D. M., ed.: Methods in Cell Physiology. Vol. I, p. 327. New York, Academic Press, 1964.

Caspersson, T.: Cell Growth and Cell Function. New York, Morton, 1950.

Coons, A. H.: Histochemistry with labeled antibody. Int. Rev. Cytol., *5:*1, 1956.

Coons, A. H.: Histochemistry with labeled antibody. Int. Rev. Cytol., *5:*1, 1956.

Coons, A. H.: Fluorescent antibody methods. *In* Danielli. J. F. ed.: General Cytochemical Methods. New York, Academic Press, 1958, p. 400.

Engström, A.: Historadiography. *In* Oster, G., and A. W. Pollister, eds.: Physical Techniques in Biological Research. Vol. I. New York, Academic Press, 1956.

Novikoff, A. B.: The intracellular localization of chemical constituents. *In* Mellors, R. C., ed.: Analytical Cytology. 2nd ed. New York, McGraw-Hill Book Co., 1959.

Pearse, A. G. E.: Histochemistry—Theoretical and Applied. 2nd ed. Boston, Little, Brown & Co., 1960.

Pelc, S. R., T. C. Appleton, and M. E. Wilton: State of light autoradiography. *In* Leblond, C. P., and K. B. Warren, eds.: The Use of Radioautography in Investigating Protein Synthesis. New York, Academic Press, 1965.

Pollister, A. W., and L. Ornstein: The photometric chemical analysis of cells. *In* Mellors, R. C., ed.: Analytical Cytology. 2nd ed. New York, McGraw-Hill Book Co., 1959.

Salpeter, M. M., and L. Bachmann: Assessment of technical steps in electron microscope autoradiography. *In* Leblond, C. P., and K. B. Warren, eds.: The Use of Radioautography in Investigating Protein Synthesis. New York, Academic Press, 1965.

Scarpelli, D. G., and N. M. Kanczak: Ultrastructural cytochemistry: Principles, limitations and applications. Int. Rev. Exp. Path., *4:*55, 1965.

Walker, P. M. B.: Ultraviolet absorption techniques. *In* Oster, G., and A. W. Pollister, eds.: Physical Techniques in Biological Research. Vol. I. New York, Academic Press, 1956.

Principles of Microscopic Analysis

Barer, R.: Phase contrast and interference microscopy in cytology. *In* Oster, G., and A. W. Pollister, eds.: Physical Techniques in Biological Research. Vol. I. New York, Academic Press, 1956.

Bennett, H. S.: Microscopical investigation of biological material with polarized light. *In* Jones, R. M., ed.: McClung's Handbook of Microscopical Technique. 3rd ed. New York, Paul B. Hoeber, Inc., 1950.

Hale, A. J.: The Interference Microscope in Biological Research. Edinburgh and London, E. & S. Livingstone Ltd., 1958.

Hale, A. J.: The interference microscope as a cell balance. *In* Walker, P. M. B., ed.: New Approaches in Cell Biology. London, Academic Press, 1960, p. 173.

Electron Microscopy

Fawcett, D. W.: Electron microscopy in histology and cytology. *In* Siegel, B. M., ed.: Modern Developments in Electron Microscopy, New York, Academic Press, 1963, p. 257.

Hall, C. E.: Introduction to Electron Microscopy. New York, McGraw-Hill Book Co., 1953.

Pease, D. C.: Histological Techniques for Electron Microscopy. New York, Academic Press, 1960.

Porter, K. R.: Ultramicrotomy. *In* Siegel, B. M., ed.: Modern Developments in Electron Microscopy. New York, Academic Press, 1963, p. 119.

CHAPTER TWO

The Cell and Cell Division

The living substance of plants and animals is described by the general term *protoplasm*. The smallest unit of protoplasm capable of independent existence is the *cell*. The simplest animals consist of a single cell, but the higher animals can be thought of as a colony or complex society of more or less interdependent cells of many kinds, specialized in various ways to carry out the many functions essential to the survival and reproduction of the organism as a whole. Cells subserving the same general function are grouped together and united by varying amounts of intercellular substance to form *tissues,* such as bones, cartilage, muscle, nervous tissue, and blood. The several basic tissues function independently in some instances, but more commonly two or more tissues are combined in particular patterns to form larger functional units called *organs*—skin, kidney, blood vessels, glands, and so on. Several organs whose functions are interrelated constitute an *organ system;* examples are the respiratory system (comprising the nose, larynx, trachea, and lungs) and the urinary system (comprising the kidneys, ureters, and urethra).

Etymologically, *histology* would seem to be the subdivision of anatomy that deals exclusively with the *tissues,* but it is in fact equally concerned with their component cellular and extracellular units and with the patterns of their interrelation in the formation of the organs. In this broader sense *histology* has come to be synonymous with *microscopic anatomy.* Formerly the boundaries of the field with respect to the dimensions of the components studied were rigidly limited by the resolution of the light microscope. The use of the electron microscope by the histologist has greatly extended the scope of his subject, so that it now includes much of cytology and tissue ultrastructure and thus embraces the study of biological structure at all levels of organization from the lower limit of direct visual inspection down to the structure of large molecules. The interests of the modern histologist do not end there, for it is impossible to account for the fine details of the structure of cells and tissues without some understanding of the chemical nature of their submicroscopic components.

CHEMICAL COMPOSITION OF PROTOPLASM

Description of the detailed composition of protoplasm is properly the domain of biochemistry, but certain aspects are essential to any consideration of cellular structure. In addition to a very high percentage of water, analysis of protoplasm reveals the presence of inorganic ions and innumerable naturally occurring organic compounds, among which are the proteins, carbohydrates, and lipid substances, and the constituents, the precursors, and some of the degradation products of these compounds.

Of the inorganic constituents one finds much potassium, little sodium, small amounts of magnesium, and even less calcium inside cells. Certain heavy metals, such as iron, are present in small amounts. Traces of two dozen or so other elements normally found in living organisms are vital to life. Of the anions, bicarbonate and phosphate predominate; chloride is present only in small amounts, if at all, except in red blood cells. This contrasts strongly with the intercellular fluids, in which sodium salts, especially the chloride, predominate.

Structurally, protoplasm may be said to

resemble a colloidal system of many phases, in that it has many of the properties of an emulsion that is composed of a number of localized areas having distinctive qualities and that is suspended in a continuous phase possessing some of the fibrous qualities of a gel. Although such comparisons have been helpful, they minimize those fundamental dynamic aspects of organization and activity that distinguish protoplasm from nonliving static models. In any event, the progressive accumulation of more information on the molecular constitution of protoplasm is throwing more and more light on its biophysical chemistry and its functions.

Macromolecules

The emphasis of this book is on the structural organization of the cellular and extracellular components forming our bodies, and this section places emphasis on those substances that do most to lend form and organization to cells and tissues—the *macromolecules*.* In the 1920's, the foundations were laid for our current understanding of the way in which the structural and mechanical properties of many naturally occurring biological materials are determined by their macromolecular constituents. It has become clear that much of the microscopic cellular structure is either mainly composed of submicroscopic, macromolecular constituents, or laid down on an organized matrix of these elements.

The macromolecules of animal cells fall into three main classes: the *polysaccharides*, *proteins*, and *nucleic acids*.

POLYSACCHARIDES. In this category are included glycogen and the mucopolysaccha-

---

*The nomenclature of this section may not be familiar to all readers of this book and is therefore briefly discussed here. *Macromolecules* are constructed from organic building blocks (*monomers*) linked together by repetitive formation of covalent bonds. Thus, the *polysaccharides* are composed of sugar monomers, the *polypeptides* and *proteins* are composed of amino acids linked together by peptide bonds, and the *polynucleotides* and *nucleic acids* are polymers of nucleotides. A molecule containing a small number of linked monomers is called an *oligomer*, and one containing a large number of these subunits is called a *polymer*. A polymer made from one monomer species is called a *homopolymer;* one made from two or more different monomers is called *copolymer* or *heteropolymer*. Many polymers contain monomer units in unbranched linear array. In others (such as glycogen), branching of molecular chains occurs. The *degree of polymerization* is given by the number of monomer units linked together in a single macromolecule.

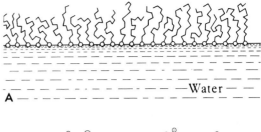

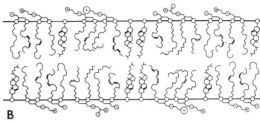

Figure 2-1. *A,* Schematic illustration of polar lipids arranged in a monomolecular layer at an oil-water interface. The polar groups are indicated by open circles and the hydrocarbon chains by the randomly zigzag lines. (From V. Luzzati, H. Mustacchi, A. E. Skoulios, and F. Husson, Acta Cryst., *13*:660, 1960.) *B,* Schematic illustration of a bimolecular layer of mixed phospholipids and cholesterol. (From Haggis, et al., Introduction to Molecular Biology. New York, John Wiley & Sons, 1964.)

rides. *Glycogen* is a highly branched polymer of D-glucose; it serves as a storage depot from which glucose needed for the chemical activities of cells may be released by degradation. Among the mucopolysaccharides are the *chondroitin sulfates* and *hyaluronic acid*. Chondroitin sulfates are copolymers of N-acetyl hexoseamine sulfate and glucuronic acid in varying proportions. Hyaluronic acid is a copolymer of glucuronic acid and N-acetyl glucosamine. Both occur widely in connective tissue (Chapter 6). In cartilage chondroitin sulfate may account for as much as 40 per cent of the dry weight (Chapter 9). Hyaluronic acid is also found in cartilage, the vitreous and aqueous humors of the eye (Chapter 34), and the fluids of the chest and joint cavities. At high concentration it provides a gelatinous matrix that lubricates the joint surface. In association with the connective tissue protein *collagen*, it endows the cornea with great mechanical strength and a considerable degree of transparency (Chapter 34).

The polysaccharides of microorganisms also play an important role in the mechanism by which one acquires immunity or becomes hypersensitive to certain foreign substances and bacteria. These constituents of the cell

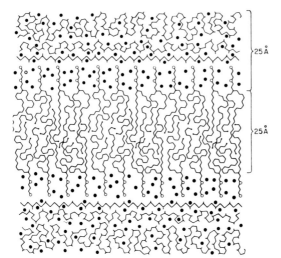

25Å

25Å

Figure 2-2. Schematic representation of the postulated molecular structure and probable osmium distribution in the stained unit membrane. The open circles represent the hydrophilic groups of the phospholipid molecules and the black dots represent the osmium deposited in the structure. (From W. Stoekenius, Circulation, *26:*1068, 1962.)

walls and capsules of some invasive bacteria, acting as *antigens,* can elicit the formation of *antibodies,* which are capable of combining specifically with the antigens that called them forth. The blood group substances, which are polysaccharide-protein complexes, also can act as antigens and thereby determine blood compatibility relationships. Although the macromolecular nature of the polysaccharides is essential for their functions in food storage, cementing, lubrication, and gel formation, the exact molecular size is not so important. Present evidence also indicates that many polysaccharides are not produced as unique molecular species but vary in their degree of polymerization.

PROTEINS. In proteins, in contrast to polysaccharides, the exquisite adjustment of the molecular structure to the biological role evidently requires the formation of polymeric molecules of precise composition and size. Each protein is a substance in which a unique number and variety of amino acids are joined in a completely specified peptide sequence. Indeed the evidence of experiments on the proteins *hemoglobin* and *ribonuclease* leads to the hypothesis that specified sequences of peptide units uniquely determine the three dimensional configuration of protein molecules and control the ability of certain small, relatively

compact proteins to form molecular chains by polymerizing into extended linear structures. In several instances these fibrous networks are formed at locations removed from sites of protein synthesis. This poses a transportation problem that can be solved by the synthesis of structural protein *precursors,* which polymerize or aggregate only under restricted circumstances. The *fibrinogen* of the circulating blood may be regarded as such a structural protein precursor. Under the catalytic action of the enzyme *thrombin* it is hydrolyzed to fibrin monomer (and small peptides); fibrin monomer, in turn, polymerizes to produce the fibrin network of the blood clot (Fig. 5-16).

The *enzymes* are by far the most numerous and most important group of proteins. They are the catalysts that determine the synthetic and degradative chemical potentialities of cells and tissues. Their proper function in the living animal depends on the control of their activity. A rich variety of such control mechanisms exists in nature, including (1) regulation of the supply of metabolites, (2) existence of specific enzyme inhibitors, some of which are proteins, (3) formation of enzyme precursors or zymogens, which require a chemical reaction for their conversion to an active form, (4) restricted localization of the enzyme, (5) inhibition of catalytic activity by products of the action of the enzyme, (6) conversion of an enzyme of a metabolic pathway to an inactive form by interaction of an end product of the pathway with a receptor site localized on the enzyme, and (7) control of the synthesis of new enzyme by products or substrates of the enzymatic reaction or by *hormones.* Undoubtedly, the efficient functioning of enzymes is often determined by their proper location in complexes, which act as chemical assembly lines. This is particularly well established in the mitochondria (p. 44).

Several of the hormones are proteins, including insulin, gonadotropin, adrenocorticotropic hormone (ACTH), and melanocyte stimulating hormone (MSH). Oxytocin and vasopressin also are polypeptide hormones.

NUCLEIC ACIDS. Of all the macromolecules of the animal cell, proteins undoubtedly play the greatest variety of roles. In contrast the nucleic acids are the most restricted in activity, being concerned exclusively (it is presently presumed) with protein synthesis and the storage of the capability of synthesizing proteins. Remarkably, however, the great diversity of cellular and organismal development and function results from this limited range of activities.

Two types of nucleic acids are known: deoxyribonucleic acid (DNA) and ribonucleic acid (RNA). Both are polymers of nucleotides, which in turn are composed of a purine or pyrimidine, a five carbon sugar, and a phosphate group. In DNA the sugar is deoxyribose; in RNA it is (with rare exceptions) ribose. Most DNAs contain a small proportion of methylated cytosine and some also contain methylated adenine. The relative ratios of these components are further restricted in DNA biosynthesis to provide equimolar proportions of adenine and thymine, as well as equimolar proportions of guanine and cytosine. This permits the regular arrangement of two "complementary" polynucleotide strands around a common axis to form the DNA *double helix*, in which adenine-thymine and guanine-cytosine

pairs are stacked above each other in a helical ladder linking two polynucleotide chains in one very long, highly regular DNA molecule. Under physiological conditions DNA exists, not as the acid, but as a polymeric anion. It must therefore be associated with positive ions. Some if not most of these are themselves macromolecules, particularly the histones and protamines, which are proteins rich in the positively charged amino acids arginine and lysine.

Although DNA is found only in the nucleus and in certain organelles of metazoan cells, RNA can be detected both in the nucleus and in the cytoplasm. The main purine and pyrimidine constituents of RNA are adenine, guanine, cytosine, and uracil, although, particularly in transfer RNA (see below), numerous substitutions have been found; their role in transfer RNA functions is still not clear. Several distinctly different types of RNA are recognized as existing in cells; compounds of

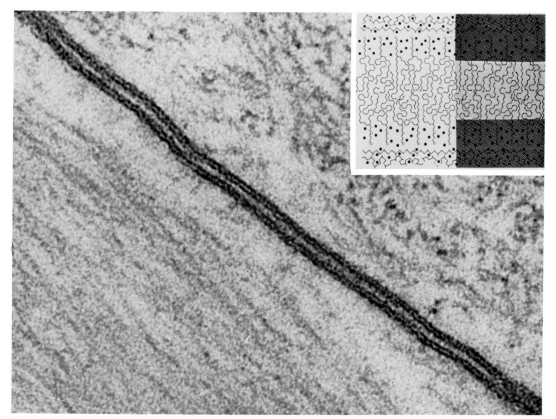

Figure 2-3. Electron micrograph of the plasma membrane of two adjoining glial cells. The cell membranes are separated by a narrow intercellular space, and each membrane appears as two dense lines about 25 Å thick separated by a less dense layer 25 Å thick. × 190,000. The inset illustrates the current interpretation of how the disposition of osmium in the protein layers and in the polar ends of the lipid molecules results in the appearance of two dense lines separated by a less dense layer.

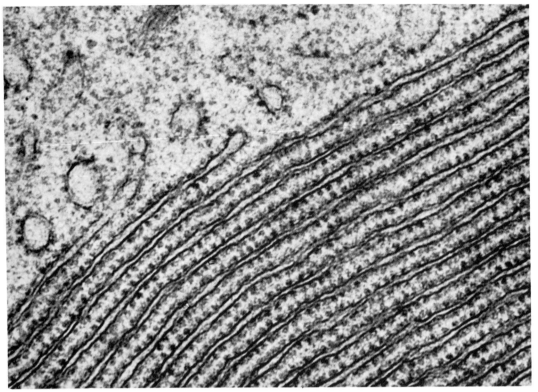

Figure 2-4. Electron micrograph of the granular endoplasmic reticulum of a pancreatic acinar cell. This form of the reticulum consists of parallel arrays of broad flat sacs or cisternae. The outer surface of their limiting membranes is studded with particles (150 Å) of ribonucleoprotein (ribosomes). Endoplasmic reticulum having such granules adhering to its membranes is often called ergastoplasm. Osmium tetroxide fixation. × 85,000.

one of these types, called *soluble,* or *transfer, ribonucleic acids* (sRNA), form compounds with the amino acids that are the immediate precursors of polypeptides. Another type of RNA, of higher molecular weight, is found associated with protein in the submicroscopic *ribosomes* present in the cytoplasm of all cells (p. 42). These nucleoprotein particles have molecular weights of several million (4.5×10^6) and are the sites of protein synthesis. A third type of RNA transmits directions for the synthesis of specific proteins from the store of genetic potentialities (DNA) to the ribosomal protein factories. It has consequently been named messenger RNA.

The possibility that the molecular basis of the structure of protoplasm might be elucidated has long fired the imagination of biologists. It is fair to say that although our fund of information about biological ultrastructure has grown enormously, generalization in terms of universal organizing forces or principles does not begin to do justice to the specificity and

regularity demonstrated by those structures that are already known. However, certain types of regular molecular patterns recur frequently, and two of these are briefly discussed below (pp. 35 and 36). For more details and more widely ranging descriptions, the reader is referred to books on ultrastructure.

LIPIDS. Up to this point in the chemical description, we have confined our attention to macromolecules and their interactions. The structural basis of biological membrane formation, on the other hand, is the interaction of smaller molecules, lipids, with proteins. The lipids are a large class of substances encompassing the triglycerides or neutral fats; the phosphatides, such as lecithin and cephalins; the cerebrosides; the sterols; and others. They contain long aliphatic chains or other nonpolar parts, as well as such polar or ionized functional groups as carboxylic or phosphate esters, amides, sugars, amines, and alcohols. There is, consequently, a tendency for these molecules to orient themselves at water interfaces with their polar groups projecting into the polar solvent, water, and their nonpolar portions pointing out of the aqueous phase, in which these portions are poorly soluble. As a result of this dual solubility, many lipids form, at water-air interfaces, monomolecular layers that are highly ordered and compact (Fig. 2-1). A wide variety of intermolecular interactions are possible in these *monolayers,* including the formation of stoichiometric compounds between different surface active substances. It is also possible to demonstrate the formation of complexes with protein molecules dissolved in the aqueous substrate.

Aspects of this layer-sandwich structure persist in lipid crystals. Bimolecular leaflets are a structural feature of these crystals. They are formed by pairs of lipid layers arranged back to back in such a way that the nonpolar groups of two layers of molecules are apposed (Fig. 2-1*B*). A crystal consists of stacks of these leaflets, so that planes of polar and nonpolar groups alternate. Water can penetrate those

regions of crystals bounded by planes of polar groups. In fact, in the presence of water, even complex lipid mixtures will yield extremely regular crystalline and liquid-crystalline phases, in which the spacings between bimolecular leaflets are determined by the quantity of water intercalated between the layers of polar groups.

Thus some of the features of the lamellar membranes of the retinal rod and cone cells (Figs. 34-26 and 34-27), the mitochondria (Figs. 2-9 and 2-10), the myelin sheath (Fig. 12-17), the endoplasmic reticulum. (Figs. 2-4 and 28-7), and the Golgi complex (Fig. 2-15) are strikingly analogized by inert lipid-protein-water complexes: mixed lipids form planar structures *whose stability is determined by the presence of water,* and these planar structures are made more rigid by their integration with a thin protein layer. In many natural lipoprotein membranes two layers of the mixed lipid-protein complex are joined back to back to form a *unit membrane* (Figs.

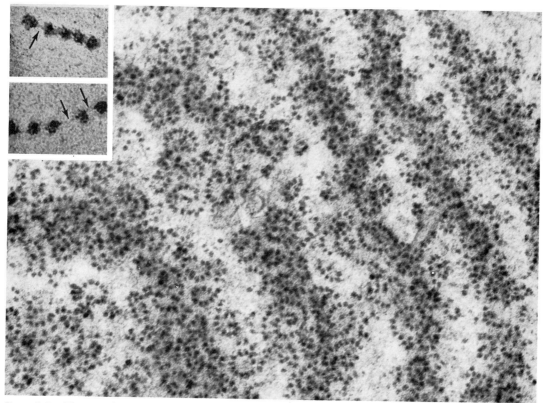

Figure 2-5. Electron micrograph of an oblique section passing tangential to several parallel cisternae of the endoplasmic reticulum, and showing numerous spiral and rosette configurations of polyribosomes. × 75,000. (Courtesy of E. Yamada.) The inset shows positively stained, isolated polyribosomes connected by a thin strand (at arrow) representing the messenger RNA. (Courtesy of C. Hall and A. Rich.)

2-2 and 2-3). The detailed arrangements then vary. In the myelin sheath of nerve fibers, layer upon layer of these unit membranes accumulate to form the extremely regular pattern shown in Figure 12-17. In the retinal rod cells, membranes are folded into continuous envelopes enclosing small cavities, and these envelopes are piled on each other in regular array (Fig. 34-26).

One other striking example of the regularity and specificity of molecular arrangement demonstrable in structural components of tissues is provided by the architecture of collagen fibrils, discussed in further detail in Chapter 6. It is appropriate at this point to emphasize that the elaborate periodic fine structure of light and dark bands shown by the electron microscope (Fig. 6-5) is the result of a chemical reaction between a stain (phosphotungstic acid) and certain groups in protein molecules (probably amino groups of lysine and arginine). The fibrils shown in Figure 6-3 extend for the dimension of many molecules in all directions. Were the aggregation of precollagenous units into fibrils a result of random clumping, the various arginine and lysine amino groups would be randomly disposed and staining would reveal no periodicity. The result observed leads to exactly the opposite conclusion, namely, that the construction of collagen fibrils from its building block, tropocollagen, involves the perfectly regular side by

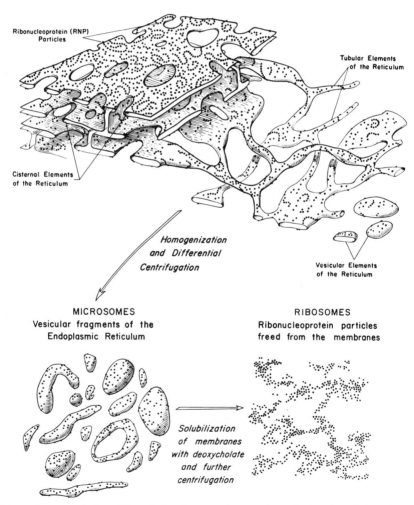

Figure 2-6. Schematic representation of the relations between the granular endoplasmic reticulum (ergastoplasm) and the *microsome* and *ribosome* fractions isolated by differential centrifugation. The ribosomes are always on the outer surface of the membrane limiting the tubules and cisternae.

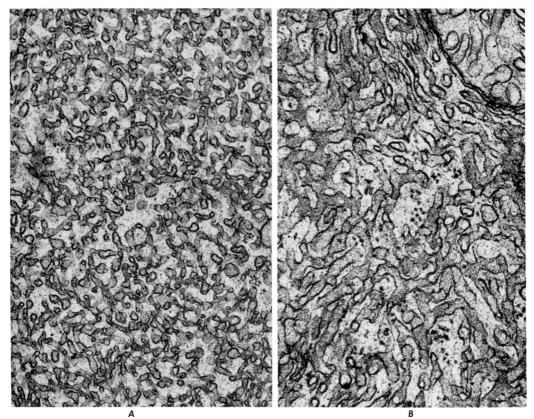

Figure 2-7. Electron micrographs of agranular or smooth-surfaced endoplasmic reticulum. *A* from liver cell of hamster, × 34,000; *B* from the human adrenal cortex, × 50,000. (Courtesy J. Long.)

side and end to end array of protein molecules. Evidently, at least two aggregation patterns are possible under different chemical conditions (Fig. 6-6), and one of these corresponds to the molecular arrangement in natural collagen fibrils.

The foregoing are two examples of structural components of cells or tissues about which some molecular architectural information is available and in which emphasis is placed on the chemical specificity of the interactions determining the structure. Undoubtedly, many elements of protoplasm lack either the regularity or the simplicity of these structures, or both.

Any discussion of cellular architecture, no matter how brief, would be incomplete without some reference to water, the major constituent of cells. Water is not only the solvent medium through which materials are transported and a participant in many biochemical reactions, it also determines the configuration

of the macromolecules dissolved in it, their ability to bind other molecules, large or small and, ultimately, the form that the structural components of cells and tissues may assume.

THE CELL

A conspicuous spherical body, the nucleus, was recognized in the interior of plant cells by Brown in 1833 and was subsequently found to be present in all animal cells as well. It has since been customary to consider the *protoplasm* of the cell as partitioned into two major regions or compartments, the nucleus, composed of *nucleoplasm* (karyoplasm), and the protoplasm surrounding the nucleus, called *cytoplasm*. Both contain a number of structural components of characteristic form and staining properties that permit them to be recognized with the light microscope. On the basis of their generality and a judgment as to their functional significance, these components have tra-

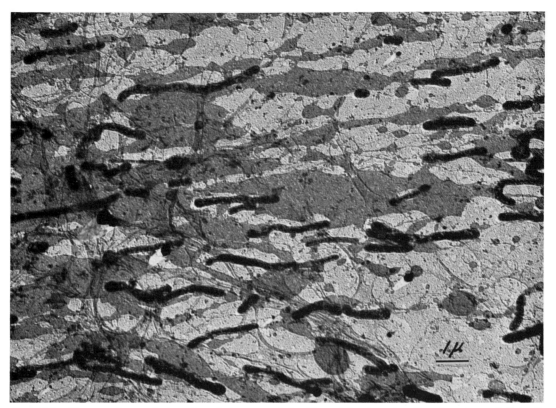

Figure 2-8. Electron micrograph through a whole mount of the thin peripheral portion of a cultured mesothelial cell. The irregular elongate rods are mitochondria. The less dense structures of exceedingly irregular size and shape and connected by thin strands are tubular and cisternal elements of the endoplasmic reticulum seen in surface view. Osmic acid fixation. (Courtesy of G. Palade and K. R. Porter.)

ditionally been classified as belonging to one or the other of two categories—*organelles* and *inclusions*. The *organelles* are structures occurring in nearly all cell types and are regarded as small internal organs of the cell—organized units of living substance having important specific functions in cell metabolism. The *inclusions*, on the other hand, are considered to be lifeless accumulations of metabolites or cell products, such as protein, fat, carbohydrate, crystals, pigment, secretory droplets, and the like, which are regarded as dispensable and often temporary constituents of cells.

Although the distinction between organelles and inclusions is still useful, it should be borne in mind that the assignment of the common cell components to one category or the other was made at a time when too little was known of their ultrastructure and chemical nature to permit a valid judgment as to whether they were physiologically active or inert, essential or dispensible. Therefore, it is not surprising that as our knowledge of cell biology has increased, the validity of the time honored classification of certain cell structures has become debatable. As a consequence of electron microscopic studies, the list of organelles has been greatly lengthened and a number of new components have been described that are difficult to categorize for lack of precise information as to their chemical nature and function.

Cytoplasm

Control of the development and function of a cell resides mainly in its nucleus, while most of the responding metabolic and synthetic activities are located in the cytoplasm. The latter, as seen with the optical microscope, appears to consist of a "structureless" medium, the *ground substance* or *cytoplasmic matrix*, and the *organelles* and *inclusions* suspended in it. The specialization of cells for different functions is often reflected in their size and shape and in variations in the number and kinds of organelles and inclusions they contain. We rely heavily upon characteristic differences in such criteria for the identification of the various cell types.

The organelles visible with the light microscope—mitochondria, Golgi apparatus, ergastoplasm—were originally described as granules, filaments, lamellae, and so on, implying that they were relatively solid structures. The electron microscope has now shown that these familiar organelles, and several of those newly discovered, are vacuolar structures bounded by thin lipoprotein membranes and, in some instances, possessing in addition a complex system of internal membranes.

Most of the important physiological processes of living organisms take place at surfaces and interfaces. Many of the thousands of enzymes in the cell, which catalyze specific chemical transformations, are strategically located in the membranes, where they participate in reactions occurring at the interface between the organelles and the cytoplasmic matrix or between the cell and its environment. The elaborate internal compartmentation of the cytoplasm represented by the organelles no doubt promotes the efficiency of numerous complex chemical reactions by extending the area of the physiologically active interfaces.

Possessing numerous membrane limited compartments may also enable the cell to maintain a separation of enzymes from substrates at some times and at others to permit their controlled interaction by varying the permeability of the membrane or the rate of active transport across it. It is clear that if there were unlimited diffusion and interaction within the cell it would be impossible to maintain the high degree of chemical heterogeneity characteristic of the cytoplasm: enzymes would attack their substrates and all of the potential interactions of the countless chemical constituents of the cell would race out of control. Actually, however, this does not occur. The cell is able to regulate its activities and to keep in reserve a very large repertoire of unexpressed biochemical potentialities. It can call each of these into play at the proper time and at the

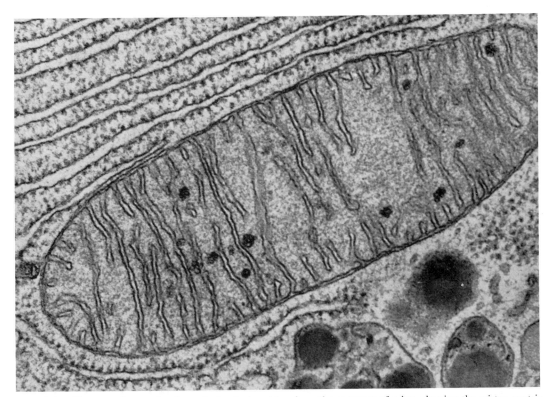

Figure 2-9. Electron micrograph of a typical mitochondrion from the pancreas of a bat, showing the cristae, matrix, and matrix granules. Endoplasmic reticulum is seen at the upper left and some lysosomes at the lower right. × 79,000. (Courtesy of K. R. Porter.)

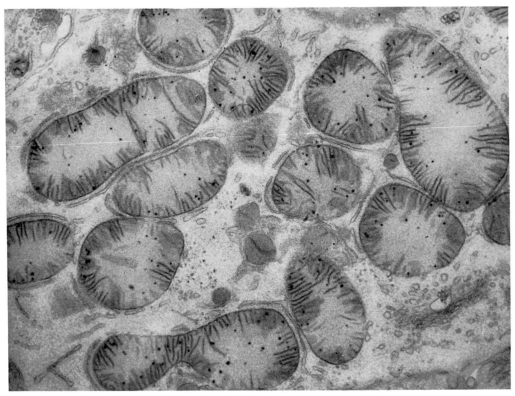

Figure 2-10. Electron micrograph of mitochondria in a bat liver cell, showing numerous cristae of varying length projecting into an amorphous matrix of low density that contains scattered small dense granules. × 17,000. (Courtesy of S. Ito.)

rate appropriate to the needs of the organism as a whole. That this is possible is probably due in large measure to the prevalence of membrane bounded organelles in the cytoplasm.

CELL MEMBRANE (PLASMALEMMA). The cell is enclosed by a thin limiting membrane, called the *plasmalemma* or simply the *cell membrane*. It is ordinarily too thin to be seen in sections with the light microscope, but its reality can be demonstrated visually by the outflow of cytoplasm when the membrane is torn by micromanipulation. Numerous physiological experiments on the swelling and shrinking of cells in solutions of different osmolarity also attest to the presence of a limiting membrane and demonstrate its selective permeability. Its low permeability to ions and high permeability to lipid soluble substances early suggested to cell physiologists that the membrane was composed of lipid or lipoprotein. Ingenious indirect measurements of its thickness, birefringence, surface tension, and other properties led Danielli and Davson in 1935 to propose that the membrane probably consists of a bimolecular

layer of mixed lipids between two layers of adsorbed proteins (Fig. 2-2).

When it became possible to examine thin sections of cells with the electron microscope, the surface membrane was visualized as a dense linear profile 80 to 100 Å thick. At higher magnification, this line could be resolved as two dense layers about 25 Å thick separated by a 30 Å light intermediate layer (Fig. 2-3). Some variation in overall thickness is encountered from one cell type to another and some asymmetry in the relative thickness of the two dense layers, but the same basic trilaminar structure is found in all cell membranes, and this is now referred to as the *unit membrane* (Robertson). Its three layers have generally been interpreted as corresponding to the two protein layers and the bimolecular leaflet of the Danielli model. An alternative interpretation of the molecular organization of the membrane, recently proposed, depicts the lipid as forming globular micelles between two layers of protein, but until more precise information is available there is little basis for making a choice between these two hypothetical models. A resolution of this problem is of the greatest importance, however, for in the structure and chemical organization of the cell membrane lies the key to its selective permeability, its specific enzymatic activity, its capacity to conduct an impulse, and many other properties upon which life depends.

The outer limit of the cell surface is not always easily defined. On the outer aspect of the unit membrane in plant cells there is an inert layer of cellulose called the *cell wall*. It has recently been found that many animal cells also have a thin external coating of material rich in polysaccharides. There is little agreement as to whether this should be regarded as an integral part of the cell membrane or as an extraneous coating. It is now a subject of intensive investigation and may prove to have a very important role in the selective uptake of substances by cells.

ERGASTOPLASM (GRANULAR ENDOPLASMIC RETICULUM). In stained histological sections, the cytoplasm of many cell types contains a substance that has a strong affinity for basic dyes. This component may be widely dispersed in the cytoplasm and stain diffusely or it may be concentrated in discrete basophilic masses or clumps of varying size. Classical cytologists referred to this deeply staining material as the *chromidial substance* or the *ergastoplasm*. Later, when reliable histochemical staining reactions and ultraviolet absorption methods and methods for isolation of cell components were developed for the detection of nucleic acids, the basophilic substance of the cytoplasm was identified as *ribonucleoprotein*.

With the advent of the electron microscope, the cytoplasm of nearly all cells was found to possess a more or less continuous network of membrane-bounded cavities. This canalicular system was soon accepted as a new organelle and called the *endoplasmic reticulum*. Its fluid-filled channels facilitate passive diffusion of metabolites throughout the cytoplasm, and its limiting membranes contain enzyme systems that play an active role in cell metabolism. In its most typical form it consists of an irregular network of branching and anastomosing tubules, often continuous with flattened saccular structures commonly referred to as *cisternae*. The latter may occur singly, but more often several become associated to form lamellar systems of parallel flat cavities (Fig. 2-4). In addition to the intercommunicating

tubules and cisternae, there are isolated vesicles that do not form part of the continuous system of cytoplasmic channels but are nevertheless considered to be portions of the endoplasmic reticulum. The degree of development of the reticulum and the relative proportions of its tubular, cisternal, and vesicular elements vary greatly in different cell types and in different phases of the physiological activity of the same cell type.

It is now generally accepted that the ergastoplasmic strands and chromidial bodies of classical cytology correspond to the aggregations of endoplasmic reticulum observed in electron micrographs, but their component tubules and cisternae usually are not resolved by the light microscope. The basophilia of these structures does not reside in the canalicular elements of the reticulum per se but in small particles of ribonucleoprotein, called *ribosomes*, which are found in great numbers adhering to the outer surface of their limiting membrane (Figs. 2-4 and 2-5). These dense particles are very uniform in size, 120 to 150 Å in diameter, and occur free in the cytoplasmic matrix as

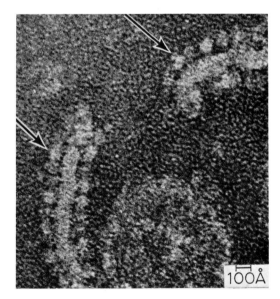

Figure 2-11. Electron micrograph of mitochondrial cristae at very high magnification. The figure shows the arrangement of structural units originally designated "elementary particles" as they appear in preparations negatively stained with phosphotungstic acid. These particles, having a diameter of about 80 Å, were originally believed to correspond to the respiratory enzyme assemblies. Evidence is now accumulating that indicates that they may instead contain ATPase and the enzymes of oxidative phosphorylation. (Courtesy of H. Fernández-Morán.)

well as being attached to the membranes. The ribosomes are the sites of synthesis of new protein in the cell. Free ribosomes are believed to be sites of the protein synthesis necessary to sustain cell proliferation and for other uses within the cell. Ribosomes attached to membranes are believed to be concerned with synthesis of protein to be secreted by the cell.

Whether free or attached, ribosomes are very often associated in clusters, called *polyribosomes* or *polysomes*, consisting of three to 30 or more ribosomes held together by a slender filament 10 to 15 Å in diameter and of variable length. This slender strand is sensitive to ribonuclease digestion and is thought to be a single long molecule of a species of nucleic acid called *messenger RNA*. This form of nucleic acid is formed in the nucleus in association with the DNA of the chromosomes and carries to the ribosomes in the cytoplasm the encoded information that determines the sequence of amino acids in the specific protein to be synthesized.

The ribosomes evidently attach to specific sites on the messenger RNA molecule and then move along its length, being released from it with the liberation of the completed polypeptide chain of the newly synthesized protein. The endoplasmic reticulum is poorly developed in embryonic and other rapidly proliferating cells, but such cells contain a large population of free ribosomes that are responsible for their diffuse basophilia. In glandular cells, on the other hand, where the basophilia resides in discrete clumps, this localized staining is attributable to the ribosomes attached to parallel arrays of cisternae of the endoplasmic reticulum.

To investigate the metabolic activities of cell components, biochemists isolate them from tissue homogenates by centrifugation. In addition to their exploration of the larger organelles—nuclei, nucleoli, and mitochondria—they have devoted much attention in the past 20 years to the properties of a fraction consist-

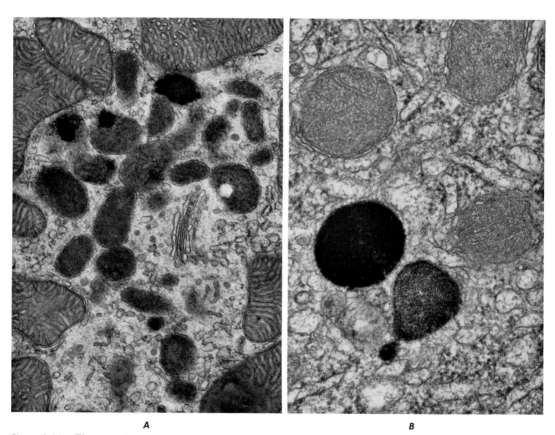

A   B

Figure 2-12. Electron micrographs of lysosomes. Those in *A* from the adrenal cortex are nonspecifically stained with osmium and lead. × 25,000. Lysosomes from the rat vas deferens in *B* have been stained for acid phosphatase activity. × 65,000. (Courtesy of D. Friend.)

ing of submicroscopic particles rich in nucleic acid and once called *microsomes*. Although it was initially believed that such particles existed as such in the intact cell, it has become evident from electron microscopic examination of this fraction that the microsomes of the biochemist are small vesicular fragments of the endoplasmic reticulum produced during homogenization of the cells (Fig. 2-6). They are membrane limited spherical vesicles with an amorphous content and variable numbers of ribosomes on their outer surfaces. By treatment of the microsome fraction with deoxycholate, their membranes can be solubilized. Further high speed centrifugation then yields a pure fraction of ribosomes.

Most of the ribonucleoprotein of cells can be isolated centrifugally as ribosomal particles 150 to 200 Å in diameter. These are identical to the small dense granules seen in electron micrographs, either free in the cytoplasmic matrix or associated with the outer surface of the membranes of the endoplasmic reticulum. They have a sedimentation coefficient of 80S and are composed of two dissimilar subunits, with sedimentation coefficients of 60S and 40S, held together by hydrogen bonds and magnesium ions. The two units can be taken apart by subjecting ribosomes in vitro to a magnesium free medium. There is no indication as yet that the subunits ever occur separately in cells. The nucleic acid in each of the units is associated with histones and structural protein. Further degradation of the subunits can be achieved by removal of the protein, which leaves two forms of RNA, one of 28S and the other of 18S sedimentation coefficient.

AGRANULAR ENDOPLASMIC RETICULUM. When it was first discovered that the distribution of parallel arrays of endoplasmic reticulum in electron micrographs was the same as that of the ergastoplasm of classical cytology, it was assumed that areas rich in endoplasmic reticulum were invariably basophilic. As experience was gained with a greater variety of tissues, it soon became clear that in some cell types the membrane limited tubules comprising the endoplasmic reticulum lack associated ribosomes. In such cells the cytoplasm is often acidophilic. Possessing no distinctive staining properties at the light microscope level that set it off from the surrounding cytoplasmic matrix, the *agranular reticulum* went undetected by cytologists.

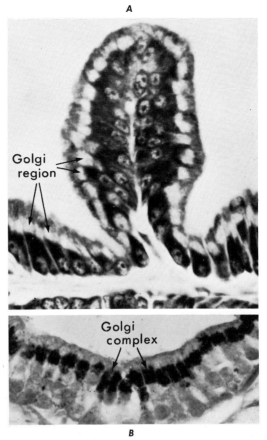

Figure 2-13. Photomicrograph of epithelial cells from the prostate, showing in *A* the Golgi zone in negative image and in *B* the Golgi complex impregnated with osmium in the Da Fano technique. × 500.

Two categories of endoplasmic reticulum are now distinguished, the granular or rough surfaced form that can be equated with the ergastoplasm or chromidial substance and the agranular or smooth surfaced reticulum that has no easily identifiable counterpart in stained histological sections. Although the two forms of this organelle are often continuous with one another, there is reason to believe that the difference between them goes beyond the mere presence or absence of ribosomes. The agranular reticulum is usually a close meshed tridimensional network of tubules and seldom takes the form of cisternae (Fig. 2-7*A* and *B*). In many cell types either one form or the other of the reticulum greatly predominates. For example, in protein secreting cells such as those of the pancreas, the endoplasmic reticulum is almost exclusively of the granular type, whereas in muscle it is mainly of the smooth surfaced variety. In other cells, such as those of the liver, the two types are represented in nearly equal proportions. It follows that the microsome fraction obtained from homogenates of different tissues will vary in its content of RNA and will contain fragments of both categories of reticulum. It has recently become possible to achieve a subfractionation of the microsomes, separating those bearing ribosomes on their surface from smooth surfaced microsomes that are derived mainly from the agranular reticulum.

The biochemical differences between the two kinds of reticulum have not been well worked out. Although there is good agreement that the granular reticulum is involved in protein synthesis, it is not yet possible to assign a single function to the agranular reticulum. In striated muscle it seems to be concerned with the release and recapture of calcium ions in the cycle of contraction and relaxation. In a number of endocrine glands it has been implicated in the biosynthesis of steroid hormones, and in the liver it is involved in cholesterol and lipid metabolism and in the hydroxylation of various endogenous and exogenous compounds.

MITOCHONDRIA. Mitochondria are organelles long recognized by light microscopists. Their discovery is commonly attributed to Altmann (1890), who described them as minute granules or filaments and erroneously interpreted them as elementary organisms existing in colonies in all cells. Their general occurrence was amply confirmed by other investigators, but little real progress was made toward an understanding of their function until about 1934 when centrifugal methods were developed for their isolation in bulk (Bensley). It is now known that their principal function is to act as mobile "power plants" supplying energy for numerous chemical reactions and active transport mechanisms of the cell. Energy is accumulated by generating a supply of the compound adenosine triphosphate (ATP). The *oxidation* of nutrients absorbed in the diet provides the energy for synthesis of ATP by *phosphorylation* of its precursors. The overall energy generating mechanism is referred to as *oxidative phosphorylation*. In addition to the enzymes involved in these important reactions,

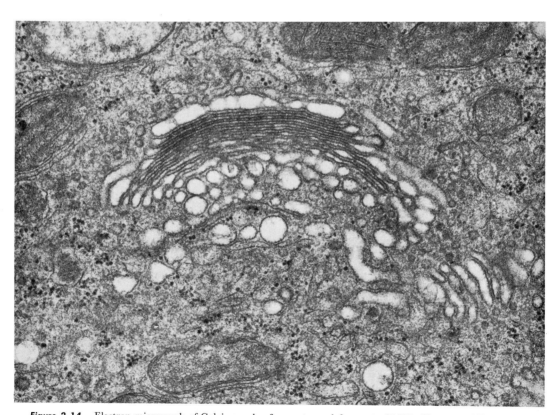

Figure 2-14. Electron micrograph of Golgi complex from rat vas deferens. × 65,000. (Courtesy of D. Friend.)

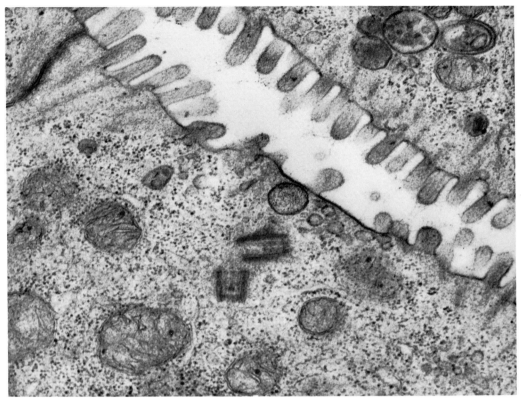

Figure 2-15. Electron micrograph of a pair of centrioles in the apical cytoplasm of an intestinal epithelial cell of a chick. The centrioles are hollow cylindrical structures, often oriented with their long axes perpendicular to each other. Osmium fixation. × 33,500. (Courtesy of S. Sorokin.)

the mitochondria contain enzymes concerned with protein synthesis and others participating in certain steps of lipid metabolism (Table 2-1).

Mitochondria can be seen in the living cell with the phase contrast microscope as slender rods or filaments 0.5 μ in diameter and 2 to 4 μ long. They can be selectively stained in the living cell by the supravital dye, Janus green. They are moved about passively in the cell in the normal streaming of the cytoplasm but also seem to be capable of active sinuous movements. To the light microscopist they appear devoid of internal organization, but when examined with the electron microscope in ultrathin sections, they have a complex and highly characteristic structure (Fig. 2-9). They are enclosed by two membranes. The outer membrane, 50 to 60 Å thick, is a smooth contoured, continuous limiting membrane. The inner membrane is of similar thickness but is thrown up into narrow pleats or folds, called *cristae*, projecting into the central cavity of the organelle, which is occupied by a moderately dense,

finely granular *mitochondrial matrix*. In this structural organization the membranes delimit two internal compartments: a large *intercristal space* occupied by matrix and a smaller compartment, the *membrane space*, comprising the space between the outer and inner membranes and extending inward between the leaves of the cristae. The membrane space is normally very narrow and has so little density in micrographs that it appears empty. The intercristal space, on the other hand, has a number of formed components.

A small number of dense granules 300 to 500 Å in diameter are usually found in the matrix occupying the intercristal space. These *matrix granules* have not been isolated and analyzed but they are believed to be concerned with the regulation of the internal ionic environment of the mitochondria. Calcium and other divalent cations accumulate in mitochondria when they are present in high concentration in intact cells or in the fluid bathing isolated mitochondria. Under these conditions unusually large dense granules are found in the mitochondria and it appears likely that the accumulated ions are organically bound to the pre-existing matrix granules to form these larger dense bodies.

Filaments of deoxyribonucleoprotein (DNA) have been identified in the mitochondrial matrix by both chemical and histochemical methods. There are also small granules about 120 Å in diameter containing ribonucleic acid (RNA). These are somewhat smaller than the ribosomes of the extramitochondrial cytoplasm. The mitochondrial DNA and RNA seem to constitute an extranuclear genetic system concerned with the protein synthesis necessary for mitochondrial proliferation. Whether it has other important functions in the cell has yet to be determined.

Much is now known about the localization of the enzymes within mitochondria. When isolated mitochondria are disrupted, some of the enzymes residing in the matrix are released into the medium as soluble protein, while others remain bound to the membranes. A partial listing of the membrane bound and soluble enzymes is given in Table 2-1. In general, the respiratory and phosphorylating enzymes are attached to the membranes, while those of the Krebs citric acid cycle and those concerned with protein and lipid synthesis are in the matrix. Indirect biochemical evidence supports the view that the enzymes and coenzymes associated with the membranes are not randomly distributed but are arranged in a highly ordered repeating pattern that facilitates the sequential catalytic reactions carried out by this organelle. The postulated spatial ordering of enzyme molecules is, for the most

part, beyond the reach of the electron microscope. However, much interest has recently centered in certain subunits of the inner mitochondrial membrane that can be visualized at very high magnification in negatively stained preparations (Fig. 2-11). These so-called mitochondrial *elementary particles* or *inner membrane subunits* project into the matrix. Each consists of a globular particle about 90 Å in diameter connected by a slender stem 35 to 45 Å long to a basal plate situated in the inner leaf of the trilaminar unit membrane. The whole matrix surface of the inner mitochondrial membrane and its cristae is covered with these subunits closely packed together. They are not found on the outer membrane. Since their first description in 1962 a lively controversy has developed as to their nature. One school has contended that each particle contains a complete set of enzymes of the electron transport chain, with cytochrome oxidase in the globular head and other cytochromes in the stem. The other school has presented evidence indicating that because of its size cytochrome oxidase could not reside in the globular particle and has proposed instead that the inner membrane subunits contain adenosine triphosphatase and the enzymes of oxidative phosphorylation.

LYSOSOMES. The *lysosomes* are newcomers to the ranks of the cell organelles, first recognized as a separate category of particles by Christian de Duve in 1955. They are usually dense bodies 0.25 to 0.5 μ in diameter, limited by a membrane and containing a number of hydrolytic enzymes capable of breaking down proteins, DNA, RNA, and certain carbohydrates under conditions of slightly acid pH. Their enzymes are therefore referred to by the

Table 2-1. *Membrane Bound and Soluble Enzymes of Mitochondria**

MEMBRANE BOUND	SOLUBLE (55% OF TOTAL PROTEIN)
Cytochromes	Most Krebs citric acid cycle enzymes except
Coenzyme Q	some dehydrogenases
Flavoproteins	Glutamate dehydrogenase
Dehydrogenases for the following substrates:	Enzymes for protein synthesis
reduced adenine dinucleotide (NADH)	Enzymes for lipid synthesis
succinate	
D-β-hydroxybutyrate	
α-glycerophosphate	
choline	
Oxidative phosphorylation enzymes	

* After D. F. Parsons. Int. Rev. Exp. Path., *4*:1, 1965.

collective term *acid hydrolases*. A partial list of the specific enzymes that have been identified in these particles includes acid phosphatase, acid ribonuclease, acid deoxyribonuclease, cathepsin, β-glucuronidase, β-galactosidase, aryl-sulfatase, and peroxidase.

In normal cells the lysosomal enzymes are safely contained within their enclosing membrane. A variety of experimental conditions and pharmacological agents may increase the permeability or cause the complete breakdown of the lysosomal membrane, allowing the enzymes to escape and digest or lyse the cell. The term *lysosome* is descriptive of this property. These particles therefore play a role in the breakdown of injured cells. They also play an important part in the intracellular digestion of foreign matter taken into cells in the process of phagocytosis. For example, two of the kinds of leukocytes or white blood corpuscles contain numerous granules with the properties of lysosomes. These cells are also capable of ingesting bacteria and are therefore in the first line of defense of the organism against invasion by pathogenic microorganisms. When bacteria are engulfed they are taken into the cell in membrane bounded phagocytosis vacuoles or *phagosomes*. Numerous lysosomes then adhere to the limiting membrane of the phagosome and fuse with it so that their hydrolytic enzymes are discharged into it, killing and ultimately digesting the bacterium.

There is also some evidence that in the life of the normal cell, mitochondria and other cell organelles that have become damaged may fuse with lysosomes to form *cytolysosomes* and may ultimately be destroyed. Apparently not all substances can be completely broken down in the cell, and with age the indigestible residues of the lysosomal activity associated with normal wear and tear accumulate in the cell in the form of *lipofuscin pigment*.

Lysosomes were discovered by biochemists subfractionating the mitochondrial fraction isolated by differential centrifugation. The presence of a membrane was inferred from the fact that mechanical disruption or treatment with surface active agents was necessary before the enzymes could act upon their substrates. Lysosomes were defined, therefore, as membrane limited particles containing acid hydrolases. The visual identification of lysosomes in electron micrographs came later, and the appearance of the structures fulfilling these two defining criteria has proved to be surprisingly diverse. Some have a smooth spherical or ovoid shape and a dense homogeneous interior; others are quite irregular in outline and inhomogeneous in density; still others are large globular structures with a rather pale matrix; and finally, a few special kinds of lysosomes, such as the specific granules of eosinophilic leukocytes, may contain dense equatorial crystals in a less dense matrix. The diversity of the appearance of this organelle from one cell type to another makes its identification on morphological grounds alone quite uncertain. The uptake by lysosomes of fluorescent vital dyes, such as acridine orange, and their histochemical reactions for acid hydrolases are valuable additional criteria for their identification (Fig. 2-13B).

The functions of lysosomes in the economy of the cell are still being defined. The subject remains somewhat confused, and a complex and cumbersome terminology has developed as an increasing number of morphological types are described. The concept that has gradually emerged is that the lysosomes and certain other vacuolar structures lacking hydrolytic enzymes collectively constitute a discontinuous intracellular digestive system for the cell. The *primary lysosomes*, containing enzymes that have not yet been engaged in digestive activities, are distinguished from *secondary lysosomes*, which are vacuolar structures that are the sites of current or past digestive activity. The material undergoing digestion may be exogenous or endogenous. When the vacuolar elements of this system are involved in digestion of components of the cell's own cytoplasm, and when morphologically recognizable fragments of normal cytoplasmic organelles are found in their interior, such structures are called *autophagic vacuoles*. If hydrolases have been added to them by fusion with lysosomes, they are called *autolysosomes*. Vacuoles containing exogenous substances are called *heterophagic vacuoles*, and if digestion is in progress, *heterolysosomes*.

MICROBODIES. The term *microbody* was introduced by Rhodin in 1954 to designate spherical cytoplasmic bodies, about 0.5 μ in diameter, surrounded by a single membrane. They were first observed in the cells of the proximal convoluted tubule of the kidney and soon thereafter were also reported in the liver. To date they have not been described in any other mammalian cell types.

The microbodies of the kidney have a

homogeneous, finely granular matrix of moderate density. Those of the liver show significant species differences. In the rat they contain conspicuous dense *cores* or *nucleoids* that exhibit a highly ordered substructure with the appearance of a crystal. At high magnification, however, this is resolved as a polytubular structure made up of minute tubules of two different sizes: large ones 95 to 115 Å in diameter and smaller ones 45Å in diameter. In transverse sections, these are arranged in a regular pattern, with each large tubule surrounded by 10 smaller ones, and this unit is repeated throughout the cross section of the core. In longitudinal section this arrangement gives rise to a pattern of parallel lines with alternate narrow and wider spacings. In certain other species, the cores of the microbodies appear to be composed only of the 45 Å tubules in regular hexagonal array. In the hamster the core takes the form of a thin flexuous sheet.

Microbodies isolated from mitochondrial and lysosome fractions by gradient centrifugation are found to contain *urate oxidase, d-amino acid oxidase,* and *catalase.* Because they contain oxidases capable of reducing oxygen to hydrogen peroxide and hydrogen peroxide to water, it has recently been suggested that a more appropriate descriptive name for the microbody would be *peroxisome.*

The matrix is believed to be mainly catalase and other soluble proteins. The cores are relatively insoluble and are thought to be the site of the urate oxidase. Consistent with this interpretation is the finding that human liver microbodies that are devoid of urate oxidase also lack cores in electron micrographs.

Although microbodies bear a superficial resemblance to secretory granules, there is no evidence that they are discharged from the cell. It is assumed that they function within the cytoplasm, but their precise role is not understood.

THE GOLGI APPARATUS. The Golgi complex is an organelle discovered by Camillo Golgi in 1898 in cells of the nervous system and named by him the *internal reticular apparatus.* It was later found to be present in nearly all cell types and gradually came to be called the *Golgi apparatus.* Ordinarily it is not visible in the living cell and it is usually not seen in routine histological preparations, but it can sometimes be identified in negative image as an unstained juxtanuclear area (Fig. 2-13*A*).

However, in tissue subjected to prolonged impregnation with osmium or silver, it can be demonstrated as a blackened network usually located in the juxtanuclear region (Fig. 2-13*B*).

At the electron microscope level it has a lamellar membranous structure instead of the reticular or canalicular configuration traditionally described. It consists of curved parallel arrays of flattened saccules or cisternae that are often expanded at their ends (Fig. 2-14). Large numbers of minute vesicles are associated with the convex outer surfaces of the stacks of cisternae, and larger vacuoles are often found at their concave inner surfaces. In secretory cells, the innermost cisternae may have a content of appreciable density and the associated vacuoles, after concentrating the cell product, develop into secretory droplets or granules.

The concept of function of the Golgi apparatus that has developed from light and electron microscopic observations is that in glandular cells it is concerned with the concentration and packaging of the secretory product. For cells elaborating a protein rich secretion, the Golgi apparatus is believed to play no significant role in its synthesis. There is now considerable evidence, however, that it may actively participate in the synthesis of secretory products rich in complex polysaccharides. The Golgi apparatus is also well developed in many cell types that are not secretory, and its function in the economy of these cells remains obscure.

ANNULATE LAMELLAE. This is the term that has been applied to a cytoplasmic organelle which consists of parallel arrays of cisternae exhibiting small annuli or circular fenestrae at very regular intervals along their length. The fenestrations are closed by a thin septum or diaphragm and thus very closely resemble the pores of the nuclear envelope (see p. 59). The lamellae or cisternae exhibit a high degree of order, being parallel and very uniformly spaced with the annuli of the successive cisternae often accurately aligned. Because of the similarity in appearance of the individual lamellae to a segment of the perinuclear cisterna, it has been suggested that they arise by delamination from the nuclear envelope, but this origin has not been firmly established. Annulate lamellae have been described in the germ cells of both invertebrate and vertebrate species, and in a large variety of normal somatic cell types. The functional significance of this organelle is still unknown.

The Centrosome and Centrioles. *Centrosome* is the term introduced by Boveri in 1888 to describe a specialized zone of cytoplasm containing the *centrioles,* a pair of small granules or short rods. The centrosome (centrosphere, cell center) is considered to be the center of a number of the activities associated with cell division. It is usually situated adjacent to the nucleus and may occupy a shallow indentation of its surface. The Golgi apparatus often partially surrounds the centrosome on the side away from the nucleus. In some epithelial cell types, however, the centrioles are not associated with the nucleus or the Golgi apparatus but are located in the apical cytoplasm immediately beneath the free surface of the cell (Fig. 2-15).

In electron micrographs each centriole is found to be a hollow cylinder 150 mμ in diameter and 300 to 500 mμ in length, closed at one end and open at the other. The central cavity is usually occupied by cytoplasm of low density, but it may contain one or more small dense granules. In transverse section, a centriole has a circular outline and its wall is seen to be composed of nine groups of longitudinally oriented parallel subunits. When these were first identified they were considered to be fibers, and this interpretation is still reflected in the terminology. With the resolution now obtained they seem to be tubular. Each of the nine groups consists of three tubules aligned and fused together so that in cross section they appear as three circles in a row. The innermost subunit of each triplet is designated subfiber A and the others subfibers B and C (Fig. 2-16). The subfibers A of the nine triplets are spaced at uniform intervals on the circumference of a circle about 150 mμ in diameter, and subfibers B and C are aligned so that the axis of each triplet diverges from a tangent to this circle at an angle of about 30°. Subfiber A of each triplet is connected to subfiber C of the next group by a slender dense line. The orientation of the triplets in cross section thus resembles a pinwheel or the vanes on a paddle wheel.

As a rule the centrioles occur in pairs, often referred to as a *diplosome.* The long axes of the two centrioles are usually perpendicular. The nature of the forces that maintain this

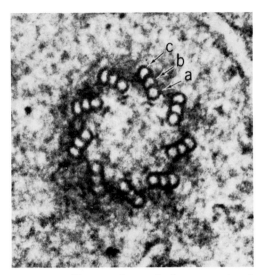

Figure 2-16. Electron micrograph of a cross section of a centriole in embryonic chick pancreas. The subunits in the wall of the centriole are triple tubular structures. The innermost element *a* is circular in cross section, while *b* and *c* are incomplete circles and share part of the wall of the adjacent element. × 180,000. (Courtesy of J. André.)

precise orientation is unknown. The centrioles are self duplicating bodies but they do not appear to reproduce by simple fission. When they replicate, early in cell division, the two pairs produced take up positions at opposite poles of the nucleus. There they serve as centers for the organization of microtubules (p. 31) to form the spindle and asters of the division figure.

Centrioles may also give rise to cilia and flagella. These motile cell processes arise from one end of the cylinder and possess nine doublet fibrils or tubules corresponding to the triplets in the wall of the centriole. The structure at the base of a cilium or flagellum has traditionally been called a *basal body* (also basal corpuscle, kinetosome, or blepharoplast), and this term persists even though it is now established that the structure is morphologically identical to a centriole. The several hundred basal bodies of a ciliated epithelial cell have long been thought to arise by repeated replication of an original pair of centrioles. There is now some evidence that basal bodies can also arise de novo during ciliogenesis and thus not all of them arise by self replication of pre-existing centrioles.

Filaments. The cytoplasmic matrix of most cells contains scattered filaments 30 to

60 Å in thickness and of indeterminate length. These may be widely dispersed and randomly oriented or they may be aggregated into bundles. The individual filaments cannot be resolved with the light microscope, but the bundles formed by their parallel association are easily visible in certain cell types and have long been referred to by histologists as *tonofibrils* (Fig. 2-17). These often terminate in the dense plaques, called *desmosomes,* adjacent to the membranes at specialized sites of cell to cell attachment. Such fibrils are especially abundant in the deeper cells of the epidermis that ultimately become transformed into devitalized scales as a consequence of accumulation in their cytoplasm of a scleroprotein called *keratin.* It has been suggested, therefore, that the filamentous subunits of the tonofibrils may be keratin or one of its precursors, but the evidence for this is not compelling.

It is possible that the filaments occurring in smaller numbers in many cell types that do not undergo keratinization may be of similar nature and may function as passive supportive elements contributing to the viscosity and elasticity of the protoplasmic gel. In certain cell types, filaments are very abundant in a thin superficial layer of the cytoplasm, the *ectoplasm,* which is believed to be more firmly gelated than the interior of the cell. On the other hand, smooth muscle cells contain filaments of rather similar appearance and dimensions but evidently of different chemical nature. These are, in part, responsible for the marked contractility of muscle. Since some degree of contractility is a universal property of

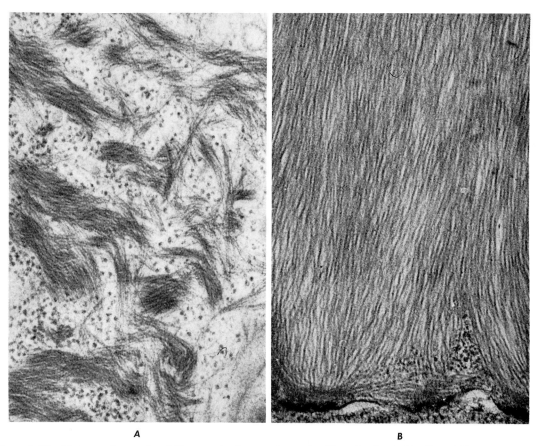

A   B

Figure 2-17. Electron micrographs of filaments in the cytoplasm of epidermal cells. *A,* Bundles of filaments corresponding to tonofibrils of epidermal cells in human skin. × 65,000. (Courtesy of G. Odland.) *B,* Filaments occupy large areas of certain basal cells in the epidermis of the lamprey. Many of these filaments terminate in dense areas of the cell surface called *hemidesmosomes.* × 80,000.

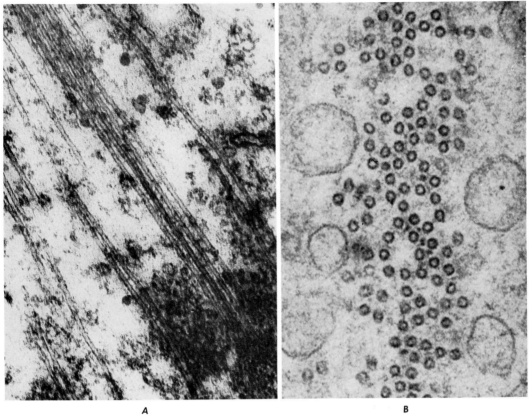

Figure 2-18.   Electron micrographs of cytoplasmic microtubules. *A*, Microtubules of the mitotic spindle seen here in longitudinal section. The chromosomes are at the lower right. × 70,000. (Courtesy E. Roth.) *B*, The microtubules in transverse section present circular profiles. Those shown here are from the manchette of a mammalian spermatid. × 140,000.

protoplasm, it can be argued that some of the filaments seen in other cell types may not be passive cytoskeletal elements but may be the structural basis for their limited contractility.

In view of the considerable variation in diameter and staining reactions of the cytoplasmic filaments, it is not clear at the present time whether the filaments that are of widespread occurrence in cytoplasm are all of the same chemical composition or whether there are two or more different types.

Microtubules.   In addition to submicroscopic filaments, the cytoplasm contains straight microtubules that can sometimes be followed in electron micrographs for two or three microns before they leave the plane of the section. They have a diameter of 200 to 270 Å and a wall 50 to 70 Å thick. The wall of the microtubule has been shown to be composed of about a dozen filamentous subunits with a center-to-center spacing of 55 to 60 Å.

Microtubules occur in small numbers in most cell types during interphase. They may be found in any part of the cytoplasm, but they often converge upon the centrosome and may terminate in satellites associated with the centrioles. In mitotic cell division, great numbers of microtubules arise and extend from the chromosomes to the poles and from pole to pole, to constitute the chromosomal and the continuous fibers of the spindle apparatus. (Fig. 2-18*A*) After cell division is completed the majority of these microtubules disappear.

In conditions other than mitosis, considerable numbers of microtubules may develop transiently at times of major alterations of cell shape. For example, during the phase of elongation in the development of spermatozoa, a cylindrical array of microtubules called the *manchette* is formed around the caudal pole of the nucleus and extends back into the region of the future neck and midpiece (Fig. 2-18*B*).

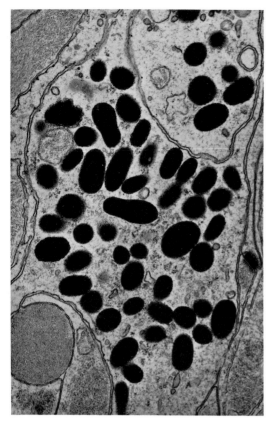

Figure 2-19. Electron micrograph of a portion of a melanocyte from an invertebrate. Numerous exceedingly dense melanosomes are present. × 18,000.

After the period of elongation is over, the manchette disappears. In nucleated erythrocytes of various species a bundle of microtubules forms the marginal band encircling the cell immediately beneath the plasma membrane. This complex of microtubules is believed to be responsible for maintaining the flattened, discoid shape of the cell.

These observations suggest that the microtubules are cytoskeletal elements influencing cell shape by imparting stiffness to certain regions of the cell. Other observations suggest that the microtubules may be capable of contraction and may therefore be directly involved in shape change or cell movements. The question as to whether they play an active or only a passive role remains unresolved.

PIGMENT GRANULES. In certain tissues scattered throughout the body, particularly in amphibia, are cells that contain large numbers of dark brown to black granules. These cells are the *melanocytes,* and the granules that contain the pigment *melanin* are called *melanosomes.* In its formative stages the melanosome is limited by a membrane and contains longitudinally oriented lamellae that exhibit a regular periodic structure along their length. As maturation of the granule proceeds, melanin is deposited upon this framework to such an extent that it obscures the internal structure. The melanosome appears as a homogeneous dense granule and its limiting membrane may no longer be evident.

In man, melanosomes are found in the melanocytes in the deep layers of the epidermis, in the basal epidermal cells, in the pigment epithelium of the retina, in the iris, and in certain cells in the brain.

Colored deposits of another pigment called *lipofuscin* are found in other cells in the body. These deposits are especially abundant in tissues of older animals and humans. They are tan or light brown in unstained preparations and fluoresce a golden brown in ultraviolet light. They also stain lightly with fat soluble dyes and are insoluble in acid, alkali, and fat solvents. Lipofuscin pigment is now thought to be an end stage of lysosomal activity and is regarded as the indigestible residues of phagocytosed material and degenerated organelles. Because such pigment progressively increases in amount with advancing age, it is sometimes referred to as "wear and tear" pigment (Fig. 2-20).

An additional category of pigment encountered in some tissues is that resulting from the destruction of *hemoglobin,* the iron-containing substance that imparts color to the red blood corpuscles and promotes their efficiency as carriers of oxygen. The red blood cells have a limited life span in the circulation and are then phagocytosed by certain cells in the spleen, liver, and bone marrow. The degradation of hemoglobin within these cells gives rise to a golden brown, iron-containing pigment called *hemosiderin,* which accumulates in irregularly granular masses in the cytoplasm of the phagocytes. There is some hemosiderin in the phagocytes of the normal spleen, liver, and bone marrow, but in diseases that involve an increased rate of destruction of the red blood cells, the amount of this pigment is markedly increased. Hemosiderin may be distinguished from other pigments by staining reactions for iron. In electron micrographs the masses of pigment include large numbers of 90 Å dense particles of the iron-containing protein *ferritin.*

GLYCOGEN. Animal cells are capable of storing carbohydrate in the form of glycogen, a large polymer of glucose. Glycogen is not apparent in routine histological sections but can be selectively stained by the Best's carmine method or by the periodic acid–Schiff reaction, which colors it a brilliant magenta. It may appear diffusely distributed in the cytoplasm or in coarse clumps, depending upon the nature of the fixative used. The coarse masses ordinarily observed with the light microscope are composed of submicroscopic particles that can be visualized only with the electron microscope.

The appearance of glycogen in electron micrographs is considerably influenced by the method of specimen preparation, but with the better fixatives it is preserved in the form of dense, roughly isodiametric, 150 to 300 Å particles that are often rather irregular in out-

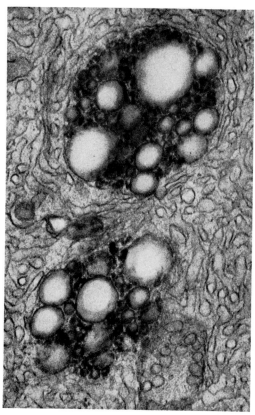

Figure 2-20. Electron micrograph of two lipofuscin pigment deposits in a human adrenal cortical cell. This type of pigment, which accumulates with age, is very heterogeneous in appearance and is thought to represent undigestible residues of lysosomal activity. × 50,000.

line. These are referred to as the *beta particles* of glycogen. In some cell types they occur individually; in others, notably the liver, they form rosette-like aggregates of larger size called *alpha particles* (Fig. 2-21A and B). The significance of these two forms of glycogen is not understood.

LIPID. Cells often contain stored lipid which, in life, is present in the form of droplets of oil. The simple lipids are neutral fats—triglycerides of fatty acids—and are of such a degree of unsaturation as to be liquid at body temperature. They serve as a local store of energy and also as a source of short carbon chains that can be utilized by the cell in the formation of membranes and other lipid rich structural components. In ordinary histological sections these are likely to appear as round clear areas in the cytoplasm, because the lipid is extracted by solvents used in the preparation of the specimen. By using sections of frozen tissue, exposure to such solvents can be avoided and the lipid can be colored with a fat soluble dye. Also, by fixation in osmium, lipid can be rendered resistant to extraction. It then appears as black spherical droplets of varying size. This is the usual appearance of lipid in electron micrographs (Fig. 2-22), but the degree of blackening depends upon the degree of unsaturation of the lipid and the nature of the fixative used. Some structures other than lipid may blacken with osmium. After preliminary aldehyde fixation, lipid may fail to blacken upon subsequent exposure to osmium, and it then appears pale gray in electron micrographs.

The Nucleus

The nucleus is an essential component of nearly all cell types. The few that lack it are incapable of growth or division and are severely limited in their metabolic activities. Every nucleus contains the genetic material, deoxyribonucleic acid (DNA), which determines the specific morphological and biochemical characteristics of each cell type and controls its metabolic activities. The DNA does not occur free in the nucleoplasm but is combined with histones and other structural proteins to form *chromatin*, which occurs in two interchangeable states of condensation and dispersion. Chromatin in the dispersed state stains poorly or not at all in contrast to condensed chromatin, which stains intensely.

In dividing cells dispersed chromatin

becomes condensed into deeply stained elongated structures, the *chromosomes*, which are present in constant number in the cells of each species (p. 71). In cells not in division some of the chromatin of the chromosomes remains condensed and is recognizable in stained nuclei as irregular clumps called *karyosomes*, or chromatin particles, of varying size and scattered through the nucleoplasm. The condensed regions of the chromosomes that persist during interphase are often referred to as the *heterochromatin*. Regions of the chromosomes that are dispersed and therefore not readily stainable comprise the *euchromatin*. The condensed regions of the chromosomes are thought to be relatively inert, while the euchromatic regions are believed to be those portions of the chromosomes that are actively participating in the control of the specific metabolic activities of the cell. Because the cells of the body vary greatly in their functions and in their synthetic activities, they also vary in the proportion of their chromatin that remains condensed. Therefore

the depth of staining and the chromatin pattern of the nucleus may differ from cell type to cell type.

In addition to the chromatin, the nucleus contains one or more prominent *nucleoli* (Fig. 2-23). These are rounded bodies that usually stain deeply because of their content of ribonucleic acid (RNA). The faintly stained or clear areas of nucleoplasm not occupied by chromatin or nucleolus have traditionally been referred to as *nuclear sap* or *karyolymph*, on the assumption that the stainable elements of the nucleus are suspended in a clear fluid or transparent gel. We now know that much of the area to which these terms were originally applied is occupied by dispersed chromatin and various submicroscopic granular components of the nucleoplasm. The terms karyolymph and nuclear sap therefore do not describe clearly definable morphological entities and should be discarded.

CHROMATIN. As seen by light microscopy, the condensed chromatin consists of ir-

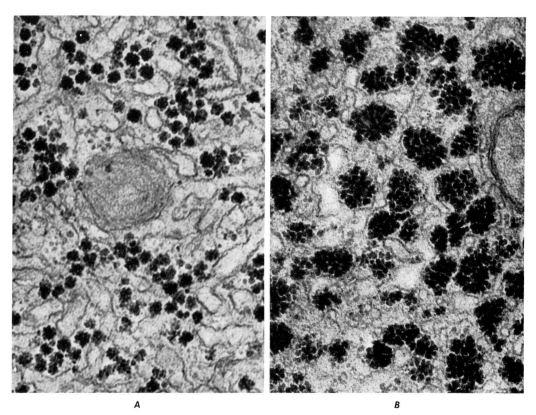

A   B

Figure 2-21.   Electron micrographs of liver glycogen of two different species at approximately the same magnification. In the salamander liver (*A*), the rosettes or alpha particles are considerably smaller than in the hamster (*B*). In both, the dense glycogen particles are aggregates of smaller subunits. × 60,000.

regular clumps of material deeply staining with dyes such as hematoxylin, methylene blue, and methyl green. Its affinity for these dyes is due principally to its content of deoxyribonucleic acid, but these dyes are also bound by other acidic substances in the cell. A widely used specific stain for identification of DNA is the Feulgen reaction. The amount of stainable chromatin and the pattern of its distribution within the nucleus is quite characteristic of certain cell types and may be useful in their identification. The chromatin pattern may also provide a rough index of a cell's activity. In interphase nuclei with little stainable chromatin, the chromosomes are mainly in the extended or dispersed condition, in which their DNA presents more synthetically active surface to the nucleoplasm. In cells with abundant coarse blocks of chromatin, on the other hand, a greater proportion of the chromosomal mass is in the condensed condition, in which its genetic material is believed to be inaccessible or inactive.

The finer structural organization of the mitotic chromosomes and of the chromatin in the interphase nucleus is still a matter of dispute. Studies of the physicochemical and optical properties of solutions of purified DNA show that the molecules are long thin threads, estimated to be about 20 Å in diameter and formed by the helical intertwining of two DNA chains in such a way that there are alternating deep and shallow helical grooves on its surface. Analysis of nucleohistones that make up the bulk of the chromatin suggests that the histones associated with the DNA molecules lie in the grooves of the double helix.

DNA double helices, when studied in vitro, undergo profound changes in form with minor changes in pH and salt concentration, and it cannot be assumed that they are in the fully extended form in the native state. If they were, one might expect to find filamentous structures 20 to 30 Å in diameter and of indefinite length in electron micrographs of chromatin. Such is not the case. After the usual fixatives containing osmium the nucleoplasm presents a bewildering array of minute punctate and elongated profiles of varying size and density.

The areas of chromatin have a complex texture that permits more than one interpretation. Some investigators consider its characteristic appearance to result from the sectioning of a feltwork of randomly oriented 100 Å

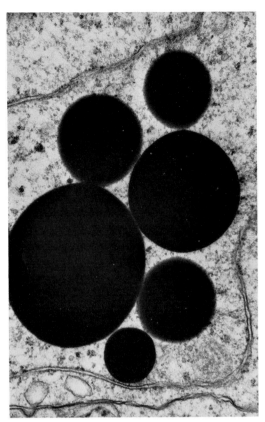

Figure 2-22. Lipid droplets in an electron micrograph of an osmium-fixed Sertoli cell. × 20,000.

filaments. Others visualize it as an interlacing pattern of 30 to 75 Å filaments that branch and anastomose to form a three dimensional lattice with interstices less than 200 Å wide. Still others, particularly those using glutaraldehyde as the primary fixative, see the areas of chromatin as a mass of 200 Å granules or filaments in cross sections. Certainly a fibrillar organization has the appeal that it can most easily be brought into accord with genetic theory and with the biophysical analysis of purified DNA, but the method of tissue preservation obviously has a profound effect upon the fine structure of the chromatin. At present there is no basis for a decision as to which among these alternative interpretations of its structure actually is closest to the condition prevailing in the living nucleus.

NUCLEOLUS. The discovery of the nucleolus is attributed to Fontana (1781). It is visible in the living cell as a conspicuous, rounded, refractile body eccentrically placed in the nucleus. In stained sections, it colors in-

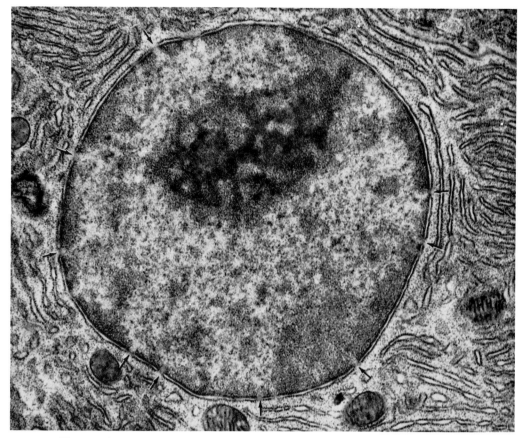

Figure 2-23. Electron micrograph of a nucleus of a pancreatic acinar cell, showing the chracteristic pattern of density variations seen in the nucleoplasm after osmium fixation. The prominent nucleolus appears to be made up of fine granules closely packed in dense anastomosing strands that form a loose irregular network. The nuclear envelope consists of two membranes bounding a narrow space, the perinuclear cisterna. At numerous points on the circumference of the nucelus (see at the arrows), the outer and inner membranes of the nuclear envelope are continuous with one another around the periphery of small circular openings, interpreted as nuclear "pores" through which the nucleoplasm communicates with the cytoplasm. × 16,000.

tensely with any of the basic dyes and with many acid dyes as well. The basophilia of the nucleolus is largely due to its content of ribonucleic acid (RNA), and therefore it is not colored in preparations stained with the Feulgen reaction for DNA. A rim of reactive material often surrounds it however, and this is commonly referred to as the *nucleolus associated chromatin*.

The number of nucleoli in most somatic cell types falls in the range from one to four, but larger numbers are encountered occasionally. The number varies from time to time in a given nucleus, as seen in time lapse movie films, which also show that nucleoli move and fuse with other nucleoli. During reconstitution of the nucleus after division the nucleolus forms at particular identifiable sites on certain chromosomes called *nucleolus organizers*. The number of nucleolus organizers determines the number of nucleoli formed and is therefore theoretically constant for each species. However, the number of nucleoli found in the tissues may depart somewhat from the basic number characteristic of the species. Polyploidy may result in multiples of the basic number. Fewer than the expected number may be present owing to fusion of nucleoli, and an excess may be produced by their budding. Although this latter phenomenon is relatively uncommon in somatic cells, it occurs regularly in oocytes, where a thousand or more nucleoli may be formed.

The nucleolus varies in size in different cell types, and within the same type it may change in volume in different physiological conditions. It is especially large in rapidly growing embryonic cells and in other cells active in protein synthesis. In electron micrographs it is typically composed of a dense central area, sometimes referred to as the *pars amorpha*, surrounded by a branching and anastomosing coarse strand 600 to 800 Å in thickness, called the *nucleolonema* (Fig. 2-24). In some cell types these components are compacted into a more or less homogeneous dense mass. In others, the nucleolonema is deployed around the pars amorpha in a loose three dimensional network. At high magnification the central region, which appears amorphous at low power, can be resolved as a dense mass of thin filaments about 50 Å thick. The bulk of the nucleolonema is made up of the same filamentous material but, in addition, usually contains granules 150 Å in diameter, closely resembling the ribosomes of the cytoplasm. The granules are not distributed uniformly throughout the nucleolonema but may be absent from some segments, which then consist only of the closely compressed fine filaments. These regions composed of filaments alone appear denser and finer textured than those made up of both filaments and granules.

The terms *pars amorpha* and *nucleolonema* are useful for describing characteristic topographical features of the nucleolus, but for other purposes it may be preferable to use *pars fibrosa* and *pars granulosa* to refer to the two distinguishable patterns of fine structural organization without regard to their distribution in the organelle as a whole.

Studies combining enzymatic digestion of protein and of ribonucleic acid with selective staining methods for nucleic acids indicate that both the filaments and the granules of the nucleolus contain ribonucleoprotein. The relation of these components to each other and to the ribosomes of the cytoplasm is not yet entirely clear, but it is believed that the nucleolus is an important way station along the path of nucleic acids from the site of their synthesis in the nucleus to the site of their functioning in the cytoplasm.

THE NUCLEAR ENVELOPE. The outer limit of the living nucleus is clearly demarcated by a thin line which has long been inter-

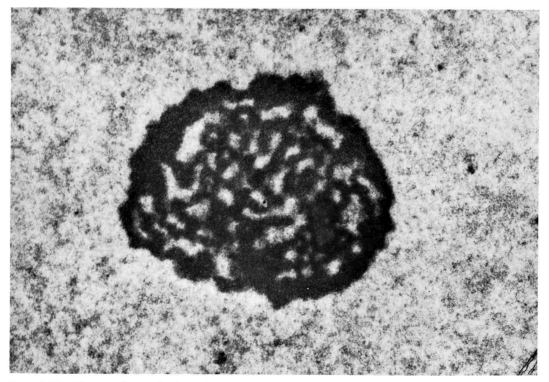

Figure 2-24. Electron micrograph of a nucleolus. It appears as a branching and anastomosing dense strand called the *nucleolonema*. At higher magnification this is found to be composed of 150 Å granules in a matrix of fine filaments. Osmium fixation. × 19,000.

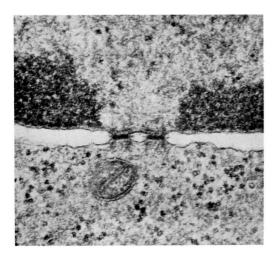

Figure 2-25. The nuclear pores appear in electron micrographs to be traversed by a thin septum or diaphragm. Polychromatophilic erythroblast from guinea pig marrow. × 45,000.

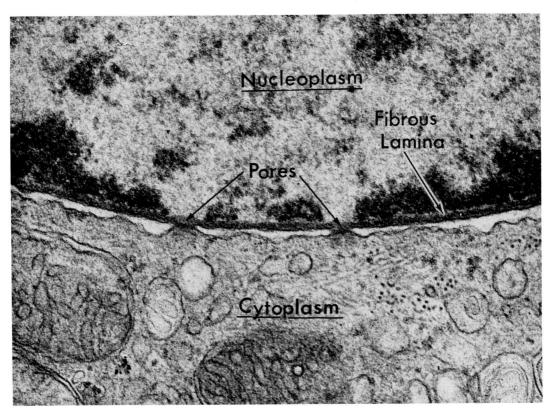

Figure 2-26. On the inner aspect of the nuclear envelope of some cell types there is a thin layer of fine filaments called the fibrous lamina. In some instances this layer appears to continue across the pores. × 60,000. (After D. W. Fawcett, Am. J. Anat., *119:*129, 1966.)

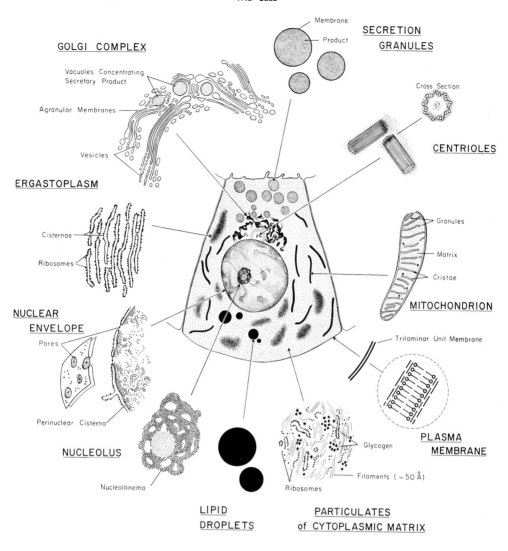

GOLGI COMPLEX

Vacuoles Concentrating
Secretory Product

Agranular Membranes

Vesicles

Membrane
Product

SECRETION
GRANULES

Cross Section

CENTRIOLES

ERGASTOPLASM

Cisternae

Ribosomes

Granules

Matrix

Cristae

MITOCHONDRION

NUCLEAR
ENVELOPE

Pores

Trilaminar Unit Membrane

Perinuclear Cisterna

NUCLEOLUS

Nucleolonema

LIPID
DROPLETS

Glycogen

Filaments (~50 Å)

Ribosomes

PARTICULATES
of CYTOPLASMIC MATRIX

PLASMA
MEMBRANE

Figure 2-27. In the center of this figure is a diagram of the cell, illustrating the form of its organelles and inclusions as they appear by light microscopy. Around the periphery are representations of the finer structure of these same components as seen in electron micrographs. The ergastoplasm of light microscopy consists of aggregations of submicroscopic membrane-limited elements with granules of ribonucleoprotein adhering to their outer surface. This component is now also called the *granular endoplasmic reticulum*. The illustration of the plasma membrane encircled by an interrupted line does not show structure that has been directly observed but represents one possible interpretation of the arrangement of lipid and protein molecules that may be related to the trilaminar appearance of cell membranes in electron micrographs. See page 60 for comment on "pores" in the nuclear envelope.

preted by cytologists as a single thin membrane. It has now been shown by electron microscopy that the *nuclear envelope* is a more complex structure than previously imagined, consisting of two parallel membranes enclosing a narrow *perinuclear space*. At many points over the surface of the nucleus, the inner and outer membranes are continuous with each other around the circumference of small

circular openings called *nuclear pores* (Fig. 2-23). Although these are considered to be potential avenues for exchange of materials between the nucleoplasm and cytoplasm, they clearly do not allow unrestricted diffusion between these two major compartments of the cell. Electrophysiological measurements of resistance have shown that the nuclear envelope constitutes a barrier to diffusion of ions that is orders of magnitude greater than would be the case if the discontinuities observed were freely communicating pores. Each pore is traversed by a delicate septum or diaphragm somewhat thinner than the usual unit membrane (Fig. 2-25). While very little is known about the molecular organization or permeability properties of this structure, it seems likely that it exercises some control over the passage of materials through the pores.

On the inner aspect of the nuclear envelope of some cell types, there is a thin layer of fine filaments called the *fibrous lamina* (Fig. 2-26). The significance of this layer is not yet clear. It is possible that it simply provides mechanical support for the nuclear envelope, but in some instances it appears to be continuous across the nuclear pores and could conceivably have an effect upon their permeability.

Ribosomes are often found on the cytoplasmic surface of the nuclear envelope, and not infrequently its outermost membrane is continuous with the limiting membranes of the system of canaliculi in the cytoplasm known as the endoplasmic reticulum. After mitotic division, the nuclear envelope re-forms by coalescence of flat saccular elements of the reticulum. The cavity of the nuclear envelope is regarded as a perinuclear cisterna and the nuclear envelope is considered to be an integral part of the endoplasmic reticulum.

CELL DIVISION

Many organs of the mature mammal show relatively few cells in division under normal conditions, and there are none in neurons of the central nervous system after the early months of fetal development in man. In some tissues the average period between divisions is measured in days or months and, in exceptional instances, years. However, nearly every microscopic section of some organs, such as the intestinal tract, contains a number of cells in division. Even greater numbers may be seen in sections of the blood cell forming tissues and huge numbers in the testis of an adult.

Such isolated sections do not indicate the full intensity of cell division in many tissues during the course of a day. To determine this, two methods are used. The first is the administration of colchicine, which stops cell division midway through the process (in metaphase, see p. 62). Sections of the tissues of an animal so treated will thus show the number of cell divisions that have accumulated in the interval

following injection of the drug. The other method is the injection of tritiated thymidine (^{3}H-thymidine), which becomes incorporated into the DNA being replicated during preparation for cell division; the amount and position of labeled thymidine can be visualized in the cells by autoradiography. The colchicine and cell labeling methods give comparable results and show that in adult warm-blooded animals, many more cells divide daily than was expected on the basis of counts made from random sections. The percentage of cell divisions in many tissues is much larger in growing animals than in the adult, where mitoses represent replacements for cells dying from wear and tear. For further details of the occurrence of cell division throughout the body, see the review by Leblond and Walker.

A typical cell division, called *mitosis,* consists of an equal division of nuclear material (*karyokinesis*) followed by a division of the cell body (*cytokinesis*) in which each of the two daughter cells receives one of the daughter nuclei. In a few cell types karyokinesis occurs normally without cytokinesis, and in certain others cytokinesis can be induced without karyokinesis. Because the small size and large number of the chromosomes in mammalian cells make detailed observations difficult, most studies of cell division have been made on more favorable material in cells of lower forms.

Mitosis.   The usual description of mitosis is based on what can be seen with optical microscopes and this convention will be followed for the present, although an imposing body of knowledge from other methods is filling some of the gaps left by optical microscopic methods. The more obvious dynamic aspects of mitosis are dramatically shown in time lapse motion pictures of this process in living cells. However, certain of the most important processes occur before any changes are visible with phase contrast or other optical microscopes.

For many decades the word "chromosome" has been generally used to refer to the thread-, rod-, hairpin-, or worm-shaped bodies characteristic of the middle stages of the mitotic process in cells of higher forms of life. However, in such cells most of the chromosomal material between mitoses (that is, in interphase) is in a dispersed condition; it condenses to assume the conventional structure of mid-mitosis and then disperses in the reconstruction of the two daughter nuclei as they, in turn, assume the interphase condition. Although the individual chromosomes in cells of higher forms have not been clearly distinguished microscopically during interphase, the science of genetics furnishes convincing evidence that each chromosome maintains its individuality throughout this period.

In preparation for mitosis, each chromosome, which was a daughter chromosome (chromatid) of the preceding mitosis, is duplicated (submicroscopically). This is followed by a complex series of microscopically visible changes by which each daughter cell normally receives an equal, full complement of chromosomal and thus of genetic material. Some of the major steps in this process are shown in diagram (Fig. 2-28) and in a sequence of photomicrographs of an individual living cell (Fig. 2-29). Further details are visible in the fixed and stained cells of Figure 2-30, and submicroscopic aspects of some of the nuclear changes are shown in Figures 2-31 to 2-39.

As a result of these activities each chromosome gives rise to another just like it, each gene being replicated in the process. These submicroscopic changes have been established by chemical analysis of the cells in the synthetic or S-period (see below) and have been visualized in the cells by autoradiographic methods. The initiating and inhibiting factors in such a sequence of events have not been identified. A good case could be made for denoting this time as the start of mitosis if there were a rapid, simple means of recognizing its beginning in the living cell. Until such a test is found, it is necessary to mark the start of mitosis as the earliest stage at which it can be recognized with optical microscopes, which is "prophase." With these instruments, especially with phase contrast optics, visible prophase is first recognized by the appearance of new, minute granules in the nucleus (see p. 62).

The first clearly demonstrated step toward mitosis is the synthesis of DNA. The DNA molecule consists of two chains twisted about each other in a helix, which is stabilized by interactions between pairs of nucleotide bases. Three mechanisms of replication can be suggested and defined in terms of the distribution of parental material between the daughter molecules: *conservative*—the original molecule remains intact and a completely new molecule is formed; *semiconservative*—replication proceeds by separation of the strands so that each daughter molecule has one new and one parental strand; *nonconservative* or *dispersive*—parental nucleotide bases are distributed in both strands of each daughter molecule. Thus in the three possible modes of replication, the whole molecule, one strand, or only the bases are concerned. The usual mode of replication in mammalian somatic cells is by the semiconservative mode.

Because the duration of this synthesis can be conveniently measured by radioautography after use of the specific DNA precursor, ^{3}H-thymidine, the cell division, or mitotic cycle, may be divided into periods designated G_1, S, G_2, and M. S is the period of DNA synthesis; G_1 and G_2 (gaps) are, respectively, the periods from the previous division to the start of DNA synthesis and from the end of DNA synthesis to the beginning of mitosis (M). The relevance of this classification is that the S-period is a constant interval characteristic of the cell type and growth conditions. Under certain controlled conditions (see next paragraph) it occupies one third to one half of the generation time. However, it should be emphasized that the increase in total mass of the cell and the synthesis of RNA and protein occurs during G_1, G_2, and S. The rates of these processes do not seem to be affected by the initiation of DNA synthesis. Of those proteins synthesized during S, with the exception of histone, nothing is known about the time during which individual protein and RNA species are synthesized.

It is important to note that this definition of G_1, G_2, and S requires that the cells of the population are undergoing a cycle of growth and division with a constant doubling time. This type of growth is rarely found in normal tissues in adults. Cells may remain for weeks or months in interphase and then undergo one or more division cycles. For this reason some authors call this phase a G_0 period, although it is not properly part of the cell division cycle.

The double nature of the chromosome has developed before the onset of optically visible mitosis, so that this part of cell division has the function of distributing to each daughter nucleus one chromatid from each chromosome in the mother nucleus. Unless chromosome replication is interfered with, genetic evidence shows that two sister chromatids contain identical linear arrays of genes.

Because of the great variation in details of mitosis as it occurs in different species, no single diagram fits all of them exactly. Direct observation of mitosis in a living cell shows that the process is a continuous one which has been arbitrarily separated into several stages

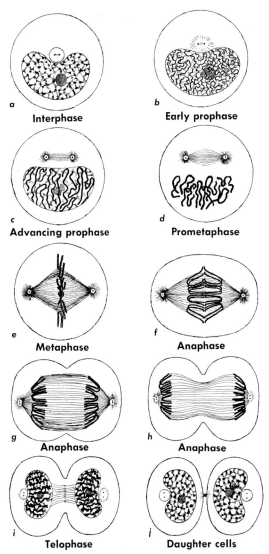

a
Interphase

b
Early prophase

c
Advancing prophase

d
Prometaphase

e
Metaphase

f
Anaphase

g
Anaphase

h
Anaphase

i
Telophase

j
Daughter cells

Figure 2-28. Diagram of various stages of mitosis in a newt cell.

for analytical purposes. In such cells, after the start of progressive condensation of dispersed, submicroscopic chromosomal material, *visible prophase* begins with the appearance of minute granules of "chromatin" near the limit of resolution of the microscope (Fig. 2-29). As more and more of these granules become visible, they aggregate into progressively larger, irregular bodies (Fig. 2-29A, B, and C). The cell center seen in interphase (Fig. 2-28a) divides and, as prophase advances, the two resulting centers move apart, and the mitotic spindle forms between them (Fig. 2-28c and d). Meanwhile the nucleolus elongates and disappears quickly into one or more of the larger,

developing, wormlike chromosomal bodies (white arrows in Fig. 2-29A, B, and C), and the nuclear membrane disappears. It is convenient to call this event the end of prophase. When all the chromatin has condensed into the newly formed chromosomes, they begin to move slowly in the residual, optically clear, nuclear material in which they are contained (Fig. 2-29E and F).

The next period is *metaphase*. The first part of this stage is often called *prometaphase*. Here the spindle (not clearly shown in the living cell by phase contrast microscopy), which had started to develop before the end of prophase, becomes larger and the centrioles are clearly visible at its poles (Fig. 2-29F, G, and H, black arrows). The wormlike chromosomes then move into the equatorial plane of the spindle. When seen in profile it appears as in Figure 2-28e. Late in metaphase a pale longitudinal stripe becomes visible in each chromosome, dividing it into two identical elongate bodies, the *chromatids*.

After this, in the rapidly following *anaphase*, the chromatids of each chromosome separate along the pale stripe into two equal groups of *daughter chromosomes*. As seen in the living cell, their separation and movement toward the poles of the spindle, and their subsequent gradual fusion into two compact daughter nuclei, is one of the most dramatic processes in cytology (Fig. 2-29I to K). The spindle elongates and with constriction of the cell body *cytokinesis* begins.

Shortly thereafter, a new nuclear membrane appears and marks the start of *telophase*. Each daughter nucleus then enlarges and, as reconstruction progresses, the mass of fused chromatids disperses, rapidly at first and then more slowly. Cytokinesis advances during reconstruction of the daughter nuclei; the spindle fibers disappear—as do the interzonal fibers—and the daughter cells remain connected for a short time by a wisp of cytoplasm containing some of the residual interzonal fibers and the *intermediate body* of Flemming (Fig. 2-28j).

During reconstruction of the nuclei, the chromosomal material becomes progressively less discernible, one or more nucleoli reappear (Fig. 2-29I and J), and the daughter cells pass into the interphase condition. Depending on the cell type, small amounts of the condensed chromosomal material fail to disperse and persist as chromatin particles.

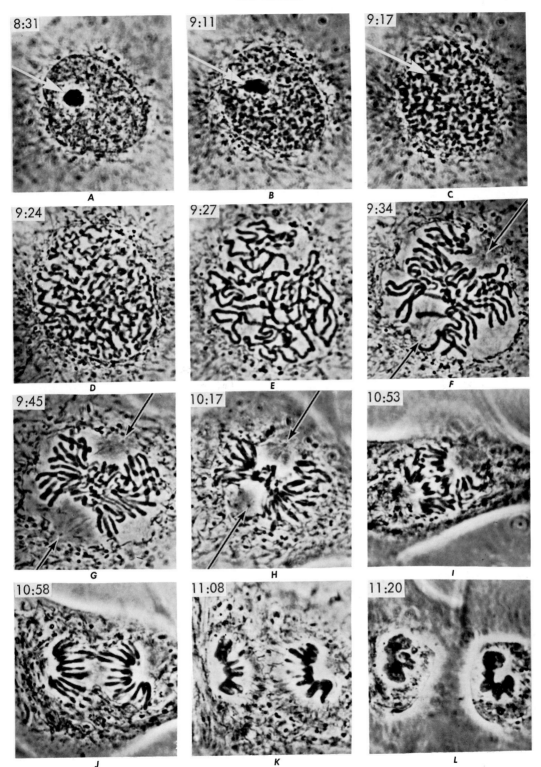

Figure 2-29. Phase contrast micrographs of stages in mitosis of the same living mesothelial cell of Amplystoma in culture. The large white arrows point to the nucleolus; the small black arrows indicate centrioles. *A* to *E*, Prophase; *F*, *G*, and *H*, metaphase; *I*, *J*, and *K*, anaphase; *L*, telophase. Mitosis proceeds much faster in cells of warm blooded animals.

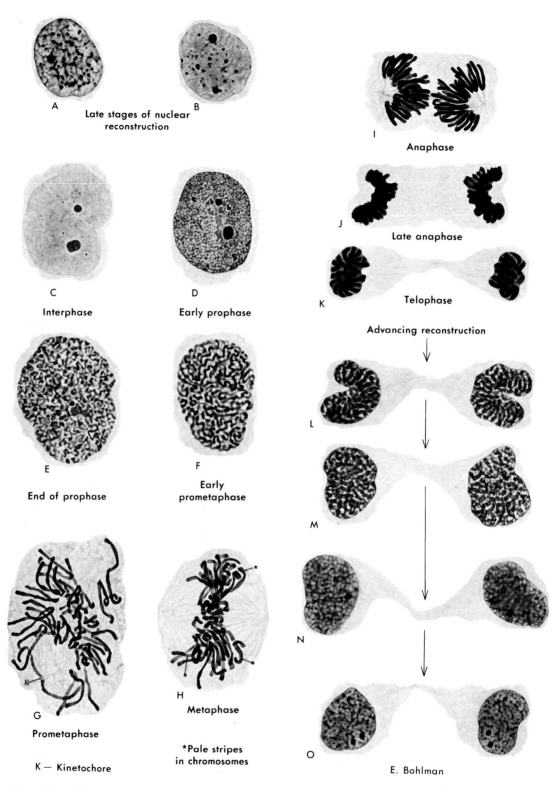

A

B

Late stages of nuclear
reconstruction

C

Interphase

D

Early prophase

E

End of prophase

F

Early
prometaphase

G

Prometaphase

K — Kinetochore

H

Metaphase

*Pale stripes
in chromosomes

I

Anaphase

J

Late anaphase

K

Telophase

Advancing reconstruction

L

M

N

O

E. Bohlman

Figure 2-30. Nuclear changes in mitotic mesothelial cells of Amblystoma in culture. (In most of these cells the cytoplasm was much more extensive than is shown.) At the end of prophase the nuclear membrane and the nucleolus are almost gone. In late anaphase, the chromosomes are fusing. With the appearance of the nuclear envelope in telophase the daughter nuclei undergo progressive reconstruction (arrows) until they attain the stage of interphase. Compare with Figure 2-29. Zenker-formol fixed, whole mounts stained with Heidenhain's iron-hematoxylin. × 800.

Although studies of the interphase and mitotic nucleus with the electron microscope have shown interesting glimpses of the striking changes undergone by this cell organ in division, the results have been disappointing in one major respect: the various acidic and basic proteins and the nucleic acids have not been clearly delineated and separated from one another at fine structural levels. ³H-labeled constituents, as seen in autoradiographs, unfortunately are localized only with an accuracy of 1000 Å or more. A much finer localization is needed to determine which filaments, seen in sections of nuclei, represent DNA in contrast to proteins. The use of labeled cytidine or uridine for RNA in the nucleoli has been more satisfactory at the topographical level but not at the near molecular level.

Valuable observations have been made with spreads of nuclei of mammalian cells and with the specialized lampbrush chromosomes of amphibian eggs, but so far these results have not been correlated satisfactorily with the thin sections of nuclear material that are indispensable for seeing many fine details in the progressive stages of mitosis.

The electron micrographs of Figures 2-31 to 2-39 were selected to show the progressive condensation of the network of filaments of the interphase nucleus (Fig. 2-31) into small clumps (Fig. 2-32), which become progressively larger and fewer (Figs. 2-33 and 2-34) until the chromosome of light microscopy appears as a compact mass of filaments (Fig. 2-35). The maximal condensation of chromosomal substance is seen in the short-lived, fused stage of late anaphase (Fig. 2-36). A new nuclear membrane then surrounds each daughter nucleus, which swells as the dense mass of filaments loosens progressively (Figs. 2-37 and 2-38). With continued dispersal of condensed chromosomal substance (Fig. 2-39), the nucleus assumes the general appearance of that in early prophase, although it is definitely smaller (Fig. 2-32). From this time on, the final change into the typical interphase nucleus proceeds more slowly.

Figures 2-31 to 2-39 are electron micrographs (EM) of important nuclear changes during mitosis in Amblystoma cells in culture. Fixation: $OsO_4 + CaCl_2$; *sections stained with uranyl acetate.* × *45,000. The insert in each figure is a phase contrast photomicrograph of the nucleus of a living cell at about the same stage of mitosis.* × *770. (Modified after Bloom.)*

(Text continued on page 70.)

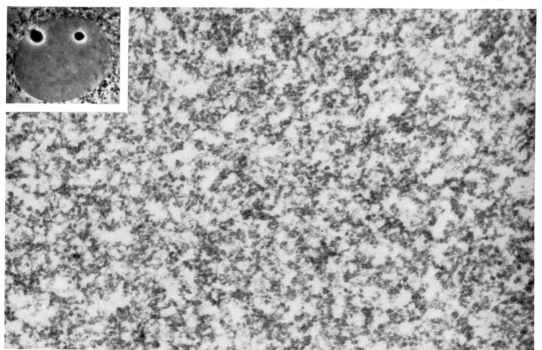

Figure 2-31. Interphase. The insert shows slight differences in texture of the nucleus and two nucleoli. The EM, typical of most of the nucleus, consists of an irregular network of filaments, gathered in places into cruciate or irregular small clumps. Narrow, irregular spaces, apparently devoid of structure, appear in the interstices of the network.

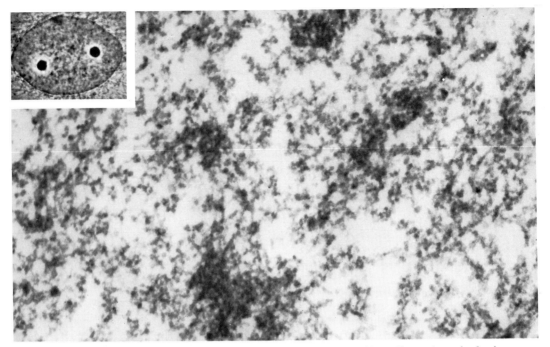

Figure 2-32.   Early prophase. The nucleus contains two nucleoli and is filled with small granules and a few larger ones. The EM reveals early stages of nuclear filaments gathering into clumps of various sizes. The open spaces between them are larger and fewer than in the previous figure.

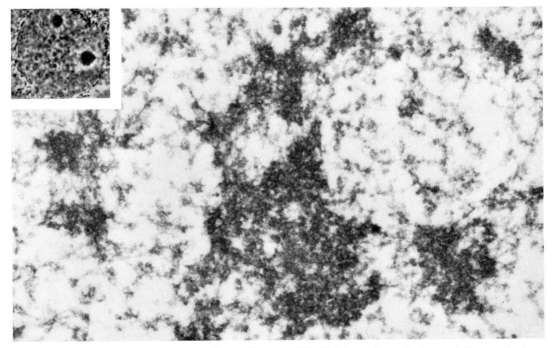

Figure 2-33.   Slightly later prophase. Nucleoli are still present. The EM shows the small clumps of filaments in stages of fusion into larger clumps.

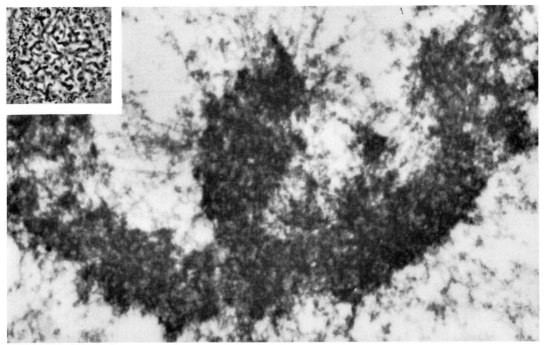

Figure 2-34. Later prophase. Nucleoli are gone. Elongate twisted bodies fill much of the nucleus. The EM is of an irregularly shaped mass of filaments, more densely packed than in the preceding figure.

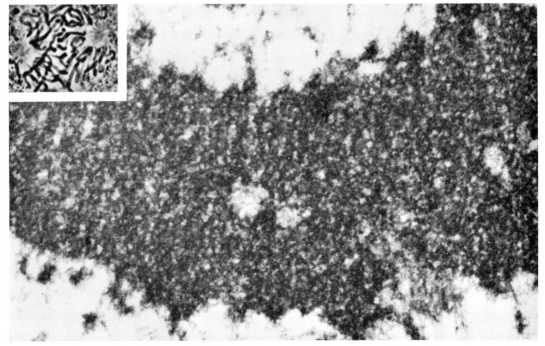

Figure 2-35. Prometaphase. The wormlike chromosomes are starting to aggregate in the mid-zone between the two pale areas containing the centrioles. The EM is of a short segment of such a condensing chromosome. There are still some open spaces within its dense tangle of filaments. Note the irregular protrusions of filaments along its surface.

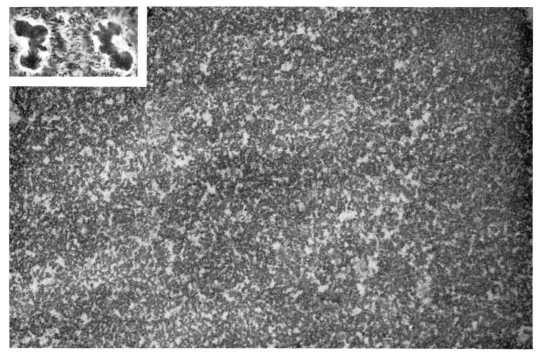

Figure 2-36. End of anaphase. The chromatids have fused to form two small, dense daughter nuclei. The EM contains a few scattered, pale-staining areas in the compact mass of filaments.

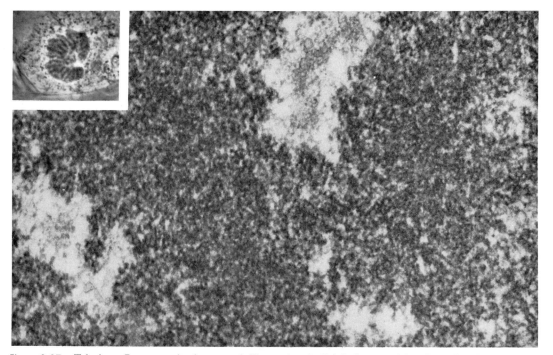

Figure 2-37. Telophase. Reconstruction has started. The nucleus is slightly larger and less dense than in Figure 2-36. Note the radiating dark stripes and the gray zones between them. The latter represent areas of loosening of the condensed mass of the previous stage. The EM shows the beginning separation of large masses of fused chromosomes and paler-staining, finely filamentous material between them. The dark filaments are now more clearly visible, especially near the right margin.

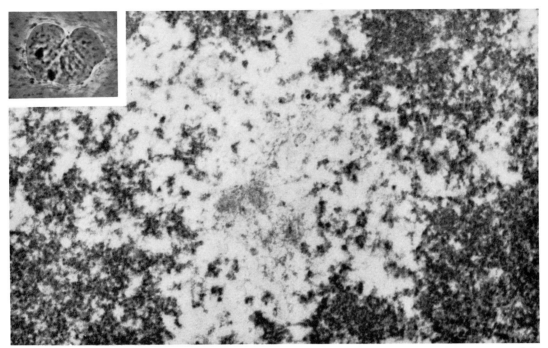

Figure 2-38. Telophase. Reconstruction is advancing. The nucleus is distinctly larger, two nucleoli are present, and the dark, condensed strips are more irregular. In the EM there is now a much looser arrangement of the coarse, dark filaments and the spaces between them are larger.

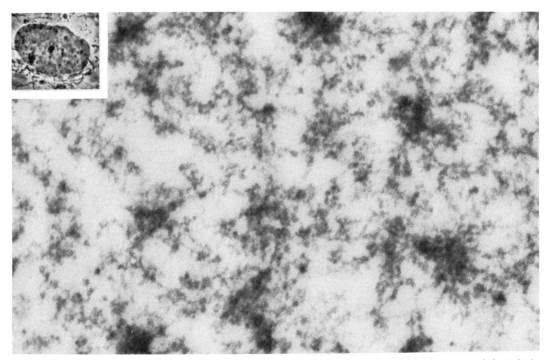

Figure 2-39. Late stage in reconstruction. A few large and many small chromatin particles are scattered through the nucleus. The large rods of Figures 2-37 and 2-38 are gone. The EM shows a later stage of the dispersal of the large masses of filaments. The nucleus now consists of an irregular network of fine filaments separated by fairly large open spaces and various-sized clumps of filaments. The picture is much like that seen in prophase—a little earlier than that shown in Figure 2-32.

The Mitotic Spindle and the Movement of Chromosomes in Mitosis. The spindle in the living cell is not clearly visualized with either the ordinary or phase contrast microscope, although its position in the cytoplasm is sometimes seen as an optically negative zone (Fig. 2-40*A*) surrounded by inclusions or organelles such as mitochondria. The spindle is clearly demonstrable with the polarization microscope (Fig. 2-40*B*) and after a variety of fixing and staining procedures. With the electron microscope, the spindle is seen to consist of great numbers of filaments 200 to 300 Å in diameter. With some preparatory methods, as after fixation with glutaraldehyde and staining with osmic acid, the filaments have a dark periphery in cross or longitudinal section and a light interior; accordingly they are interpreted as *microtubules.* With other fixatives, especially Zenker formol osmic, a clear central area in each filament is usually not seen. Spindle filaments may be found attached to the sides of chromosomes as well as to an apparently more specific organelle, the *kinetochore* or *centromere.* This has been seen, occasionally, with the electron microscope as a slightly curved disk to the spindle filaments and to the chromosome or near it. More delicate filamentous aggregates in the region of the kinetochore have also been considered to be spindle fiber attachments.

None of the movements of cell parts involved in mitosis have been satisfactorily explained, although many theories have been advanced to account for the forces evidently at work. If the kinetochore containing region of a chromosome is irradiated with ultraviolet light, this chromosome will not join those in the metaphase group but will form a separate little nucleus. If the mitotic spindle is destroyed by exposure to cold, or to chemicals as different as colchicine and chloramphenicol, or to ultraviolet irradiation of any small part of the cytoplasm, the chromosomes will not form a regular metaphase configuration and their daughter halves (chromatids) will not separate as in normal anaphase. Instead, two irregularly sized groups of whole chromosomes move apart despite the absence of the spindle; cytokinesis occurs and the result is two cells with incomplete and haphazard numbers of chromosomes, each consisting of two chromatids. Thus the spindle fibers must play an important part in guiding the daughter chromosomes apart, but the mechanism is not known at this time.

The isolated spindle consists largely of proteins and a small percentage of RNA. None of the proteins has been characterized satisfactorily. The solubilized spindle possesses weak ATP-hydrolyzing activity, but the possibility that this is due to a cytoplasmic contaminant

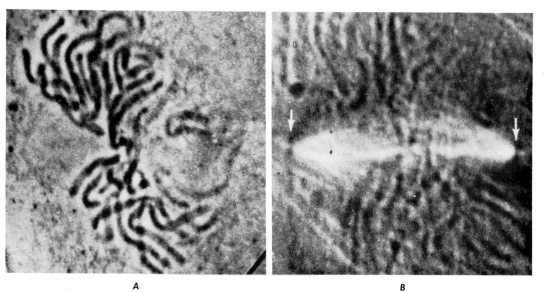

A   B

Figure 2-40. Metaphase of a cell of newt heart in tissue culture. *A,* By phase-contrast microscopy, *B,* by polarization microscopy, which demonstrates the oriented structure of the spindle. The arrows point to the centrioles. (Courtesy of R. Uretz.)

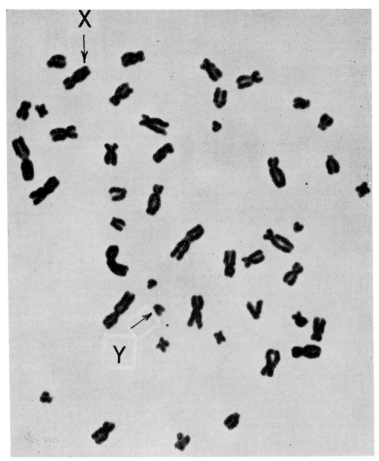

Figure 2-41. Photomicrograph of the 46 metaphase chromosomes from a cell of a human male grown in tissue culture and treated by a technique which spreads out the 23 pairs of autosomes and the X and Y chromosomes so that their characteristic shapes and sizes can be studied. × 1700. (Courtesy of J. H. Tjio and T. T. Puck.)

has not been ruled out. This compound (ATP) is usually regarded as the source of energy for a variety of cellular processes, ranging from protein and nucleic acid synthesis to muscle contraction and active transport. An analogy has often been drawn between the supposed participation of the spindle in chromosome movement and muscle contraction. Although both systems convert chemical energy into mechanical work, the small amount of evidence now available suggests that the protein components are not identical.

Many theories, both early and recent, of chromosome movements in mitosis were based on physical forces, such as those arising from attraction or repulsion of electric charges, diffusion of cytoplasmic constituents, changes in viscosity, or vortex streaming. Since these theories failed to assign a role to the spindle,

they may now be rejected. An understanding of the detailed mechanisms by which the chromosomes move awaits further structural and chemical studies.

CHROMOSOME NUMBER IN MAN. Since the work of Tjio and Lavan it seems clear that human somatic cells of males have 22 pairs of autosomes and an X and a Y (Fig. 2-41), whereas females have 22 pairs of autosomes and two X chromosomes. Each human chromosome has been given a number, largely on the basis of its size, and they have been arranged in groups (see Fig. 2-41). There are slight differences of opinion among the workers in this field about the enumeration, but fortunately they have agreed on a simple method of designating the chromosomes so that confusion in the numbering will be obviated. In a few diseases in man it has been shown that one

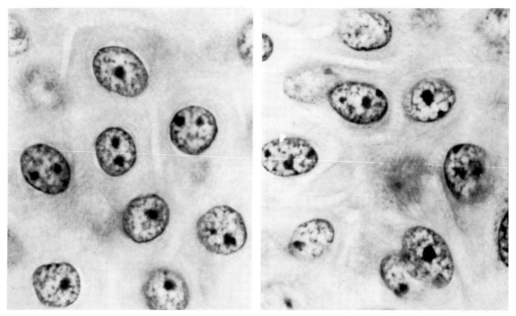

Figure 2-42. Photomicrographs of sections of skin from a male subject on the left and a female subject on the right. In three of the nuclei in the figure at the right a peripherally placed mass of sex chromatin can be seen. × 1800. (Courtesy of M. Barr.)

or even two chromosomes are characteristically missing.

Barr and his associates have found that in a number of species, including man, the sex of an individual can be ascertained by a sex difference in the nuclei of many types of interphase cells—for example, neurons or squamous epithelium. In females, but not in males, there is a small chromatin particle which they believe to be the sex chromosome (Fig. 2-42). This criterion has been of use in the diagnosis of the nature of some sex abnormalities in man.

CYTOKINESIS. In mitotic animal cells the cell body is typically divided by a constriction that begins in late anaphase or early telophase (Figs. 2-28 to 2-30) and advances in a plane perpendicular to the spindle axis and between the two groups of anaphase chromosomes. This provides that each daughter cell shall have one nucleus. Since there is no mechanism to ensure similar equal distribution of cytoplasmic organelles, inclusions, and genetic factors (plasmagenes), these are apparently apportioned more or less equally between the two daughter cells, depending on the degree of randomness of their distribution and on the location of the spindle in the mother cell. The forces producing the constriction are not understood.

MEIOSIS. The special type of nuclear division (meiosis) that occurs during the formation of the sex cells is discussed in the chapters on the genital organs.

AMITOSIS. In sharp contrast to the precisely operating mechanism of mitosis is the mode of karyokinesis called amitosis, or direct cell division. In this case the nucleus is reported as merely constricting until it finally divides into two more or less equal daughter nuclei. Most investigators doubt that this process occurs under normal conditions. There seems to be no well authenticated instance in which a complete cytokinesis has been observed to follow an amitotic karyokinesis in the same individual cell. In any event, there is no mechanism for equal distribution of chromosomes, so that the daughter nuclei would be grossly imbalanced.

REFERENCES

The references of the first group are important source books in the fields of histology and cytology. In seeking detailed information on the histology of particular tissues or organs, the student would do well to consult the handbooks edited by von Möllendorf and Bargmann and by Cowdry.

The references in the second group are concerned with topics of current interest and investigation on the structure of the cell and its various microscopic and submicroscopic components. They have been arranged under a number of subject headings to facilitate the student's search for additional information on the several cell organelles. The most extensive modern source book in English is the six volume work *The Cell: Biochemistry, Physiology, Morphology* edited by J. Brachet and A. E. Mirsky. Assistance in the visual identification of cell components at the electron microscope level can be obtained by referring to atlases of fine structure such as *An Introduction to the Fine Structure of Cells and Tissues* by K. R. Porter and M. Bonneville, and *An Atlas of Fine Structure: The Cell* by D. W. Fawcett.

I

von Bardeleben, K., and H. von Eggeling: Handbuch der Anatomie des Menschen. Jena, G. Fischer, 1896–1926.

Bolk, L., E. Göppert, E. Kallius, and W. Lubosch: Handbuch der vergleichenden Anatomie der Wirbeltiere. Berlin, Urban & Schwarzenberg, 1931 et seq.

Brachet, J., and A. E. Mirsky: The Cell: Biochemistry, Physiology, Morphology. 6 vols. New York, Academic Press, 1959–1964.

Cowdry, E. V., ed.: General Cytology. Chicago, University of Chicago Press, 1924.

Cowdry, E. V., ed.: Special Cytology. 3 vols. 2nd ed. New York, Paul B. Hoeber, Inc., 1932.

De Robertis, E. D. P., W. W. Nowinski, and F. A. Saez: Cell Biology. 4th ed. Philadelphia, W. B. Saunders Co., 1965.

Fawcett, D. W.: An Atlas of Fine Structure: The Cell. Philadelphia, W. B. Saunders Co., 1966.

Giese, A. C.: Cell Physiology. 2d ed. Philadelphia, W. B. Saunders Co., 1962.

Graumann, W., and K. Neumann: Handbuch der Histochemie. Stuttgart, G. Fischer, 1958 et seq.

Heidenhain, M.: Plasma und Zelle. Jena, G. Fischer, 1907–1911.

Hughes, A.: A History of Cytology. London, Abelard-Schuman, 1959.

Kölliker, R. A., and V. von Ebner: Handbuch der Gewebelehre des Menschen. 3 vols. 6th ed. Leipzig, Engelmann, 1899–1902.

von Möllendorf, W., and W. Bargmann: Handbuch der mikroskopischen Anatomie des Menschen. Berlin, Julius Springer, 1927 et seq.

Oppel, A.: Lehrbuch der vergleichenden mikroskopischen Anatomie der Wirbeltiere. Jena, G. Fischer, 1896.

Porter, K. R., and M. Bonneville: An Introduction to the Fine Structure of Cells and Tissues. Philadelphia, Lea & Febiger, 1963.

Swanson, C. P.: Cytology and Cytogenetics. Englewood Cliffs, N. J., Prentice-Hall, Inc., 1957.

Willmer, E. N.: Cytology and Evolution. New York, Academic Press, 1960.

Wilson, E. B.: The Cell in Development and Heredity. New York, Macmillan Co., 1925.

II

The Cell Membrane

Ponder, E.: The cell membrane and its properties. *In* Brachet, J., and A. E. Mirsky, eds.: The Cell. New York, Academic Press, 1961, Vol. II, p. 1.

Robertson, J. D.: Unit membranes: A review with recent new studies of experimental alterations and a new subunit in synaptic membranes. *In* Cell Membranes in Development. New York, Ronald Press, 1964.

Sjöstrand, F. S.: A comparison of plasma membrane, cytomembranes, and mitochondrial membrane elements with respect to ultrastructural features. J. Ultrastruct. Res., *9:*561, 1961.

Stoeckenius, W.: Some electron microscopic observations on liquid-crystalline phases in lipid-water systems. J. Cell Biol., *12:*221, 1962.

Yamamoto, T.: On the thickness of the unit membrane. J. Cell Biol., *17:*413, 1963.

Granular Endoplasmic Reticulum (Ergastoplasm)

Fawcett, D. W.: The membranes of the cytoplasm. Lab. Invest., *10:*1162, 1961.

Fawcett, D. W.: Structural and functional variations in the membranes of the cytoplasm. *In* Seno, S., and E. V. Cowdry, eds.: Intracellular Membranous Structure. Ohayama, Japan, Chugoku Press, 1965.

Garnier, C.: Contribution à l'étude de la structure et du fonctionnement des cellules glandulaires séreuses. Du rôle de l'ergastoplasme dans la sécrétion. Thesis, Nancy, No. 50, 1899.

Haguenau, F.: The ergastoplasm: Its history, ultrastructure and biochemistry. Int. Rev. Cytol., *7:*425, 1958.

Littlefield, J. W., E. Keller, J. Gross and P. C. Zamecnik: Studies on cytoplasmic ribonucleoprotein particles from the liver of the rat. J. Biol. Chem., *217:*111, 1955.

Palade, G. E.: A small particulate component of the cytoplasm. J. Biophys. & Biochem. Cytol., *1:*59, 1955.

Palade, G. E.: Studies on the endoplasmic reticulum. II. Simple dispositions in cells in situ. J. Biophys. & Biochem. Cytol., *1:*567, 1955.

Palade, G. E.: The endoplasmic reticulum. J. Biophys. & Biochem. Cytol., *2* (Suppl):85, 1956.

Palade, G. E., and K. R. Porter: Studies on the endoplasmic reticulum. I. Its identification in cells in situ. J. Exper. Med., *100:*641, 1954.

Palade, G. E., and P. Siekevitz: Pancreatic microsomes. J. Biophys. & Biochem. Cytol. *2:*671, 1956.

Porter, K. R.: Observations on a submicroscopic basophilic component of the cytoplasm. J. Exper. Med., *97:*727, 1953.

Porter, K. R.: The ground substance: Observations from electron microscopy. *In* Brachet, J., and A. E. Mirsky, eds.: The Cell. New York, Academic Press. 1961, Vol. II, p. 621.

Porter, K. R., A. Claude, and E. F. Fullam: A study of tissue culture cells by electron microscopy. Methods and preliminary observations. J. Exper. Med., *81:*233, 1945.

Agranular Endoplasmic Reticulum

Christensen, A. K.: Fine structure of testicular interstitial cells in the guinea pig. J. Cell Biol., *26:*911, 1965.

Christensen, A. K., and D. W. Fawcett: The fine structure of testicular interstitial cells in the opossum. J. Biophys. & Biochem. Cytol. *9:*653, 1961.

Christensen, A. K., and D. W. Fawcett: The fine structure of the interstitial cells of the mouse testis. Am. J. Anat., *118:*551, 1966.

Doyle, W. L.: Tubule cells of the rectal salt gland of *Urolophus.* Am. J. Anat., *111:*223, 1962.

Enders, A. C., and W. R. Lyon: Observations on the fine structure of lutein cells. II. The effects of hypophysectomy and mammotropic hormones in the rat. J. Cell Biol., *22:*127, 1964.

Ito, S.: The endoplasmic reticulum of gastric parietal cells. J. Biophys. & Biochem. Cytol., *11:*333, 1961.

Jones, A. L., and D. W. Fawcett: Hypertrophy of the agranular endoplasmic reticulum in hamster liver induced by phenobarbital. J. Histochem. & Cytochem., *24:*215, 1966.

Philpott, C. W., and D. E. Copeland: Fine structure of chloride cells from three species of *Fundulus.* J. Cell Biol., *18:*389, 1963.

Porter, K. R.: The sarcoplasmic reticulum: Its recent history and present status. J. Biophys. & Biochem. Cytol., *10:*219, 1961.

Porter, K. R., and E. Yamada: Studies on the endoplasmic reticulum. V. Its form and differentiation in pigment epithelial cells of frog retina. J. Biophys. & Biochem. Cytol., *8:*181, 1960.

Remmer, H., and H. J. Merker: Effect of drugs on the formation of smooth endoplasmic reticulum and drug metabolizing enzymes. Ann. N. Y. Acad. Sci., *123:*79, 1965.

Ross, M. H., G. Pappas, and J. T. Lanman: Electron microscopic observations on the endoplasmic reticulum of the human fetal adrenal. J. Biophys. & Biochem. Cytol., *4:*659, 1958.

Sedar, A. L.: Electron microscopy of the oxyntic cell in the gastric glands of *Rana catesbiana.* II. The acid secreting gastic mucosa. J. Biophys. & Biochem. Cytol., *10:*47, 1961.

Mitochondria

Altmann, R.: Die Elementarorganismen und ihre Beziehungen zu den Zellen. Leipzig, Veit, 1890.

Benda, C.: Weitere Mitteilungen über die Mitochondrien. Verh. d. Physiol. Ges., 376, 1899.

Bensley, R. R., and N. Hoerr: Preparation and properties of mitochondria. Anat. Rec., 60:449, 1934.

Cowdry, E. V.: The mitochondrial constituents of protoplasm. Carnegie Contributions to Embryol., 8:39, 1918.

Fernandez-Moran, H.: Subunit organization of mitochondrial membranes. Science, 140:381, 1963.

Gibor, A., and S. Granick: Plastics and mitochondria: Inheritable systems. Science, 145:890, 1964.

Hogeboom, G. H., W. C. Schneider, and G. H. Palade: Isolation of intact mitochondria from rat liver; some biochemical properties of mitochondria and submicroscopic particulate material. J. Biol. chem., 172:619, 1948.

Lazarow, A., and S. J. Cooperstein: Studies on the enzymatic basis for the Janus green B staining reaction. J. Histochem. & Cytochem., 1:234, 1953.

Lehninger, A. L.: The Mitochondrion, New York, W. A. Benjamin, Inc., 1964.

Luck, D. J. L.: DNA in mitochondria of *Neurospora crassa.* Proc. Nat. Acad. Sci., 52:931, 1964.

Nass, M. M. K., and S. Nass: Intramitochondrial fibers with DNA characteristics. I. Fixation and electron staining reactions. J. Cell Biol., 19:593, 1963.

Nass, M. M. K., and S. Nass: Intramitochondrial fibers with DNA characteristics. II. Enzymatic and other hydrolytic treatments. J. Cell Biol., 19:613, 1963.

Novikoff, A. B.: Mitochondria. In Brachet, J., and A. E. Mirsky, eds.: The Cell. New York, Academic Press, 1961, Vol. II, p. 299.

Palade, G.: An electron microscope study of mitochondrial structure. J. Histochem. & Cytochem., 1:188, 1953.

Parsons, D. F.: Recent advances correlating structure and function in mitochondria. Int. Rev. Exp. Path., 4:1, 1965.

Peachey, L. D: Electron microscopic observations on the accumulation of divalent cations in intramitochondrial granules. J. Cell Biol., 20:95, 1964.

Rabinowitz, M., J. Sinclair, L. DeSalle, R. Haselkorn, and H. H. Swift: Isolation of deoxyribonucleic acid from mitochondria of chick embryo heart and liver. Proc. Nat. Acad. Sci., 53:1126, 1964.

Stoeckenius, W.: Some observations on negatively stained mitochondria. J. Cell Biol., 17:443, 1963.

Swift, H., N. Kislev, and L. Bogorad: Evidence for DNA and RNA in mitochondria and chloroplasts. J. Cell Biol., 23:91A, 1964.

Lysosomes

Allison, A. C., and M. R. Young: Uptake of dyes and drugs by living cells. Life Sciences, 3:1407, 1964.

deDuve, C.: Lysosomes. Scientific American 208:5, 1963.

deDuve, C.: Lysosomes. Ciba Foundation Symposium. London, J. & A. Churchill, 1963.

deDuve, C., and R. Wattiaux: Functions of lysosomes. Annual Rev. Physiol., 28:435, 1966.

Essner, E., and A. B. Novikoff: Localization of acid phosphatase activity in hepatic lysosomes by means of electron microscopy. J. Biophys. & Biochem. Cytol., 9:773, 1961.

Holt, S. J., and R. M. Hicks: The localization of acid phosphatase in rat liver cells as revealed by combined cytochemical staining and electron microscopy. J. Biophys. & Biochem. Cytol., 11:47, 1961.

Miller, F., and G. E. Palade: Lytic activities in renal protein absorption droplets. An electron microscopical cytochemical study. J. Cell Biol., 23:519, 1954.

Novikoff, A. B.: Lysosomes and related particles. In Brachet, J., and A. E. Mirsky, eds.: The Cell. New York, Academic Press, 1961, Vol. II, Chapter 6.

Robbins, E., P. I. Marcus, and N. K. Gonatas: Dynamics of acridine orange cell interaction. II. Dye induced ultrastructural changes in multi-vesicular bodies. J. Cell Biol., 21:49, 1964.

Trump, B. F., and J. L. E. Ericsson: Electron microscopic observations on the localization of acid phosphatase in mouse hepatic parenchymal cells. Exper. Cell Res., 33:598, 1964.

Microbodies (Peroxisomes)

Afzelius, B. A.: The occurrence and structure of microbodies. A comparative study. J. Cell Biol., 26:835, 1965.

deDuve, C., and P. Baudhuin: Peroxisomes. Physiol. Rev., 46:323, 1966.

Hruban, Z., and H. Swift: Uricase: Localization in hepatic microbodies. Science, 146:1316, 1964.

Golgi Apparatus

Bowen, R. H.: The cytology of glandular secretion. Quart. Rev. Biol., 4:299, 484, 1929.

Burgos, M. H., and D. W. Fawcett: Studies on the fine structure of the mammalian testis. I. Differentiation of the spermatids in the cat. J. Biophys. & Biochem. Cytol., 1:287, 1955.

Dalton, A. J.: Golgi apparatus and secretion granules. In Brachet, J., and A. E. Mirsky, eds.: The Cell. New York, Academic Press, 1961, Vol. II, p. 603.

Dalton, A. J., and M. D. Felix: Cytologic and cytochemical characteristics of the Golgi substance of epithelial cells of the epididymis—in situ, in homogenates and after isolation. Am. J. Anat., 94:171, 1964.

Friend, D. S., and M. J. Murray: Osmium impregnation of the Golgi apparatus. Am. J. Anat., 117:135, 1965.

Golgi, C.: Sur la structure des cellules nerveuses des ganglions spinaux. Arch. ital. Biol., 30:278, 1898.

Hibbard, H.: Current status of our knowledge of the Golgi apparatus in the animal cell. Quart. Rev. Biol., 20:1, 1945.

Mollenhauer, H. H., and W. G. Whaley: An observation on the functioning of the Golgi apparatus. J. Cell Biol., 17:222, 1963.

Nassanov, D.: Das golgische Binnennetz und seine Beziehungen zu der Sekretion. Arch. f. Mikr. Anat., 100:433, 1924.

Novikoff, A. B., and W. Y. Shin: The endoplasmic reticulum in the Golgi zone and its relations to microbodies, Golgi apparatus and autophagic vacuoles in rat liver cells. J. Microscopie, 3:187, 1964.

Palay, S. L.: The morphology of secretion. In Frontiers of Cytology. New Haven, Yale University Press, 1958, p. 305.

Palade, G. E., P. Siekewitz, and L. G. Caro: Structure, chemistry and function of the pancreatic exocrine cell. In The Exocrine Pancreas. Ciba Foundation Symposium. Boston, Little, Brown & Co., 1962.

Peterson, M., and C. P. Leblond: Synthesis of complex carbohydrates in the Golgi region as shown by radiography after injection of labeled glucose. J. Cell Biol., 21:143, 1964.

Pollister, A. W., and P. F. Pollister: The structure of the Golgi apparatus. Int. Rev. Cytol., 6:85, 1957.

Schneider, W. C., and E. L. Kuff: On the isolation and some biochemical properties of the Golgi substance. Am. J. Anat., 94:209, 1954.

Zeigel, R. F., and A. J. Dalton: Speculations based on the morphology of the Golgi systems in several types of protein-secreting cells. J. Cell Biol., 15:45, 1962.

Centrosome and Centrioles

André, J.: Le centriole et la région centrosomienne. J. Microscopie, 3:23, 1964.

Costello, D. P.: On the orientation of centrioles in dividing cells and its significance: A new contribution to spindle mechanics. Biol. Bull., 120:285, 1961.

Dalcq, A. M.: Le centrosome. Bull. de l'Acad. Roy. de Belgique (Classe des Sciences), 50:1408, 1964.

DeHarven, E., and W. Bernhard: Étude au microscope électronique de l'ultrastructure du centriole chez les vertébrés. Zeitschr. f. Zellforsch., 1956.

Gachet, J., and J. P. Thiery: Application de la méthode de tirage photographique avec rotations ou translations à l'étude de macromolécules et de structures biologiques. J. Microscopie, 3:253, 1964.

Gall, J. G.: Centriole replication. A study of spermatogenesis in the snail *Viviparus.* J. Biophys. & Biochem. Cytol., 10:163, 1961.

Gall, J. G., and J. Mizukami: Centriole replication in the water fern *Marsilea.* J. Cell Biol., 10:26A, 1961.

Henneguy, L. F.: Sur les rapports des cils vibratiles avec les centrosomes. Arch. Anat. Micr., 1:481, 1897.

Huetter, A. F.: Continuity of the centrioles in *Drosophila melanogaster.* Zeitschr. f. Zellforsch., 19:119, 1933.

Randall, J., and J. M. Hopkins: Studies of cilia basal bodies and some related organelles. II. Problems of genesis. Proc. Linnaean Soc. Lond., *174*:pt.1: 37, 1963.

Renaud, F. L., and H. Swift: The development of basal bodies and flagella in *Allomyces arbusculus.* J. Cell Biol., *23*:339, 1964.

Stockinger, L., and E. Cirelli: Eine bisher unbekannte Art der Zentriolenvermehrung. Zeitschr. f. Zellforsch., *68*:733, 1965.

Szollosi, D.: Centrioles, centriolar satellites and spindle fibers. Anat. Rec., *148*:343, 1964.

Filaments and Microtubules

Behnke, O.: A preliminary report of "microtubules" in undifferentiated and differentiated vertebrate cells. J. Ultrastruct. Res., *11*:139, 1964.

Brody, I.: The ultrastructure of the tonofilaments in the keratinization process. J. Ultrastruct. Res., *4*:265, 1960.

Burgos, M. H., and Fawcett, D. W.: An electron microscope study of spermatid differentiation in the toad, *Bufo arenarum* Hensel. J. Biophys. & Biochem. Cytol., *2*:223, 1956.

Byers, B., and Porter, K. R.: Oriented microtubules in elongating cells of the developing lens rudiment after induction. Proc. Nat. Acad. Sci., *52*:1090, 1964.

Fawcett, D. W., and Witebsky, F.: Observations on the ultrastructure of nucleated erythrocytes and thrombocytes, with particular reference to the structural basis of their discoidal shape. Zeitschr. f. Zellforsch., *62*:785, 1964.

Gray, E. G.: Electron microscopy of neuroglial fibrils of the cerebral cortex. J. Biophys. & Biochem. Cytol., *6*:121, 1959.

Hepler, P. K., and Newcomb, E. H.: Microtubules and fibrils in the cytoplasm of *Coleus* cells undergoing secondary wall deposition. J. Cell Biol., *20*:529, 1964.

Ledbetter, M. C., and Porter, K. R.: A "microtubule" in plant cell fine structure. J. Cell Biol., *19*:239, 1963.

Ledbetter, M. C., and Porter, K. R.: Morphology of microtubules of plant cells. Science, *144*:872, 1964.

Robbins, E., and Gonatas, N. K.: The ultrastructure of a mammalian cell during the mitotic cycle. J. Cell Biol., *21*:429, 1964.

Roth, L. E., and Daniels, E. W.: Electron microscopic studies of mitosis in amebae. II. The giant ameba *Pelomyxa carolinensis.* J. Cell Biol., *12*:57, 1962.

Silveira, M., and Porter, K. R.: The spermatozoids of flatworms and their microtubular systems. Protoplasma, *59*:240, 1964.

Slautterback, D. B.: Cytoplasmic microtubules. I. Hydra. J. Cell Biol., *18*:367, 1963.

Tilney, L. G., and Porter, K. R.: Studies on microtubules in Helioza I. Protoplasma, *60*:317, 1965.

Pigment

Barnicot, N. A., and M. S. C. Birbeck: The electron microscopy of human melanocytes and melanin granules. *In* Montagna, W., and R. A. Ellis, eds.: The Biology of Hair Growth. New York, Academic Press, 1958.

Billingham, R. E., and W. K. Silvers: The melanocytes of mammals. Quart. Rev. Biol., *35*:1, 1960.

Björkerud, S.: Isolation of lipofuscin granules from bovine cardiac muscle. J. Ultrastruct. Res. (Suppl.), *5*:5, 1963.

Connors, C. L.: Studies on lipochromes. Am. J. Path., *4*:292, 1928.

Drochmans, P.: Melanin granules. Their fine structure, formation and degradation in normal and pathological tissues. Int. Rev. Exp. Path., *2*:357, 1963.

Fitzpatrick, T. B., and G. Szabo: The melanocyte: Cytology and cytochemistry. J. Invest. Derm., *32*:197, 1959.

Malkoff, D., and Strehler, B.: The ultrastructure of isolated and in situ human cardiac age pigment. J. Cell Biol., *16*:611, 1963.

Moyer, F. H.: Genetic variations in the fine structure and ontogeny of mouse melanin granules. American Zoologist, *6*:43, 1966.

Seiji, M., T. B. Fitzpatrick, and M. S. C. Birbeck: The melanosome: A distinctive subcellular particle of mammalian melanocytes and the site of melanogenesis. J. Invest. Derm., *36*:243, 1961.

Glycogen

Biava, C.: Identification and structural forms of human particle glycogen. Lab. Invest., *12*:1179, 1963.

Drochmans, P.: Morphologie du glycogene. J. Ultrastruct. Res., *6*:141, 1962.

Revel, J. P.: Electron microscopy of glycogen. J. Histochem. & Cytochem., *12*:104, 1964.

Nuclear Envelope

Barnes, B. G., and J. M. Davis: The structure of nuclear pores in mammalian tissue. J. Ultrastruct. Res., *3*:131, 1959.

Baud, C. A.: Nuclear membrane and permeability. *In* Seno, S., and E. V. Cowdry, eds.: Intracellular Membranous Structure. Okayama, Japan, Chugoku Press, 1965, p. 323.

Callan, S. G., and S. G. Tomlin: Experimental studies on amphibian oocyte nuclei. I. Investigation of the structure of the nuclear envelope by means of the electron microscope. Proc. Roy. Soc. Lond., *137B*:367, 1950.

Fawcett, D. W.: On the occurrence of a fibrous lamina on the inner aspect of the nuclear envelope in certain cells of vertebrates. Am. J. Anat. *119*:129, 1966.

Feldherr, C. M.: The nuclear annuli as pathways for nucleocytoplasmic exchanges. J. Cell Biol., *14*:65, 1962.

Ito, S., and W. R. Lowenstein: Permeability of a nuclear membrane. Changes during normal development and changes induced by growth hormone. Science, *150*:909, 1965.

Kanno, Y., and W. R. Lowenstein: A study of the nucleus and cell membranes of oocytes with an intracellular electrode. Exper. Cell Res., *31*:149, 1963.

Lowenstein, W. R., and Y. Kanno: The electrical conductance and potential across the membrane of some cell nuclei. J. Cell Biol., *16*:421, 1963.

Merriam, R. W.: On the fine structure and composition of the nuclear envelope. J. Biophys. & Biochem. Cytol., *11*:559, 1961.

Moses, M.: Breakdown and reformation of the nuclear envelope at cell division. *In* Internat. Cong. Electron Micros., Berlin, 1958. Berlin, Springer, 1958, p. 230.

Pappas, G. D.: The fine structure of the nuclear envelope of *Amoeba proteus.* J. Biophys. & Biochem. Cytol. 2 (Suppl.):431, 1965.

Watson, M.: Further observations on the nuclear envelope of the animal cell. J. Biophys. & Biochem. Cytol., *6*:147, 1959.

Watson, M. L.: Pores in the mammalian nuclear membrane. Biochim. Biophys. Acta, *15*:475, 1954.

Wiener, J., D. Spiro, and W. R. Lowenstein: Ultrastructure and permeability of nuclear membranes. J. Cell Biol., *27*:107, 1965.

Nucleolus

Amenta, P. S.: Fusion of nucleoli in cells from the heart of *Triturus viridescens.* Anat. Rec., *139*:155, 1961.

Bernhard, W., and N. Granboulan: The fine structure of the cancer cell nucleus. Exper. Cell Res. (Suppl.), *9*:19, 1963.

Caspersson, T., and J. Schultz: Ribonucleic acids in both nuclei and cytoplasm and the function of the nucleolus. Proc. Nat. Acad. Sci., *26*:507, 1940.

Clyman, M. J.: A new structure observed in the nucleolus of the human endometrial epithelial cell. Am. J. Obst. & Gynec., *86*:430, 1963.

Estable, C., and J. R. Sotelo: Una nueva estructura celular; el nucleolonema. Publ. Inst. Invest. Ciencias. Biol., *1*:105, 1951.

Hay, E. D., and J. P. Revel: The DNA component of the nucleolus studied in autoradiographs viewed with the electron microscope. Proc. V Internat. Cong. Electron Micros. Academic Press, New York, Vol. 2, p. O-7.

Hyde, B. B., K. Sankaranarayanan, and M. L. Birnstiel: Observations on the fine structure of pea nucleoli in situ and isolated. J. Ultrastruct. Res., *12*:652, 1965.

Jones, K. W.: The role of the nucleolus in the formation of ribosomes. J. Ultrastruct. Res., *13*:257, 1965.

Maggio, R., P. Siekevitz, and G. E. Palade: Studies on isolated nuclei. II. Isolation and chemical characterization of nucleolar and nucleoplasmic sulfractions. J. Cell Biol., *18*:293, 1963.

Marinozzi, V.: Cytochimie ultrastructurale du nucléole—RNA et protéins intranucléolaires. J. Ultrastruct. Res., *10*:443, 1964.

Marinozzi, V., and W. Barnhard: Présence dans la nucléole de deux types de ribonucléoprotéins morphologiquement distinctes. Exper. Cell Res., *32*:595, 1964.

Perry, R. P., and M. Errera: The influence of nucleolar ribonucleic acid metabolism on that of the nucleus and cytoplasm. *In* Mitchell, J. S., ed.: The Cell Nucleus. London, Butterworths, p. 24.

Schoefl, G.: The effect of actinomysin D on the fine structure of the nucleolus. J. Ultrastruct. Res., *10*:224, 1964.

Terzakis, J. A.: The nucleolar channel system of the human endometrium. J. Cell Biol., *27*:293, 1965.

Uretz, R. B., and R. P. Perry: Improved ultraviolet microbeam apparatus. Rev. Sci. Instr., *28*:861, 1957.

Vincent, W. S.: Structure and chemistry of nucleoli. Int. Rev. Cytol., *4*:269, 1965.

Vincent, W. S., and O. L. Miller, Jr., eds.: International Symposium on the Nucleolus, Its Structure and Function. National Cancer Institute, Monograph No. 23, 1967. Washington, United States Government Printing Office, 1967.

Cell Division

Barnicot, N. A., and H. E. Huxley: Electron microscope observations on mitotic chromosomes. Quart. J. Micr. Sci., *106*:197, 1965.

Bloom, W., and S. Özarslan: Electron microscopy of ultraviolet-irradiated parts of chromosomes. Proc. Nat. Acad. Sci., *53*:1294, 1965.

Bloom, W., R. E. Zirkle, and R. B. Uretz: Irradiation of parts of individual cells. III. Effects of chromosomal and extrachromosomal irradiation on chromosome movements. Ann. N. Y. Acad. Sci., *59*:503, 1955.

Cantor, K. B., and J. E. Hearst: Isolation and partial characterization of metaphase chromosomes of a mouse ascites tumor. Proc. Nat. Acad. Sci., *55*:642, 1966.

Coleman, J. R., and M. J. Moses: DNA and the fine structure of synaptic chromosomes in the domestic rooster (*Gallus domesticus*). J. Cell Biol., *23*:63, 1964.

DeRobertis, E. D. P., W. W. Nowinski, and F. A. Saez: Cell Biology. 4th ed. Philadelphia, W. B. Saunders Co., 1965.

Forer, A.: Local reduction of spindle fiber birefringence in *Nephrotoma suturalis* (Loew) spermatocytes induced by ultraviolet microbeam irradiation. J. Cell Biol., *25*:95, 1965.

Frenster, J. H.: Mechanisms of repression and de-repression within interphase chromatin. In Dawe, C. J., ed.: The Chromosome: Structural and Functional Aspects. Tissue Culture Association Symposium. In Vitro, *1*:78, 1965.

Gaulden, M. E., and R. P. Perry: Influence of the nucleolus on mitosis as revealed by ultraviolet microbeam irradiation. Proc. Nat. Acad. Sci., *44*:553, 1958.

Gross, P. R., ed.: Second conference on the mechanisms of cell division. Ann. N. Y. Acad. Sci., *90*:345, 1960.

Harris, M.: Cell Culture and Somatic Variation. New York, Holt, Rinehart and Winston, 1964.

Hughes, A.: The Mitotic Cycle: The Cytoplasm and Nucleus During Interphase and Mitosis. New York, Academic Press, 1952.

Inoué, S.: On the physical properties of the mitotic spindle. In Gross, P. R., ed.: Second conference on the mechanisms of cell division. Ann. N. Y. Acad. Sci., *90*:529, 1960.

Lafontaine, J. G.: A light and electron microscope study of small, spherical nuclear bodies in meristematic cells of *Allium cepa, Vicia faba* and *Raphanus sativus*. J. Cell Biol., *26*:1, 1965.

Lafontaine, J. G., and L. A. Chouinard: A correlated light and electron microscope study of the nucleolar material during mitosis in *Vicia faba*. J. Cell Biol., *17*:167, 1963.

Leblond, C. P., and B. E. Walker: Renewal of cell populations. Physiol. Rev., *36*:255, 1956.

Levine, L., ed.: The Cell in Mitosis. New York, Academic Press, 1963.

Locke, M., ed.: The Role of Chromosomes in Development. New York, Academic Press, 1964.

Mazia, D.: Mitosis and the physiology of cell division. In Brachet, J., and A. E. Mirsky, eds.: The Cell: Biochemistry, Physiology, Morphology. New York, Academic Press, 1961, Vol. III, p. 77.

Moses, M. J.: The nucleus and chromosomes: A cytological perspective. In Bourne, G. H., ed.: Cytology and Cell Physiology. 3rd ed. New York, Academic Press, 1964, p. 424.

Nicklas, R. B.: Chromosome micromanipulation. II. Induced reorientation and the experimental control of segregation in mitosis. Chromosoma, *21*:17, 1967.

Perry, R. B.: Changes in ultraviolet absorption spectrum of parts of living cells following irradiation with an ultraviolet microbeam. Exper. Cell Res., *12*:546, 1957.

Perutz, M. F.: Proteins and Nucleic Acids: Structure and Function. New York, Elsevier Publishing Co., 1962.

Porter, K. R., and R. D. Machado: Studies on the endoplasmic reticulum. IV. Its form and distribution during mitosis in cells of onion root tip. J. Biophys. & Biochem. Cytol., *7*:167, 1960.

Prescott, D. M.: Comments on cell life cycle. Nat. Cancer Inst. Monogr., *14*:55, 1964.

Revel, J. P., and E. D. Hay: Autoradiographic localization of DNA synthesis in a specific ultrastructural component of the interphase nucleus. Exper. Cell Res., *25*:474, 1962.

Ris, H.: Ultrastructure and molecular organization of genetic systems. Canad. J. Genet. Cytol., *3*:95, 1961.

Robbins, E., and N. K. Gonates: The ultrastructure of a mammalian cell during the mitotic cycle. J. Cell Biol., *21*:429, 1964.

Seed, J.: X-irradiation of the nucleolus and its effect on nucleic acid synthesis. In Mitchell, J. S., ed. (for the Faraday Society): The Cell Nucleus. New York, Acadamic Press, 1960.

Serlin, J. L.: The intracellular transfer of genetic information. Int. Rev. Cytol., *15*:35, 1963.

Swift, H. S.: Molecular morphology of the chromosome. In Vitro, *1*:26, 1966.

Taylor, E. W.: Control of DNA synthesis in mammalian cells in culture. Exp. Cell Res., *40*:316, 1965.

Taylor, H. J.: The replication and organization of DNA in chromosomes. In Molecular Genetics. New York: Academic Press, 1963, Part I, p. 65.

Tjio, J. H., and T. T. Puck: Genetics of somatic mammalian cells: chromosomal constitution of cells in tissue culture. J. Exper. Med., *108*:259, 1958.

Watson, J. D.: Molecular Biology of the Gene. New York: W. A. Benjamin, Inc., 1965.

Zirkle, R. E.: Partial-cell irradiation. In Lawrence, L. H., and C. A. Tobias, eds.: Advances in Biological and Medical Physics. New York, Academic Press, 1957, Vol. V, p. 103.

CHAPTER THREE

Epithelium

In the foregoing chapter the microscopic and submicroscopic components of cells were described in some detail. This emphasis upon the cell as the fundamental unit of structure in higher organisms is appropriate, but it is important to realize that isolated cells are seldom encountered in the body. Instead, cells that work together to perform a particular function are usually assembled in coherent associations and bound together by varying amounts of fibrous and amorphous intercellular substance to form *tissues*.

The early chapters of this book are devoted to descriptions of the basic tissues: epithelium, connective tissue, muscular tissue, and nervous tissue. The later chapters will describe the characteristic patterns in which the various tissues are combined to form the larger functional units known as *organs*.

Epithelium, the subject of this chapter, is a tissue composed of closely aggregated cells in apposition over a large part of their surface of contact and having very little intercellular substance. In its simplest form, epithelium consists of a single continuous layer of cells of the same type covering an external or internal surface. Quite commonly, however, multiple layers develop and the cells may differentiate into two or more kinds. To describe the resulting diversity in appearance, various types of epithelium are identified by different terms.

ORIGIN AND DISTRIBUTION OF EPITHELIUM. Two of the primary germ layers of the early embryo, the *ectoderm* and *endoderm,* are clearly epithelial in their pattern of growth, and most of the epithelial organs of the body are derived from these germ layers. For example, the epi-

dermis of the skin and the epithelium of the cornea, which together cover the entire external surface of the body, develop from the ectoderm. By invagination and proliferation, this outer covering epithelium gives rise to tubes or solid cords that form the glandular appendages of the skin, such as the sudoriparous, sebaceous, and mammary glands. Similarly, the alimentary tract is lined with epithelium of endodermal origin, and its associated glands—liver, pancreas, gastric glands, and intestinal glands—arise in the embryo by invagination and specialization of epithelial outgrowths from the lining of the primitive fore- and hindgut. Each *exocrine gland* of the adult communicates with an internal cavity or an external surface by way of ducts that open onto the epithelium of the inner or outer surface layer from which it developed during embryonic life. The *endocrine glands,* on the other hand, usually lose their connection with the surface epithelium from which they originally develop.

In addition to the epithelial structures that develop from the ectoderm and endoderm, there are several organs and lining layers having an epithelial pattern of growth that arise from mesoderm. Examples are the kidney and the epithelia of the male and female reproductive tracts.

The linings of the peritoneal cavity and of other serous cavities in the adult, and the linings of blood and lymph vessels, are all derivatives of mesenchyme. They were formerly called *false epithelia* to distinguish them from derivatives of the epithelial germ layers, but this distinction is no longer considered to be important. From a morphological point of view they are in all respects typical epithelia. Nevertheless, it is convenient and customary to refer to the lining of blood and lymph vessels as *endothelium* and to the lining of serous cavities as *mesothelium.*

Epithelia are specialized for many different functions. Those that form the outer surface of the body are often adapted for protection of the organism against loss of moisture and mechanical damage. They may also play a role in sensory reception, containing nerve endings that provide the warnings of pain that make the organism avoid injury. Others contain neural elements, such as taste buds and olfactory cells, specialized to function as chemical receptors. All substances received or given off by the body must traverse an epithelium; thus many of those lining internal surfaces are modified for *absorption* or *secretion.* Those concerned with secretion may contain only occasional individual cells specialized for production and release of a secretion, or the whole epithelium may give rise to a gland in which most of the cells are specialized for elaboration of a particular product. Other epithelia concerned with excretion become modified to increase their efficiency in transport of solutes and water or in elimination of substances from the body.

CLASSIFICATION OF EPITHELIA

Epithelia are classified and named according to the number of cell layers and the shape of the cells. If there is one layer of cells the epithelium is described as *simple;* if there are two or more layers it is said to be *stratified.* The superficial cells can usually be described as *squamous, cuboidal,* or *columnar.* Thus a single layer of flat cells is a *simple squamous epithelium.* A single layer of tall prismatic cells is a *simple columnar epithelium.* The corresponding multi-layered epithelia are called *stratified squamous epithelium* and *stratified columnar epithelium.*

Within the same general category of epithelium the cells may or may not have

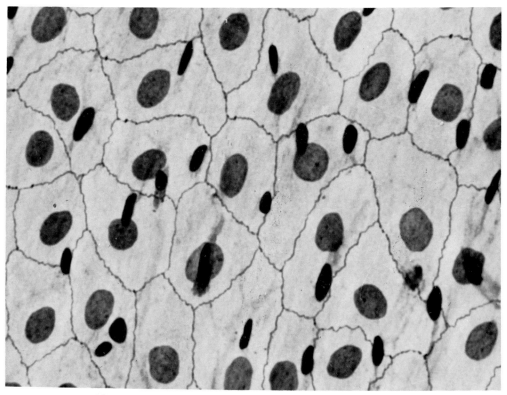

Figure 3-1.   A thin spread of guinea pig mesentery treated with silver nitrate and subsequently stained with May-Grünwald and Giemsa stains. The limits of the simple squamous mesothelial cells have been blackened by the silver. The large round or oval nuclei are those of the mesothelial cells. The elongate darker nuclei are those of fibroblasts beneath the layer of mesothelium. × 750.

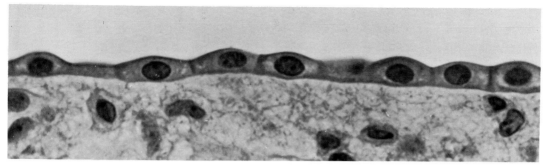

Figure 3-2.   The epithelium of the collecting ducts of the dog kidney may be flattened so as to form a thick squamous epithelium such as is shown here, or the cells may be cuboidal. × 960.

motile cell processes called *cilia* on their free surfaces. In the interest of more precise description it is customary to make note of this surface specialization in naming the epithelium. When such a border is present, the tissue is described as a *ciliated simple columnar epithelium* or a *ciliated stratified columnar epithelium*. Similarly in stratified squamous epithelium, the superficial cells in some cases accumulate in their cytoplasm a fibrous protein called *keratin* and are reduced to scalelike lifeless residues of cells. To distinguish such epithelia from others in which the superficial cells do not undergo this change, it is customary to describe them as *keratinized stratified squamous epithelium.*

Among the simple columnar epithelia one category is described as *pseudostratified* because the cells are so arranged that the nuclei occur at two or more levels and the epithelium thus appears to be stratified. It can be shown by maceration, however, that there is actually only one layer, all of the cells being fixed to the basement membrane but only some of

them reaching the free surface. In truly stratified epithelia only the cells of the lowermost layer touch the underlying tissue.

Among the stratified epithelia there are two types that cannot adequately be described by reference to the shape of their surface cells. These are the *transitional epithelium* of the urinary tract and the *germinal epithelium* of the male gonad. Their distinguishing characteristics will be described later.

SIMPLE SQUAMOUS EPITHELIUM.   Thin platelike cells are arranged in a single layer on the surface of the connective tissue and adhere closely to one another by their edges. On examination from the surface, especially after the cell limits are stained with silver nitrate, a typical mosaic pattern is seen (Fig. 3-1). The individual cells have regular (usually hexagonal) or irregular wavy outlines, and each contains a nucleus. In perpendicular sections a thin stripe is seen, subdivided into small segments which correspond to the single cells. A given section will not pass through the nucleus

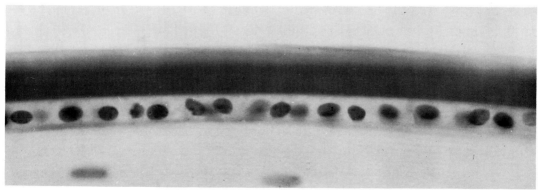

Figure 3-3.   The epithelium underlying the capsule of the lens of the human eye is a single layer of cuboidal cells. The capsule itself is a thick cuticle 11 to 18 μ thick on the surface of the epithelium. × 720.

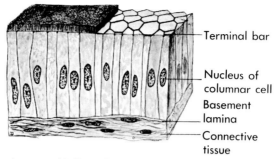

Figure 3-4. Diagram of the columnar epithelium of the small intestine. The striated border has been removed in the right half to show the terminal bars. (Redrawn and slightly modified from Stöhr-von Möllendorff.)

of every cell. In profile the cell may appear as a plump spindle or a thin rectangle (Fig. 3-2).

Epithelia of this variety are found in the human body on the inner surface of the wall of the membranous labyrinth and on the inner surface of the tympanic membrane of the ear; in the parietal layer of the capsule of Bowman and in the descending limb of the loop of Henle in the kidney; in the rete testis; and in the smallest excretory ducts of many glands. Also included in this category are the *mesothelium* lining the serous cavities (Fig. 3-1), the *mesenchymal epithelium* lining cavities in the connective tissue, and the *endothelial* cells lining the walls of the blood and lymph vessels.

SIMPLE CUBOIDAL EPITHELIUM. The low prismatic cell bodies adhere to one another by their lateral surfaces. On surface view this epithelium appears as a mosaic of small, usually six-sided, polygons; in vertical section the sheet of cells appears subdivided into squares.

This epithelium is found in many glands, as in the thyroid, on the free surface of the ovary, on the choroid plexus, on the inner surface of the capsule of the lens (Fig. 3-3), in

some areas of the labyrinth, in the excretory ducts of many glands, and as the pigmented epithelium of the retina. Secreting epithelia in the terminal portions of many glands can often be placed in this class, although the cells comprising acini or the walls of tubules are usually in the form of truncated pyramids rather than cubes.

SIMPLE COLUMNAR EPITHELIUM. The tall prismatic cells adhere to one another by their lateral surfaces. In sections parallel to the surface one sees a mosaic much like that in other simple epithelia, but one in which the polygonal outlines of the cells are considerably smaller (Figs. 3-4 and 3-5). In sections perpendicular to the surface the rectangular outlines of the cells may be but little taller than those of cuboidal epithelium (Fig. 3-6*A*) or they may be tall and slender, standing upright like columns or fence palings (Fig. 3-6*C*). In many examples of columnar epithelium all the oval nuclei are at approximately the same level (Fig. 3-6*D*). An epithelium of this type lines the surface of the digestive tract from the cardia of the stomach to the anus and is also common in the ex-

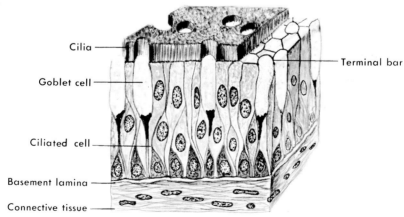

Figure 3-5. Diagram of pseudostratified columnar ciliated epithelium. (Redrawn and slightly modified from Stöhr-von Möllendorff.)

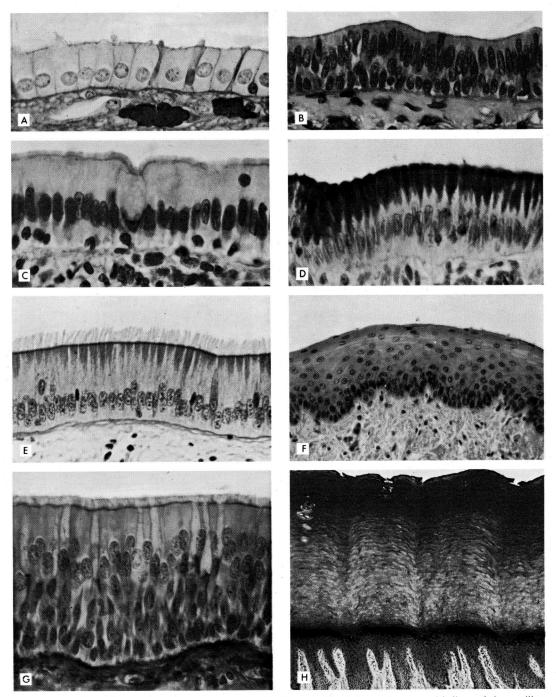

Figure 3–6. Photomicrographs of various types of epithelium: *A*, Simple low columnar epithelium of the papillary duct of the dog kidney. Mallory trichrome stain.

B, Stratified columnar epithelium from a large salivary gland duct. Mallory-azan stain.

C, Simple columnar epithelium from the intestinal mucosa of a cat. The epithelium has a striated border. Notice the presence of a single goblet cell among the columnar cells. Heidenhain's azan stain.

D, Simple columnar epithelium of mucous cells from the stomach. The mucus is stained a deep magenta. PAS-hematoxylin stain.

E, Simple ciliated columnar epithelium from the typhlosole of a mollusc. Notice the long cone of rootlets extending from the basal bodies of the cilia downward into the apical cytoplasm. Chrome alum-hematoxylin-phloxine stain.

F, Stratified squamous epithelium from the esophagus of a macaque. Hematoxylin and eosin stain.

G, Ciliated pseudostratified columnar epithelium from the human trachea. Mallory-azan stain.

H, Keratinized stratified squamous epithelium of the epidermis of the sole of the foot. Notice the very thick superficial stratum of fully keratinized devitalized cells.

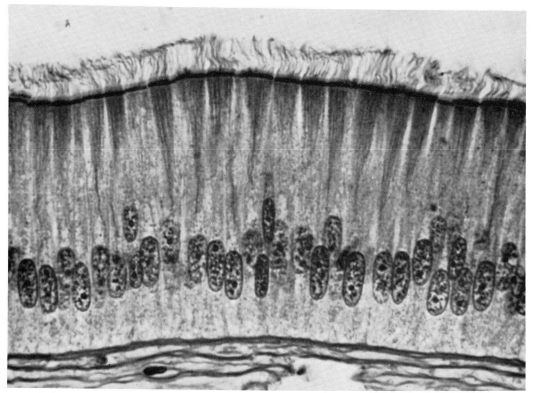

Figure 3-7. Simple columnar ciliated epithelium from the alimentary tract of a fresh water mussel. Notice the dark row of ciliary basal bodies just beneath the free surface of the cells and the cones of fibrous rootlets that extend downward from the basal bodies into the apical cytoplasm. Observe also the distinct "basement membrane" upon which the epithelium rests. Chrome alum-hematoxylin-phloxine stain. × 1200.

cretory ducts of many glands. *Ciliated simple columnar epithelium* (Fig. 3-7) is found in the uterus and oviducts, in the small bronchi of the lung, in some of the paranasal sinuses, and in the central canal of the spinal cord.

STRATIFIED SQUAMOUS EPITHELIUM. The epithelial sheet is thick, and a perpendicular section shows the cells to vary in shape (Figs. 3-6*F* and 3-8). The layer next to the underlying tissue consists of cuboidal or even columnar cells, sometimes with rounded upper ends. Then follow a varying number of layers of more or less irregular polyhedral cells, often provided with excavations which fit the convex surfaces of their neighbors. The nearer to the free surface, the more the cells are flattened (Fig. 3-8). The superficial layers consist of thin squamous cells.

Epithelia of this kind are found in the epidermis, the mouth, the esophagus, a part of the epiglottis, a part of the conjunctiva, the cornea, the vagina, and a part of the female urethra. On most inner surfaces of the body the superficial cells of such epithelia are viable, nucleated elements, but on the exposed outer surfaces of the body the superficial cells have lost their nuclei and are dry, dead scales. Such epithelia are most accurately described as *keratinized stratified squamous epithelia* (Fig. 3-6*H*).

STRATIFIED COLUMNAR EPITHELIUM. The deeper layer or layers consist of small, irregularly polyhedral or fusiform cells which do not reach the free surface. The superficial cells are tall and prismatic and are not connected with the underlying tissue. Stratified columnar epithelium is relatively rare and is confined to small areas. It is found in the fornix of the conjunctiva, in the cavernous part of the urethra, in some places in the anal mucous membrane, in the pharynx, on the epiglottis, and in the large excretory ducts of some glands (Fig. 3-6*B*). Some authors place the epithelium of the enamel organ in this group.

On the nasal surface of the soft palate, in

the larynx, and transiently in the fetal esophagus one finds *ciliated stratified columnar epithelium* (Fig. 3-9).

PSEUDOSTRATIFIED COLUMNAR EPITHELIUM. In pseudostratified columnar epithelium the nuclei are at different levels and the cells are quite variable in shape (Figs. 3-5 and 3-6G). Some are attached to the underlying connective tissue but do not extend to the free surface. These basal or supporting cells are overlaid by tall superficial cells which maintain a connection with the underlying tissue via slender processes. The cells are thus irregular in shape and the nuclei are at several levels, giving the appearance of a stratified epithelium. Pseudostratified epithelium occurs in the large excretory ducts of the parotid and several other glands and in the male urethra. *Ciliated pseudostratified columnar epithelium* is found on the greater part of the mucous membrane of the respiratory passages, in the eusta-

chian tube, in a part of the tympanic cavity, in the lacrimal sac, and in the excretory passages of the male reproductive system.

TRANSITIONAL EPITHELIUM. This was originally believed to represent an intermediate or transitional form between stratified squamous and columnar epithelium. The term *transitional epithelium* persists, even though its implication of change from one type to another is no longer considered appropriate. This kind of epithelium varies greatly in appearance because it is found lining hollow organs which are subject to great mechanical changes due to contraction and distention. In the contracted condition it consists of many cell layers (Fig. 3-10). The deepest elements have a cuboidal or even a columnar shape; above these are several layers of irregularly polyhedral cells, and the superficial layer consists of large cells with a characteristic convex free surface. In the stretched condition the relations of the cells

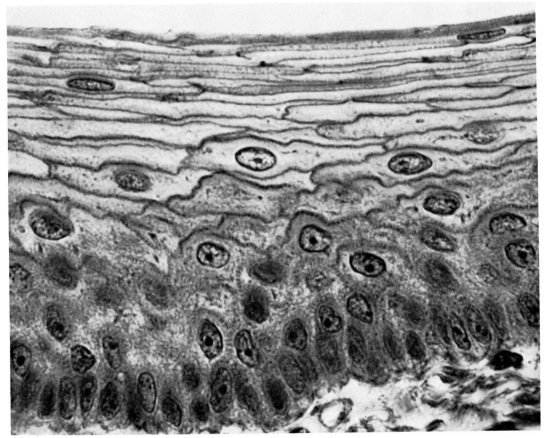

Figure 3-8. Photomicrograph of stratified squamous epithelium from the gingiva of a kitten. Observe the darker-staining cuboidal cells of the basal layer and the progressive flattening of cells in the more superficial layers. × 1500.

change to accommodate to the distention of the organ, and usually only two layers can then be distinguished: a superficial layer of large squamous elements over a layer of irregular cuboidal cells. This type of epithelium is characteristic of the mucosa of the excretory passages of the urinary system from the renal calyces to the urethra.

The classification of epithelia that has been presented applies primarily to the higher vertebrates. Other categories would be necessary to describe adequately the patterns of cell association found in invertebrates and lower vertebrates. In the adult the type of epithelium is characteristic of the particular organ and does not change under normal conditions. However, in chronic inflammation or in the development of tumors one type of epithelium may change into another, a process called *metalplasia*. As an example of metaplasia, if one nostril of a dog is surgically closed, the greater evaporative loss of moisture that accompanies the increased ventilation through the remaining nasal passage causes its pseudostratified ciliated columnar epithelium to transform into stratified squamous epithelium.

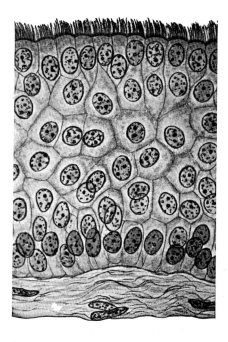

Figure 3-9. Stratified columnar ciliated epithelium from the laryngeal surface of the epiglottis of a 31 week human embryo. × 795. (After V. Patzelt, from Schaffer.)

SPECIAL STRUCTURAL FEATURES OF EPITHELIAL CELLS

A fundamental property of epithelial cells is their inherent tendency to maintain extensive contacts with one another and thus to form coherent sheets covering surfaces and lining cavities. As structural correlates of this property, characteristic specializations of the plasmalemma are found on the lateral surfaces of the cells for maintaining close cell to cell contact. The free surfaces of the superficial cells may also be modified in various ways to increase the efficiency of the epithelium in carrying out one or more of the diverse functions of *protection, absorption, secretion, excretion, transport,* and *special sensation.* Because substances entering or leaving the body must traverse an epithelium in a direction perpendicular to the sheet, the epithelial cells are structurally and functionally *polarized*—that is to say, the distal end, toward the free surface, differs from the proximal end, toward the underlying connective tissue. This polarity is evident not only in the specialization of the respective surfaces but also in the arrangement of the organelles in the interior of the cell. The centrosome and Golgi apparatus are usually at the apical pole of the nucleus. An imaginary line passing through the centrosome and the center of the nucleus defines the *cell axis,* and this is usually perpendicular to the epithelial sheet. The long filamentous mitochondria of columnar epithelia tend to be oriented parallel to the cell axis (Fig. 3-11).

The evidence of polarity of the cells is less obvious in stratified squamous epithelia, which are more concerned with protection than with absorption or secretion. In these, the devices for cell attachment are especially well developed, and the cytoplasm contains a conspicuous internal reinforcement or *cytoskeleton* composed of submicroscopic filaments, aggregated in bundles that comprise the *tonofibrils* visible with the light microscope. Such an internal supporting framework is not a prominent feature of columnar epithelia, but in some of these a *terminal web,* consisting of a feltwork of fine filaments, can be seen immediately beneath the free surface, where it apparently provides support for specialized striated or ciliated borders.

SPECIALIZATIONS FOR CELL ATTACHMENT. Adjacent epithelial cells cohere so tightly that

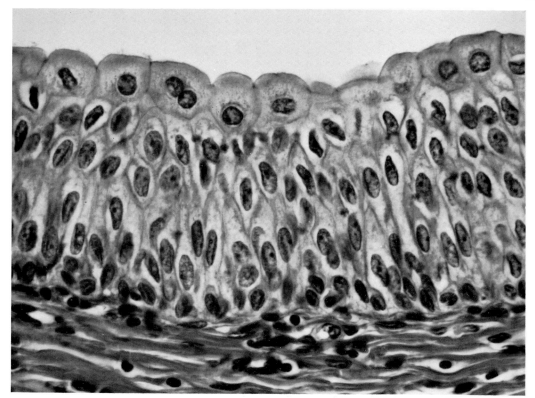

Figure 3-10. Photomicrograph of stratified transitional epithelium from the renal pelvis of a monkey, showing the characteristic superficial layer of large rounded cells, often binucleate. Hematoxylin and eosin. × 700.

relatively strong mechanical force must be applied to separate them. Views as to the basis for their firm adherence have changed greatly. It was the traditional interpretation that a thin layer of an interstitial substance existed between cells that acted as an adhesive. This hypothetical substance has long been referred to as the *intercellular cement.*

Certain epithelial cells, particularly those of the epidermis, appeared with the light microscope to adhere to one another by many small processes distributed over the entire surface of the cell. These seemed to extend from cell to cell and were called "intercellular bridges." Between the bridges was a labyrinthine system of expanded intercellular spaces called *interfacial canals* (Fig. 3-12). Midway in each bridge was a dense-staining dot called a *desmosome.* Although some histologists insisted that there was protoplasmic continuity from cell to cell through the bridges, others interpreted the desmosomoes as special sites of attachment at the end to end junctions of short

processes on the neighboring cells. With special preparative procedures desmosomes could be demonstrated on the lateral surfaces of columnar epithelial cells that adhered tightly with no apparent intercellular bridges. Also, on the boundary between adjacent columnar epithelial cells, near their free surface, dark dots or dense bars could be seen. These were called *terminal bars* (Fig. 3-4). In horizontal sections at their level, they are seen to form a dense band that is continuous around the polygonal perimeter of each cell. Traditionally these bars were interpreted as local accumulations of intercellular cement and they were assumed to close the intercellular space at the free surface.

The electron microscope has greatly clarified these relationships and has led to the definition of several additional types of specialization for attachment. Intercellular bridges with cytoplasmic continuity do not exist in stratified squamous epithelium. The structures so interpreted by classical histologists are short processes attached end to end by desmosomes (Fig.

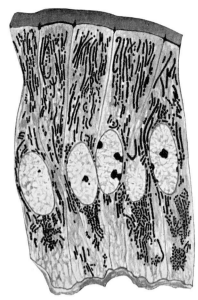

Figure 3-11. Columnar epithelium from rat intestine, showing striated border, terminal bars, and filamentous supranuclear and granular infranuclear mitochondria. Iron-hematoxylin stain. × 1000. (After A. A. Maximow.)

3-12). The desmosome is a bipartite structure consisting of local differentiations of the opposing cell membranes. The plasmalemma at the desmosome is of normal dimensions but appears thickened because of the presence of a thin dense layer on its cytoplasmic surface (Fig. 3-13). Immediately subjacent to this is a somewhat thicker layer consisting of a feltwork of fine filaments embedded in a condensation of the cytoplasmic matrix. Bundles of tonofilaments from the cytoplasm often converge upon the desmosomes and appear to terminate in them, but studies at high magnification have shown that many of the filaments form narrow hairpin loops in the dense layer of the matrix and turn back into the cytoplasm (Kelly). A thin intermediate line may be resolved in the intercellular space parallel to the plasma membranes and midway between them, but as a rule no transverse structural elements can be observed connecting the symmetrical halves of the desmosome. The nature of the forces that hold the cells together more tightly at these points is not known.

Half desmosomes are never observed along the boundaries between cells, the formation of one half evidently inducing the nearly simultaneous formation of the complementary half by the neighboring cell. Half desmosomes

are found, however, on the basal surface of stratified squamous epithelia where the cells are exposed to the underlying connective tissue (Fig. 3-14).

The term *macula adherens* has recently been proposed to replace *desmosome* (Farquhar and Palade). This new term is descriptive of the cohesive function of this structure and its plaquelike or discoid configuration in the plane of the membrane, but the older name, meaning "a connecting body," is equally appropriate and continues to be widely used.

In the juxtaluminal region of columnar epithelia, where *terminal bars* are seen with the light microscope, the electron microscope often reveals a *junctional complex* consisting of three distinct components (Fig. 3-15). Near the free surface the membranes of adjoining cells converge and the outer leaflets of their unit membranes appear to fuse into a single linear density. The intercellular space is thus completely obliterated. This zone of membrane fusion is usually less than half a micron long in sections perpendicular to the epithelium, but in subtangential sections just below the free surface it can be shown to extend around the entire perimeter of the cell. There is no condensation of the adjacent cytoplasm. This component of the juxtaluminal junctional complex is called a "tight junction" or *zonula occludens*. Deep to it is the *zonula adherens*, where the membranes diverge again to the normal distance of 150 to 200 Å and are supported on their inner aspect by moderately dense filamentous material forming a continuous band parallel to the zonula occludens. This band of dense filamentous cytoplasm has ill defined outer limits, sometimes blending with the terminal web.

The third component of the typical junctional complex of columnar epithelium is the *macula adherens* or desmosome, whose fine structure has already been described. A number of these are distributed in a discontinuous row around the cell parallel to and deep to the zonula adherens. They are easily distinguished by their sharply defined limits and by the presence of a dense homogeneous layer immediately subjacent to the plasmalemma—a feature lacking in the other two elements of the junctional complex. Desmosomes may also be found elsewhere on the lateral boundaries of epithelial cells, whereas the zonula occludens and zonula adherens are confined to the juxtaluminal region.

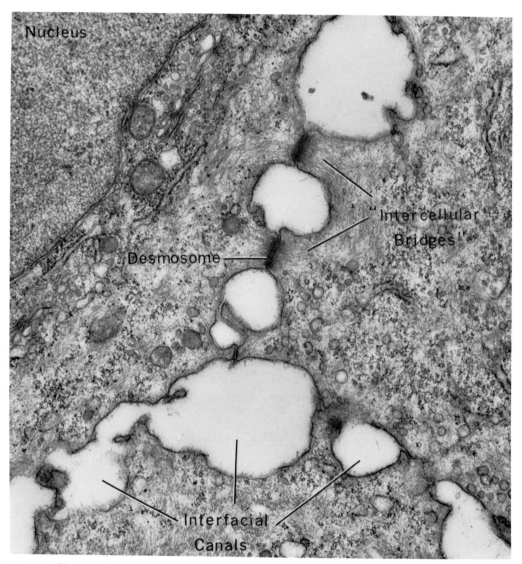

Figure 3-12. Electron micrograph showing the junction of three cells in the epidermis of an amphibian larva. The "intercellular bridges" of light microscopy are not open communications between cells but are sites of end to end contact of short processes on adjacent cells. At the points of contact the cells are firmly attached by means of surface specializations called desmosomes. The labyrinthine system of communicating intercellular spaces, called "interfacial canals," between the cell processes may play a role in the nutrition of the more superficial cells of the epithelium. × 25,000. (Courtesy of E. D. Hay.)

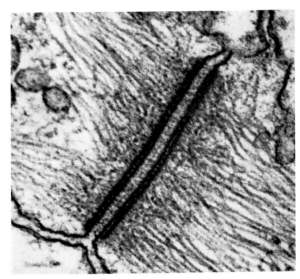

Figure 3-13. Electron micrograph of a desmosome from the epidermis of a larval newt, showing the thickening of the inner leaflet of the cell membrane and the tonofilaments forming "loops" in the condensation of cytoplasm adjacent to the specialized area of the membrane. × 93,000. (Courtesy of Douglas Kelly.)

All three of these surface specializations help maintain cell to cell cohesion and contribute to the structural integrity of the epithelium. The zonula occludens has the additional function of sealing the contact between cells and denying access to the intercellular space from the lumen. This has important implications for absorption and transport, for it probably means that substances traversing the epithelium must pass through the apical cytoplasm of such cells in the initial portion of their transit. It is also becoming apparent that these zones of membrane fusion are sites offering a low resistance to flow of ions, for it has been shown by impaling epithelia with microelectrodes that the cells are electrically coupled. It is possible, therefore, that the low resistance connections at the zonulae occludentes may play a role in the coordination of the activities of the epithelial cells.

THE BASAL SURFACE OF EPITHELIA. Between an epithelium and the underlying connective tissue is an extracellular supporting layer that has long been called the *basement membrane* and has been interpreted as a condensation of the ground substance of the connective tissue at its interface with the epithelium. The basement membrane is often difficult to see in routine hematoxylin and eosin preparations but can be clearly demonstrated by staining with the periodic acid-Schiff reaction or with silver impregnation methods (Fig. 3-16). It then appears as a thin continuous layer closely applied to the base of the epithelium. It is now apparent that what was formerly identified as the "basement membrane" is not a single structural entity but has two or more distinct components that are not resolved as such with the light microscope. In electron micrographs its most consistent component is a continuous sheet 500 to 800 Å thick and composed of moderately dense material that has a fine filamentous texture. This boundary layer is now often called the *basement lamina* or *basal lamina*. It is in contact with the basal plasma membrane and conforms closely to its contours. The density of this layer is very low immediately adjacent to the cell but increases a short distance away from the membrane. Because this outer condensed zone is more conspicuous in sections, the basal lamina may appear as a linear density running parallel to the cell surface at a distance of 300 to 400 Å from the membrane.

Outside the basal lamina are small fascicles of unit fibrils of collagen (reticular fibers) embedded in an amorphous protein-polysaccharide *ground substance*. All these components —basal lamina, reticular fibers, and ground substance—contribute to the image of the "basement membrane" seen with the light microscope. The reticular fibers are mainly responsible for its impregnation with silver salts, while the periodic acid–Schiff reaction involves the polysaccharides of the basal lamina and ground substance. Because the *basal lamina* immediately underlies the epithelium and is the most consistent component of the complex, it is now commonly thought of as synonymous with "basement membrane," and the latter term is now falling into disuse.

Chemical studies of isolated basal laminae from the kidney indicate that their main structural component is a form of collagen. There is now considerable evidence that this layer is a product of the overlying epithelium and not a condensation of the underlying connective tissue ground substance, as it was formerly thought to be. The reticular fibers and their associated polysaccharide matrix, on the other hand, are mainly the products of connective tissue fibroblasts.

SPECIALIZATIONS OF THE FREE SURFACE

STRIATED BORDER. A number of columnar epithelia possess a refractile border that exhibits delicate vertical striations when examined at high magnification. This is called a *striated* or *brush border* (Fig. 3-6*b*). It was long debated whether the vertical striations were attributable to narrow parallel channels in an amorphous cuticle or to a great many slender, rodlike processes. This uncertainty has now been resolved with the demonstration by electron microscopy that such borders consist of large numbers of slender cylindrical cell processes 80 to 90 mμ in diameter and 0.5 to 1μ long. These are now called *microvilli* (Fig. 3-17). They are enclosed in an extension of the plasmalemma that has the typical trilaminar structure but which often bears delicate filamentous excrescences 25 to 50 Å in diameter on its outer surface. When present, these can

Figure 3-14. Hemidesmosomes along the basal cell membrane in newt epidermal cell. Notice the tonofilaments converging on the dense cytoplasmic component of the hemidesmosomes. At the lower left are cross sections of the collagen fibrils of the basal lamellae. × 80,000. (Courtesy of Douglas Kelly.)

be shown by histochemical staining reactions to be rich in complex polysaccharides (see Fig. 26-7). The cytoplasm in the interior of the microvilli is fine textured and homogeneous except for a bundle of straight parallel filaments that run longitudinally for their entire length and often extend a half micron or so down into the apical cytoplasm. Here the filaments are anchored in the terminal web, which crosses the end of the cell immediately beneath the striated border.

In such well developed striated borders as those of the intestinal epithelium and proximal convoluted tubule of the kidney, the microvilli are uniform in length and diameter and stand erect in close parallel array. On other epithelia where they are less numerous, their orientation is more variable. In these cells the terminal web and the internal filaments in the microvilli are relatively inconspicuous. These fibrous elements, when present, evidently contribute to the structural stability and to the maintenance of the orderly arrangement of microvilli in the border.

Microvilli occur in limited numbers on the free surface of a great many epithelial cell types including some that are secretory, but they are present in greatest profusion on cells whose principal function is absorption. Biochemical analysis of isolated striated borders from intestinal epithelium has shown that they contain enzymes that hydrolyze sugar phosphates and split disaccharides to monosaccharides. These enzymes reside in or near the membranes of the microvilli. The brush border thus appears to be a structural device for greatly increasing the surface area of membrane exposed to substances that are to be absorbed. This amplification of the interface, which is a site of important chemical events in digestion and transport, greatly enhances the efficiency of the epithelium in its absorptive function.

STEREOCILIA. The epithelium lining part of the male reproductive tract, specifically the epididymis, has an unusual surface specialization in which a long pyriform tuft projects into the lumen from each cell (Fig. 3-18). At high magnification, this appears to be composed of thin hairlike processes that cohere so as to form a tuft that bears a superficial resemblance to the hairs of a watercolor brush. The individual processes are as long as the vibratile processes called cilia, but are non-

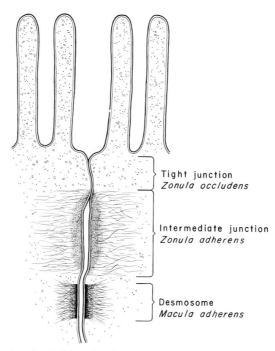

Tight junction
Zonula occludens

Intermediate junction
Zonula adherens

Desmosome
Macula adherens

Figure 3-15. Diagram of the juxtaluminal junctional complex of a columnar epithelium, consisting of a tight junction immediately beneath the surface, followed by an intermediate junction and then by a desmosome.

Parietal cell   Vessels   Cells of lamina propria

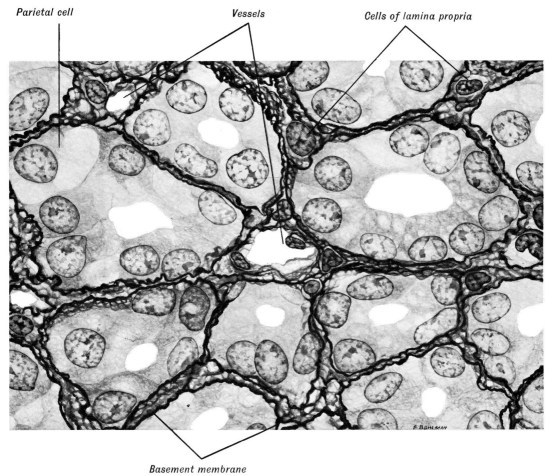

Basement membrane

Figure 3-16. "Basement membranes" surrounding cross sections of fundic glands of human stomach. The Bielschowsky stain used here impregnates the reticular fibers of the classical basement membrane. × 1500.

motile. They were therefore called *stereocilia* in classical histology, and the name persists, although their resemblance to cilia at the submicroscopic level is very slight indeed. In electron micrographs they are found to be very long flexuous microvilli. They seem to lack the filamentous cores that lend a certain degree of stiffness to the shorter microvilli of brush borders, and although they are parallel at their base, they become increasingly sinuous and entwined toward their tips.

CILIA. These motile cell processes are larger than microvilli and much more complex in their internal structure. They are arranged in parallel rows and there may be hundreds on a single epithelial cell. They are 5 to 10 μ long and about 0.2 μ in diameter and are resolved with the light microscope. At the base of each

is a dense granule called the *basal body*. In living cells cilia can be observed to have a rapid to and fro beat in a consistent direction. When the rate of beat is slowed down in cinematographic analysis, each cilium is found to stiffen on the more rapid forward or *effective stroke* and to become flexible on the slower *recovery stroke*. Cilia may have an *isochronal rhythm*, in which all cilia beat together, but more commonly they exhibit a *metachronal rhythm*, in which the successive cilia in each row start their beat in sequence so that each is slightly more advanced in its cycle than the preceding one. This sequential activation of the cilia results in the formation of waves that sweep slowly over the surface of the epithelium as a whole. When viewed from above with the microscope, this activity is reminiscent of the waves that run

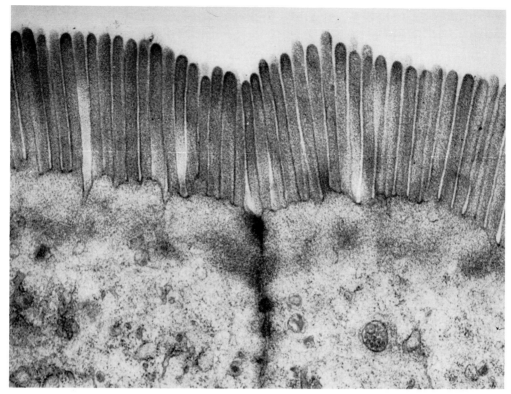

Figure 3-17. Electron micrograph of the microvilli forming the striated border of the intestinal epithelium of a hamster. × 40,000. (Courtesy of S. Ito, after D. W. Fawcett, Circulation, *26*:1105, 1962.)

before the wind across a field of grain. The metachronal waves of ciliated epithelial, however, are regular in the periodicity of their occurrence and constant in direction.

The effect of this coordinated activity of the cilia is to move a blanket of mucus slowly over the epithelium or to propel fluid and particulates through the lumen of a tubular organ. No internal structure to account for the movement of cilia is discernible with the light microscope, but under the electron microscope cilia are found to have longitudinal fibrils in their interior that are constant in their number and arrangement. In transverse sections, two single fibrils are in the center and nine double fibrils are uniformly spaced around them (Fig. 3-20). The structure of the basal body is identical to that of a centriole, with nine triplet fibrils embedded in its wall. The ciliary fibrils extend from the tip to the base. There the central fibrils terminate, but the peripheral doublets are continuous with the inner pair of subunits of the triplets in the wall of the basal body.

It should be noted that although it is customary to refer to the longitudinal components of the cilia and of the basal bodies as "fibrils," they appear to be tubular structures with a dense wall and less dense center. They have much in common with the microtubules that are found in the cytoplasm of many kinds of cells. The doublets are not composed of two similar tubules adherent along one side but seem to be made up of one complete tubule, *subfibril A,* that is circular in transverse section, and an incomplete tubule, *subfibril B,* that has a C-shaped cross section. The latter is fused to the former by its edges so that the resulting doublet has a figure-of-eight cross section with part of the wall of the complete tubule closing the defect in the incomplete tubule. Each doublet bears a pair of short arms that project from subfiber A of each doublet toward the next. From the point of view of an observer looking along the cilium from base to tip, the arms are directed clockwise.

It is an interesting example of the unity of Nature that the same basic structural organization is found in cilia and flagella throughout the plant and animal kingdoms. Those that enable the protozoan *Paramecium* to swim about in a drop of pond water have exactly the same cross sectional appearance as those that help to remove dust and bacteria from the sinuses and respiratory passages of man. The longitudinal fibrils of cilia are presumed to be the contractile elements responsible for their movement, but the functional advantage of the 9 + 2 arrangement is not understood.

Fascination with cilia as a system in which to study the basis of the fundamental contractile properties of protoplasm has led to numerous efforts to pursue their structure down to the molecular level of organization. By mechanical disruption and negative staining it has been shown that the walls of the ciliary fibrils contain about 13 longitudinally oriented filamentous subunits approximately 40 Å in thickness. It has been possible to separate the principal structural components of cilia by exploiting their different solubilities and thus to achieve a kind of chemical dissection of

this organelle (Gibbons, 1965). Purified preparations of the central fibrils or *axonemes*, the outer doublets, and the membranes have been obtained. A protein with adenosine triphosphatase activity, called *dynein*, has been isolated and partially characterized. Extraction of dynein results in disappearance of the arms from the outer fibrils, and when dynein is added to a suspension of outer fibrils under appropriate conditions, the arms can be restored to the fibrils. Further studies of this kind may soon provide the information necessary for an understanding of the mechanism of ciliary motility.

BLOOD VESSELS AND NERVE FIBERS. As a rule epithelium lacks blood vessels. The nutritive substances from the blood vessels of the underlying connective tissue reach the epithelial elements after passing through the thin intercellular spaces between the epithelial cells. If the epithelium is unusually thick, as in the skin, the surface of the underlying connective tissue is usually provided with *papillae*, outgrowths carrying blood capillaries. These

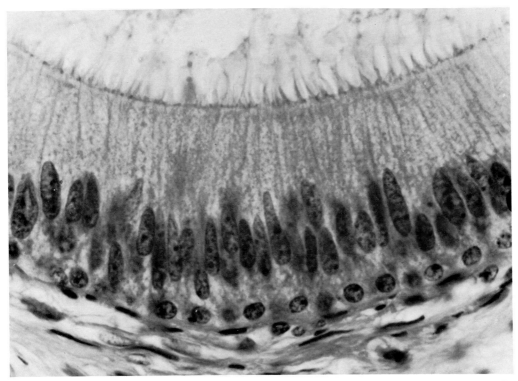

Figure 3-18. Photomicrograph of pseudostratified columnar epithelium of the human epididymis. Notice the tufts of long flexible stereocilia projecting from each cell. × 720.

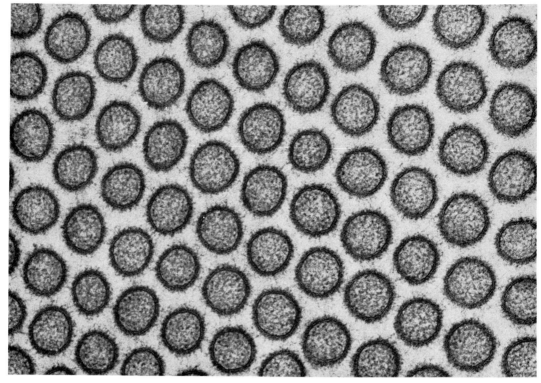

Figure 3-19. Electron micrograph of a horizontal section through the striated border of the intestinal epithelium, showing the microvilli in transverse section. They are remarkably uniform in their size and distribution. Compare their lack of internal structure with similar sections of cilia (Fig. 3-20). × 98,000. (Courtesy of S. L. Palay.)

project into the deep surface of the epithelium and probably facilitate nutrition by shortening the diffusion distance to the cells in the superficial layers. In a few places, such as the stria vascularis of the cochlea and the maternal layer of certain epitheliochoreal placentae, loops of blood capillaries with a thin sheath of connective tissue may penetrate among the cells of the epithelium.

In the epidermis, olfactory mucosa, and many other epithelia, numerous terminal branches of sensory nerve fibers pierce the basement lamina and run in the interstices among the epithelial cells. The epithelia of the stomach and intestine and the cervix of the uterus, on the other hand, seem to lack sensory nerve endings and the mucous membranes of these organs can be rubbed or cauterized in the unanaesthetized patient without discomfort.

EXTRANEOUS CELLS. Wandering cells may enter the epithelium from the connective tissue. For example, individual lymphocytes are very often found migrating through the epithelium of the intestinal tract and into the lumen. Peyer's patches in the intestinal submucosa are large accumulations of lymphoid cells, and the overlying epithelium is often infiltrated by a multitude of lymphocytes that may push aside and distort the epithelial cells. At certain phases of the reproductive cycle of rodents and to a lesser extent in the human, a great number of leukocytes of various kinds migrate through the vaginal epithelium. It is not surprising that these actively motile cells can insinuate themselves between the sessile epithelial cells, but how they breach the basement lamina and separate the desmosomes, and even the so-called "tight junctions" of epithelium, and how these are restored to their former relations after the migratory cell has passed, are problems that remain unsolved.

REGENERATION OF EPITHELIUM. The epithelial layers, especially those that cover the outer surface of the body and the intestinal tract, are subject to constant mechanical and other trauma. Under physiologic conditions their cells perish continuously and are shed. This is especially manifest in the epidermis, where the superficial cells are continuously undergoing a peculiar kind of differentiation called keratinization, which leads to death and desquamation of the superficial cells. The cells lost are replaced by new ones, which arise through the transformation of the cells of the deeper layers. In the gastrointestinal tract, cells are continually exfoliated at the tips of the villi. On the other hand, in the respiratory passages and especially in most of the glands, degeneration of the epithelium is rare.

The physiological loss of cells in the epithelium is balanced by a corresponding regeneration. In vertebrates this is always effected through mitotic proliferation of relatively undifferentiated epithelial elements. In the stratified squamous epithelium the mitoses are found mainly in the deeper columnar and polyhedral cell layers near the base (the stratum germinativum). The simple columnar epithelium of the stomach and the intestine is regenerated from special areas of proliferating undifferentiated epithelial cells in the base of the gastric foveolae or in the crypts of Lieberkühn. The rate of normal physiological loss and replacement is so great that the epithelial covering of the intestinal villi is entirely replaced every few days.

In the body, the epithelial elements are nonmotile as a rule. In healing wounds, however, epithelial cells flatten out into a thin sheet that rapidly spreads to cover large denuded areas of connective tissue. In the initial stages of this repair there is no mitotic activity, but proliferation later begins at the margins of the

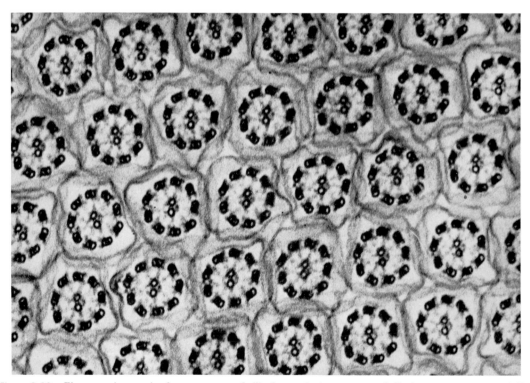

Figure 3-20. Electron micrograph of cross sections of cilia from a fresh water mussel. Each contains two central filaments surrounded by nine double ones. This number and arrangement of internal filaments has been found to be of universal occurrence in cilia throughout the plant and animal kingdoms. Notice that one member of each outer doublet appears tubular, whereas the other has a more dense interior and bears, on its outer surface, short arms that project toward the next filament. × 76,000. (After I. R. Gibbons, J. Biophys. & Biochem. Cytol., *11:*179, 1961.)

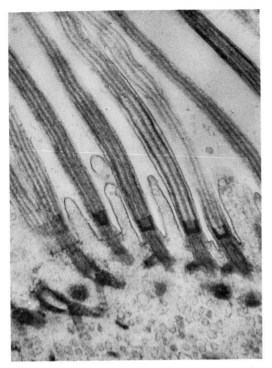

Figure 3-21. Electron micrograph of a longitudinal section of cilia on the epithelium lining the pharynx of a salamander. The internal longitudinal filaments of the cilia, and their junction with the curved basal bodies, can be seen. Cross striated rootlets are visible on some of the basal bodies. × 40,000. (Courtesy of E. D. Hay.)

wound, providing the cells necessary for restoration of the covering epithelium to its normal thickness.

REFERENCES

André, J.: Sur quelques details nouvellement connus de l'ultrastructure des organites vibratiles. J. Ultrastruct. Res., 5:86, 1961.

Arey, L. B.: Wound healing. Physiol. Rev., 16:327, 1936.

Bennett, H. S.: Morphological aspects of extracellular polysaccharides. J. Histochem. & Cytochem., 11:2, 1963.

Bertalanffy, F. D., and K. P. Nagy: Mitotic activity and renewal rate of the epithelial cells of human duodenum. Acta Anat., 45:362, 1961.

Brandt, P. W.: A consideration of the extraneous coats of the plasma membrane. Circulation (Suppl.), 26:1075, 1962.

Farquhar, M. G., and G. E. Palade: Junctional complexes in various epithelia. J. Cell Biol., 17:375, 1963.

Fawcett, D. W.: Cilia and flagella. In Brachet, J., and A. E. Mirsky, eds.: The Cell: Biochemistry, Physiology, Morphology. New York. Academic Press, 1961, Vol. II, p. 217.

Fawcett, D. W.: Intercellular bridges. Exper. Cell. Res., (Suppl.), 8:174, 1961.

Fawcett, D. W.: Physiologically significant specializations of the cell surface. Circulation, 26:1105, 1962.

Fawcett, D. W.: Surface specializations of absorbing cells. J. Histochem. & Cytochem., 13:75, 1965.

Fawcett, D. W., and K. R. Porter: A study of the fine structure of ciliated epithelia. J. Morphol., 94:221, 1954.

Gibbons, I. R.: The relationship between the fine structure and direction of beat in gill cilia of a lamellibranch mollusc. J. Biophys. & Biochem. Cytol., 11:179, 1961.

Gibbons, I. R.: Chemical dissection of cilia. Arch. de Biol. (Liège), 76:317, 1965.

Gibbons, I. R., and A. J. Rowe: Dynein: A protein with adenosine triphosphatase activity from cilia. Science, 149:424, 1965.

Hay, E. D., and J. P. Revel: Autoradiographic studies of the origin of the basement lamella in Ambystoma. Develop. Biol., 7:152, 1963.

Ito, S.: The surface coat of enteric microvilli. J. Cell Biol., 27:475, 1965.

Kelly, D.: Fine structure of desmosomes, hemidesmosomes and an adepidermal globular layer in developing newt epidermis. J. Cell Biol., 2B:51, 1966.

Leblond, C. P., and B. E. Walker: Renewal of cell populations. Physiol. Rev., 36:255, 1956.

Leblond, C. P., R. C. Greulich, and J. P. M. Pereira: Relationship of cell formation and cell migration in the renewal of stratified squamous epithelia. In Montagna, W., and R. E. Billingham, eds.: Advances in Biology of the Skin. New York, Pergamon Press, 1964, Vol. 5, p. 39.

Leblond, C. P., H. Puchtler, and Y. Clermont: Structures corresponding to terminal bars and terminal web in many types of cells. Nature, 186:784, 1960.

Lipkin, M., P. Sherlock, and B. Bell: Cell proliferation kinetics in the gastrointestinal tract of man. Gastroenterology, 45:721, 1963.

Marcus, P. I., S. J. Cieciura, and T. T. Puck: Clonal growth in vitro of epithelial cells from normal human tissues. J. Exper. Med., 104:615, 1956.

Messier, B., and C. P. Leblond: Cell proliferation and migration as revealed by radioautography after injection of thymidine-H3 into male rats and mice. Am. J. Anat., 106:247, 1960.

Miller, F.: Hemoglobin absorption by the cells of the proximal convoluted tubule in mouse kidney. J. Biophy. & Biochem. Cytol., 8: 689, 1960.

Moscona, A. A.: Patterns and mechanisms of tissue reconstruction from dissociated cells. In Rudnick, D., ed.: Developing Cell Systems and Their Control. New York, Ronald Press, 1960, p. 45.

Salpeter, M. M., and M. Singer: Differentiation of the submicroscopic adepidermal membrane during limb regeneration in adult Triturus, including a note on the use of the term basement membrane. Anat. Rec., 136:27, 1960.

Schaffer, J.: Das Epithelgewebe. In von Möllendorff, W., and W. Bargmann, eds.: Handbuch der mikroskopischen Anatomie des Menschen. Berlin, Julius Springer, 1927, Vol. 2, part 1, p. 1.

Speidel, E., and A. Lazarow: Chemical composition of glomerular basement membrane in diabetes. Diabetes, 12:355, 1963.

Taylor, A. C.: Attachment and spreading of cells in culture. Exper. Cell Res., (Suppl.), 8:154, 1961.

Weiss, P.: Cell contact. Int. Rev. Cytol., 7:391, 1958.

Weiss, P.: Interactions between cells. In Oncley, J. L., et al., eds.: Biophysical Science—A Study Program. New York, John Wiley & Sons, 1959, p. 449.

Weiss, P.: The biological foundations of wound repair. The Harvey Lectures, 55:13, 1961.

Weiss, P., and Moscona, A.: Type-specific morphogenesis of cartilages developed from dissociated limb and scleral mesenchyme in vitro. J. Embryol. & Exper. Morphol., 6:238, 1958.

Yamada, E.: The fine structure of the gall bladder epithelium of the mouse. J. Biophys. & Biochem. Cytol., 1:445, 1955.

CHAPTER FOUR

Glands and Secretion

The mesothelial linings of the major body cavities are kept moist by a small amount of watery fluid that arises as a transudate of the blood. Such epithelial layers are referred to as *serous membranes.* The surface of the epithelium lining of various internal organs is moistened and lubricated by a viscous mucus which is secreted by certain of the cells of the epithelium itself, or by glands opening onto it. Such layers are often called *mucous membranes.* They line most of the internal hollow organs that connect with the exterior—those of the alimentary, respiratory, and reproductive tracts.

Secretion, which is usually a function of epithelium, is the elaboration and release by cells of a fluid which may contain any of a variety of substances such as mucin, hormones, or enzymes. The cells perform work in the production of their secretion, whereas in *excretion,* such as that occurring in the kidney, a fluid is produced by filtration of the blood plasma without any significant expenditure of energy on the part of the cells. Epithelial cells specialized for the function of secretion constitute organs called *glands.* Much has been learned in recent years from correlated biochemical and electron microscopic studies about the intracellular sites of synthesis and processing of the secretory product. These primary events at the level of the cell will be reviewed before we proceed to a discussion of the histological organization and classification of glands.

SECRETORY PATHWAY WITHIN EXOCRINE GLANDULAR CELLS

In addition to the organelles common to all cells, gland cells often contain specific granules or droplets that represent intracytoplasmic accumulations of precursors of their secretion. Gland cells, like others, must be considered to be in a state of continual activity. Even "resting" cells are performing work in maintaining their integrity and internal organization and in synthesizing and secreting their specific products at minimal levels. By observation of the changes in the appearance of the gland cells during different stages of exaggerated secretory activity, cytologists have been able to recognize a sequence of cytological events associated with secretion (Fig. 4-1). When the cell is stimulated to secrete, the number of specific granules decreases and watery vacuoles increase. After depletion of the granules, the chromophilic substance or ergastoplasm seems to become more prominent, the mitochondria become larger and more numerous, and the Golgi apparatus hypertrophies. Coincident with these changes in the cytoplasm, the nucleus increases in volume and the amount of stainable chromatin diminishes, while the nucleolus becomes larger and more deeply stained. As the secretory granules begin to reaccumulate, they first appear in very close association with the Golgi apparatus.

Although the older literature was replete with conflicting claims of "transformation" of mitochondria, ergastoplasm, or Golgi bodies directly into the secretory product, a consensus gradually developed that the Golgi apparatus was the site of concentration of material synthesized throughout the cytoplasm (Bowen).

Progress in molecular biology and electron microscopy has now greatly clarified the role of the various organelles in the synthesis and secretion of protein rich cell products. The

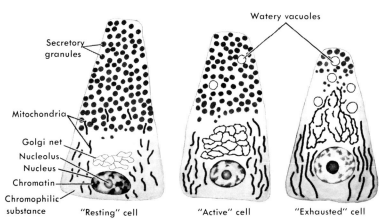

Figure 4-1. Diagrams of serous type of secretory cell in different stages of secretion to illustrate changes in cytoplasmic and nuclear structures that may take place during marked activity. (Courtesy of I. Gersh.)

cell that has been most thoroughly studied is the pancreatic acinar cell, which secretes a large volume of digestive juice containing several protein enzymes. The nature of the cell product is now known to be determined by the active regions of the chromosomal DNA in the nucleus. Encoded in the sequence of nucleotides in the molecular structure of DNA is the blueprint for the construction of all of the proteins of the cell. The organelles that respond to this information by synthesis of the specific proteins are in the cytoplasm, so that there must be intermediaries and also pathways of communication between these two major cell compartments. Three classes of ribonucleic acid molecules have been identified that serve to transfer and translate the genetic information: these are *messenger RNA, transfer RNA,* and *ribosomal RNA.* The nucleolus is regarded as an important way station for one or more of these nucleic acids, and their principal pathway to the cytoplasm is presumably through the "pores" in the nuclear envelope, although the morphological evidence for this is still far from compelling.

Messenger RNA formed on certain segments of the DNA molecules in the nucleus moves out into the cytoplasm carrying in its molecular structure, the information that determines the correct sequence for the assembly of amino acids in the synthesis of the specific protein. Another RNA from the nucleus combines with protein to form the ribosomes of the cytoplasm. Several ribosomes become attached to each molecule of messenger RNA to form

the polysomes that are attached to the membranes of the endoplasmic reticulum. There is a special transfer RNA for each of the 20 amino acids. Each attaches to its own specific type of amino acid, selected from among those entering the cell from the blood, and transports this amino acid to a ribosome. There, the transfer RNA recognizes and attaches itself to the appropriate complementary site on the messenger RNA molecule and inserts its amino acid into the protein molecule developing on the ribosome. This process, repeated hundreds of thousands of times on polysomes associated with the endoplasmic reticulum throughout the gland cell, is the means by which the information residing in the chromosomes is translated into the correct sequence of amino acids to produce the polypeptide chains of the specific proteins. The newly synthesized protein is transferred from the ribosomes across the limiting membrane of endoplasmic reticulum and accumulates in its lumen (Fig. 4-2).

The events described thus far take place at an amicroscopic level and have been inferred from biochemical studies on centrifugal cell fractions. The subsequent events in the formation of secretory material are accessible to electron microscopic and autoradiographic analysis. The product segregated within the reticulum appears to be transported through its labyrinthine system of channels to the region of the Golgi complex. The lumen of the reticulum is not continuous with the cavities of the Golgi complex, but smooth surfaced *intermediate vesicles* are budded off from the margins of the cisternae, and these appear to carry small amounts of the newly synthesized protein from the reticulum to the Golgi complex (Palade; Ziegel and Dalton). There they coalesce with membrane limited saccules of this organelle (Fig. 4-3). The functional activities of the Golgi complex are still poorly understood, but it is clear that, in glandular cells, it receives the products of protein synthesis and concentrates them in membrane limited vacuoles (Fig. 4-4). These leave the Golgi region and collect in the apical cytoplasm (Fig. 4-5). They are large enough to be visible with the light microscope. In the past they have commonly been called *secretory granules,* but because in most instances their content appears to be a viscous fluid, *secretory droplet* would seem more appropriate. In the process of secretion, the membrane enclosing the secretory droplet contacts the plasmalemma and coa-

lesces with it in such a way that it becomes continuous with and incorporated into the cell surface. The secretory product flows out and is thus discharged into the exterior without any discontinuity being produced in the plasmalemma. In summary, it is the current view that the ribosomes on the endoplasmic reticulum are the site of synthesis; the product is segregated in the lumen of the reticulum and transported through it to the Golgi complex, which then functions as a center for concentration and packaging of the product. The mitochondria participate only as an energy source (Fig. 4-6).

The validity of these interpretations is strongly supported by autoradiographic methods. An animal is given tritium labeled amino acid and its pancreas is examined at successive time intervals. In an animal killed within five minutes the silver grains in radioautographs

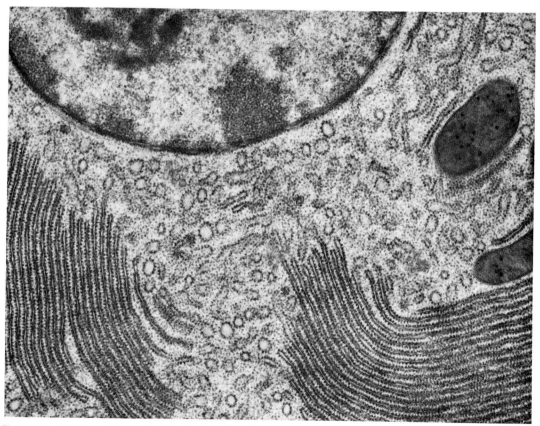

Figure 4-2.   Electron micrograph of the basal region of a pancreatic acinar cell. In all protein secreting exocrine glands the granular endoplasmic reticulum (ergastoplasm) is well developed. The associated ribosomes are the sites of synthesis of new protein. × 22,000.

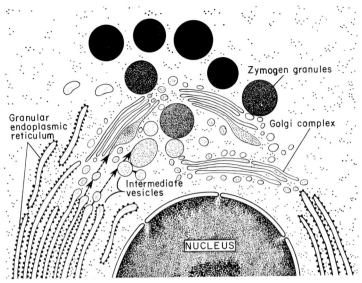

Figure 4-3. Diagram depicting the postulated mechanism of transfer of the secretory product from the reticulum to the Golgi apparatus. Smooth surfaced vesicles are believed to bud off from the margins of the cisternae and transport the product to the Golgi cisternae.

are found over the ergastoplasm where amino acid is being incorporated into protein. In 20 minutes the label is mainly over the Golgi region, and in one hour it is over the secretory droplets in the cell apex or is already in the lumen of the gland (Fig. 4-7). The rapidity of these events is far greater than previously believed. It is now estimated that the mean life span of exportable protein molecules in the pancreatic acinar cell is about 53 minutes (Warshawsky et al.).

Although this description is based upon studies of the pancreatic acinar cell, there are enough parallel observations in other organs to indicate that it applies to most glandular cells producing a secretion rich in protein. There is evidence that in cells secreting protein-polysaccharide, the Golgi complex may play a role in the synthesis of the polysaccharide moiety as well as in concentration of the final secretory product (Peterson and Leblond).

CLASSIFICATION OF GLANDS

Glands are classified in several different ways. Three major categories are defined with respect to their mode of secretion: *exocrine glands,* which discharge their product at an external or internal surface; *endocrine glands,* which release their product into the blood or lymph vessels; and *mixed glands,* which have both exocrine and endocrine portions. Glands may also be described with respect to the method by which the cells discharge their product: *merocrine* secretion involves release through the cell membrane with the cell remaining intact; *apocrine* secretion is accompanied by loss of part of the apical cytoplasm along with the material secreted; and *holocrine* secretion consists of discharge and destruction of the whole cell. There are *unicellular* and *multicellular* glands, and the latter are further classified according to the organization and geometry of the epithelial component (*tubular, alveolar, tubuloalveolar, saccular,* etc.).

Despite the great variety of schemes of classification, it is not always possible to characterize all glands adequately because of a lack of fundamental information on the histophysiology of the organ. Moreover, the added resolution of the electron microscope has considerably changed our concept of the cellular mechanisms of *apocrine* and *merocrine* secretion. According to the traditional view of merocrine secretion, the secretory material diffused through the surface membrane or the secretory granules passed out through transient discontinuities in the membrane. The electron microscopic observations presented above for the pancreas (traditionally regarded as a merocrine gland) reveal a mechanism of release not envisioned by classical cytologists but one that can now be accepted as typical of this kind of gland. Fine structural observations on the mammary gland, generally regarded as *apocrine*, substantiate the belief that some of the cell is lost in the process of secretion, but apparently less of it than was imagined by light microscopists. The lipid component of the secretion is discharged in an envelope of plasma membrane and a thin rim of cytoplasm pinched off from the cell. The same cells, however, appear to secrete a proteinaceous material that leaves the cell in much the same way as the zymogen of the pancreas. This cell type, therefore, cannot be regarded as purely apocrine but exhibits two distinct mechanisms for release of its secretory product. The terms developed by light microscopists to describe mechanisms of secretion are thus proving to be imprecise, but until a more consistent terminology is developed, they will continue to be useful.

EXOCRINE GLANDS

UNICELLULAR GLANDS. In mammals, virtually the only example of a unicellular gland is the *mucous* cell or *goblet cell* found scattered among the columnar cells of the epithelium on many mucous membranes. It secretes *mucin*, a protein-polysaccharide, which, with water, forms a lubricating solution called *mucus*. A fully developed cell of this type has an expanded, oval apical end filled with pale droplets of *mucigen* and a slender basal end containing a compressed nucleus and a small amount of deeply staining basophilic cytoplasm.

The common term *goblet cell* is descriptive of the form of the cell, with its expanded cup-shaped rim of cytoplasm called the *theca* filled with secretory droplets and the thin stem of the cell extending to the base of the epithelium.

The mucigen droplets tend to swell and

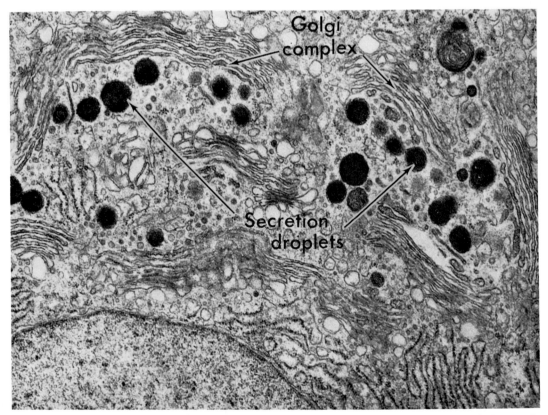

Figure 4-4. Electron micrograph of the Golgi region of a cell from Brunner's gland, illustrating the typical close association of the secretory droplets with the inner aspect of the parallel stacks of Golgi cisternae. × 22,000. (Courtesy of D. Friend.)

coalesce during specimen preparation and are seldom resolved as separate entities. They are better preserved by freeze-drying. They stain with the periodic acid–Schiff reaction or Hale's colloidal iron method because of their polysaccharide content. Mucicarmine and other less specific stains may also be used.

The fine structure of goblet cells is difficult to study because of the degree to which their organelles are compressed into the basal cytoplasm. The basophilia of the cytoplasm is due to the abundance of free and attached ribosomes. The latter are deployed on the surface of cisternae arranged roughly parallel to the cell surface in the paranuclear and basal cytoplasm. The Golgi complex is well developed and located between the nucleus and the mucigen droplets of the theca. The nucleus is

deformed by the accumulated mucigen above and by the narrow confines of the slender cell base. The individual droplets of mucigen are enveloped by extremely delicate membranes that are usually broken in preparation of the specimen (Moe).

The synthesis of mucigen involves the synthesis of protein in the manner described for zymogen secretion. However, autoradiography after administration of ^{35}S or ^{3}H-glucose, as precursors of the polysaccharide, indicates that the label goes directly to the supranuclear region, suggesting that the synthesis and sulfation of the polysaccharides of the mucigen probably take place in the Golgi complex (Belanger; Florey; Peterson and Leblond). In the discharge of the secretion, the membrane of individual secretory droplets or of groups of

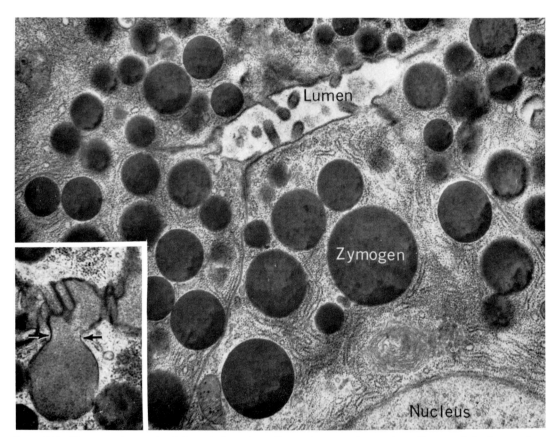

Figure 4-5. Electron micrograph of the apical portions of several pancreatic exocrine cells around the lumen of an acinus. The apical cytoplasm contains numerous dense secretory (zymogen) droplets. The inset illustrates the mechanism of release of the cell product. The zymogen droplet approaches the cell surface and its membrane becomes continuous with the plasma membrane (at arrows). The contents of the granule or vacuole thus become extracellular and are emptied into the lumen without having passed through a discontinuity in the plasma membrane. × 19,000. (After D. W. Fawcett, Circulation 26, Part 2:1105, 1962.)

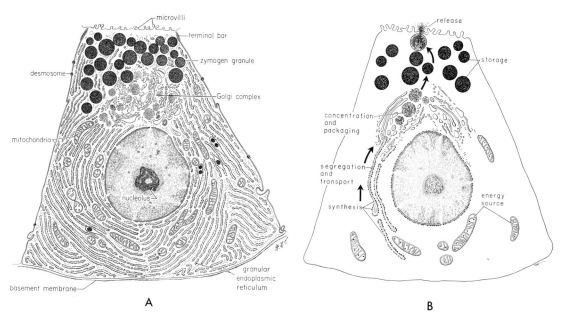

Figure 4-6. *A*, Diagram of the disposition of organelles in a pancreatic acinar cell. *B*, Schematic representation of the current views concerning the secretory pathway in the pancreatic acinar cell and the functional interrelations of its organelles. New protein synthesized at the ribosomes is segregated in the lumen of the endoplasmic reticulum and transported to the Golgi region. There it is concentrated and formed into zymogen granules that are stored in the apical cytoplasm and ultimately released at the free surface of the cell. (After D. W. Fawcett, *in* S. Seno and R. V. Cowdry, eds., Intracellular Membranous Structure. Tokyo, Chugoku, Ltd., 1965.)

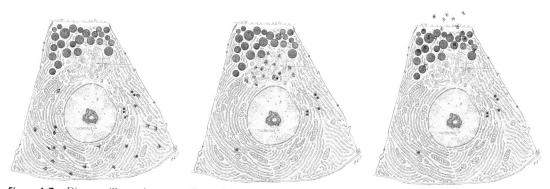

Figure 4-7. Diagram illustrating autoradiographic localization of labeled amino acid in various sites along the secretory pathway. At early time intervals the grains are over the ergastoplasm in the basal region of the cell where the amino acid is being incorporated into newly synthesized protein. At later time intervals they are found over the Golgi complex and still later over the zymogen granules at the cell apex or over the secretion in the lumen of the acinus. Diagram based upon the studies of L. G. Caro. (After D. W. Fawcett, *in* S. Seno and R. V. Cowdry, eds., Intracellular Membranous Structure. Tokyo, Chugoku, Ltd., 1965.)

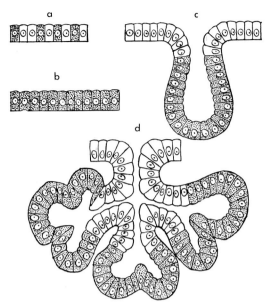

Figure 4-8. Diagram of unicellular and multicellular glands. *a,* Granular; glandular cells are scattered singly among clear, common epithelial cells; *b,* glandular cells arranged in a continuous sheet—secretory epithelial surface; *c,* simplest type of multicellular gland; the area lined with glandular cells forms a saclike invagination into the subjacent tissue; *d,* multicellular gland of greater complexity; the glandular spaces are lined partly with glandular cells (terminal portions), partly with common epithelium (excretory ducts).

coalesced droplets fuses with and becomes part of the plasma membrane, permitting the mucus to pour out onto the surface (Trier).

The elimination of mucigen proceeds more or less continuously and the cell may retain its goblet form for most of its life span, which in the intestine is only two to four days. Although goblet cells normally pass through only one long secretory cycle of continuous secretion, they may be made to expel nearly all of their secretion at once. Under these conditions, they soon resume mucosynthesis and refill their theca.

MULTICELLULAR GLANDS. The simplest form of multicellular gland is an epithelial *secretory sheet*, consisting of secreting cells alone (Fig. 4-8). In mammals the surface epithelium of the gastric mucosa and of the mucous membrane of the uterus at certain stages, belong to this category.

Intraepithelial glands are a special form of secretory sheet. They are small accumulations of glandular cells (usually mucous) that lie wholly within the thickness of the epithelium but are arranged around a small lumen of their own (Fig. 4-9). They are found in the human in the pseudostratified columnar epithelium of the nasal mucosa and of the ductuli efferentes and the urethra.

All other multicellular glands arise as invaginations of the epithelial sheet that extend into the underlying connective tissue (Fig. 4-10). The gland cells are usually confined to the *secretory* or *terminal* portions of the tubular invagination. The secretion elaborated by the gland cells reaches the surface directly, or through an *excretory* duct consisting of less specialized cells. In many glands the secreting surface is further increased by many extremely fine canals, the *secretory capillaries*, which arise from the lumen of the terminal portion and penetrate between the glandular cells. They are extracellular, often branching and ending blindly before reaching the basement lamina. They have no walls of their own but are formed by groovelike excavations in adjoining cells (Fig. 4-12). Exceptionally, glandular cells such as the parietal cells of the gastric glands may appear to contain an intracellular system of fine canaliculi. Electron microscopy has shown, however, that these so-called "intracellular canaliculi" are not actually within the cytoplasm but are deep invaginations of the cell surface. They are, therefore, limited by the plasma membrane and their lumen is actually extracellular, like that of other secretory canaliculi.

SIMPLE EXOCRINE GLANDS. A simple exocrine gland consists of a secretory unit connected to the surface epithelium of origin either directly or by an *unbranched* duct. The simple glands of man are classified as *tubular, coiled tubular, branched tubular,* and *acinar* or *alveolar* (Fig. 4-10).

In *simple tubular glands* there is no excretory duct, and the terminal portion is a straight tubule that opens directly on the epithelial surface. The intestinal glands (crypts) of Lieberkühn are examples.

In *simple coiled tubular glands* the terminal portion is a long coiled tubule, which passes into a long excretory duct. The sweat glands belong to this category. In the large axillary sweat glands of the apocrine type, the terminal portions branch.

In *simple branched tubular glands* the tubules of the terminal portion bifurcate into two or more branches, which are sometimes coiled near their ends. An excretory duct may be absent, as in the glands of the stomach and uterus, or there may be a simple short excretory duct, as in some of the small glands of the oral cavity, the tongue, and the esophagus, and in the glands of Brunner in the duodenum.

In the *simple branched acinar (or alveolar) glands* the terminal portion is expanded to form a spherical or elongated sac. If only one acinus is associated with one excretory duct, the gland is a simple acinar gland. This type is thought not to occur in mammals. If the acinus is subdivided by partitions into several smaller compartments, or if several acini are arranged along a duct, it is a simple branched acinar gland. Examples are the sebaceous glands of the skin and the meibomian glands of the eyelids.

COMPOUND EXOCRINE GLANDS. In contrast to the unbranched duct of a simple exocrine gland, the duct of a compound exocrine gland branches repeatedly. A compound gland can be thought of as consisting of a variable number of simple glands at the ends of an arborescent system of ducts of steadily diminishing caliber.

The compound glands are sometimes classified according to the nature of the secretion they produce and are therefore called *mucous, serous,* or *mixed*. Another common classification is based upon the form of the terminal elements of the gland: tubular, acinar, tubuloacinar, or saccular (Fig. 4-11).

In *compound tubular glands* the terminal portions of the smallest lobules are more or less coiled tubules, usually branching. To this category belong the pure mucous glands of the oral cavity, glands of the gastric cardia, some of the glands of Brunner, the bulbourethral glands, and the renal tubules. In special cases, as, for instance, in the testis, the terminal coils anastomose.

In the *compound acinar (alveolar) glands* the terminal portions are thought of as having the form of egg-shaped or spherical units with a small lumen. As a rule, however, the form is that of irregularly branched tubules with numerous saccular outgrowths from the wall and on the blind ends. These glands would be more correctly designated *compound tubuloacinar (tubuloalveolar)*. To this group belong most of the larger exocrine glands—the serous and mixed glands of the oral cavity and respiratory passages, and the pancreas.

Some authors add another category called *compound saccular glands*, which differ from the compound alveolar only in the larger size, and particularly in the larger lumen of their secretory endpieces. The examples commonly cited are the mammary gland and the prostate gland. Other authors include these among the compound tubuloacinar glands.

In some cases the excretory ducts do not all join into a single main duct but open independently on a restricted area of a free epithelial surface. Such is the case in the lacrimal, mammary, and prostate glands.

HISTOLOGICAL ORGANIZATION OF GLANDS

There are certain common features in the general plan of organization of most of the larger glands. They are enclosed in a condensation of connective tissue constituting the capsule of the organ and are divided into grossly visible subdivisions called *lobes,* by *septa* of connective tissue extending inward from the capsule. These in turn are partitioned by thin septa into smaller units called *lobules,* still visible with the naked eye (Fig. 4-12). These are separated to some extent into microscopic *lobules* of glandular units, but as a rule collagenous connective tissue penetrates for only a short distance into the lobule before giving way to a delicate network of reticular fibers surrounding the terminal ducts and secretory elements.

Blood vessels, lymphatics, and nerves of glands usually show a pattern of distribution similar to that of the connective tissue. They

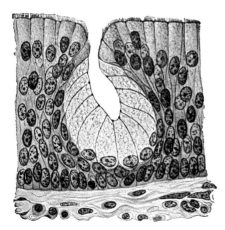

Figure 4-9. Intraepithelial gland from the pseudostratified ciliated epithelium of the laryngeal surface of the epiglottis of a woman of 72 years. × 534. (After V. Patzelt, from Schaffer.)

penetrate the capsule and follow the collagenous septa or the strands between the lobules
and from there send branches inward. Within
the lobule they are ultimately enclosed by
reticular connective tissue. The blood and
lymph capillaries form networks around small
masses of gland cells and the terminal ducts.
The major vascular supply is supplemented
in most glands by a collateral circulation mediated through capsular vessels of small caliber. The terminal nerve fibers branch, and
their final divisions end in a multitude of small
enlargements on the surfaces of gland cells.

The duct system of a complex exocrine
gland conducts the product of the gland cells
to a free external or internal body surface. It
may also modify the secretion during its passage. The *main* duct of the gland divides in the
connective tissue to form *lobar ducts.* Their fur-

ther branchings in the septa between lobules
are called *interlobular ducts,* while the ducts of
the microscopic lobules are called *intralobular*
ducts. The latter are accompanied by very little connective tissue and are continuous with
the *intercalary ducts,* whose branches communicate with the secretory acini either directly or
via intercellular canaliculi or by a combination
of these arrangements (Fig. 4-12). The epithelium of the largest ducts may be stratified
squamous or columnar-cuboidal. As the duct
becomes smaller, the epithelium is first simple
columnar, then cuboidal, and finally squamous.

ENDOCRINE GLANDS

These glands arise in the embryo as tubular invaginations or solid outgrowths from
surface epithelium, but in the course of their

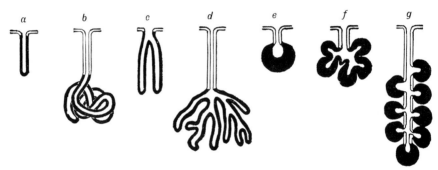

Figure 4-10. Diagrams of simple exocrine glands. *a,* Simple tubular; *b,* simple coiled tubular; *c* and *d,* simple branched tubular; *e,* simple alveolus; *f* and *g,* simple branched acinar. Secretory portions black; ducts double-contoured.

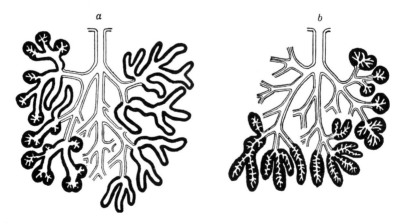

Figure 4-11. Diagram of compound exocrine glands. *a,* Mixed compound tubular and tubuloacinar; *b,* compound acinar. Secretory portions black; ducts doubly contoured.

subsequent development, their connection with the surface is lost. The endocrine glands are quite diverse and do not lend themselves to classification on the basis of their histological organization. In some examples, the gland consists of closed sacs of epithelium surrounded by highly vascular connective tissue. In most instances, however, the invagination of epithelium loses its lumen or is solid from the outset, and after separating from the surface epithelium it becomes penetrated by a rich network of blood vessels. Since there are no excretory ducts, the secretions find their way into the capillaries irrigating and draining the gland and from those into the general circulation. Other glands, which are not entirely dissociated from the excretory duct system, are called *mixed glands.* In the liver, for example, the hepatic cells, which secrete bile into the duct system, also release internal secretions directly into the blood vessels. In the testes and pancreas, on the other hand, one group of cells secretes into the external duct system while another group delivers its internal secretion into the blood.

The principal endocrine glands are the *hypophysis,* the *thyroid, parathyroids, pancreas, adrenals, pineal, testes,* and *ovaries.* To these, the *placenta* must be added as a transient endocrine organ. The central nervous system, in addition to its production of the humoral agents of impulse transmission such as acetylcholine and norepinephrine, also contains neurons secreting substances into the bloodstream that are capable of acting at distant points in the organism. Certain areas of the brain, therefore, function as endocrine "glands." The neurosecretory cells can receive impulses from other neurons and in some instances can also transmit impulses, but their axons do not synapse with other neurons, muscles, or exocrine glands. Instead they end at blood vessels and, like the cells of endocrine glands, release their product into the blood or body fluids.

CYTOLOGICAL CHARACTERISTICS OF ENDOCRINE CELLS

If one considers the chemical diversity of the hormonal products of the ductless glands, it is not surprising that it is impossible to define cytological features common to all endocrine cells. Those that produce protein, glycoprotein, or polypeptide hormones and store them in secretory granules or droplets are generally

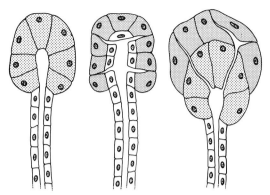

Figure 4-12. Diagram to show relations of terminal portions of duct system (intercalary duct) and intercellular canaliculi to the secreting cells. Lighter stippled portion generally mucous; darker portion serous. (Modified from Zimmermann.)

similar in their fine structure to cells of exocrine glands. All available evidence indicates that the cytological events associated with synthesis and consolidation of the product into granules are much the same and that the same organelles are involved. Relatively little is known, however, about the mechanism of release of the hormones from the cell or how they pass across the perivascular spaces and endothelium to enter the circulation.

Electron micrographs frequently show the membrane-bounded secretory granules lying immediately beneath the cell membrane. Occasionally, granules lacking a membrane are seen lying outside of the cell in shallow depressions between the plasma membrane and the basement lamina. Such images suggest that the granules are extruded by coalescence of their membranes with the plasmalemma. The naked granules are presumed to undergo dissolution, and the hormones liberated are then free to diffuse through the basement lamina, across the perivascular space, and through fenestrations of the endothelium. This is rather widely accepted as the principal mechanism, but granules with an intact membrane are occasionally observed in the perivascular spaces and even in the cytoplasm of the endothelial cells. This finding is hard to explain and has led some workers to entertain the possibility that secretory granules released from processes of the endocrine cells may be transported intact across the perivascular space and endothelium.

The endocrine glands that produce steroid hormones accumulate no visible precursors of their secretion. They may contain many lipid droplets, but there is little evidence that these are sites of storage of the hormones. The cytoplasm of cells engaged in the synthesis of steroids contains mitochondria of unusual internal configuration and a very extensively developed agranular endoplasmic reticulum. These are presumed to be the organelles chiefly concerned with steroid hormone synthesis. Morphological observations to date have provided no insight into the mechanism of steroid hormone release.

GENERAL PROPERTIES AND INTEGRATIVE FUNCTION OF ENDOCRINE GLANDS

Phylogenetically three main integrative mechanisms developed in animals, and these are recapitulated in vertebrate ontogeny. The earliest to appear involves substances that diffuse in the intercellular spaces and influence cells in a limited region. This humoral mechanism is later supplemented by a nervous system. Discrete endocrine glands appear considerably later in phylogeny. The first system of integration during diffusion is poorly con-

trolled and slow, and it has a limited usefulness in larger metazoa. The nervous system reaches its highest development in dealing with highly complicated integrated patterns of behavior, involving delicate, precise, and rapid motor events. These systems are supplemented by the endocrine glands, which secrete substances that have a longer latent period (because they are distributed by the circulating blood) and produce sustained results.

The endocrine system consists of specialized glands that secrete specific substances, *hormones,* into the circulation. Their primary morphological orientation is not toward ducts but toward the vascular system, and it is not surprising that they are all characteristically highly vascular. Endocrine glands are subject to control by the central nervous system, or by other endocrine glands, or by a combination of these factors. There is a complicated series of *endocrine interrelationships,* which are highly important in the integration of various physiological activities. Some of these are indicated in Figure 4-14.

Hormones are defined as products of specialized tissues that are carried by the blood

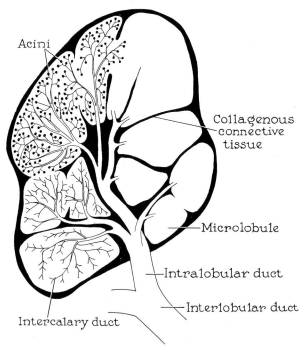

Figure 4-13. Diagram to show branches of duct system and relations to secretory portion in a lobule of a compound tubuloacinar gland. Collagenous stroma separates (often incompletely) the microscopic lobules. The main duct shown is a branch of the interlobular duct. The interlobular duct branches into intralobular ducts of several orders. These are continuous with fine terminal intercalary ducts which end in the secretory portion. (Modified from Heidenhain.)

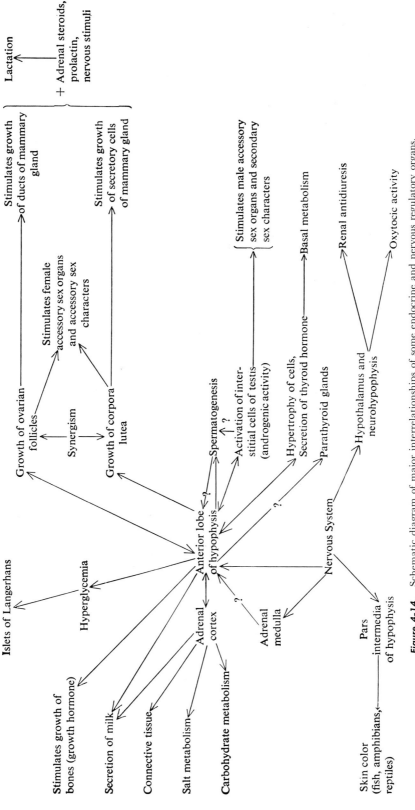

Figure 4-14. Schematic diagram of major interrelationships of some endocrine and nervous regulatory organs.

vascular system to influence other cells, tissues, or organs, or the organism as a whole. The integrative action of hormones consists in the depression, activation, or maintenance of cells other than those responsible for their secretion. Some hormones affect certain organs and tissues almost specifically. The organs so affected are called *target organs*. Other hormones have a more general effect that probably influences basic cell reactions in ways that are as yet poorly understood. The hormones may be secreted almost as rapidly as they are formed (as in the adrenal cortex), or they may be stored intracellularly (as in insulin, in the cells of the islets of the pancreas) or extracellularly (e.g., thyroglobulin, in the thyroid gland colloid). Hormones differ greatly in chemical composition, and like vitamins and trace elements, they may be effective in minute concentrations.

The definition of a hormone as given here arbitrarily excludes a wide range of other chemical integrators that may be transmitted by diffusion, others that may be intracellular, and still others that may arise either outside the body or as metabolites from all cells. The first class of integrators, those transmitted by diffusion, includes embryonic *inductors* and *neurohumoral agents* such as norepinephrine and acetylcholine, which are involved in transmission of nerve impulses across synapses and at nerve endings. The second class of integrators, those remaining intracellular, includes *genes* and certain *enzymes*. The third class of integrators, which arise outside the organism, includes certain *vitamins* as well as the *secretogogues* that are involved in the control of the secretory activities of certain parts of the gastrointestinal tract. Related to these are the integrators which arise from metabolic activity. These include carbon dioxide, which aids in the regulation of respiration, and glucose released from the glycogen of the liver, which maintains the constancy of the blood sugar level. Except for its general origin from all of the tissues, carbon dioxide so nearly resembles a hormone in its action in the body that it is classified as a *parahormone,* and the release of glucose from the liver was, in fact, the first process characterized as *internal secretion*.

REFERENCES

Bowen, R. H.: The cytology of glandular secretion. Quart. Rev. Biol., *4*:299, 484, 1929.

Florey, H. W.: The secretion and function of intestinal mucus. Gastroenterology, *43*:326, 1962.

Jennings, M. A., and H. W. Florey: Autoradiographic observations on the mucous cells of the stomach and intestine. Quart. J. Exper. Physiol., *41*:131, 1956.

Nassonov, D.: Das Golgische Binnennetz und seine Beziehungun zu der Sekretion. Morphologische und experimentelle Untersuchungen an einigen Saugetierdrüsen. Arch. f. mikr. Anat., *100*:433, 1924.

Palade, G. E.: Functional changes in the structure of cell components. *In* Hayashi, T., ed.: Subcellular Particles. New York, Ronald Press, 1959, p. 64.

Palade, G. E., P. Siekevitz, and L. G. Caro: Structure, chemistry and function of the pancreatic exocrine cell. *In* de Reuck, A. V. S., and M. P. Cameron, eds.: The Exocrine Pancreas. Boston, Little, Brown & Co., 1962.

Palay, S. L.: The morphology of secretion. *In* Frontiers in Cytology. New Haven, Yale University Press, 1958, pp. 305–342.

Peterson, M., and C. P. Leblond: Synthesis of complex carbohydrates in the Golgi region as shown by radioautography after injection of labeled glucose. J. Cell Biol., *21*:143, 1964.

Scharrer, E.: Principles of neuroendocrine integration. *In* Endocrines and the Central Nervous System. Baltimore, Williams and Wilkins Co., 1966.

Scharrer, E., and B. Scharrer: Neurosekretion. *In* von Möllendorff, W., and W. Bargmann, eds.: Handbuch der mikroskopischen Anatomie des Menschen, Berlin, Springer Verlag, 1954, Vol. 6, part 5, p. 953.

Trier, J. S.: Studies on small intestinal crypt epithelium. I. The fine structure of the crypt epithelium of the proximal small intestine of fasting humans. J. Cell Biol., *18*:599, 1963.

Turner, C. D.: General Endocrinology. 4th ed. Philadelphia, W. B. Saunders Co., 1965.

Warshawsky, H., C. P. Leblond, and B. Droz: Synthesis and migration of proteins in the cells of the exocrine pancreas as revealed by specific activity determination from radioautographs. J. Cell Biol., *16*:213, 1963.

Zeigel, R. F., and A. J. Dalton: Speculations based on the morphology of the Golgi systems in several types of protein-secreting cells. J. Cell Biol., *15*:45, 1962.

CHAPTER FIVE

Blood

The embryonic connective tissue, the *mesenchyme,* gives rise to the blood, the blood vessels, and the various types of connective tissue. The mesenchyme develops from the mesoderm immediately after the formation of the germ layers and soon accumulates in masses between them. The mesenchymal cells at first are irregularly stellate and connected by their processes, and their cell bodies are separated by a jelly-like intercellular substance. The cells undergo many changes to form the various blood and connective tissue cells.

There are four main types of connective tissue, all characterized by an abundant intercellular substance: blood and lymph, connective tissue proper, cartilage, and bone. In the blood and lymph the intercellular substance is liquid. In the connective tissue proper, of which there are many types, the intercellular substance always contains fibers and varies from a soft jelly to a tough fibrous mass. In cartilage the intercellular substance contains masked fibers and has a rubbery consistency. In bone the fibrous intercellular substance is impregnated with calcium salts.

In the adult organism the various connective tissues cannot be sharply separated from one another in all respects. The fibers of the connective tissue proper continue into both cartilage and bone, and certain characteristic chemical substances are common to the intercellular substance in the connective tissue proper, cartilage, and bone. Similarly, the cells of the blood cannot be separated from those of the connective tissue proper, because there is a constant exchange of cells between them. Certain cells of the blood and the other connective tissues may display marked differences in form and function when their environment is changed. Thus a leukocyte that seems to be inactive while in the blood may previously have been active while in the connective tissue proper and may become active again on re-entering this tissue from the blood.

In the earliest stages of development the endothelial cells of the blood vessels and the blood cells arise simultaneously from the same mesenchymal elements. Moreover, the embryonic endothelium occasionally turns into blood cells. In the later stages, however, the endothelium becomes more differentiated and independent, and new vessels arise only through sprouting of pre-existing ones. Thus all the vessels including the heart become a comprehensive specialized system, described in Chapter 13. The blood vessels are always accompanied by connective tissue. However, as we shall see, some cells with the developmental potencies of mesenchymal cells persist in the adult organism around the blood vessels and in the blood cell forming organs.

FORMED ELEMENTS OF THE BLOOD

The blood of adult vertebrates is a red liquid which circulates in a closed system of tubes, the blood vessels. Its quantity in man is estimated as about 7 per cent of the body weight. The liquid menstruum of the blood, the *plasma,* appears colorless in a thin film examined under the microscope but varies from gray to yellow, according to species, when seen in large amounts with the naked eye. Suspended in the plasma are several kinds of formed elements: the *red corpuscles (erythrocytes),*

111

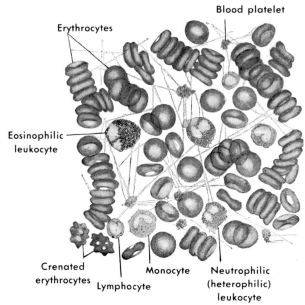

Figure 5-1. Fresh preparation of human blood. Note the strands of fibrin and rouleaux of erythrocytes. × 780. (After A. A. Maximow.)

colorless corpuscles (white blood corpuscles or leukocytes) and, in mammals, the *blood platelets.**

In the last two decades, the cells of the blood and of the blood cell forming tissues have been the subject of especially intensive investigation. This has been due in part to a great medical interest in transplantation of all tissues including blood and in part to the wide exploitation of significant old knowledge on the sensitivity of these cells to destruction by ionizing radiations. The nature and interrelationships of the blood cells and cells of the other connective tissues are discussed in Chapter 6 and especially in the latter part of Chapter 8 (pp. 209 et seq.).

Erythrocytes, or Red Blood Corpuscles

In mammals, the red blood corpuscles are nonmotile, highly differentiated cells which have lost their nucleus, Golgi net, RNA, mito-

---

* In an attempt to eliminate confusion connected with many of the names of cells then in use, a new nomenclature was introduced in this country some years ago for the various blood cells and their precursors. For instance, it was proposed to supplant *erythrocyte* by *rubricyte.* This terminology has been adopted by only a few individuals. Until this or another new terminology has been accepted internationally, we shall continue to use the conventional names.

chondria, and centrioles during maturation. In the other vertebrates they retain the nucleus.

A normal adult has about 35 ml. of red cells per kg. of body weight. The red cell volume is slightly lower in the adult female, and is higher in both male and female at birth. The normal "red count" (a measure of red cell concentration) averages 5.2 million per ml. for men and 4.5 million per ml. for women. Both red cell volume and red cell count are increased by residence at high altitude. Changes in pathologic conditions may be even more marked.

The size of the erythrocytes, under normal conditions, is remarkably uniform; in man the diameter averages 7.74 μ and the thickness at the edge 1.9 μ. According to some estimates, the erythrocytes of man have a diameter well over 8 μ, and the smaller figure given here may be due to dehydration during preparation. The total surface area of all the red blood corpuscles in the human body is computed as about 3500 square meters. The specific gravity of the erythrocytes is higher than that of the plasma; the estimates vary from 1.02 to 1.08.

The red blood corpuscles are a pale, greenish yellow. This is especially marked at the periphery of the corpuscle, where the layer of the colored substance is thickest. In dense masses of erythrocytes the color is a distinct red. Hemoglobin, the pigment which gives the erythrocytes their color, can be easily separated from the corpuscles by *hemolysis*. It then dissolves in the plasma and gives it a distinct reddish color, while the corpuscles become colorless, although they more or less keep their form. The colorless part of the cell which remains after the hemoglobin leaves is called the *stroma* or, preferably, the ghost. Hemoglobin and the colorless substances are believed by some to form a colloidal mixture, of which hemoglobin forms about 95 per cent of the dried weight, but the details of erythrocyte structure are subject to debate. Each cubic centimeter of red cells contains approximately 1 mg. of iron in the form of hemoglobin. There are at least 10 genetically differentiated molecular species of hemoglobin.

The erythrocytes of mammals are biconcave disks. In profile they have elongated bodies with rounded ends and a constricted middle part (Fig. 5-19). Some investigators claim that they are shallow cups and that the biconcave form is the result of shrinkage due to an increase in the osmotic pressure of the plasma during examination. It is possible that in the normal blood, both forms, as well as all transitions between them, are present at the same time (Figs. 5-1, 5-2, and 5-19). In the camel and the llama the erythrocytes are biconcave ovals devoid of nuclei.

The erythrocytes are extremely soft and flexible. The slightest mechanical influence distorts them, but the usual form is restored as soon as the mechanical factor ceases to act. This can be seen easily during observation of circulating blood in living capillaries. When an erythrocyte is forced through a blood vessel of small caliber, it becomes considerably drawn out, but it resumes the disk shape as soon as it enters a larger vessel. In the living condition

the substance of erythrocytes appears homogeneous even with dark-field illumination. With the electron microscope erythrocytes appear finely granular. Ultracentrifuged erythrocytes are stratified into two or three layers; this indicates that they are composed of at least three substances.

Under physiological conditions the interior of the erythrocytes and the plasma are in a state of osmotic equilibrium. If the molecular concentration of the plasma is lowered through addition of water, water enters the erythrocyte. If the osmotic pressure of the plasma is increased, the interior of the erythrocyte gives up water to the plasma and becomes irregular in outline, or crenated (Figs. 5-1 and 5-2). A solution of 0.9 per cent of NaCl is isotonic with normal human plasma and therefore does not alter the size or form of the erythrocytes; it is often called "physiologic salt solution."

Erythrocytes have a marked tendency to adhere to one another by their broad surfaces and to assemble in long, curved columns resembling piles of coins (Fig. 5-1). This can be observed in a drop of fresh, undiluted blood. The piles or *rouleaux* form at once; a slight pressure on the coverslip breaks them up. They may also be formed in the living body while erythrocytes are circulating in the blood vessels. The adhesion is so strong that, if the motion of the bloodstream in the vessel is not too swift, the piles are seen gliding, serpent-like, through the smaller vessels. The cause of the rouleau formation is not known. Some believe that it is a display of surface tension forces, which cause bodies suspended in a fluid to apply to one another by their greatest surfaces.

Agglutination of erythrocytes occurs in the circulating blood in a variety of pathological conditions, usually as a result of the action of an agglutinin, occasionally as a nonspecific effect of an abnormal protein. Irregular clumps of erythrocytes are found in the circulating blood in many diseases. This phenomenon, called sludging, has been studied extensively by Knisely, Bloch, and others.

Although lacking a nucleus the red cells are not physiologically or biochemically inert. Energy is needed to maintain a gradient of osmotic pressure between ions in and outside of the red cells, to preserve the form of the red cell, and to convert methemoglobin to hemoglobin. Energy is supplied by oxidation of glucose to lactic acid, a complicated, stepwise process, most of which is anaerobic. Each step

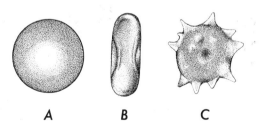

Figure 5-2. An erythrocyte in 0.9 per cent sodium chloride solution, seen from the broad surface (*A*) and in profile (*B*). *C* is a crenated erythrocyte. (Redrawn and slightly modified from Broderson.)

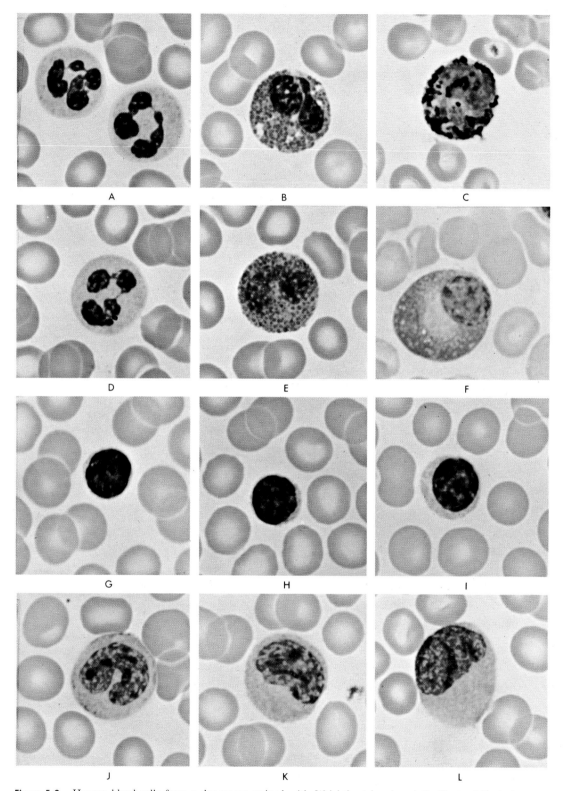

Figure 5-3. Human blood cells from a dry smear stained with Wright's stain. *A* and *D,* Neutrophilic leukocytes. *B* and *E,* Eosinophilic leukocytes. *C,* Basophilic leukocyte. *F,* Plasma cell. This is not a normal constituent of the peripheral blood but is included here for comparison with the mononuclear leukocytes. *G* and *H,* Small lymphocytes. *I,* Medium lymphocyte. *J, K,* and *L,* Monocytes.

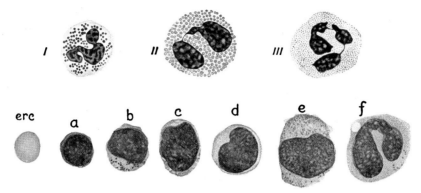

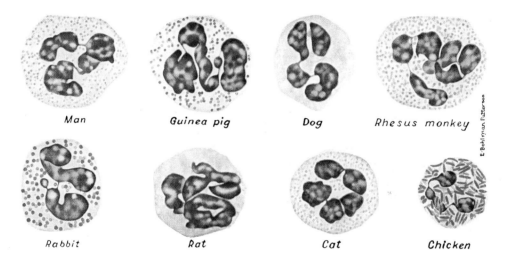

Figure 5-4. *I,* Basophilic leukocyte; *II,* eosinophilic leukocyte; *III,* neutrophilic (heterophilic) leukocyte; *erc,* erythrocyte; *a, b, c,* and *d,* lymphocytes; *e* and *f,* monocytes. From Romanowsky-stained dry smears of human blood, except *I,* which is stained with thionine. (After A. A. Maximow.)

Figure 5-5. Heterophilic leukocytes of several species. Note the variation in size and staining of the granules in those species in which they are present. Wright's stain. (Courtesy of M. Bloch.)

in the oxidation of glucose is under enzymatic control. An abnormality in a single enzyme system, usually the result of an inherited defect, frequently results in excessively rapid destruction of red cells.

Normally, the erythrocytes in a dry smear of the peripheral blood stain red (that is, they are acidophilic) with the Wright or Giemsa stain. Some of the developing red blood corpuscles which have lost their nuclei but are not yet completely mature are called *reticulocytes.* In stained dry smears they are slightly larger than the mature erythrocytes and have a diffuse, slightly bluish appearance (*polychromato-*

philia or *polychromasia*) which is due to the staining of residual ribosomes. When stained with brilliant cresyl blue the polychromatophilic substance is precipitated into a network, or reticulum, whence the name reticulocyte.

The percentage of reticulocytes in the circulating blood, depends on the rate of transformation of normoblasts to reticulocytes and on the length of time the reticulocytes circulate in the peripheral blood before becoming red blood cells. Normally this period in the circulating blood is 24 hours. They probably reside longer in the marrow prior to release into the circulation. The number of reticulocytes

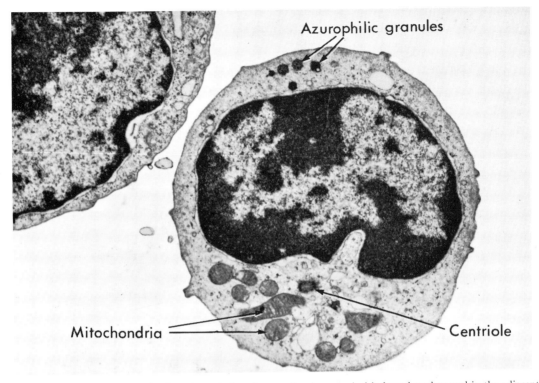

Azurophilic granules

Mitochondria   Centriole

Figure 5-6. Electron micrograph of a guinea pig lymphocyte, showing a typical indented nucleus and in the adjacent cytoplasm a centriole and several mitochondria. Although a nongranular leukocyte, the lymphocyte may contain a few azurophilic granules. × 14,000.

may be used as a rough index of the rate of red cell formation, provided other causes of elevation of the reticulocyte count are excluded. In adult man the reticulocyte count averages about 0.8 per cent.

Heinz bodies may be found in small numbers in normal red cells but are best demonstrated by incubating the cells with phenylhydrazine and staining with methyl violet. They are the result of polymerization of denatured hemoglobin molecules and are present in increased number in the erythrocytes of patients with hemolytic anemia that is caused by congenital susceptibility to specific drugs such as primaquine, used in treatment of malaria. This susceptibility is due to a defect in a specific enzyme, glucose-6-phosphate dehydrogenase, needed in aerobic metabolism of glucose.

ABNORMAL FORMS OF ERYTHROCYTES. A detailed description of abnormal forms of erythrocytes belongs to the textbooks of pathology. A variation in size is known as *anisocytosis.* Red cells that are larger than normal are *macrocytes,* those smaller, *microcytes.* Deviation from normal shape is *poikilocytosis.*

The concentration of hemoglobin per red cell is less than normal when the rate of red cell formation is relatively greater than the rate of hemoglobin synthesis. Each red cell in this instance contains an abnormally small quantity of hemoglobin and appears paler (*hypochromic*) than the normal red cells (*normochromic*).

Erythrocytes may have a basophilic (blue) stippling after Romanowsky staining. This occurs normally in the embryo but very rarely in the adult. In postnatal life basophilic stippling is particularly common in diseases in which an excessive rate of production is a reaction to an excessive rate of destruction of erythrocytes. It is probable that this stippled substance is similar to the basophilic material in the polychromatophilic erythrocytes.

Quite different from the basophilic granules of the mottled erythrocytes are the peculiar granular *Howell-Jolly bodies,* remnants of the nuclear chromatin, which occur in seemingly normal erythrocytes of adult and especially of embryonic mammals. They are small, sharply outlined, round or angular bodies which stain intensely with nuclear dyes, and especially with methyl green, which never stains the basophilic granulation. Their number is limited to one or two in an erythrocyte.

FUNCTION OF THE ERYTHROCYTES. The erythrocytes are carriers of oxygen. In the blood vessels of the lungs (or gills) their hemoglobin combines with oxygen and is transformed into oxyhemoglobin. In the tissues of the body, where the oxygen tension is much less than in the respiratory organs, oxyhemoglobin is reduced and its oxygen is used in the metabolic processes of the cells. Hemoglobin plays an equally important part in the transport of carbon dioxide from the tissues to the lungs. As it loses oxygen it becomes a weaker acid, the diminution in its acid strength being nearly sufficient to compensate for the carbonic acid formed from the oxygen it delivers to the tissues. In the lungs, as oxygen is taken up and carbon dioxide is lost, hemoglobin again becomes a stronger acid. In addition, part of the carbon dioxide carried from the tissues to the lungs is combined directly with hemoglobin in the form of hemoglobin carbamate.

Colorless Corpuscles: Leukocytes or White Blood Corpuscles

The blood of all animals contains a number of colorless cells, *leukocytes*. They are more resistant to change in the surrounding medium than are the erythrocytes. In a drop of fresh blood, they remain alive for a considerable time and can be studied easily. Their number is far smaller than that of the erythrocytes, averaging in normal human blood 5000 to 9000 per ml. In children the figures are higher. The number of leukocytes in the circulating blood varies at different times of the day, during digestion, and in the various parts of the circulatory system. In addition, it may change rapidly under the influence of numerous conditions that are hard to control. Consequently,

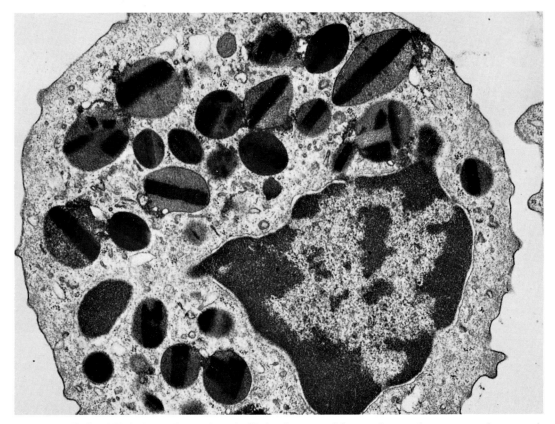

Figure 5-7.   Eosinophilic leukocyte from guinea pig. Notice that most of the granules contain one or more dense crystals. × 17,000.

leukocyte counts frequently have only a relative value.

The leukocytes are true cells with a nucleus and cytoplasm. They are all more or less ameboid. In fresh human blood several types can be distinguished: *lymphocytes,* small cells, about the size of an erythrocyte or slightly larger, with a round or indented nucleus and a thin rim of clear, homogeneous cytoplasm; *monocytes,* slightly larger cells with an oval or reniform nucleus and a somewhat greater amount of cytoplasm; *heterophilic granular leukocytes*—called *neutrophilic leukocytes* in man—cells with a lobulated nucleus and a cytoplasm filled with fine granules; *eosinophilic granular leukocytes,* which are fewer in number and characterized by the presence of yellowish, refractile granules and a bilobed nucleus; and *basophilic granular leukocytes,* which also contain coarse granules but are hard to identify when unstained.

The white blood corpuscles may thus be separated into two groups: nongranular leukocytes and granular leukocytes. It must be emphasized that cells examined in the living organism, or seen in sections, are quite different in appearance from the same cells seen in dry smears, where they are no longer spherical but flattened to thin disks and therefore appear relatively larger. In the process of drying, many structural details are greatly changed and often distorted. For instance, the nucleolus of small lymphocytes, obvious in the living, is obscured in dry smears.

NONGRANULAR OR LYMPHOID LEUKOCYTES (AGRANULOCYTES). This group contains the lymphocytes and the monocytes. The largest lymphocytes of lymphatic tissue (Chapter 8) do not gain access to the bloodstream under normal conditions, and the *large lymphocyte* of the blood as seen in dry smears corresponds to the medium-sized lymphocyte of the lymphatic

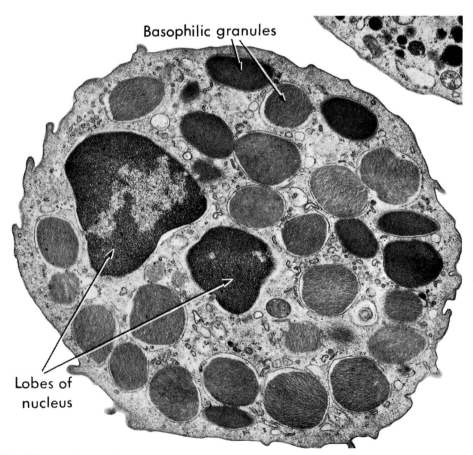

Figure 5-8. Electron micrograph of a basophilic granular leukocyte of the guinea pig. The large granules are somewhat irregular in outline and vary in their density. × 16,000.

tissue as studied in tissue sections. Under abnormal conditions exceedingly large lymphocytes of the lymphatic tissue may appear in the blood. They are usually called *lymphoblasts* by histologists, although most clinical hematologists speak of them as *stem cells.*

Lymphocytes. In man the lymphocytes form 20 to 25 per cent of the total number of colorless corpuscles in the blood. They are spherical cells 6 to 8 μ in diameter, although a few of them may be even a little larger. On the average, they are slightly larger than erythrocytes.

The characteristic feature of a small lymphocyte is a relatively large nucleus surrounded by a thin layer of cytoplasm. The nucleus is nearly spherical, but on one side it has a more or less obvious indentation. This is nearly always obscured in dry smears of the blood but is usually seen in the living cell with phase contrast microscopy and in well prepared histological sections (Fig. 8-3), and in the thin sections used for electron microscopy if the plane of section is appropriate (Fig. 5-6). In stained preparations the chromatin forms a thick layer at the nuclear envelope and several darkly staining masses in the interior. The nucleus accordingly appears dark. All lymphocytes have prominent nucleoli as seen in the living cells and in well prepared microscopic sections. They are also visible with the electron microscope. Unfortunately, they are rarely seen in dry smear preparations. The cytoplasm forms a slightly larger accumulation on the indented side of the nucleus. It is homogeneous and basophilic; in dry smears it stains pale blue with Romanowsky eosin-methylene-azure mixtures.

The larger lymphocytes are relatively scarce. Their larger size is due to a somewhat greater amount of cytoplasm, while the nucleus remains unchanged or is slightly less compact. The cytocentrum is represented by a pair of centrioles at the indentation of the nucleus; it is surrounded by a small Golgi apparatus. The mitochondria are scarce and have the form of small dots or short rods. They stain supravitally with Janus green. With the electron microscope, these cytological constituents can be seen more clearly (Fig. 5-6). Supravital staining with neutral red seldom reveals more than a very few inclusions in the lymphocytes of man. In many lymphocytes of some animals, such as the rat, a considerable number of small neutral red stained vacuoles can be seen

Figure 5-9. High-magnification electron micrograph of part of a guinea pig basophilic granule, showing its limiting membrane (*above*) and its highly ordered internal structure. $\times$ 100,000.

around the cytocentrum. Except for occasional small lipid droplets, no other inclusions are found in the living, unchanged lymphocytes.

Although the lymphocytes are nongranular leukocytes, Romanowsky stained dry smears occasionally reveal in their cytoplasm a few round granules of different sizes and of a bright purple color. These are called *azurophilic granules.* They are not a constant feature of this cell type and are different from the characteristic granules of the granulocytes.

In the guinea pig many lymphocytes and monocytes contain a large spherical inclusion, the *Kurloff body.* In dry smears it stains in the same way as do the azurophilic granules, although it has other staining reactions that differentiate it from them. In living cells the Kurloff body is a homogeneous yellowish green body.

One of the most interesting advances in the study of the white blood corpuscles has

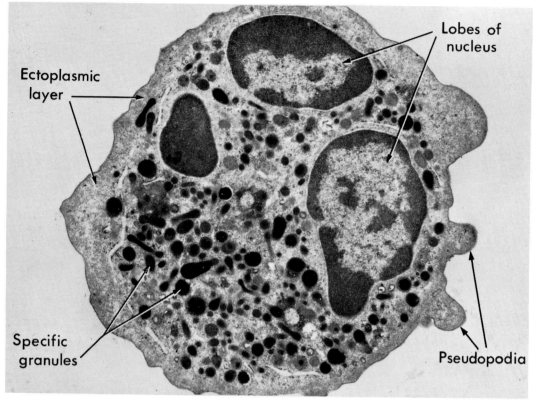

Ectoplasmic layer

Lobes of nucleus

Specific granules

Pseudopodia

Figure 5-10. Electron micrograph of a heterophilic leukocyte of a guinea pig. The nucleus has several lobes and the cytoplasm is filled with specific granules of varying shape. A thin ectoplasmic layer of cytoplasm that is devoid of granules forms pseudopodia and is probably important in the ameboid locomotion of this cell type. × 12,000.

been the growing body of knowledge indicating that there are several kinds of functionally different small lymphocytes, which are not morphologically distinguishable from one another with current techniques. How many types there are and whether they represent two, three, or more cell strains are subjects of intense study. The circulating blood contains at least two types of such lymphocytes: those arising in lymph nodes and those from the thymus. This conclusion is based on studies of lymphocytes labeled with tritiated thymidine. Those that develop in lymph nodes have very long lives. There are also reports that lymphocytes recognizable by chromosomal markers have lived for years in persons who have been transfused with blood containing them. Lymphocytes originating in the thymus, sometimes called *thymocytes,* are believed to survive in the blood for only a few days. In addition to their origins in lymph nodes and thymus, lymphocytes also arise in the spleen, tonsils, lym-

phatic nodules beneath the epithelium of the gastrointestinal tract, and in the bone marrow (Chapter 14). Whether lymphocytes from all of these sources circulate under normal conditions is not known.

Monocytes. There is much confusion as to just what a monocyte is, because the definition of this cell type has been obscured by the contradictory opinions of the proponents of the various theories of blood formation. When preparations of blood are examined objectively, the nongranular leukocytes are seen to consist of a series of transitional forms that begins with the smaller lymphocytes and ends with larger cells of quite different appearance, the *monocytes.* But in the midportion of this series of transitions is a group of cells which cannot easily be classified as either typical lymphocytes or typical monocytes (Fig. 5-3*J*, *K*, and *L* and Fig. 5-4). The following description refers to the typical monocytes of the blood; a discussion of their origin is found on page 207.

The typical monocytes measure 9 to 12 μ in diameter. In dry smears, in which they are flattened and stretched, their diameter may reach 20 μ. They constitute 3 to 8 per cent of the leukocytes of the circulating blood. Their enumeration is especially difficult because, as mentioned before, they cannot always be sharply differentiated from the larger lymphocytes of the blood.

In the monocytes the cytoplasm is far more abundant than in the lymphocytes. In older monocytes the nucleus has an eccentric position and is oval or kidney-shaped. A few monocytes have a horseshoe-shaped or deeply constricted nucleus, and these are the oldest ones (Fig. 5-37). The chromatin granules are much finer and more numerous than in the lymphocytes. Therefore the nucleus stains less intensely, especially in dry smears. One or several small nucleoli are always present, although they are not usually seen in dry smears.

The abundant cytoplasm has a pale grayish blue color in dry smears stained with eosin-methylene-azure. Special methods show that it contains the usual diplosome and a considerable number of mitochondria. Near the indentation of the nucleus is a Golgi apparatus. Supravital staining with Janus green and neutral red reveals a spherical group of fine red vacuoles, the rosette, which surrounds the cytocentrum; its position corresponds with that of the Golgi apparatus. The bluish green stained mitochondria are arranged in a wreath around the rosette. The claim that this rosette is specific for monocytes is incorrect, for closely allied cell types may have neutral red rosettes (lymphocytes in the rat, plasma cells, macrophages, and some of the septal cells of the lung). Neutral red is now believed to stain cytoplasmic granules having the properties of lysosomes. The number of circulating monocytes may be increased experimentally in rabbits by infection with *Listeria monocytogenes,* or by injections of the phospholipids of the tubercle bacillus.

GRANULAR LEUKOCYTES OR GRANULOCYTES. In contrast to the lymphocytes and monocytes, the granulocytes always contain specific granules. These are of the same kind in any given cell type, but are distinctly different in the various classes of granulocytes in a given species and in the homologous cells of

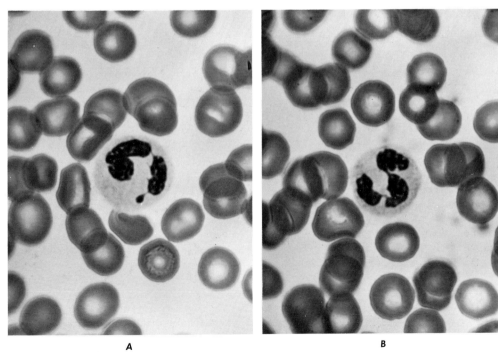

A   B

Figure 5-11. Erythrocytes and neutrophilic leukocytes from a normal female (*A*) and a normal male (*B*). The female leukocyte shows the "drumstick" appendix of the nucleus that was discovered by Davidson and Smith. From dry smears of human blood. Giemsa stain. × 1800. (Courtesy of Murray Barr.)

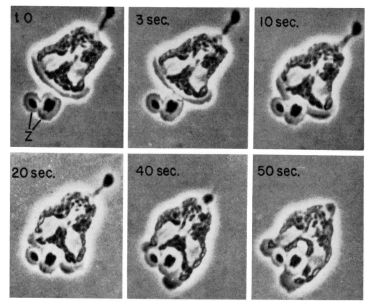

Figure 5-12. Frames from a motion picture of phagocytosis of zymosan particles of yeast cell wall (*Z*) by a chicken heterophilic leukocyte with its large granules. Note the close apposition of the leukocytic membrane to the zymosan granules. Clear zones seen in the cytoplasm in the 40 and 50 second prints are the result of granule lysis, demonstrated more clearly in following illustrations. Note the reduction in content of granules in that part of the cell containing the zymosan particles. Phase contrast microscopy. Approximately × 1000. (Courtesy of J. G. Hirsch, J. Exp. Med., *116*:827, 1962.)

different species. They may be relatively large or small, spherules or ovoids, or they may be irregular in outline, filamentous, or rod-shaped (Fig. 5-5). Another general characteristic of the mature granular leukocyte is the shape of its nucleus. Instead of being spherical, slightly indented or kidney-shaped, as in the majority of the nongranular leukocytes, the nucleus of the granulocyte is constricted into a varying number of lobes. The lobated nucleus of the mature cell gradually develops from the compact, spherical nucleus of the young form. Although different classes of granulocytes may be identified on the basis of their nuclear form and the morphology of the cytoplasmic granules, the most convenient classification is based on a combination of the morphology and staining reactions of the granules.

In such a classification the granulocytes fall into three general groups designated as acidophilic, basophilic, and heterophilic leukocytes (neutrophilic in man). In the first, the granules in the cytoplasm are most often spherical or egg-shaped and are electively stained with acid dyes; in the second they are of similar form, but stain electively with basic dyes; while in the third group the granules, although constant in a particular species, differ as to form, size, and staining reaction according to species (Fig. 5-5).

Acidophilic or Eosinophilic Leukocytes. The diameter of these cells, which are spherical in the fresh condition, is about 9 μ. In dry smears the size of the flattened cells is about 12 μ. Their number in normal adult blood varies from 2 to 5 per cent of the total leukocyte count.

The nucleus usually has two oval lobes connected by a thin chromatin thread (Figs. 5-3*B*, and 5-4*II*). In fixed and stained preparations, the lobes of the nucleus show a fairly dense chromatin network but no nucleoli. A similar nucleus is found in the eosinophilic leukocytes of the other mammals. In the rat and mouse the nucleus is a thick, irregular ring. Centrally located in the cell body is a small area free of granules and occupied by the cytocentrum with its diplosome.

The coarse granules, in man, are spherical and are stained with acid dyes; with Romanowsky type stains they are red or pink. In the electron microscope the eosinophilic granules of rodents contain a flat discoid crystal made up of many parallel lamellae (Fig. 5-7). In man the crystals are quite variable in form. Supravital staining with Janus green reveals a few mitochondria between the eosinophilic granules. With the exception of some fishes, all vertebrates have typical eosinophilic leukocytes in their blood.

Basophilic Leukocytes. These cells are difficult to find in human blood because they form only about one half of 1 per cent of the total number of leukocytes. Their size is about the same as that of the neutrophilic leukocytes (Fig. 5-3*C*). In a dry smear they measure 10 μ in diameter. The nucleus is elongated, often bent in the form of an **S**, and provided with two or more constrictions. The chromatin network is looser and paler than in the eosinophilic leukocytes and nucleoli are usually not seen. The granules in the cytoplasm of the living cells have a low refractive index. Their substance, in man, is soluble in water; therefore, in preparations stained with the usual watery dye solutions, the granules are partly dissolved and disfigured. In dry smears or in sections of alcohol fixed material, the cyto-plasm contains round granules of different sizes, which stain a metachromatic purple with alcoholic thionine or toluidine blue. Supravital application of neutral red stains the granules a dark red color.

The solubility of the basophilic granules has created confusion in regard to the nature of these cells, but the use of suitable methods leaves no doubt as to their specific nature. In the guinea pig, the granules are large, oval, and insoluble in water, and they stain but faintly. In the dog, the granules are fine and are assembled in a small, compact group. In the cat, rat, and mouse, the basophilic leukocytes seem to be normally absent from the blood. In the lower vertebrates the variations are still greater.

In electron micrographs (Fig. 5-8), each coarse granule is limited by a membrane and has an internal fine structural pattern that varies from species to species. In the guinea pig (Fig. 5-9), the content of the granules has a crystalline structure; in man, they appear to consist of closely compacted dense granules

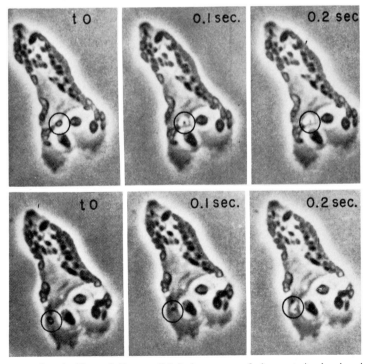

Figure 5-13. The same cell as in Figure 5-12 at a slightly later stage of phagocytosis, showing, in the circled areas, the rapid lysis of two heterophilic granules, one in each of the two rows of micrographs. The area occupied by the circled granule in the upper row appears only as a small vesicle in later micrographs in the lower row. Phase contrast microscopy. Approximately × 2000. (Courtesy of J. G. Hirsch, J. Exp. Med., *116*:827, 1962.)

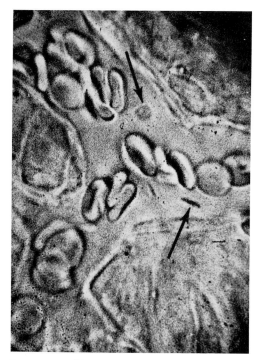

Figure 5-14. Blood vessel of a chamber in the skin of a mouse, showing blood platelets in profile and surface view (arrows). From a frame of a 16 mm. motion picture film. (Courtesy of G. Algire.)

of uniform size but exhibiting no crystalline order.

Heterophilic Leukocytes (Neutrophilic in Man). This type of leukocyte is the most numerous in the blood of all vertebrates. In fresh human blood these cells can be recognized easily by their fine granulation. The diameter of the spherical cells in the fresh condition is 7 to 9 μ. In a dry smear they measure 10 to 12 μ and constitute 65 to 75 per cent of the total number of leukocytes.

The nucleus is highly polymorphous. It is an elongated, bent or twisted body consisting of several irregularly oval or angular lobes connected by thin chromatin threads (Fig. 5-3A and D). During ameboid motion the nucleus undergoes passive changes of its form, but the constrictions and the thickenings are constant. The number of the lobes usually varies from three to five and increases with the age of the cell. Under physiological conditions the majority of the cells have a three-lobed nucleus. In pathological conditions these relations may change considerably. A dark chromatin network is seen in the lobes in stained sections. Nucleoli appear to be absent.

In dry smears of the peripheral blood of human females, but not of males, David and Smith found a specific nuclear appendage. It is about 1.5 μ in diameter and is joined to a lobe of the nucleus by a fine strand of chromatin (Fig. 5-11A). This "drumstick," visible in about 3 per cent of the cells in smears, is presumably present in most of them and represents the chromatin of the XX chromosome pair. It has the same diagnostic value as the chromatin body shown in Figure 2–42. It can be distinguished by its size and shape from the larger and smaller nuclear excrescences which are not related to the sex chromatin.

The cytoplasm has a peripheral, homogeneous layer which forms the pseudopodia. The inner, slightly acidophilic mass is full of fine granules, except for a small, clear area in the center of the cell body which contains the diplosome. In man the granules are stained with neutral dyes and are therefore called neutrophilic. The Romanowsky mixture gives them a purple hue. They can also be stained with acid dyes, such as eosin. Supravital staining with Janus green reveals the presence of a few mitochondria. Neutral red applied supravitally gives the granules an indistinct, pale yellowish hue. Occasionally, small vacuoles and inclusions of fat or glycogen can be found between the granules.

In other mammals the granules have a variable size and staining reaction more or less typical for the species. In the guinea pig and rabbit the granules are stainable with either acid or basic dyes, although they show a predilection for acid dyes and, therefore, were called *pseudoeosinophils*. In some species the granules are so small that they are hardly visible with the highest powers of the light microscope (see Fig. 5-5).

Abnormal Forms of Leukocytes. In some diseases the blood may contain degenerating leukocytes. Vacuoles or droplets of lipid may appear in the cytoplasm. In degenerating granular leukocytes the nucleus may undergo fragmentation into separate parts (*karyorrhexis*) or shrinkage (*pyknosis*). Atypical and immature leukocytes enter the blood in certain diseases.

Free Macrophages of the Blood. Many investigators have described macrophages in the blood. They have a large, eccentric nucleus and a vacuolated, ameboid cytoplasm, which often contains phagocytosed inclusions. In animals which have had intravenous injections of vital dyes or particulate matter, large quantities of these substances accumulate in the free macrophages (see p. 144). Such cells originate in the spleen, liver, and bone marrow from fixed macrophages by withdrawal of their processes and migration into the bloodstream. They are found especially in the blood of the veins and of the right heart; the majority of them are filtered off in the capillaries of the lungs, but some may occasionally enter the general circulation.

Free macrophages may appear in the blood in certain diseases, especially those of septic nature. Their presence in normal blood is doubtful. Confusion has been caused because many authors did not distinguish the blood macrophages from the monocytes. The cells described by some authors in leukemias and other diseases under the name of hemohistioblasts are for the most part the same free macrophages. In some cases, artificially damaged hemocytoblasts or myelocytes in dry smears have been mistaken for free macrophages or hemohistioblasts.

Functions of the Leukocytes. Little is known of the functions of the leukocytes while in the bloodstream. Occasionally some of them phagocytose particulate material, such as bacteria or carbon particles. When leukocytes are outside the vascular system, they show active movement. Some leukocytes are phagocytic; some can turn into other cell types and some are important in immune reactions.

Movement. All leukocytes are capable of active movement, provided they have a solid substrate to move on. The movement can be observed in a drop of fresh blood protected from desiccation and kept at body temperature or, better, in tissue cultures. The movement of the leukocytes is identical in essential details with that of an ameba. Factors concerned in the movement of leukocytes are discussed by Allen.

The motility of the leukocytes explains why they are not confined to the system of blood or lymph vessels but may be found everywhere in the connective tissue and occasionally even in other tissues. Under physiological conditions, single leukocytes, especially lymphocytes, migrate out of the vessels into the

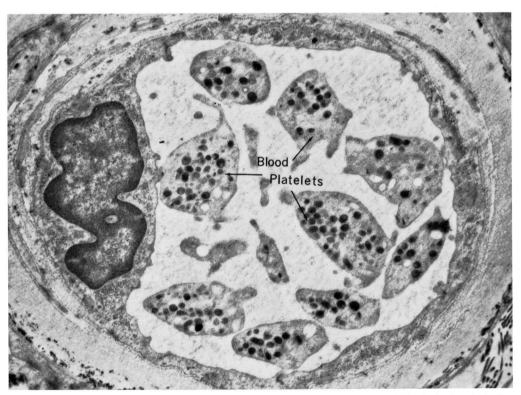

Figure 5-15. Electron micrograph of a capillary in the human eye, containing several blood platelets in its lumen. × 11,500. (Courtesy of M. Jakus.)

Figure 5-16. Electron micrograph of fibrin, showing the periodic cross striation. × 55,000. (After Porter and Hawn.)

tissue, and may return again into the blood or lymph channels. In inflammation—the reaction of a tissue to local injury—the leukocytes assemble rapidly in the blood vessels of the region and migrate in enormous numbers through the vessel walls into the tissue.

Chemotaxis. The migration of the leukocytes into the tissue toward the site of a local injury is believed to be caused by their chemotactic properties. According to in vitro studies it is primarily the granulocytes that show chemotaxis when tested with bacterial products, products of damaged tissue, and a number of carbohydrates. Although the lymphocytes do not react chemotactically to any of these substances, they and the monocytes accumulate in great numbers in injured tissues.

Phagocytosis. The heterophilic granulocytes display a marked capacity for ingesting small, discrete particles, such as cinnabar, carbon, and, very importantly, many types of bacteria and other microorganisms. In this process, the specific granules of the leukocytes break down and disappear (Figs. 5-12 and 5-13). In so doing they liberate hydrolytic enzymes, which destroy the bacteria. The granules are thus a special type of lysosome. They also liberate a bactericidal agent called *phagocytin.* The phagocytosis and digestion of bacteria by the heterophilic granulocytes is one of

the means by which the host destroys bacteria, and the outcome of some infections may depend on the extent of phagocytosis by leukocytes.

Phagocytosis can be watched outside the body when living leukocytes and bacteria are brought together under suitable conditions in vitro. Phagocytosis may occur within the circulating bloodstream but is distinctly more effective in extravascular locations.

The eosinophilic and basophilic leukocytes rarely, if ever, display phagocytosis. The agranulocytes in the bloodstream are seldom phagocytic, although, under suitable extravascular conditions, the monocytes are able to engulf particulate matter.

Other Properties of the Leukocytes. A positive oxidase reaction occurs in the granulocytes and in most of the monocytes. The lymphocytes do not give this reaction. The leukocytes contain many enzymes whose significance is poorly understood. Most of the *neutrophilic* leukocytes of patients with chronic granulocytic leukemia do not contain the same amount of phosphatase normally found in these cells. During infections, on the other hand, this enzyme increases in concentration.

The number of leukocytes in the peripheral blood can vary as a result of certain pathological conditions. The neutrophils increase greatly in most bacterial infections. The number of eosinophils increases greatly when certain animal parasites are in the body and also during various allergic disorders. Administration of adrenocorticotropic hormone or cortisone causes a disappearance of the eosinophils from the blood. This cell type may accumulate in enormous numbers in local tissue areas, as in the mucous membranes of the respiratory passages in bronchial asthma, or about animal parasites. Further details on the eosinophils are given in Chapter 6.

The basophils increase in number in the bloodstream of guinea pigs infected with *L. monocytogenes.* They appear in great numbers in the inflamed area caused by the local injection of egg albumin or ventriculin in guinea pigs.

Blood Platelets

The *platelets* in the circulating blood of all mammals are small, colorless corpuscles. They are round or oval, biconvex disks; seen in profile, they look like small, plump spindles or rods (Fig. 5-14). Their spindle shape and their content of granules are clearly shown in electron micrographs (Fig. 5-15). Their size is not quite uniform, the average being 3 μ. The number varies considerably and is usually given as 250,000 per cu. mm. of blood, although some authors give much higher figures. It is difficult to determine the real number because as soon as the blood leaves the vessel, the platelets adhere to one another and to all surfaces with which they come in contact.

In a fresh drop of blood the platelets at once agglutinate into small and large clusters and stick to the glass. They are the lightest elements of the blood, so that in centrifuged blood they form the uppermost white layer. On standing they lose their smooth outlines, and finally disintegrate into small groups of granules. Simultaneously, around and radiat-

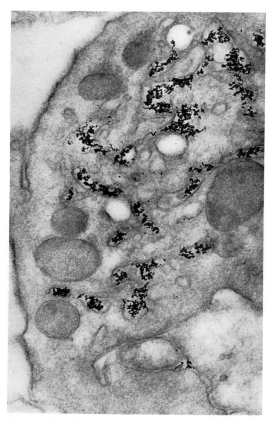

Figure 5-17. Electron micrograph of a platelet from the lung of a rabbit injected 24 hours before with colloidal thorium dioxide. The dense granules in the interior of the platelet are thorium taken up and stored in membrane limited vesicles or canaliculi. × 56,000. (Courtesy of David Ferriera.)

ing from them, strands of fibrin appear in the plasma (Fig. 5-16). They may be preserved for observation by rendering the blood incoagulable through the addition of sodium citrate or heparin. Of all fixing reagents, solutions of osmic acid preserve them best. In rapidly prepared dry smears, the platelets are preserved as round corpuscles.

In dry smears stained with a Romanowsky mixture, each platelet is seen to consist of two parts. One is highly refractile and contains purple granules. This is the *granulomere* or *chromomere*. The other is pale and homogeneous and stains a pale blue—the *hyalomere*. The chromomere usually occupies a central position. The hyalomere often sends out pointed processes. Sometimes the platelets contain small vacuoles. Platelets can take up and store finely divided inorganic material (Fig. 5-17) and contain considerable amounts of glycogen (Fig. 5-18).

Platelets originate from peculiar giant cells, the *megakaryocytes*, which are found in the bone marrow of all mammals. It is believed that excrescences become pinched off the surface of the megakaryocytes and enter the bloodstream as platelets (see p. 191). Platelets play several roles in hemostasis. Either they or compounds absorbed on them stimulate contraction of injured vessels to prevent loss of blood following interruption of the continuity of the lining of blood vessels. Another major property of platelets is adhesiveness, which is manifested by their agglutination at the site of injury to the endothelial lining of the vessel in such a way as to plug the defect. Platelets participate in the formation of thromboplastin, a major step in the initiation of clotting. The blood of inframammalian vertebrates does not contain platelets. These animals have, instead, nucleated spindle cells which play a similar role in blood clotting. The term *thrombocyte* should be reserved for them.

BLOOD CLOTTING. Under normal circumstances, as a result of an equilibrium between forces initiating and preventing its clotting, blood remains a fluid, circulating tissue. This equilibrium is disturbed when the circulation halts, when blood is removed from the body, and in a wide variety of pathological circumstances.

Clotting of the blood may be analyzed in three stages. The first step is the formation of thromboplastin, the result of the interaction of substances derived from platelets, vessels, or tissue, and from plasma. The second is the transformation of prothrombin to thrombin through the action of thromboplastin, calcium ions, and other plasma factors. The third step is conversion of fibrinogen, which is normally in solution in plasma, into fibrin.

With the electron microscope it can be seen that fibrin fibers are "cross striated." The width of these bands is about 250 Å (Fig. 5-16). The liquid fraction which remains after removal of a clot is known as *serum*.

LYMPH

The lymph, the liquid that fills the lymphatic vessels, is collected from all over the body and returned to the blood. The composition of the lymph arising in different organs varies markedly. There are no cells in the smallest lymph vessels, the lymph capillaries. As it passes through the lymph nodes, however, more and more cells are added to the lymph. In the thoracic duct it is a more or less opaque,

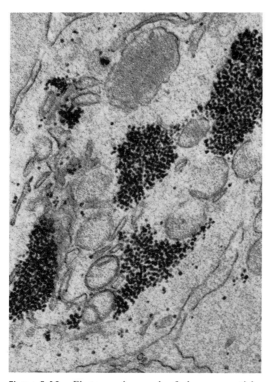

Figure 5-18. Electron micrograph of glycogen particles in normal human platelets fixed in potassium permanganate and stained with uranyl acetate. × 45,500. (Courtesy of David Ferriera.)

sometimes pinkish liquid which contains large numbers of cells. The lymph here is similar to the plasma of the blood; it also clots, although the clot is much looser and softer. The number of cells in the lymph varies within wide limits, although their character is uniform. As a rule, besides some few erythrocytes and occasional eosinophilic leukocytes, about 99 per cent of the cells are lymphocytes, of which the small lymphocytes form up to 95 per cent, depending on the animal species. Medium-sized and, especially, large lymphocytes are relatively rare. Cells of monocytic character are exceedingly rare under physiological conditions; the same is true of larger cells of the macrophage type. Under some pathological or experimental conditions, including tissue cultures of lymph, the cellular aspect of the lymph may change rapidly, and numerous macrophages may develop from the lymphocytes.

The lymphocytes in the thoracic duct do not represent the number of new lymphocytes being made in the lymphatic tissue, as was believed until recently. Many of those in the thoracic duct lymph come from the circulating blood via postcapillary venules in the lymph nodes (Fig. 14-11). The continuous movement of lymphocytes from their sources in all the hemopoietic and connective tissues to the blood passing through all the tissues and organs, then to the lymph nodes, thence into the lymph of the thoracic duct, and into the blood again repetitively has been named the *fourth circulation*.

LIFE SPAN OF BLOOD CORPUSCLES IN THE CIRCULATION

The red blood cells of man live in the circulation for approximately 120 days and the platelets a maximum of 10 to 12 days. It has been a difficult problem to determine the length of time spent in the blood by circulating granular leukocytes. The best estimates are that the heterophils survive for 12 hours or less. Even less is known about the longevity of eosinophilic or basophilic leukocytes. The lymphocytes of the blood live for either a few days or for many months or even years (p. 146). There are no data on the survival time of monocytes, in large part owing to the difficulty of separating all monocytes from lymphocytes and to the uncertain state of knowledge of the site of formation of these cells.

The investigators who have believed that

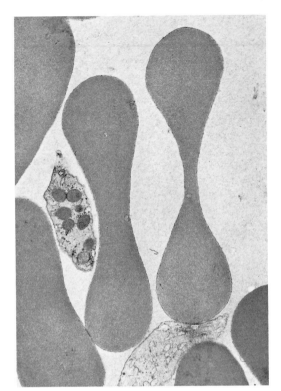

Figure 5-19. Electron micrograph of mature erythrocytes and platelets. × 11,000.

the small lymphocytes of the blood can turn into larger ones, and also into plasma cells, granulocytes, erythrocytes, monocytes, and macrophages, have thought of the circulating lymphocytes as forming an easily mobilizable source of cells with mesenchymal potentialities for development. On the basis of recent experiments with cultures of peripheral blood, it is now widely accepted that the circulating small lymphocytes can transform into large lymphocytes, capable of mitotic division, and into plasma cells. It is not generally agreed that they can turn into the other cell types mentioned above. These questions are discussed on page 204.

The small lymphocytes, directly and through plasma cells which arise from them, play important roles in certain general and local defense mechanisms of the body, including the elaboration of specific immune bodies against invading microorganisms or foreign proteins. They help maintain the "defense" of the individual against grafts of foreign tissue, even within the same species. Since the lymphocytes containing antibodies are of the long-lived type, it has also been suggested that they

may be responsible for immunological memory.

It is believed by some that small lymphocytes of the blood participate in the inflammatory reaction to local injuries by transforming into monocytes and inflammatory macrophages. Rebuck and coworkers have published drawings of successive stages in the transformation of individual lymphocytes as they develop into macrophages in blister fluid.

REFERENCES

The Handbook of Hematology, edited by H. Downey (New York, Paul B. Hoeber, Inc. 1938), contains detailed discussions of the older literature dealing with the morphology, origin and interrelationships of the blood cells. More modern approaches are contained in Leukopoiesis in health and disease (H. R. Bierman, editor), Ann. N. Y. Acad. Sci., *113:* 511, 1964.

Erythrocytes

Bessis, M., and J. P. Thiéry: Les cellules du sang vués au microscope à interférences (Système Nomarski). Revue d'Hématologie, *12:*518, 1957.

Bierman, H. R., ed.: Leukopoiesis in health and disease. Ann. N. Y. Acad. Sci., *113:*511, 1964.

Bishop, C., and D. M. Surgenor, eds.: The Red Blood Cells. New York, Academic Press, 1964.

Cowles, J., J. Saikkonen, and B. Thorell: On the presence of hemoglobin in erythroleukemia cells. Blood, *13:*1176, 1958.

Davidson, W. M., and D. H. Smith: A morphological sex difference in the polymorphonuclear leukocytes. Brit. M. J., *2:*6, 1954.

Davies, H. G.: Structure in nucleated erythrocytes. J. Biophys. & Biochem. Cytol., *9:*671, 1961.

Eck, R. V., and M. O. Dayhoff: Evolution of the structure of ferredoxin based on living relics of primitive amino acid sequences. Science, *152:*363, 1966.

Ingram, V.: The Hemoglobins in Genetics and Evolution. New York, Columbia University Press, 1963.

Knisely, M. H.: The settling of sludge during life; first observations, evidences, and significances; a contribution to the biophysics of disease. Acta Anat., *44:* suppl. 41, 1961.

Macfarlane, R. G., and Robb-Smith, A. H. T., eds.: Functions of the Blood. New York, Academic Press, 1961.

Perutz, M. F.: X-ray analysis of hemoglobin. Science, *140:*863, 1963.

Wintrobe, M.: Clinical Hematology. 5th ed. Philadelphia, Lea & Febiger, 1961.

Granulocytes

Ackerman, G. A.: Cytochemical properties of the blood basophilic granulocyte. Ann. N. Y. Acad. Sci., *103:*376, 1963.

Allen, R. D.: Ameboid movement. *In* Brachet, J., and A. E. Mirsky, eds.: The Cell: Biochemistry, Physiology, Morphology. New York, Academic Press, 1961, Vol. II, p. 135.

Anderson, D. R.: Ultrastructure of normal and leukemic leukocytes in human peripheral blood. J. Ultrastruct. Res., Suppl. 9, 1966.

Bond, V. B., T. M. Fliedner, E. P. Cronkite, J. R. Rubini, and J. S. Robertson: Cell-turnover in blood and blood-forming tissues studied with tritiated thymidine. *In* Stohlman, F., Jr., ed.: The Kinetics of Cellular Proliferation. New York, Grune & Stratton, 1959.

Horn, R. G., and S. S. Spicer: Sulfated mucopolysaccharide and basic protein in certain granules of rabbit leukocytes. Lab. Invest., *13:*1, 1964.

Nongranular Leukocytes

Berman, L., and C. S. Stulberg: Primary cultures of macrophages from normal human peripheral blood. Lab. Invest., *11:*1322, 1962.

Bloom, W.: Origin and nature of the monocyte. Folia haematol., *37:*1, 1928.

Caffrey, R. W., W. O. Rieke, and N. B. Everett: Radioautographic studies of small lymphocytes in the thoracic duct of the rat. Acta. Haemat., *28:*145, 1962.

Everett, N. B., R. W. Caffrey, and W. O. Rieke: Recirculation of lymphocytes. *In* Bierman, H. R., ed.: Leukopoiesis in health and disease. Ann. N. Y. Acad. Sci., *113:*887, 1964.

Gowans, J. L.: Life-span, recirculation and transformation of lymphocytes. Int. Rev. Path., *5:*1, 1966.

Gowans, J. L., and E. J. Knight: The route of re-circulation of lymphocytes in the rat. Proc. Roy. Soc. B, *159:*745, 1965.

Hirsch, J. G.: Cinemicrophotographic observations on granule lysis in polymorphonuclear leucocytes during phagocytosis. J. Exper. Med., *116:*827, 1962.

Maximow, A. A.: The lymphocytes and plasma cells. *In* Cowdry, E. V., ed.: Special Cytology. 2nd ed. New York, Paul B. Hoeber, Inc., 1932, p. 601.

Norman, A., M. S. Sasaki, R. E. Ottoman, and A. G. Fingerhut: Lymphocyte lifetime in women. Science, *147:*745, 1965.

Nossal, G. J. V., A. Szenberg, G. L. Ada, and C. M. Austin: Single cell studies on 19S antibody production. J. Exper. Med., *119:*485, 1964.

Rebuck, J. W., ed.: The Lymphocyte and the Lymphocytic Tissue. New York, Paul B. Hoeber, Inc., 1960.

Reinhardt, W. O.: Some factors influencing the thoracic-duct output of lymphocytes. *In* Bierman, H. R., ed.: Leukopoiesis in health and disease. Ann. N. Y. Acad. Sci., *113:*844, 1964.

Rieke, W. O.: Lymphocytes from thymectomized rats: Immunologic, proliferative, and metabolic properties. Science, *152:*535, 1966.

Sabesin, S. M.: Lymphocytes of small mammals: Spontaneous transformation in culture to blastoids. Science, *149:*1385, 1965.

Shelton, E.: Prolonged survival of rabbit thoracic duct lymphocytes in a diffusion chamber. J. Cell Biol., *12:*652, 1962.

Speirs, R. S.: The action of antigen upon hypersensitive cells. *In* Bierman, H. R., ed.: Leukopoiesis in health and disease. Ann, N. Y. Acad. Sci., *113:*819, 1964.

Symposium on differentiation and growth of hemoglobin- and immunoglobin-synthesizing cells. J. Cell Physiol., *67:* Suppl. 1, 1966.

Weiss, L., and D. W. Fawcett: Cytochemical observations on chicken monocytes, macrophages and giant cells in tissue culture. J. Histochem. & Cytochem., *1:*47, 1953.

Yoffey, J. M.: The lymphocyte. Ann Rev. Med., *15:*125, 1964.

Yoffey, J. M., G. C. B. Winter, D. G. Osmond, and E. S. Meek: Morphological studies in the culture of human leukocytes with phytohaemagglutinin. Brit. J. Haemat., *11:*488, 1965.

Platelets

Biggs, R., and R. G. Macfarlane: Human Blood Coagulation and Its Disorders. 3rd ed. Philadelphia, F. A. Davis Co., 1962.

David-Ferreira, J. F.: Sur la structure et le pouvoir phagocytaire des plaquettes sanguines. Zeitschr. f. Zellforsch., *55:*89, 1961.

Davie, E. W., and O. D. Ratnoff: The proteins of blood coagulation. *In* Neurath, H., ed.: The Proteins. 2nd ed. New York, Academic Press, 1965. Vol. III, p. 359.

Johnson, S. A., R. W. Monto, J. W. Rebuck, and R. C. Horn, Jr., eds.: Blood Platelets (A Symposium). Boston, Little, Brown & Co., 1961.

Marcus, A. J., and M. B. Zucker: The Physiology of Blood Platelets. New York, Grune & Stratton, 1965.

Porter, K. R., and C. van Z. Hawn: Sequences in the formation of clots from purified bovine fibrinogen and thrombin; a study with the electron microscope. J. Exper. Med., *90:*225, 1949.

Seegers, W. H.: Prothrombin. Commonwealth Fund. Cambridge, Harvard University Press, 1962.

CHAPTER SIX

Connective Tissue Proper

Connective tissue proper always consists of *cells* and extracellular *fibers* embedded in an amorphous *ground substance* containing *tissue fluid.* Traditionally the fibers have been considered to be of three kinds, *collagenous, reticular,* and *elastic,* but recent evidence indicates that collagenous and reticular fibers may simply be different morphological expressions of a single fibrous protein. There are several types of cells in connective tissue, which can be categorized either as *fixed cells* or as *wandering cells.* The relative abundance of the various kinds of fibers, cells, and ground substance varies greatly from one region of the body to another, and for convenience of description an effort is made to classify connective tissues. Classification is difficult and inexact and should not be interpreted too rigidly, for the various types grade into one another through transitional forms, and one type may be transformed into another if the local conditions change.

Names are usually assigned according to whether the fibers are loosely woven or densely packed. Thus we distinguish *loose connective tissue* and *dense connective tissue.* Within the second category it is useful to add modifiers to indicate whether the fibers have an ordered or a disordered arrangement. Thus in *dense irregular connective tissue* the fibers are closely interwoven in a random way, whereas in *dense regular connective tissue* the fibers are arranged in parallel bundles, as in tendons, or in flat sheets, as in aponeuroses. In addition, a number of kinds of connective tissue with special properties are so named as to indicate the predominating component or the identifying feature: *mucous* connective tissue, *elastic* tissue, *reticular* tissue, *adipose* tissue, *pigment* tissue, etc. These and the cellular lamina propria of the intestinal and uterine mucosa are all variants of loose connective tissue, which is a common and simple form that can be taken as the prototype of the connective tissues.

LOOSE CONNECTIVE TISSUE

Loose connective tissue develops from the mesenchyme remaining after the other tissues of the embryo have been formed. An interlacing fabric of fine reticular fibers is deposited in the meshes of the stellate reticulum of mesenchymal cells. As the fibers become more numerous, they associate in coarser bundles and take on the staining properties of collagen. The mesenchymal cells gradually change their character, elongating and stretching out along the surface of the fiber bundles to become the principal cells of the connective tissue. Other cell types, either differentiating from mesenchymal cells or emigrating from the blood, take up residence in the interstices of the fabric of interwoven fibers. Like a collapsed sponge this tissue contains innumerable potential spaces, normally occupied by a small amount of amorphous ground substance but capable of becoming enlarged and distended with fluid.

131

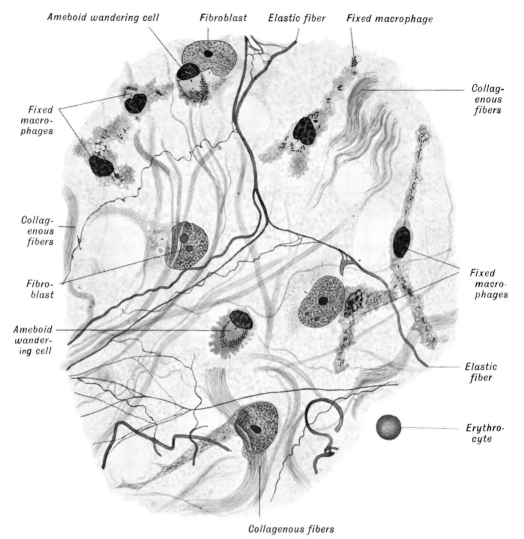

Ameboid wandering cell   *Fibroblast*   *Elastic fiber*   *Fixed macrophage*

*Collag-
enous
fibers*

*Fixed
macro-
phages*

*Collag-
enous
fibers*

*Fibro-
blast*

*Fixed
macro-
phages*

*Ameboid
wander-
ing cell*

*Elastic
fiber*

*Erythro-
cyte*

Collagenous fibers

Figure 6-1.   Section through slightly edematous, subcutaneous, loose connective tissue from the thigh of a man. The figure illustrates various types of cells and fibers found in normal connective tissue. The erythrocyte at the lower right (7μ) is for size comparison. × 950. (After A. A. Maximow.)

These extracellular interstitial spaces are the minute chambers or compartments seen by the early histologists, who are responsible for the term *areolar tissue* (from *areola*, a small space or area), a synonym for loose connective tissue still in common use.

The Extracellular Components

The functions of connective tissue depend largely upon the properties of its extracellular substance. The fibers are responsible for its tensile strength and resilience, while the aqueous phase of the ground substance is the essential medium between cells and the blood,

through which all nutrients and wastes must pass. Its consistency and degree of hydration can exert an important influence upon this vital exchange.

COLLAGENOUS FIBERS.   Collagenous fibers are present in all types of connective tissue but vary greatly in their abundance. In unstained preparations of loose connective tissue the collagen fibers appear as colorless strands 1 to 12 μ in thickness and of indefinite length. They run in all directions, and if the connective tissue is not under tension, they tend to have a slightly wavy course (Fig. 6-2). At high magnification, faint longitudinal striations can be detected in the larger collagenous fibers, suggesting that they consist of bundles of smaller parallel fibrils 0.3 to 0.5 μ in thickness. With polarization microscopy, even the smallest visible collagen fibrils show form birefringence, indicating the presence of elongated submicroscopic units oriented in the direction of the fiber axis. When the examination is carried down to the electron microscope level, the smallest collagen fibrils detectable with the light microscope are found, in turn, to be composed of parallel submicroscopic fibrils, 200 to 1000 Å in diameter. These are the oriented subunits responsible for the form birefringence observed in polarized light. In electron micrographs, they are cross striated, with transverse bands repeating on an average of every 640 Å along their length (Fig. 6-3). When collagenous fibers are stained with phosphotungstic acid and viewed at high magnification, several additional bands can be resolved within each 640 Å period (Fig. 6-5A).

The collagenous fibers are flexible but offer great resistance to a pulling force. The breaking point of human collagenous fibers (as in tendon) is reached with a force of several hundred kg./cm.² and their elongation at this point is only a few percentage points. If collagen is denatured by boiling or by chemical treatment, it yields the familiar substance *gelatin*. With more gentle treatment, some collagen fibrils can be put into solution in vitro without denaturation. When this is done the fundamental units or molecules in solution are called *tropocollagen* and consist of long, slender particles about 2800 Å in length and 14 Å thick. The tropocollagen molecules are made up of three polypeptide chains, two of which are identical while one differs slightly from the others in amino acid composition. Each has a helical configuration, and all three are coiled around one another in a right handed direction (Fig. 6-4). Of the amino acids comprising the polypeptide chains of collagen, two, hydroxyproline and hydroxylysine, do not occur

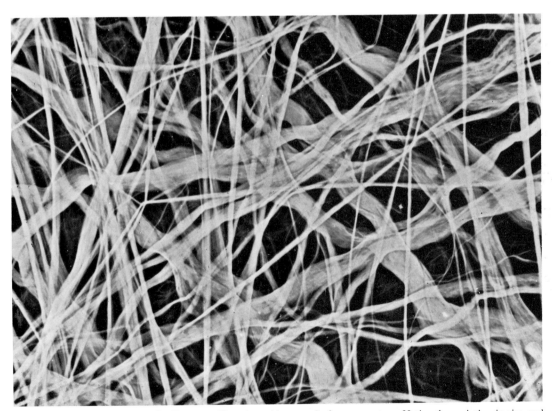

Figure 6-2. Photomicrograph of collagenous fibers in a thin spread of rat mesentery. Notice the variation in size and the wavy course of the larger fibers. The preparation was stained with Paps' silver method and the photograph printed as a negative to simulate more closely their appearance in fresh material. × 550. (After D. W. Fawcett, *in* R. O. Greep, ed.: Histology. Philadelphia, The Blakiston Co., 1953. Reproduced with the permission of the McGraw-Hill Book Co.)

in significant amounts in other animal proteins. The hydroxyproline content of a tissue can therefore be taken as a measure of its collagen content. This circumstance has proved useful in quantitative chemical studies and in the autoradiographic localization of sites of collagen synthesis.

Tropocollagen molecules are present in the ground substance of growing connective tissue and can be extracted in cold neutral salt solution. Warming such solutions to body temperature results in spontaneous polymerization of tropocollagen into typical cross striated fibrils. In this process the long tropocollagen molecules are believed to come together in a parallel arrangement and overlap each other by about a quarter of their length to produce a staggered array that results in cross striations at 640 Å intervals (Fig. 6-4). The finer lines within each of these periods are presumed to result from alignment of asymmetries along the length of the tropocollagen units.

Banded patterns that do not occur in

Figure 6-3. Shadowed electron micrograph of collagen fibrils from human skin, showing the characteristic cross banding at intervals of 640 Å along their length. (Courtesy of J. Gross and F. O. Schmitt.)

nature can be produced by altering the conditions under which the collagen is reconstituted. If a solution of collagen and α-acid glycoprotein of serum is dialyzed against water, the collagen fibers that are formed have a period of 2400 Å instead of the 640 Å characteristic of the native fibers. This form is called *fibrous long spacing (FLS) collagen* (Fig. 6-6B). Precipitation from acid solution by addition of adenosine triphosphate (ATP) yields segments about 2400 Å long, instead of fibers (Fig. 6-6C). This form is called *segment long spacing (SLS) collagen*. Both of these as well as the native form can be redissolved and precipitated in either of the other forms, depending upon the physicochemical conditions. In the long spacing forms, the tropocollagen molecules are believed to come together side to side in register, so that the length of the period or of the segment is approximately the same as the length of the tropocollagen molecules.

The explanation of the 640 Å period of native collagen on the basis of a staggered arrangement of the tropocollagen molecules was deduced from electron microscopic studies of the various highly ordered fibrils and crystallites precipitated from collagen solutions (Hodge and Schmitt). Although this interpretation has been accorded widespread acceptance, it may not be the only one that will account for the observations.

Application of the negative staining technique to high resolution studies of native collagen fibers has made it possible to visualize directly the tropocollagen macromolecules within the fiber (Fig. 6–5C), but this method does not permit identification of the position of the ends of the molecules. Observations with negative staining have failed to provide evidence supporting the quarter-staggered arrangement. Accordingly, another model has been proposed in which the tropocollagen molecule is presumed to have nine zones along its length, five bonding zones 265 Å long alternating with four nonbonding zones 375 Å long. Thus random aggregation and lateral association of the bonding zones could account for the patterns of crossbanding observed and the images obtained by negative staining (Grant, et al.) Further study is needed before this model can be accepted.

Collagen has been identified as a substance capable of inducing the formation of nuclei of hydroxyapatite crystal growth from

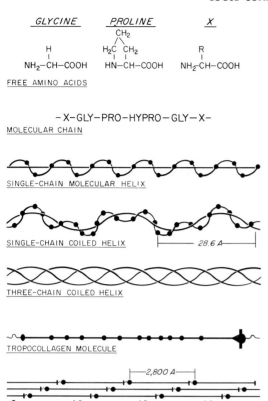

GLYCINE

$NH_2-CH-COOH$
H

PROLINE

CH_2
H_2C CH_2
$HN-CH-COOH$

X

$NH_2-CH-COOH$
R

FREE AMINO ACIDS

$-X-GLY-PRO-HYPRO-GLY-X-$
MOLECULAR CHAIN

SINGLE-CHAIN MOLECULAR HELIX

SINGLE-CHAIN COILED HELIX   28.6 Å

THREE-CHAIN COILED HELIX

TROPOCOLLAGEN MOLECULE

2,800 Å

COLLAGEN FIBRIL   640 Å

Figure 6-4. Diagram depicting the formation of collagen, which can be visualized as taking place in seven steps. The starting materials (*a*) are amino acids, of which only two are shown and the side chain of any of the others is indicated by R in amino acid X. (*b*) The amino acids are linked together to form a molecular chain. (*c*) This then coils into a left handed helix (*d* and *e*). Three such chains then intertwine in a triple stranded helix, which constitutes the tropocollagen molecule (*f*). Many tropocollagen molecules become aligned in staggered fashion, overlapping by a quarter of their length to form a cross striated collagen fibril (*g*). (Redrawn and slightly modified from J. Gross, Scientific American, May 1961.)

metastable solutions of calcium and phosphate (Glimcher). These conditions do not prevail in ordinary connective tissue, but this property of collagen appears to be important in the calcification of bone matrix (see Chapter 10).

For the study of histological sections there are no specific staining reactions for collagen, but its recognition usually presents no problem. It takes the eosin in hematoxylin and eosin

preparations and binds various acid aniline dyes, such as the acid fuchsin of van Gieson's stain and the aniline blue of Mallory's stains. In silver staining methods, such as those of Paps or Bielschowsky, the collagen is tinted tan to brown, in contrast to the blackening of the reticular fibers. Collagen may present physical and possibly chemical differences in different parts of the body and may not always take the form of fibers.

ELASTIC FIBERS. The extracellular fibers composed of *elastin* are difficult to identify in histological sections prepared by routine methods, but they can be selectively stained by orcein, by Weigert's resorcin-fuchsin, or by Verhoeff's stain. In unstained spreads of loose connective tissue, they are not plentiful, but they form a network of refractile fibers 0.2 to 1.0 μ in diameter (Fig. 6-7). Elastic fibers stretch easily, and when released after stretching they return almost completely to their original length. Their breaking point occurs when they are stretchd to about 150 per cent of their original length. For this degree of stretch, a force of only 20 to 30 kg./cm.² is necessary. When a fiber is broken the ends retract and spiral or coil. Elastic fibers are not made up of visible fibrillar subunits but usually appear homogeneous. Under polarized light they show, at most, only weak positive birefringence, but on stretching they become strongly birefringent. This change is presumably caused by an orientation of the submicroscopic components in the direction of the fiber axis.

When present in sufficient numbers, elastic fibers impart a yellowish color to the tissue. Certain elastic ligaments, such as the ligamenta flava of man and the ligamentum nuchae of ruminants, are distinctly yellow and are composed of coarse parallel elastic fibers up to 4 or 5 μ in diameter. Elastin is not always in the form of fibers. In the walls of arteries it occurs in a fenestrated sheet, the *elastica interna*.

Elastin is a protein that bears some resemblance to collagen in its content of glycine and proline but differs in its high content of valine and in containing a new amino acid, *desmocine*. Elastin is highly resistant to boiling and to dilute acids and alkalis. It is isolated by taking advantage of its resistance to alkali under conditions that destroy other tissue constituents. It is resistant to digestion by trypsin, but treatment of tissue with the enzyme *elastase*, prepared from pancreas, will digest the elastic

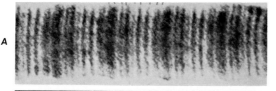

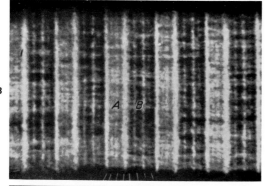

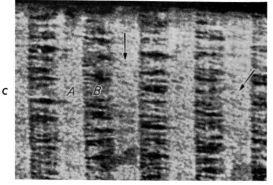

Figure 6-5. Electron micrographs of collagen. *A*, Collagen fibril from rat tail tendon stained with phosphotungstic acid. × 257,000. *B*, Collagen from same source negatively stained with phosphotungstate. × 257,000. *C*, Collagen precipitated from citrate extract of rat skin, negatively stained. Notice that the tropocollagen molecules can be resolved. × 257,000. (After B. R. Olsen, Zeitschr. f. Zellforsch, *59:*184, 1963.)

fibers from sections and leave cells and collagenous fibers intact.

Like collagen, purified elastin has been reported to be capable of inducing the formation of nuclei of hydroxyapatite crystal growth from metastable solutions of calcium and phosphate. It is possible that this process may be involved in pathological calcifications of the aorta, skin, and other sites (Sobel et al.).

Reticular Fibers. These minute fibers tend to form delicate networks rather than coarse bundles, and they stain more intensely with silver methods than do typical collagenous fibers. The reticular fibers are not appar-

ent in ordinary histological preparations but can be demonstrated by reason of their property of absorbing metallic silver when treated with alkaline solutions of reducible silver salts (Fig. 6-8). Fibers of this character are the first to appear in the differentiation of mesenchyme into loose connective tissue, but they gradually give way to increasing numbers of collagenous fibers in the loose connective tissue of adults. Reticular fibers persist, however, in delicate networks surrounding adipose cells, supporting the endothelium of capillaries, the sarcolemma of muscle, and the endoneurium of nerves. They are also found in close association with the basal lamina (basement membrane) of epithelia (Fig. 6-11). They constitute the fibrous supporting tissue of lymphoid and blood forming organs and the stroma of the liver and other epithelial organs.

Because of their arrangement and distinctive staining properties the *reticular fibers* were formerly considered to be a separate kind of protein fiber, but in electron micrographs they are found to be made up of unit fibrils with the periodic structure typical of collagen. It appears therefore that the difference in argyrophilia of reticular and collagenous fibers is not due to a chemical difference but has a physical basis, depending upon the number and arrangement of unit fibrils of collagen and their relation to the protein-polysaccharide matrix that binds them together. Although it now appears that collagen and reticulin are essentially identical, the terms *reticulum* and *reticular fibers* continue to be useful to designate fibrous elements whose size and arrangement are different from those of mature collagenous fibers.

Ground Substance. The formed elements of connective tissue are embedded in a matrix of *amorphous ground substance* having the properties of a very viscous solution or thin gel. It is difficult to characterize this material morphologically because, in the fresh state, it is optically homogeneous and transparent. It is extracted by most of the aqueous fixatives in common use and therefore can seldom be demonstrated in histological sections. The ground substance is preserved to some extent by the method of freeze-drying if the fresh frozen sections are subsequently fixed in ether-formol vapor. In such preparations it gives a periodic acid–Schiff reaction for carbohydrates and stains metachromatically with toluidine blue. These reactions are attributable to the *protein-*

polysaccharides (formerly called mucopolysaccharides) of the ground substance. These are of several kinds that vary in their proportions from one kind of connective tissue to another. The commonest are *hyaluronate, chondroitin-4-sulfate (chondroitin sulfate A)*, and *chondroitin-6-sulfate (chondroitin sulfate C)*. Each of these polysaccharides is composed of two different saccharide units, which alternate regularly along a long unbranched chain. The saccharides of the *chondroitin sulfates* are galactosamine and glucuronate, and there is one sulfate group in each repeating period of the molecule. Multiple chains of chondroitin sulfate appear to be bound to protein, which accounts for 15 per cent or more of the protein-polysaccharide molecule. The strongly acid sulfate groups are responsible for the basophilia of this component of the extracellular substance. The other polysaccharides, though not sulfated, also carry a very large number of negatively charged groups along their length and are therefore described as polyanions. In the tissues they are always associated with an equivalent number of cations, mostly sodium. The ability of the polyanionic polysaccharides to bind polyvalent cations is the basis for the staining reaction with Hale's iron method or with Alcian blue, which are used for the demonstration of these compounds in tissue sections. These same polyelectrolyte properties are probably also of fundamental importance to the functions of the polysaccharides in the connective tissues.

In hyaluronate, the alternating saccharide units are glucosamine and glucuronate. Its molecular weight is 200,000 to 500,000, and if straightened out, the chain would be up to 2.5 μ in length. The hyaluronate is bound to a protein, but this makes up only about 2

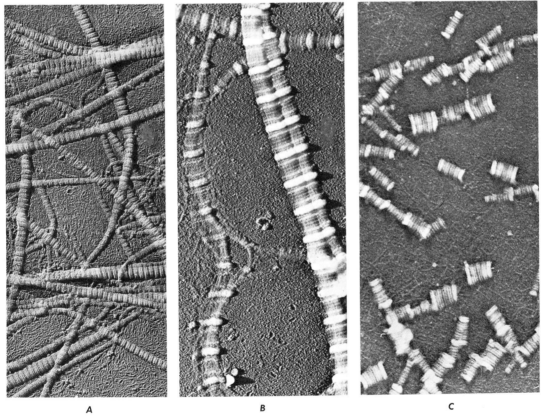

A   B   C

Figure 6-6. Electron micrographs of collagen. *A*, Fibrils with typical collagen period (640 Å). Precipitated from collagen solution by dialysis against 1 per cent NaCl. Chromium shadowed. *B*, Fibrous long spacing (FLS). Produced by dialysis against water of a mixture of α_1 acid glycoprotein of serum and collagen solution. Stained with phosphotungstic acid hematoxylin. *C*, Segment long spacing (SLS). Precipitation from acid solution of collagen by addition of ATP. Chromium shadowed. (Courtesy of J. Gross, F. O. Schmitt, and J. H. Highberger.)

per cent of the whole molecule. One of the most important properties of this substance is its very high viscosity in aqueous solutions. This is largely responsible for the consistency of the ground substance. If fluid is injected into the connective tissue it does not immediately diffuse away from the site but remains localized for a while in a discrete bleb, as though walled off by the viscous interstitial substance. This property is thought to act as a barrier to the spread of bacteria that may gain access to the tissues. In this connection, it is interesting that some of the most invasive bacteria produce the enzyme *hyaluronidase*, which enables them to depolymerize the hyaluronate of the ground substance. The viscosity of hyaluronate in the synovial fluid of joints makes it well suited for its lubricating function, and it is not inconceivable that in dense connective tissues also, it acts as a plasticizer to diminish friction and wear between collagen fibrils as they move over one another in the flexuous movements of the tissues. The volume of solution occupied by these large diffuse molecules, called their domain, is large (about 4000 Å in diameter), and when molecules are present in a high enough concentration, they become entangled with each other and with the collagen fibrils that penetrate their domain. The resistance of collagen fibrils to compression in hyaluronate solution or in the ground substance appears to be in part a reflection of the resistance of the hyaluronate molecule to compression of its domain (Schubert). Though difficult to demonstrate microscopically, the hyaluronate of connective tissue is of great importance in determining the structural and physiological properties of the ground substance.

The ground substance also contains variable amounts of *tropocollagen*, which cannot be demonstrated histologically but can be extracted in neutral salt solution and precipitated as cross striated collagen fibers in vitro.

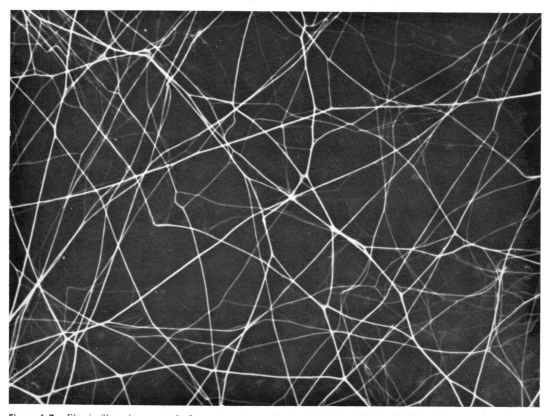

Figure 6-7. Elastic fibers in a spread of rat mesentery stained with resorcin-fuchsin; the photomicrograph is printed as a negative. Notice that the fibers are smaller and less variable in size than collagen fibers and they branch and anastomose to form a network. × 550. Philadelphia, The Blakiston Co., 1953. (After D. W. Fawcett, *in* Greep, R. O., ed.: Histology. Reproduced with the permission of the McGraw-Hill Book Co.)

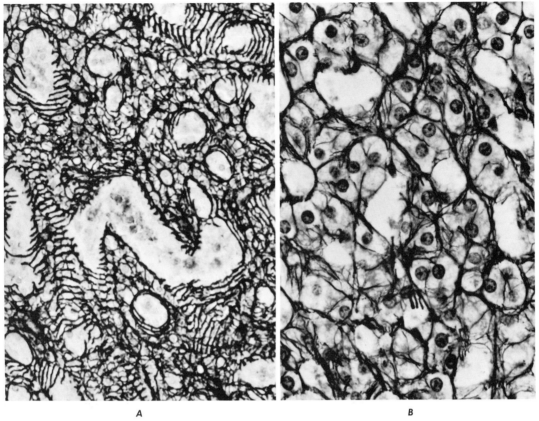

A   B

Figure 6-8. Reticular fibers are distinguished from collagenous fibers by their smaller size, their branching pattern, and the fact that they blacken with silver stains. The pattern of reticular fibers is different and characteristic of each organ. *A*, Reticulum of the spleen. × 400. (Preparation by K. Richardson.) *B*, Reticular fibers of the adrenal cortex. × 550.

ORIGIN OF CONNECTIVE TISSUE FIBERS. The sequence of morphological events in formation of collagen is similar whether studied in the embryo, in young scar tissue, or in tissue cultures. Delicate networks of branching and anastomosing argyrophilic fibrils appear among the fibroblasts (Fig. 6-9). The fibrils may follow the outlines of the cells and their processes, but they also extend far into the intercellular substance. When studied in electron micrographs the finest of the developing fibrils are apparently extracellular and have the cross striations of collagen. As the fibrils increase in number they rearrange into parallel wavy bundles of appreciable thickness. These lose their ability to be blackened with silver (Fig. 6-10) and instead accept stains for collagen (Mallory or van Gieson).

The constant association of fibroblasts with developing collagenous fibers both in vivo and in vitro early suggested that these cells are involved in fibrogenesis, but their exact role

has been a subject of debate. The area of controversy has been considerably narrowed in recent years. It is now widely accepted that reticular and collagenous fibers arise extracellularly by condensation or crystallization of tropocollagen secreted into the ground substance by fibroblasts. Consistent with this view is the electron microscopic observation that fibroblasts of growing connective tissue have the extensive endoplasmic reticulum and well developed Golgi complex that we have come to expect of cells actively engaged in protein synthesis. Moreover, if a ^{14}C labeled amino acid, proline, is given to animals in which inflammatory new formation of connective tissue has been induced, labeled collagen can be detected in the microsome fraction isolated from connective tissue cells. Incorporation of labeled amino acid in fibroblasts can also be followed radioautographically in animals with healing wounds. At early time intervals after administration of tritiated proline, the silver grains

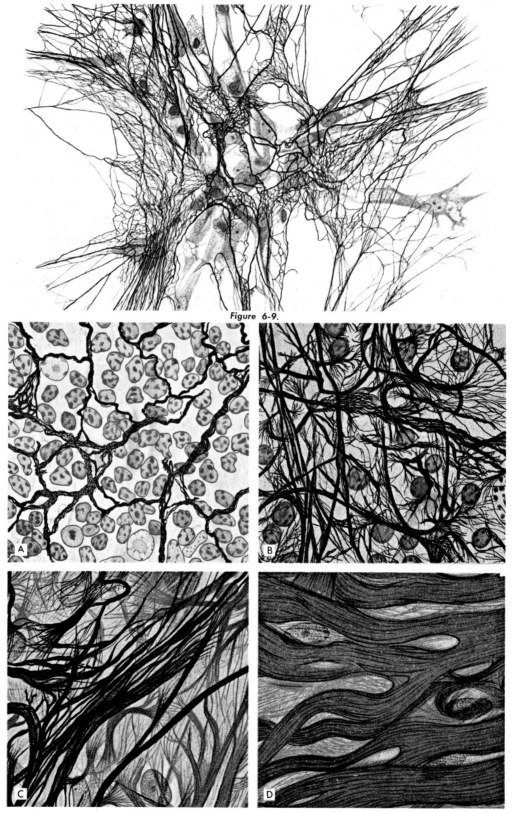

Figure 6-9.

Figure 6-10. *See opposite page for legend.*

betraying the location of the labeled precursor are over the endoplasmic reticulum; later they are over the Golgi region and still later outside of the cell over newly formed collagen fibers.

The evidence thus points to a synthetic pathway for collagen, similar to that described for secretion of other proteins (Fig. 6-14). Amino acids enter the fibroblast, and there proline and lysine are hydroxylated to hydroxyproline and hydroxylysine. On the ribosomes of the endoplasmic reticulum these and other activated amino acids are assembled into peptides that consist of about 250 amino acid residues and have a molecular weight of about 30,000. Four such peptides are linked together by a carbohydrate of unknown composition to form an alpha chain having a molecular weight of about 120,000. Three alpha chains associate in a coil to form tropocollagen with a molecular weight of 360,000. The exact intracellular site where these events take place is not known for certain, but it seems likely that the peptides formed on the ribosomes accumulate in the lumen of the reticulum and are transported to the Golgi complex, where the further steps in their conversion to tropocollagen probably take place. Tropocollagen segregated in Golgi vacuoles is released from the fibroblast when these vacuoles move to the cell surface and discharge their contents into the surrounding ground substance.

A remaining point of uncertainty concerns the possible role of the cells in determining the arrangement of the fibers. Some assume that the cells simply maintain the appropriate physicochemical conditions in the surrounding ground substance to permit collagen fibers to form extracellularly by a process of spontaneous polymerization similar to that occurring in vitro. Such a process could presumably take place at some distance from the fibroblast. The orientation of the fibrils would be in response to mechanical stresses in the tissue and would not be influenced by the cells. Other investigators believe that new fibrils arise only

in very close relation to the cell surface, and that the cells exercise a direct control over their formation and their orientation in the connective tissue. According to this view, local discontinuities appear in the fibroblast membrane and there is a shedding of noncollagenous fibrous material from the cortical cytoplasm to form protofibrils that remain for a time closely associated with the cell surface. These protofibrils then become the sites of deposition of the tropocollagen from the surrounding ground substance and develop into typical collagen fibrils by progressive accretion of tropocollagen molecules to their surface (Porter). It is contended that the orthogonal patterns and other precisely ordered arrangements of collagen fibers in the body are difficult to explain if collagen deposition is a completely independent extracellular phenomenon, whereas, if collagen is deposited on protofibrils that are oriented by fibroblasts, a mechanism is provided for ordering of collagen fibrils by the cells rather than by purely mechanical forces. Further study is needed to resolve this problem.

Elastic fibers appear in the embryo much later than collagen fibers, and very little is known about their formation. It is presumed that a precursor is secreted by fibroblasts, chondroblasts, and possibly other mesenchymal derivatives; there is as yet no chemical or morphological evidence of incorporation of labeled precursors of elastin by any of these cells.

The Cellular Elements

It is convenient to think of the cells of loose connective tissue in two categories, a relatively stable population of *fixed cells* (fibroblasts) that are responsible for production and long term maintenance of the extracellular components, or for storage of reserve fuel (adipose cells), and a population of mobile *wandering cells* that are mainly concerned with the shorter term events involved in tissue reaction

---

Figure 6-9. Development of reticular fibers in a 20 day culture of adult rabbit thymus. The reticular fibers stain black. Bielschowsky-Foot and Mallory-azan stains. About × 500. (After A. A. Maximow.)

Figure 6-10. Four stages in the development of collagenous fibers in tissue cultures of rabbit lymph node. *A,* Section of lymph node showing cells and blackened reticular fibers. *B,* After four days in vitro the black reticular fibers are branching and more numerous. *C,* After five days in culture the black reticular fibers contrast with the newly developed collagenous fibers stained blue. *D,* After six days in culture only thick bundles of collagenous fibers are present. It is now realized that both types of fiber are composed of collagen, but their staining properties depend upon their size and mode of aggregation. Bielschowsky-Foot and Mallory-azan stains. About × 500. (After R. McKinney.)

to injury (lymphoid cells, free macrophages, eosinophils, plasma cells, mast cells).

FIBROBLASTS. These are the common fixed cells of the connective tissue that elaborate the precursors of the extracellular fibrous and amorphous components.* Their shape depends to some extent upon their physical substrate. They are usually deployed along bundles of collagen fibers and appear in sections as fusiform (spindle-shaped) elements with long tapering processes. In other situations they may be flattened, stellate cells with several slender processes. Their cytoplasm is often eosinophilic like the neighboring collagen. The outlines of the cell bodies are therefore difficult to make out. They are more easily visualized after staining with iron-hematoxylin. These cells have been extensively studied in tissue culture, where they can be observed free of the interlacing fabric of fibers in which they reside in vivo. In this environment the cells migrate out from the explant into the surrounding medium, with their processes adhering to form a cellular network (Fig. 6-12). It is not unlikely that the fibroblasts in the body also maintain tenuous contacts with one another, but for technical reasons this is difficult to demonstrate.

The elliptical nucleus is usually smoothly contoured but may sometimes be slightly folded. There are one or two nucleoli, and the chromatin is sparse and distributed in very small karyosomes. A diplosome and a small Golgi apparatus are situated near the nucleus. The mitochondria are long slender filaments found mainly in the cell body, but they may

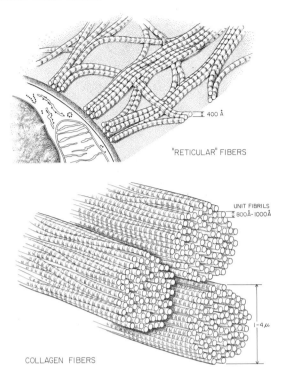

"RETICULAR" FIBERS

UNIT FIBRILS
800Å - 1000Å

1 - 4 μ

COLLAGEN FIBERS

Figure 6-11. Diagram showing that the "reticular fibers" associated with the basal lamina of an epithelial cell (*above*) and the "collagen fibers" of the connective tissue in general (*below*) are both composed of unit fibrils of collagen. Those of reticulum are somewhat smaller and interwoven in loose networks instead of in large bundles.

---

* The student should be aware of troublesome inconsistency in terminology with respect to this cell type. The suffix -*blast* (Greek *blastos*, germ) is often used in naming the formative stages of various cell types. Thus an *erythroblast* is an early developmental stage of the fully differentiated cell called an *erythrocyte*. Some authors, therefore, use the term *fibroblast* to designate a relatively immature cell actively proliferating and producing components of the extracellular substance, and they apply *fibrocyte* to the relatively quiescent cells of adult connective tissue. This interpretation loses sight of the fact that the term "fibroblast" was originally intended to describe a "fiber forming cell" and not to name an immature form of a cell called a fibrocyte. Moreover, because most histologists recognize *mesenchymal cells*, persisting in postnatal life, as the undifferentiated progenitors of the connective tissue cells, to use "fibroblast" in this sense is to make an unnecessary distinction and to introduce a redundant term. The term *fibroblast*, therefore, is properly used to describe the differentiated cell of adult connective tissue, and it can be considered synonymous with *fibrocyte* (as used by other authors).

also occur in the processes. Under conditions of stimulation, as in wound healing, when fibroblasts are dividing and actively synthesizing extracellular components, they enlarge and their cytoplasm becomes moderately basophilic. In electron micrographs the quiescent fibroblasts contain a small Golgi complex and a few cisternal profiles of granular endoplasmic reticulum, but in growing or repairing connective tissue, the Golgi complex becomes very prominent and the endoplasmic reticulum is much more extensive. The cytoplasm usually contains few inclusions except for occasional small fat droplets. Granules staining with the periodic acid–Schiff reaction become numerous under some conditions and may represent intracellular precursors of the polysaccharides of the ground substance. In electron micrographs, these granules are represented by small vacuoles in the Golgi region and elsewhere, containing a flocculent material that is interpreted as a secretory product.

Fibroblasts normally show no tendency to take up foreign matter, but under intense and prolonged stimulation by injection of a colloidal vital dye, such as trypan blue, they may come to contain a few minute deposits of the dye. Majority opinion holds that fibroblasts are differentiated cells that ordinarily do not give rise to other types of cells in the connective tissue. There is evidence, however, that in pathological states and under certain experimental conditions, they can develop into bone cells. It is also widely accepted that fibroblasts may accumulate lipid and become typical adipose cells, but in both of these instances, it is difficult to establish with certainty whether it is actually the fibroblasts or their undifferentiated mesenchymal progenitors that undergo these transformations.

UNDIFFERENTIATED CELLS (MESENCHYMAL Cells). Many investigators believe that some cells persist in the adult organism that retain the potencies of mesenchymal cells. They are often smaller than the fibroblasts but have the same general appearance. In the loose connective tissue they are usually arranged along the blood vessels, particularly along the capillaries

(Marchand, 1924) (Fig. 6-15). The conviction that they are not common fibroblasts but are undifferentiated cells is gathered from numerous observations that show that under the influence of certain stimuli, as in tissue cultures, inflammation, and the effects of injection of toxins, they may develop into new cell types. They probably have much the same properties as the primitive reticular cells of the blood forming tissues and of the free lymphoid stem cells (see page 204).

ADIPOSE CELLS. Among the fixed cells in the loose connective tissue are some that are specialized for the synthesis and storage of lipid. These *adipose cells* or *fat cells* accumulate lipid to such an extent that the nucleus is flattened and displaced to one side, and the cytoplasm becomes so thinned out that it is resolved only as a thin line around the rim of the single large lipid droplet. So inconspicuous are the nucleus and cytoplasm that the fat cells in fresh connective tissue have the appearance of large glistening drops of oil. They may occur singly in the connective tissue but are more often in groups. There is a marked tendency for them to be deployed along the course of

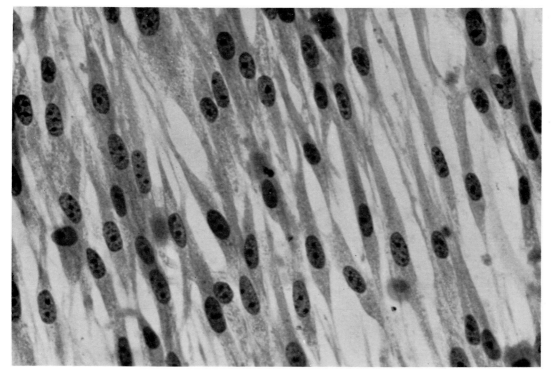

Figure 6-12. Photomicrograph of mouse fibroblasts in tissue culture, illustrating their common spindle shape. Harris hematoxylin stain. × 600.

small blood vessels. Where they accumulate in such large numbers that they become the predominant component, crowding out other cell types, the resulting tissue is called *adipose tissue* or *fat* (see Chapter 7).

In the usual histological section the lipid droplets of the adipose cells are dissolved out during dehydration, and there remains only the thin layer of cytoplasm, slightly thickened in one area to accommodate the nucleus. Despite the extreme thinness of the rim of cytoplasm, a juxtanuclear Golgi apparatus can be demonstrated, and filamentous mitochondria are distributed around the entire circumference of the lipid droplet. The individual fat cells are surrounded by a delicate network of argyrophilic fibers.

Adipose cells appear to develop from spindle-shaped cells that resemble fibroblasts, but these are generally believed to be undifferentiated mesenchymal cells that persist into postnatal life in the adventitia of the small blood vessels of the connective tissue. During their early development they may contain multiple small lipid droplets, but these ultimately coalesce into a single drop (Fig. 6-16). The fully formed fat cell is apparently incapable of mitotic division. Any new areas of adipose cells that develop in adult life differentiate from fusiform precursors, probably mesenchymal cells.

MACROPHAGES (HISTIOCYTES). Stretched out along the bundles of collagen fibers are stellate or fusiform cells that in some regions of the body are almost as abundant as the fibroblasts and are often difficult to distinguish from them. These are the *fixed macrophages* or *histiocytes.* Their nuclei tend to be somewhat smaller and more darkly staining than those of fibroblasts. Near the nucleus is the cytocentrum, containing a diplosome and a closely associated Golgi apparatus. The mitochondria are short rods usually congregated around the centrosome. The cytoplasm is more heterogeneous than that of fibroblasts, often containing a variety of granules and small vacuoles that stain supravitally with neutral red.

The majority of the macrophages in nor-

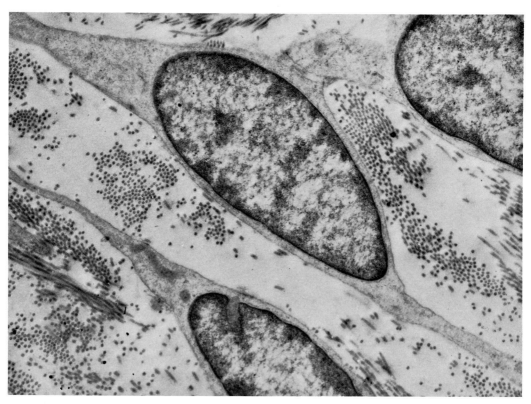

Figure 6-13. Electron micrograph of fibroblasts and bundles of collagen fibrils in the loose connective tissue of the lamina propria in the toad urinary bladder. Osmium fixation. × 12,000. (Courtesy of A. Keller.)

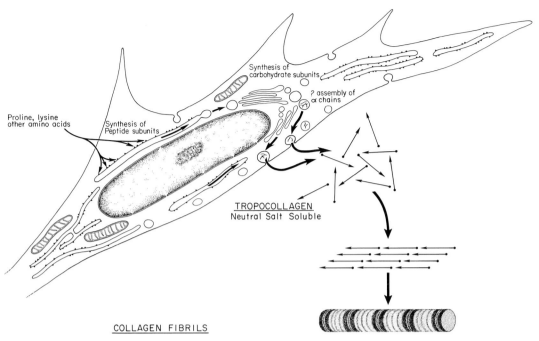

Proline, lysine other amino acids

Synthesis of Peptide subunits

Synthesis of carbohydrate subunits

? assembly of α chains

TROPOCOLLAGEN
Neutral Salt Soluble

COLLAGEN FIBRILS

Figure 6-14. Schematic representation of the intracellular and extracellular events in the elaboration of collagen. Amino acids entering the fibroblast are synthesized into polypeptide subunits at the ribosomes. These are transported to the Golgi complex, where carbohydrate subunits are believed to be synthesized. The α chains of collagen are presumed to be assembled in the Golgi complex into tropocollagen molecules. Tropocollagen molecules released at the cell surface aggregate extracellularly in staggered array to form collagen fibrils. (Redrawn after J. Gross.)

mal connective tissue are sessile, but when they are stimulated in inflammation they withdraw their processes, detach from the fibers and become actively motile as *free macrophages.* If such macrophages chance to be fixed in different stages of their ameboid migratory movements, they may be highly variable in outline, but as a rule they are more or less rounded cells distributed singly or in small clusters in the fibrous meshes of the connective tissue.

These cells have a remarkable capacity for *phagocytosis,* the process wherein blunt pseudopodia are extended around foreign particulate matter that is then taken into the cytoplasm in vacuoles. This behavior can be elicited experimentally by injecting into the living animal nontoxic colloidal dyes, such as lithium carmine or trypan blue. The macrophages take up ultramicroscopic particles of the dye by phagocytosis and concentrate them within cytoplasmic vacuoles. Under the same conditions, the fibroblasts and other cell types take up little or none of the dye. The use of such vital dyes is the most certain means of identifying macrophages. They are equally avid in

their ingestion of extravasated erythrocytes, debris of dead cells, bacteria, and inert foreign matter. Because of their motility and great phagocytic capacity, the macrophages constitute a mobile reserve of scavenger cells important in the maintenance of the connective tissues and in the local defenses of the body against bacterial invasion.

The macrophages of the loose connective tissue have also been called *clasmatocytes, rhagiocrine cells, histiocytes, resting wandering cells,* and many other names. The macrophages along the blood vessels, together with the perivascular undifferentiated cells, have also been called *adventitial cells.*

MONONUCLEAR WANDERING CELLS. The smallest of the wandering cells of the connective tissues are the lymphocytes. These are identical with the small mononuclear leukocytes of the blood and display similar variations in size. The smallest are 7 to 8 μ in diameter with a round or slightly indented darkly staining nucleus surrounded by a narrow rim of clear basophilic cytoplasm. In electron micrographs a nucleolus can be identified among

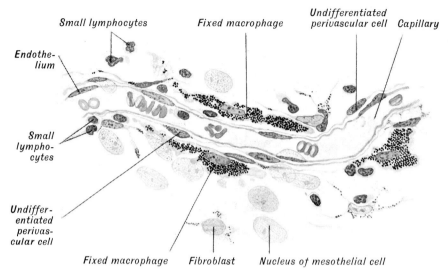

Figure 6-15. Stretch preparation of rabbit omentum vitally stained with lithium carmine, showing indifferentiated perivascular cells, macrophages, and other cellular elements of the connective tissue. Hematoxylin stain. × 500. (After A. A. Maximow.)

the clumps of chromatin. A juxtanuclear diplosome, a small Golgi complex, and a few mitochondria are found in the cytoplasm. The endoplasmic reticulum is sparse, but free ribosomes are present in great abundance. Lymphocytes, as seen in tissue sections, are spheroidal and smoothly contoured, showing little evidence of motility. When observed in cell cultures, however, they are actively ameboid and presumably are also migratory in the tissues. They are not phagocytic, but there is considerable evidence that when properly stimulated in vivo they can differentiate into macrophages.

Some of the lymphocytes found in the connective tissues may have originated in embryonic mesenchyme and remained there, but the majority of them probably are emigrants from the blood and, after a sojourn in the tissues, may return to the blood or lymph. Those that populate the lamina propria of the alimentary tract migrate in great numbers through the intestinal epithelium into the lumen of the bowel and are lost to the body. The highly contradictory reports as to the life span of these cells have, in part, been resolved by radioautographic studies, which indicate that there are two distinct populations of lymphocytes—one with a life span measured in days and the other living for months and possibly for the lifetime of the individual. It is principally the long-lived lymphocytes that recirculate between the blood and lymph and may be transient inhabitants of the connective tissues.

The potentiality of the lymphocytes for differentiation into other cell types has long been a subject of controversy. Some have considered the lymphocyte a potential stem cell for all of the formed elements of the blood; others have regarded it as a specialized cell type with very limited developmental potentialities. This dispute is still not completely settled. It has now been clearly established, however, that in cultures of blood leukocytes, addition of phytohemagglutinin, tuberculin-purified protein derivative, or leukocytes from another individual, will stimulate lymphocytes to undergo a transformation to large pyroninophilic cells that divide freely and are morphologically indistinguishable from primitive blood forming cells called hemocytoblasts. Although appropriate conditions for further differentiation of these cells have not been attained in vitro, it is likely that in the connective tissue they can give rise to new lymphocytes, to plasma cells, to macrophages, and possibly to other cell types (p. 204).

The number of lymphocytes in normal loose connective tissue is quite small but is increased in the primary response of the tissue to foreign protein and in chronic inflammatory conditions. It is not yet clear to what extent lymphocytes participate directly in the synthesis of immune globulins, and to what extent they simply serve as a reservoir of cells capable of differentiating into plasma cells, which are known to be active in antibody synthesis.

Many of the wandering cells in connective tissue appear to be *monocytes*. The largest of these may be 12 μ or more in diameter and have an eccentric kidney-shaped nucleus and a highly ameboid cytoplasm containing various inclusions that stain supravitally with neutral red.

In local inflammatory reactions, additions may be made to the resident population of phagocytes in connective tissue by emigration of more monocytes from the blood and their transformation into macrophages (Figs. 6-17 and 6-18). In chronic inflammatory reactions the macrophages may become closely packed and take on the appearance of *epithelioid cells*. Around foreign objects in the tissues that are too large or too resistant to be engulfed and destroyed by intracellular digestion, the phagocytic cells may coalesce to form huge multinucleate masses called *foreign body giant cells*.

The same sequence of transformations of mononuclear wandering cells that occurs in inflamed connective tissue can be observed when leukocytes from blood are cultivated in vitro. Under the conditions prevailing in such cultures the lymphocytes and the monocytes are the only leukocytes capable of prolonged survival. The monocytes are rapidly transformed into macrophages (Fig. 6-17). The lymphocytes are capable of undergoing a similar transformation in inflamed connective tissue but do so less readily in cell cultures. The effete and dying cellular elements of other kinds are phagocytosed and eliminated. Thus after a few days, pure cultures of macrophages are obtained. These may later assume an epithelioid

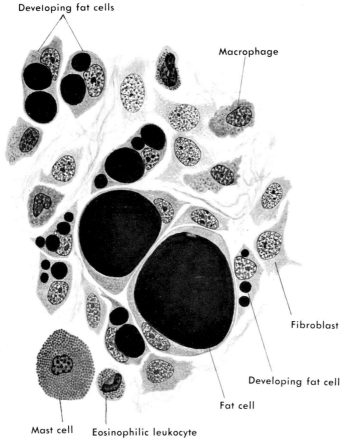

Developing fat cells

Macrophage

Fibroblast

Developing fat cell

Fat cell

Mast cell   Eosinophilic leukocyte

Figure 6-16.   Several fat cells from the subcutaneous, loose connective tissue of a rat. The fat has been stained black by the osmic acid of the fixation fluid. About $\times$ 1000. (After A. A. Maximow.)

appearance and after prolonged cultivation, giant cells are formed. The ability to follow in vitro the same sequence of cellular transformations that occurs in inflamed tissues in vivo has made it possible to study in considerable detail the fine structural and cytochemical changes associated with the transition from monocytes to macrophages and to epithelioid and giant cells. Accompanying the acquisition of phagocytic properties, there is a progressive increase in cell volume and a striking enlargement of the Golgi apparatus, which becomes the site of active formation of many small lysosomes. During the intracellular digestion of ingested material, the lysosomes discharge their content of hydrolytic enzymes into the phagocytosis vacuoles, and hence the number of lysosomes diminishes during active phagocytosis. They accumulate again in great numbers in the epithelioid and giant cells that develop after the cellular debris and other material available for phagocytosis has been largely eliminated.

The possible portals of entry of infectious microorganisms are many and the body's defenses need to be widely deployed. The fixed and free macrophages of the connective tissue share the property of phagocytosis and storage of vital dyes with a variety of other cell types broadly distributed in the body. These include the *monocytes* of the blood, the *alveolar phagocytes* of the lung, the *reticular cells* in the sinuses of the lymph nodes and spleen, the *endothelium of the blood sinusoids* in the liver and bone marrow, and the *microglia* of the central nervous system. Although these cells are normally quite dissimilar in appearance, all react similarly to bacterial invasion and other noxious stimuli. These cells, having common properties and

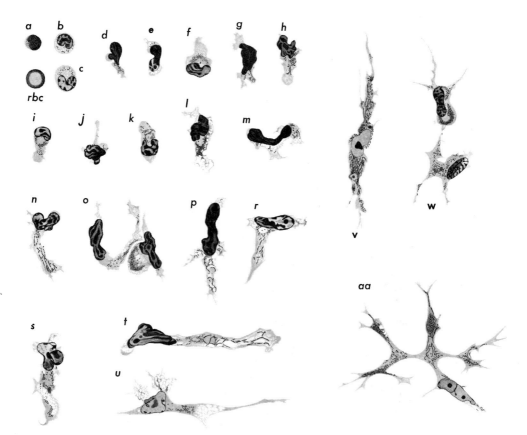

Figure 6-17. Cells from sections of cultures of the leukocytes of the blood of a guinea pig, showing the development of lymphocytes and monocytes into macrophages (polyblasts). *a* and *b*, lymphocytes, and *c*, monocyte from centrifuged blood; *d* and *e*, ameboid lymphocytes, and *f*, ameboid monocyte, from a three-hour culture; *g* to *k*, cells from a 10 hour culture; *l* to *r*, from a 25 hour culture; *s* to *u*, from a two day culture; *v* and *w*, from a five day culture, *w* in mitosis; *aa*, macrophage from 12 day culture. Note mitochondria in all cells. Iron-hematoxylin stain. × 750. (After A. A. Maximow.)

sharing the same defensive function, are thought of as constituting a single physiological system. This widely dispersed but functionally integrated system of cells is described by the collective terms *macrophage system* or *reticuloendothelial system* (Aschoff). It has great importance for understanding the pathology and natural history of infectious disease.

PLASMA CELLS. Another cell type that has a very important function in resistance to disease is the *plasma cell*, which is now known to be the principal producer of *antibodies*, the immune globulins of the blood that participate in the body's humoral defenses against bacterial infection. Plasma cells are relatively uncommon in typical loose connective tissue, but they are plentiful in the highly cellular connective tissue comprising the lamina propria of the gastrointestinal tract. They also occur in lymphoid tissues throughout the body. They may be as small as lymphocytes or two or three times that size. They are ovoid cells with a slightly eccentric, round, or oval nucleus and an intensely basophilic cytoplasm. The nuclear chromatin is distributed in unusually coarse clumps or blocks that tend to be spaced around the periphery of the nucleus so as to produce a characteristic radial pattern that is helpful in identification of the cell. Adjacent to the nucleus is a conspicuous lightly staining area, the centrosome. The remainder of the cell body has a strong affinity for basic dyes (Fig. 6-19). The basophilia and pyroninophilia of the cytoplasm are abolished by digestion with ribonuclease and hence are attributed to its high content of ribonucleoprotein. Plasma cells seldom divide. They exhibit a sluggish motility and have no demonstrable phagocytic activity. They arise from large lymphoid elements resembling the stem cells of hemopoietic tissues. In the course of this differentiation there is a progressive relative increase in cytoplasm, while the nucleus becomes smaller and more chromophilic.

The coarse chromatin pattern seen in plasma cells with the light microscope is also evident in electron micrographs (Fig. 6-20). The juxtanuclear pale zone is the site of a pair of centrioles and a well developed Golgi complex. A few membrane bounded spherical bodies associated with the inner face of the Golgi complex resemble secretory granules. The peripheral cytoplasm is occupied by an extensive system of cisternae of the endoplas-

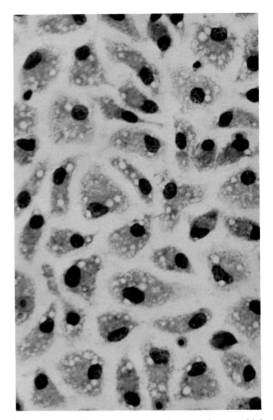

Figure 6-18. Photomicrograph of macrophages which developed from monocytes of chicken blood after a few days in tissue culture. May-Grünwald-Giemsa. × 500.

mic reticulum. Ribosomes are very numerous, both on the membranes of the reticulum and in the cytoplasmic matrix. The abundant ribosomes and highly developed reticulum are believed to be involved in the synthesis of the immune globulins or antibodies. In some plasma cells the cisternae are flat and generally parallel in their arrangement. In others they are greatly distended with flocculent material of relatively low density. These different cytological appearances may reflect different degrees of activity or varying degrees of storage of the product. Occasional plasma cells accumulate granular masses in the cisternae of the reticulum, corresponding to the Russell bodies of light microscopy. These stain with the periodic acid–Schiff reaction and appear to be rich in glycoprotein. In rare plasma cells the material deposited in the cisternae may condense to form large crystals of varying shape. The chemical relationship, if any, between the Russell bodies and the crystalline inclusions is

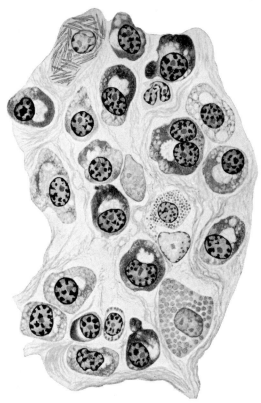

Figure 6-19. Plasma cells from connective tissue near human tonsil. There are transitions from small lymphocytes to plasma cells. Several of the latter contain globular or crystalloid inclusions. Hematoxylin-eosin-azure II. (After A. A. Maximow.)

obscure. Upon degeneration of these plasma cells, these inclusions may be set free and remain for some time between the other elements of the connective tissue.

The chain of evidence for the participation of plasma cells in antibody formation extends back over the past 30 years and includes observations and experiments from various disciplines. Human patients with an excess of circulating antibody *hyperglobulinemia* also have a high concentration of plasma cells in their tissues. Persons with congenital *agammaglobulinemia* have a complete failure of antibody synthesis and develop no plasma cells at sites of antigenic stimulation. Intensive immunization of normal animals, on the other hand, is attended by a marked increase in the numbers of these cells in the connective tissues of nearly every organ. Although these correlations strongly supported the inference that plasma cells were the source of antibody, compelling

experimental evidence has been obtained only recently. The production of antibody in vitro by individual plasma cells isolated by micromanipulation has now been demonstrated. An ingenious immunohistochemical method adapted for use at the electron microscope level has also made it possible to localize antibody within the cisternae of the endoplasmic reticulum in plasma cells from animals immunized to ferritin (de Petris et al.) (Figs. 6-21 and 6-22).

EOSINOPHILIC CELLS.   The eosinophils of the connective tissue appear to be identical with the eosinophilic leukocytes of the blood and evidently emigrate through the walls of the capillaries and venules to settle in the tissues. They are numerous in the loose connective tissue of the rat, mouse, and guinea pig. They are less plentiful in man but are occasionally found in the stroma of certain glands, particularly the mammary gland, in the interstitial connective tissue of the lung, and in the omentum. They are abundant in the lamina propria of the small intestine.

In man they usually have a bilobed nucleus, while in the mouse and rat the nucleus is annular (doughnut-shaped). The most distinctive cytological characteristic of the eosinophil is the presence of coarse cytoplasmic granules that stain intensely with eosin and other acid dyes. In electron micrographs the granules are membrane bounded and contain one or more flat crystals embedded in a finely granular matrix. The form of the crystal varies from species to species. In the cat it is cylindrical; in the mouse and rat it is a single flat equatorial disk; in man the crystals tend to be multiple and variable in their shape and orientation.

The eosinophilic granules have been isolated in bulk from horse and rat blood and their chemical properties have been studied. Their eosinophilia appears to reside in their protein matrix, which contains several enzymes including peroxidase, ribonuclease, aryl-sulfatase, cathepsin, beta glucuronidase, and acid and alkaline phosphatase. Of these enzymes the first four have the highest activity. The range of the hydrolytic enzymes of eosinophilic granules is similar to those of heterophilic leukocytes and rat liver lysosomes. They differ mainly in their higher content of peroxidase and in the absence of lysozyme and phagocytin. The absence of the latter two antibacterial agents is consistent with the fact that eosinophils do not have as one of their major functions the ingestion and destruction of bacteria.

Eosinophils of the connective tissue increase in number in various parasitic infections, in conditions involving allergic hypersensitivity, such as asthma and hay fever, and in the late phases of inflammatory reactions. An accumulation of histamine in the tissues is also associated with these conditions. Studies on experimentally induced inflammatory exudates rich in eosinophils have shown that the total histamine content of the exudate is correlated with the number of eosinophils. Thus there is evidence that these cells contain histamine, but the amount is relatively small compared to the histamine content of mast cells. It is estimated that the mast cell contains 20 to 2000 times as much histamine as the eosinophil.

An accumulation of eosinophils in the tissues can be induced experimentally by repeated injections of foreign protein. The requirement for repeated injections over a considerable period suggests that the appearance of the eosinophils depends in some way upon the development of *antibodies* against the foreign protein. It has now been shown that intraperitoneal injection of serum from a sensitized guinea pig into a normal guinea pig results in an increase in eosinophils in the peritoneal fluid. If the antigenic foreign protein and serum containing antibody are injected together, 15 million or more eosinophils can be recovered by lavage of the peritoneal cavity 24 hours later. These observations have been interpreted as indicating that the presence of antigen-antibody complexes induces eosinophils to emigrate from the bloodstream and accumulate in the connective tissues (Litt).

By ingenious application of immunohistological techniques it has been shown that antigen-antibody complexes not only attract eosinophils but are phagocytosed by them. A suitable fluorochrome was conjugated with bovine serum albumin to provide a *red* fluorescing *antigen*. Another fluorochrome was used to

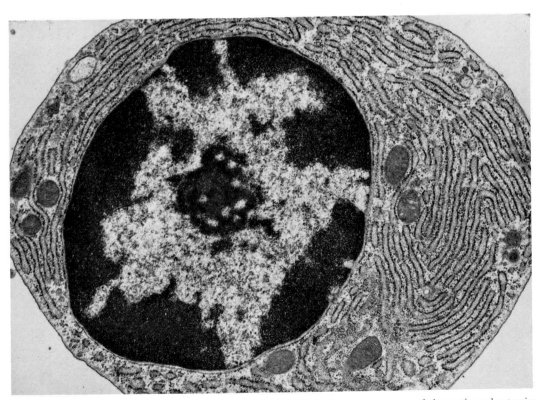

Figure 6-20. Electron micrograph of a guinea pig plasma cell. Notice the coarse pattern of chromatin and extensive granular endoplasmic reticulum. × 16,000.

produce a *green* fluorescing *antibody*. The antigen-antibody complex fluoresced a brilliant *yellow*. Neither the antigen nor the antibody alone were taken up by eosinophils, but when the doubly labeled complex was injected into the peritoneal cavity of guinea pigs and smears of the exudate were examined with the fluorescence microscope one hour later, numerous eosinophils contained bright yellow intracytoplasmic material. Thus one of the functions of eosinophils may be to phagocytize and destroy immune complexes. Other functions will undoubtedly be discovered for these cells in the future.

MAST CELLS. Mast cells are found widely distributed in the connective tissues of most vertebrates. They are often especially abundant along small blood vessels. Their cytoplasm is filled with granules that are *metachromatic* when stained with certain basic aniline dyes. That is to say, the granules, in taking up the dye, change their color. Thus with methylene blue or thionine (also a blue dye), the granules assume a purple hue. Their metachromasia appears to be due to their content of strongly acidic, sulfated protein-polysaccharides. When stained supravitally with neutral red they take on a dark brick-red color (Fig. 6-23).

The size and shape of mast cells vary greatly from species to species. They are large round or ovoid cells in the rat and mouse. They are similar in shape but smaller in man, and in guinea pigs they tend to be slender and fusiform. The round nucleus is small relative to the size of the cell and is often obscured by the large number of intensely stained granules. Binucleate mast cells are not uncommon. The granules are relatively large in murine rodents (0.6μ) and smaller in other species. In most species the granules are soluble in aqueous fixatives.

In electron micrographs, mast cells have numerous small surface folds or villous projections. The Golgi complex is well developed; the endoplasmic reticulum is sparse and the mitochondria relatively few. The granules are limited by a membrane and display considerable variability in their fine structure, depending upon the species. Their interior is finely granular in rodents, but in man they tend to appear heterogeneous with coarse subunits made up of lamellar whorls.

The function of mast cells in the connective tissues is poorly understood, and they continue to be a subject of intense investigation. Mast cells have been found to contain at least two compounds of physiological interest, *heparin* and *histamine*. Many years ago it was discovered that a good correlation exists between the number of mast cells in a tissue and the efficacy of extracts of that tissue in preventing coagulation of the blood. It was suggested, therefore, that the mast cells contained the potent anticoagulant *heparin*. This has since been abundantly verified. In recent years methods have been developed for isolating mast cells from peritoneal fluid in a high degree of purity. When such preparations are analyzed, heparin is the only major protein-polysaccharide (mucopolysaccharide) found, and it is present in the amount of about 20 $\mu\mu$gm. per cell.

There is a similar correlation between the number of mast cells and the histamine content of tissues. Histamine is a potent substance that increases the permeability of capillaries and venules and also has a marked effect upon the blood pressure. Pharmacological agents that cause a release of histamine in the tissues have been shown to induce mast cells to release their granules, and the amount of histamine released varies directly with the degree of mast cell degranulation. The synthesis and release of histamine thus appears to be another of the activities of mast cells.

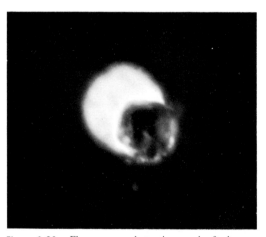

Figure 6-21. Fluorescence photomicrograph of a human plasma cell reacted with fluorescent antibody against γ_2-globulin. The strong fluorescence of the plasma cell cytoplasm identifies this cell type as one of the sites of origin of human immunoglobulins. $\times$ 1300. (After R. Mellors and L. Korngold, J. Exper. Med., *118*:387, 1963.)

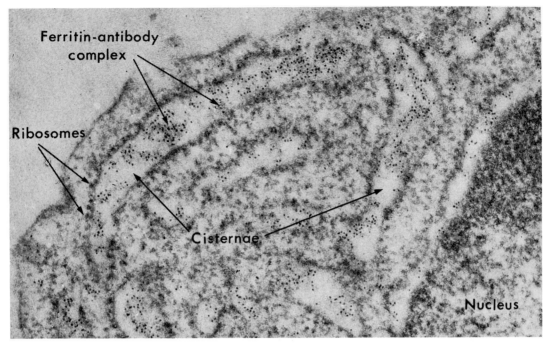

Figure 6-22. Electron micrograph of a plasma cell of a rabbit hyperimmunized against ferritin. The cell was incubated with the antigen (ferritin) under conditions permitting ferritin to enter the cell. Antigen-antibody complexes are localized in the cisternae of the endoplasmic reticulum, thus demonstrating that the plasma cells are involved in antibody synthesis. × 82,000. (After S. de Petris, G. Karlsbad, and B. Pernis, J. Exper. Med., *117*:849, 1963.)

In the rat and mouse but not in other species, mast cells also contain *serotonin* (5-hydroxytryptamine), a substance that causes constriction of small blood vessels and influences blood pressure.

In mammals the mast cells of the connective tissue and the basophilic leukocytes of the blood are independent cell types, despite similar staining properties of their granules.

The Serous Membranes

The serous membranes, the *peritoneum,* the *pleura,* and the *pericardium,* are thin layers of loose connective tissue covered by a layer of mesothelium. When the membranes are folded, to form the omentum or the mesentery, both free surfaces are covered with mesothelium. The serous cavities always contain a small amount of serous liquid, the *serous exudate.* The cells floating in it originate from the serous membrane (Fig. 6-25).

All the elements of the loose connective tissue are found in the serous membranes, where they are arranged in a thin layer (Fig. 6-24). The mesentery contains a loose network of collagenous and elastic fibers, scattered fibroblasts, macrophages, mast cells, and a varying number of fat cells along the blood vessels.

Physiologically the most important and histologically the most interesting part of the serous membranes in mammals is the omentum. In places the membrane is pierced by innumerable holes and is thus reduced to a fine lacelike net formed by collagenous bundles covered by mesothelial cells. Such areas have few or no vessels.

In those areas of the omentum that are not provided with holes, undifferentiated cells occur along the vessels and macrophages are numerous. There are also many small lymphocytes and plasma cells and, occasionally, eosinophilic leukocytes and mast cells. The number of lymphocytes and plasma cells varies considerably in different animals.

In certain areas the macrophages are accumulated in especially dense masses. Such macroscopically visible areas are often arranged along the blood vessels as small or large round or oval patches called *milky spots.* These

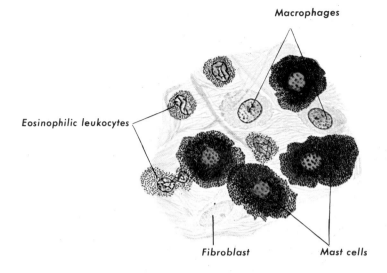

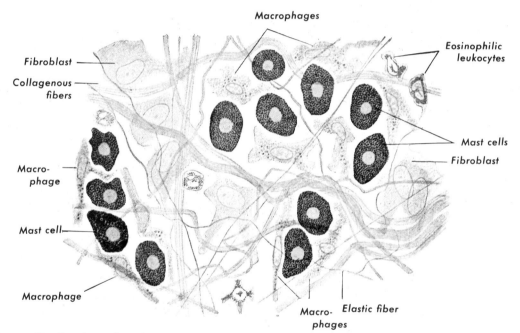

Figure 6-23. Two figures from the loose connective tissue of the rat. *Above,* Fixed and stained with hematoxylin-eosin-azure II. × 600. *Below,* Stained supravitally with neutral red. × 800. (After A. A. Maximow.)

are sometimes also found in the netlike part of the omentum. They are characteristic in the omentum of the rabbit. In the serous membrane which lines the pleural cavities there are cellular areas much like the milky spots of the omentum.

FREE CELLS OF THE SEROUS EXUDATE. Normally, the amount of serous exudate is small, but in pathological conditions it may increase enormously. The exudate contains a number of freely floating cells. Among them the following can be distinguished:

1. Free macrophages that originate in the milky spots of the omentum and migrate into the cavity. They correspond with those inflammatory exudate mononuclear cells that originate from the local macrophages (Fig. 6-25).

2. Desquamated mesothelial cells that keep their squamous form or become spherical with small budlike protuberances. The nu-

cleus usually contains a heavily staining nucleolus. In inflammation and in tissue culture they develop into fibroblasts.

3. Small lymphocytes, the vast majority of which have migrated from the blood vessels of the omentum. A few may have developed through proliferation of the undifferentiated mesenchymal cells of the omentum. In inflammatory exudates, transitions from lymphocytes to large macrophages can be found in great numbers.

4. Eosinophilic leukocytes of hematogenous origin occur in some animals (guinea pig).

5. Free connective tissue mast cells occur in the rat and mouse.

6. In pathological inflammatory exudates

there are great numbers of heterophilic leukocytes from the blood.

DENSE CONNECTIVE TISSUE

Dense connective tissue differs from the loose form mainly in the great preponderance of the fibers over the cellular and amorphous components. Where the fiber bundles are randomly oriented the tissue is described as *dense irregular connective tissue,* and where the fibers are oriented in a consistent pattern it is called *dense regular connective tissue.*

Dense Irregular Connective Tissue. This tissue is found in the dermis, the capsules of organs, sheaths of tendons and nerves, and

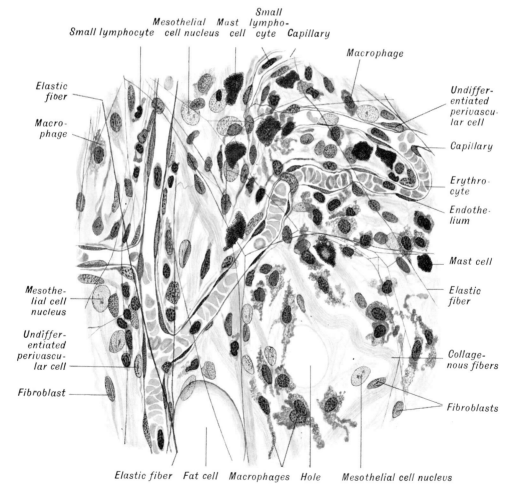

Figure 6-24. Stretch preparation of human omentum. Hematoxylin-eosin-azure II stain. × 450. (After A. A. Maximow.)

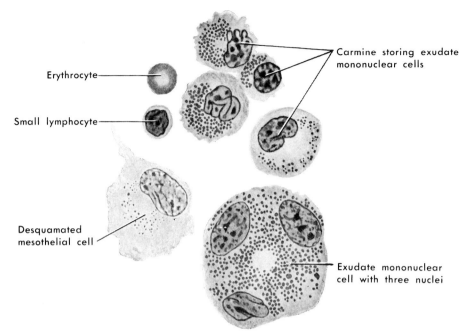

Erythrocyte

Small lymphocyte

Carmine storing exudate mononuclear cells

Desquamated mesothelial cell

Exudate mononuclear cell with three nuclei

Figure 6-25. Cells from the peritoneal exudate of a rabbit which had several intravenous injections of lithium carmine. Note carmine granules (dark gray). Hematoxylin stain. × 1000. (After A. A. Maximow.)

parts of the urinary tract. Its constitution in the dermis is typical. The elements are the same as in the loose variety, but the collagenous bundles are thicker and are woven into a compact feltwork (Fig. 6-26). They are accompanied by extensive elastic networks. All the fibers from the dermis continue directly into those of the loose subcutaneous tissue, where their arrangement is correspondingly looser. There is less amorphous ground substance in the dense connective tissue. Among the two kinds of fibers and the ground substance are the cells; these are much more difficult to identify than in the loose tissue. The macrophages are easily recognized in vitally stained animals. Along the small vessels there are always many inconspicuous nuclei, which probably belong to undifferentiated mesenchymal cells.

DENSE REGULAR CONNECTIVE TISSUE. The constituents of the regular connective tissue, especially the collagenous bundles, are arranged according to a definite plan. The specific arrangement reflects the mechanical requirements of the particular tissue. In *tendons* the fibers form a flexible tissue, which offers great resistance to pulling force. Macroscopically, the tissue has a distinct fibrous structure and a characteristic shining white appearance.

Its chief constituents are thick, closely packed, parallel, collagenous bundles, the same in structure as those in the loose connective tissue. They show a distinct longitudinal striation and in many places fuse with one another at acute angles. In cross section they appear as finely dotted areas, usually separated from one another by broken angular lines, although often continuing into one another. Fine elastic networks have been described between the collagenous bundles.

The fibroblasts are the only cells present; they are arranged in long parallel rows in the spaces between the parallel collagenous bundles. The cell bodies are rectangular, triangular, or trapezoidal when seen from the surface and rod-shaped when seen in profile. Their cytoplasm stains darkly with basic dyes and contains a clear centrosome adjacent to the single, round nucleus. Although the limits between the successive cells in a row are distinct, the lateral limits of the cells are indistinct, because here the cytoplasm continues into a thin membrane. Sometimes it can be followed in the transverse direction to another cell row. In a stained cross section of a tendon the cells appear as dark star-shaped figures between the collagenous bundles (Fig. 6-30). A tendon consists of a varying number of small tendon bundles bound by loose connective tissue into larger bundles (Fig. 6-31).

The *ligaments* are similar to the tendons, except that the elements are less regularly arranged.

In other examples of dense regular connective tissue, such as the *fasciae* and *aponeuroses* the collagenous bundles and fibroblasts are arranged regularly in multiple sheets or lamellae. In each sheet the fibers follow a parallel and often slightly wavy course. In the different sheets the direction may be the same or it may change. The fibers often pass from one sheet into another. Therefore a clear isolation of the sheets is seldom possible. Between the collagenous bundles, fine networks of elastic fibers are usual. The cells correspond to the tendon cells and adapt themselves to the spaces between the collagenous bundles.

In the fibrous membranes with somewhat less regularly arranged elements, such as the periosteum, sclera, and the like, a section perpendicular to the surface shows successive layers of collagenous bundles cut in the longitudinal, oblique, or transverse direction, and cells which are irregular, flat, or fusiform. In these tissues there are always gradual transitions to places where the elements have a quite irregular, dense arrangement. There is also no sharp distinction between them and the surrounding loose connective tissue.

The *cornea* is an example of dense regular connective tissue that is made up of successive layers of collagen with the fibrils of one layer oriented at approximately 90 degrees to those in the next layer (Fig. 6-28).

CONNECTIVE TISSUE WITH SPECIAL PROPERTIES

Mucous Connective Tissue.   This tissue is found in many parts of the embryo, es-

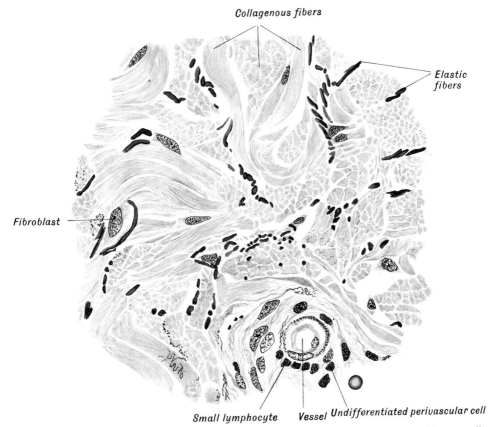

Figure 6-26.   Section of derma of man: dense, irregularly arranged connective tissue. Orcein and hematoxylin stains. × 500. (After A. A. Maximow.)

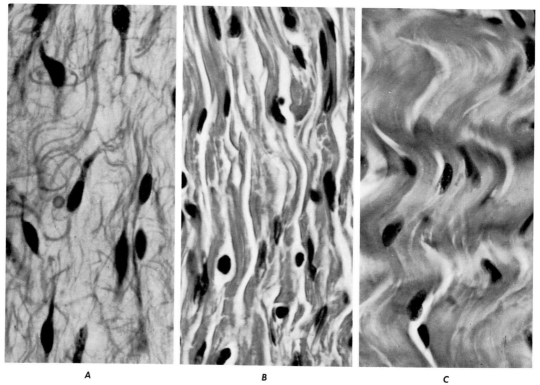

A   B   C

Figure 6-27. Photomicrographs illustrating connective tissue with varying amounts of collagen. *A,* Loose connective tissue from an eight month fetus showing relatively few slender collagen fibers. × 650. *B,* Moderately dense, irregular connective tissue with coarse, irregularly oriented bundles of collagen. × 500. *C,* Dense connective tissue with very abundant collagen in parallel wavy bundles. × 500.

pecially under the skin, and is a form of the loose connective tissue. The classic object for its study is *Wharton's jelly* of the *umbilical cord* of the human fetus. The cells are large, stellate fibroblasts whose processes often are in contact with those of neighboring cells. A few macrophages and lymphoid wandering cells are also present. The intercellular substance is very abundant, soft, jelly-like, and homogeneous in the fresh condition; when fixed, much of the ground substance is extracted and it contains granules and fibrillar precipitates. It gives the reaction for mucin and contains thin, collagenous fibers which increase in number with the age of the fetus.

Examples of mucous connective tissue in adult animals are limited to the dermis and hypodermis of the so-called sex skin of monkeys, where the ground substance is extraordinarily abundant, and the cock's comb, where the ground substance has a very firm consistency.

ELASTIC TISSUE. In the dense connective tissue of a few parts of the body elastic fibers predominate, and the tissue has a yellow color macroscopically. It may appear in the form of strands of coarse parallel fibers, as in the ligamenta flava of the vertebrae, in the true vocal cords, in the ligamentum stylohyoideum, the ligamentum suspensorium penis, and in the tendons of the smooth muscle of the trachea. In these situations the elastic fibers are thick, refringent, and round or flattened; they branch frequently and fuse with one another at acute angles, as in a stretched fishing net. In cross section the angular or round areas representing the fibers form small groups; the spaces between the elastic fibers are filled with a delicate feltwork of collagenous fibers and a few fibroblasts.

An example of dense regular elastic connective tissue is found in the massive ligamentum nuchae of grazing animals, which consists of coarse elastic fibers 10 to 15 μ in diameter closely associated in parallel bundles (Fig. 6-32).

Scarpa's fascia of the human anterior abdominal wall, which aids in the support of the viscera, consists largely of elastic fibers. The corresponding layer in the large quadrupeds, the tunica abdominalis, is a thick yellow sheet of dense elastic tissue several millimeters in thickness.

The elastic tissue forms membranes in the walls of hollow organs upon which a changing pressure acts from within, as in the largest arteries, in some parts of the heart, and in the trachea and bronchi.

In the large arteries the structural unit of the elastic tissue is a *fenestrated membrane,* a lamella of *elastin* of variable thickness provided with many irregular openings. The fenestrated membranes are arranged in many layers around the cavity of the organ and are connected with one another by oblique ribbon-like branches. The spaces between the lamellae contain a mucoid amorphous mass and smooth muscle cells with irregular outlines. It is impossible to distinguish sharply between the fibrous elastic networks and the fenestrated elastic membranes.

RETICULAR TISSUE. The fibrous elements of some types of connective tissues are *reticular fibers.* These occur in the lymphatic tissue, myeloid tissue, spleen, and in the wall of the sinusoids of the liver. The cell types usually associated with the fibers of this reticulum are the primitive reticular cells and phagocytic reticular cells or macrophages (Fig. 6-33). There are many transitions from the first cell type into the latter. In the meshes of this fibrous and cellular reticulum are free cells, varying in type and number, depending on the type and functional state of the tissue. This tissue is discussed at length in Chapter 8.

PIGMENT TISSUE. In the tunica supra-

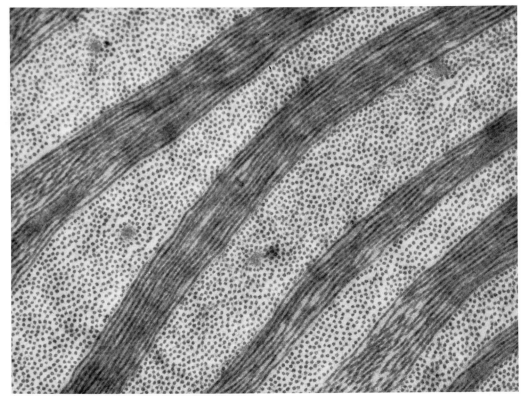

Figure 6-28. An example of dense regular connective tissue in the cornea. The collagen is arranged in lamellae with the fibrils in alternate layers oriented at right angles to those in the intervening layers. Electron micrograph. Osmium fixation. × 35,000. (Courtesy of M. Jakus.)

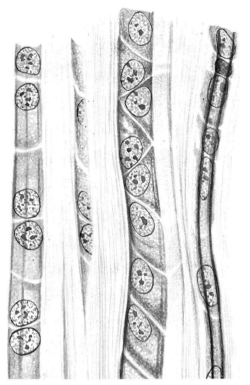

Figure 6-29. Freshly teased tendon of the tail of a rat, stained with methylene blue. The rows of tendon cells run between collagenous bundles. × 380. (After A. A. Maximow.)

and the tissues, *storage* of fuel in adipose cells, *protection* against infection, and *repair* after injury. For its mechanical role its fibrous components are most important, and their abundance and distribution are adapted to the local structural requirements. Delicate networks of *reticular* fibers support the basement lamina of epithelia, surround the capillaries and sinusoids, and envelop individual muscle fibers or the groups of parenchymal cells that form the functional units of organs. The coarser *collagenous* fibers abound where greater tensile strength is required. They form the tendons, aponeuroses, and septa and fibrous capsules of organs. *Elastic fibers* give the tissues their suppleness and their ability to spring back to their normal relations after stretching. They are especially abundant in hollow organs subject to periodic distention. Loose connective tissue with an abundant, highly hydrated ground substance is commonly found beneath the integument, between muscles, and in other sites where mobility of the parts is advantageous. On the other hand, where strength is more important than mobility, dense connective tissue is formed, and its bundles of collagen fibers tend to be oriented so as to resist most efficiently the local mechanical stresses.

Connective tissue plays a significant role in the nutrition of the other tissues that it surrounds and permeates. It is evident that all substances reaching the cells of these other tissues from the blood, and all the products of their metabolism that are returned to the blood and lymph, must pass through a layer of connective tissue. These metabolites are believed to diffuse through the aqueous phase of the gelatinous ground substance or along thin films of fluid coating the fibers. The exchange of materials is probably influenced by the viscous properties of the ground substance.

The polyelectrolyte properties of the protein-polysaccharides suggest that the connective tissue ground substance may also participate in maintaining water and electrolyte balance. In addition to the storage of energy in adipose cells, it is noteworthy that approximately half of the circulating proteins of the body are in the interstitial spaces at every moment and, because the proportions of albumin and globulin differ from those of plasma, the connective tissue may exercise some selectivity in its depot function.

INFLAMMATION. Of great importance in

choroidea and in the lamina fusca of the sclera of the eye, the majority of the cells in the loose connective tissues are melanocytes. Such a tissue can be termed "pigment tissue" (see Chapter 34).

CONNECTIVE TISSUE (LAMINA PROPRIA) OF THE INTESTINAL AND UTERINE MUCOUS MEMBRANES, AND INTERSTITIAL CONNECTIVE TISSUE OF THE LUNG, TESTIS, AND OVARY. The connective tissue which surrounds and supports the epithelial elements in these organs acquires a specifically differentiated structure. It is described in the chapters that deal with these organs.

HISTOPHYSIOLOGY OF CONNECTIVE TISSUE

Connective tissue is the medium surrounding the structural elements of the other tissues and organs. It functions in mechanical *support*, exchange of metabolites between blood the defenses of the organism against disease is the part played by connective tissue as the arena of the local reactive process called *inflammation*. Bacteria and other exogenous noxious substances call forth an intense local reaction, in which the cells of the blood and connective tissues are mobilized to bring about the destruction of the foreign substance and the repair of the damage caused. In inflamed connective tissue, leukocytes in great numbers migrate from the capillaries and venules at the very beginning of the process. The majority of these are heterophils that are capable of phagocytizing bacteria and other foreign matter and digesting it intracellularly through the action of the hydrolytic enzymes in their specific granules (lysosomes). The mononuclear blood cells (lymphocytes and monocytes) hypertrophy in the first day or two after the onset of inflammation and become transformed into phagocytic cells, the *hematogenous macrophages*, which supplement the macrophages already present in the tissue. Stimulated by the noxious material, many of these are mobilized at the site as free macrophages (histogenous macrophages). It has also been claimed that fibroblasts can turn into macrophages, but this transformation is denied by most investigators. Evidence is accumulating that in injured tissue the mast cells may act as migratory unicellular glands, supplying biologically active compounds in the region of local stress. Their liberation of histamine may serve to increase the

blood flow and contribute to the local inflammatory edema that dilutes the irritant and promotes its inactivation by antibodies. There is also some indication that release of histamine helps activate the phagocytosis of the other cell types.

REPAIR. The regenerative capacity of fibroblasts and the fact that they respond so readily to injury by proliferation and fibrogenesis make them the principal agents of repair. They are involved in the healing of defects, not only in connective tissue proper, but also in other tissues that have little or no regenerative capacity of their own. For example, the heart muscle that degenerates following a heart attack is replaced by a connective tissue scar.

Although much has been learned about the production of collagen in the histogenesis and repair of connective tissue, it must be realized that there are also mechanisms for the removal of collagen. This is of great importance in the growth and remodeling of bone and other tissues. Systematic study of this process has begun only recently, but it has already been shown that some tissues of tadpoles contain collagenase, and that the activity of this enzyme is enhanced by thyroid hormone, which induces metamorphosis and brings about resorption of the tail. Collagenases are now being detected in mammalian tissues as well.

HORMONAL EFFECTS. The adrenocorti-

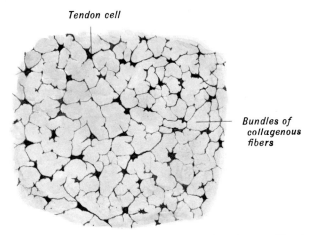

Figure 6-30. Cross section of a tendon from tail of a rat. Hematoxylin-eosin-azure II stain. About × 350. (After A. A. Maximow.)

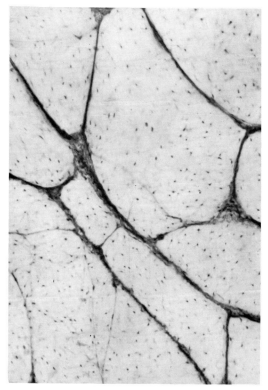

Figure 6-31. Cross section of a human tendon, showing the separation of the tendon bundles by loose connective tissue, which stains dark. Hematoxylin-eosin-azure II stain. Photomicrograph. About × 120.

has long been known that *scurvy*, the disease resulting from deficiency of vitamin C (ascorbic acid), is attended by an inability to form collagen fibers in normal abundance. It has now been found that addition of ascorbic acid to suspensions of scorbutic fibroblasts in vitro enhances the conversion of proline to hydroxyproline in collagen, suggesting that the basic defect of collagen metabolism in scorbutic animals may be impaired synthesis of hydroxyproline, one of the amino acids peculiar to collagen.

A disease of domestic animals characterized by bone deformities has been traced to the ingestion of the sweet pea *Lathyrus odoratus.* All of the abnormalities of this disease, called *lathyrism,* can be reproduced by administration of β-aminoproprionitrile, the toxic agent extracted from the sweet pea plant. Tropocollagen appears to be synthesized normally in such animals but is defective in its ability to form stable collagen fibrils. When tropocollagen is extracted at 0° C. from *normal* animals and induced to form fibers by an increase in the temperature to 37° C., the longer it is held at that temperature the less soluble it becomes at 0° C. This time dependent loss of solubility is believed to be due to formation of increased numbers of bonds between the tropocollagen units. In *lathyritic* animals there is a marked

cotropic hormone of the pituitary and cortisone of the adrenal cortex both tend to lower the protein-polysaccharide content of the ground substance. They also diminish the intensity of the cellular response in inflammation. The response of connective tissues to sex hormones varies greatly with the species, the sex, and the site in the body. The most dramatic effects are on the sex skin of monkeys, where estrogens greatly increase the protein-polysaccharides of the ground substance, and in the cock's comb, where testosterone stimulates accumulation of hyaluronic acid and formation of collagen.

DISTURBANCES OF COLLAGEN METABOLISM. Collagen metabolism is affected by age and nutritional state and may be rather specifically disturbed in a number of disease states. In some of these specific disorders, recent knowledge of the mechanisms of fibrogenesis has provided a partial explanation of the defect or made it possible to identify the step in the process where the normal biosynthetic mechanism fails. It

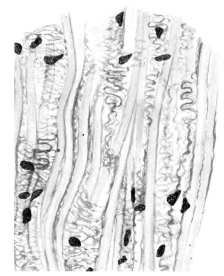

Figure 6-32. Longitudinal section from ligamentum nuchae of an ox. The thick elastic fibers form most of the tissue. Between them are dark fibroblast nuclei and wavy collagenous fibers. Eosin-azure II stain. × 300. (After A. A. Maximow.)

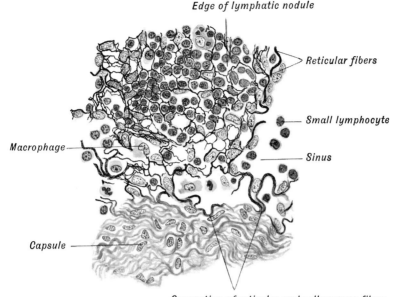

Edge of lymphatic nodule

Reticular fibers

Small lymphocyte

Macrophage

Sinus

Capsule

Connection of reticular and collagenous fibers

Figure 6-33.   Portion of cortex and capsule of human mesenteric lymph node. Bielschowsky stain. × 500. (After A. A. Maximow.)

increase in the extractability of tropocollagen from connective tissue at 0° C., and although the extracted tropocollagen is capable of forming typical cross striated fibers on warming, these retain the ability to redissolve upon cooling even after prolonged periods at 37° C. This and other evidence suggests that lathyritic agents result in synthesis of abnormal chains that are not able to crosslink adequately (Gross).

REFERENCES

General

Asboe-Hansen, G., ed.: Connective Tissue in Health and Disease. Copenhagen, E. Munksgaard, 1954.

Maximow, A. A.: Bindegewebe und blutbildende Gewebe. *In* von Möllendorff, W., and W. Bargmann, eds.: Handbuch der mikroskopischen Anatomie des Menschen. Berlin, Julius Springer, 1927, Vol. 2, part 1, p. 232.

Extracellular Components

Bensley, S. H.: On the presence, properties, and distribution of the intercellular ground substance of loose connective tissue. Anat. Rec., *60:*93, 1934.

Grant, R. A., R. W. Horne, and R. W. Cox: New model for the tropocollagen macromolecule and its mode of aggregation. Nature, *207:*822, 1965.

Gross, J., J. H. Highberger, and F. O. Schmitt: Extraction of collagen from connective tissue by neutral salt solutions. Proc. Nat. Acad. Sci., *41:*1, 1955.

Gross, J., and C. I. Levene: Effect of β-aminoproprionitrile on extractability of collagen from skin of mature guinea pigs. Am. J. Path., *35:*687, 1959.

Hodge, A. J., and F. O. Schmitt: The charge profile of the tropocollagen macromolecule and the packing arrangement in native-type collagen fibrils. Proc. Nat. Acad. Sci., *46:*186, 1960.

Hodge, A. J., and F. O. Schmitt: The tropocollagen macromolecule and its properties of ordered interaction. *In* Edds, M. V., ed.: Macromolecular Complexes. New York, Ronald Press, 1961.

Levene, C. I., and J. Gross: Alterations in the state of molecular aggregation of collagen induced in chick embryos by β-aminoproprionitrile. J. Exper. Med., *110:*771, 1959.

Olsen, B. R.: Electron microscope studies on collagen. I. Native collagen fibrils. II. Mechanism of linear polymerization of tropocollagen molecules. Zeitschr. f. Zellforsch., *59:*184, 199, 1963.

Petruska, J. A., and A. J. Hodge: A subunit model for the tropocollagen macromolecule. Proc. Nat. Acad. Sci., *51:*871, 1964.

Porter, K. R., and G. D. Pappas: Collagen formation by fibroblasts of the chick embryo dermis. J. Biophys. & Biochem. Cytol., *5:*153, 1959.

Ramachandran, G. N., Ed.: Treatise on Collagen. Vol. 1, Chemistry of Collagen; G. N. Ramachandran, ed. Vols. 2A and 2B, Biology of Collagen; B. S. Gould, ed. Vol. 3, Chemical Pathology of Collagen; R. A. Milch, ed. New York, Academic Press, in press.

Robertson, W. v.B.: D-ascorbic acid and synthesis of collagen. Biochim. Biophys. Acta, *74:*137, 1963.

Robertson, W. v.B., and J. Hewitt: Augmentation of collagen synthesis by ascorbic acid *in vitro.* Biochim. Biophys. Acta, *49:*404, 1961.

Schmitt, F. O., J. Gross, and J. H. Highberger: Tropocollagen and the properties of fibrous collagen. Exper. Cell Res., *3*(Suppl.): 326, 1955.

Schubert, M.: Intercellular macromolecules containing polysaccharides. *In* Connective Tissue: Intercellular Macromolecules, London. J. & A. Churchill Ltd. 1964. p. 119.

Wolbach, S. B.: Controlled formation of collagen and reticulum; a study of the source of intercellular substance in recovery from experimental scorbutus. Am. J. Path., *9* (Suppl.):689, 1933.

Cellular Elements

Allgöwer, M.: The Cellular Basis of Wound Repair. Springfield, Charles C Thomas, 1956.

Benditt, E. P., R. L. Wong, M. Arase, and E. Roeper: 5-Hydroxytryptamine in mast cells. Proc. Soc. Exper. Biol. and Med., *90:* 303, 1955.

Cohn, Z. A., M. E. Fedorko, and J. G. Hirsch: The *in vitro* differentiation of mononuclear phagocytes. IV. The ultrastructure of macrophage differentiation in the peritoneal cavity and in culture. V. The formation of macrophage lysosomes. J. Exper. Med., *123:*747, 757, 1966.

Cohn, Z. A., and J. G. Hirsch: The isolation and properties of the specific cytoplasmic granules of rabbit polymorphonuclear leucocytes. J. Exper. Med., *112:*982, 1960.

Cohn, Z. A., and E. Weiner: The particulate hydrolases of macrophages. I. Comparative enzymology, isolation and properties. II. Biochemical and morphological response to particle ingestion. J. Exper. Med., *118:*991, 1009, 1963.

Deane, H. S.: Some electron microscopic observations on the lamina propria of the gut, with comments on the close association of macrophages, plasma cells and eosinophils. Anat. Rec., *149:* 453, 1964.

de Petris, S., G. Karlsbad, and B. Pernis: Localization of antibodies in plasma cells by electron microscopy. J. Exper. Med., *117:*849, 1963.

Downey, H.: The development of histiocytes and macrophages from lymphocytes. J. Lab. & Clin. Med., *45:*499, 1955.

DuShane, G. P.: The development of pigment cells in vertebrates. *In* Biology of Melanomas: Results of a Conference held at the New York Academy of Sciences in 1946. New York, New York Academy of Sciences. (Special Publication 4, 1948, p. 1.)

Ebert, R. H., and H. W. Florey: The extravascular development of the monocyte observed *in vivo.* Brit. J. Exper. Path. *20:*342, 1939.

Evans, H. M., and K. J. Scott: On the differential reaction to vital dyes exhibited by the two great groups of connective tissue cells. Carnegie Contributions to Embryol., *10:*1, 1921.

Fawcett, D. W.: An experimental study of mast cell degranulation and regeneration. Anat. Rec., *121:*29, 1955.

Gowans, J. L., D. D. McGregor, and D. M. Cowen: Initiation of immune responses by small lymphocytes. Nature, *196:*651, 1962.

Harris, H.: Chemotaxis and phagocytosis. *In* Macfarlane, R. G., and A. H. T. Robb-Smith, eds.: The Functions of the Blood. New York, Academic Press, 1961, p. 413.

Hirsch, J. G.: Cinematographic observations on granule lysis in polymorphonuclear leucocytes during phagocytosis. J. Exper. Med., *116:*827, 1962.

Hirsch, J. G., and Z. A. Cohn: Degranulation of polymorphonuclear leucocytes following phagocytosis of micro-organisms. J. Exper. Med., *112:*1005, 1960.

Kolouch, F., Jr.: The lymphocyte in acute inflammation. Am. J. Path., *15:*413, 1939.

Lewis, M. R., and W. H. Lewis: Transformation of mononuclear blood cells into macrophages, epithelioid cells, and giant cells in hanging drop cultures of lower vertebrates. Carnegie Contributions to Embryol., *18:*95, 1926.

Litt, M.: Eosinophils and antigen-antibody reaction. Ann. N. Y. Acad. Sci., *116:*964, 1964.

Lowther, D. A., N. M. Green, and J. A. Chapman: Morphological and chemical studies of collagen formation. II. Metabolic activity of collagen associated with subcellular fractions of guinea pig granulomata. J. Biophys. & Biochem. Cytol., *10:*373, 1961.

Marchand. F.: Der Prozess der Wundheilung mit Einschluss der Transplantation. Stuttgart, F. Enke, 1901.

Marchand, F.: Die örtlichen reaktiven Vorgänge (Lehre von der Entzündung). *In* Krehl, and F. Marchand: Handbuch der allgemeinen Pathologie. Leipzig, 1924, Vol. 4, part 1, p. 78.

Maximow, A. A.: Über die Zellformen des lockeren Bindegewebes. Arch. f. Mikr. Anat., *67:*680, 1906.

Maximow, A. A.: The morphology of the mesenchymal reactions. Arch. Path. Lab. Med., *4:*557, 1927.

Maximow, A. A.: The macrophages or histiocytes. *In* Cowdry, E. V., ed.: Special Cytology. 2nd ed. New York, Paul B. Hoeber, Inc., 1932, Vol. II, p. 709.

Mellors, R. C., and L. Korngold: The cellular origin of human immunoglobulins. J. Exper. Med., *118:*387, 1963.

Movat, H. Z., and N. V. P. Fernando: The fine structure of connective tissue. I. The fibroblast. II. The plasma cell. Exp. & Mol. Pathol., *1:*509, 535, 1962.

Nossal, G. J. V.: Genetic control of lymphopoiesis, plasma cell formation and antibody production. Int. Rev. Exp. Path. *1:*1, 1962.

Odor, D. L.: Observations of the rat mesothelium with the electron and phase microscopes. Am. J. Anat., *95:*433, 1954.

Olsen, B. R.: Electron microscope studies on collagen. I. Native collagen fibrils. Zeitschr. f. Zellforsch., *59:*184, 1963.

Padawer, J., ed.: Mast cells and basophils. Ann. N. Y. Acad. Sci., *103:*1, 1963.

Porter, K. R.: Cell fine structure and biosynthesis of intercellular macromolecules. *In* New York Heart Association: Connective Tissue: Intercellular Macromolecules. Boston, Little, Brown & Co., 1964, p. 167.

Porter, K. R., and G. D. Pappas: Collagen formation by fibroblasts of the chick embryo dermis. J. Biophys. & Biochem. Cytol., *5:* 153, 1959.

Ranvier, L.: Traité technique d'histologie. Paris, F. Savy, 1875.

Ranvier, L.: Des clasmatocytes. Arch. Anat. Micr., *3:*123, 1900.

Rawles, M. E.: Origin of pigment cells from neural crest in the mouse embryo. Physiol. Zool., *20:*248, 1948.

Rebuck, J. W., and J. H. Crowley: A method of studying leukocytic functions *in vitro.* Ann. N. Y. Acad. Sci., *59:*757, 1955.

Rifkin, R. A., E. F. Osserman, K. C. Hsu, and C. Morgan: The intracellular distribution of gamma globulin in a mouse plasma cell tumor as revealed by fluorescence and electron microscopy. J. Exper. Med., *116:*324, 1962.

Riley, J. F.: The Mast Cells. Edinburgh and London, E. & S. Livingstone, Ltd., 1959.

Robineaux, J., and J. Fréderic: Contribution a l'étude des granulations neutrophilis de polynucléares par le microcinématographie en contrast de phase. Compt. rend. soc. biol., *149:*486, 1955.

Ross, R., and E. P. Benditt: Wound healing and collagen formation. III. A quantitative radioautographic study of the utilization of proline-H³ in wounds from normal and scorbutic guinea pigs. J. Cell Biol., *15:*99, 1962.

Ross, R., and J. W. Lillywhite: The fate of buffy coat cells grown in subcutaneously implanted diffusion chambers. Lab. Invest., *14:* 1568, 1965.

Sharp, J. A., and R. G. Burwell: Interaction of macrophages and lymphocytes after skin grafting or challenges with soluble antigens. Nature, *188:*474, 1960.

Speirs, R. S., and Y. Osada: Chemotactic activity and phagocytosis of eosinophils. Proc. Soc. Exper. Biol. Med., *109:*929, 1962.

Sutton, J. S., and L. V. Weiss: Transformation of monocytes in tissue cultures into macrophages, epithelioid cells and multinucleated giant cells. An electron microscope study. J. Cell Biol., *28:*303, 1966.

Taliaferro, W. H.: The cellular basis of immunity. Annual Rev. Microbiol., *3:*159, 1949.

Thiéry, J. P.: Microcinematographic contributions to the study of plasma cells. *In* Ciba Foundation Symposium: Cellular Aspects of Immunity. Boston, Little, Brown & Co., 1960, p. 59.

Trowell, O. A.: The lymphocyte. Int. Rev. Cytol., *7:*236, 1958.

Uvnäs, B.: Release processes in mast cells and their activation by injury. Ann. N. Y. Acad. Sci., *116:*880, 1964.

Weiss, L. P., and D. W. Fawcett: Cytochemical observations on chicken monocytes, macrophages, and giant cells in tissue culture. J. Histochem. & Cytochem., *1:*47, 1953.

CHAPTER SEVEN

Adipose Tissue

Twenty-five years ago adipose tissue was considered to be a metabolically inert tissue which passively stored fat, provided insulation against heat loss, and functioned in mechanical support in certain regions of the body. The allocation of a separate chapter to it in recent textbooks of histology is a consequence of its belated recognition as a diffuse organ of primary metabolic importance.

Most animals feed intermittently but consume energy continuously; there must therefore be provision for temporary storage of fuel. Lipid is the most favorable substance for this purpose because it weighs less and occupies less volume per calorie of stored chemical energy than either carbohydrate or protein. Although many tissues contain small amounts of carbohydrate and fat, the adipose tissue serves as the body's most capacious reservoir of energy. About 10 per cent of the total body weight of an average man is fat, representing approximately a 40 day reserve of energy. In obese individuals this may increase to the equivalent of a year or more of normal metabolism. By accumulating lipid in periods of excess food intake and releasing fatty acids in periods of fasting, adipose tissue plays an important role in maintaining a stable supply of fuel. Far from being inert, the cells of this tissue actively synthesize fat from carbohydrate and are highly responsive to hormonal and nervous stimulation.

HISTOLOGICAL CHARACTERISTICS OF THE ADIPOSE TISSUES

In most mammals there are two more or less distinct types of adipose tissue, which differ in their color, distribution, vascularity, and metabolic activity. One is the familiar yellow or *white adipose tissue,* which comprises the bulk of body fat. The other, called *brown adipose tissue,* is less abundant and occurs only in certain specific areas. There are marked species differences in the relative amounts of the two types of fat. Brown adipose tissue is most abundant in hibernating species. Although it is present in primates, including man, it is relatively inconspicuous and probably does not assume great importance in the economy of these animals.

The peripheral parts of lobules of brown adipose tissue often have an appearance strongly suggestive of a transition from one form of fat to the other. This has fostered the widespread belief that brown fat is simply an immature or transitional form of ordinary adipose tissue. For this reason it is commonly referred to in the literature of pathology as *fetal fat.* This term does not seem to be appropriate, however, for in those species in which it is best developed, brown fat persists throughout adult life and is morphologically and metabolically sufficiently different to warrant its designation as a distinct type of adipose tissue. We will return to this point in discussing the histogenesis of the adipose tissues.

ORDINARY ADIPOSE TISSUE. Fat varies in color from white to deep yellow, depending in part upon the diet. The color resides mainly in the stored lipid. The cells are very large, ranging up to 120 μ in diameter. They are typically spherical but may assume polyhedral shapes because of mutual deformation (Fig. 7-1). A single droplet of lipid occupies most of the volume of the cell. Therefore, fat cells of

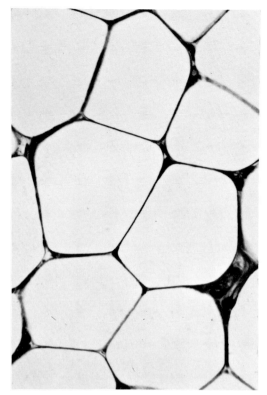

Figure 7-1. Ordinary adipose tissue of a mouse prepared by usual methods of fixation and dehydration. The lipid droplet has been extracted and only a thin rim of cytoplasm of each cell remains. × 400.

compartmentation, visible with the naked eye, is most obvious in regions where the fat is subjected to pressure and has a cushioning or shock absorbing effect. In other regions, the connective tissue septa are thinner and the lobular organization of the tissue is less apparent.

Examined with the electron microscope, the cytoplasm around the nucleus is found to contain a small Golgi complex, a few filamentous mitochondria, occasional short profiles of endoplasmic reticulum and a moderate number of free ribosomes. Attenuated as it is, the thin layer of cytoplasm around the lipid droplet nevertheless includes a few mitochondria, fine filaments, and minute vesicles, which may represent the agranular reticulum. The lipid droplet is not enclosed by a membrane, but it is often set off from the surrounding cyto-

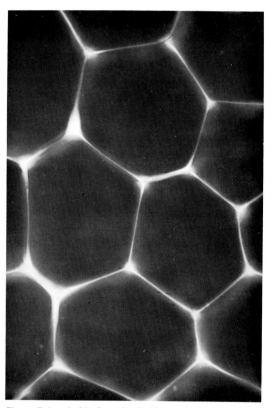

Figure 7-2. A thin formalin fixed spread of adipose tissue in rat mesentery stained with Sudan black without previous dehydration. Here the lipid has been retained and is stained by the fat soluble dye, while the surrounding rim of cytoplasm is essentially unstained. × 400. (After D. W. Fawcett, *in* Greep, R. O., ed.: Histology. Philadelphia, The Blakiston Co.,, 1953. Reproduced with the permission of the McGraw-Hill Book Co.)

this kind are sometimes described as *unilocular* to distinguish them from brown fat cells, which contain multiple small droplets and are termed *multilocular*. The nucleus is displaced to one side by the accumulated lipid and the cytoplasm is reduced to a thin rim comprising only about one fortieth of the total volume of the cell. The lipid is usually dissolved out during preparation of histological sections, so that only the plasmalemma and a thin shell of cytoplasm remain. With silver stains each cell is found to be surrounded by delicate reticular fibers. In the angular spaces between the cells are cross sections of capillaries that form a loose plexus throughout the tissue. If well preserved, adipose tissue appears in section as a delicate network with large polygonal meshes (Figs. 7-1 and 7-2), but the cell rims often collapse to varying degrees during preparation, giving the cells an irregular outline.

Adipose tissue is often subdivided into small lobules by connective tissue septa. This

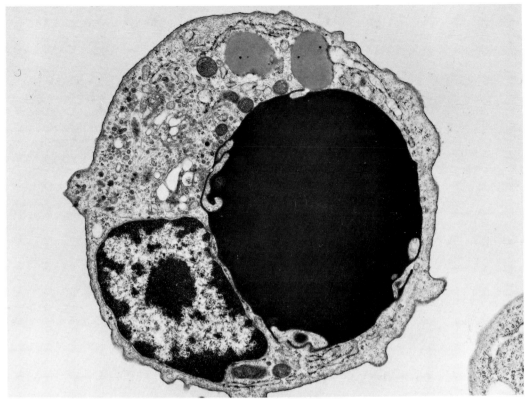

Figure 7-3. Electron micrograph of a small developing fat cell from guinea pig bone marrow. The cell still has a thick rim of cytoplasm and a relatively small droplet of lipid that is intensely blackened with osmium. Its irregular outline is an artifact of fixation. Two smaller gray droplets nearby show less affinity for osmium, possibly because their lipid is less unsaturated. × 16,000.

plasm by 40 to 50 Å filaments in an orthogonal arrangement (Figs. 7-4 and 7-5). Similar filaments occurring singly or in small bundles are found randomly oriented elsewhere in the cytoplasm. The plasma membrane shows numerous minute inpocketings of the kind that are usually interpreted as evidence for a submicroscopic form of pinocytosis. Each adipose cell is invested by a layer of glycoprotein corresponding to the boundary layer or basal lamina of epithelia.

In prolonged fasting or in the emaciation associated with chronic illness, adipose tissue may give up much of its stored lipid and revert to a highly vascular connective tissue containing aggregations of ovoid or polygonal cells with multiple small lipid droplets. The cells seldom or never revert to simple fusiform elements resembling fibroblasts.

DISTRIBUTION OF ORDINARY ADIPOSE TISSUE. This type of fat is widely distributed in the subcutaneous tissue but exhibits regional differences in amount, which are influenced by age and sex. In infants and young children there is a continuous subcutaneous layer of fat, the *panniculus adiposus,* of rather uniform thickness over the whole body. In adults it thins out in some regions but persists and grows thicker in certain sites of predilection. These sites differ in the two sexes and are largely responsible for the characteristic differences in body form of males and females. In the male, the principal areas are the nape of the neck and the region overlying the seventh cervical vertebra, the subcutaneous area overlying the deltoid and triceps, the lumbrosacral region, and the buttocks. In the female, subcutaneous fat is most abundant in the breasts, the buttocks, the epitrochanteric region, and the anterior aspect of the thigh.

In addition to these superficial fat deposits, there are extensive accumulations in both sexes in the omentum, mesenteries, and retroperitoneal areas. All of these areas readily

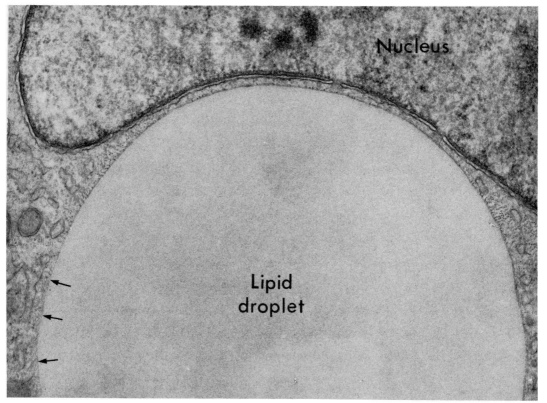

Figure 7-4. Electron micrograph of the nucleus and adjacent lipid droplet of a developing fat cell from chick bone marrow. After glutaraldehyde fixation the lipid shows less staining with osmic acid and the interface between the lipid and the cytoplasm (at arrows) can be seen more clearly. Notice the absence of a membrane around the droplet. × 34,000. (Courtesy of Eunice M. Wood.)

give up their stored lipid during fasting. There are other areas of fat, however, that do not give up their stored fuel so readily. For example, the adipose tissue in the orbit, in the major joints, and on the palms of the hands and soles of the feet does not seem to be grist for the metabolic mill but instead has the mechanical function of support or protection. These areas diminish in size only after very prolonged starvation.

BROWN ADIPOSE TISSUE. The color of this form of fat ranges from tan to a rich reddish brown. Its cells are smaller than those of white fat and polygonal in cross section. The cytoplasm is more abundant, and there are multiple lipid droplets of varying size (Fig. 7-6). The spherical nucleus is somewhat eccentric in position but seldom displaced to the periphery of the cell. A small Golgi apparatus is present, as well as numerous large spherical mitochondria. In electron micrographs the mitochondria occupy a large part of the cyto-

plasm and have numerous cristae that may extend across the full width of the organelle (Fig. 7-7). The endoplasmic reticulum is not well developed, and only a few profiles of the smooth surfaced form can be found. The lipid droplets do not appear to develop within the reticulum but are free in the ground substance of the cytoplasm. Scattered ribosomes and variable amounts of particulate glycogen are also present in the cytoplasmic matrix.

The connective tissue stroma of brown adipose tissue is very sparse and the blood supply exceedingly rich (Fig. 7-8). The cells are therefore in more intimate association with one another and with the capillaries than is the case in ordinary fat. Numerous small unmyelinated nerve fibers can be demonstrated among the brown fat cells by silver staining methods and in electron micrographs. Naked axons are frequently encountered in apposition to the surface of adipose cells.

The histological organization of brown fat

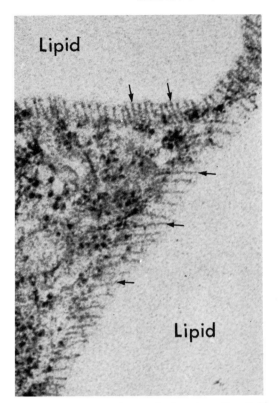

Figure 7-5. Electron micrograph of portions of two lipid droplets and the intervening cytoplasm in a developing adipose cell from the chick. The arrows point to the ordered array of fine filaments at the interface between the lipid and the cytoplasm. × 87,000. (Courtesy of Eunice M. Wood.)

along the central aspect of the thoracic aorta. Small lobules are found in the mediastinum, along the great vessels in the neck, and in the hilus of the kidney. Although brown fat is not so extensively developed in primates, a sizable mass can be found in the axillae of the macaque.

Whether brown adipose tissue occurs in well nourished human adults is a subject of debate. In such individuals, all the fat seems to be of the unilocular variety, but in starvation or chronic wasting disease, glandlike masses of multilocular fat cells indistinguishable from typical brown fat appear in those same regions where brown adipose tissue is found in rodents. Two types of fatty tumors called *lipomas* also occur in man. One resembles ordinary fat and the other resembles brown fat. These observations lend support to the view that both types are represented in man, but that under normal nutritional conditions the lipid droplets of cells of multilocular fat coalesce into a single droplet, so that the principal distinguishing morphological characteristic is lost. In prolonged

is always distinctly lobular, and the pattern of distribution of the blood vessels within lobes and lobules closely resembles that found in glands. In animals subjected to prolonged fasting the brown fat becomes more deeply colored and reverts to a compact, glandlike mass of epithelioid cells bearing no resemblance to connective tissue (Fig. 7-9). The color of brown fat is in large part attributable to the high concentration of cytochromes in its mitochondria.

DISTRIBUTION OF BROWN ADIPOSE TISSUE. Ordinary adipose tissue may develop in almost any area of loose connective tissue in the body, and new areas may appear at any time in postnatal life. But brown adipose tissue arises in embryonic life in certain specific sites, and no new areas develop after birth. In common laboratory rodents, brown fat occurs in two large, symmetrical interscapular fat bodies, in thin lobules between the muscles around the shoulder girdle, and in the axillae. It fills the costovertebral angle and forms a long strand

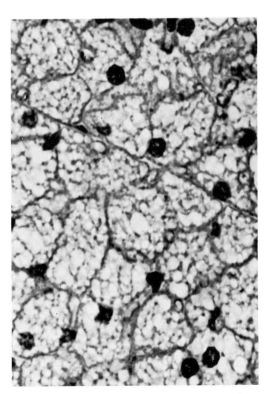

Figure 7-6. Photomicrograph of typical brown adipose tissue. The polygonal cells contain more cytoplasm than those of ordinary fat and many small lipid droplets. × 650.

starvation the tendency for multiple droplets is re-expressed, and two types can then be identified. The differences in interpretation of the adipose tissues have their basis in diverging views as to the histogenesis of fat (Fig. 7-10).

HISTOGENESIS OF ADIPOSE TISSUE

An early view that still has some adherents is that of Flemming (1870), who contended that adipose tissue was merely ordinary connective tissue in which fat had been deposited in the fibroblasts. This view assumes that any and all connective tissue can serve as a repository for fat when dietary intake exceeds energy expenditure. Although connective tissue is ubiquitous, the fact is that in obesity, fat does not become universally and evenly distributed but is deposited in certain sites preferentially, while other areas are spared. For example, the backs of the hands

and feet, the eyelids, nose, ears, scrotum, and genitalia seldom accumulate fat. This fact is hard to explain if adipose cells can arise from common fibroblasts wherever they occur. Toldt (1870–1888), on the other hand, maintained that adipose tissue is derived from special formative cells "lipoblasts," set apart in the embryo in primitive fat forming organs. According to this interpretation the characteristic distribution of fat in the adult would then reflect the distribution and relative abundance of these special fat forming cells. Many would now make no distinction between Toldt's lipoblasts and persisting mesenchymal cells.

Hammar's (1895) interpretation was, in effect, a combination of these two views. He distinguished two processes, the first taking place during embryonic life and called *primary fat formation*. In this process special cells were laid down in lobular, glandlike arrangements of epithelioid cells. These cells first developed multiple small lipid droplets, which later coalesced to form a single large droplet. In addi-

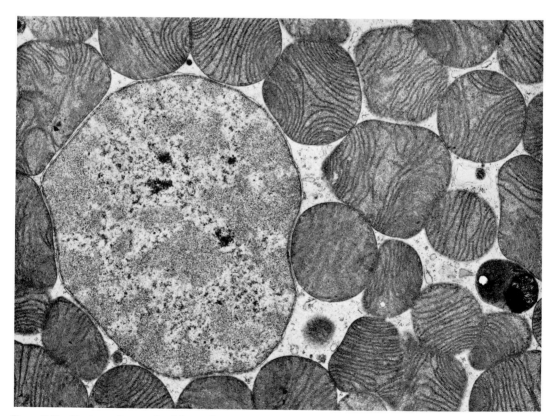

Figure 7-7. Electron micrograph of the nucleus and adjacent cytoplasm of a brown adipose cell from a bat recently aroused from hibernation. Notice the abundance of large spherical mitochondria with numerous long cristae. × 14,000.

HISTOPHYSIOLOGY OF ADIPOSE TISSUE

The histophysiology of adipose tissue can best be understood in relation to the analogy of deposits and withdrawals from a metabolic reserve bank. The deposits may be in the form of (1) fatty acids of the chylomicrons absorbed from the diet, (2) fatty acids synthesized from glucose in the liver and transported to the adipose tissue in the form of serum lipoprotein, or (3) triglyceride synthesized from carbohydrate in the adipose cells themselves. Withdrawals are made by enzymatic hydrolysis of triglyceride and release of free fatty acids into the blood. With a continuous supply of glucose, lipolysis and release of free fatty acids are negligible. With alternation of fasting and feeding, which is the usual feeding pattern, lipolysis is increased several times during periods of fasting. The normal balance is greatly affected by

Figure 7-8. A thick section of brown and white adipose tissue in which the blood vessels have been injected with India ink. The vascular bed of the brown fat (*above*) is extraordinarily rich and has a typical glandlike pattern, while that of the white fat (*below*) is relatively sparse. × 70. (After D. W. Fawcett, J. Morphology, *90:*363, 1952.)

tion to this primary fat formation, he believed that fat could form at any time during late fetal or postnatal life directly from relatively undifferentiated connective tissue cells by accumulation of lipid, without these cells becoming arranged in recognizable glandlike lobules. The end products of primary and secondary fat formation in man were said to be indistinguishable in normally nourished individuals.

Certainly two distinct methods of histogenesis of fat are recognizable in human embryos. In postnatal life, however, the cells in those areas that correspond in their anatomical distribution to the brown fat of rodents continue to accumulate lipid. The multiple droplets ultimately coalesce into a single droplet, and the cells thus become morphologically indistinguishable from those which develop directly from primitive connective tissue. Thus, in the adult human, there seems to be only one morphological type of adipose tissue.

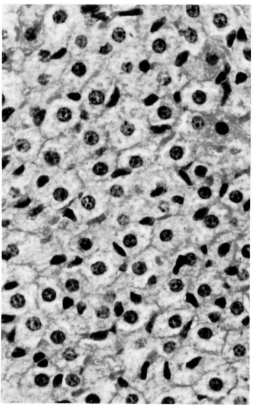

Figure 7-9. Brown adipose tissue that has become depleted of lipid after prolonged fasting, or as a consequence of hypophysectomy, takes on the appearance of a gland. Its cells resemble epithelium rather than fibroblasts. × 750.

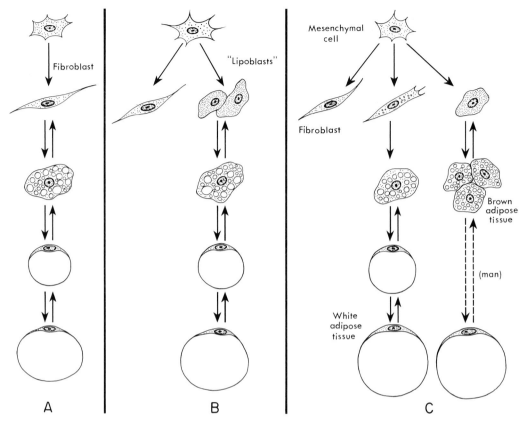

Figure 7-10. Diagrammatic representation of the three principal views concerning the histogenesis of adipose tissue. *A,* This represents the view that adipose cells are merely fibroblasts which have accumulated excess lipid (Flemming). *B,* The view that adipose tissue develops from special formative cells ("lipoblasts") set apart early in embryonic life (Toldt). *C,* The compromise interpretation that recognizes two processes, one leading to the formation of lobular, glandlike masses of epithelioid cells that develop into brown adipose tissue and one in which persisting mesenchymal cells develop directly into ordinary white adipose tissue (Hammar). In rodents that have brown fat in adult life the two types of adipose tissue remain morphologically distinct. In man, the multiple droplets of the brown fat gradually coalesce so that it comes to resemble the white fat except after fasting or prolonged illness.

hormones and by the action of the nervous system.

HORMONAL INFLUENCES. In mobilization of depot fat the pituitary probably acts in most instances on the adrenal cortex and thyroid rather than directly upon the adipose tissue. There are marked species differences, and the mechanisms involved are still obscure. It has yet to be clearly established that in response to a need for fuel the pituitary secretes a substance that promotes liberation of fatty acids from adipose tissue.

The characteristic differences in adipose tissue distribution in males and females has already been alluded to. Because hormones circulate freely in the blood and presumably reach all tissues in approximately equal con-

centrations, these differences in fat distribution imply either that there are genetically determined differences in distribution of cells having the capacity to develop into fat cells, or that there are regional differences in sensitivity of the cells to circulating *sex hormones.*

This regional difference in sensitivity does not seem to be restricted to the effects of sex hormones, for an excess of *adrenal cortical hormone* results in a characteristic distribution of fat, of which a prominent feature is an accumulation of fat over the lower cervical region, producing a deformity referred to as "buffalo hump."

The hormone *insulin* is the main physiological factor controlling the uptake of glucose by adipose tissue and secondarily the synthesis of fat from carbohydrate. Whether given in vivo or added to the medium of adipose tissue incubated in vitro, it appears to stimulate the transport of glucose into the cell and to accelerate its metabolism along all of the paths open to it. It seems to have a specific effect upon the rate at which glucose is converted to glycogen. Oxygen consumption is stimulated because of the accelerated conversion of glucose to fatty acid. These effects of insulin in promoting glycogen deposition can be demonstrated morphologically and are very much more pronounced in brown than in white fat (Figs. 7-11 and 7-12).

In the absence of insulin, as in diabetes, there is a rise in blood glucose, a diminished utilization of glucose, an increase in unesterified fatty acids in the plasma, and an increase in blood lipoproteins. Carbohydrates are normally used preferentially as an energy source, but in the diabetic, in whom carbohydrates cannot be utilized because of a deficiency of insulin, the required energy is derived principally from fat.

INFLUENCE OF THE AUTONOMIC NERVOUS SYSTEM. Adipose tissue is fairly richly innervated, especially the brown fat. The function of the nerves can be demonstrated experimentally by cutting the nerves of the interscapular fat body on one side of the midline, leaving the nerve supply to the other side intact. Within the first postoperative days it becomes apparent that the fat cells on the denervated side are larger than those on the normal side. The differences in the two sides are more dramatic if the animal is then deprived of food and placed in a cold environment. These conditions ordinarily lead to a rapid mobilization of lipid from the fat depots. In animals unilaterally denervated the fat cells on the side with the nerves intact are rapidly depleted of lipid, while the fat cells on the de-

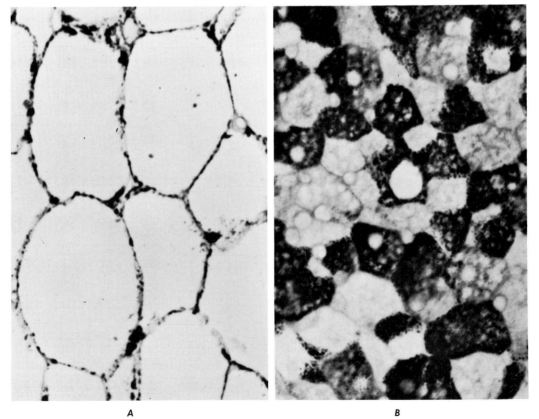

A   B

Figure 7-11.   *A,* White adipose tissue of a rat refed after a period of fasting. The dark granular deposits in the rim of cytoplasm are glycogen. The glycogen subsequently disappears as the carbohydrate is used in the synthesis of fat. × 650. *B,* Under the same conditions, considerably more glycogen is deposited in brown adipose tissue. Not all of the cells respond to the same degree. A similar deposition of glycogen results from administration of the hormone insulin. × 650. (After D. W. Fawcett, J. Morphology, *90:*363, 1952.)

nervated side retain a nearly normal content of lipid. It is thus demonstrated that the presence of nerves is necessary for mobilization of lipid from adipose tissue.

The chemical mediator, norepinephrine, is present in abundance in innervated adipose tissue but low or absent after denervation. It is apparently through release of norepinephrine from the nerve endings that the nerves control the mobilization of fatty acids from adipose tissue. Injection of small amounts of exogenous norepinephrine approximately doubles the amount of free fatty acid in the blood plasma. The norepinephrine brings about the activation of adipose tissue lipase, increasing the rate of hydrolysis of triglycerides (Fig. 7-12).

BROWN ADIPOSE TISSUE AS A HEAT GENERATOR. It has long been noted that brown adipose tissue is more abundant in animal species that hibernate and it was assumed to have a function related to winter dormancy. There is now evidence that one of its functions is to serve as a chemical furnace—an oil burner to heat the animal during arousal from hibernation.

There is a marked increase in oxygen consumption and a generation of heat when fatty acid released from triglyceride is oxidized in the fat cells or reconverted to triglyceride. When a hibernating animal begins to arouse, nerve impulses to the brown adipose tissue release norepinephrine at the nerve endings, which leads to activation of lipase in the fat cells and results in the breakdown of triglyceride to fatty acid and glycerol. Re-esterification of the fatty acid then occurs, with further consumption of oxygen and a generation of heat that serves to warm the blood flowing through the fat and secondarily to raise the temperature of the animal as a whole.

Correlated with this function are some unusual features of the mitochondria. Oxidative phosphorylation is difficult to demonstrate in mitochondrial fractions from brown adipose tissue. Moreover, the elementary particles or inner membrane subunits that are usually present on the cristae and are thought to be the sites of phosphate transfer enzymes have not been demonstrated in negatively stained mitochondria of brown adipose tissue. A lack of oxidative phosphorylation in mitochondria would be a surprising finding in any other tissue, but it is consistent with the needs of a system concerned mainly with heat production (Afzelius). The heat generation by brown fat can be demonstrated visually by the new technique of thermography (Fig. 7-13). The thermograph scans the infrared radiation from surfaces and registers the temperature-dependent intensity of radiation on a photographic plate. When a bat arousing from hibernation is scanned, the thin wing membranes rapidly equilibrate with the ambient temperature and most of the body is still relatively cool.

INSULIN   NOREPINEPHRINE

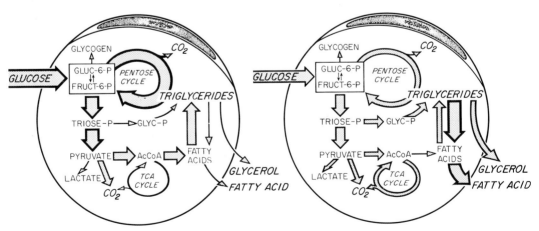

Figure 7-12. Diagram depicting effects of insulin and norepinephrine upon adipose tissue. The widths of the arrows are a rough measure of the quantitative effects on the respective metabolic pathways. (Modified after B. Jeanrenaud, Metabolism, *10*:535, 1961.)

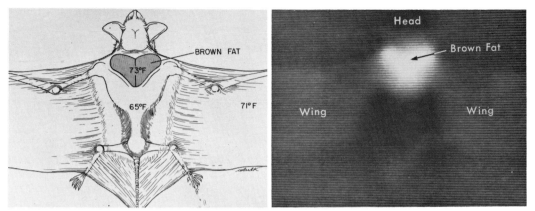

Figure 7-13. Thermograph of a bat made during arousal from hibernation. By scanning for detection of infrared radiation, a "hot spot" is revealed in the area corresponding to the location of the interscapular brown adipose tissue. During arousal this tissue acts as a chemical "furnace" producing heat that helps warm the rest of the body. (Courtesy of J. Hayward.)

However, a sharply delineated "hot area" is found on the thermograph, coinciding with the location of the interscapular brown fat. Thus in hibernating species brown adipose tissue performs two important roles during the arousal from dormancy: the oxidation of lipid to produce heat within the brown fat, and the release into the circulation of large amounts of oxidizable substrates for utilization by other tissues. What other functions this tissue may perform in the many species that do not hibernate remain to be discovered.

REFERENCES

Afzelius, B. A.: The fine structure of brown fat mitochondria. Proc. 6th Internat. Congr. Electron Microscopy. Tokyo, Maruzen Co., 1966, p. 359.

Ball, E. G., and R. L. Jungas: On the action of hormones which accelerate the rate of oxygen consumption and fatty acid release in rat adipose tissue *in vitro*. Proc. Nat. Acad. Sci., *47*:932, 1961.

Fawcett, D. W.: Histological observations on the relation of insulin to the deposition of glycogen in adipose tissue. Endocrinol., *42*:454, 1948.

Fawcett, D. W.: A comparison of the histological organization and histochemical reactions of brown fat and ordinary adipose tissue. J. Morphol., *90*:363, 1952.

Fawcett, D. W., and I. C. Jones: The effects of hypophysectomy, adrenalectomy, and of thiouracil feeding on the cytology of brown adipose tissue. Endocrinol., *45*:609, 1949.

Hausberger, F. X.: Influence of nutritional state on size and number of fat cells. Zeitschr. f. Zellforsch., *64*:13, 1964.

Hausberger, F. X.: Effect of dietary and endocrine factors on adipose tissue growth. *In* Renold, A. E., and G. F. Cahill, Jr., eds.: Handbook of Physiology, Section 5, p. 519. Washington, American Physiological Society, 1965.

Havel, R. J.: Autonomic nervous system and adipose tissue. *In* Renold, A. E., and G. F. Cahill, Jr., eds.: Handbook of Physiology, Section 5, p. 575. Washington, American Physiological Society, 1965.

Hayward, J. S., and E. G. Ball: Quantitative aspects of brown adipose tissue thermogenesis during arousal from hibernation. Biol. Bull., *131*:94, 1966.

Hayward, J. S., C. P. Lyman, and C. R. Taylor: The possible role of brown fat as a source of heat during arousal from hibernation. Ann. N. Y. Acad. Sci., *131*:441, 1965.

Jeanrenaud, B.: Dynamic aspects of adipose tissue metabolism: A review. Metab. Clin. Exp., *10*:535, 1961.

Joel, C. D.: The physiological role of brown adipose tissue. *In* Renold, A. E., and G. F. Cahill, Jr., eds.: Handbook of Physiology, Section 5, p. 59. Washington, American Physiological Society, 1965.

Joel, C. D., and E. G. Ball: The electron transmitter system of brown adipose tissue. Biochem., *1*:281, 1962.

Luckenbill, L. M., and A. S. Cohen: The association of lipid droplets with cytoplasmic filaments in avian subsynovial adipose cells. J. Cell Biol., *31*:195, 1966.

Napolitano, L.: The differentiation of white adipose cells. J. Cell Biol., *18*:663, 1963.

Napolitano, L.: The fine structure of adipose tissues. *In* Renold, A. E., and G. F. Cahill, Jr., eds.: Handbook of Physiology, Section 5, p. 109. Washington, American Physiological Society, 1965.

Napolitano, L., and D. W. Fawcett: The fine structure of brown adipose tissue in newborn mice and rats. J. Biophys. & Biochem. Cytol., *4*:685, 1958.

Napolitano, L., and H. T. Gagne: Lipid depleted white adipose cells. Anat. Rec., *147*:273, 1963.

Rémillard, G. L.: Histochemical and microchemical observations on the lipids of the interscapular brown fat of the female verpertilionid bat, *Myotis lucifugus lucifugus*. Ann. N. Y. Acad. Sci., *72*:1, 1958.

Renold, A. E., A. Marble, and D. W. Fawcett: Action of insulin on deposition of glycogen and storage of fat in adipose tissue. Endocrinol., *46*:55, 1950.

Sidman, R. L.: The direct effect of insulin on organ cultures of brown fat. Anat. Rec., *124*:723, 1956.

Sidman, R. L., and D. W. Fawcett: The effect of peripheral nerve section on some metabolic responses of brown adipose tissue in mice. Anat. Rec., *118*:487, 1954.

Sidman, R. L., M. Perkins, and N. Weiner: Noradrenaline and adrenaline content of adipose tissues. Nature, *193*:36, 1962.

Smith, R. E., and R. J. Hock: Brown fat: Thermogenic effector of arousal in hibernators. Science, *140*:199, 1963.

Weiner, N., M. Perkins, and R. L. Sidman: Effect of reserpine on noradrenaline content of innervated and denervated brown adipose tissue of the rat. Nature, *193*:137, 1962.

Wells, H. G.: Adipose tissue, a neglected subject. J.A.M.A., *114*:2177, 2284, 1940.

Wertheimer, E., and B. Shapiro: The physiology of adipose tissue. Physiol. Rev., *28*:451, 1948.

CHAPTER EIGHT

Blood Cell Formation and Destruction

The short-lived blood corpuscles are kept at a constant number in the blood by the continuous formation of new cells. Under normal conditions, blood cells are regenerated only within the lymphatic and the myeloid tissues and organs (*hemopoietic* organs and tissues). The process of their formation is called *hemopoiesis*.

The cells of the circulating blood may be divided into two groups, according to their origin. To the first group belong the lymphocytes (and probably the monocytes), which originate in the lymphatic tissue and are called *lymphoid elements*. The second group consists of the erythrocytes and the granular leukocytes; these originate in the myeloid tissue and are called *myeloid elements*. This separation of myeloid and lymphatic tissues, however, is not absolute, since there is no such separation in the early embryonic stages of the mammals or throughout life in most of the lower vertebrates. Moreover, the usual separation between the two hemopoietic tissues is effaced in certain abnormal conditions in postnatal mammals (p. 207).

All the blood cell forming tissues of adult mammals have the same fundamental structure—a fibrous and cellular stroma in whose meshes hemopoiesis takes place. This framework is composed of reticular fibers and cells. The reticular fibers are sheathed by a thin layer of cytoplasm in which are scattered pale oval nuclei (Fig. 8-1). These *primitive reticular cells* show distinct cell limits in the electron microscope (Clark) and they thus do not form a syncytium as was believed on the basis

of optical microscopy. They are not active phagocytes and only rarely contain a few granules of waste pigment; they do not take up appreciable amounts of vital dyes (Fig. 8-2), although they can become active macrophages (see below and discussion on p. 209). Like the mesenchymal cells of the embryo, they are endowed with the ability to turn into all types of blood and connective tissue cells.

From these primitive reticular cells there are many transitions to larger cells, which are active phagocytes called *phagocytic reticular cells* or *fixed macrophages*. These have an abundant cytoplasm and a large pale nucleus. Most of them are stellate or spindle-shaped and adhere to the reticular fibers. They may contain debris of dead cells, foreign materials, engulfed erythrocytes in various stages of disintegration, and, in vitally stained animals, numerous large dye granules (Fig. 8-2). In fresh preparations stained supravitally with neutral red, the inclusions and vacuoles of the macrophages stain deeply. The fixed macrophages may become *free macrophages*.

LYMPHATIC TISSUE

In mammals the lymphatic tissue forms distinctly outlined organs, the *lymph nodes*, which are arranged along the course of the lymph vessels. It is present in small amounts in the *bone marrow* and in large amounts in the *spleen*, where it may undergo specific modifications depending on the peculiar type of blood circulation in this organ (see Chapter

15). In addition, lymphatic tissue is scattered in the mucous membranes of the alimentary canal and the respiratory passages, in the conjunctiva, and elsewhere. The *thymus,* also an important lymphoid organ, differs from the rest of the lymphatic tissue in that it has, intermixed with the lymphocytes, a large epithelial component, which is currently believed to be an important gland of internal secretion (see Chapter 16).

Two microscopic constituents can be distinguished in the lymphatic tissue: a sponge-like framework, or stroma, and free cells in the meshes of the stroma. These constituents are present in different proportions in various parts of the lymphatic tissue, so that we may distinguish *loose lymphatic tissue,* consisting predominantly of stroma; *dense lymphatic tissue,* in which the free cells predominate; and *nodular lymphatic tissue,* especially dense accumulations of free cells within the loose or dense lymphatic tissue. Under various physiological and pathological conditions, each of these types of tissue may turn into either of the other two types.

The loose lymphatic tissue, as found in the lymph nodes, forms sinuses or pathways for the lymph, which flows through the organ. Unlike the lymph vessels, which have a free lumen and a wall of their own, the sinuses are merely portions of the lymphatic tissue that are especially loose in structure (see Chapter 14).

Stroma

The framework of lymphatic tissue is made up of reticular fibers and reticular cells (Fig. 8-1).

FIBERS.   The fibers are of the reticular type and are best shown by the silver impregnation method for optical microscopy. The electron microscope shows that they are composed of bundles of collagenous fibrils. At the periphery of the nodules the framework is dense and the meshes are small, while the stroma within the nodules is loose, with thin fibers. In the loose tissue of the sinuses the large meshes are composed of coarse fibers. Along the walls of all the blood vessels the reticulum is condensed.

CELLS.   The cells of the stroma are the primitive reticular cells and the phagocytic reticular cells or fixed macrophages. The primitive reticular cells of the lymphatic tissue have the ability to develop into phagocytes and lymphocytes, as well as into myelocytes in ectopic myelopoiesis (p. 207). Under certain conditions the fixed macrophages may become free macrophages anywhere in the lymphatic tissue; they are especially numerous in the sinuses. When the lymph contains foreign substances, such as lithium carmine or bacteria, the number of free macrophages increases greatly.

The fixed and free macrophages of the lymphatic tissue correspond closely with those of the loose connective tissue (p. 144). In the lymphatic tissue they increase by division and by development from primitive reticular cells.

The macrophages, which help form the walls of the sinuses and which are attached to the fibers passing through the cavities of these spaces, are often flattened and resemble endothelial cells. For this reason they have been called endothelium, but the term is not justified because the ability to store vital dyes and to transform into free macrophages has not been proved for the endothelium of the common blood or lymph vessels. The flattened form of these macrophages is an adaptation to their position on the wall of the channels through which the lymph flows. The terms *littoral* or *lining cells* of the system of macrophages are perhaps the best to use.

The lymphatic tissue does not contain

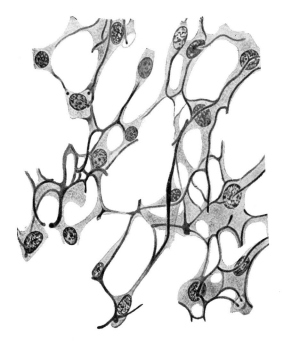

Figure 8-1.   Section of a lymph node after the lymphocytes have been removed, showing the network of reticular cells and their intimate relations with the reticular fibers. Mallory-azan stain. (Redrawn after Heidenhain.)

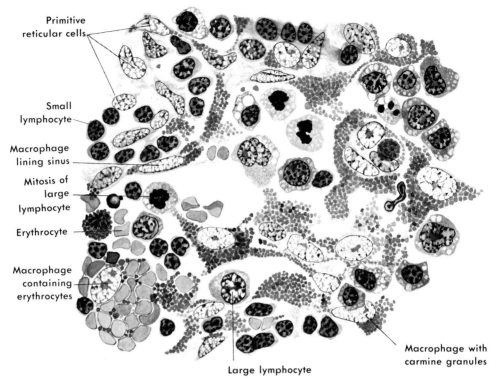

Figure 8-2. Medullary sinus of mesenteric lymph node of a rabbit which had repeated intravenous injections of lithium carmine. Hematoxylin-eosin-azure II stain. × 950. (After A. A. Maximow.)

fibroblasts (except along the arteries and veins and in the trabeculae of the lymphatic organs), although, in inflammation and in cultures of this tissue, fibroblasts develop from the primitive reticular cells and from the macrophages.

Free Cells

The meshes of the fibrous and cellular reticulum contain free cells. In dense lymphatic tissue and in the nodules the free cells are so densely crowded that the nuclei of the primitive reticular cells can be clearly seen among them only in thin sections. The free cells are much less numerous in the meshes of the sinuses; here they float in the lymph, which passes slowly through the channels. Except for the free macrophages described earlier, the free cells are all *lymphocytes*.

In the lymphatic tissue several groups of lymphocytes can be distinguished. The *small lymphocytes* form the vast majority (Fig. 8-3) (see Chapter 5). The *medium-sized lymphocytes,* scattered everywhere among the small lymphocytes, are present in a much smaller number. They are slightly larger than the small lymphocytes, are present in a much smaller number. They are slightly larger than the small lymphocytes, are present in a much smaller number. They are slightly larger than the small lymphocytes, are present in a much smaller number. They are slightly larger than the small lymphocytes, are present in a much smaller number. They are slightly larger than the small lymphocytes, are present in a much smaller number. They are slightly larger than the small

variety, and the nucleus is clearer and contains less chromatin; one or two nucleoli are prominent, and there is more cytoplasm. These cells divide mitotically. *Large lymphocytes,* or *macrolymphocytes,* are scattered singly among the other lymphocytes. In the living tissues they are spherical and measure up to 15 μ in diameter, although an occasional one may measure 20 μ or more. In dry smears, the spherical shape is spread into a thin, flattened, much larger circle. They occur everywhere, even in the sinuses, but are more numerous in the lymphatic nodules, their number varying with the functional condition of the lymphatic tissue. Often, especially in human lymph nodes, they may be absent. Their cytoplasm is strongly basophilic, owing to its ribosomes, and forms a broad layer around the nucleus. It may contain a few vacuoles at the indentation of the nucleus; the hemispherical cytocentrum with a diplosome is surrounded by a Golgi net. There are more rod-shaped mitochondria than in the smaller forms, and they are arranged around the cytocentrum. The large, usually kidney-shaped nucleus occupies a slightly eccentric position, with the excavation directed toward the large accumulation of cytoplasm. The nuclear membrane is coarsely outlined; the chromatin particles are widely scattered in a large quantity of clear nuclear sap. Always there are one or more large irregularly shaped nucleoli. The large lymphocytes divide by mitosis.

These three types of lymphocytes are connected with one another by an uninterrupted series of transitional forms. In the small ones mitoses are extremely rare under normal conditions, the main, immediate source of the lymphocytes of the blood being the medium-sized lymphocyte.

Under suitable conditions the small lymphocyte may hypertrophy into a larger one and regain the ability to divide. This transformation is probably a rare occurrence in the lymphatic tissue. The small lymphocytes of the blood can hypertrophy into typical large lymphocytes within a day or two in culture (p. 205).

Plasma cells are common in the lymphatic tissue, especially in the medullary cords of the lymph nodes; their number is subject to marked variation, particularly under pathological conditions. In some animals (rat, mouse) plasma cells are unusually numerous. Sometimes, eosinophilic leukocytes are found in the lymphatic tissue. Heterophilic granulocytes are a sign of an inflammatory lesion. Young forms of granulocytes (myelocytes) are found only in *extramedullary myelopoiesis* (p. 207). A few mast cells are scattered along the fibers of the reticulum; monocytes usually do not occur.

DEVELOPMENT OF LYMPHOCYTES. In postnatal mammals most lymphocytes arise by mitosis of pre-existing lymphocytes within the lymphatic tissue. This occurs mainly in the nodular lymphatic tissue but also to some extent in the diffuse and loose tissue. The mother cell is usually a medium-sized lymphocyte, although dividing larger ones are not uncommon. In some instances it has been possible to trace lymphocytes to their origin from primitive reticular cells—a source probably active only when the pre-existing lymphocytes are unable, because of their mitoses, to fill the demand for lymphocytes.

LYMPHATIC NODULES. The lymphatic nodules are dense accumulations of lymphocytes embedded in a relatively scanty cellular and fibrous reticulum, and are usually the expression of some stage of lymphocytopoietic activity focused at a small area in the lymphatic tissue. The nodules appear and disappear, or pass through a series of cyclic changes during which an intense new formation of lymphocytes proceeds through proliferation of pre-existing lymphocytes and to a lesser extent through transformation of the primitive reticular cells.

In its fully developed form, a nodule consists of a central portion and a peripheral zone, sometimes called the *corona*. The central portion of a nodule that is actively producing lymphocytes is called the *germinal center* or secondary nodule (Figs. 8-4 and 8-5). This germinal center may attain a diameter of 1 mm. It often has a small artery supplying it with blood. This central area in such a nodule appears paler than the surrounding mass of small lymphocytes with their dark nuclei, for the majority of its cells are medium-sized lymphocytes. They contain more mitotic figures than do the medium-sized lymphocytes in loose and dense lymphatic tissue. Scattered among them are a few large lymphocytes and all transitions between them. A few small lymphocytes are also found. Among the lymphocytes of an actively lymphocytopoietic nodule are scattered primitive reticular cells with indistinct cytoplasm (Fig. 8-5). These also show occasional mitoses. Macrophages with phagocytosed inclusions are distributed along the capillaries in the nodule.

At the end of a proliferative phase, mitosis ceases in the germinal center, which gradually becomes depleted of lymphocytes. Such an *inactive center* contains reticular cells, macrophages, and a few lymphocytes. In certain

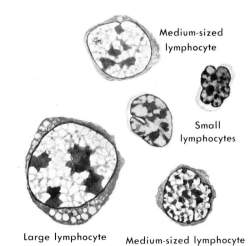

Figure 8-3. Lymphocytes from a human lymph node. Hematoxylin-eosin-azure II stain. × 1500. (After A. A. Maximow.)

pathological conditions—diptheria, burns, and severe bacterial and plasmodial infections— the central portion may have a similar appearance, although there are usually more active macrophages. Such central areas have been described as *"reaction centers."* Some of the stages of their development are much like the *"inactive centers."*

The *peripheral zone* or *corona* appears in sections darker than the central portion of the nodule, for the majority of its cells are densely crowded small lymphocytes with their dark nuclei. These small lymphocytes are frequently seen arranged in concentric layers.

In a stage of complete rest the lymphatic nodule consists mainly of small lymphocytes, so compactly arranged that the nodule stands out as a dense, darkly stained area in the diffuse

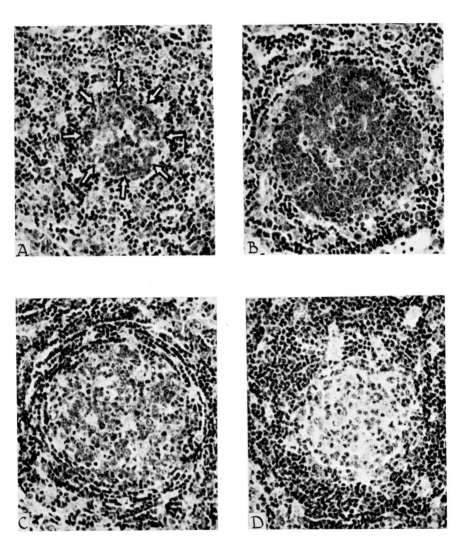

Figure 8-4. Photomicrographs showing four nodules at different stages of development in mesenteric lymph node of guinea pigs, five days after injection of *Listeria monocytogenes. A,* Small new "bare" germinal center consisting of dividing medium-sized lymphocytes. Its margins are indicated by the arrows. *B,* Later stage in the development of a nodule. This "bare" germinal center contains 27 mitoses in medium-sized lymphocytes. *C,* Corona of densely packed small lymphocytes has been formed around the germinal center, which is actively lymphocytopoietic and contains 15 mitoses in medium-sized lymphocytes. This is the type of nodule which is often regarded as typical, consisting of an outer, dark-staining zone and a lighter central area. *D,* Nodule with inactive center. It has a pale-staining central portion consisting mainly of reticular cells, free macrophages, and a few scattered lymphocytes. This nodule, with its center depleted of lymphocytes, resembles the "reaction center" type. Hematoxylin-eosin-azure II. × 300. (After Conway.)

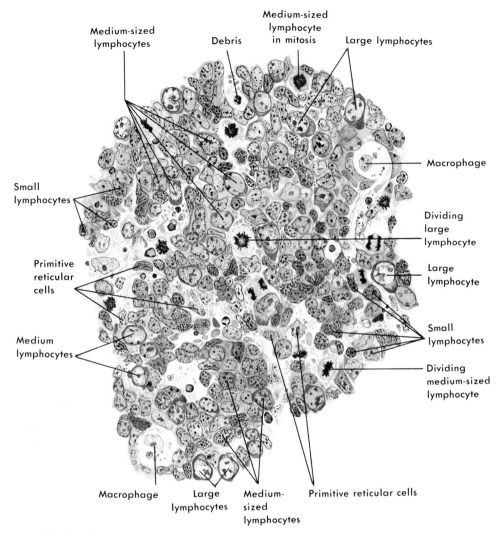

Figure 8-5. Portion of actively lymphoctyopoietic nodule of human lymph node. Hematoxylin-eosin-azure II. × 750. (After A. A. Maximow.)

lymphatic tissue. New nodules may develop anywhere in the loose or dense lymphatic tissue. Indeed, they may even develop in a preexisting nodule. These new areas of lymphocytopoiesis start with many, rapidly repeated mitoses in medium-sized lymphocytes (Fig. 8-5). In some instances these have been shown to arise as free cells, with a narrow rim of cytoplasm, by individual transformation or through mitoses of the primitive reticular cells (Fig. 8-17).

Such a small isolated mass of densely packed medium-sized lymphocytes is in every respect similar to a germinal center. Because of the absence of a corona of small lympho-

cytes, it may be described as a "bare" or "naked" *germinal center*. Many of the medium-sized lymphocytes become large lymphocytes, and some of the primitive reticular cells become macrophages. The bare germinal center increases in size because of the continued mitosis of the medium-sized lymphocytes. The growth pressure may cause development of a corona of densely packed small lymphocytes, depending on the density of the surrounding lymphatic tissue. As a lymphocyte forming nodule becomes inactive, mitoses become less numerous, and the last divisions of the medium-sized cells give rise to small lymphocytes; some of the latter may originate from shrinkage

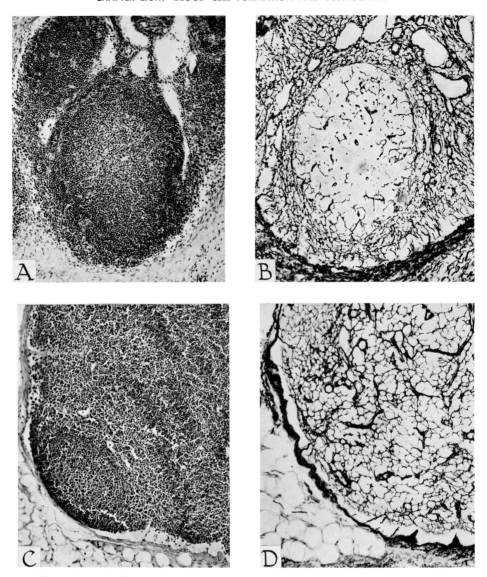

Figure 8-6. Photomicrographs from sections of mesenteric lymph nodes of rabbits after injection of *L. monocytogenes. A* and *B* are from the same block, 36 hours after injection. *C* and *D* are from the same block, 48 hours after injection. When Nodular lymphatic tissue (*A*) becomes diffuse lymphatic tissue (*C*) the reticular fiber framework characteristic of the nodules (*B*) is lost (*D*). In all sections the subcapsular sinus is prominent. *A* and *C*, stained with hematoxylin; *B* and *D*, impregnated for reticular fibers by the Foot method. × 107. (After Conway.)

of the larger cells. Plasma cells also appear. Decrease of the growth pressure effaces the sharp boundary line between the center and the periphery of the nodule, which then becomes uniform in appearance and composition.

NEW FORMATION OF LYMPHATIC TISSUE. New foci of lymphatic tissue and even lymph nodes can develop in any part of the loose connective tissue in the adult organism. When this happens, the lymphocytes and the ele-

ments of the stroma develop from the ubiquitous undifferentiated elements of the adult connective tissue (p. 143). When the lymphatic tissue involutes and disappears, the lymphocytes degenerate or wander away, while the reticular cells seem to be transformed into fat cells, or, perhaps, fibroblasts.

FUNCTION OF THE LYMPHATIC TISSUE. The most conspicuous function of the lymphatic tissue is the production of lymphocytes.

The lymphocytes that are newly formed in the lymph nodes—the vast majority of them are of the small variety—migrate into the sinuses and are carried away by the lymph stream into the lymphatics and the thoracic duct, and thence into the blood. In addition, numbers of small lymphocytes from the blood migrate directly into the lymphatic tissue through the endothelium of its venous capillaries (Fig. 14-8 and p. 143). In extramedullary myelopoiesis the lymphatic tissue can also become a source of granulocytes (see p. 207).

In the early stages of infection of rabbits and guinea pigs with *Listeria monocytogenes*, the lymphocytes of the lymph nodes, and occasionally even of the nodules, turn into monocytes. Lymphoid hyperplasia in malaria builds up a reserve from which new macrophages are formed. The other functions of the lymphatic tissue are concerned mainly with its macrophages, lymphocytes, and plasma cells; they will be discussed with the structure of the lymph nodes and spleen.

The marked atrophy of lymphoid tissues that result from the action of a variety of noxious agents (part of the "alarm reaction" of Selye) is believed to be due to the liberation of adrenal cortical hormones; it does not occur if the adrenal cortex is removed.

Some authors deny the importance of the nodules for the regeneration of the lymphocytes, believing them to be only centers of reaction of the lymphatic tissue to various toxic agents. As proof, they point to the degeneration of lymphocytes and reticular cells, as evidenced by the nuclear debris in the macrophages of the centers, in intoxications, burns, inflammatory lesions, and certain infectious diseases. It is true that cellular debris occurs in the center of the nodule (Fig. 8-4). However, this is not evidence that the center of the nodule is exclusively a site of cell destruction, since lymphocytes continue to proliferate (see mitoses in lymphocytes in Fig. 8-4), and the germinal center can increase in size, while debris is present. Just as in all areas of rapid new formation

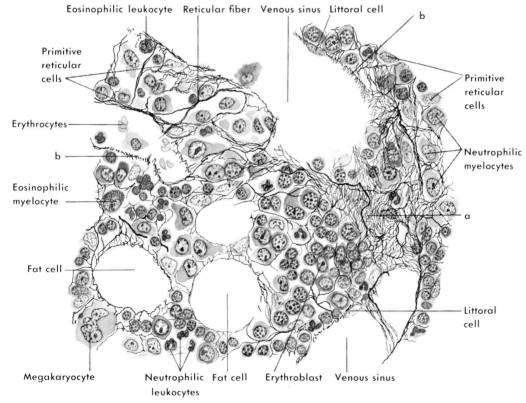

Figure 8-7. Bone marrow from upper epiphysis of a femur of a 6 year old child. The fibrous network of the wall of a vessel is seen from the surface at *a* and in cross section at *b*. Bielschowsky stain. × 500. (After A. A. Maximow.)

of cells, some of the newly formed cells degenerate, so do a number of the newly formed lymphocytes in the germinal center. Some of the clearest pictures of regeneration of lymphatic tissue are to be found in the work of Conway and after high doses of x-irradiation (see DeBruyn). In such material it is relatively easy to follow the regenerative process and the cyclic changes in the nodules.

The lymphocytes are among the most sensitive cells in the body to ionizing radiations, toxins such as mustard gas, and steroids. Unexpectedly, reticular cells, which are more primitive than lymphocytes, are remarkably radioresistant.

Embryonic lymphatic tissue has nodules that are dense masses of small lymphocytes, lacking pale-staining central areas. It is claimed that guinea pigs which have been reared for 60 days on sterile media do not show centers in the nodules.

LYMPHATIC TISSUE IN THE LOWER VERTEBRATES. In the lower vertebrates, although lymphocytes are plentiful, their regeneration is not localized in special lymphatic organs but occurs in many places in the connective tissue. In fact, lymph nodes are usually absent. The most important difference in comparison with the mammals is that the lymphatic tissue is not sharply separated from the myeloid tissue.

MYELOID TISSUE: THE BONE MARROW

The bone marrow weighs approximately 2600 gm., or about 4.5 per cent of the body weight. The marrow may be divided into *red* (active, hemopoietic) and *yellow* (inactive, fatty) marrow. In the embryo and newborn, only red marrow is found. With progressing age the red marrow is partially converted to yellow marrow, so that in the normal adult approximately equal amounts of red and yellow marrow are found. Vertebrae, ribs, sternum, diploë, and often the proximal epiphyses of the femur and humerus contain red marrow. Under normal conditions approximately 70 per cent of the red marrow is occupied by fat.

No sharp limit can be drawn between the two types of bone marrow. The amount of myeloid tissue increases at the expense of the fat when there is an increased rate of formation of myeloid cells. After prolonged starvation or in some wasting diseases, the amount of myeloid tissue decreases and the fat acquires a peculiar gelatinous appearance, a condition known as serous fat atrophy. Figure 8-19 shows the effect of raising the temperature of fatty marrow.

The myeloid tissue, like the lymphatic, consists of the spongelike framework or stroma, which is intimately connected with the blood vessels, and the free cells in the meshes of the stroma.

Stroma

As in the lymphatic tissue, the stroma consists of primitive and phagocytic reticular cells attached to the argyrophilic fibers (Figs. 8-7 and 8-8). The network of cells and fibers is looser and its meshes are larger than in the lymphatic tissue. Particulate matter and vital dyes injected into the blood are taken up rapidly by the fixed macrophages of the bone marrow.

Circulation in the bone marrow is characterized by the presence of many large vessels, called *sinusoids,* through whose walls innumerable cells pass into the bloodstream. The sinusoids are lined by flattened, fixed macrophages (littoral cells), like those forming the walls of the lymph node sinuses. These dye storing and phagocytosing cells have indistinct limits and are in direct connection with similar cells of the stroma. Preformed openings between the littoral cells have not been demonstrated with the electron microscope. They can round off and appear as free macrophages in the blood of the sinusoids. The manner in which the arteries connect with the sinusoids needs further study.

The stroma of the myeloid tissue is distinguished by the constant presence of fat cells. These are scattered singly in the red marrow (Fig. 8-8), but in the yellow bone marrow they occupy most of the tissue (Fig. 8-19*A*); between them, except for the blood vessels and reticular fibers, there remain only scattered fixed macrophages and primitive reticular cells. The latter are probably the main local source of the new blood cells when the yellow bone marrow is transformed into red marrow. Small accumulations of lymphatic tissue with nodules occur regularly in the bone marrow, but lymph vessels have not been found.

Free Cells

In contrast to the free cells of the lymphatic tissue, those of the myeloid tissue are

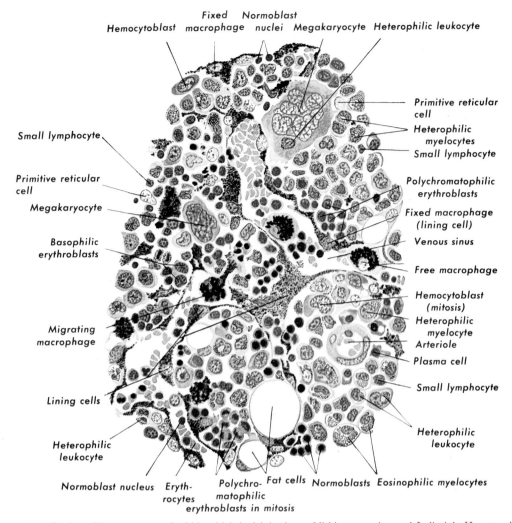

Figure 8-8. Section of bone marrow of rabbit which had injections of lithium carmine and India ink. Hematoxylin-eosin-azure II. × 460. (After A. A. Maximow.)

extremely varied in form and are scattered irregularly throughout the tissue. The vast majority of them are immature myeloid elements.

MATURE MYELOID ELEMENTS. Mature, non-nucleated erythrocytes, and the three types of granular leukocytes as they occur in the circulating blood, are found everywhere between the other cells. Thus the tissue that produces these elements always contains a ready supply of them and, in case of need, can forward large quantities at once into the blood (Fig. 8-8).

IMMATURE MYELOID ELEMENTS. The other free cells in the bone marrow are *hemocytoblasts* (free stem cells); *erythroblasts,* the precursors of the red blood corpuscles; *myelocytes,* the precursors of the three principal types of granular leukocytes; and *megakaryocytes,* the precursors of blood platelets. In postnatal mammals the myeloid cells develop extravascularly in the bone marrow.

Hemocytoblasts. The myeloid tissue of all adult mammals contains ameboid, nongranular, basophilic cells of lymphoid nature. They vary in size, the largest measuring 15μ or more, and are scattered singly or in groups of two or four. Their structure corresponds exactly to that of the lymphocytes. They are the *free stem cells* of all other myeloid elements. (Fig. 8-9). A suitable name for them is hemocytoblast. The small cells of this type are connected with the larger ones by a complete series of transitional forms.

Erythroblasts. The young forms of the

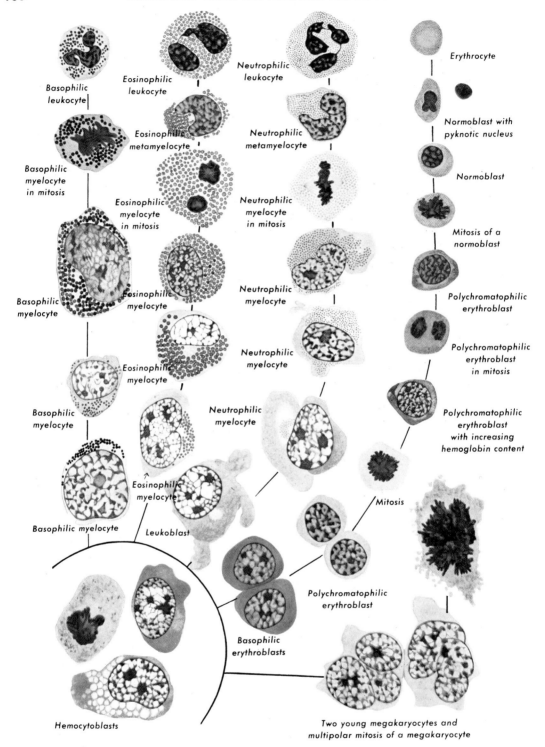

Figure 8-9. Development of the myeloid elements of human bone marrow from a common lymphoid stem cell as seen in sections stained with hematoxylin-eosin-azure II. The basophilic myelocytes were fixed in absolute alcohol and stained with alcoholic thionine. The mature cells are from dry smears of human blood stained with May-Grünwald-Giemsa, except the basophilic leukocyte, which is stained with alcoholic thionine. × 1500. (After A. A. Maximow.)

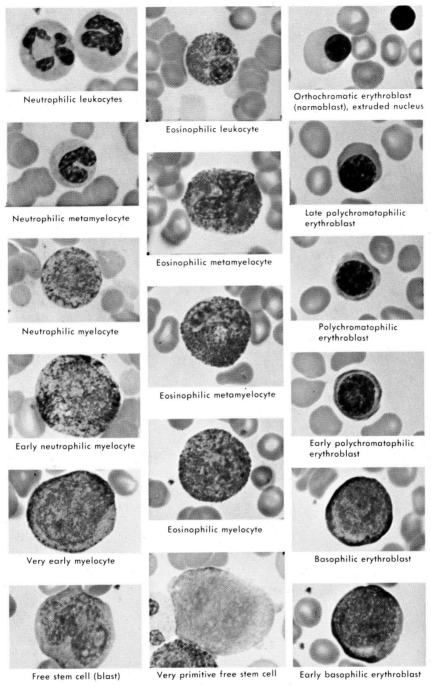

Neutrophilic leukocytes

Eosinophilic leukocyte

Orthochromatic erythroblast (normoblast), extruded nucleus

Neutrophilic metamyelocyte

Eosinophilic metamyelocyte

Late polychromatophilic erythroblast

Neutrophilic myelocyte

Eosinophilic metamyelocyte

Polychromatophilic erythroblast

Early neutrophilic myelocyte

Eosinophilic myelocyte

Early polychromatophilic erythroblast

Very early myelocyte

Basophilic erythroblast

Free stem cell (blast)

Very primitive free stem cell

Early basophilic erythroblast

Figure 8-10. Photomicrographs of developing blood cells in human bone marrow, showing steps in the transformation of stem cells into neutrophilic and eosinophilic leukocytes and into erythrocytes, as seen in dry smears stained with Wright's blood stain. Compare with Figure 8-9 which shows similar cells as seen in sections of bone marrow.

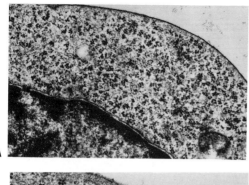

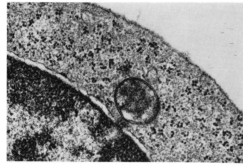

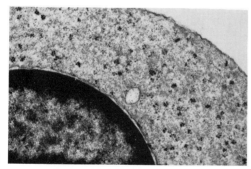

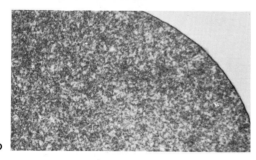

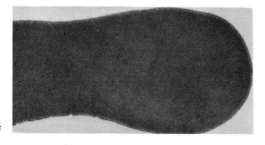

red blood corpuscles are spherical cells with spherical nuclei and are called erythroblasts. In living cells their cytoplasm is homogeneous and of a yellow color, which intensifies as the cells develop into erythrocytes. Supravital staining with neutral red produces red precipitates in their cytoplasm. Erythroblasts never show ameboid motion. In fixed and stained sections, mitochondria, a Golgi net, and a cytocentrum are seen. The round nucleus of the erythroblasts always presents a checkerboard distribution of angular particles of chromatin. The nucleoli gradually involute. The number of mitotic divisions in the cell lineage is not known, although it is believed that development into the mature red cell takes about three days. The changes in the erythroblasts as they develop into erythrocytes are shown in Figures 8-9 and 8-10, and in the electron micrographs of Figures 8-11, 8-12, and 8-13.

The erythroblasts closest to the stem cell are called *basophilic erythroblasts,* because of the intense basophilia of their cytoplasm, which stains deeper than that of the hemocytoblasts. An intermediate cell (*proerythroblast*) has been described.

The erythroblasts of the next youngest generation have a small amount of hemoglobin. After staining with Wright or Giemsa stain the cytoplasm varies from a purplish blue to lilac or gray. These erythroblasts are, therefore, called *polychromatophilic.* This staining reaction is due to the appearance of pink-staining hemoglobin in the basophilic cytoplasm of the erythroblast, which stains blue with these methods because of its RNA.

The polychromatophilic erythroblasts divide mitotically. Some of them remain in the tissue in a resting condition for future use. In the others the amount of hemoglobin increases while the basophilia of the cytoplasm diminishes; in this way *normoblasts* arise, in which the cytoplasm stains a bright pink with Wright or Giemsa stain. Normoblasts are smaller than polychromatophilic erythroblasts and only slightly larger than mature erythrocytes. The small round nucleus contains a dense accumu-

Figure 8-11. A series of electron micrographs illustrating the decline in number of ribosomes and progressive increase in hemoglobin in the cytoplasm during the differentiation of the guinea pig erythrocyte. *A,* Basophilic erythroblast. *B,* Polychromatophilic erythroblast. *C,* Orthochromatic erythroblast (normoblast). *D,* Reticulocyte. *E,* Erythrocyte. About × 25,000.

lation of angular chromatin particles. After a number of mitotic divisions, the nucleus is condensed to a homogeneous, dark body. Each mature normoblast extrudes its pyknotic nucleus and becomes a red blood corpuscle.

Some of the changes occurring in the cells are morphologic manifestations of the synthesis of nucleotides and hemoglobin. These syntheses consist of a series of enzymatically controlled steps, presumably under genetic control. Hemoglobin is formed from heme, globin, and iron. Heme is a porphyrin synthesized from glycine and acetate. Human globin consists of two complex polypeptide chains, each of which is made up of a specific number of amino acids arranged in a characteristic sequence. Variation from the normal in this chain results in an abnormal hemoglobin often associated with a shortened red cell survival.

A total of about 30 mg. of iron, attached to a beta globulin, transferrin, passes through the plasma daily. About 20 mg. comes from the destruction of some 20 ml. of erythrocytes every day. This is reutilized in the daily, compensatory formation of 20 ml. of new erythrocytes. Nine of the additional 10 mg. of iron in daily transit through the plasma is derived from the solution and deposition of iron in the form of ferritin and hemosiderin, and 1 mg. from iron entering the body from food to replenish the total of 1 mg. lost in the exfoliation of skin and intestinal tract and in the excreta. One of the most important facets of iron metabolism is that in man there is no means to excrete more than 1 mg. of iron except by loss of red blood cells from the body.

The normal adult man stores approximately 1200 mg. of iron (women 1000 mg. or less) as ferritin or hemosiderin. Both of these are complexes of a protein, apoferritin, with $FeOH_3$, 23 per cent in the case of ferritin and 25 per cent in hemosiderin. With the increase in iron storage, the ratio of $FeOH_3$ to apoferritin increases and an increased percentage of the iron is stored as hemosiderin. Both complexes are stored primarily in the fixed and free macrophages of the hemopoietic tissues and in the Kuppfer and epithelial cells of the liver (p. 588). The 1 to 2 μ granules, staining greenish blue with eosin-azure II, are relatively easily available for hemoglobin synthesis. Hemosiderin is stored as larger, yellow-green, sharply delimited deposits, staining green with azure II, and is less easily available for hemoglobin synthesis.

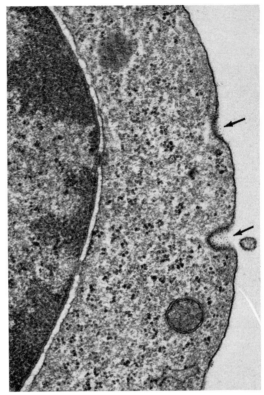

Figure 8-12. An electron micrograph of a portion of a guinea pig polychromatophilic erythroblast showing (at the arrows) two stages in the uptake of ferritin particles by micropinocytosis. Notice that the cell membrane is generally smooth but acquires a fuzzy surface coating at those sites destined to invaginate to form vesicles. The ferritin is adsorbed onto the surface coat. × 36,000. (After D. W. Fawcett, J. Histochem. and Cytochem., *13*:85, 1965.)

Granules of iron in the cytoplasm of erythroblasts, before being incorporated into hemoglobin, can be demonstrated by the Prussian blue reaction. Erythroblasts, including normoblasts, containing such granules are called *sideroblasts;* reticulocytes and erythrocytes containing these granules are called *siderocytes.*

Ascorbic acid, folic acid, vitamin B_{12}, and undoubtedly other substances, function as coenzymes or as precursors of coenzymes in nucleotide synthesis. A deficiency in any of these may cause the formation of abnormal erythrocytes (megalocytes) with a decreased life span. Vitamin B_{12} is absorbed by action of an "intrinsic factor" secreted by the fundic part of the stomach. A deficiency in this vitamin also causes abnormalities in white cell and platelet formation, in mucous membranes, and in the nervous tissues.

Myelocytes. Besides the erythroblasts, the young forms of the three types of leukocytes (heterophilic, eosinophilic, and basophilic) are common cell types of the myeloid tissue. The myelocytes of each of the three types are provided with their characteristic granulation and cannot be transformed into myelocytes of another type or into elements of another kind. They have a compact, round or kidney-shaped nucleus and proliferate intensely by mitotic division. Some of their progeny remain unchanged, while others undergo progressive maturation. Finally, each cell is transformed individually into a mature polymorphonuclear granular leukocyte. These details are shown in Figures 8-9 and 8-10, which also illustrate the differences resulting from the use of the two techniques of preparation. Electron micrographs (Figs. 8-15 and 8-16) show further details of the structure of myelocytes. Estimates of the duration of maturation of a myeloblast up to the time of entry of the granular leukocyte into the circulation vary from three to four days.

Myelocytes with Heterophilic Granules (Neutrophilic Myelocytes of Man). The heterophilic myelocytes are larger than the mature heterophilic leukocytes. In the youngest generation, sometimes called *promyelocytes,* the oval or kidney-shaped nucleus contains a loose chromatin network and several nucleoli. At the indentation of the nucleus there is a distinct cytocentrum. The cytoplasm is slightly basophilic, although it often shows acidophilic areas. The first specific granules are scarce and are usually confined to the periphery of the cytocentrum and the acidophilic areas. With Wright's stain on dry smears the azure granules are seen before the specific granules appear; for a time both types of granules are present and later the azure granules disappear.

The promyelocytes are often in mitosis. In the following generation, the cytoplasm of the heterophilic myelocytes becomes diffusely acidophilic, while the specific granules increase in number and fill the whole cell body, except for the cytocentrum. The chromatin network of the nucleus becomes coarser and stains

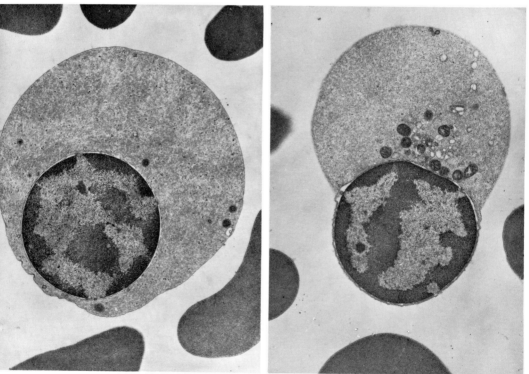

Figure 8-13. Electron micrographs of human orthochromatic erythroblasts (normoblasts). The cell at the right is extruding its nucleus. Notice that the nucleus is pinched off, enclosed in a portion of the cell membrane and a thin layer of cytoplasm, and does not pass through a break in the membrane as was previously believed. × 8000.

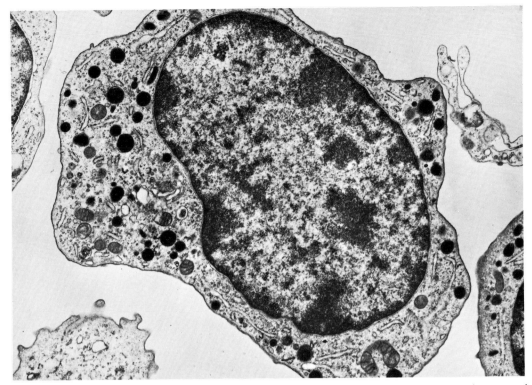

Figure 8-14. Electron micrograph of an early heterophilic myelocyte from guinea pig bone marrow. A sparse endoplasmic reticulum persists. The granules are not as numerous or as variable in shape as in the mature heterophilic leukocyte. Many of those shown here correspond to the azurophilic granules seen in dry smears. × 10,000.

darker, and the nucleoli become indistinct. Mitoses are common; during division the granules are evenly distributed among the daughter cells and continue to increase in numbers as the latter grow.

After an unknown number of mitoses, a generation of heterophilic myelocytes appears that does not divide. The nucleus in these cells shows a beginning polymorphism and has the shape of a horseshoe. Such cells are called *metamyelocytes;* each of them matures with a progressive constriction of the nucleus into a mature heterophilic leukocyte.

Myelocytes with Eosinophilic Granules. Less numerous than the heterophilic myelocytes are the myelocytes with eosinophilic granules, which undergo in general the same changes. Among them also different generations can be distinguished. They all have a slightly basophilic protoplasm. The eosinophilic promyelocytes contain a small number of specific granules which do not stain alike. The youngest among them show a distinct basophilia and stain bluish with eosin-azure;

from these there are all transitions to mature purely eosinophilic granules. Mitoses are common in the eosinophilic myelocytes, especially in the large ones. The horseshoe-shaped nucleus of the metamyelocytes becomes constricted, often into two lobes in the mature leukocytes.

Myelocytes with Basophilic Granules. These are much scarcer than the heterophilic myelocytes and are difficult to study because their granules, in man, are easily soluble in water.

For the most part the basophilic myelocytes are small cells with a paler nucleus than the other myelocytes. The protoplasm contains a widely varying number of specific, basophilic, metachromatic granules of unequal size.

Megakaryocytes. These giant cells with a polymorphous nucleus are characteristic of the red bone marrow; they also occur in the liver, spleen and other blood cell forming organs of the embryo. The megakaryocytes are distributed among the other hemopoietic ele-

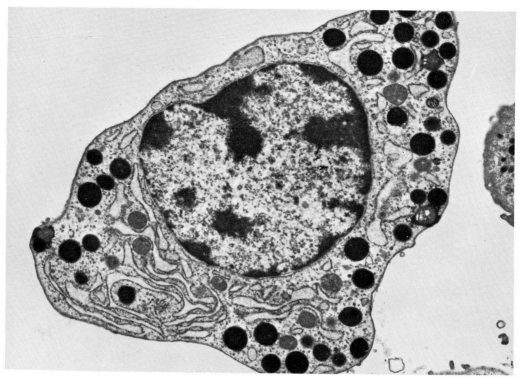

Figure 8-15. Electron micrograph of an eosinophilic myelocyte from guinea pig bone marrow. There is a well developed endoplasmic reticulum and numerous granules that are distinctly larger than those of heterophilic myelocytes. The characteristic equatorial crystal found in the granules of mature eosinophils develops quite late and is not seen at this stage. × 9500.

ments of the marrow and are its most conspicuous cell because of their very large size, some attaining a diameter of 40 μ. The cell body is roughly spherical in form but often has blunt irregular pseudopods on its surface. The nucleus is extraordinarily elaborate with multiple lobes of varying size interconnected by constricted regions (Fig. 8-8). It has a coarse chromatin pattern and numerous nucleoli. With routine methods the cytoplasm appears homogeneous, but after appropriate fixation and special staining a concentric zonation of the cytoplasm can be demonstrated. A relatively large inner zone is surrounded by a broad central region stippled with large numbers of fine granules that are either uniformly distributed or gathered in small dense clusters. At the periphery of the cell is a rim of clear cytoplasm of irregular contour and variable thickness devoid of granules. There are groups of centrioles among the folds of the nucleus. Mitochondria are numerous and small. A compact juxtanuclear Golgi apparatus can be demonstrated in young megakaryocytes, but in more

mature forms it tends to be dispersed as multiple small Golgi bodies widely scattered in the cytoplasm.

The origin of platelets from the megakaryocytes was discovered by Wright in 1906, when he noted the similarity of the chromomeres of platelets to the coarse granules in the cytoplasm of mature megakaryocytes and saw the fragmentation of megakaryocyte processes into platelets. This was confirmed in Yamada's electron microscopic study in 1957, which revealed the mechanism by which the cytoplasm of the developing megakaryocyte is progressively partitioned into small units that are ultimately shed as platelets.

Megakaryocytes develop from hemocytoblasts whose nuclei hypertrophy and become horseshoe-shaped and constricted in several places as the cytoplasm gradually increases in amount. There follows a series of peculiar divisions which involve only the nucleus. The centrioles replicate and a complex spindle with several poles arises. The chromosomes become arranged in several equatorial planes and give rise to multiple daughter nuclei, which fuse at once into a new larger nucleus without constriction of the cytoplasm. After an interval, a new mitosis with still more centers occurs, the daughter nuclei again fuse in telophase, and the quantity of chromatin, number of nucleoli, and number of centrioles again increase. There is evidence that five or six mitoses occur during this process.

During the early period of growth of the young megakaryocytes, the cytoplasm is relatively poor in membranes but rich in ribosomes. Some of the latter are associated with a sparse endoplasmic reticulum but the majority occur in clusters free in the cytoplasmic matrix. As differentiation proceeds, small, membrane-bounded, dense granules appear and gradually become widely distributed in the cytoplasm. These seem to arise in close association with the Golgi bodies and correspond to the azurophilic granules of the light microscope. Concurrently with the development of

the granules, increasing numbers of small vesicles are formed. In electron micrographs these are deployed in meandering rows. Such linear arrays of membranous profiles are actually sections of vesicles that are arranged, in tridimensional perspective, in curved planes that interact to partition the cytoplasm into oblong masses 1 to 2 μ in diameter, each enclosing a number of granules and representing a future platelet. These discontinuous vesicular profiles subsequently elongate and coalesce to form a more or less continuous system of paired membranes, the *platelet demarcation membranes* (Fig. 8-16), which bound narrow clefts outlining the future platelets. In the mature megakaryocytes, these demarcation membranes evidently extend to the cell surface membrane and masses of platelets are shed, leaving around the polymorphous nucleus a thin residual layer of cytoplasm bounded by an intact membrane. It is generally assumed, but not proved, that the megakaryocytes degenerate

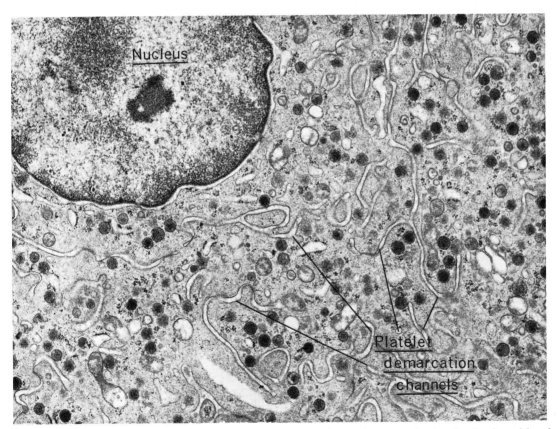

Figure 8-16. Electron micrograph of a small area from a guinea pig megakaryocyte showing the tip of one lobe of the giant nucleus and numerous platelet demarcation channels in the cytoplasm. The granules correspond to the azurophilic granules bound in the central region of the mature platelet. × 18,000.

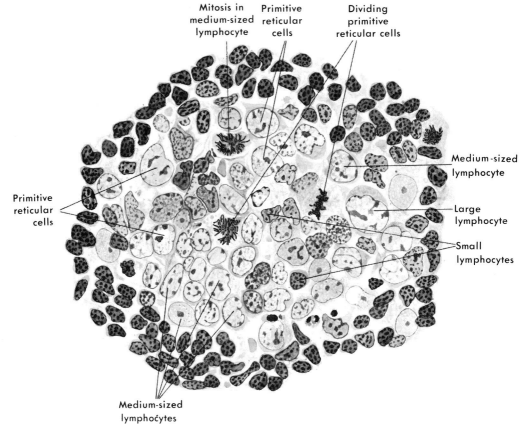

Figure 8-17. Heteroplastic development of lymphocytes from primitive reticular cells in a human lymph node. Hematoxylin-eosin-azure II. × 750. (After A. A. Maximow.)

and are replaced by differentiation of new megakaryocytes from stem cells. Degenerate megakaryocytes not infrequently find their way into the sinusoids of the marrow and are carried with the blood into the capillaries of the lungs, where they remain for a time and then presumably autolyse. Under pathological conditions, embolism of the lung vessels by megakaryocytes may occur on a large scale.

LYMPHOCYTES. Nodules of lymphatic tissue are found normally in the marrow. In some vertebrates, the chicken for example, these nodules are present in large numbers. In man, in physiological states, the amount of lymphatic tissue in the marrow varies with age. In infancy, nodular and even dense diffuse lymphatic tissue is normally found. With adolescence the dense diffuse lymphatic tissue largely disappears. Beginning at the age of about 40 or 50, nodules of lymphatic tissue increase in number. These nodules have the same structure as those in the splenic white pulp and cortex of lymph nodes.

PLASMA CELLS. Plasma cells constitute 1 to 3 per cent of the free cells of normal human marrow. They are found primarily within the reticular fiber sheath of the terminal portions of the arterial capillaries, but also occur as isolated cells or in small foci throughout the marrow. In certain diseases the level of globulins in the plasma seems to vary with the number of plasma cells in the marrow.

MONOCYTES. Many hematologists believe that monocytes are formed in the myeloid tissue. However, the evidence for this transformation is inconclusive. In the marrow, under normal conditions, the monocytes are found only in the lumen of the venous sinusoids. The origin of these cells is discussed on page 207.

Entry of Myeloid Elements into the Blood

Because the myeloid elements arise outside the bloodstream, the newly formed mature myeloid cells must pass through the walls of the blood vessels to enter the circulation. The thin-walled venous sinusoids make this possible. Through them pass not only the ameboid mature granular leukocytes, but also the non-motile erythrocytes. When these are ready for circulation, they slip through the membrane into the bloodstream in the lumen of the sinusoid. The mechanism of this phenomenon is not known.

The claim that red blood corpuscles in the adult, normal man are formed intravascularly is based on unconvincing evidence. In the embryonic mammalian liver and bone marrow the red blood cells develop extravascularly, while in the yolk sac they are preponderantly of intravascular origin.

Functions of the Myeloid Tissue

The myeloid tissue has a variety of functions, the most important of which is the production of myeloid elements for the blood. It is an important site for storage of iron, which is readily available for synthesis of hemoglobin; the heterophilic leukocytes produced in it are actively phagocytic for some bacteria and so are fixed macrophages. Little is known about the function of the large amount of fat stored in it.

The cellular composition of the blood depends on the rate at which blood cells are formed and released from the blood forming tissues, the rate at which they are destroyed, and the rate of leakage from the vessels. Under physiologic conditions these factors remain relatively unchanged, so that the numbers of precursors of each cell type in the blood forming tissues and of each cell type in the blood stay relatively fixed.

Blood formation may be analyzed in terms of three compartments of cells, each of which ordinarily maintains its numbers in a steady state. Most immature are the undifferentiated cells (reticular cells and hemocytoblasts) with the ability to form all blood cells; next are the precursors of the peripheral blood cells (myelocytes, erythroblasts, and megakaryocytes); third are the blood cells. The three compartments are in dynamic equilibrium with one another.

Blood cell formation may be either *heteroplastic* or *homoplastic*. In heteroplastic formation, stem cells become basophilic erythroblasts or myelocytes or megakaryocytes; in homoplastic, blood cells originate from younger elements of the same type. In either

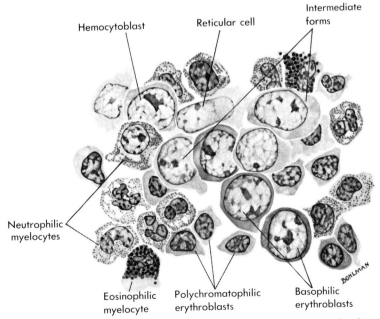

Figure 8-18. Section of human bone marrow from a patient with polycythemia vera, showing stages in development of primitive reticular cells into hemocytoblasts and basophilic erythroblasts. Zenker-formol and hematoxylin-eosin-azure II. × 1380. (From a preparation of C. Huggins.)

case there must be a mitosis in which one daughter cell matures and the other remains in its original form, or two types of mitoses, one resulting in two cells that mature and another in two cells that do not mature, or both. Otherwise the hemopoietic tissues would be depleted in the process of forming blood cells.

In the embryo, hemocytoblasts producing myeloid cells originate from outstretched mesenchymal cells. In the adult under physiological conditions blood formation is largely homoplastic. Some believe that it is always heteroplastic, but against this view is the great infrequency of mitoses in the primitive reticular cells. Pathological stimuli sometimes call forth the new formation of hemocytoblasts from the primitive reticular cells (Fig. 8-18) and the further differentiation of hemocytoblasts into myeloid elements. As mentioned on page 179, heteroplastic formation of lymphocytes may also occur (Fig. 8-17).

Measurement of the rate of production of blood cells is extremely difficult. Most of our knowledge is related to the formation of red cells, hence the following description is based on the formation of red cells. The same *principles* apply to the production of other blood cells.

The rate of red cell formation depends on several factors: the flow of immature precursors into the erythroblastic lineage (heteroplastic formation); the number of mitoses in the maturation process between basophilic erythroblasts and reticulocytes; the time elapsed in this process; and the number of cells dying (wastage) during hemopoiesis. If the last two factors are constant, the number of erythroblasts is determined by the first two. Only then is the number of erythroblasts a measure of the rate of red cell production.

In anemia or when there is insufficient oxygen in the air, there is a low oxygen content of the blood. In this condition, called hypoxia, and also after administration of cobalt salts, there is an accelerated formation of red blood cells in the otherwise normal individual.

A hormone called *erythropoietin* is believed to induce erythroid stem cells to develop into erythroblasts and thus erythrocytes. The hormone increases the rate of synthesis of hemoglobin and of erythrocyte stroma in vitro. It stimulates what appears to be messenger RNA synthesis within 15 minutes after cells are exposed to it. It is present in the blood plasma and is stored in the kidney. The hormone, first

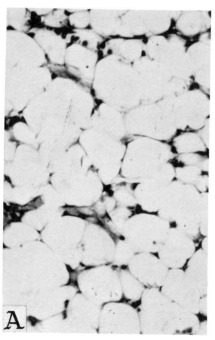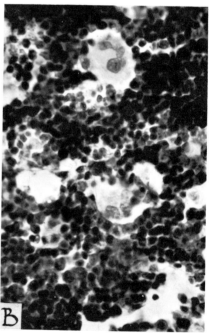

Figure 8-19. A tail loop was constructed in a 23 day old rat by skinning the distal half of the tail and inserting it surgically in the peritoneal cavity, where it was kept for 125 days. *A*, Section from the cool outside loop, showing fatty bone marrow. *B*, Section from the warm region of the tail in the abdominal cavity, showing hemopoietic marrow. × 500. (Courtesy of C. Huggins.)

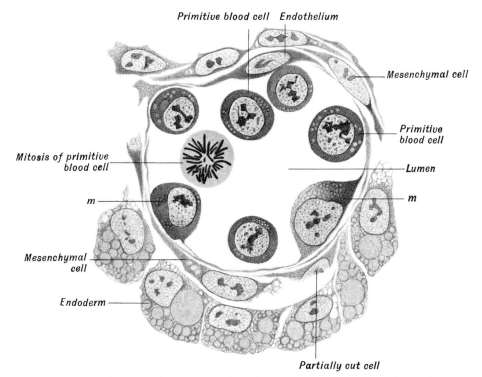

Primitive blood cell   Endothelium

Mesenchymal cell

Primitive
blood cell

Mitosis of primitive
blood cell

Lumen

m   m

Mesenchymal
cell

Endoderm

Partially cut cell

Figure 8-20. Cross section of a vessel of the area vasculosa of a rabbit embryo of 8½ days (five somites). *m,* Rounding off of endothelial cells and their transformation into primitive blood cells. Eosin-azure stain. × 1000. (After A. A. Maximow.)

isolated by Borsook in crude form, has since been purified, although still incompletely, about 400,000 times the concentration in the plasma. It appears to be a protein of fairly large molecular weight (see review by Gold-wasser). Specific antisera against erythropoietin inhibit the action of the hormone (Lange, O'Grady, Lewis and Trobaugh).

The precursors of the blood cells are especially sensitive to ionizing radiations. The decrease in hemopoiesis resulting from irradiation occurs because of an inhibition of mitoses and an increase in wastage.

In most general or severe local infections the heterophilic granulocytopoietic apparatus is stimulated. Whenever there is an increased need for production of erythrocytes there is an increased rate of formation of these cells, usually manifested by a proliferation of red cell precursors in the marrow. That temperature plays some role in the control of hemopoiesis in the marrow is shown by the conversion of fatty into hemopoietic marrow of the tail bones of a rat when the temperature of the bone is raised to that of the body, as by placing it within the body (Fig. 8-19).

DESTRUCTION OF BLOOD CORPUSCLES

Little is known about the mechanisms and sites of the normal destruction of senescent red cells, white cells, and platelets.

The life span (normally 120 days in man) and in some circumstances the site of destruction of red cells may be measured by the various techniques for determination of red cell survival. It is believed that red cells are normally destroyed by tissue macrophages and do not disintegrate in the blood. As a result of the destruction of red cells, hemoglobin is split into hematin and globin. The hematin is further fragmented into iron, which is reutilized or stored, and into bilirubin, which is excreted by the liver into the bile.

Estimates of the life span of white blood cells vary widely. The presence of degenerating leukocytes in the circulating blood, often described, has never been confirmed conclusively. Destruction of granular leukocytes through phagocytosis by the Kupffer cells has been described. However, the destruction in these sites does not account for the total number of white cells destroyed.

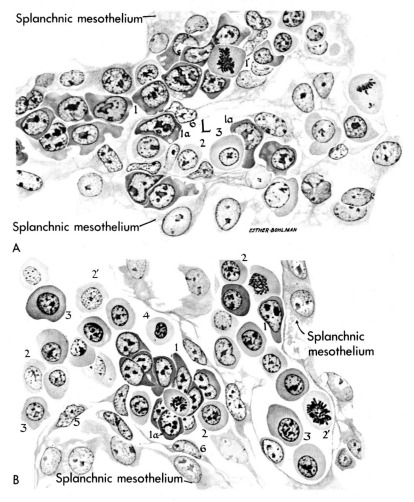

Figure 8-21. Two sections through folds of the wall of the yolk sac of a 24 day human embryo (H1516 Univ. Chicago Emb. Coll.). *A,* Early stage of hemopoiesis, consisting of proliferating extravascular hemocytoblasts (*1, 1′*); *L,* lumen of a small vessel containing a few primitive polychromatophilic erythroblasts. *B,* Later stage of hemopoiesis showing transformation of hemocytoblasts (*1*) into primitive basophilic erythroblasts (*1a*), primitive polychromatophilic erythroblasts (*2, 3*), and primitive erythrocytes (*4*); *5,* mesenchymal cells; *6,* endothelium. Hematoxylin-eosin-azure II. × 1100. (From Bloom and Bartelmez, Am. J. Anat., *67*:21, 1940.)

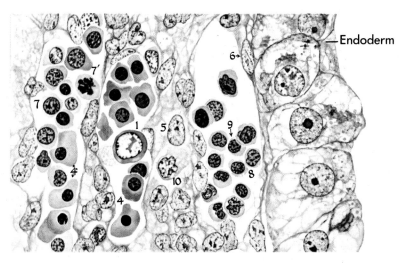

Figure 8-22. Section through yolk sac of a 20-mm. human embryo. In addition to circulating primitive erythrocytes, there are two foci developing polychromatophilic definitive erythroblasts. *1,* Hemocytoblast; *4,* primitive erythrocytes; *5,* mesenchymal cells; *7* and *8,* early and late definitive polychromatophilic erythroblasts with one in mitosis at *7; 9,* normoblast; *10,* lymphoid wandering cell. Hematoxylin-eosin-asure II. × 1100. (From Bloom and Bartelmez, Am. J. Anat., *67*:21, 1940).

It has been claimed that platelets survive for approximately 10 days in the circulating blood. It has also been claimed that the lung is an important site of their destruction.

An increased rate of destruction of red cells, white cells, and platelets is common in certain diseases. The details have been most accurately analyzed in the case of the red cells, whose accelerated destruction is due either to formation of an abnormal red cell (intra-erythrocytic) or change in environment (exo-erythrocytic).

EMBRYONIC DEVELOPMENT OF BLOOD AND CONNECTIVE TISSUE

The manner in which blood cells develop in embryonic and postnatal animals is still uncertain and is now the object of more study than ever. Downey's *Handbook of Hematology*, although published nearly 30 years ago, contains quite a few chapters which are still apposite in this rapidly advancing field.

Blood is formed in practically the same manner in all embryonic mammals. Beginning hemopoiesis is the same in almost all situations (with the possible exception of the thymus, p. 420) and consists in the rounding up of outstretched mesenchymal cells into free basophilic cells, which in turn give rise to all types of blood cells. The first site of this process is the walls of the yolk sac, succeeded by the body mesenchyme, thymus, liver, bone marrow, spleen, and lymph nodes. In the yolk sac most of the *primitive stem cells* become *primitive red blood corpuscles,* which serve as oxygen carriers until they are replaced by the permanent erythrocytes. The remaining stem cells give rise to the *definitive* or *permanent red blood cells, granulocytes,* and *megakaryocytes.* In all other situations in which blood formation occurs, the process is the same except that primitive erythroblasts are not formed.

In all areas of embryonic blood formation the free stem cells are morphologically the same as the various-sized lymphocytes (or hemocytoblasts) of the adult. Even in the primordia of the lymphatic tissue some erythrocytes, myelocytes, and megakaryocytes are formed. It is only in the late embryonic stages that an apparent division of blood forming tissues into myeloid and lymphatic takes place, and this division seems to hold for most of the normal adult life. Under abnormal conditions, however, the myeloid potencies of the cells of the lymphatic and loose connective tissues may become apparent even in the adult mammalian organism. *Blood formation in the embryo thus takes place through the development of a hemopoietic tissue whose connstituent cells are qualitatively the same but vary quantitatively in the successive locations in which this process occurs.*

ORIGIN OF MESENCHYME. The mesenchyme arises from the mesoderm through the isolation, from this layer, of cells which become distributed singly and in groups in the spaces between the three germinal layers. The sclerotomes are an especially abundant source of the mesenchyme. Some mesenchymal cells also arise from the surface of the parietal mesoderm facing the ectoderm, from the surface of the visceral mesoderm facing the endoderm, and from the lateral layer of the somites, the skin plate.

YOLK SAC. In early human ova irregular strands of primitive mesodermal cells traverse the small chorionic "cavity." As fluid accumulates in the blastocyst, these strands cover the surfaces of the chorionic, amniotic, and yolk sac vesicles. As the embryo develops, the yolk sac becomes larger and its mesoderm assumes a more typical epithelium-like arrangement. This yolk sac mesoderm is apparently the source of the yolk sac mesenchyme, which then develops hemopoietically as in other mammals. The mesenchyme between the splanchnopleure and the endoderm gives rise to groups of spherical basophilic cells (the *blood islands*) connected with one another by strands of elongated cells. The peripheral cells of the islands and those of the strands become transformed into endothelial tubes. The endothelium secretes the blood plasma, which fills the tubes. In this way the first blood vessels, the yolk sac vessels, arise. The round cells of the islands are the first blood cells. In the first stages of development, the endothelial cells of the blood vessels in the area vasculosa are often seen to swell and become free in the lumen as additional primitive blood cells.

The first blood elements are hemocytoblasts. They are free mesenchymal cells and are usually called *primitive blood cells* (Figs. 8-20 and 8-21*A*). Almost immediately after their formation most of them elaborate hemoglobin and become *primitive erythroblasts* (Fig. 8-21*B*). They accumulate large quantities of hemoglobin and finally cease dividing, although the nucleus remains in the vast majority of them. Such older forms are called *primitive erythrocytes;* they serve the growing embryo as oxygen carriers, but finally die out. They do not form de-

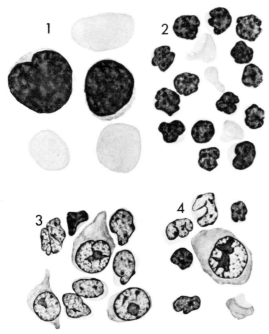

Figure 8-23. Development of large lymphocytes (hemocytoblasts) from small lymphocytes in cultured blood (from a child with leukemia) in which 96 per cent of the leukocytes were small lymphocytes. *1*, Dry smear of blood just before explantation. *2*, Section of centrifuged lymphocytes before explantation. *3* and *4*, Sections of 24 hour culture with stages in the transformation of small lymphocytes into medium-sized and very large ones with huge nucleoli and more basophilic cytoplasm. Zenker-formol and hematoxylin-eosin-azure II. (Reproduced from the color plate of Pierce, 1932.)

finitive erythrocytes. A few of the primitive blood cells remain unchanged as ameboid basophilic hemocytoblasts. The intravascular hemocytoblasts at these early stages sometimes form atypical megakaryocytes. Free phagocytes arise from the primitive endothelial cells are are shed into the lumen. These are the first macrophages of the embryo; they engulf degenerating blood cells. In the human yolk sac vessels, the hemocytoblasts later produce a few secondary erythroblasts identical with those in adult bone marrow (Fig. 8-22). Elsewhere in the mesenchyme they produce a few heterophilic and eosinophilic granulocytes. The hemopoietic activity of the yolk sac in man continues but a short time, and the organ soon atrophies. When the yolk sac of the rat is transplanted to the anterior chamber of the eye, the hemocytoblasts produce great numbers of myelocytes, definitive erythroblasts and megakaryocytes instead of primitive erythroblasts.

Body Mesenchyme. In the diffuse mesenchyme of the body, wandering cells of hemocytoblastic and macrophage appearance occasionally give rise to small extravascular groups of myelocytes and erythrocytes; most of these degenerate. The hemopoietic activity of the wandering cells in the diffuse mesenchyme soon subsides, but these same elements in the specialized blood forming areas of the mesenchyme are the source of a most intense hemopoiesis.

Vascular Endothelium. In early embryonic stages the endothelium of the blood vessels is identical in its potencies with the common mesenchymal cells. Thus, in the yolk sac vessels and in the caudal portion of the aorta, the endothelial cells form clusters of hemocytoblasts. The endothelium of the vessels of the embryonic liver, bone marrow, and spleen may take part for a short time in the production of hemocytoblasts. Later, this endothelium becomes the littoral cells of the macrophage system, which either have lost or do not use their hemopoietic powers in the adult organism. In all the other vessels the endothelium apparently loses its hemopoietic potency early (Chapter 13).

Liver. The liver, the second blood forming organ of the embryo, develops as a network of branching epithelial strands from the epithelium of the intestine. Large, thin-walled blood vessels are located in the meshes of this network from the very beginning. Between this endothelium and the epithelium are thin layers of mesenchyme, which give rise to hemocytoblasts. They proliferate hemopoietically. The liver cells are soon outnumbered by the dense masses of extravascular definitive erythroblasts; a few megakaryocytes and myelocytes are also present.

The erythroblasts produce mature erythrocytes, which slip through the walls of the sinusoids and enter the general circulation. The endothelium of these vessels is transformed into a layer of macrophages, which become the Kupffer cells of the adult. Toward the end of gestation the hemopoietic activity of the liver gradually subsides, so that only small foci of erythroblasts can be found in the liver of the newborn. These, too, soon disappear.

Thymus. The embryogenesis of this organ is considered on page 420.

Bone Marrow. The next hemopoietic organ of the mammalian embryo is the bone marrow. The myeloid tissue develops from the primitive bone marrow, the mesenchyme, which resorbs the cartilage in the bones of endochondral origin and fills the spaces between the bone trabeculae of the endochondral or periosteal bone. Here, again, the process is the same in principle as in the diffuse mesenchyme of the body and in the liver. Some of the fixed mesenchymal cells become wandering cells of hemocytoblastic or macrophage type. These proliferate and form dense, extravascular clusters of erythroblasts, groups of myelocytes of the three different types, and megakaryocytes. Soon, especially in the older regions, as in the diaphyses of the long bones, a solid mass of myeloid tissue develops. Of the original fixed mesenchymal elements, only a few stellate cells remain between the meshes

of the young blood cells; some of them remain as the primitive reticular cells of the stroma of the bone marrow, while the others develop into macrophages and fat cells. Argyrophilic fibrils develop about them. The primitive endothelium of the vessels becomes the littoral macrophages in later stages.

LYMPHATIC ORGANS.   The lymph nodes arise along the course of the lymphatics or in the walls of the primitive lymph sacs in relatively large stages of embryonic development. Here again, in circumscribed areas of the diffuse mesenchyme, many fixed mesenchymal cells are transformed into wandering cells. As in the other blood forming organs, cells of hemocytoblastic and free macrophage types can be distinguished (Fig. 14-11). Wandering

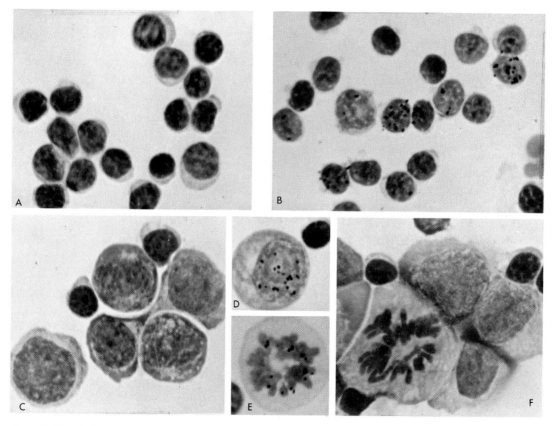

Figure 8-24.   *A*, Smear preparation of thoracic duct lymphocytes used in the cultures. Non-radioautographic preparation. × 1200. *B*, Radioautograph of rat thoracic duct lymph cells obtained two weeks after ³H-thymidine administration. At this time only the long-lived small lymphocytes were labeled. × 1200. *C* and *F*, Non-radioautographic preparation of enlarged lymphocytes of the rat which arose from small lymphocytes cultured three days on monolayer of mouse embryo cells. These cells are division products of the enlarged cells which first arose by direct transformation of the stimulated small lymphocytes. × 1200; × 1200. *D* and *E*, Radioautographs of enlarged cells which arose from the labeled long-lived small lymphocytes of the rat after two days culture on monolayer of mouse embryonic cells. Note that the grain count is essentially the same as that of the labeled small lymphocytes and that the hypertrophy precedes division. × 1200. (Courtesy of N. B. Everett.)

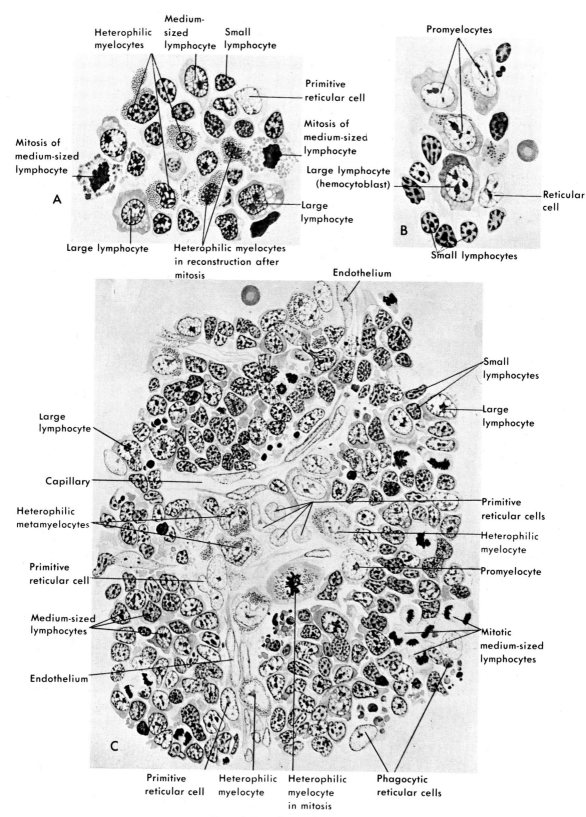

Figure 8-25. *See opposite page for legend.*

cells of the small lymphocyte type, rarely found in the bone marrow, now appear in large numbers. The number of large and small lymphocytes increases, in part, through continued mobilization of new, fixed mesenchymal cells, but mainly through intense mitotic proliferation of the free lymphocytes. The fixed mesenchymal cells which remain between the free cells become the cellular components of the reticular stroma, and in later stages elaborate argyrophilic fibrils. Lymphatic nodules develop relatively late, ordinarily not until after birth and at about the time that plasma cells and immunologic competence also develop. Large lymphocytes are rare until after lymphatic nodules have formed.

The lymphatic tissue in the embryo always contains many heterophilic and eosinophilic myelocytes and a few megakaryocytes and erythroblasts; these develop from the same wandering cells from which the small lymphocytes arise. Thus in the embryo of a mammal the myeloid and the lymphoid elements are not sharply separated.

SPLEEN. This organ is first recognizable as a thickening of mesenchyme in the dorsal mesentery of the stomach. Then, isolated mesenchymal cells contact to become hemocytoblasts, which thereafter develop into clones of erythroblasts and granulocyte precursors, and also into megakaryocytes, as has been described for the liver and marrow. This rapidly proliferating myeloid tissue eventually fills the spleen prior to the appearance of lymphatic tissue.

Subsequently, presumably under the influence of the thymus, periarteriolar myeloid hematopoiesis is suppressed and medium and small lymphocytes appear in the stroma of the periarteriolar mesenchymal tissue to initiate formation of the white pulp. According to one theory the lymphocytes arise from this mesenchyme; according to another they arise by migration from the thymus. In man, with further development of the white pulp, myeloid hematopoiesis is almost completely suppressed and the myeloid tissue is converted into

red pulp. In most mammals, especially rodents, a significant amount of splenic myeloid hematopoiesis persists during postnatal life.

LOOSE CONNECTIVE TISSUE. When connective tissue fibers appear in the mesenchyme, this tissue becomes the connective tissue. The exact moment when a mesenchymal cell changes into a fibroblast has not been determined, because there is no appreciable change in structure. In fact, in all regions of the body some fixed mesenchymal cells remain undifferentiated, mainly along the capillaries.

At the later embryonic stages the vast majority of the wandering cells in the connective tissue are macrophages; hemocytoblasts are rare except in the primordia of the lymphatic organs and the bone marrow.

Many of the wandering cells persist as such in the adult connective tissue. Most of them, however, become fixed macrophages. The primitive wandering cells also give rise to mast cells, which then proliferate mitotically.

The appearance of the primordia of the white and of the brown fat tissue is closely connected with the development of networks of blood vessels. The fibrillar intercellular substance of the connective tissue around the growing capillaries undergoes a peculiar dissolution, and the mesenchymal cells in these areas proliferate and form loose, cellular networks. Although some consider such accumulations of cells as specific, primitive fat organs, it is more probable that these elements are common mesenchymal cells, which accumulate fat droplets and become fat cells. In the primordia of the brown fat tissue, stellate cells assume a polyhedral form, and the accumulated fat droplets fail to fuse.

Normally plasma cells are not found in mammalian embryos except possibly in the guinea pig, which is unusually mature at birth. This observation, and the allegedly poor response of newborn mammals to antigenic stimulation, led to acceptance of the concept that embryonic and newborn mammals are immunologically incompetent. It is true that plasma cells and immunologic competence de-

Fig. 8-25. Ectopic myelopoiesis, showing three sources of heterophilic myelocytes in germinal centers of lymphatic nodules. In *A* the myelocytes developed by transformation of small and medium-sized lymphocytes. In *B* the early myelocytes arose from large lymphocytes (hemocytoblasts) with prominent nucleoli and variable amounts of basophilic cytoplasm, whereas in *C* the myelocytes came from pericapillary primitive reticular cells with inconspicuous nucleoli and slightly basophilic cytoplasm. *A* is from the spleen of a guinea pig injected intravenously with lithium carmine and chicken erythrocytes; *B* and *C* are from a mesenteric lymph node of a rabbit chronically poisoned with sapotoxin and phenylhydrazine. Zenker-formol and hematoxylin-eosin-azure II. (*A* after Bloom, 1926; *B* and *C*, after Lang, 1926.)

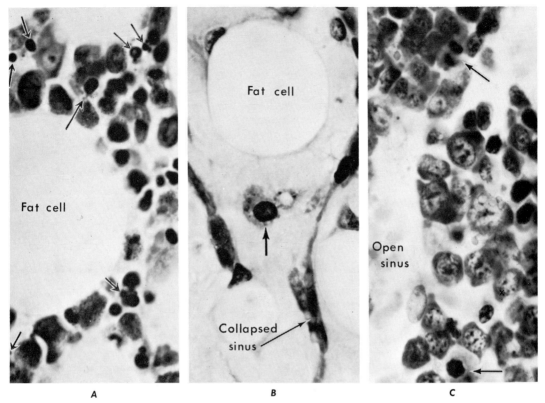

A   B   C

Figure 8-26. Some of the changes which occur in the bone marrow of rabbits after total body irradiation with 800 R of 200 kV x-rays. *A*, 24 hours after irradiation the marrow consists mainly of fat cells, stages in the formation of granulocytes, and debris of erythrocyte precursors (arrows). *B*, after nine days the marrow is completely depleted of hematopoietic cells and is reduced to fat cells, a jelly-like intercellular substance, an occasional macrophage (arrow) and some collapsed sinuses. *C*, 10 days after irradiation, hematopoiesis appears in scattered foci. Note the very large, young marrow cells with darkly stained cytoplasm (basophilia) and prominent nucleoli. × 1030. (After W. Bloom and M. A. Bloom.)

velop only after formation of extrathymic lymphatic tissue. However, mammalian embryos late in embryonic life, and newborn mammals, can form plasma cells and antibodies.

DEVELOPMENTAL POTENCIES OF THE LYMPHOID STEM CELLS OF THE LYMPHOID AND MYELOID TISSUES

Probably no problems in histology have been the subject of as long and intense a debate as those dealing with the development and interrelationships of blood cells. The use of conventional histologic techniques for six or seven decades failed to bring a consensus on many of the questions involved. With complete disregard of the hemopoietic tissues, too many of the observations and conclusions were based exclusively on studies of the cells of the peripheral blood of man in health and disease. Moreover, the cytologic methods were often of such inferior quality that they have rarely been considered adequate for study of fine details of cells in other tissues.

All the conventional morphological criteria proposed for distinguishing the various stem cells (lymphoblasts, myeloblasts, and monoblasts), such as differences in their nuclear structure, number of nucleoli, mitochondria, supravital staining, oxidase and peroxidase reactions, proved to be unreliable. Despite a claim to the contrary, lymphocytes and myeloblasts have the same type of movement in tissue culture (De Bruyn). They also have identical sensitivities to ionizing radiations and radiomimetic substances. Further, many clinical hematologists, unable to classify 10 to 30 per cent of cases of acute leukemia as either lymphoblastic or myeloblastic on the morphology of the peripheral blood cells (Fig. 8-27), now speak of such cases as "undifferentiated" or "blast cell" leukemias until changes in the blood picture or in the clinical course of the disease permit their classification as myeloid or lymphatic.

An adequate understanding of the interrelationships between cells of the several blood cell forming and other connective tissues in man must rest on a comprehensive analysis of these tissues from many points of view. These include the study of hemopoiesis of embryonic, postnatal, and adult stages in the lower vertebrates and in mammals including man. Not all of the developmental relationships between these cells are clearly discernible during the relatively slow changes of physiological conditions, but they may be analyzed more easily in those pathological and experimental states in which increased destruction of cells has induced rapid reparative cell formation and transformation. Especially informative are responses to ectopic myelopoiesis, inflammation, tissue cultures, certain hormones, noxious chemicals, ionizing radiations, and tissue grafts (including transfusion of hemopoietic cells). Some of the most striking recent advances were made possible by modern techniques, including the use of cells identifiable by specific radioactive or fluorescent labels or easily detectable genetic markers. With these methods some unexpected and revolutionary concepts have entered hematology, leading to the solution of some of the old problems, and, as often in science, to the appearance of new and apparently more complicated ones.

In the lower vertebrates, the developing lymphoid and myeloid cells are intimately mixed without segregation into lymphoid and myeloid tissues, although spatial and temporal differences may occur between the formation of erythrocytes and that of granular leukocytes. In the development of hemopoietic foci in mammalian embryos, both lymphoid and myeloid cells arise in each focus from apparently identical cells and are present together, although in greatly varying proportions, in all hemopoietic primordia.

Nearly all hematologists agree that the myeloid elements of the bone marrow develop through proliferation and differentiation from a free basophilic stem cell—designated in this book as a hemocytoblast. In the lymphatic tissue, small lymphocytes develop from larger ones, which have, when seen with optical microscopes, exactly the same structure as the hemocytoblasts in the bone marrow. It is still unsettled whether the lymphoid cells in both tissues have identical or different developmental potencies. If they are identical, then all blood elements of the adult originate from a common free cell, which may appropriately be called the *hemocytoblast*. If, however, the large lymphoid cells of the lymphatic and myeloid tissues differ in their potencies, then each of these tissues has a specific free stem cell, one of which could be called *lymphoblast* and the other *myeloblast*. There is also no agreement on whether the monocyte has a specific free stem cell, a *monoblast*, different from that (or those) giving rise to the other blood cells (see p. 207).

One of the most important steps forward in the analysis of the developmental potentialities of allegedly different hemopoietic stem cells came with the widespread verification of an old observation by Pierce that small lymphocytes in cultures of human blood hypertrophied into large ones (Fig. 8-23). In the recent experiments lymphocytes in blood or lymph were cultured in a medium containing phytohemaglutinin, tuberculin, tetanus toxoid, or one of many vaccines, as those against typhoid-paratyphoid, pertussis, poliomyelitis, or smallpox. In a few days the small lymphocytes developed into larger lymphocytes which multiplied by division and developed into plasma cells and pale staining larger cells not as yet identified (Fig. 8-24). Thoracic duct lymphocytes of rabbits were reported to develop into macrophages in culture (Bloom, 1928). Confirmation of this potentiality of lymphocytes has come from the crucial experiments of Howard, Christie, Boak and Evans-Anfom (1965). They injected thoracic duct lymphocytes (p. 128) from a parental strain of mice into the veins of F_1 hybrid mice. Eleven days later they found a greatly increased number of Kupffer cells (p. 588) in the livers of the recipient mice. These macrophages had the karyotype of the injected lymphocytes, not that of cells of the recipient. It is thus beyond question that some thoracic duct lymphocytes have the potential of becoming macrophages. The chemical nature of the stimulus evoking this transformation remains to be discovered. All of these findings thus negate a basic idea long maintained by most hematologists, that the small lymphocyte is devoid of potential for progressive development and that it is capable only of degeneration and death.

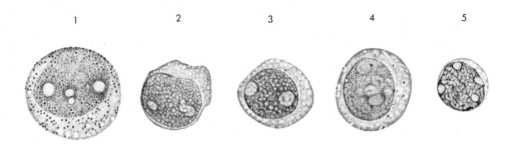

Figure 8-27. *1*, Myeloblast with azure granules from normal human bone marrow; *2*, myeloblast from the blood in chronic myeloid leukemia; *3* and *4*, lymphoblasts from the blood in chronic lymphatic leukemia; *5*, lymphoblast from the blood in subacute lymphatic leukemia. (Cells 2 to 5 are from pathological human blood.) May-Grünwald-Giemsa—stained dry smears. (After Downey.)

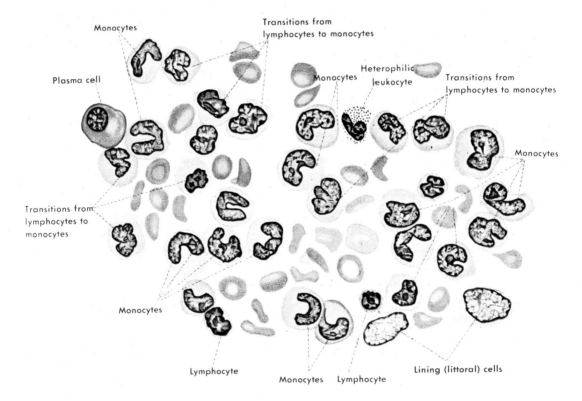

Figure 8-28. Section through a splenic sinus of a rabbit infected with *L. monocytogenes.* Hematoxylin-eosin-azure II stain. × 1200. (After Bloom.)

ECTOPIC HEMOPOIESIS. In most adult mammals, lymphocytes are normally formed in the lymphatic tissues and myeloid elements in the bone marrow. New lymphatic tissue may develop in practically any part of the body and especially in glands associated with the gastrointestinal tract, and to a lesser extent in the respiratory, urinary, and reproductive systems. Lymphatic tissue may become overdeveloped in certain diseases, not always of neoplastic type. Lymphatic nodules are regular constituents of human bone marrow (p. 176).

In some abnormal conditions formation of the myeloid cells may occur in tissues and organs other than the bone marrow. This is called *ectopic* or *extramedullary myelopoiesis* or *myeloid metaplasia.* Local myelopoiesis may occur in the sclerotic aortic wall, in the adrenal glands, liver, lymph nodes, and spleen, and in the connective tissue surrounding the pelvis of the kidney after ligation of the renal arteries and veins of the adult rabbit. It may also occur in other parts of the body in certain intoxications, infections, repeated bleeding, or continued use of blood cell destroying substances. Usually the first cells to develop in the new sites are heterophilic and eosinophilic myelocytes: megakaryocytes appear later, and erythroblasts develop still later. There are several sources of ectopic myelopoiesis. Sometimes the first myeloid elements appear within venous capillaries, where they originate from circulating lymphoid cells (presumably lymphocytes). The stem cells and newly formed myelocytes pass through the walls of the vessels into the tissues, where they continue to proliferate. In lymph nodes and spleen, myelocytes have been reported as arising from small, medium-sized and large lymphocytes, even in the germinal centers (Fig. 8-25*A* and *B*). Myelocytes have also been described as arising from local undifferentiated, perivascular cells or from primitive reticular cells in the lymphatic tissues, apparently without passing through a free hemocytoblast stage (Fig. 8-25*C*). If the myeloid metaplasia is intense, all kinds of immature myeloid cells occur in the circulating blood, whence they may colonize other tissues.

In view of the great number of mice being used for experiments with transfused myeloid and lymphoid cells, it is of special interest to note that in these animals the formation of granulocytes, erythrocytes, and megakaryocytes in the spleen is of such frequent occurrence as to be considered the normal condition.

In fragments of lymph node of adult rabbits cultured in a medium of plasma and bone marrow extract, large lymphocytes were found to develop into myelocytes and megakaryocytes. It has also been reported that thoracic duct lymphocytes of ascaris immunized rabbits, when cultured in plasma with bone marrow and ascaris extracts, were observed to develop into heterophilic myelocytes. Neither of these experiments has been confirmed. The myeloblasts of the blood in myeloblastic leukemia and lymphocytes in lymphatic leukemia develop into macrophages in tissue cultures. The claim that myeloblasts can produce only myelocytes and erythroblasts, and perhaps megakaryocytes, thus seems untenable.

Since the turn of the century it has been known that the blood cell forming tissues are among the most sensitive to ionizing radiations. When x-rays are applied in sufficient amounts over the whole body of an animal, damage to the hemopoietic tissues is a major cause of death (Figs. 8-26 and 14-12). However, shielding the spleen against x-rays prevents death after an otherwise lethal irradiation by producing a great increase in hemopoiesis in the spleen; this enables blood cell formation to start again in the bone marrow, lymph nodes, and thymus. Lethally irradiated mice can also be saved by timely injections of blood and hemopoietic cells, which colonize the depleted blood cell forming organs. Lymphoid cells from bone marrow when injected intravenously into mice are able to colonize and restore to apparent normal condition the x-ray depleted spleen, lymph nodes, thymus, and bone marrow, whereas no lymphoid cells of the thymus or lymph nodes were found capable of recolonizing bone marrow to any substantial extent (Micklem et al.).

Other experiments with lethally irradiated mice show that injections of lymph node cells from a compatible donor can repopulate the nodes with lymphocytes. Curiously, it has further been found that such lymphocytes in the repopulated nodes are replaced later by other small lymphocytes, which come from injected bone marrow lymphocytes with characteristically marked chromosomes. This has not been explained.

ORIGIN AND NATURE OF THE MONOCYTE. The source of these cells was obscured for years by the assumed identity of the artificially flattened blood monocyte of dry smears with the roughly globular free macrophage as seen in

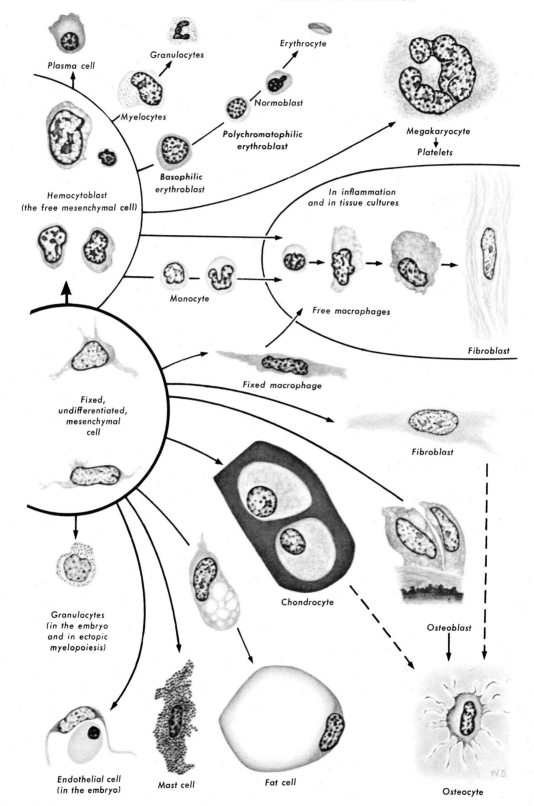

Figure 8-29. Interrelationships of the cells of human blood and connective tissues, which are the same for all mammals. The dotted lines indicate unusual transformations. The lymphocytes are included with the hemocytoblasts. Hematoxylin-eosin-azure II. × 720.

tissue sections. Some believe the monocytes develop from a hypothetical *monoblast* in the bone marrow. Monocytes in the blood do not store vital dyes, but do store them when they develop into macrophages in inflammation or in culture of blood leukocytes. It is impossible to separate all monocytes as a cell type distinct from all lymphocytes in the circulating blood. In the early stages of inflammation, hematogenous lymphocytes and monocytes rapidly become ameboid phagocytic cells (p. 146). In this development, lymphocytes pass through a transitory stage, in which many of them cannot be distinguished from monocytes. In cultures of normal and leukemic blood leukocytes, and of lymphocytes of rabbit lymph, the small lymphocytes have been described as changing into monocytoid cells and then into large macrophages. In rabbits in which an extensive monocytosis has been produced by infection with *L. monocytogenes* or after double vital staining, monocytes develop by individual hypertrophy from the smaller lymphocytes. There is no substantial evidence for the existence of a specific monoblast different from a lymphocyte or hemocytoblast. Apparently, monocytes are lymphocytes (hemocytoblasts) that have developed slightly in the phagocytic direction. The main site of this transformation seems to be in the blood of the venous sinuses of the liver, bone marrow, and spleen (Fig. 8-29).

GENETIC INTERRELATIONSHIPS AND POTENCIES OF THE CELLS OF THE BLOOD AND LYMPH, THE CONNECTIVE TISSUES, AND ENDOTHELIUM. From a general point of view, three large groups of cells may be recognized in the blood and the other connective tissues: *(1) Hemocytes* —free cells that circulate in the blood or are scattered throughout the connective and hemopoietic tissues. To be distinguished among them are (a) the hemocytoblasts (lymphocytes), which serve as stem cells for (b) three types of granular leukocytes, monocytes, erythrocytes, megakaryocytes, plasma cells, and lymphoid wandering cells. *(2) Specialized connective tissue cells.* As fibroblasts they produce collagen and the amorphous ground substance of connective tissue. As chondrocytes and osteocytes they form the collagen and other interstitial substances of cartilage and bone. *(3) Macrophages*—fixed or free cells that phagocytose, store vital dyes and other colloidal substances, and play important roles in some of the "defense" reactions. In animals in which fixed macrophages have been labeled with

vital dyes, new lymphocytes and other blood cells develop from the presumably more primitive, not actively phagocytic, reticular cells.

The question is not settled whether a phagocytic reticular cell (a fixed macrophage) can cease being a phagocyte and return to the status of a more primitive reticular cell with the potentialities of this cell type. It has been widely accepted that fixed cells with unrestricted mesenchymal potencies are present in the connective tissues of adult mammals. Although there are protagonists of the beliefs that such cells are fibroblasts, or common vascular endothelial cells or fixed macrophages, the most convincing evidence indicates that the original mesenchymal potencies are retained by perivascular cells in the loose connective tissue, by the primitive reticular cells of the hemopoietic tissues, and by some of the cells lining the venous sinuses of the liver. In the lymphatic and myeloid tissues, the development of fixed and free macrophages from the primitive reticular cells can be observed, both in the body and in cultures of these tissues. Lymphoid cells—that is, hemocytoblasts—also originate from the same source. In the omentum, the new formation of fixed macrophages from perivascular, undifferentiated cells has been described. In extramedullary myelopoiesis, myelocytes have also been traced directly to perivascular, fixed cells. When certain foreign substances are introduced into the organism, the macrophage system, which disposes of them, shows an increase in size and number of its cells over much of the body.

This is written at a time when the problems of developmental potentialities of lymphoid and myeloid stem cells are under intense and productive experimental study. Some of the major differences of the past are disappearing, as evidenced by general agreement that small lymphocytes can become larger ones that divide and may also become plasma cells. The latter and some of the lymphocytes are importantly concerned in antibody formation. At present it appears that there are at least two kinds of morphologically identical but functionally different lymphocytes, one arising in the thymus and the other in lymphatic tissue; there is no agreement on whether there are more lymphocytic types, or, if there are, how many. The isolation of subtle chemical differences, perhaps of genetic nature, between various lymphocyte types is an alluring problem.

It is undecided whether lymphocytes, or some of them, have the ability to turn into granulocytes or erythrocytes, or whether they are a late phylogenetic differentiation concerned largely with monocyte and plasma cell production and with the defense mechanisms of inflammation and immunity.

In view of contradictory experimental results, definitive answers cannot be given to many questions involving the nature of the hemopoietic stem cells and the factors which stimulate, mediate, or prevent their development into blood cells. However, the prospect is excellent that the flood of current ingenious studies will bring answers to many of the problems. One conclusion is assured: The era of building theories of blood cell formation solely on the morphology of circulating blood cells belongs to the past.

REFERENCES

Handbook of Hematology, edited by H. Downey (New York, Paul B. Hoeber, Inc., 1938), contains several chapters which are important for older material on the topics discussed in this chapter.

Ackerman, A. G.: Histochemical differentiation during neutrophil development and maturation. In Bierman, H. R., ed.: Leukopoiesis in health and disease. Ann. N.Y. Acad. Sci., 113:511, 1964.

Alpen, E. L., and D. Granmore: Observations on regulation of erythropoiesis and on cellular dynamics by Fe59 autoradiography. In Stohlman, F., Jr., ed.: The Kinetics of Cellular Proliferation. New York, Grune & Stratton, Inc., 1959.

Bennett, M. and G. Cudkowicz: Functional and morphological characterization of stem cells: The unipotential role of "lymphocytes" of mouse marrow. In The Lymphocyte in Immunology and Haemopoiesis (Symposium). London. Edward Arnold. Ltd., 1967.

Bierman, H. R., ed.: Leukopoiesis in health and disease. Ann. N.Y. Acad. Sci., 113:511, 1964.

Block, M.: An experimental analysis of hematopoiesis in the rat yolk sac. Anat. Rec., 96:289, 1946.

Block, M.: The blood forming tissues and blood of the newborn opossum (Didelphys Virginiana). I. Normal development. Ergeb. Anat. Entwickl., 37:237, 1964.

Bloom, M. A.: Bone marrow. In Bloom, W., ed.: Histopathology of Irradiation from External and Internal Sources. National Nuclear Energy Series, Vol. 22-I. New York, McGraw-Hill Book Co., 1948.

Bloom, W.: The hemopoietic potency of the small lymphocyte. Folia haematol., 33:122, 1926.

Bloom, W.: The origin and nature of the monocyte. Folia haematol., 37:1, 1928.

Bloom, W.: Mammalian lymph in tissue culture; from lymphocyte to fibroblast. Arch. f. exper. Zellforsch., 5:269, 1928.

Bloom, W.: Transformation of lymphocytes into granulocytes in vitro. Anat. Rec., 69:99, 1937.

Bloom, W.: Embryogenesis of mammalian blood. In Downey, H., ed.: Handbook of Hematology. New York, Paul B. Hoeber, Inc., 1938, Vol. 2, p. 865.

Bruce, W. R., and E. A. McCulloch: The effect of erythropoietic stimulation on the hematopoietic colony-forming cells in mice. Blood, 23:216, 1964.

Caffrey, R. W., N. B. Everett, and W. O. Rieke: Radioautographic studies of reticular and blast cells in the hemopoietic tissues of the rat. Anat. Rec., 155:41, 1966.

Clark, S. L., Jr.: The reticulum of lymph nodes in mice studied with the electron microscope. Am. J. Anat., 110:217, 1962.

Conway, E. A.: Cyclic changes in lymphatic nodules. Anat. Rec., 69:487, 1937.

Conway, E. A.: Reaction of lymphatic tissue in early stages of Bacterium monocytogenes infection. Arch. Path., 25:200, 1938.

Coons, A. H.: Some reactions of lymphoid tissues to stimulation by antigens. The Harvey Lectures, Series 53, 113:129, 1959.

Cottier, H., N. Odartchenko, G. Keiser, M. Hess, and R. D. Stoner: Incorporation of tritiated nucleosides and amino acid into lymphoid and plasmocytoid cells during secondary response to tetanus toxoid in mice. In Bierman, H. R., ed.: Leukopoiesis in health and disease. Ann. N.Y. Acad. Sci., 113:511, 1964.

Cronkite, E. P., C. R. Jansen, H. Cottier, Kanti Rai, and C. R. Sipe: Lymphocyte production measured by extracorporeal irradiation, cannulation, and labeling techniques. In Bierman, H. R., ed.: Leukopoiesis in health and disease. Ann. N.Y. Acad. Sci., 113:511, 1964.

Davies, H. G.: Structure in nucleated erythrocytes. J. Biophys. & Biochem. Cytol., 9:671, 1961.

DeBruyn, P. P. H.: Locomotion of blood cells in tissue culture. Anat. Rec., 89:43, 1944.

Detta, N., B. Thorell, and L. Ackerman: Cytoplasmic nucleotides in the megakaryocytes. Acta Haemat., 14:176, 1955.

Dougherty, T. F., M. L. Berliner, G. L. Schneebell, and D. L. Berliner: Hormonal control of lymphatic structure and function. In Bierman, H. R., ed.: Leukopoiesis in health and disease. Ann. N.Y. Acad. Sci., 113:511, 1964.

Downey, H.: The myeloblast—its occurrence under normal and pathological conditions and its relations to lymphocytes and other blood cells. Folia haemat., 34:65, 145, 1927.

Downey, H.: The megaloblast-normoblast problem; a cytological study. J. Lab. & Clin. Med., 39:837, 1952.

Everett, N. B., W. O. Rieke, and R. W. Caffrey: The kinetics of small lymphocytes in the rat, with special reference to those of thymic origin. In Good, R. A., and A. E. Gabrielsen, eds.: The Thymus in Immunology. New York, Hoeber Medical Division, Harper & Row, 1964.

Ford, C. E., H. S. Micklem, E. P. Evans, J. G. Gray, and D. A. Ogden: The inflow of bone marrow cells to the thymus: Studies with part-body irradiated mice injected with chromosome-marked bone marrow and subjected to antigenic stimulation. Proc. 7th Internat. Transplantation Conf. Ann. N.Y. Acad. Sci., 129:283, 1966.

Goldwasser, E.: Biochemical control of erythroid cell development. In Moscona, A., A. Monroy. eds.: Current Topics in Developmental Biology. New York, Academic Press, 1966.

Goodman, J. W.: On the origin of peritoneal fluid cells. Blood, 23:18, 1964.

Gowans, J. L.: Life-span, recirculation and transformation of lymphocytes. Int. Rev. Exper. Path., 5:1, 1966.

Gowans, J. L., and D. D. McGregor: The immunological activities of lymphocytes. Progress in Allergy, 9:1, 1965.

Hamre, C. J.: Hematopoiesis in the bone marrow of rats recovering from nutritional anemia. J. Lab. & Clin. Med., 32:756, 1947.

Howard, J. G., J. L. Boak, and G. H. Christie: Further studies on the transformation of thoracic duct cells into liver macrophages. Ann. N.Y. Acad. Sci., 129:327, 1966.

Howard, J. G., J. L. Boak, and G. H. Christie: Macrophage-type cells in the liver derived from thoracic duct cells during graft-vs.-host reactions. In The Lymphocyte in Immunology and Haemopoiesis (Symposium). London, Edward Arnold, Ltd., 1967.

Howard, J. G., G. H. Christie, J. L. Boak, and E. Evans-Anfom: Evidence for the conversion of lymphocytes into liver macrophages during graft-vs.-host reaction. Colloq. Int. Centre Nat. Rech. Sci., Paris, No. 147, 1965, p. 95.

Jones, O. P.: The influence of disturbed metabolism on the morphology of blood cells. In Macfarlane, R. G., and A. H. Robb-Smith: Functions of the Blood. New York, Academic Press, 1961, p. 171.

Jones, O. P.: Selective binding sites for the transfer of ferritin into erythroblasts. I. Preliminary report. J. Nat. Cancer Inst., 35:139, 1965.

Jordan, H. E.: The relation of lymphoid tissue to the process of blood production in avian bone marrow. Am. J. Anat., 59:249, 1936.

Kindred, J. E.: A quantitative study of the hemopoietic organs of young adult albino rats. Am. J. Anat., 71:207, 1942.

Lajtha, L. G., C. W. Gilbert, D. D. Perteous, and R. Alexanian: Kinetics of a bone-marrow stem-cell population. In Bierman,

H. R., ed.: Leukopoiesis in health and disease. Ann. N.Y. Acad. Sci., *113*:511, 1964.

Lang, F. J.: Experimentelle Untersuchungen über die Histogenese der extramedulären Myelopoese. Zeitschr. f. mikr.-anat. Forsch., *4*:417, 1926.

Lange, R. D., L. F. O'Grady, J. P. Lewis, and F. E. Trobaugh, Jr.: Application of erythropoietin antisera to studies of erythropoiesis. Ann. N.Y. Acad. Sci., in press.

Leduc, E. H., A. H. Coons, and J. M. Connolly: Studies on antibody production. II. The primary and secondary responses in the popliteal lymph node of the rabbit. J. Exper. Med., *102*:61, 1955.

Lewis, J. P., and F. E. Trobaugh, Jr.: Haematopoietic stem cells. Nature, *204*:589, 1964.

McCulloch, E. A., J. E. Till, and L. Siminovitch: Genetic factors affecting the control of hemopoiesis. Proc. 6th Canadian Cancer Res. Conf., 1964, p. 336.

Mechanik, N.: Untersuchungen über das Gewicht des Knochenmarkes des Menschen. Zeitschr. f. d. ges. Anat., *79:*part 1:58, 1926.

Micklem, H. S., C. E. Ford, E. P. Evans, and J. G. Gray: Interrelationships of myeloid and lymphoid cells: Studies with chromosome-marked cells transfused into lethally irradiated mice. Proc. Roy Soc. B, *165:*78, 1966.

Nossal, G. J. V.: How cells make antibodies. Scientific American, *211:*106, 1964.

Patt, H. M., and M. A. Maloney: A model of granulocyte kinetics. *In* Bierman, H. R., ed.: Leukopoiesis in health and disease. Ann. N.Y. Acad. Sci., *113:*511, 1964.

Pierce, M.: Cultures of leukemic blood leukocytes. Arch. Path., *14:*295, 1932.

Rebuck, J. W., ed.: The Lymphocyte and Lymphocytic Tissue. New York, Paul B. Hoeber, Inc., 1960

Rebuck, J. W., H. I. Coffman, G. B. Bluhm, and C. L. Barth: A structural study of reticulum and monocyte production with quantitation of lymphocytic modulation of nonmultiplicative type to histiocytes. *In* Bierman, H. R., ed.: Leukopoiesis in health and disease. Ann. N.Y. Acad. Sci., *113:*511, 1964.

Reinhardt, W. O.: Some factors influencing the thoracic-duct output of lymphocytes. *In* Bierman, H. R., ed.: Leukopoiesis in health and disease. Ann. N.Y. Acad. Sci., *113:*511, 1964.

Richter, G. W.: A study of hemosiderosis with the aid of electron microscopy, with observations on the relationship between hemosiderin and ferritin. J. Exper. Med., *106:*203, 1957.

Robbins, J. H.: Tissue culture studies of the human lymphocyte. Science, *146:*1648, 1964.

Sabesin, S. M.: Lymphocytes of small mammals: Spontaneous transformation in culture to blastoids. Science, *149:*1385, 1965.

Shelton, E.: Differences in the potentialities of normal and malignant lymphocytes grown in diffusion chambers. Pathologie-Biologie, *9:*542, 1961.

Stohlman, F., Jr.: Observation on the kinetics of red cell proliferation. *In* The Kinetics of Cellular Proliferation. New York, Grune & Stratton, Inc., 1959.

Symposium on differentiation and growth of hemoglobin and immunoglobin-synthesizing cells. J. Cell Physiol., *67:*Suppl. 1, 1966.

Trowell, O. A.,: Lymphocytes. *In* Willmer, E. N., ed.: Cells and Tissues in Culture: Methods, Biology, and Physiology. New York, Academic Press, 1965, Vol. 2, p. 96.

Wintrobe, M.: Clinical Hematology. 5th ed. Philadelphia, Lea & Febiger, 1961.

Wright, J.: Histogenesis of the blood platelets. J. Morphol., *21:*263, 1910.

Yamada, E.: The fine structure of the megakaryocyte in the mouse spleen. Acta Anat., *29:*267, 1957.

Yoffey, J. M.: The lymphocyte. Annual Rev. Med., *15:*125, 1964.

Yoffey, J. M.: Bone Marrow Reactions. London, Edward Arnold, Ltd., 1966.

Zamboni, L., and D. Pease: The vascular bed of the red bone marrow. J. Ultrastruct. Res., *5:*65, 1961.

CHAPTER NINE

Cartilage

Cartilage is a specialized form of connective tissue consisting of cells, *chondrocytes,* and extracellular fibers embedded in an amorphous, gel-like *matrix.* The intercellular components predominate over the cells, which are isolated in small cavities within the matrix. Unlike other connective tissues, cartilage has no nerves or blood vessels of its own. The colloidal properties of its matrix are therefore important to the nutrition of its cells and are in large measure responsible for its firmness and resilience. The capacity of cartilage for rapid growth while maintaining a considerable degree of stiffness makes it a particularly favorable skeletal material for the embryo. Most of the axial and appendicular skeleton is first formed in cartilage models, which are later replaced by bone.

Cartilage is of more restricted occurrence in postnatal life, but it continues to play an indispensable role in the growth in length of the long bones throughout the growth of the individual, and it persists in the adult on their articular surfaces. Except where it is exposed to the synovial fluid in joints, cartilage is invariably enclosed in a dense fibrous connective tissue covering called the *perichondrium.* Three kinds of cartilage, *hyaline, elastic,* and *fibrocartilage,* are distinguished on the basis of the amount of amorphous matrix and the relative abundance of the collagenous and elastic fibers embedded in it. Hyaline cartilage is the most common and characteristic type and the others can be regarded as modifications of it (Fig. 9-1).

HYALINE CARTILAGE

In the adult, hyaline cartilage is found on the ventral ends of the ribs, in the tracheal rings and larynx, and on the joint surfaces of bones. It is a somewhat elastic, semitransparent tissue with an opalescent bluish tint. Its histological appearance is most easily understood from a consideration of how it develops.

HISTOGENESIS OF CARTILAGE. At sites of future cartilage formation in the embryo, the mesenchymal cells first withdraw their processes and become crowded together in dense aggregations called *protochondral tissue* or *centers of chondrification.* The nuclei of the cells are very close together and the cell boundaries indistinct (Fig. 9-2*A* and *B*). As the cells enlarge and differentiate, they secrete around themselves a metachromatic hyaline matrix (Fig. 9-2*C*). Tropocollagen is secreted at the same time, but the fibrils that form extracellularly tend to be masked by the hyaline ground substance in which they are embedded. As the amount of interstitial material increases, the cells become isolated in separate compartments or *lacunae* and take on the cytological characteristics of mature cartilage cells or *chondrocytes* (Fig. 9-3).

The continuing growth of cartilage takes place by two different mechanisms. Mitoses are observed among the cells for a rather long period. After the constriction of the cytoplasm in such a division, a new partition of interstitial substance quickly develops and separates the two daughter cells. These in turn may divide, giving rise to clusters of four, and so on. The mitotic division of the chondrocytes and the secretion of new matrix between the daughter cells lead to an expansion of the cartilage from within, which is referred to as *interstitial growth.*

The mesenchyme surrounding the cartilage primordium condenses into a special layer, the perichondrium, which merges with the cartilage on one side and the adjacent connective tissue on the other (Fig. 9-4). Throughout embryonic life the cells on the inner or chondrogenic layer of the perichondrium constantly differentiate into chondrocytes, secrete matrix around themselves, and in this way contribute new cells and matrix to the surface of the mass of cartilage. This process is called *appositional growth.* The ability of the perichondrium to form cartilage persists but remains latent in the adult.

THE CHONDROCYTES. In the layers of cartilage immediately beneath the perichondrium or under the free surface of articular cartilage, the lacunae are elliptical in section

with the long axis parallel to the surface, while deeper in the cartilage they are semicircular or angular. The cells in living cartilage usually conform to the shape of the lacunae that they occupy, but fixation and dehydration may result in their retraction from the wall of the lacuna, so that they appear stellate. Actually, mature cartilage cells in higher vertebrates rarely if ever have processes visible with the light microscope, but in electron micrographs their surface is quite irregular. The cells tend to be clustered in small groups (Fig. 9-1). Each group is said to be *isogenous* because it represents the progeny of a single chondrocyte that underwent a few mitotic divisions in the course of the interstitial growth of the cartilage. In the cartilage of the epiphyseal plates of long bones, cell division in a consistent plane results in an arrangement of the cartilage cells in long columns that are later invaded by advancing bone (Fig. 9-5).

The nucleus of the chondrocyte is round or oval and contains from one to several nucleoli depending upon the species. There is a

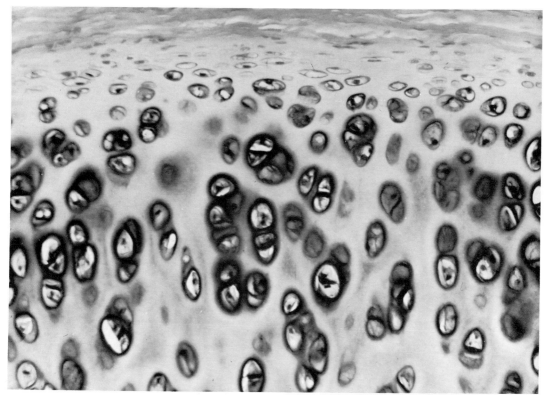

Figure 9-1. Hyaline cartilage from the trachea of a guinea pig. Notice the more intense staining of the capsular or territorial matrix immediately surrounding the groups of isogenous cells. The cells immediately beneath the perichondrium (*top*) recently added in appositional growth are single and elongated. Hematoxylin and eosin. × 400.

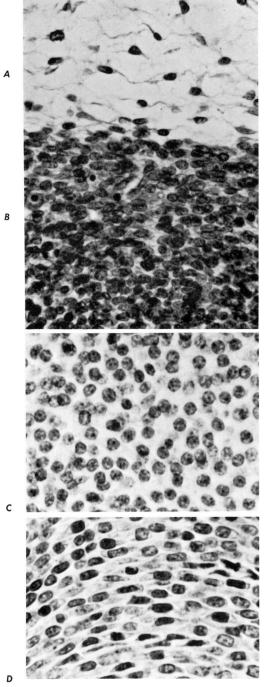

Figure 9-2. In the histogenesis of cartilage, mesenchymal cells (*A*) withdraw their processes and become crowded together to form an area of precartilage (*B*). In newly formed embryonic cartilage (*C*), the densely aggregated cells of the precartilaginous stage have been moved apart by deposition of clear hyaline matrix between them. The cells then become angular (*D*) and isolated by clearly demarcated lacunae. Hematoxylin and eosin stain. ×375.

juxtanuclear cell center with a pair of centrioles and a well developed Golgi apparatus. The surrounding cytoplasm contains elongated mitochondria, occasional lipid droplets, and variable amounts of glycogen. When new matrix is being formed in growing or regenerating cartilage, the cytoplasm becomes more basophilic and the Golgi region becomes unusually large. Under these conditions of active growth, electron micrographs show a well developed granular endoplasmic reticulum with moderately distended cisternae. The saccules of the Golgi complex tend to be dilated, and there are numerous associated vacuoles of varying size that sometimes contain a flocculent precipitate. Similar vacuoles are also seen at the cell surface, where they appear to be discharging their contents into the surrounding matrix. In cartilage that is not actively growing, the endoplasmic reticulum is less extensive and the Golgi complex not as prominent.

CARTILAGE MATRIX. In fresh hyaline cartilage the matrix appears homogeneous. This is due in part to the fact that the ground substance and the collagen embedded within it have approximately the same refractive index and in part to the very small size and random orientation of the collagen fibrils. The amorphous ground substance is deeply colored with the periodic acid–Schiff reaction for complex carbohydrates. It also has a marked affinity for basic dyes and stains metachromatically with toluidine blue. The principal constituent of the ground substance is *chondromucoprotein,* a copolymer of a mucoprotein, chondroitin-4-sulfate (chrondroitin sulfate A) and chondroitin-6-sulfate (chondroitin sulfate C). It is the strongly acidic sulfate groups of these mucopolysaccharides that are responsible for the basophilia and the metachromasia of cartilage matrix.

The matrix immediately surrounding each group of isogenous cells usually stains more deeply than elsewhere (Fig. 9-1). This deeply basophilic rim is called the *capsular* or *territorial matrix,* while the less basophilic matrix between cell groups is called the *interterritorial matrix.* The deeper staining of the territorial matrix suggests that the concentration of the acid mucopolysaccharides is higher in the immediate vicinity of the cells.

Up to 40 per cent of the dry weight of cartilage matrix is collagen in the form of an interlacing fabric of fine fibrils 100 to 200 Å in diameter. These fibrils do not exhibit the 640

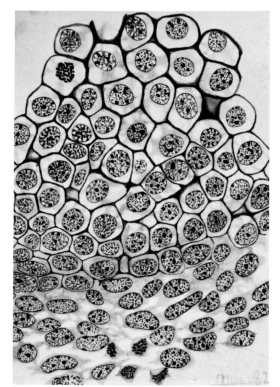

Figure 9-3. Development of cartilage from mesenchyme in a 15 mm. guinea pig embryo. The mesenchyme (*below*) gradually merges into the protochondral tissue with interstitial substance (*above*). Note mitoses. × 750. (After A. A. Maximow.)

Å periodic cross banding characteristic of collagen fibers in connective tissue or bone. They are sparse or absent in the immediate vicinity of the cells but abundant in the intercapsular matrix.

SECRETION OF MATRIX COMPONENTS. The chondrocytes have long been assumed to have some role in the elaboration of the ground substance and fibers of the matrix, but in the absence of obvious precursors in cytoplasm there was no real evidence that they had a secretory function. With the advent of radioautography it was shown that injected ^{35}S can be detected at early time intervals in the chondrocytes and later in the matrix (Bélanger). Recent adaptations of radioautography for use at the electron microscope level of resolution leave no doubt as to the role of the chondrocyte in the production of both collagen and chondromucoprotein. After injection of tritiated proline into animals actively forming

cartilage, this precursor of collagen could be localized after 10 to 15 minutes over the endoplasmic reticulum of the chondrocytes. At 30 minutes the label was over the Golgi region, and at four hours it was over vacuoles at the periphery of the cell and in the adjacent matrix (Revel and Hay). At longer time intervals the cells were cleared and all of the label was over the matrix.

Thus it has now been demonstrated that the secretion of collagen precursors follows the same intracellular path as the secretion of protein by a glandular cell (Fig. 9-6). Recent studies using tritiated glucose and ^{35}S strongly suggest that the Golgi complex of the chondrocyte is the site of synthesis of the complex

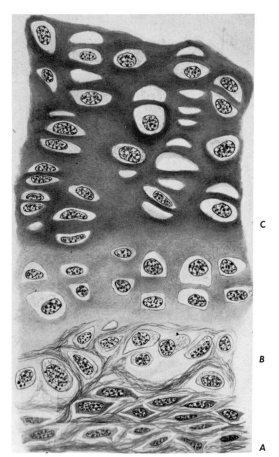

Figure 9-4. Hyaline cartilage from xiphoid process of rat. *A*, Transition layer adjacent to perichondrium. *B*, Continuation of collagenous fibers from perichondrium into interstitial substance of cartilage. *C*, Columns of isogenous groups of cartilage cells, some of which have fallen out of the lacunae in processing. Eosin-azure stain. × 750. (After A. A. Maximow.)

carbohydrate constituents of the extracellular matrix. It is probable that sugars and sulfate go directly to the Golgi region, where they are incorporated in the synthesis of sulfated polysaccharide. Labeled amino acid precursors, on the other hand, appear to go to the granular endoplasmic reticulum, where they are incorporated into protein that is later conjugated with polysaccharide in the Golgi apparatus and released from the cell as chondromucoprotein.

ELASTIC CARTILAGE

In mammals this variety of cartilage is found in the external ear, the walls of the external auditory and eustachian tubes, the epiglottis, and in parts of the corniculate and cuneiform cartilages. It differs from hyaline cartilage macroscopically in its yellowish color and its greater opacity, flexibility and elasticity.

Its cells are similar to those of hyaline cartilage; they are of the same rounded shape, are also surrounded by capsules, and are scattered singly or in isogenous groups of two or three cells. The interstitial substance differs from that of hyaline cartilage by being permeated by frequently branching fibers, which give all the tests for elastin (Fig. 9-7). They form a network that is often so dense that the ground substance is obscured. In the layers beneath the perichondrium, the feltwork of the elastic fibers is looser. The elastic fibers of the cartilage continue into the perichondrium.

In the histogenesis of elastic cartilage in the embryo, a primitive connective tissue develops containing fibroblasts and wavy fibrillar bundles that do not give reactions characteristic of either collagen or elastin. These indifferent fibers apparently are transformed later into elastic fibers with typical staining properties. The cells secrete matrix around themselves and become recognizable as chondrocytes. As in hyaline cartilage, a perichondrium is formed and initiates appositional growth.

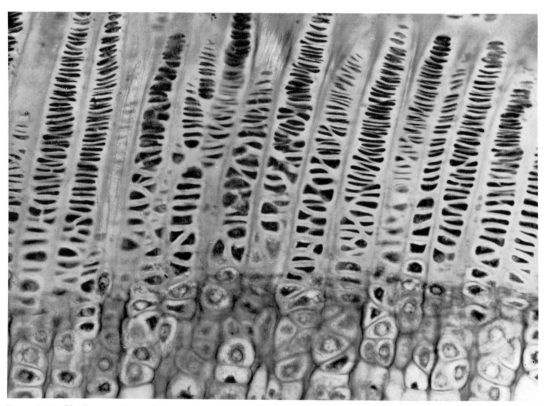

Figure 9-5. Hyaline cartilage of the epiphyseal plate of rabbit tibia. Here the cartilage cells are arranged in long parallel columns. From above downward, zones of cartilage cell proliferation, maturation, hypertrophy, and degeneration can be recognized. Hematoxylin and eosin stain. × 375.

FIBROCARTILAGE

Fibrocartilage occurs in a few regions of dense connective tissue in the bodies of mammals as small areas with poorly defined limits where typical cartilage cells and a small amount of matrix are found among the abundant fibrous elements. It occurs in the intervertebral disks, certain articular cartilages, in the symphysis pubis, in the ligamentum teres femoris, and in the sites of attachment of certain tendons to bones. The encapsulated cartilage cells lie singly or in pairs or sometimes aligned in rows between bundles of collagen fibers (Fig. 9-8). The ground substance is quite inconspicuous except in the immediate vicinity of the cells, where its presence can be inferred from the characteristic form of the lacunae.

Fibrocartilage is closely associated with the connective tissue of the capsules and ligaments of joints. It is a transitional form between cartilage and dense connective tissue, and the gradual transformation from one to the other can be observed in the adult as in its histogenesis in the embryo. In the intervertebral disks, for example, the hyaline cartilage connected with the vertebrae shows distinct collagenous fibers in its matrix. These then become associated into thick bundles, which almost entirely displace the homogeneous ground substance while the cartilage cells retain their spherical form and their capsular matrix. Finally this typical fibrocartilage merges into connective tissue, the cells of which are provided with processes and are not enclosed in lacunae.

Fibrocartilage develops in much the same way as ordinary connective tissue. In the beginning there are typical fibroblasts separated by a large amount of fibrillar substance. Then these cells become rounded, are transformed into cartilage cells, and surround themselves with a thin layer of capsular matrix. The abundant fibrous interstitial substance becomes infiltrated only slightly, if at all, with amorphous cartilaginous ground substance.

OTHER VARIETIES OF CARTILAGE AND CHONDROID TISSUE

There is a transitory phase in the embryonic development of hyaline cartilage when it is composed of closely adjacent vesicular cells and provided with thin capsules and with col-

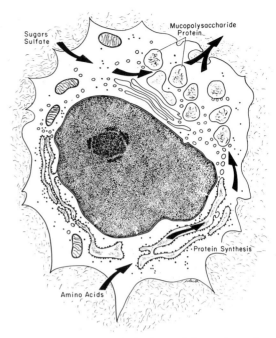

Figure 9-6. Diagram of the intracellular pathway for synthesis of matrix components. Amino acids are incorporated into protein at the ribosomes. Sugar and sulfates are believed to be incorporated into polysaccharide in the Golgi region and combined to form the protein-polysaccharide mucopolysaccharide released into the surrounding matrix. (Courtesy of E. Hay and J. P. Revel.)

lagenous fibers in its interstitial substance. In this undeveloped condition the cartilage may remain throughout life in certain parts of the bodies of higher organisms. It occurs often in lower vertebrates (fishes and amphibians, as in the sesamoid cartilage of the tendon of Achilles in frogs) and is still more common in invertebrates. Such tissue has been called *pseudocartilage, fibrohyaline tissue, vesicular supporting tissue,* and *chondroid tissue.* This tissue serves as a mechanical support for other parts of the body.

The tissue composing the *notochord* of vertebrates has a similar structure. Here, there is a shaft of variable thickness which consists of large, closely packed vesicular cells distended with fluid and having an elastic membrane. The notochordal tissue has a different embryological origin from that of the cartilage and of the other connective tissues.

REGENERATION OF CARTILAGE

In amphibians, cartilage is regenerated in a manner resembling histogenesis of carti-

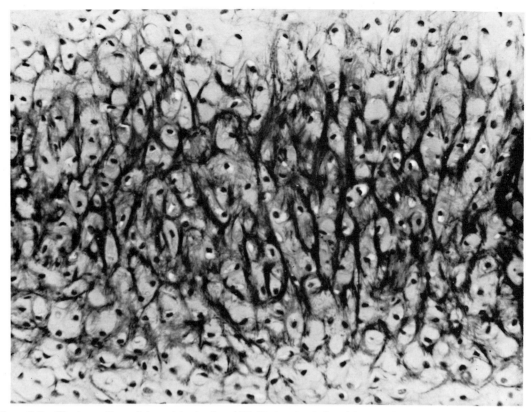

Figure 9-7. Elastic cartilage of the epiglottis of a child. Notice the dark-staining elastic fiber bundles in the matrix between cell groups. Hematoxylin and eosin stain. × 300. (After D. W. Fawcett, *in* R. O. Greep, ed.: Histology. Philadelphia, The Blakiston Co., 1953. Reproduced with the permission of the McGraw-Hill Book Co.)

lage in the embryo, but most workers agree that after a wound or excision of a portion of cartilage in adult mammals, no such independent regeneration takes place. Instead one sees at first in the injured area only necrotic and atrophic changes. The defect is then filled by newly formed connective tissue, which grows in from the perichondrium or from fascia in the vicinity of the injured area. The fibroblasts of this ingrowing granulation tissue may then round up, produce capsules around themselves and become transformed into new cartilage cells. Thus, if cartilage is replaced in the adult mammal, this takes place mainly by metaplasia of loose connective tissue.

Such a metaplasia sometimes takes place in connective tissue under the influence of simple mechanical forces acting from the outside, such as pressure, particularly when combined with friction. It is claimed that the presence of cartilage on the joint surfaces of

bones is related to the constant mechanical influences to which a normal joint is subjected while functioning. When these mechanical conditions disappear, as happens in dislocation of bones, the cartilage often undergoes dedifferentiation. On the other hand, cartilage is laid down in the primordia of the joint surfaces in the embryo at a time when there are probably no mechanical forces acting on the joint.

Although cartilage has only limited regenerative capacity if the cells have been damaged, it has been shown that components of the matrix can be rapidly reformed if the cells remain intact. Injection of a crude preparation of papain into young rabbits results in a collapse of their ears. This is attended by a loss of basophilia of the cartilage matrix and by a loss of its amorphous and elastic components, demonstrable in electron micrographs. After 48 hours the regeneration of matrix components is already far advanced and the ears are largely restored to their normal erect position.

REGRESSIVE CHANGES IN CARTILAGE

The most important regressive change in cartilage, calcification, normally precedes the type of bone formation called *intracartilaginous ossification* (Fig. 9-9). The cartilage cells in a center of ossification undergo a regular sequence of changes referred to as the cytomorphosis of the cartilage cells. In the epiphyseal plate, where the cells become arranged in parallel columns, these changes are observed in successive zones along the length of the column. A *zone of proliferation, zone of maturation, zone of cartilage cell hypertrophy,* and *zone of cell degeneration* can be recognized (Fig. 9-5). In the zone of hypertrophic cartilage cells, there is a strong histochemical reaction for the enzyme alkaline phosphatase. Its function here is not known. The matrix in this region undergoes calcification. Minute nests of calcium phosphate and carbonate crystals are deposited in the vicinity of the cells (Fig. 9-10). As these enlarge and merge, the cartilage becomes opaque, hard, and brittle. Because of these changes in the matrix, the zone of cartilage cell hypertrophy is also known as the *zone of provisional calcification.* The relation of these events to the process of ossification will be discussed in greater detail in Chapter 10. In man, ossification of certain cartilages is a normal age change and may take place in some parts of the larynx as early as 20 years of age.

Another form of regressive change in cartilage is called *asbestos transformation.* Within the homogeneous intercellular substance, parallel fibers are deposited that have nothing in common with collagenous fibers. They do not swell in acetic acid, but dissolve in boiling water and in low concentrations of alkalis. They give the tissue a silky, glossy appearance similar to that of asbestos; they spread over wide areas and may lead to a softening of the tissue and even to the formation of spaces in it. It has been reported that new cartilage may develop in these spaces. In elastic as well as in hyaline cartilage, calcification and asbestos transformation may take place with advancing age.

HISTOPHYSIOLOGY OF CARTILAGE

Cartilage in joints has the remarkable property of sustaining great weight and at the same time allowing the bones, which carry this weight, to move easily and smoothly against one another. In other places, such as the ear and the respiratory passages, cartilage serves as a pliable yet resistant framework that prevents the collapse of the tubular organs. Finally, cartilage in many bones makes pos-

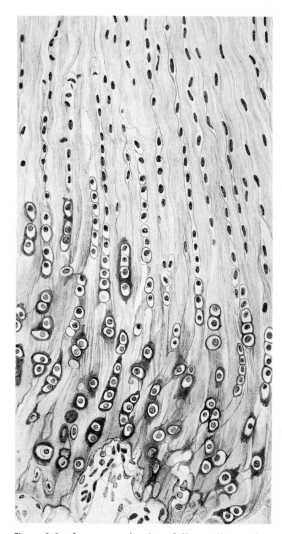

Figure 9-8. Low-power drawing of fibrocartilage at insertion of tendon into the tibia of a rat. Note the direct transformation of rows of tendon cells (*top*) into cartilage cells surrounded by deeply staining matrix. Hematoxylin-eosin-azure II. From a preparation of F. C. McLean. (Drawn by Miss A. Nixon.)

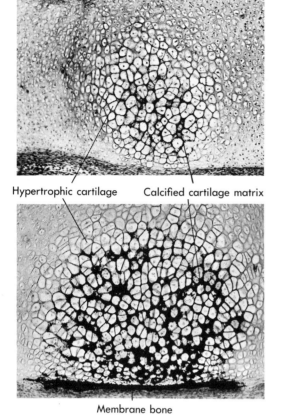

Hypertrophic cartilage   Calcified cartilage matrix

Membrane bone

Figure 9-9. Two stages in the calcification of the cartilage model of the calcaneus in rats. *Above*, Two days and *below*, four days after birth. The calcium salts appear black because of the silver nitrate stain. Undecalcified preparations stained with von Kōssa's method and hematoxylin and eosin. × 75. (After W. Bloom and M. A. Bloom.)

sible their growth in length and is important in determining their size and shape.

Far from being an inert tissue, cartilage, through its participation in the growth of bones, is a fairly delicate indicator of certain metabolic disturbances. It reflects *nutritional deficiencies,* especially of protein, minerals, or vitamins. For example, the thickness of the epiphyseal cartilage plate diminishes rapidly when a young rat is placed on a protein deficient diet or on one lacking in vitamin A. When vitamin C is withheld from guinea pigs, giving them *scurvy,* cessation of matrix formation may be accompanied by changes in the cells and by distortion of their columnar arrangement. Absence of vitamin D is attended by a deficient absorption of calcium and phosphorus from the diet and leads to *rickets,* in which the epiphyseal cartilages continue to proliferate

but fail to calcify and the growing bones become deformed by weight bearing.

The participation of cartilage in the growth in length of bones is in part under control of several hormones, of which the most important is the pituitary *growth hormone.* Hypophysectomy in young rats leads to a thinning of the epiphyseal plate of long bones, with cessation of mitosis and a decrease in the number and especially in the size of its cells. After a short time the cartilage fails to be eroded, and growth of the bone ceases. When growth hormone is injected into such animals, the cartilage undergoes a striking metamorphosis and within a few days resembles that of a normal, young, growing animal, and the bone resumes its growth (Fig. 9-12). The response of the cartilage varies with the dose level and has been used to assay extracts containing the hormone. Long continued administration of the hormone produces giant rats, this being made possible in part by growth of cartilage after it would normally have ceased growing.

Figure 9-10. Electron micrograph of a small area of cartilage matrix in the epiphyseal plate of a kitten humerus. Calcification of the cartilage has begun with the appearance of dense aggregations of minute crystals. Buffered osmic acid fixation. × 60,000. (Courtesy of B. Scott and D. C. Pease.)

Arrow indicates amount of growth
in length after administration of
growth hormone.

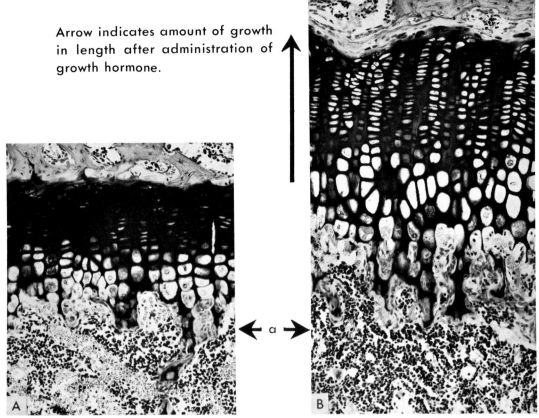

Figure 9-11. Photomicrographs of proximal metaphysis of tibias of young rats to show effects of growth hormone. *A,* Atrophic cartilage of hypophysectomized rat; *B,* hypertrophy and growth of cartilage with new bone formation in hypophysectomized rat after injection for four days with purified growth hormone. *a,* tip of spongiosa. Zenker-formol, hematoxylin and eosin. × 165. (Courtesy of I. Gersh.)

Further, the injection of the hormone into older rats, in which cartilage proliferation has stopped, can to some extent reactivate its growth, with subsequent increase in the size of its bones.

When growth of cartilage has been retarded by removal of the thyroid from rats shortly after birth, renewed activity can be stimulated by administering *thyroxine.*

An excess of vitamin A accelerates the normal growth sequences of epiphyseal cartilage cells. It has been shown that these responses are not mediated by the pituitary. Mechanical injury to the cartilage may result in localized disturbance of growth. Lesions produced in the cartilage by x-rays or other high energy radiations frequently result in a marked stunting of growth.

Although much has been learned about the relation of cartilage cells to other mesenchymal cells, the interstitial substance is less well understood. Its mode of formation and growth, even its physical state, the organization of its polysaccharides, and the mechanism of calcification, all are fundamental problems that need further study. Perhaps the most difficult problem is the mechanism of interstitial growth in the center of this supporting tissue with its dense intercellular substance.

REFERENCES

Amprino, R.: On the incorporation of radiosulfate in the cartilage. Experientia, *11:*65, 1955.

Becks, H., C. W. Asling, M. E. Simpson, C. H. Li, and H. M. Evans: The growth of hypophysectomized female rats following chronic treatment with pure pituitary growth hormone. III. Skeletal changes—tibia, metacarpal, costochondral junction and caudal vertebrae. Growth, *13:*175, 1949.

Bélanger, L. F.: Autoradiographic studies of the formation of the organic matrix of cartilage, bone and the tissues of teeth. *In* Wolstenholme, G. E. W., and O'Connor, C. M., eds., Bone Structure and Metabolism. London, J. & A. Churchill Ltd., 1956.

Cameron, D. A., and R. A. Robinson: Electron microscopy of epiphyseal and articular cartilage matrix in the femur of the newborn infant. J. Bone & Joint Surg., *40:*163, 1958.

Campo, R. D., and D. D. Dziewiatkowski: A consideration of the permeability of cartilage to inorganic sulfate. J. Biophys. & Biochem. Cytol., 9:401, 1961.

Clark, E. R., and E. L. Clark: Microscopic observations on new formation of cartilage and bone in the living mammal. Am. J. Anat., 70:167, 1942.

Dziewiatkowski, D. D., and H. Q. Woodard: Effect of irradiation with x-rays on the uptake of S^{35} sulfate by the epiphyseal cartilage of mice. Lab. Invest., 8:205, 1959.

Fell, H. B., and E. Mellanby: The biological action of thyroxine on embryonic bones grown in tissue culture. J. Physiol., 127:427, 1955.

Glücksmann, A.: Studies on bone mechanics in vitro. II. The role of tension and pressure in chondrogenesis. Anat. Rec., 73:39, 1939.

Godman, G. C., and N. Lane: On the site of sulfation in the chondrocyte. J. Cell. Biol., 21:353, 1964.

Godman, G. C., and K. R. Porter: Chondrogenesis, studied with the electron microscope. J. Biophys. & Biochem. Cytol., 8:719, 1960.

Leblond, C. P., L. F. Bélanger, and R. C. Greulich: Formation of bones and teeth as visualized by radioautography. Ann. N. Y. Acad. Sci., 60:629, 1955.

McCluskey, R. T., and L. Thomas: The removal of cartilage matrix in vivo by papain. J. Exper. Med., 108:371, 1958.

Pelc, S. R., and A. Glücksmann: Sulphate metabolism in the cartilage of the trachea, pinna and xiphoid process of the adult mouse as indicated by autoradiographs. Exper. Cell Res., 8:336, 1955.

Revel, J. P., and E. D. Hay: An autoradiographic and electron microscopic study of collagen synthesis in differentiating cartilage. Zeitschr. f. Zellforsch., 61:110, 1963.

Sheehan, J. F.: A cytological study of the cartilage cells of developing long bones of the rat, with special reference to the Golgi apparatus, mitochondria, neutral-red bodies and lipid inclusions. J. Morphol., 82:151, 1948.

Sheldon, H., and F. B. Kimball: Studies on cartilage. III. The occurrence of collagen with vacuoles of the Golgi apparatus. J. Cell Biol., 12:599, 1962.

Sheldon, H., and R. A. Robinson: Studies on cartilage. I. Electron microscopic observations on normal rabbit ear cartilage. II. Electron microscopic observations on rabbit ear cartilage following the administration of papain. J. Biophys. & Biochem. Cytol., 4:401, 1958, and 8:151, 1960.

Silberberg, R., M. Hasler, and M. Silberberg: Submicroscopic response of articular cartilage of mice treated with estrogenic hormone. Am. J. Path., 46:289, 1965.

Silberberg, R., M. Silberberg, and D. Feir: Life cycle of articular cartilage cells: an electron microscope study of the hip joint of the mouse. Amer. J. Anat., 114:17, 1964.

Streeter, G. L.: Developmental horizons in human embryos (fourth issue); A review of the histogenesis of cartilage and bone. Carnegie Contributions to Embryol., 33:149, 1949.

Thomas, L.: Reversible collapse of rabbit ears after intravenous papain and prevention of recovery by cortisone. J. Exper. Med., 104:245, 1956.

Weiss, P., and A. Moscona: Type-specific morphogenesis of cartilages developed from dissociated limb and scleral mesenchyme in vitro. J. Embryol. & Exper. Morphol., 6:238, 1958.

Wolbach, S. B., and C. L. Maddock: Vitamin-A acceleration of bone growth sequences in hypophysectomized rats. Arch. Path., 53:273, 1952.

CHAPTER TEN

Bone

Bone, in common with other connective tissues, consists of cells, fibers, and ground substance, but it is unlike the others in that its extracellular components are calcified, making it a hard, unyielding substance ideally suited for its supportive and protective function in the skeleton. It provides for the internal support of the body and for the attachment of the muscles and tendons essential for locomotion. It protects the vital organs of the cranial and thoracic cavities, and it encloses the blood forming elements of the bone marrow. In addition to these mechanical functions, it plays an important metabolic role as a mobilizable store of calcium, which can be drawn upon as needed in the homeostatic regulation of the concentration of calcium in the blood and other fluids of the body.

Although bone approaches cast iron in tensile strength, it is less than one third as heavy. At all levels of its organization from the gross to the submicroscopic, the principles of its construction ensure the greatest strength with the greatest economy of material and the least weight. Despite its strength and hardness, bone is a dynamic living material constantly being renewed and reconstructed throughout the lifetime of the individual. Owing to its continual internal reconstruction and its responsiveness to external mechanical stimuli, it can be modified to some extent by the surgical procedures or appliances of the orthopedic surgeon or the orthodontist. It is also surprisingly responsive to metabolic, nutritional, and endocrine factors. Disuse is followed by *atrophy* with loss of substance; increased use is accompanied by *hypertrophy* with an increase in the mass of bone.

MACROSCOPIC STRUCTURE OF BONES

Upon inspection with the naked eye or hand lens, two forms of bone are distinguishable, *spongy* (substantia spongiosa) and *compact* (substantia compacta). Spongy bone consists of a three dimensional lattice of branching bony spicules or *trabeculae* delimiting a labyrinthine system of intercommunicating spaces that are occupied by bone marrow. Compact bone appears as a solid continuous mass, in which spaces can be seen only with the aid of the microscope. The two forms of bone grade into one another without a sharp boundary (Fig. 10-1).

In typical long bones, such as the femur or the humerus, the *diaphysis* (shaft) consists of a thick walled hollow cylinder of compact bone with a voluminous central *medullary cavity* (marrow cavity) containing the bone marrow. The *epiphyses,* at the ends of the shaft, consist mainly of spongy bone covered by a thin peripheral cortex of compact bone. The intercommunicating spaces among the trabeculae of epiphyseal spongy bone, in the adult, are directly continuous with the marrow cavity of the diaphysis. In the growing animal, the epiphysis and diaphysis are separated by the cartilaginous *epiphyseal plate,* which is united with the diaphysis by columns of spongy bone in a transitional region called the *metaphysis.* The epiphyseal cartilage and the adjacent spongy bone of the metaphysis constitute a growth zone, in which increment in length occurs. On the articular surfaces of the epiphyses of long bones the thin cortical layer of compact bone is covered by a layer of hyaline cartilage, the *articular cartilage.*

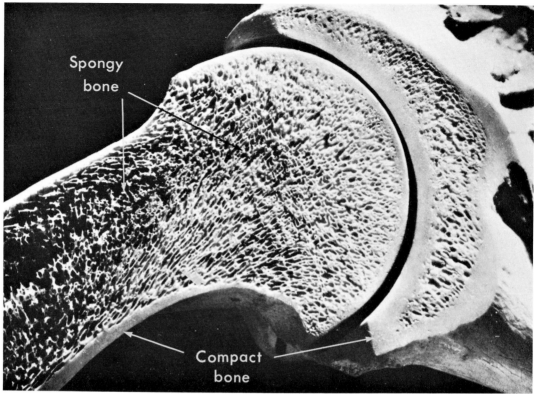

Spongy bone

Compact bone

Figure 10-1.   Photograph of a sagittal section of the proximal end of the humerus in relation to the glenoid fossa of the scapula at the shoulder joint. These are dry bones and the cartilaginous articular surfaces of the joint are not present. The figure is presented here to illustrate the appearance and distribution of spongy and compact bone. (After A. Feininger, from *Anatomy of Nature.* Crown Publishers. With permission of Time, Inc.)

With few exceptions, bones are invested by *periosteum,* a layer of specialized connective tissue, which is endowed with *osteogenic potency.* That is to say, it has the ability to form bone. A covering of periosteum is lacking on those areas of the epiphysis of long bones that are covered with articular cartilage. It is also absent at the sites where tendons and ligaments are inserted, on the surfaces of the patella and other sesamoid bones that are formed within tendons, and on the subcapsular areas of the neck of the femur and of the astragalus. Where functional periosteum is absent, the connective tissue in contact with the surfaces of bone lacks osteogenic potency and does not contribute to the healing of fractures. The marrow cavity of the diaphysis and the cavities of spongy bone are lined by a more delicate layer, the *endosteum,* which also possesses osteogenic properties.

In the flat bones of the skull, the substantia compacta forms, on both surfaces, relatively thick layers that are often referred to as the *outer* and *inner tables.* Between them is a layer of spongy bone of varying thickness called the *diploë.* The periosteum on the outer surface of the skull is called the *pericranium,* while the inner surface is lined by the *dura mater.* Although different terms are applied to these connective tissue coverings of the flat bones, they do not differ greatly in their structure or osteogenic potency from the periosteum and endosteum of long bones. However, defects in the calvarium resulting from injury do not heal completely in adults.

MICROSCOPIC STRUCTURE OF BONES

If a thin ground section of the shaft of a long bone is examined with the microscope, it is apparent that the contribution of the cellular elements of bone to its total mass is small. Compact bone is largely composed of the calcified interstitial substance, *bone matrix,* deposited in layers or *lamellae* 3 to 7 μ thick (Figs. 10-2 and 10-3). Rather uniformly spaced throughout the interstitial substance of bone are lenticular cavities, called *lacunae,* each completely filled by a bone cell or *osteocyte.* Radiating in all directions from the lacunae are exceedingly slender, branching tubular passages, the *canaliculi,* that penetrate the interstitial substance of the lamellae, anastomosing with the canalculi of neighboring lacunae (Figs. 10-4 and 10-5). Thus although the lacunae are spaced some distance apart, they form a continuous system of cavities interconnected by an extensive network of minute canals. These slender passages are believed to be essential to the nutrition of the bone cells. Whereas cartilage cells can be sustained by diffusion through the aqueous phase of the gel-like hyaline matrix, the deposition of calcium salts in the interstitial substance of bone evidently reduces its permeability. However, the maintenance of a system of intercommunicating canaliculi provides avenues for exchange of metabolites between the cells and the nearest perivascular space.

The lamellae of compact bone are disposed in three common patterns. (1) The great majority are arranged concentrically around longitudinal vascular channels within the bone to form cylindrical units of structure called *haversian systems* or *osteons.* These vary in size, being made up of 4 to 20 lamellae. In cross section, the haversian systems appear as concentric rings around a circular opening (Fig. 10-4). In longitudinal section, they are seen as closely spaced bands parallel to a long slit (Fig. 10-3). (2) Between the haversian systems are angular fragments of lamellar bone of varying size and irregular shape. These are the *interstitial systems* (Fig. 10-2). The limits of the haversian systems and interstitial systems are sharply demarcated by refractile lines called *cementing lines.* In cross section, the interior of compact bone thus has the appearance of a mosaic of round and angular pieces cemented together (Fig. 10-6). (3) At the external surface of the cortical bone, immediately beneath the periosteum, and on the internal surface, subjacent to the endosteum, there may be several lamellae that extend uninterruptedly around much of the circumference of the shaft. These are the *outer* and *inner circumferential lamellae.*

Two categories of vascular channels are distinguished in compact bone on the basis of their orientation and their relation to the lamellar structure of the surrounding bone. The longitudinal channels in the centers of the

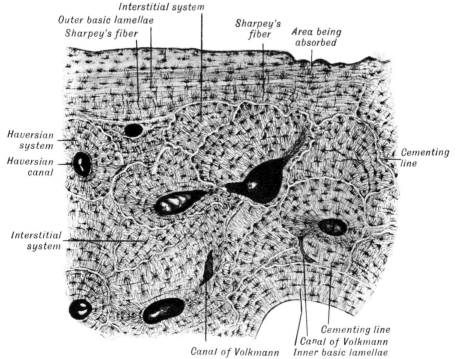

Figure 10-2. Portion of a ground cross section of a human metacarpal bone. Stained with fuchsin, mounted in Canada balsam. × 160. (After Schaffer.)

haversian systems are called *haversian canals*. They are 22 to 110 μ in diameter and contain one or two blood vessels ensheathed in loose connective tissue. The vessels are, for the most part, capillaries and postcapillary venules, but occasional arterioles may also be found. The haversian canals are connected with one another and communicate with the free surface and with the marrow cavity via transverse channels called *Volkmann's canals*. These can be distinguished from the haversian canals in section by the fact that they are not surrounded by concentrically arranged lamellae but traverse the bone in a direction perpendicular or oblique to the lamellae. The blood vessels from the endosteum and, to a lesser extent, from the periosteum, communicate with those of the haversian systems via the Volk-

mann's canals. The vessels are often larger than those in the osteons.

Although basically correct, the traditional description of haversian canals as longitudinal, and Volkmann's canals as oblique or transverse, is an oversimplification. Reconstruction of osteons from serial sections has shown that they are not always simple cylindrical units but may branch and anastomose and have a rather complex three dimensional configuration (Cohen). Thus one may encounter obliquely oriented vascular channels that are surrounded by concentric lamellae. Despite their atypical orientation, these are clearly cross connecting haversian canals.

Spongy bone is also composed of lamellae with lacunae embedded in the interstitial substance. The trabeculae of the spongiosa are

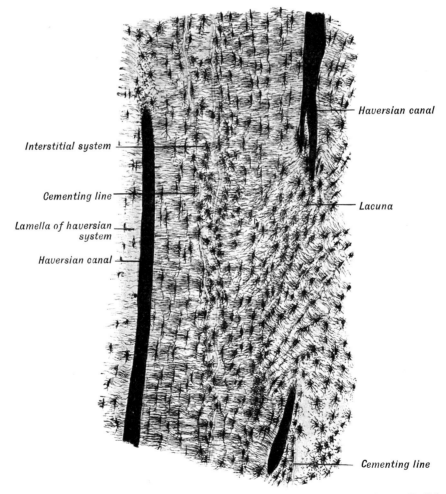

Interstitial system

Cementing line

Lamella of haversian system

Haversian canal

Haversian canal

Lacuna

Cementing line

Figure 10-3.   Portion of a longitudinal, ground section of the ulna of man; stained with fuchsin. × 160. (After Schaffer.)

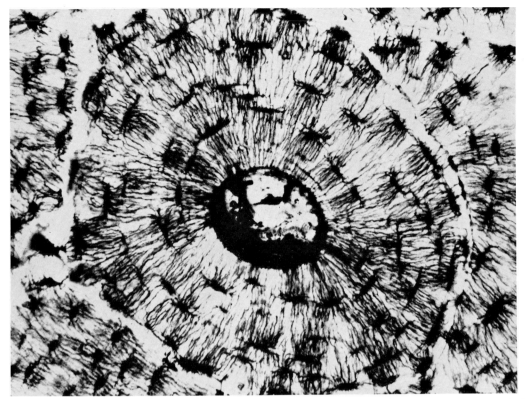

Figure 10-4. Ground section of human femur, showing a typical haversian system and the lacunae and canaliculi. × 300. (After D. W. Fawcett, *in* R. O. Greep, ed.: Histology. Philadelphia, The Blakiston Co., 1953. Reproduced with the permission of the McGraw-Hill Book Co.)

relatively thin, however, and are usually not penetrated by blood vessels. Therefore, there are usually no complete haversian systems, the bone cells being nourished from the free, endosteal surface via the network of canaliculi.

The periosteum is subject to considerable variation in its microscopic appearance depending upon its functional state. During embryonic and postnatal growth there is an inner layer of bone forming cells, *osteoblasts*, in direct contact with the bone. This has sometimes been called the *cambium layer*, by a fancied analogy with the wood forming zone of trees. In the adult, the osteoblasts assume a resting form and are indistinguishable from other spindle-shaped connective tissue cells. If a bone is injured, however, the bone forming potentiality of these cells is reactivated; they take on the appearance of typical osteoblasts and participate in the formation of new bone. The outer layer of the periosteum is a relatively acellular dense connective tissue containing blood vessels. Branches of these vessels traverse

the deeper layer and enter Volkmann's canals, through which they communicate with the vessels of the haversian canals. These numerous small vessels entering Volkmann's canals from the periosteum may contribute to maintaining its attachment to the underlying bone. In addition, coarse bundles of collagenous fibers from the outer layer of the periosteum turn inward, penetrating the outer circumferential lamellae and interstitial systems of the bone. These are called *Sharpey's fibers* or *perforating fibers* (Fig. 10-7). They arise during growth of the bone when thick collagenous bundles become incarcerated in the bone matrix deposited during the subperiosteal formation of new lamellae. When uncalcified, they occupy irregular canals penetrating the compact bone from the periosteal surface in a direction perpendicular or oblique to the lamellae. When calcified, they appear as irregular radial stripes in the outer portion of the cortical bone. They serve to anchor the periosteum firmly to the underlying bone.

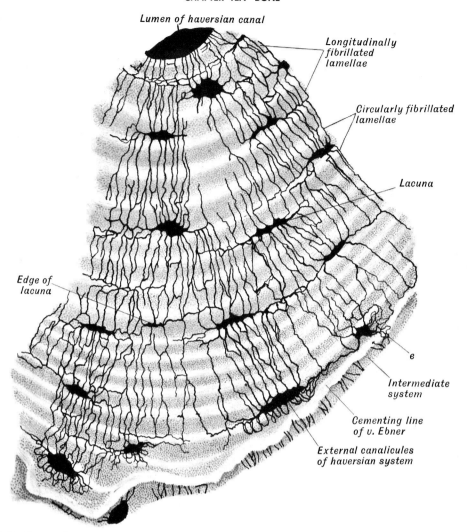

Lumen of haversian canal

Longitudinally
fibrillated
lamellae

Circularly fibrillated
lamellae

Lacuna

Edge of
lacuna

e

Intermediate
system

Cementing line
of v. Ebner

External canalicules
of haversian system

Figure 10-5. Sector of a cross section of a haversian system of a macerated human hip bone. The cavities and canalicules are filled with a dye: *e*, connection of canalicules of the haversian system with those of an intermediate system. × 520. (After A. A. Maximow.)

They vary greatly in number in different regions, being particularly numerous in some of the bones of the skull and at sites of attachment of muscles and tendons to the periosteum of long bones. In addition to Sharpey's fibers, some elastic fibers penetrate the cortical bone from the periosteum, either together with or independent of the collagenous bundles.

The endosteum is a thin connective tissue layer lining the walls of those cavities in the bone that house the bone marrow. It is the condensed peripheral layer of the stroma of the bone marrow where it is in contact with bone, and it resembles the periosteum in some respects. All the cavities of bone, including the haversian canals and the marrow spaces within spongy bone, are lined with endosteum after osteoblasts are no longer recognizable. The endosteum lining the compact bone of the shaft, however, is more prominent than elsewhere. The endosteum has both osteogenic and hemopoietic potencies.

SUBMICROSCOPIC STRUCTURE AND CHEMICAL COMPOSITION OF BONE MATRIX

The interstitial substance of bone is of similar composition in different species and consists of two main components, an organic matrix and inorganic salts. The organic matrix of bone consists of collagenous fibers embedded in an amorphous ground substance consisting of protein-polysaccharides. The chondroitin sulfate content of the ground substance is lower than that of hyaline cartilage, and, therefore, bone matrix is usually acidophilic.

In electron micrographs, the collagenous fibers of bone, unlike those of cartilage, have the characteristic cross banding of native collagen. Those within each lamella of an haversian system are consistent in their orientation, but their direction in the successive lamellae changes. It is widely accepted that this change in orientation of the fibers is responsible for the alternation of bright and dark layers in haversian systems viewed with polarizing optics (Fig. 10-6*B*). There is still no general agreement, however, as to the precise arrangement of the fibers. In decalcified preparations viewed at high magnification, refractile lamellae with a fine circumferential striation alternate with less refractile layers having a stippled or punctate aspect. This appearance was originally interpreted as indicating a regular alternation of lamellae with circularly and longitudinally oriented fibrils. This was apparently an oversimplification. Some investigators have insisted that collagen-rich lamellae alternate with collagen-poor lamellae and that this difference is as important as the direction of the fibers in accounting for the microscopic appearance of the haversian systems. Others have suggested that the fibers within a given collagen-rich lamella are not parallel but form two sets of fibers intersecting in a lattice-like pattern (Rouiller). The majority of histologists, however, seem to follow Gebhardt (Fig. 10-8) in believing that the fibrils in all of the lamellae run helically with respect to the axis of the haversian canal, but differ sufficiently in the pitch of the helix from layer to layer to account for the observed appearance under the polarization microscope.

During development and growth the amount of organic material per unit volume remains relatively constant, but the amount of water decreases and the proportion of inorganic matter or *bone mineral* increases, attaining a maximum of about 65 per cent of the fat-free dry weight in the adult. In the poorly calcified bone of individuals with *rickets* or *osteomalacia* the mineral content may be as low as 35 per cent.

The inorganic matter of bone consists of submicroscopic crystals of an apatite of calcium and phosphate resembling hydroxyapatite $(Ca_{10}(PO_4)_6(OH)_2)$. The bone mineral always contains significant amounts of the citrate ion, $C_6H_5O_7^{\equiv}$, and the carbonate ion, $CO_3^=$. Citrate is considered to be in a separate phase, located on the surfaces of crystals. The location of carbonate is still a matter of debate; it may be located on the surface of crystals, or it may substitute for $PO_4^{\equiv}$ in the crystal structure, or both. Substitution of the fluoride ion, F^-, for OH^- in the apatite crystal is common; its amount depends mainly on the fluoride content of the drinking water.

The crystals of apatite are deposited in the form of slender needles 200 to 400 Å in length by 15 to 30 Å in thickness, and these are located within the substance of the collagen fibers of the organic matrix—a very efficient arrangement for effectively resisting mechanical stresses. Magnesium and sodium, which are normal constituents of the body fluids, are always present in the bone mineral, which serves as a storage depot for these elements. ^{45}Ca and ^{32}P can, of course, substitute for the stable ^{40}Ca and ^{31}P in the hydroxyapatite crystal. Foreign cations, such as Pb^{++}, Sr^{++}, and Ra^{++} (^{226}Ra), if ingested, may also substitute for Ca^{++}. In the fission of uranium in nuclear reactors or of uranium or plutonium in the detonation of nuclear weapons, a large number of radioactive elements is liberated. Some of these, on gaining access to the body, are incorporated in bone. The most hazardous of these *bone seeking isotopes* is ^{90}Sr. As a result of their radioactivity, they may cause severe damage to bone and to the marrow. A few of these bone seeking isotopes, including ^{259}Pu, do not enter the bone mineral but have instead a special affinity for the organic constituents of bone. Study of the rate of turnover of the inorganic substances in bone is greatly aided by the use of bone seeking isotopes (Fig. 10-9).

If bone is exposed to a weak acid or a chelating agent (such as EDTA) the inorganic salts are removed. The bone thus decalcified has lost most of its hardness and is tough and flexible, and it retains its gross form and a near normal microscopic appearance. If a bone is ignited, or if the organic constituents are extracted, the remaining inorganic constituents retain the gross form of the bone and to a certain extent its microscopic topography, but the bone has lost its tensile strength and is as brittle as porcelain. Thus it is clear that the hardness of bone depends upon its inorganic constitu-

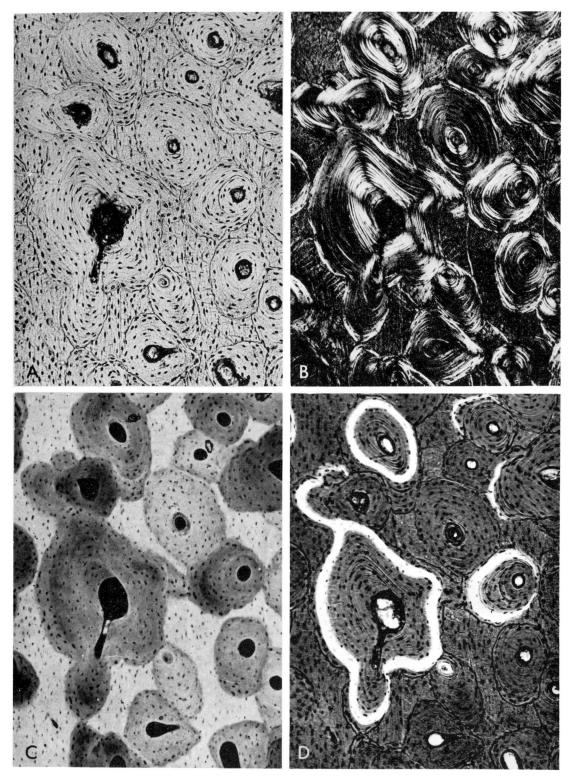

Figure 10-6. *See opposite page for legend.*

ents, while its great toughness and resilience reside in its organic matrix, particularly the collagen. Without either, it would be a poor skeletal material, but with both, it is a highly ordered, remarkably resistant tissue, superbly adapted, at all levels of its organization, for its chemical and mechanical function.

THE CELLS OF BONE

In actively growing bones three kinds of bone cells are distinguishable: *osteoblasts, osteocytes,* and *osteoclasts.* Although they are usually described as distinct cell types, there is clear evidence of transformation from one to the other, and it is evidently more reasonable to regard them as different functional states of the same cell type. Such reversible changes in appearance are examples of cell *modulation,* in contrast to *differentiation,* which is the term applied to progressive and apparently irreversible specialization in structure and function. In addition to these three, there are other cells in bones that have latent potentialities for developing into bone cells under appropriate stimulation. Like other connective tissues, bone develops from the embryonic mesenchyme, and, as has been pointed out in previous chapters, cells with some if not all mesenchymal potencies persist into postnatal life. Among the pluripotential cells in adult mammals are the stellate reticular cells of hemopoietic tissue, certain elongate cells in the adventitia of small blood vessels, and primitive spindle-shaped cells in the endosteum and periosteum that are indistinguishable from fibroblasts. The osteogenic potentialities of these cells may be activated during normal growth of bone; as a result of experimental

intervention; or in the healing of fractures and other forms of injury to bone. When this occurs, these precursors of bone cells may undergo mitosis and may then be identified by their uptake of tritiated thymidine; their contribution to new bone may be demonstrated by radioautography. They may also be recognized morphologically as they gradually assume the form and acquire the cytological characteristics of osteoblasts, osteocytes, and osteoclasts.

OSTEOBLASTS. The osteoblasts are associated with the formation of osseous tissue and are invariably found on the advancing surfaces of developing or growing bones. During active deposition of new bone matrix they form an epithelioid layer of cuboidal or low columnar cells connected to one another by short slender processes. The nucleus with its single prominent nucleolus is often at the end of the cell farthest from the bony surface (Fig. 10-10). Adjacent to the nucleus is a pale-staining cell center in which a diplosome and an associated well developed Golgi apparatus can be demonstrated by use of special stains. The mitochondria are elongated and fairly numerous. The cytoplasm is intensely basophilic owing to its content of ribonucleic acid (RNA). When new bone is being formed the osteoblasts give a strong histochemical reaction for alkaline phosphatase, and the periodic acid–Schiff reaction reveals in the cytoplasm small pink-staining granules that are believed to represent precursors of the bone matrix. When active new formation of bone ceases and the osteoblasts revert to spindle form, these granules disappear from the cytoplasm, and the phosphatase reaction of the cells rapidly declines.

Figure 10-6. Section of bone from the midshaft of the human fibula as revealed by four different optical methods. *A,* Ground section photographed through the ordinary bright field microscope. The lacunae, the haversian systems, and interstitial lamella are clearly shown. *B,* The same section photographed through the polarizing microscope shows the alternating bright and dark concentric layers in the haversian systems that result from the differing orientation of collagen fibers in the successive lamellae. *C,* In a historadiogram of the same section, the differing shades of gray in the scale from white to black reflect the differing concentrations of calcium. In the haversian canals, there has been no absorption of the x-rays and the film is therefore black. The most recently deposited haversian systems are incompletely calcified and appear dark gray, whereas older ones containing higher concentrations of calcium are lighter. The old interstitial lamellae, being fully calcified, are most highly absorptive and therefore appear white. *D,* The 14 year old girl from whom this specimen was taken had been given a daily dose of the antibiotic Achromycin for 15 consecutive days at one period of her illness. Amputation of the leg was carried out 230 days later. Achromycin is incorporated into the matrix of bone being deposited at the time of its administration and imparts a fluorescence to the newly formed bone. In the section shown here, transilluminated with ultraviolet light in a fluorescence microscope, the white areas represent areas of bone laid down during the 15 day Achromycin treatment. The nonfluorescent central portions of the same haversian systems represent bone deposited after cessation of the treatment. × 125. (Courtesy of R. Amprino.)

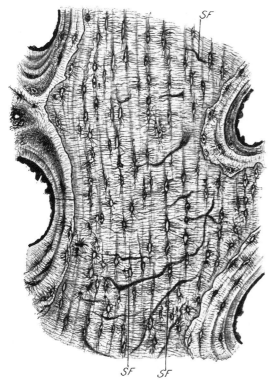

Figure 10-7. Portion of a cross section of a human fibula. *SF,* Sharpey's fibers. × 160. (After Schaffer.)

In electron micrographs, osteoblasts are seen to have the structure expected of a cell actively engaged in protein synthesis (Figs. 10-14 and 10-15). The cisternae of the endoplasmic reticulum are extensive and often in parallel array. Their membranes are studded with ribosomes and these are also present in great numbers in the cytoplasmic matrix. The Golgi membranes are well developed and have numerous associated vacuoles. Sizable vesicles containing an amorphous or flocculent material of appreciable density apparently correspond to the PAS staining granules observed with the light microscope (Fig. 10-11). Small lipid droplets and membrane limited dense bodies, interpreted as lysosomes, are also encountered occasionally.

OSTEOCYTES. The principal cells of fully formed bone are the *osteocytes,* which reside in lacunae within the calcified interstitial substance. The cell body is flattened, conforming to the shape of the lenticular cavity that it occupies, but there are numerous slender processes that extend for some distance into the canaliculi in the surrounding matrix. How far they penetrate into the canaliculi of adult

mammalian bone has not been determined, but the processes on osteocytes occupying neighboring lacunae are not thought to be in contact. The nuclear and cytoplasmic characteristics of osteocytes at the light microscope level are similar to those of osteoblasts, except that the Golgi region is less conspicuous, the cytoplasmic processes are longer, and the cytoplasm exhibits relatively little affinity for basic dyes. In electron micrographs osteocytes that have only recently been incorporated into bone still have the well developed Golgi apparatus and extensive rough surfaced endoplasmic reticulum characteristic of osteoblasts (Fig. 10-15). In more quiescent osteocytes the Golgi complex is smaller, there are fewer cisternal profiles of the reticulum, and free ribosomes are relatively sparse. These are the fine structural features of a cell that is by no means metabolically inert, but one that is not actively secreting.

The osteocyte is essentially an osteoblast that has been surrounded by bone matrix. In this location, within the lacuna, the cell is no longer forming new matrix at a rapid rate but is presumably engaged in maintenance of the

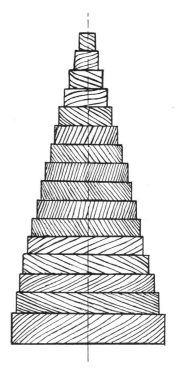

Figure 10-8. Diagram of the direction of the fibrils in successive lamellae of a haversian system. (Redrawn and slightly modified from Gebhardt.)

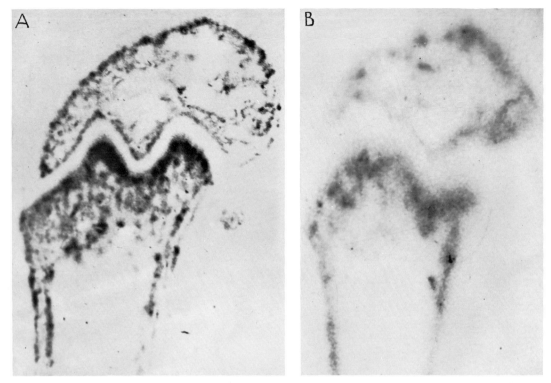

Figure 10-9. Radioautographs of distal end of femur of rats to show deposition of bone-seeking, radioactive isotopes. Note the sharp localization of an α-emitting element (plutonium) in *A*, and the more indefinite localization of a long range β emitter (^{32}P) in *B*. Both sections of undecalcified bones after fixation in alcohol. About 10×.

interstitial substance and of the system of fine channels that permeate it. The osteocytes may also participate in the mechanism by which materials are transported from blood to bone and from bone to blood. Beginning with the paper of Heller-Steinberg (1951), evidence has accumulated that the osteocytes exert an influence on the osseous matrix immediately surrounding the lacunae that results in increased reactivity of the bone mineral (Fig. 10-12).

This view is well stated in Bélanger's (1963) definition of the process of *osteolysis* as "an active physiological phenomenon taking place within the intimacy of the bone under the influence of the osteocytes, whereby bone matrix is modified and bone salt is lost." Thus it is the current belief that the osteocytes play an active role in the release of mineral from bone to blood, and hence participate in the homeostatic regulation of the concentration of calcium in the fluids of the body.

Like the osteoblast, the osteocyte is thought to undergo transformations to other forms. When released from its lacuna in the process of bone resorption it may assume the form of an osteoblast or of a reticular cell, or it may be incorporated into a multinucleate osteoclast.

OSTEOCLAST. Closely associated with areas of bone resorption are the osteoclasts, giant cells with a variable number of nuclei, often as many as 15 to 20. They are frequently found in concavities in the surface of bone, called *Howship's lacunae*. This relationship suggested to the early investigators of the histology of bone that the lacunae were formed by an erosive action of the osteoclasts (Fig. 10-10). In the growth and reformation of the trabeculae of spongy bone in rapidly growing animals, they are commonly seen enveloping the tip of each spicule of bone undergoing resorption. These relationships led to the widely accepted belief that osteoclasts play an active and major role in bone resorption. Although no one questions the close topographical relations of these cells to sites of resorption, it is only fair to state that some workers believe that the observations are equally consistent with the alternative interpretation that osteo-

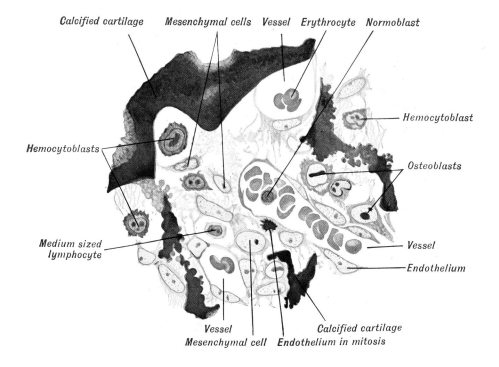

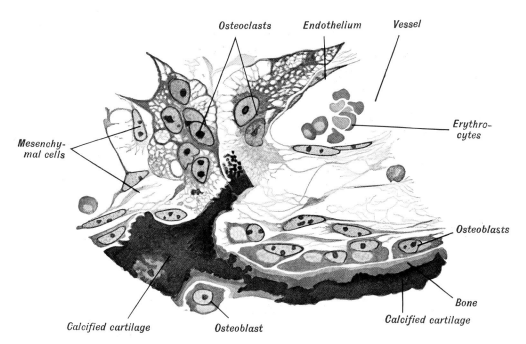

Figure 10-10. Two areas from sections of bone marrow cavity near the zone of endochondral ossification of the humerus of a 70 mm. human embryo. Hematoxylin-eosin-azure stain. About 700×. (After A. A. Maximow.)

clasts arise by coalescence of osteocytes liberated in the course of bone resorption and that they may therefore be by-products, rather than the active agents, of bone resorption. This view now has fewer adherents, as the evidence for an active role of osteoclasts in bone resorption becomes more and more compelling.

The nuclei of the osteoclasts resemble those of osteoblasts and osteocytes, which are considered to be their principal source in mammals. There is radioautographic evidence, however, that in amphibians mononuclear wandering cells, presumably monocytes, may contribute to the formation of osteoclasts (Fischman and Hay). The cytoplasm is slightly basophilic and highly heterogeneous in texture, often appearing vacuolated or foamy. In contrast to osteoblasts and osteocytes, vacuoles in the cytoplasm of osteoclasts stain positively with neutral red and with tests for acid phosphatase. On the side adjacent to the bone, the cytoplasm may have a faintly striated appearance. This specialization has been considered by some to be comparable to the brush borders of absorptive cells. Electron micrographs have revealed that although this surface of the osteoclast is elaborately specialized it bears no real resemblance to a brush border (Figs. 10-18 and 10-19). Instead of a regular arrangement of microvilli there appears to be a deep infolding of the cell membrane, delimiting a large number of irregularly shaped lobopodia or clavate processes separated by narrow extracellular clefts. Small crystals of bone mineral liberated from the bone matrix are often found deep in these clefts (Fig. 10-18). Observations of living osteoclasts in tissue culture show that

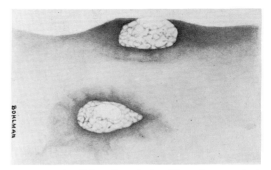

Figure 10-12. Edge of a spicule of bone from a rat, six hours after injection of 1000 units of parathyroid extract. The dark staining matrix around the osteocyte in the center and at the margin of the spicule indicates bone resorption. The upper osteocyte is partially liberated from the matrix. Cytoplasmic granules are absent. Frozen-dried and undecalcified; periodic acid–leukofuchsin stain. × 3000. (After Heller.)

this is not a stable surface specialization but is highly active and constantly changing its configuration. Despite the evidence of surface activity at the interface between the osteoclasts and the bone, there is little evidence that they are mechanically erosive or even highly phagocytic. The mechanisms by which they accomplish the simultaneous degradation of the organic matrix and dissolution of bone mineral remain to be elucidated, but there is suggestive evidence that they may secrete proteolytic enzymes with collagenolytic activity.

HISTOGENESIS OF BONE

Bone always develops by transformation of a pre-existing connective tissue. Two different modes of osteogenesis are recognized in embryos. When bone formation occurs directly in primitive connective tissue it is called *intramembranous ossification*. When it takes place in pre-existing cartilage it is called intracartilaginous or *endochondral ossification*. In endochondral ossification the bulk of the cartilage must be removed before bone deposition begins, and the distinctive features of this mode of ossification are more concerned with resorption of cartilage than with deposition of bone. The actual deposition of bony tissue is essentially the same in the two modes of ossification. Bone is first laid down as spongy bone, but some of it is subsequently converted to compact bone by a filling in of the interstices between trabeculae. Occasionally bone may arise in tissues not belonging to the osseous system, and from

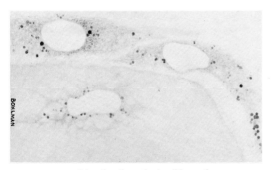

Figure 10-11. Margin of a spicule of bone from a young rat; frozen-dried, undecalcified, and stained with periodic acid–leukofuchsin. The cytoplasm of the osteocyte and two osteoblasts contains granules; the nuclei do not stain, and the matrix stains feebly. × 3000. (After Heller.)

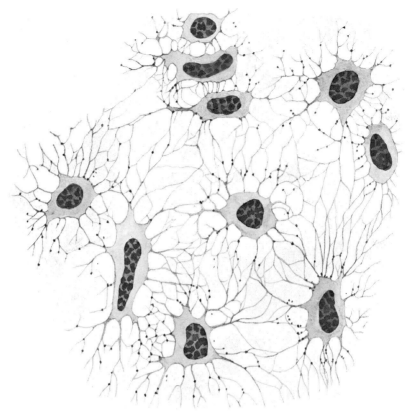

Figure 10-13. Thin, transparent membrane bone of a white mouse, stained supravitally with methylene blue, in glycerin. The interstitial substance appears homogeneous and is not stained; the angular osteocytes with their nuclei fill the cavities. From the cells arise anastomosing processes which lie in the canalicules and in cross section appear as dots. × 1040. (After A. A. Maximow.)

connective tissues not ordinarily manifesting osteogenic properties. This is called *ectopic bone formation.*

INTRAMEMBRANOUS OSSIFICATION. Certain flat bones of the skull—the frontal, parietal, occipital, and temporal bones and part of the mandible—develop by intramembranous ossification and are referred to as *membrane bones.* The mesenchyme condenses into a richly vascularized layer of connective tissue, in which the cells are in contact with one another by long tapering processes and the intercellular spaces are occupied by randomly oriented delicate bundles of collagen fibrils embedded in a thin gel-like ground substance. The first sign of bone formation is the appearance of thin strands or bars of a denser eosinophilic matrix (Fig. 10-20). These tend to be deposited approximately equidistant between neighboring blood vessels, and since the vessels form a network, the earliest trabeculae of bone matrix

also develop in a branching and anastomosing pattern (Fig. 10-21). Simultaneously with their appearance, the surrounding primitive connective tissue cells enlarge and gather on their surface, assuming a cuboidal or columnar form while still remaining connected by shortened processes (Figs. 10-22 and 10-23). Concurrently with this change in size and shape of the cells they become intensely basophilic and are thenceforth identified as osteoblasts. Through their secretory activity additional bone matrix is deposited and the trabeculae become longer and thicker.

Tropocollagen macromolecules are secreted, together with the amorphous protein-polysaccharide of the matrix, and these aggregate extracellularly to form randomly interwoven fibrils of collagen. This early bone, in which the collagen fibers run in all directions, is sometimes called *woven* bone to distinguish it from that formed in subsequent remodeling, which is laid down in lamellae containing collagen in ordered parallel array. At a certain stage in the transformation of the interstitial substance of primitive connective tissue to bone matrix it becomes calcifiable and calcium phosphate is deposited in it and in all of the matrix formed later by the osteoblasts. The property of calcifiability is evidently conferred upon the matrix by the osteoblasts.

As successive layers are added to the periphery of the calcifying trabeculae, some of the osteoblasts at their surface become incarcerated in the newly deposited matrix and one by one become buried within its substance. These are the first bone cells or osteocytes occupying lacunae within the calcifying matrix. The osteoblasts that become osteocytes by being included in the bone remain connected to osteoblasts at the surface by slender processes. The canaliculi of bone are formed by deposition of calcified matrix around these

processes. As rapidly as the ranks of osteoblasts on the surface of the trabeculae are depleted by their incorporation into the bone, their numbers are restored by differentiation of new osteoblasts from cells of the surrounding connective tissue. Mitotic division is frequent in these precursor cells but is rarely observed in osteoblasts themselves.

In areas of the primary spongiosa that are destined to become compact bone the trabeculae continue to thicken at the expense of the intervening connective tissue until the spaces around the blood vessels are largely obliterated. The collagen fibrils in the layers of bone that are deposited on the trabeculae in this progressive encroachment upon the perivascular spaces gradually become more regularly arranged and come to resemble lamellar bone. The irregularly concentric layers formed may bear a superficial resemblance to haversian systems. In those areas where spongy bone will persist, the thickening of the trabeculae

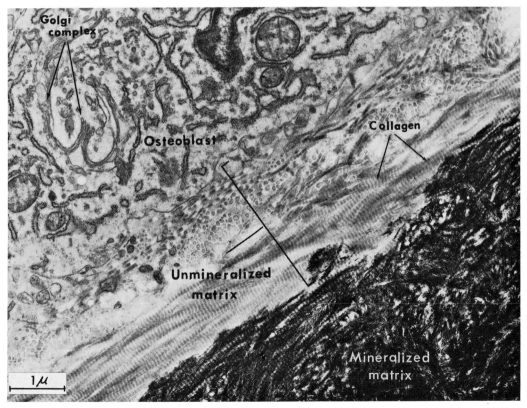

Figure 10-14. Edge of a resorption canal being filled in by lamellar bone. At the upper left is a portion of an osteoblast containing a prominent Golgi zone and abundant granular reticulum. Subjacent to it are the collagen fibrils of two unmineralized lamellae, and at the lower right is the dense mineralized bone. (After R. R. Cooper et al., J. Bone and Joint Surg., *48A*:1239, 1966.)

ceases and the intervening vascular connective tissue is gradually transformed into hemopoietic tissue. The connective tissue surrounding the growing mass of bone remains on its surface and condenses to form the periosteum. The osteoblasts that have remained on the surface of the bone during its development assume a fibroblast-like appearance as growth ceases and persist as the deepest cells of the periosteum. Their osteogenic potentialities are recognized only if they are again called upon to form bone, whereupon they again assume morphological characteristics of osteoblasts.

ENDOCHONDRAL OSSIFICATION.   Bones at the base of the skull, in the vertebral column, the pelvis, and the extremities are called *cartilage bones* because they are first formed of hyaline cartilage; this is then replaced with bone by the process of *endochondral ossification.* This can best be studied in one of the long bones of an extremity. The first indication of

the establishment of a primary *center of ossification* is a striking enlargement of the chondrocytes at the middle of the shaft of the cartilage model (Fig. 10-24). The cells in this region hypertrophy, glycogen accumulates within them, and their cytoplasm becomes highly vacuolated. The enlargement of their lacunae takes place at the expense of the intervening cartilage matrix, which is gradually reduced to thin fenestrated septa and irregularly shaped spicules. The hyaline matrix that remains in the region of *hypertrophic cartilage cells* becomes calcifiable, and if there are adequate concentrations of calcium and phosphate in the blood plasma and tissue fluid, small nests of calcium phosphate crystals are deposited within it (Fig. 10-28*C*). Regressive changes in the hypertrophied cartilage cells, including swelling of their nuclei and loss of chromatin, are followed by their death and degeneration.

Concurrently with these cytological changes in the chondrocytes in the interior of

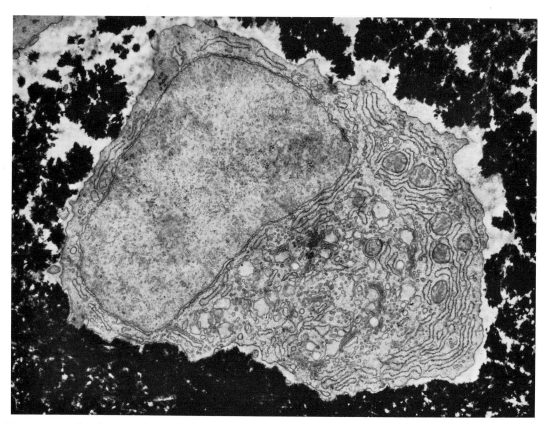

Figure 10-15.   An electron micrograph of an osteocyte from alveolar bone of a 20 day rat embryo. The cell has only recently been incorporated into the bone and still retains the well developed Golgi apparatus and extensive endoplasmic reticulum characteristic of the osteoblast. The black deposits are nests of crystals of bone mineral. × 15,500. (Courtesy of J. D. Decker).

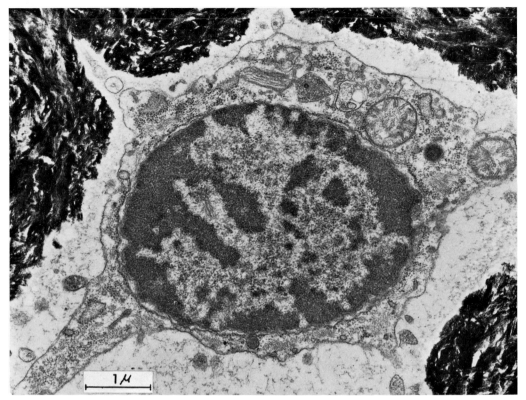

Figure 10-16. An osteocyte in its lacuna. There is a larger nuclear cytoplasmic ratio than in the more active osteoblast. The cytoplasm contains abundant ribosomes but the Golgi complex and endoplasmic reticulum are less prominent. (After R. R. Cooper et al., J. Bone and Joint Surg., *48A*:1239, 1966.)

the cartilage model, the osteogenic potencies of cells in the *perichondrium* are activated and a thin layer of bone is deposited around the midportion of the shaft, the *periosteal band* or *collar* (Figs. 10-25*B* and 10-28*A* and *B*). At the same time, blood vessels from the investing layer of connective tissue, now called the periosteum, grow into the diaphysis, invading the irregular cavities in the cartilage matrix created by the enlargement of the chondrocytes and confluence of their lacunae (Figs. 10-27 and 10-25*E* and *F*). The thin walled vessels branch and grow toward either end of the cartilage model, forming capillary loops that extend into the blind ends of the cavities. Cells with mesenchymal potencies are carried into the interior of the cartilage in the perivascular connective tissue that accompanies the invading blood vessels. Some of these cells differentiate into hemopoietic elements of the bone marrow. Others, coming into contact with the cartilage, differentiate into osteoblasts. These gather in an epithelioid layer on the surfaces of persisting spicules of calcified cartilage matrix and

deposit bone matrix upon them. The earliest trabeculae formed in centers of endochondral ossification thus have a core of calcified cartilage covered by a layer of bone of varying thickness. Owing to the different staining affinities of calcified cartilage and bone, these trabeculae are easily distinguished from the more homogeneous trabeculae formed by intramembranous ossification.

GROWTH IN LENGTH OF LONG BONES. In the continuing growth in length of the cartilage model after the appearance of the primary center of ossification in the diaphysis, the chondrocytes in the epiphyses become arranged in longitudinal columns instead of in the small isogenous groups usually found in hyaline cartilage (Fig. 9-5). The cells within the columns are separated by thin transverse septa, while adjacent columns are separated by wider longitudinal bars of hyaline matrix. As endochondral ossification progresses from the center of the shaft toward either end of the cartilage model, the chondrocytes undergo the same sequence of changes as described for the establishment of the primary center, but the process is now more orderly. Along the length of the epiphyseal cell columns are several recognizable zones, corresponding to various stages in the cytomorphosis of the cartilage cells. At some distance from the diaphyseo-epiphyseal junction is a *zone of proliferation,* where frequent division of the small flattened cells provides for the continual elongation of the columns. Next comes a *zone of maturation,* in which the cells that are no longer dividing gradually enlarge. This is followed by a *zone of hypertrophy* with very large vacuolated cells. Since the matrix in this region becomes the site of calcium deposition, this may also be called the *zone of provisional calcification.* And finally at the diaphyseal end of the columns is a zone wherein the chondrocytes are degenerating and the open ends of their enlarged lacunae are being invaded by capillary loops and perivascular connective tissue from the marrow spaces of the diaphysis (Fig. 10-29). As the spaces at the lower ends of the columns are invaded, osteoblasts are mobilized on the surfaces of the

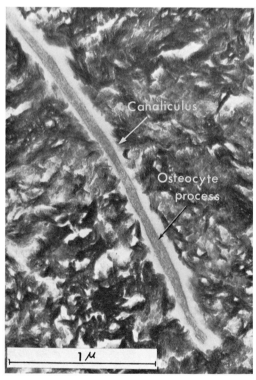

Figure 10-17. Electron micrograph of a slender osteocyte process extending far into a canaliculus. (After R. R. Cooper et al., J. Bone and Joint Surg., *48A*:1239, 1966.)

irregularly shaped longitudinal bars of calcified cartilage between them. A thin new layer of bone matrix is then deposited on the surface of the cartilage. Under favorable conditions it begins to calcify as it is laid down, and thus it becomes bone. Electron microscopy has shown, however, that a superficial layer of uncalcified *preosseous tissue* or *osteoid,* a micron or less in thickness, is always present on forming bony surfaces. There may be a further lag in calcification even under physiological conditions, owing to a local failure in the supply of calcium or phosphate. When such a failure becomes general and osteoid accumulates in excess, the condition is known as *rickets* in growing children or as *osteomalacia* in adults (Fig. 10-38). The calcification of new bone is best demonstrated in undecalcified sections in which the bone mineral has been stained black with silver by the von Kóssa method (Fig. 10-29*A*). The transitional zone where the cartilage is being replaced by advancing bone is called the *metaphysis.* The primary spongy bone in this zone undergoes extensive reorganization as the growth processes pass it by. As the bone grows longer the diaphyseal ends of the trabeculae are continually being resorbed at about the same rate that additions are made at the epiphyseal end, with the result that the spongiosa of the metaphysis tends to remain relatively constant in length.

Primary centers of ossification have appeared in the diaphysis of each of the principal bones of the skeleton by the third month of fetal life. Much later, usually after birth, the epiphyses show in their interior the characteristic chondrocyte hypertrophy that heralds the onset of ossification, and they in turn are invaded by blood vessels and osteogenic tissue from the perichondrium to establish *secondary centers of ossification* at either end of the developing long bones (Fig. 10-25*G* and *H*). The expansion of these secondary centers gradually replaces all of the epiphyseal cartilage except for what persists as the *articular cartilage* and a transverse disk between the epiphysis and diaphysis called the *epiphyseal plate* (Fig. 10-25*J*). The latter contains the cartilage columns whose proliferative zone is responsible for all subsequent growth in length of long bones. Under normal conditions the rate of multiplication of cartilage cells in this zone is in balance with the rate of their degeneration and removal from the diaphyseal end of the columns. The epiphyseal plate therefore retains

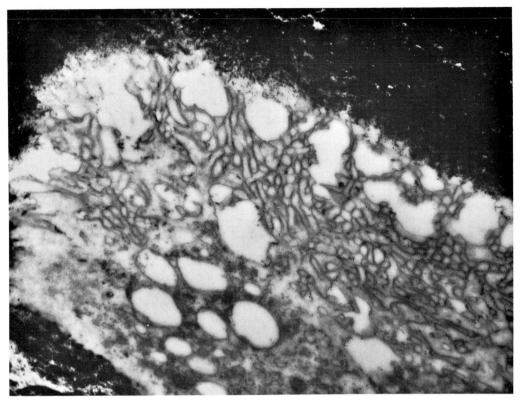

Figure 10-18. Electron micrograph of a portion of an osteoclast, illustrating the elaborate infolding of its surface where it is in contact with bone. The bone appears black owing to the density of the mineral salts in its matrix. × 10,000. (Courtesy of F. Gonzales and M. Karnovsky.)

approximately the same thickness. Growth is the result of the cartilage cells continually growing away from the shaft and being replaced by bone as they recede. The net effect is an increase in the length of the shaft.

At the end of the growing period, proliferation of cartilage cells slows and finally ceases when the epiphyseal plates are replaced replaced by spongy bone and marrow (Fig. 10-25*J*). This is called the *closure of the epiphyses*. Thereafter the bony epiphyses and diaphyses are continuous, and no further longitudinal growth of the bone is possible. The times of closure and the relative contribution of each of the two epiphyses of a long bone to its growth may differ markedly. Growth in length of the femur, for example, takes place mainly at the distal epiphysis; growth of the tibia, at the proximal. Such information is of clinical value in radiology and orthopedic surgery.

Because all increment in length of a bone is limited to its epiphyseal plates, injury to this region may result in serious impairment of growth. In cases of the retarded growth of one leg, attributable to general neurovascular disturbances such as may occur in the limb of a child who has had poliomyelitis, the orthopedic surgeon can take advantage of existing knowledge of the normal rates of growth at the various epiphyseal plates and of the times of their normal closure to select the appropriate time and site for a surgical obliteration of an epiphysis in the normal leg. Such a procedure, if appropriately timed, may retard growth of the normal leg just enough to permit the slower growing leg to catch up and thus achieve an equalization of leg length by the time growth in stature of the individual ceases.

GROWTH IN DIAMETER OF LONG BONES. The long bones of the extremities are classified as cartilage bones because they are first laid down in cartilage models, and, as indicated in the foregoing section, their growth *in length* depends upon endochondral ossification. Their growth *in diameter*, however, is the result of deposition of new membrane bone beneath the periosteum. The compact bone forming the shaft of a fully developed long bone is almost entirely the product of subperiosteal *intramembranous* ossification.

After establishment of the primary ossification center, the ends of the cartilage model continue to elongate and expand by proliferation and elaboration of new matrix by the chondrocytes, but such interstitial growth is no longer possible in the center of the diaphysis, where the cartilage is regressing and being replaced by bone. The diameter of the endochondral component in the middle of the diaphysis, therefore, cannot be appreciably greater than the diameter of the cartilage model in the early embryo at the time of establishment of the primary center of endochondral ossification. Increase in thickness of the shaft, to keep pace with the rapid interstitial growth of the cartilage at the ends, is accomplished by a progressive thickening of the *periosteal band* or *collar* formed around the middle of the cartilaginous diaphysis at the onset of ossification. This results in a three dimensional lattice of trabeculae of intramembranous woven bone that forms the wall of the diaphysis.

Bone resorption is as important to the growth of bones as is bone deposition, and the deposition of new bone on the outside of the shaft is accompanied by the appearance of osteoclasts on the inside and erosion of bone from within to enlarge the marrow cavity. The rates of external apposition of new bone and internal resorption are so adjusted that the cylindrical shaft expands rapidly while the thickness of its wall increases more slowly.

Because of the continual internal reorganization of bone during development, the record of the topographical distribution of endochondral and intramembranous ossification in earlier stages of development is continually erased. Therefore, the extent of the contribution of the periosteum to the fully formed long bone is seldom fully appreciated. It is informative in this regard to examine developing long bones of the manatee, an aquatic mammal in which resorption of bone to form the secondary marrow cavity does not take place. In fetal bones of this species (Fig. 10-30), the primary spongiosa of endochondral bone has a characteristic hourglass distribution. The two conical regions, with their apices meeting at the site of the original ossification center, result from uniform growth in length and cir-

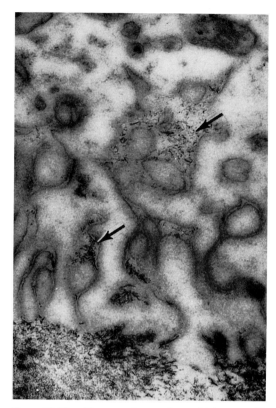

Figure 10-19. Electron micrograph, at a higher magnification than Figure 10-15, of the active border of an osteoclast in contact with the bone at the bottom of the figure. The arrows point to crystals of bone salt liberated from the matrix and occupying labyrinthine extracellular clefts between the processes of the osteoclast. × 28,000. (Courtesy of F. Gonzales and M. Karnovsky.)

cumference of the ends of the cartilage model. The area between the diverging sides of the two cones is filled in by a thick collar of spongiosa of periosteal origin. Such bones, lacking the capacity for the resorption that occurs in the histogenesis of long bones in other species, provide an instructive view of the basic topography of the cartilaginous and membranous components of all long bones (Fig. 10-31).

SURFACE REMODELING OF BONES. Although growing bones are constantly changing their internal organization they retain approximately the same external form from an early fetal stage into adult life. It is apparent that this would not be so if new bone were deposited at a uniform rate at all points beneath the periosteum. Instead, the shape of a bone is maintained during growth by a continual remodeling of its surface, which involves bone deposition in some areas of the periosteum and bone absorption in other areas. That this is true was demonstrated in the middle of the eighteenth century by madder feeding experiments. With this method of vital staining the bone deposited during a period of feeding on madder root is stained red, while areas that were stable or were undergoing resorption remain unstained. It was clearly shown that some areas of the surface of long bones stained while others did not. The general features of these early experiments have now been confirmed and extended by means of newer techniques employing bone seeking isotopes or the antibiotic tetracycline, both of which are deposited preferentially in newly forming bone.

Typical of such experiments are those localizing the sites of osteogenesis in the growing rat tibia (Leblond et al.). This bone supports a large articular surface, and the epiphysis is considerably broader than the shaft. Thus it is possible to distinguish a cylindrical region in the middle of the shaft and a conical region toward the end, where it expands to the width of the epiphysis. If a bone-seeking isotope is given to a growing rat and radioautographs are then made of longitudinal sections of the tibia, the sites of new bone formation are disclosed by the distribution of silver grains in the overlying emulsion. In the conical region of the bone the silver grains are aligned immediately subjacent to the endosteum, whereas in the cylindrical portion of the shaft they are found beneath the periosteum (Fig. 10-33). Study of parallel histological sections reveals numerous osteoclasts beneath the periosteum of the conical region and beneath the endosteum of the cylindrical segment. Thus it is clear that in the surface remodeling of this bone, the periosteum plays opposite roles in neighboring regions on the surface of the same bone. Subperiosteal bone deposition is occurring in the cylindrical portion of the shaft while subperiosteal bone absorption is taking place in the conical region. Similarly, bone is being formed at the endosteal surface of the cone and absorbed on the inner aspect of the cylinder. As a consequence of these activities the midportion of the shaft is expanding radially while its marrow cavity is being enlarged. While the bone as a whole is elongating by growth at the epiphyseal plate, the diverging wall of the conical region of the shaft is being straightened and is contributing, at its lower end, to the lengthening of the cylindrical region of the shaft.

It is insufficient to assume that growth of

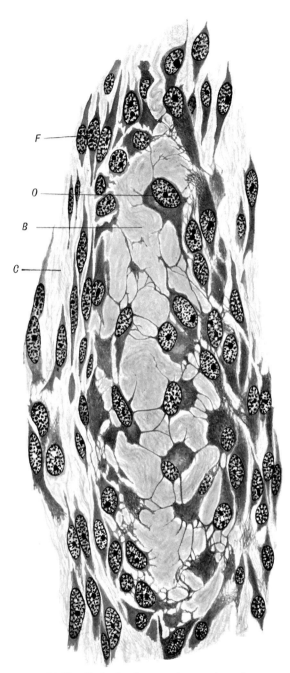

Figure 10-20. Beginning intramembranous bone formation in the skull of a 5.5 cm. cat embryo; *B,* homogeneous thickened collagenous fibers, which become the interstitial bone substance; *C,* collagenous interstitial substance; *F,* connective tissue cells; *O,* connective tissue cells, with processes, which become osteoblasts and later bone cells. Eosin-azure stain. × 520. (After A. A. Maximow.)

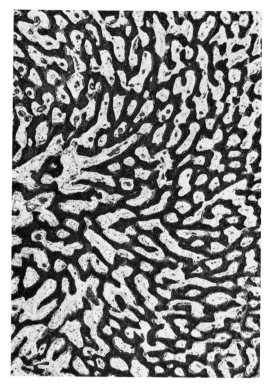

Figure 10-21. Photomicrograph of the pattern of trabeculae in the primary spongiosa of intramembranous bone formation.

the flat bones at the sutures could account for enlargement of the cranial cavity to accommodate the growing brain. As the radius of curvature of the growing skull vault increases, the bones become less convex. Therefore, not only must bone resorption take place on the inside of the calvarium concurrently with bone deposition on the outer surface, but also the rates of deposition and absorption must differ from the center to the periphery of each cranial bone in order to account for its flattening as the radius of curvature of the skull vault increases. How these local variations in function of endosteum and periosteum are controlled in space and time to mold and shape the bone constantly during its growth is a fascinating unsolved problem in morphogenesis.

INTERNAL REORGANIZATION OF BONE. The conversion of primary spongy bone to compact bone was attributed in an earlier section to thickening of the trabeculae and a progressive encroachment of bone upon the perivascular spaces until these are largely obliterated. As this process advances, bone is

deposited in layers and since these are disposed more or less concentrically around vascular channels, they come to bear a superficial resemblance to haversian systems. They are called *primitive haversian systems* to distinguish them from the more precisely ordered lamellar systems comprising the definitive *haversian systems* of adult bone. The latter arise only in the course of the internal reorganization of primary compact bone that is referred to as *secondary bone formation.*

At scattered points in the compacta, usually in those areas laid down earliest, cavities appear as a result of osteoclastic erosion of primary bone. The formation of such *absorption cavities* was first described by Tomes and DeMorgan in 1853. They enlarge to form long cylindrical cavities occupied by blood vessels and embryonic bone marrow. When they reach a considerable length, destruction of bone ceases; the osteoclasts give way to osteoblasts, and concentric lamellae of bone are laid down on the walls of the cavity. The lamellae of this and subsequent generations of haversian systems have the ordered arrangement of collagen and the change in its orientation in successive layers that are characteristic of osteons in adult bone. In man from about the age of one year onward, only lamellar bone of this character is deposited within the shafts of long bones. The outer limits of secondary haversian systems are defined by distinct *cement lines.* This secondary bone eventually replaces all of the *primitive haversian systems.*

The internal bone destruction and reconstruction do not end with the replacement of primary by secondary bone, but continue ac-

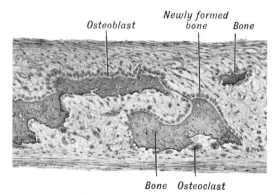

Figure 10-22. Cross section through primordium of the parietal bone of a 4 month embryo. × 100. (After Schaffer.)

tively throughout life. Resorption cavities continue to appear and to be filled in by third, fourth, and higher orders of haversian systems (Fig. 10-34). The interstitial lamellae of adult bone represent persisting fragments of earlier generations of haversian systems. At any one time there may be seen in a cross section: (1) mature osteons, in which all rebuilding activity has come to an end and which form the great mass of structural bone upon which the weight bearing function of the skeleton depends; (2) actively forming new osteons, in which concentric layers of preosseous tissue are being laid down and progressively calcified; (3) absorption cavities being hollowed out in preparation for formation of new osteons. The rate of lamellar bone formation can be determined by administration of tetracycline at two different times and measurement of the thickness of bone between the two resulting bands of labeled bone (Fig. 10-35). Such studies show that 1 μ per day is a fair average for man, and for any given haversian system, the rate of dep-

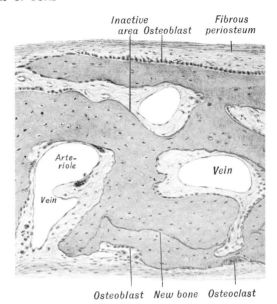

Figure 10-23. Cross section through primordium of the parietal bone of a 6 month embryo, analogous to the section shown in Figure 10-19. × 100. (After Schaffer.)

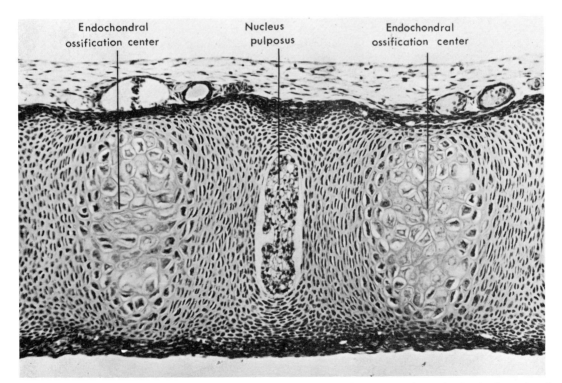

Figure 10-24. Photomicrograph of the cartilaginous vertebral column of a mouse embryo, showing in the center of each vertebra an area of hypertrophied cartilage cells that represents an early stage in the establishment of a center of endochondral ossification.

osition as the osteon nears completion. The formation time for an haversian system in the adult is 4 to 5 weeks. Different values are found in young growing bone and in pathological states. The newly deposited lamellar bone continues to calcify over a considerable period of time. A historadiogram therefore reveals a mixture of haversian systems of varying age displaying all degrees of mineralization (Fig. 10-6C). By this continuous turnover the organism is assured a continuing supply of new bone to carry out its skeletal and metabolic functions. It also provides the plasticity that enables bone to alter its internal architecture to adapt to new mechanical conditions.

REPAIR OF BONE. After a fracture there are, first, the usual reactions of any tissue to severe injury, including hemorrhage and organization of the clot by ordinary granulation tissue, forming the *procallus*. The granulation tissue becomes dense connective tissue, and then cartilage and fibrocartilage develop within it, forming a *fibrocartilaginous callus* that fills the gap between the ends of the fragments. The new bone, which will ultimately unite the fragments, begins to form at some distance from the fracture line, originating from the deeper layers of the periosteum and endosteum and subsequently invading the fibrocartilaginous callus. It extends toward the center of this, replacing the tissues of the callus with new bone matrix, the *bony callus*. This new matrix is calcifiable as it is laid down and, under favorable conditions, calcifies as it is formed. Ossification of the callus, then, like intracartilaginous bone formation, is essentially a replacement of the earlier tissue by bone, with only enough of the fibrocartilaginous callus remaining to furnish a framework for the deposition of new bone. *Bony union* of the fracture is accomplished when the new spongy bone, invading the callus from the periosteum of the two fragments of bone, makes contact and unites. After this there is reorganization, with resorption of excess bone, and internal reconstruction, resulting finally in a bridging of the gap with compact bone.

In certain locations, where the connective tissue surrounding the bone lacks osteogenic potency, such as the subcapsular areas of the neck of the femur and of the astragalus, and the surfaces of the bones formed within tendons (the patella and sesamoid bones), healing of fractures occurs without a periosteal reaction and without a fibrocartilaginous callus. If there is good apposition of the fragments, the cancellous bone of the marrow cavity unites, as it were, by first intention, without any callus formation. If apposition is poor or nonexistent, repair may occur only as a relatively weak, fibrous union.

ECTOPIC BONE FORMATION. As already stated, bone forms from a connective tissue, with the transformation of mesenchymal cells, fibroblasts, and reticular cells into osteoblasts, osteocytes, and osteoclasts. The return of these cells to fibroblast-like cells and reticular cells has also been described. A common feature in all these transformations, as described heretofore, is that bone has developed only in connection with the osseous system—the skeleton. The influences under which ordinary connective tissue gives rise to bone in the embryo are but little understood, but it is clear that previously undifferentiated connective tissue cells are capable of transformation to the cells characteristic of bone.

It would appear that, once cells have exhibited osteogenic potencies, these can be readily evoked again for an indeterminate period after the cells have returned to an indifferent morphologic state. Thus, in the healing of fractures, cells in the deepest layers of the periosteum and endosteum, under the stimulus of trauma, reassume the form of osteoblasts and once again are actively engaged in osteogenesis. Moreover, cells grown from bone in tissue culture, and having lost the morphologic characteristics of osteoblasts, once again

Figure 10-25. Diagram of the development of a typical long bone as shown in longitudinal sections (*A* to *J*) and in cross sections *A'*, *B'*, *C'* and *D'* through the centers of *A*, *B*, *C* and *D*. Pale blue, cartilage; purple, calcified cartilage; black, bone; red, arteries. *A*, Cartilage model; *B*, periosteal bone collar appears before any calcification of cartilage. *C*, Cartilage begins to calcify. *D*, Vascular mesenchyme enters the calcified cartilage matrix and divides it into two zones of ossification (*E*). *F*, Blood vessels and mesenchyme enter upper epiphyseal cartilage and the epiphyseal ossification center develops in it, *G*. A similar ossification center develops in the lower epiphyseal cartilage, *H*. As the bone ceases to grow in length the lower epiphyseal plate disappears first (*I*) and then the upper epiphyseal plate, *J*. The bone marrow cavity then becomes continuous throughout the length of the bone and the blood vessels of the diaphysis, metaphyses, and epiphyses intercommunicate.

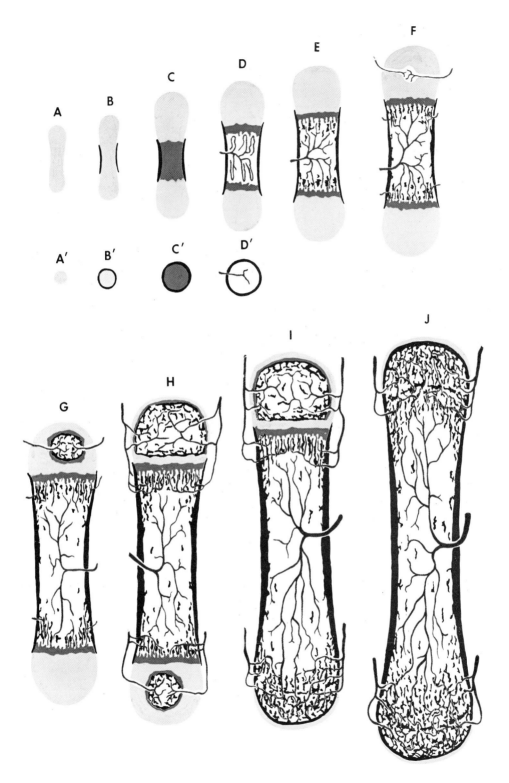

Figure 10-25. *See opposite page for legend.*

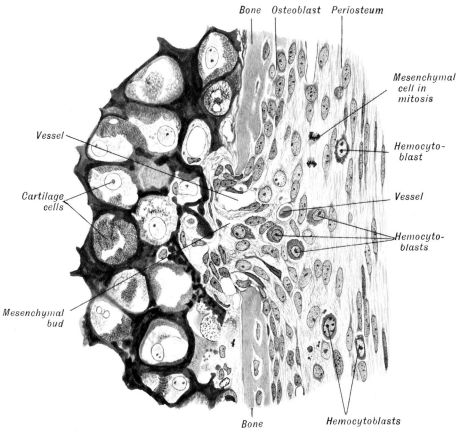

Figure 10-26. Part of longitudinal section through the middle of the diaphysis of the femur of a 25 mm. human embryo. Mesenchyme with vessels entering calcified cartilage through an opening in the periosteal bone collar. Eosin-azure stain. × 560. (After A. A. Maximow.)

form bone when implanted into the anterior chamber of the eye (Heinen).

Furthermore, under certain conditions, bone may be formed spontaneously from connective tissue that is not in association with the skeleton. This *ectopic ossification* has been described in such diverse locations as the pelvis of the kidney, the walls of arteries, the eyes, muscles, and tendons. In the long tendons of the legs of turkeys, bone formation is a normal event, occurring regularly. From these observations it may be inferred that many types of connective tissue have latent osteogenic potencies that are exhibited only rarely. This conconclusion is supported by experimental production of bone in connective tissue after ligation of the renal artery and vein, after transplantation of bladder epithelium to the fascia of the anterior wall of the abdomen, and after injection of alcoholic extracts of bone into muscle. In fact, alcohol alone may induce

osteogenesis in muscle, and it shares this ability with other irritating chemicals.

Many attempts have been made to utilize the osteogenic potencies of periosteum and bone by transplanting these tissues to areas in which it is desired that new bone be formed. The modern "bone bank," which supplies fragments of bone preserved by freezing or by other means, is the fruit of these efforts. Transplants of fresh autogenous bone ordinarily survive and proliferate. Homografts are antigenic and give rise to an immune response characterized by accumulations of lymphocytes and plasma cells containing specific antibodies, leading ultimately to death of the transplanted tissue. Heterografts will not survive, but if calf bone is refrigerated and stored it loses some of its antigenicity and may therefore be suitable for preservation in bone banks and later use. Grafts of such tissue favor induction of new bone formation by the cells of the host.

Reticular cells within the orbit of advancing bone, as in the formation of medullary bone in birds, assume the form of osteoblasts before they actually participate in osteogenesis. This observation, together with those upon the behavior of bone grafts just cited, suggests that the presence of bone itself may be an important factor in activating osteogenic potencies. There is thus histological evidence in favor of *induction* of bone formation, although attempts to isolate a specific *inductor substance* have so far given equivocal results.

HISTOPHYSIOLOGY OF BONE

As the principal tissue making up the skeletal system, bone functions in support of the soft tissues; it carries the articulations and provides attachment for the muscles involved in locomotion; it forms a rigid covering for protection of the nervous system and the hemopoietic tissue. In addition to these mechanical functions it plays an important role as a large store of calcium and phosphorus that can be drawn upon to maintain the normal levels of these elements in the blood and to provide for the mineral requirements of other tissues.

CALCIUM DEPOSITION IN BONE. The mechanism of deposition of calcium in bone is still poorly understood. At least two factors, local and humoral, are thought to be involved. The humoral factor relates to the concentration of mineral in the body fluids and the solubility of the salts of calcium and phosphate. But discovery of the local factors that operate to determine when and where bone mineral will be deposited has proved to be elusive.

It has recently been suggested that acid hydrolases, liberated from the lysosomes of hypertrophic cartilage cells in the epiphyseal

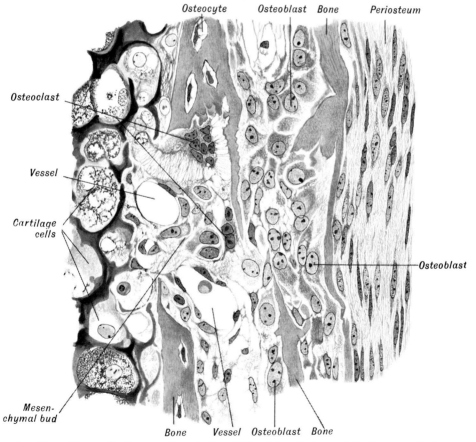

Figure 10-27. Part of longitudinal section through the middle of the diaphysis of the humerus of a human embryo of eight weeks. The process of ossification has advanced slightly farther than in Figure 10-26. Eosin-azure stain. × 560. (After A. A. Maximow.)

cartilage, degrade the cartilage matrix in the zone of provisional calcification and render it calcifiable.

An alternative explanation (Glimcher) proposes that the intial seeding or nucleation of apatite crystals requires a specific stereo-chemical configuration present in collagen. In support of this concept, it was demonstrated that reconstituted collagen with the common 640 Å period is capable of inducing formation of hydroxyapatite crystals when exposed to otherwise stable solutions of calcium and phos-phate ions. Only this native form of collagen was effective. Results were uniformly negative with tropocollagen, unstructured fibrils, and fibrous long-spacing and segment long-spacing collagen. To account for the fact that tendon and other connective tissues do not calcify, it has been suggested that some component of the ground substance is responsible for inhibi-tion and control of calcification.

BONE AS A STORE OF MOBILIZABLE CAL-CIUM. There is a constant interchange of calcium between bone and the blood, which

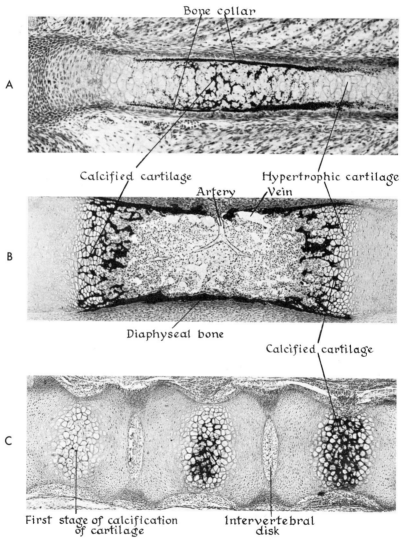

Figure 10-28. Photomicrographs showing several stages of bone formation in developing rats. From formalin-fixed, undecalcified sections stained with silver nitrate to show bone salt (black). *A,* Longitudinal section through second rib of 18 day rat embryo; calcification of the periosteal bone collar is further advanced than that of the cartilage. *B,* Section of metatarsal of 4 day rat, in which ossification is proceeding toward the epiphyses; the hypertrophic cartilage is not completely calcified. *C,* Three stages in calcification of vertebrae in 20 day rat embryo. × 117, 63, and 57, respectively. (W. Bloom and M. A. Bloom.)

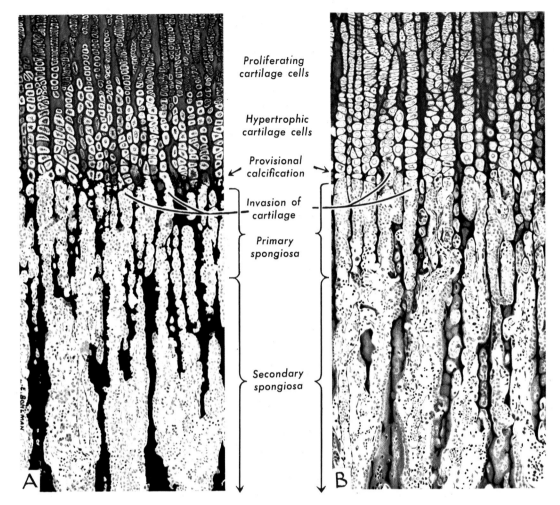

Figure 10-29. Endochondral ossification in longitudinal sections through the zone of epiphyseal growth of the distal end of the radius of a puppy. *A,* Neutral formalin fixation; no decalcification. Von Kóssa and hematoxylin-eosin stain. All deposits of bone salt are stained black; thus, bone and calcified cartilage matrix stain alike. *B,* Zenker-formol fixation; decalcified. Hematoxylin-eosin-azure II stain. Persisting cores of cartilage matrix in trabeculae of bone take a deep blue or purple stain, whereas bone stains red. It is impossible to tell where calcium deposits had been. × 95.

results in the maintenance of a relatively constant calcium ion concentration in the plasma. The minute hydroxyapatite crystals, 25 to 40 Å thick and 200 to 400 Å long, present a surface area for exchange with the extracellular fluids that is on the order of 100 to 300 square meters per gram. It has been estimated that during every minute in the life of an adult man, one of every four calcium ions present in the blood exchanges with similar ions in the bones. A dual mechanism for homeostatic regulation of the blood calcium level has been postulated. One part, acting by diffusion and simple equilibrium between blood and the labile fraction of bone mineral, is adequate to maintain a constant but low calcium level of approximately 7 mg. per 100 ml. of blood plasma. Not all of the bone contributes equally to this function. The most labile calcium apparently is located in the younger and incompletely calcified osteons. It is these that are most sensitive to ionic variations in the internal environment. Therefore, the continued remodeling of the adult skeleton has metabolic as well as mechanical significance (Vincent). It provides a pool of young osteons, which can rapidly respond in homeostatic regulation by taking up or releasing calcium. As these osteons mature, they become progressively less available to the extracellular fluids and they contribute more

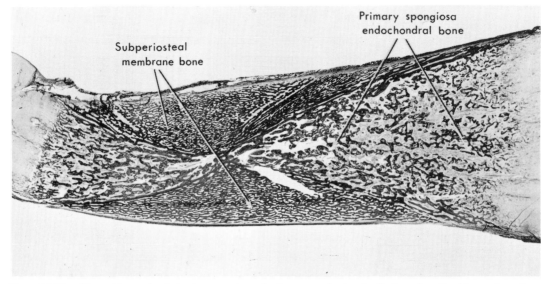

Figure 10-30. Photomicrograph of the humerus in a fetal manatee in longitudinal section. In this species, whose bones lack a secondary marrow cavity, the respective contributions of subperiosteal and endochondral bone to the formation of the shaft of a long bone are more evident than in bones of other species. × 5. (After D. W. Fawcett, Am. J. Anat., *71:*271, 1942.)

to the mechanical function of the skeleton. They are replaced in their physiologic function by a new generation of osteons. These two categories are sometimes referred to as *metabolic bone* and *structural bone*. The second part of the dual mechanism required to elevate and maintain the plasma calcium at the normal level of 10 mg. per 100 ml. is mediated by *parathyroid hormone* (Chapter 19), and involves resorption of bone mineral and organic matrix through the action of osteoclasts.

The responsiveness of the skeleton to the metabolic needs of other organ systems is best illustrated in those species in which there are unusual periodic demands for calcium. Perhaps the most striking example is found in birds in the laying cycle, where considerable amounts of calcium are required in the reproductive tract for deposition of the egg shell. To meet this need, many trabeculae in the marrow cavities of the long bones are resorbed, only to be restored after the egg is laid and again removed to provide the shell for the next egg in the clutch. Less dramatic examples of mobilization of calcium from the skeleton are also observed in mammals. While the antlers of deer are growing, there is a mild rarefaction of bone throughout the skeleton, and in dairy cows producing large amounts of milk there may be a detectable osteoporosis. Human reproduction does not involve such unusual demands for calcium. There is no doubt, however, that the maternal skeleton is drawn upon to some extent during pregnancy for calcification of the fetal skeleton and during prolonged lactation to make up the calcium lost in the milk. In normal individuals there is no detectable radiological change in the skeleton, but when pregnancy or lactation is superimposed upon severe nutritional deficiency or impaired absorption of calcium, osteomalacia results and may become so severe as to result in pathological fractures.

ENDOCRINE EFFECTS UPON BONE. The skeletal system is affected by several hormones. The most important of these is *parathyroid hormone*. Its participation in maintenance of the normal levels of circulating calcium was referred to earlier. The activity of the parathyroid glands appears to be regulated by a *negative feedback* mechanism, in which the blood Ca^{++} level itself exerts a direct effect upon parathyroid activity. Since bone resorption under the influence of parathyroid hormone results in destruction of stable crystals of hydroxyapatite, as well as of the organic matrix, this mechanism makes available, for homeostatic regulation, an otherwise inaccessible source of calcium. Opposing the action of parathyroid hormone is another hormone called *calcitonin* or *thyrocalcitonin,* which originates in the thyroid gland. It interferes with bone resorption and tends to lower the blood calcium (Chapter 18).

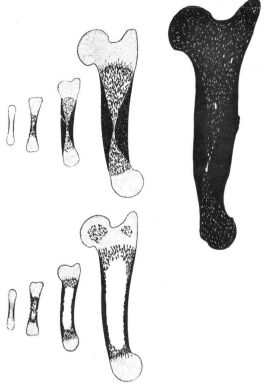

brous tissue. This phenomenon has been reported only in rats.

The effects of the gonadal hormones upon bone vary greatly with the species. In the examples of the laying bird, cited above, an entire new system of trabeculae of *medullary bone* is produced by outgrowth from the endosteal lining in the estrogenic phase of the egg laying cycle. These trabeculae serve to accumulate calcium for later use in formation of the egg shell. The same changes can be induced by administration of exogenous *estrogens*. Concurrently with the storage of calcium in medullary bone, the liver forms a phosphoprotein that appears in the blood and is transported to the ovarian follicle, where it is stored in the egg yolk as *phosphovitellin*, the major source of phosphate for growth and development of the chick embryo.

Mice react to administration of estrogens in a manner qualitatively similar to that of birds. Endosteal bone formation is enhanced but, in this case, does not seem to serve any physiological function. Endosteal bone formation has not been reported in rats. In this species, estrogens inhibit normal resorption of the spongiosa during endochondral ossification, resulting in a greatly elongated and dense spongiosa in the metaphysis. The osteoporosis

Figure 10-31. Diagrammatic representation of the development of a manatee bone (*above*) compared with that of a typical mammal (*below*). (After D. W. Fawcett, Am. J. Anat., *71*:271, 1942.)

Grafts of parathyroid to bone in vivo (Barnicot) and confronted cultures in vitro (Gaillard) have demonstrated that the gland causes resorption by direct action on bone. In clinical *hyperparathyroidism,* bone is extensively absorbed and is replaced by fibrous tissue containing large numbers of osteoclasts. This results in the pathological condition described as *osteitis fibrosa* (von Recklinghausen's disease). When large doses of parathyroid extract are given to animals, changes in the bones are profound. Within a few hours many osteoblasts disappear, the majority reverting to fibroblast-like cells, changing into phagocytic cells, or coalescing to form osteoclasts (Fig. 10-37). There is widespread necrosis of the elements of the bone marrow and, in young rats, of the osteocytes. The calcium containing trabeculae are rapidly resorbed and replaced by fibrous tissue. Recovery occurs when large numbers of osteoblasts develop again and new bone, formed intramembranously, replaces the fi-

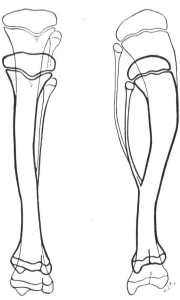

Figure 10-32. Diagram to illustrate remodeling during growth of tibia and fibula of rat, viewed from anterior aspect and in profile. (After Wolbach.)

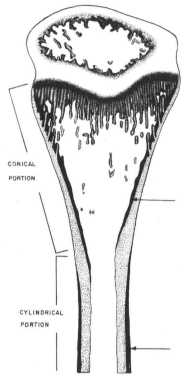

CONICAL
PORTION

CYLINDRICAL
PORTION

Figure 10-33. A diagram based upon an autoradiograph of the head of the tibia of a growing rat killed a few hours after receiving an injection of ^{32}P. The localization of high concentrations of silver grains in the autoradiograph is depicted here in black. In addition to the new bone in the epiphysis and at the metaphysis, bone is being deposited under the endosteum in the conical portion and beneath the periosteum in the cylindrical portion of the shaft (arrows). (Drawing based upon studies of Leblond et al., Am. J. Anat., *86*:289, 1950. (After D. W. Fawcett, *in* R. O. Greep, ed.: Histology. Philadelphia, The Blakiston Co., 1954. Reproduced with the permission of the McGraw-Hill Book Co.)

occasionally seen in women after the menopause is attributed by some to the decline in ovarian function but it does not respond favorably to treatment with estrogens.

The gonadal hormones, in some way, play an important part in determining the rate of skeletal maturation. In normal human development the time of appearance of the various ossification centers and the time of fusion of the epiphyses with their diaphyses is remarkably constant. The progress of these events at any given time during development is intimately related to the developmental state of the reproductive system. Thus in precocious sexual development, skeletal maturation is accelerated and growth is stunted owing to premature epiphyseal closure. On the other hand, in testicular hypoplasia or prepubertal

castration, epiphyseal union in the long bones is delayed and the arms and legs become disproportionately long.

The growth of bone is also markedly influenced by the *growth hormone* (somatotropin) of the anterior hypophysis (Chapter 17). Hypophysectomy results in cessation of growth at the epiphyseal plate; administration of growth hormone reinstates growth. Growth hormone injected into rats that have been both thyroidectomized and hypophysectomized produces skeletal growth, whereas thyroxine produces maturation but only moderate growth. Coordination between growth and maturation may be restored by administration of both hormones.

NUTRITIONAL EFFECTS UPON BONE. Growth of the skeleton is quite dependent upon nutritional factors, and deficiencies of minerals or of essential vitamins are often detected more easily in bone than in other tissues. A gross dietary deficiency of either calcium or phosphorus leads to rarefaction of bone and increased liability to fractures. Even if the intake of these elements is adequate, a deficiency of *vitamin D* may interfere with their intestinal absorption and lead to *rickets*. In this condition, ossification of the epiphyseal cartilages is disturbed, the regular columnar arrangement of the cartilage cells disappears, and the metaphysis becomes a disordered mixture of uncalcified cartilage and poorly calcified bone matrix (Fig. 10-38). Such bones are easily deformed by weight bearing.

In long-standing deficiency of calcium and of vitamin D, especially when aggravated by pregnancy, the bones of adults come to contain much uncalcified osteoid tissue, a condition known as *adult rickets* or *osteomalacia*. Although the condition is aggravated by the increased demands of pregnancy, the diminution in calcium content in this condition is due mainly to failure of calcification of new bone formed in the turnover of this tissue rather than to decalcification of previously calcified bone.

Deficiency of *vitamin C* leads to profound changes in tissues of mesenchymal origin, producing the condition known as *scurvy* or *scorbutus*, in which the primary defect is an inability to produce and maintain the intercellular substance of connective tissues. In the case of bone it results in deficient production of collagen and bone matrix with consequent retardation of growth and delayed healing of fractures.

Deficiency of *vitamin A* results in a diminu-

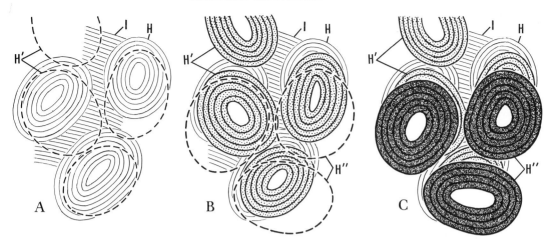

Figure 10-34. Diagram of stages in formation of three generations of haversian system, *H, H',* and *H''. I,* Interstitial lamellae. (Modified from Prenant.)

tion in the rate of growth of the skeleton. The vitamin controls the activity, distribution, and coordination of osteoblasts and osteoclasts during development. Among other things, there is a failure of resorption and remodeling to enlarge the cranial cavity and spinal canal at a rate sufficient to accommodate growth of the brain and spinal cord. Serious damage therefore results to the central nervous system. In hypervitaminosis A there is an acceleration of the erosion of the cartilage columns without a compensating increase in the rate of multiplication of cells in the proliferative zone. The

epiphyseal plates may therefore be completely obliterated and growth may cease prematurely.

JOINTS AND SYNOVIAL MEMBRANES

Bones are joined to one another by connective tissue structures that permit varying degrees of movement between the adjoining bones. Such structures are called joints or articulations. These present extreme variations in character, which depend primarily upon the type of bones which are joined and

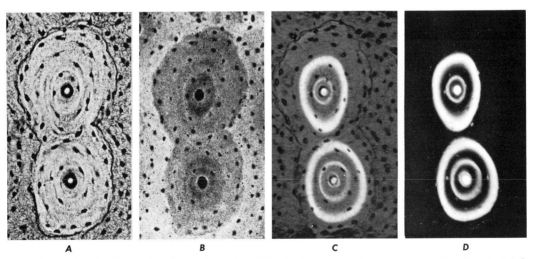

Figure 10-35. A pair of haversian systems from the midshaft of the tibia of a 9 month old dog given two 5 day courses of treatment with a tetracycline separated by an interval of 19 days. *A,* Ordinary microscopy. *B,* Historadiogram. *C* and *D,* Fluorescence microscopy. The bone deposited during Ledermycin treatment fluoresces, and the design of this experiment permits one to visualize the amount of bone deposited in each 5 day period. Of particular interest is the fact that the inner band, corresponding to the second period of administration, is narrower than the first, demonstrating that in this instance there is a slowing down in the rate of concentric bone deposition as the formation of the haversian system progresses. (Courtesy of R. Amprino.)

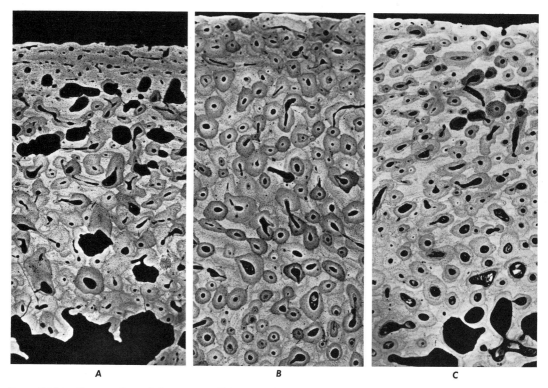

A   B   C

Figure 10-36. Cross sections of the anteromedial sector of the midshaft of the femur as revealed by negative histo-radiography. *A,* At age 7. *B,* At age 20. *C,* At age 65. Notice in the child (*A*) there are large resorption cavities (black) and large irregularly shaped haversian systems. At the surface of the compacta, the thick zone of periosteal bone is invaded by resorption cavities. Large remnants of periosteal primary bone are found in the interstices between the secondary osteons in the middle zone of the compacta. These remnants are fewer and smaller in the older perimedullary zone at the bottom of the figure. In the 20 year old man (*B*), the compacta is much thicker. Secondary haversian systems and remnants of primary bone persist in the subperiosteal zone. Elsewhere, the osteons are fairly regular in outline and are separated by remnants of pre-existing osteons. (Courtesy of R. Amprino.)

the varying degrees of motion permitted by the articulation. Thus, in some cases, as in the skull, the joints are immovable, and the connected bones are separated only by a thin connective tissue layer, the sutural ligament. Other joints are slightly movable, such as the intervertebral articulations. Here the succeeding vertebrae are joined by dense fibrous tissue and cartilage. Still other bones are freely movable upon one another, and here the bones are completely separated by cartilage and fibrous capsules.

Joints in which there is little or no movement are called *synarthroses.* There are three types of these: if the connection between the bones is of bone, it is a *synostosis;* if of cartilage, a *synchondrosis;* and if of connective tissue, a *syndesmosis.* Joints that permit free movement of the bones are called *diarthroses.*

In the diarthrodial joints there is a cavity.

Because this was thought by some to have a continuous lining of flattened, epithelium-like cells, the tissue was called "mesenchymal epithelium." However, the walls of the joint cavities are composed of a dense connective tissue whose cells are irregularly distributed and seldom suggest epithelium in arrangement. Occasionally, small amounts of cartilage and all transitions between the cartilage cells and the joint or synovial cells can be found.

The articular surface of the bones is covered with hyaline cartilage. Where the opposing cartilages touch, they are not covered with dense connective tissue, but at their bases a small area of perichondrium is reflected backward into the membrane of the joint capsule. At this point there are many cartilage cells extending into the synovial membrane. As is true of most of the cartilage of the body, the articular cartilages contain no blood vessels; it is generally believed that they are nourished by diffusion from the surrounding tissues. The articular cartilages are intimately adherent to a layer of compact bone which lacks haversian systems and has large lacunae, and is said to be free of canaliculi.

Most of the joint capsules are composed of two fairly distinct layers. The external consists of dense fibrous tissue and is called the *fibrous layer*. The inner is the *synovial layer*, which is more cellular and is thought to secrete the viscid, colorless liquid of the joint cavity. However, the joint membrane exhibits many variations in structure. The synovial layer is sometimes thrown into marked folds, which may project for surprising distances into the cavity. The larger of these folds frequently contain vessels. In other cases the two layers appear fused, or the synovial layer may rest directly on muscle or fatty tissue or periosteum. It has been suggested that the synovia be classified according to the tissues on which they lie: that is, loose connective, dense fibrous, or adipose tissue.

Synovial membranes that rest on loose connective tissue usually cover those parts of the joints not subjected to strain or pressure. As a rule they have a definite surface

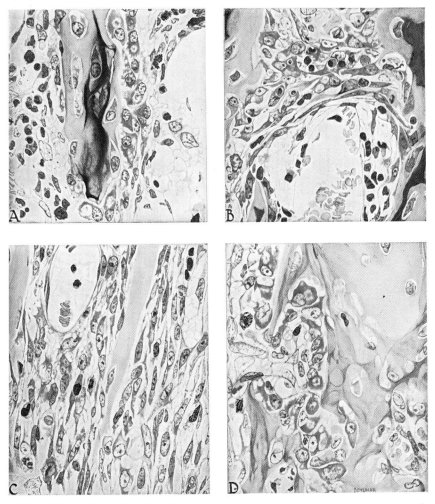

Figure 10-37.   Effect of large doses of parathyroid extract on proximal epiphysis of rat tibiae. The sections are from four members of a 7 week litter. *A*, Normal control, with prominent osteoblasts; *B*, 9 hours, *C*, 24 hours, and *D*, 96 hours after injection of 1000 units of parathyroid extract. *B* shows extensive development of osteoblasts into fibroblast-like cells. In *C*, bone marrow and osteoblasts have been replaced by densely packed fibroblast-like cells. In *D*, the fibrous tissue has been replaced by newly formed bone, many of its cells having changed into osteoblasts. Hematoxylin-eosin-azure II. × 505. (After Heller, McLean, and Bloom.)

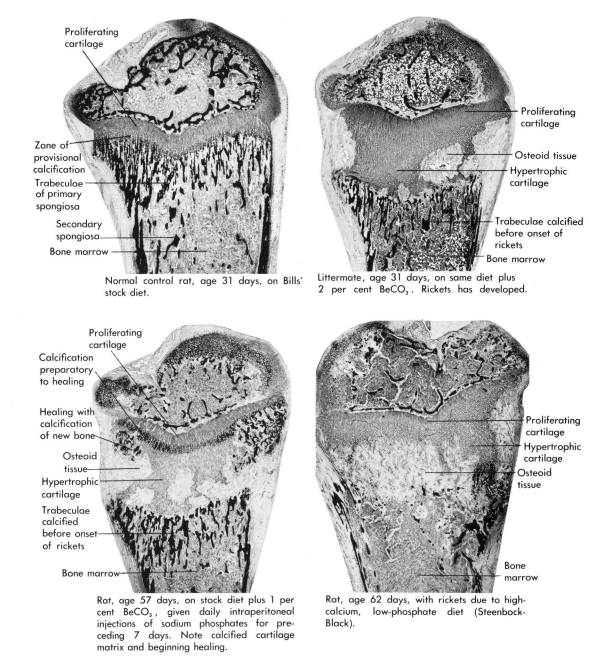

Proliferating cartilage

Zone of provisional calcification

Trabeculae of primary spongiosa

Secondary spongiosa

Bone marrow

Normal control rat, age 31 days, on Bills' stock diet.

Proliferating cartilage

Osteoid tissue

Hypertrophic cartilage

Trabeculae calcified before onset of rickets

Bone marrow

Littermate, age 31 days, on same diet plus 2 per cent BeCO₃. Rickets has developed.

Proliferating cartilage

Calcification preparatory to healing

Healing with calcification of new bone

Osteoid tissue

Hypertrophic cartilage

Trabeculae calcified before onset of rickets

Bone marrow

Rat, age 57 days, on stock diet plus 1 per cent BeCO₃, given daily intraperitoneal injections of sodium phosphates for preceding 7 days. Note calcified cartilage matrix and beginning healing.

Proliferating cartilage

Hypertrophic cartilage

Osteoid tissue

Bone marrow

Rat, age 62 days, with rickets due to high-calcium, low-phosphate diet (Steenbock-Black).

Figure 10-38. Photomicrographs of head of tibia in experimental rickets in rats. All sections from undecalcified bones stained with silver nitrate to show calcification, and counterstained with hematoxylin and eosin. All rats weaned to experimental diet at 21 days. × 15. (Courtesy of F. C. McLean.)

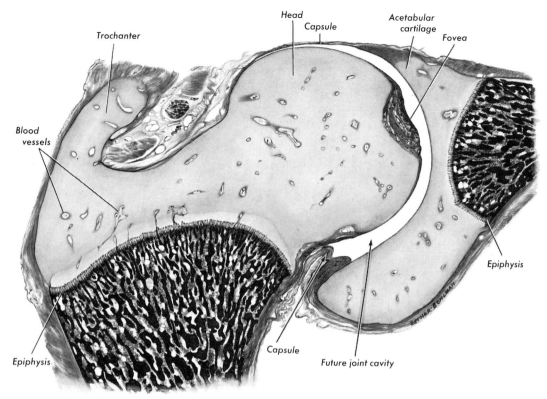

Figure 10-39.   Section through head of the femur of a 26 cm. human fetus. × 6. From a preparation of H. Hatcher.

layer, separated from the underlying tissue of the joint by loose connective tissue. The surface layer consists of collagenous fibers interspersed with fibroblasts whose processes may extend for long distances, although sometimes the cells are rounded. The collagenous fibers are either irregularly arranged or may be oriented along the main lines of stress. In addition to the fibroblasts, there are a few macrophages, leukocytes and lymphoid wandering cells. In addition to blood vessels, the loose connective tissue contains many lymphatics.

The fibrous synovial membrane covers the interarticular ligaments and tendons and lines those parts of the joints that are subject to strain. It consists of dense connective tissue; the surface zone is slightly more cellular than the rest. Some of the fibroblasts have capsules. When unusual pressure is applied to the synovial membrane, fibrocartilage develops.

The adipose type of synovial membrane covers the fat pads that project into the joint cavities. The synovial membrane in this case usually consists of a single layer of cells resting on a thin layer of connective tissue.

The fibroblasts of the synovial membrane rarely show mitoses. They may occasionally contain one or two vacuoles. There are no vacuoles within them that stain with neutral red. Mitochondria and a Golgi net have been demonstrated in them.

Folds of the synovial membrane may be either temporary formations, which depend on the position of the joint, or they may form permanent *villi*, which project into the joint cavity. Some of these villi have a broad base and a rather short stalk, while others may be thin and long. The larger folds contain blood vessels, lymphatics, and occasionally lobules of adipose tissue. There is an increase in the size and number of the villi with age. New islets of cartilage are formed in them, mainly by metaplasia of the synovial fibroblasts.

Blood vessels probably do not lie free on the surface of the synovial membrane. There are two plexuses of lymphatics, as a rule, within

Articular surface

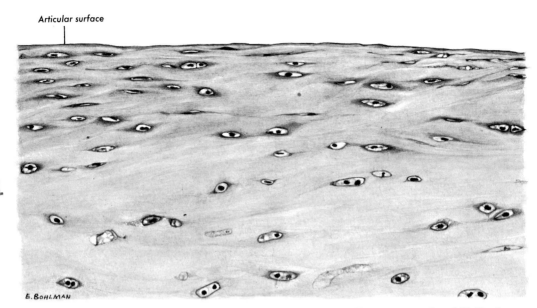

Figure 10-40.   Articular surface of head of the femur of a man. × 300. From a preparation of H. Hatcher.

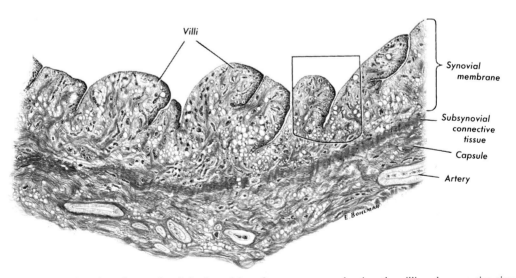

Villi

Synovial membrane

Subsynovial connective tissue

Capsule

Artery

Figure 10-41.   Section through capsule of the knee joint of a young man, showing the villi and connective tissue components. The area outlined is shown at higher magnification in Figure 10-39. × 15. From a preparation of H. Hatcher.

Villus

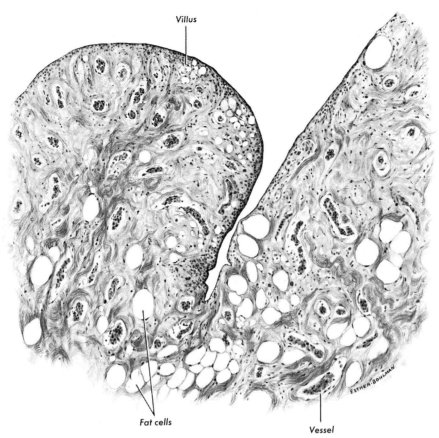

Fat cells

Vessel

Figure 10-42. Synovial membrane of young adult. (Higher magnification of the area outlined in Figure 10-38.) Note the irregularity in the concentration of cells toward the free surface of the villus and the irregular distribution of fat cells. × 85. From a preparation of H. Hatcher.

the synovial membranes, a superficial and a deep plexus. The nerves which accompany the blood vessels end in the layer beneath the surface in terminal arborizations or end-bulbs or plates. Pacinian corpuscles are always present.

When injured, the synovial membrane reacts like any other connective tissue by the formation of granulation tissue, and after some weeks may be completely regenerated. The synovial fluid is normally small in amount and seems to be a dialysate of blood to which have been added small amounts of mucin and a very few cells, chiefly lymphocytes, monocytes, and macrophages.

REFERENCES

Current surveys of bone from different points of view range from the relatively brief *Bone: An Introduction to the Physiology of Skeletal Tissue,* by F. C. McLean and M. R.

Urist (3rd ed. Chicago, University of Chicago Press, 1967), to the larger and more specialized presentation by many authors in *The Biochemistry and Physiology of Bone,* edited by G. H. Bourne (New York, Academic Press, 1956); in *Bone as a Tissue,* edited by K. Rodahl, J. T. Nicholson, and E. M. Brown, Jr. (New York, McGraw-Hill Book Co., 1960); in *Bone Biodynamics,* edited by Harold M. Frost (Boston, Little, Brown & Co., 1963); and in *Structure and Function of Connective and Skeletal Tissue,* Scientific Committee: S. Fitton-Jackson, R. D. Harkness, S. M Partridge, and G. R. Tristram (London, Butterworths, 1965).

Amprino, R., and A. Engström: Studies on x-ray absorption and diffraction of bone tissue. Acta Anat., *15*:1, 1952.

Barnicot, N. A.: The local action of the parathyroid and other tissues on bone in intracerebral grafts. J. Anat., *82*:233, 1948.

Bélanger, L. F., J. Robichon, B. B. Migicovsky, D. H. Copp, and J. Vincent: Resorption without osteoclasts (osteolysis.) *In* Sognnaes, R. F., ed.: Mechanisms of Hard Tissue Destruction. Washington, D.C., American Association for the Advancement of Science, 1963, p. 531.

Bloom, W., M. A. Bloom, and F. C. McLean: Calcification and ossification: Medullary bone changes in the reproductive cycle of female pigeons. Anat. Rec., *81*:443, 1941.

Cohen, J., and W. H. Harris: The three dimensional anatomy of haversian systems. J. Bone & Joint Surg., *40A*:419, 1958.

Cooper, R. R., J. W. Milgram, and R. A. Robinson: Morphology of the osteon. An electron microscopic study. J. Bone & Joint Surg., *48A:*1239, 1966.

Dudley, H. R., and D. Spiro: The fine structure of bone cells. J. Biophys. & Biochem. Cytol., *11:*627, 1961.

Engström, A.: Structure of bone from the anatomical to the molecular level. *In* Bone Structure and Metabolism. London, J. & A. Churchill, Ltd., 1956.

Fawcett, D. W.: The amedullary bones of the Florida manatee. Am. J. Anat., *71:*271, 1942.

Fernández-Morán, H., and A. Engström: Electron microscopy and x-ray diffraction of bone. Biochem. Biophys. Acta, *23:*260, 1957.

Fischman, D. A. and E. D. Hay: Origin of osteoclasts from mononuclear leucocytes in regenerating new limbs. Anat. Rec., *143:*329, 1962.

Gaillard, P. J.: Parathyroid gland and bone in vitro. VI. Devel. Biol., *1:*152, 1959.

Glimcher, M. J.: Molecular biology of mineralized tissues with particular reference to bone. *In* Oncley, J. L., et al., eds.: Biophysical Science—A Study Program. New York, John Wiley & Sons, 1959, p. 359.

Glimcher, M. J., A. J. Hodge, and F. O. Schmitt: Macromolecular aggregation states in relation to mineralization: The collagen-hydroxyapatite system as studied in vitro. Proc. Nat. Acad. Sci., *43:*860, 1957.

Gonzales, F., and M. J. Karnovsky: Electron microscopy of osteoclasts in healing fractures of rat bone. J. Biophys. & Biochem. Cytol., *9:*299, 1961.

Hancox, N. M., and B. Boothroyd: The osteoclast in resorption. *In* Sognnaes, R. F., ed.: Mechanisms of Hard Tissue Destruction. Washington, D.C., American Association for the Advancement of Science, 1963.

Heinen, J. H., G. H. Dabbs, and H. A. Mason: The experimental production of ectopic cartilage and bone in the muscles of rabbits. J. Bone & Joint Surg., *31:*765, 1949.

Heller, M.: Bone. *In* Bloom, W., ed.: Histopathology of Irradiation from External and Internal Sources. National Nuclear Energy Series. New York, McGraw-Hill Book Co., 1948, Chapter 5, pp. 70–161.

Heller, M., F. C. McLean, and W. Bloom: Cellular transformations in mammalian bones induced by parathyroid extract. Am. J. Anat., *87:*315, 1950.

Heller-Steinberg, M.: Ground substance, bone salts, and cellular activity in bone formation and destruction. Am. J. Anat., *89:*347, 1951.

Jackson, S. F.: The fine structure of developing bone in the embryonic fowl. Proc. Roy. Soc. B., *146:*370, 1957.

Lacroix, P.: Bone and cartilage. *In* Brachet, J., and A. E. Mirsky, eds.: The Cell: Biochemistry, Physiology, Morphology. New York, Academic Press, 1961, Vol. V, p. 219.

Lacroix, P., and A. Budy, eds.: Radioisotopes and bone: A symposium. Oxford, Blackwell Scientific Publications, Ltd., 1962.

Leblond, C. P., et al.: Radioautographic visualization of bone formation in the rat. Am. J. Anat., *86:*289, 1950.

McLean, F. C., and W. Bloom: Calcification and ossification; calcification in normal growing bone. Anat. Rec., *78:*333, 1940.

McLean, F. C., and A. M. Budy: Radiation, Isotopes, and Bone. New York, Academic Press, 1964.

McLean, F. C., and R. E. Rowland: Internal remodeling of compact bone. *In* Sognnaes, R. F., ed.: Mechanisms of Hard Tissue Destruction. Washington, D.C., American Association for the Advancement of Science, 1963.

Maximow, A. A.: Untersuchungen über Blut und Bindegewebe. III. Die embryonale Histogenese des Knochenmarks der Säugetiere. Arch. f. mikr. Anat., *76:*1, 1910.

Neuman, W. F., and M. W. Neuman: The Chemical Dynamics of Bone Mineral. Chicago, University of Chicago Press, 1958.

Robinson, R. A., and D. A. Cameron: Bone. *In* Electron Microscopic Anatomy. New York, Academic Press, 1964, p. 315.

Sledge, C. B.: Some morphologic and experimental aspects of limb development. Clin. Ortho. & Rel. Res., *44:*241, 1966.

Sognnaes, R. F., ed.: Calcification in Biological Systems. Washington, D.C., American Association for the Advancement of Science, 1960.

Sognnaes, R. F., ed.: Mechanisms of Hard Tissue Destruction, Washington, D.C., American Association for the Advancement of Science, 1963.

Vincent, J.: Microscopic aspects of mineral metabolism in bone tissue with special reference to calcium, lead, and zinc. Clin. Orthopedics, *26:*161, 1963.

Weidenreich, F.: Das Knochengewebe. *In* von Möllendorff, W., and W. Bargmann, eds.: Handbuch der mikroskopischen Anatomie des Menschen. Berlin, Julius Springer, 1930, Vol. 2, part 2, p. 391.

CHAPTER ELEVEN

Muscular Tissue

Muscular tissue is responsible for locomotion and for the movements of the various parts of the body with respect to one another. The fundamental protoplasmic property of contractility is highly developed in this tissue, whose cells are elongated in the direction of contraction and organized in long units of structure called *muscle fibers*.

The recognition of two general categories of muscle, *smooth* and *striated,* depends upon the presence or absence of regular transverse bands along the length of the fibers. Smooth muscle is innervated by the autonomic nervous system and its contraction is not subject to voluntary control. Striated muscle is subdivided into two distinct types, *skeletal* and *cardiac.* The fibers of skeletal muscle are syncytial. They are innervated by the cerebrospinal system of nerves, and their contraction is under *voluntary* control. The fibers of cardiac muscle are made up of separate cellular units, and their rhythmical contraction is *involuntary.*

In general, the visceral musculature is composed of *smooth muscle.* The somatic musculature comprising the flesh of the body wall and of the extremities is *striated skeletal muscle. Cardiac muscle* makes up the wall of the heart and may extend into the proximal portions of the pulmonary veins.

SMOOTH MUSCLE

Smooth muscle forms the contractile portion of the wall of the digestive tract from the middle of the esophagus to the internal sphincter of the anus. It provides the motive power for mixing the ingested food with digestive juices and for its propulsion through the absorptive and excretory portions of the tract. Smooth muscle is found in the walls of ducts in the glands associated with the alimentary tract, in the walls of the respiratory passages from the trachea to the alveolar ducts, and in the urinary and genital ducts. The walls of the arteries, veins, and larger lymphatic trunks contain smooth muscle. In the skin it forms minute muscles called arrectores pilorum, responsible for elevation of hairs. In the areola of the mammary gland it participates in the erection of the nipple, and in the subcutaneous tissue of the scrotum it causes the wrinkling of the skin that accompanies elevation of the testes. In the eye, it forms the musculature of the iris and ciliary body that is concerned with accommodation and with constriction and dilation of the pupil.

THE SMOOTH MUSCLE FIBERS. Smooth muscle fibers are long, spindle-shaped cells. Where they are closely associated in bundles or sheets, their boundaries are difficult to resolve with the light microscope, but by special maceration techniques the fibers can be isolated and their long fusiform shape is then evident (Fig. 11-1). They vary greatly in length in different organs. In the pregnant human uterus, they may reach a half millimeter in length. Their average length in the musculature of the human intestine is about 0.2 mm. with a thickness of about 5 μ. The smallest smooth muscle cells in the walls of small blood vessels may be only 20 μ long.

In longitudinal sections the elongated single nucleus is found to occupy the thickest part of the fiber about midway along its length. Its long cylindrical profile is rounded at the ends (Fig. 11-2). The chromatin usually forms a delicate pattern uniformly dispersed in the

Figure 11-1. Isolated smooth muscle cells from the wall of the stomach of a cat. × 220. (After A. A. Maximow.)

The cytoplasm of muscle cells is called *sarcoplasm*. In smooth muscle it is quite homogeneous in the living state and is almost equally devoid of structure after routine fixation and staining. However, after use of special stains, or after gentle maceration in nitric or trichloracetic acid, fine longitudinal striations can be demonstrated, running the full length of the cell. These are the *myofibrils* and are interpreted as the contractile material of smooth muscle. They are doubly refractile under the polarizing microscope but show no sign of the alternating isotropic and anisotropic transverse bands that are characteristic of the myofibrils of striated muscle (p. 275).

After appropriate cytological staining methods, mitochondria can be seen throughout the sarcoplasm, but they tend to congregate near the poles of the elongated nucleus. A pair of centrioles and a small Golgi apparatus can also be demonstrated. In some organs the sarcoplasm of smooth muscle may contain considerable glycogen.

In the development of mammary and sweat glands, certain cells of ectodermal origin become specialized for contraction. The cell body of these *myoepithelial cells* has some of the characteristics of epithelial cells but their base is drawn out into several radiating processes that contain myofilaments. In electron micrographs these portions of the cell have an appearance closely resembling the sarcoplasm of smooth muscle cells (Figs. 22-32 and 33-8).

MODE OF ASSOCIATION OF SMOOTH MUSCLE FIBERS. Smooth muscle cells may occur singly or in small groups in ordinary connective tissue, as in the lamina propria of the intestinal villi, where their contraction shortens the villi and helps expel lymph from the lacteals. In the walls of blood vessels, where smooth muscle fibers serve only to change the caliber of the lumen, they are oriented circumferentially, occurring as isolated fibers in the smallest arterioles and as a continuous layer in vessels of larger size. In the wall of the intestine, smooth muscle is arranged in separate longitudinal and circumferential layers. The coordinated action of these layers forms constrictions that move along the intestine as peristaltic waves, propelling the contents through the lumen. In other hollow organs, such as the bladder or uterus, the smooth muscle forms poorly defined layers of elaborately interlacing coarse bundles oriented in different directions.

nucleoplasm, but in the smooth muscle of some organs it tends to be aggregated along the inner surface of the nuclear envelope. There are two to several nucleoli, depending upon the species. In smooth muscle fixed in contraction the passively distorted nuclei may be deeply indented along their margins or may take on a helical form.

The cells of smooth muscle are offset with respect to one another, so that the thick middle portion of one is juxtaposed to the thin ends of adjacent cells. In transverse sections, smooth muscle therefore presents a mosaic of rounded or irregularly polygonal profiles varying from less than a micron to several microns across (Fig. 11-3). Only the largest profiles, those representing sections through the thick middle portion of the fibers, contain a centrally placed cross section of the nucleus. No nucleus is found in the smaller profiles, which represent sections at various levels in the tapering ends of the fusiform cells.

The connective tissue fibers outside the muscle continue into the spaces between the cells and bind them into bundles. Between the thicker bundles and layers of smooth muscle cells is a small amount of loose connective tissue containing fibroblasts, collagenous and elastic fibers, and a network of capillaries and nerves. Connective tissue cells are seldom found within smooth muscle bundles, but the clefts between muscle cells are nevertheless penetrated by thin collagenous, elastic, and reticular fibers. The reticular fibers branch irregularly, and their delicate network invests the individual smooth muscle cells. They can be stained with Mallory's aniline blue method and still more sharply with the Bielschowsky silver impregnation method (Fig. 11-4A and B). The reticular fibers are embedded in an intercellular layer of protein-polysaccharide that appears in sections stained with the periodic acid–Schiff (PAS) reaction as a continu-

ous pattern of magenta lines outlining every muscle cell (Fig. 11-3).

The pull of each contracting cell in smooth muscle is transmitted to the surrounding sheath of reticular fibers, and these continue directly into those of the surrounding connective tissue. This arrangement permits the force of contraction of the entire layer of the smooth muscle to be uniformly transmitted to the surrounding parts.

THE FINE STRUCTURE OF SMOOTH MUSCLE. In electron micrographs the elongated nucleus of the extended smooth muscle cell is smoothly contoured and rounded at the ends. The juxtanuclear sarcoplasm contains long slender mitochondria, a few tubular elements of granular endoplasmic reticulum, and numerous clusters of free ribosomes. A small Golgi complex is located near one pole of the nucleus. The bulk of the cytoplasm is occupied by exceedingly thin parallel myofilaments as-

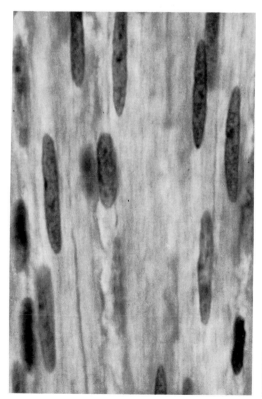

Figure 11-2

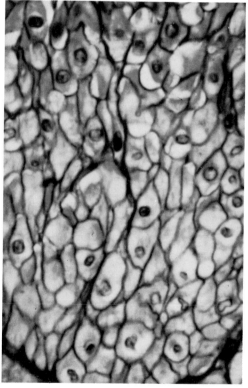

Figure 11-3

Figure 11-2. Photomicrograph of longitudinal section of smooth muscle from the tunica muscularis of intestine. × 1100.
Figure 11-3. Photomicrograph of transverse section of smooth muscle from the tunica muscularis of human stomach. The section was treated with the periodic acid–Schiff reaction, which stains the protein-polysaccharide coating of the muscle cells, thus accentuating their outline. × 1100.

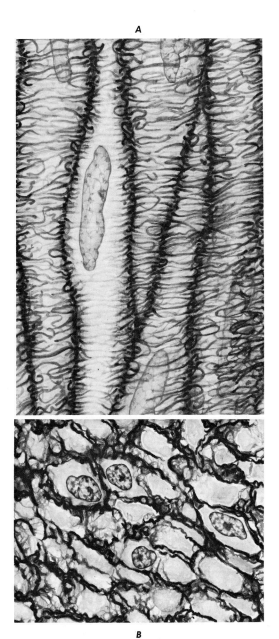

A

B

Figure 11-4. *A,* Longitudinal section through smooth muscle from human intestine, stained with the Bielschowsky silver method for reticular fibers, and hematoxylin. The fibers form continuous networks about each of the muscle cells. *B,* Transverse section through smooth muscle of human intestine, stained with Bielschowsky silver method for reticular fibers, and hematoxylin. × 1875. (Drawn by Miss E. Bohlman.)

sociated in bundles of varying width that evidently correspond to the myofibrils seen with the light microscope. These are oriented, for the most part, parallel to the long axis of the muscle cell. Interspersed among the tracts of myofilaments are mitochondria, occurring singly or in small clusters and having a prevailing longitudinal orientation. Scattered fairly uniformly through the contractile substance of the cell are oval or fusiform dense areas (Fig. 11-6). At high magnification these appear to contain filaments embedded in a dense amorphous matrix. Similar dense areas are distributed at intervals along the inner aspect of the plasmalemma. The exact nature of these dense areas in the sarcoplasm is not known. Their fine structural resemblance to the dense regions found at desmosomes, at zonulae adherentes of epithelia, and at the Z bands of striated muscle suggests that the dense component of all of these may be similar and may have a cohesive function. The occurrence of dense bodies in smooth muscle at nodal points where myofilaments seem to be bonded together laterally, and also where they are attached to the cell surface, is consistent with this speculation. The plasmalemma between the specialized sites of myofilament attachment is characteristically studded with small vesicular inpocketings or caveoli like those seen in endothelial cells and commonly interpreted as evidence of micropinocytosis.

A number of unstriated invertebrate muscles and all striated muscles of vertebrates have been found with the electron microscope to have two distinct sets of parallel filaments, which are believed to slide past one another during contraction. The widespread occurrence of a two-filament sliding mechanism of muscle contraction (see p. 279) led to the expectation that all muscle cells would be found to have two kinds of filaments. Early electron microscopic studies, however, failed to demonstrate more than one class of myofilament in vertebrate smooth muscle. It has been difficult to determine to what degree this is a technical problem. The myofilaments are very thin, less ordered, and less easily preserved than those of striated muscle. In cross sections at high magnification, it is sometimes possible to distinguish pointlike profiles of two sizes, about 30 Å and about 80 Å (Figs. 11-5 and 11-8). These have been interpreted by some investigators as end-on views of two kinds of filaments. The thicker filaments are relatively

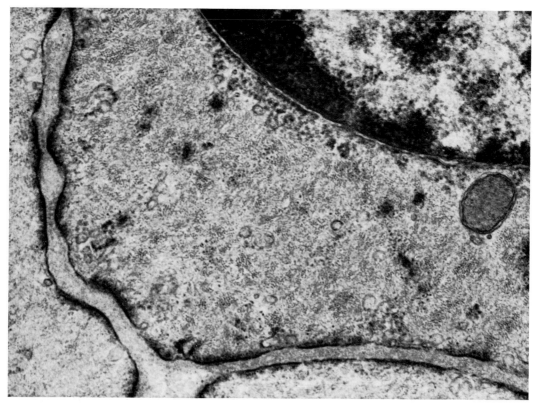

Figure 11-5. Electron micrograph of a small area of a smooth muscle cell in which the myofilaments in cross section are seen as small dots. In the so-called dense bodies of the smooth muscle cell the myofilaments appear to be embedded in a material denser than that making up the rest of the cytoplasmic matrix. × 80,000.

few and are not distributed uniformly or in any precise topographical relation to the thin filaments. The question remains unsettled as to whether the smallest contractile unit of smooth muscle is a single filament capable of shortening, or a specific grouping of two kinds of filaments that slide past one another during contraction as seems to be the case in striated muscle.

In studies of the chemical composition of muscle two fibrous proteins can be isolated, *actin* and *myosin*. When these are mixed in vitro they form a complex (actomyosin) which is capable of contracting on addition of adenosine triphosphate. It is reasonable to believe therefore that these are the major proteins involved in the contractile mechanism. The localization of actin and myosin to the two, microscopically identifiable, filamentous components of the sarcoplasm has been achieved for striated muscle (p. 278), but their exact relation to the myofilaments in smooth muscle has not been as clearly established.

CELL TO CELL RELATIONS IN SMOOTH MUSCLE. The surface of each smooth muscle cell is invested by a thick extracellular coating that corresponds in its fine structure to the *basal lamina* (basement membrane) of epithelia and to the *external lamina* or boundary layer of many other cell types. This is clearly the component responsible for the PAS reaction of the intercellular spaces already described (Fig. 11-3). Small bundles of collagen fibrils, which correspond to the argyrophilic reticulum of smooth muscle, are lodged in clefts between or within the surface coatings of adjacent cells (Fig. 11-7).

Owing to the presence of this thick extracellular layer, adjacent smooth muscle cells are separated by a distance of 400 to 800 Å. Typical desmosomes are not found. However, the specialized dense areas of adjacent cells, in which the myofilaments terminate, are too often opposite one another for their distribution to be entirely random. An intermediate dense line may be found in the intercellular

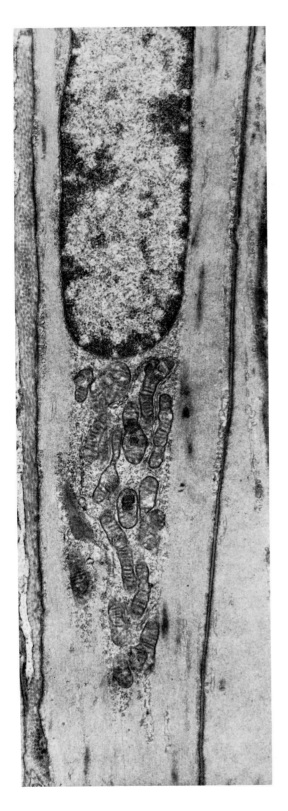

material between two such opposing dense regions. Thus, in spite of the considerable distance that separates the cells, there is a complementarity of the specialized areas of their surfaces that suggests a cell to cell cohesion at these sites, as at the desmosomes of epithelia. Contraction results in force applied at many points of insertion of myofilaments on the periphery of the cell. The contracted cell becomes ellipsoid and may exhibit numerous invaginations of its surface at points of attachment of myofilament bundles. The force is probably transmitted to neighboring cells mainly through the reticular connective tissue sheath, but long range forces of attraction acting at multiple dense areas of specialization on the opposing cell surfaces may also be involved.

In certain limited areas of the surface of visceral smooth muscle, the intercellular substance is lacking and the membranes of neighboring cells come into very close association. At these sites the intercellular space is obliterated and the outer leaves of the opposing unit membranes appear to have fused. Such sites of close apposition have been given various names, including *tight junction, fascia occludens,* and *nexus.* They are believed to constitute low resistance pathways, permitting a spread of excitation from one cellular unit to another throughout the muscle mass.

PHYSIOLOGICAL PROPERTIES AND CONTRACTILE MECHANISM OF SMOOTH MUSCLE. Smooth muscle is distinguished from striated muscle not only by its histological and cytological appearance but by its physiological and pharmacological properties. Its contractions are slower than those of other types of muscle, but it is able to sustain forceful contraction for long periods with relatively little expenditure of energy. Depending upon the site, contraction may be initiated by nerve impulses, hormonal stimulation, or local changes arising within the muscle itself. One of the more important local stimuli initiating contraction is stretching of the muscle fibers,

Figure 11-6. Electron micrograph of a portion of a smooth muscle cell from mouse ductus epididymidis cut longitudinally. The periphery of the fiber is occupied by myofilaments. Conical regions of cytoplasm extending from either pole of the elongated nucleus contain numerous mitochondria, a few profiles of endoplasmic reticulum, and many free ribosomes. × 20,000.

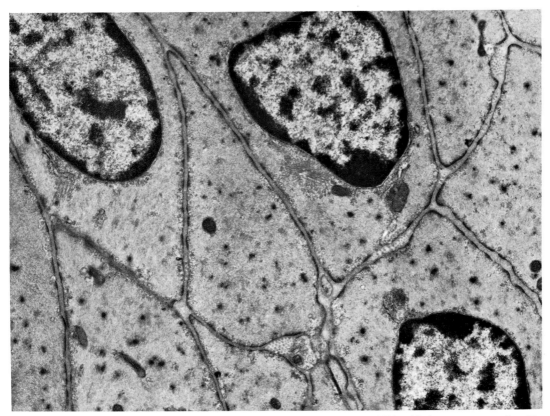

Figure 11-7. Electron micrograph of smooth muscle from the mouse ductus epididymidis in transverse section. The cells are separated by a rather wide extracellular space occupied by amorphous protein-polysaccharide and small bundles of collagen fibers. Scattered through the cytoplasm are dense bodies and around the periphery of the cell are condensations of cytoplasm of similar density that are probably sites of insertion of the myofilaments into the cell surface. × 14,000.

which can change the membrane potential and initiate a wave of contraction. The ability of smooth muscle to respond to stretch is particularly important in the physiology of the bladder, gastrointestinal tract, and other hollow viscera, whose contents are evacuated by peristaltic contractions.

Although usually treated by morphologists as a single type of muscle, smooth muscle in different organs is adapted to a variety of functions and differs markedly in its physiological properties in different organs. *Vascular smooth muscle*, in the blood vessels, behaves rather like skeletal muscle in that its activity is usually initiated by motor nerve fibers, and there is little evidence of conduction between cellular units. *Visceral smooth muscle*, on the other hand, bears certain functional resemblances to cardiac muscle in that it has a myogenic autorhythmicity; the cells behave like single muscular units and impulses are freely conducted from cell to cell presumably through the specialized areas of close membrane contact revealed in electron micrographs. Two forms of contraction are recognized in visceral smooth muscle: *rhythmic contraction* and *tonic contraction*. In the former, periodic spontaneous impulses are generated and spread through the muscle, accompanied by a wave of contraction. In addition, smooth muscle maintains a continuous state of partial contraction called *muscle tone*. The cause of the tonic contraction is no better understood than the genesis of the rhythmic contractions. The degree of *tonic contraction* may change greatly without any change in the frequency of the *rhythmic contraction* and vice versa. The two forms of contraction thus appear to be independent.

There are several other physiological and pharmacological differences in smooth muscle of different organs. For example, the amounts of *actin* and *myosin* in smooth muscle of the uterus are under endocrine control. Its cells hypertrophy during pregnancy and show a striking increase in the size of the Golgi apparatus and the extent of the granular endoplasmic reticulum. There are also marked changes during the normal estrus cycle. Ribonucleic acid synthesis is one of the early responses of the uterus to estrogen stimulation, and the organelles concerned with protein synthesis become much more prominent during estrus than at other times. Uterine musculature in the terminal stages of pregnancy is also responsive to the hormone *oxytocin,* elaborated by the posterior lobe of the hypophysis. Smooth muscle in other parts of the body is relatively unresponsive to hormones other than epinephrine.

SKELETAL MUSCLE

HISTOLOGICAL ORGANIZATION.   The unit of histological organization of skeletal muscle is the fiber, a long cylindrical multinucleate cell visible with the light microscope. Large numbers of parallel muscle fibers are grouped into *fascicles,* which are visible to the naked eye in fresh muscle. The fascicles are associated in various patterns to form the several types of *muscles* recognized by the anatomist—unipennate, bipennate, and so on. The muscle fibers, the fascicles, and the whole muscle are each invested by connective tissue that forms a continuous stroma, but its different parts are designated by separate terms for convenience of description. The muscle as a whole is enclosed by a connective tissue layer called the *epimysium* (Fig. 11-9). Thin collagenous septa that extend inward, surrounding all of the fascicles, collectively comprise the *perimysium,* and the exceedingly delicate reticulum that invests the individual muscle fibers constitutes the *endomysium.* The connective tissue serves to bind together the contractile units and groups of units and to integrate their action; it also allows a certain degree of freedom of motion between them. Thus, although the muscle fibers are very closely packed together, each is somewhat independent of adjacent fibers, and each fascicle can move independently of neighboring fascicles.

The blood vessels supplying skeletal muscle course in the connective tissue septa and ramify into a rich capillary bed around the individual muscle fibers (Fig. 11-10). The capillaries are sufficiently tortuous to permit their accommodation to changes in length of the fibers, by straightening during elongation and contorting during contraction.

In muscles, such as the sartorius, that do not taper at the ends, the fibers apparently continue without interruption through the entire length of the muscle. It is generally believed, however, that in most muscles the fibers are shorter than the muscle as a whole, seldom extending from its origin to its insertion but being connected at one end to connective tissue septa within the muscle and at the other to the tendon.

The thickness of the muscle fibers ranges from 10 to 100 μ or more depending upon the species and the particular muscle examined. Fibers within the same muscle may vary considerably in their caliber. During the growth of the organism the diameter of the fibers in-

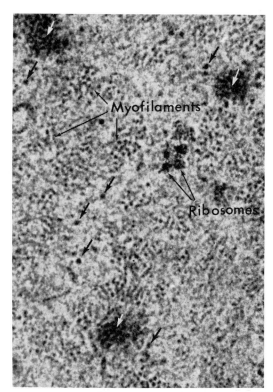

Figure 11-8.   At high magnification, the individual myofilaments, in cross section, are resolved as small dots of rather uniform size. A smaller number of larger dots (at arrows) suggest the presence of two size categories of filaments. The dense bodies (white arrows) appear to consist of myofilaments embedded in a dense matrix. $\times$ 118,-000.

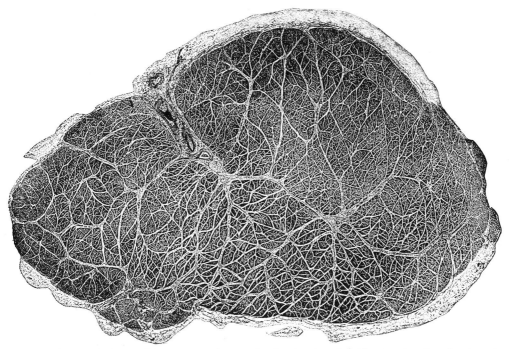

Figure 11-9. Cross section through human sartorius muscle, showing the subdivision into bundles of various sizes by connective tissue. × 4. (Photograph by Müller, from Heidenhain.)

creases with age, and in the grown individual it may undergo further increase in response to strenuous muscular activity—a phenomenon referred to as *hypertrophy of use* and exemplified in the bulging biceps of the boxer and the leg muscles of the ballerina. Conversely, the fibers may become thinner in muscle immobilized for long periods as in the treatment of fractures —the *atrophy of disuse.*

CYTOLOGY OF THE MUSCLE FIBER. The individual fibers can be separated by teasing fresh muscle apart under a dissecting microscope. In addition to the obvious transverse striations that give this type of muscle its name, a more delicate longitudinal striation is also discernible within the muscle fiber. The structural basis of this longitudinal striation becomes apparent when samples of muscle are treated with dilute nitric acid. In such macerated specimens, the limiting membrane of the fiber, the *sarcolemma*, is destroyed, the cytoplasmic matrix, called the *sarcoplasm*, is extracted, and the contractile substance of the muscle fiber separates into a large number of thin, parallel, cross striated fibrils, the *myofibrils*. The fine longitudinal striation detectable within the fresh muscle fiber is thus attributable to the parallel arrangement of myriad myofibrils.

The transverse striation comes about because each myofibril is made up of cylindrical segments or bands of different refractility that alternate regularly along its length. The corresponding segments of the closely packed parallel myofibrils are usually in register, so that the striations appear to extend across the whole width of the fiber (Figs. 11-14 and 11-15).

Each muscle fiber is invested by a delicate membrane just visible with the compound microscope. In teased fresh preparations where the fiber has been torn or crushed, it appears as a thin transparent film (Fig. 11-12). This has traditionally been called the sarcolemma. It has recently become apparent from electron microscopic studies that this film, visible with the light microscope, is not a single component but a compound structure consisting of the plasmalemma of the muscle fiber, its protein-polysaccharide external coating, and a delicate network of associated reticular fibers. In current usage, the term *sarcolemma* is reserved for the plasmalemma of the muscle fiber. It differs in no essential respect from the limiting membrane of any other cell. It should be realized that this lipoprotein membrane alone is not resolved by the ordinary microscope under

A   B   C

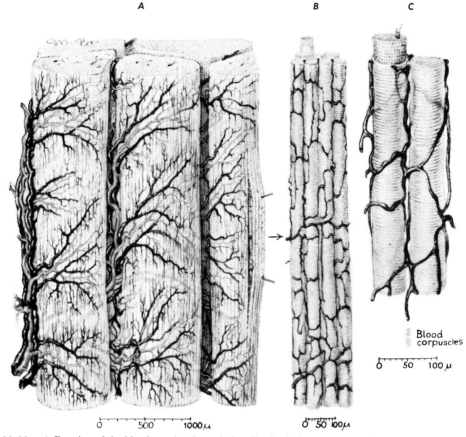

Blood
corpuscles

Figure 11-10. *A,* Drawing of the blood supply of muscle bundles in the human rectus abdominis muscle. *B,* The capillary network of muscle fibers; note thick loops crossing the fibers. *C,* The same at higher magnification showing red blood cells to establish scale. (From M. Brödel, Johns Hopkins Hosp. Bull., *61:*295, 1937.)

usual conditions of observation, but with the added thickness of its associated amorphous and fibrous investments a limiting layer is visible.

The nuclei of the striated muscle fiber are numerous. No actual number can be specified, for this depends upon the length of the muscle, but in a fiber several centimeters long there would be several hundred nuclei. They are elongated in the direction of the fiber. Their position varies according to the type of muscle and the animal species, but in the great majority of skeletal muscles of mammals, the nuclei are located at the periphery of the fiber immediately beneath the sarcolemma. This is especially apparent in transverse sections (Fig. 11-13). This characteristic position is a helpful criterion for distinguishing skeletal from cardiac muscle. It should be borne in mind, however, that in many of the so-called red muscles of mammals and in the muscles of lower verte-

brates the nuclei may be scattered through the whole fiber.

The nuclei of the muscle cells usually have one or two nucleoli and moderately abundant chromatin distributed along the inner aspect of the nuclear envelope. A small number of other nuclei of similar elongated form but with a coarser chromatin pattern are closely associated with the surface of the muscle fibers. These belong to elongated *satellite cells,* which are flattened against the muscle fiber or occupy shallow depressions in its surface and are enclosed within the same investing layer of protein-polysaccharide and reticular fibers. The cytoplasm of the satellite cell is scanty and its boundary with the muscle fiber usually cannot be resolved with the light microscope. The ontogenetic and functional relationships of these cells to the muscle fibers are not known. It is nevertheless of some importance to be aware that nuclei of slightly different appear-

SKELETAL MUSCLE

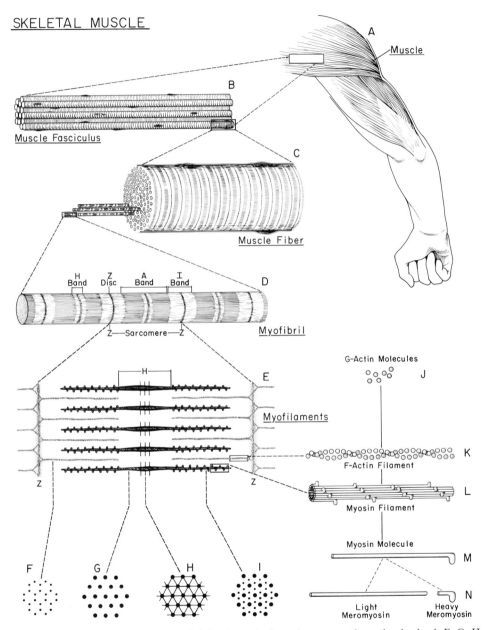

Figure 11-11. Diagram of the organization of skeletal muscle from the gross to the molecular level. F, G, H, and I are cross sections at the levels indicated. (Drawing by Sylvia Colard Keene.)

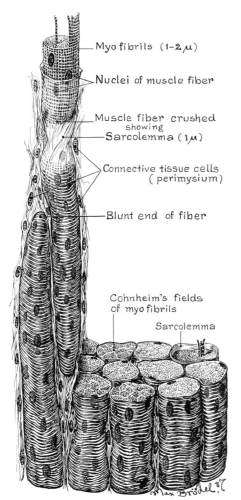

Myo fibrils (1-2 μ)

Nuclei of muscle fiber

Muscle fiber crushed
showing
Sarcolemma (1μ)

Connective tissue cells
(perimysium)

Blunt end of fiber

Cohnheim's fields
of myofibrils

Sarcolemma

Figure 11-12. Schematic representation of the structure of muscle fibers. (From M. Brödel, Johns Hopkins Hosp. Bull., *61*:295, 1937.)

ance found at the periphery of muscle fibers belong to a separate cell type.

The sarcoplasm of a muscle fiber corresponds to the cytoplasm of other cell types and can be defined as the contents of the sarcolemma exclusive of the nuclei and the myofibrils. It consists, therefore, of a typical cytoplasmic matrix and the usual cell organelles and inclusions as well as the myofibrils peculiar to muscle. Though not visible in routine preparations, the Golgi apparatus can be demonstrated by special staining methods. As might be expected in a multinucleate syncytium, there are multiple small Golgi bodies, which are located near one pole of each nucleus throughout the muscle fiber. The mitochondria (formerly called *sarcosomes*) are most abundant near the poles of the nuclei and

immediately beneath the sarcolemma, but they also occur in the interior of the fiber, where they are distributed in longitudinal rows between the myofibrils (Fig. 11-14). Several early cytologists examining preparations of muscle that were impregnated with heavy metals described in addition to the common organelles a lacelike network of dark strands in the interfibrillar sarcoplasm that appeared to surround all of the myofibrils. This was called the *sarcoplasmic reticulum* (Veratti). It was demonstrated with difficulty with the light microscope and many doubted its reality, but the presence of this organelle has now been verified in electron micrographs (Porter).

Lipid droplets are found in varying numbers in the muscle of some species. They may be situated between the myofibrils or among

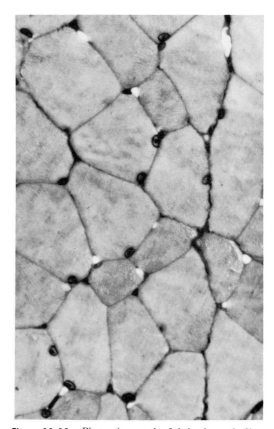

Figure 11-13. Photomicrograph of skeletal muscle fibers in cross section illustrating their polygonal outline and the peripheral position of their nuclei. In well fixed muscle the fibers are quite homogeneous in cross section. It is only where there has been considerable shrinkage that the myofibrils are separated into polygonal areas called Cohnheim's fields. × 450.

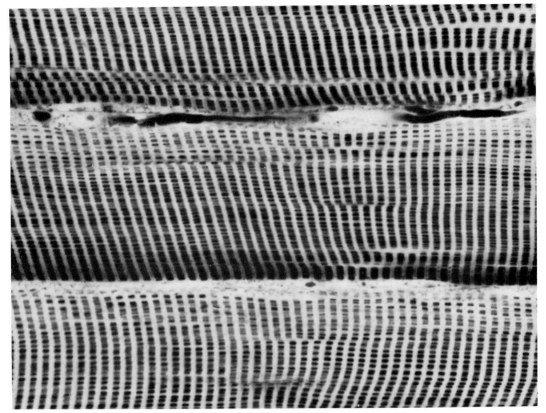

Figure 11-14. Photomicrograph of three muscle fibers from the dog in longitudinal section. The dark transverse A bands and light I bands are clearly differentiated. The dark longitudinal striations visible in the A bands correspond to the myofibrils, the smallest unit of the contractile material visible with the light microscope. Iron-hematoxylin stain. × 1200.

the clusters of mitochondria at the poles of the nuclei and at the periphery of the fiber. In appropriately stained preparations, small amounts of glycogen can be demonstrated throughout the sarcoplasmic matrix. In addition to these microscopically visible inclusions, the sarcoplasm of the living muscle contains the protein *myoglobin*, which imparts to muscle some of its color. There are also numerous metabolites of small molecular weight in sarcoplasm, which are extracted in the course of tissue preparation for histological examination.

Most of the interior of the muscle fiber is occupied by myofibrils 1 to 2 μ in diameter. In transverse sections they are resolved as fine dots either uniformly distributed or grouped in polygonal areas called the *fields of Cohnheim*. Whether this polygonal pattern represents the true distribution of myofibrils or is a consequence of shrinkage was long debated. The weight of evidence now favors its interpretation as an artifact, and no functional signifi-

cance is now attached to Cohnheim's fields. In longitudinal sections, the feature of greatest interest is the identification of the bands of the cross striated myofibrils. The cylindrical segments of the myofibrils that are markedly refractile and dark in fresh muscle, stain intensely with iron-hematoxylin in histological sections, while the less refractile, alternate segments remain essentially unstained (Fig. 11-14).

When muscle is examined with the polarizing microscope, the contrast of the bands is reversed. The dark-staining bands are now doubly refractile or anisotropic (A bands) and therefore appear bright, whereas the *light* staining bands are isotropic (I bands) or only very weakly anisotropic and thus appear *dark*. In the most commonly used terminology, the principal bands are named A band and I band, according to their appearance in polarized light. The relative lengths of the bands vary, depending upon whether the muscle is examined at resting length, during contraction, or when passively stretched. The length of the A band remains constant in all phases of contraction, but the I band is most prominent in stretched muscle, shorter at resting length, and extremely short in contraction.

In stained preparations and in living muscle viewed with dark phase contrast, a dark transverse line, the Z *line,* bisects each I band. The repeating structural unit to which all of the morphological events of the contractile cycle are referred is the *sarcomere,* which is defined as the segment between two successive Z lines and therefore includes an A band and half of the two contiguous I bands (Fig. 11-16). In histological sections of skeletal muscle, the A bands, I bands, and Z lines are usually the only cross striations that are discernible, but in exceptional preparations a paler zone, called the *H band,* may be seen traversing the center

of the A band. In its center is a narrow dark line, the *M band* or M line, located precisely in the middle of the A band. Although all of these features of the cross banded pattern of striated muscle can be seen with the light microscope, they can be demonstrated and interpreted more clearly in electron micrographs.

THE FINE STRUCTURE OF THE SARCOPLASM. The common organelles observed in the sarcoplasm with the light microscope do not depart significantly in fine structure from those in other cell types. The small Golgi complex found near many of the nuclei does not appear especially active. The mitochondria are abundant at the poles of the nuclei and beneath the sarcolemma. In addition a considerable number are lodged in narrow clefts between the myofibrils. In keeping with the high energy requirements for muscle contraction, the mitochondria have very numerous closely

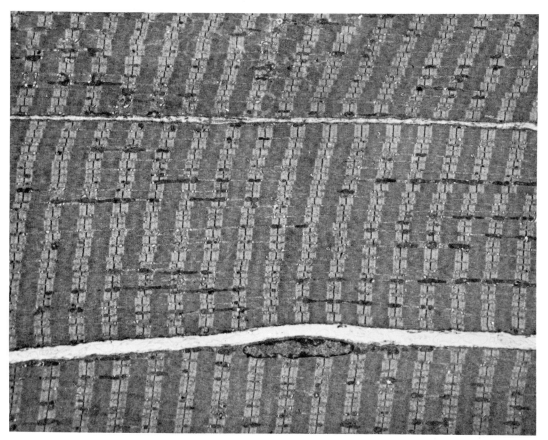

Figure 11-15. Electron micrograph of a longitudinal section of three skeletal muscle fibers from a mouse. Although the magnification is not very much higher than in the photomicrograph in Figure 11-14, the greater resolution of the electron optical image makes it possible to identify the A, I, and Z bands and the mitochondria between the myofibrils. × 3400. (Courtesy of J. Venable.)

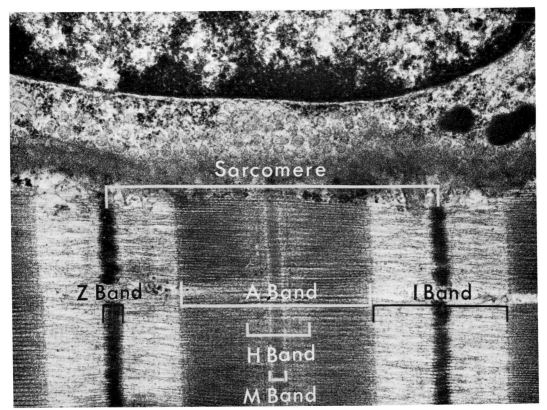

Figure 11-16. Electron micrograph of parts of two muscle fibers with the nucleus of one (*above*) and the most superficial myofibrils of the other (*below*). The principal features of the pattern of cross striations are identified on the figure. × 34,000.

spaced cristae. Their intimate association with the contractile elements brings the source of chemical energy (adenosine triphosphate, ATP) close to the sites of its utilization in the myofibrils.

An important organelle that cannot profitably be studied with the light microscope is the *sarcoplasmic reticulum,* a continuous system of membrane limited *sarcotubules* that extend throughout the sarcoplasm and form a closely meshed canalicular network around each myofibril (Fig. 11-18). This organelle corresponds to the endoplasmic reticulum of other cell types, but in muscle it is largely devoid of associated ribosomes and exhibits a highly specialized repeating pattern of local differentiations that bear a constant relationship to particular bands of the striated myofibrils. The tubules of the reticulum overlying the A bands have a prevailing longitudinal orientation but anastomose freely in the region of the H band (Fig. 11-20). At regular intervals along the length of the myofibrils the longitudinal *sarcotubules* are

confluent with transversely oriented channels of larger caliber called *terminal cisternae.* Pairs of parallel terminal cisternae run transversely across the myofibrils in close apposition to a slender intermediate element, the *T tubule.* These three associated transverse structures constitute the so-called *triads* of skeletal muscle (Figs. 11-18, 11-19, and 11-20). In amphibian muscle, the triads are found encircling each I band at the level of the Z line (Fig. 11-20). In mammalian muscle there are two triads to each sarcomere, situated at the junctions of each A band with the adjacent I bands. The lumen of the slender T tubule does not open into the adjacent cisternae and, strictly speaking, is not a part of the sarcoplasmic reticulum. Its limiting membrane is continuous with the sarcolemma and its lumen does communicate with the extracellular space at the cell surface. It is therefore to be regarded as a slender tubular invagination of the sarcolemma penetrating deep into the interior of the muscle fiber. To emphasize their separate iden-

Figure 11-17. Electron micrograph of four myofibrils from rabbit psoas muscle showing their characteristic pattern of cross banding. The broad dark band is the A band. The less dense central region of the A band is called the H band, and the narrow dark stripe across the middle of the H band is the M band. The broad light region between successive A bands is the I band, which is bisected by the dense, narrow Z line. × 24,000. (After H. E. Huxley, Scientific American, 1960.)

tity and to distinguish the T tubules from elements of the sarcoplasmic reticulum, they are referred to collectively as the *T system* of the muscle fiber.

The Substructure of the Myofibrils. The myofibrils, the smallest units of the contractile material visible with the light microscope (Fig. 11-11C and D), are found in electron micrographs to be composed of smaller units, the *myofilaments* (Fig. 11-11E). These are of two kinds, differing in dimensions and chemical composition. The cross banded pattern of striated muscle reflects the arrangement of these two sets of submicroscopic filaments. The thicker *myosin* filaments, 100 Å in diameter and 1.5 μ long, are parallel and about 450 Å apart. The parallel arrays of myosin filaments are the principal constituent of the A band and determine its length (Figs. 11-11E and 11-23). The filaments are slightly thicker in the middle and taper toward both ends. They are held in register by slender cross connections that are

aligned at the midpoint of the A band, giving rise to the transverse density recognized as the M line. In cross sections at the level of the H band, the filaments are disposed in an extremely regular hexagonal array (Fig. 11-11G). The thinner *actin* filaments, 50 Å in diameter, extend about 1 μ in either direction from the Z line and thus constitute the I band. They are not limited to this band, however, but extend some distance into the adjacent A bands, where they occupy the interstices between the hexagonally packed thick filaments. Thus in cross sections near the ends of the A band, the pointlike profiles of six thin actin filaments are evenly spaced around each myosin filament (Figs. 11-11 and 11-22). The depth to which the ends of the actin filaments penetrate into the A band varies with the degree of contraction (Fig. 11-23). In the relaxed condition the thin filaments that extend into the A band from opposite ends do not meet. The distance between their ends determines the width of the H band, which is defined as the central region of the A band that is not penetrated by the actin filaments. In stretched myofibrils the H band is therefore broad, whereas in the contracted state it is very narrow or entirely absent (Fig. 11-23). In the region of their interdigitation at the ends of the A band, the parallel thick and thin filaments are only 100 to 200 Å apart, and this narrow interval is traversed by regularly spaced cross bridges that extend radially from each myosin filament toward the neighboring actin filaments (Figs. 11-11 and 11-21).

The details of the interrelation of the actin filaments at the Z line are still under investigation, but certain points seem adequately established. Each thin filament approaching the Z line appears to be continuous with four diverging thin strands called Z filaments. Each of these runs obliquely through the Z line to one of the actin filaments on the other side. The actin filaments approaching the Z line from opposite sides are offset, so that when seen in longitudinal sections the cross connecting Z filaments produce a characteristic zig-zag pattern (Fig. 11-24). The Z filaments are believed to contain the muscle protein *tropomyosin,* and it is probable that this substance is associated both with the Z filaments and with the actin in the thin filaments of the I band.

Although no further detail can be observed in electron micrographs of thin sections of muscle, the analysis of the contractile material has been carried further by mechanical disintegration of myofibrils under conditions that permit the release of the individual myofilaments. These have been studied with the electron microscope after metal shadowing and with negative staining procedures. When isolated in this way, the thin filaments are about 1 μ in length and smooth contoured and have the chemical properties of *F-actin*. At very high magnification they have a beaded appearance and seem to consist of globular subunits (55 Å) forming two strands entwined in a helix (Fig. 11-11K). Further dissociation of the thin filaments yields globular units with the same size, molecular weight, and other properties of *G-actin* (Fig. 11-11 J). Each of the two strands making up the thin filaments of muscle is therefore considered to be a polymer of G-actin. Artificial actin filaments formed in vitro from globular actin molecules have an electron microscopic appearance essentially identical to that of naturally occurring thin

filaments prepared by dissociation of myofibrils (Fig. 11-25). Several lines of evidence indicate that tropomyosin is intimately associated with the actin filaments in intact muscle, but the manner in which they are related has not been visually demonstrated.

The isolated thick filaments of muscle are 1.5 μ long. They have a smooth central segment 0.15 to 0.2 μ in length, but toward their ends they are beset with many short projections corresponding to the cross bridges seen between the thick and thin filaments in intact myofibrils. When further dissociation of such fibrils is carried out, myosin molecules are obtained (Fig. 11-11L and M). These are rod-shaped and about 1500 Å long, with a globular projection at one end (Fig. 11-26). The thick filaments of muscle are believed to be formed by an antiparallel arrangement of myosin molecules in such a way that the smooth central region of the filament is occupied only by the rodlike parts of the molecules, with the globular heads projecting outward nearer the ends of the fibrils. It has been known for some time that the myosin molecule can be cleaved by brief tryptic digestion into two fragments called *light meromyosin* and *heavy meromyosin* (Fig. 11-11N). It now appears that the light meromyosin makes up the major part of the rodlike backbone of the molecule and the heavy meromyosin comprises the segment bearing the globular lateral projection. The ability to combine with actin, and the adenosine triphosphatase activity that are essential to muscular contraction, reside in the heavy meromyosin fragments, whose lateral projections correspond to the bridges seen between the myosin and actin filaments in micrographs of intact myofibrils.

SLIDING FILAMENT MECHANISM OF CONTRACTION. Though classical cytologists described the changes in the relative lengths of the bands during muscle shortening, these observations suggested no satisfactory explanation of the contractile mechanism. Until fairly recently the commonest speculation envisioned a process of shortening due to reversible folding and cross linking of long molecules. In the past few years, however, the detailed analysis of the submicroscopic organization of muscle by electron microscopy and x-ray diffraction has not only revealed the structural relationships responsible for the cross striations but has led to an entirely new concept of the mechanism of contraction. Basic to the new

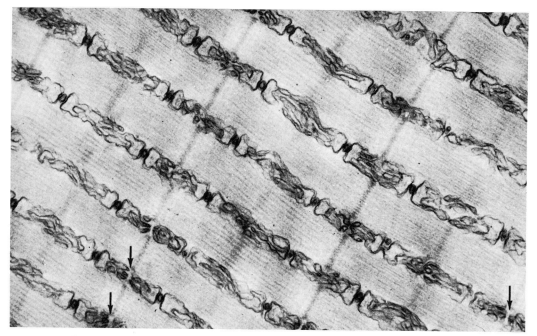

Figure 11-18. Electron micrograph of a longitudinal section of a muscle fiber from a fast-acting fish muscle, illustrating the extensive development and regular arrangement of its sarcoplasmic reticulum, which occupies the clefts between myofibrils. The "triads" of the reticulum run across the myofibrils in a direction perpendicular to the page and hence are seen here in cross section. They consist of a slender intermediate tube (30 mμ) flanked by two larger channels (100 mμ). They are consistently located at either end of each A band near the A-I junction. The longitudinally oriented tributaries of the triads form close-meshed networks parallel to the surface of the myofibrils. The branches of the two triads in the same sarcomere are continuous in the region of the H band, but there often appears to be discontinuity at the level of the Z bands (see at arrows). $\times$ 28,000. (After D. W. Fawcett and J. P. Revel, J. Biophys. & Biochem. Cytol., 1961.)

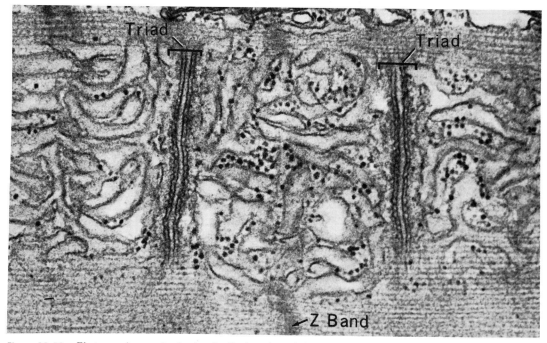

Figure 11-19. Electron micrograph of a longitudinal section of the cricothyroid muscle of a bat. The section passes tangential to a myofibril and provides a view of the topography of the sarcoplasmic reticulum closely applied to its surface. The triads are oriented transverse to the long axis of the myofibril at the A-I junction. Numerous dense particles of glycogen are seen between the longitudinal sarcotubules which form a close-meshed network over the A and I bands. $\times$ 50,000. (Courtesy of J. P. Revel.)

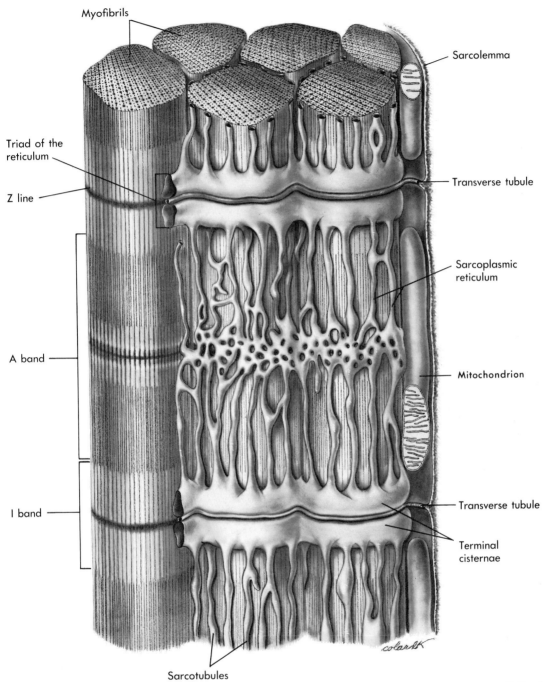

Figure 11-20. Schematic representation of the distribution of the sarcoplasmic reticulum around the myofibrils of skeletal muscle. The longitudinal sarcotubules are confluent with transverse elements called the terminal cisternae. A slender transverse tubule (T tubule) extending inward from the sarcolemma is flanked by two terminal cisternae to form the so-called triads of the reticulum. The location of these with respect to the cross banded pattern of the myofibrils varies from species to species. In frog muscle, depicted here, the triads are at the Z line. In mammalian muscle there are two to each sarcomere, located at the A-I junctions. (Modified after L. Peachey: J. Cell Biol., *25:*209, 1965, from D. W. Fawcett and S. McNutt. Drawn by Sylvia Colard Keene.)

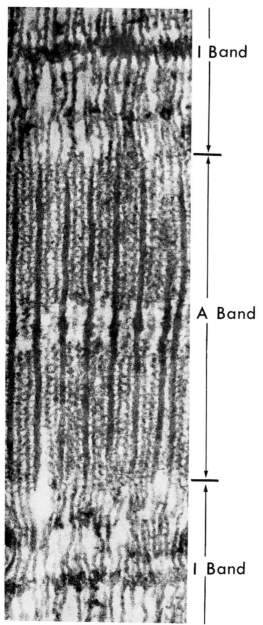

I Band

A Band

I Band

Figure 11-21. Electron micrograph of a thin longitudinal section of rabbit psoas muscle, showing the arrangement of thick and thin filaments. The figure includes one sarcomere length. In the I band at either end, only thin filaments are found. In the A band, occupying the central portion of the figure, the thin filaments of the I band interdigitate with a set of thicker filaments. × 135,000. (Courtesy of H. E. Huxley.)

theory was the observation that the length of the A band remains constant during contraction, while the lengths of the H band and the I band both decrease. A possible explanation for these changes in the pattern of cross banding became apparent when the electron microscope revealed two interdigitating sets of filaments. According to the *sliding filament hypothesis* (Hanson and Huxley), when a muscle contracts, the thick and thin filaments maintain the same length but slide past each other, so that the ends of the actin filaments extend farther into the A bond, narrowing and ultimately obliterating the H band. As a consequence of the deeper penetration of the A band by the I filaments, the Z line is drawn closer to the ends of the adjacent A bands, and there is an overall shortening of the myofibril (Fig. 11-23).

The chemical events responsible for the longitudinal displacement of one set of fibrils with respect to the other have yet to be elucidated. The evidence to date suggests that the force is produced by some cyclic process occurring at the cross bridges and that each cross bridge on the myosin filament may attach to a succession of sites along the neighboring actin filament, causing the filaments to move past one another. The breakdown of ATP by myosin ATPase localized in the bridges is thought to play a significant role in energizing this process.

COUPLING OF EXCITATION TO CONTRACTION. The attention of physiologists has long been focused upon the problem of explaining how the myofibrils throughout the muscle fiber are activated simultaneously and almost instantaneously after arrival of an impulse at the sarcolemma. These events take place too rapidly to be explained by inward diffusion of an activating substance liberated from an excitable surface membrane. In a new approach to this problem, Huxley and Taylor applied a microelectrode to the surface of an isolated muscle fiber and showed that a local reduction in membrane potential was not equally effective at all points on the surface. It resulted in inward spread of an impulse leading to contraction only if the tip of the microelectrode was over certain sensitive spots. In frog muscle these sensitive points were located only over the I band. There appeared therefore to be a structural component at the center of each I band responsible for inward conduction.

The discovery of the sarcoplasmic reticulum by Porter and Palade and the finding of transversely oriented triads at the level of each Z line led to the suggestion that these might be the submicroscopic structures involved in the inward spread of activation. The recent demonstration that the membranes of the T tubules are continuous with the sarcolemma and that their lumen is open to the extracellular space has provided the necessary final link in the evidence for the participation of the T tubules in excitation-contraction coupling.

The functions of the longitudinal elements of the sarcoplasmic reticulum are not as well understood, but evidence that they play a part in muscle relaxation is rapidly accumulating. Calcium is required in the external fluid for muscular contraction and it is now believed to have an important triggering role in initiating contraction. A "relaxing factor" isolated from muscle homogenates has been shown by electron microscopy to consist of membrane bounded vesicles derived by fragmentation of the sarcoplasmic reticulum. In vitro, these vesicles, in the presence of adenosine triphosphate, rapidly and reversibly bind calcium. It is now speculated that, in the resting state, most of the calcium in muscle is concentrated in the sarcoplasmic reticulum. Excitation of the sarcolemma is conducted inward by the membranes of the T system, somehow causing the sarcoplasmic reticulum to release calcium ions to the myofibrils, triggering their contraction. When contraction is completed calcium ions are recaptured by the sarcoplasmic reticulum and relaxation ensues. Enzymes splitting ATP and ADP have been demonstrated by histochemical methods at the electron microscope level in the cisternal expansions of the sarcoplasmic reticulum adjacent to the T tubules. The location of a structure containing ATPase in close topographic relation to the T system further suggests that this contact may play a significant role in excitation-contraction coupling by energizing the postulated ATP-driven calcium pump.

THE MYONEURAL JUNCTION. The specialized junctional region at the termination of a motor nerve on skeletal muscle fibers is called the *motor end plate*. It is recognized with the microscope as a slightly elevated plaque on the muscle fiber marked by a local accumulation of nuclei (Figs. 11-27 and 11-28). The nuclei are of at least two morphologically distinguishable types. The so-called "arborization

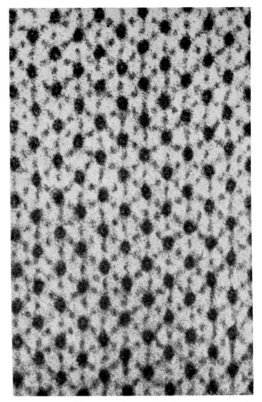

Figure 11-22. Electron micrograph of a transverse section of insect flight muscle showing the regular hexagonal array of thick and thin filaments in the A band of a myofibril. (After Hanson and Huxley, Scientific American, 1960.) ×350,000.

nuclei" belong to cells referred to collectively as the *teloglia* or terminal Schwann cells associated with the motor nerve endings. The second category of nuclei, usually larger and less intensely stained, are called "fundamental nuclei" or "sole nuclei" in the classical literature. These are simply the nuclei of the underlying muscle fiber that congregate in the region of the myoneural junction. With special methods of metallic impregnation it can be shown that the axon of the motor nerve, after losing its myelin sheath, forms a terminal arborization among the clustered nuclei of the end plate. The terminal branches of the axons occupy recesses in the surface of the muscle fiber called *synaptic troughs* or *primary synaptic clefts*. When selectively stained, the surface of the underlying muscle fiber is found to be highly differentiated to form what appear to be evenly spaced, ribbon-like lamellae attached to the sarcolemma by their edges and projecting from the myoneural interface into the underlying sarcoplasm. This specialization of the muscle fiber surface is called the subneural apparatus.

Electron microscopy has greatly clarified the relationships at the myoneural junction. The teloglial cells cover the outer surface of the axon terminals but never penetrate into the synaptic clefts. Here the nerve and muscle are directly exposed to one another. The so-called "lamellae" of the subneural apparatus are found to be narrow *secondary synaptic clefts* formed by plication of the sarcolemma lining the primary synaptic trough (Fig. 11-27). The axolemma and the sarcolemma are separated at all points by a protein-polysaccharide boundary layer similar to that investing the rest of the surface of the muscle fiber. The axoplasm in the nerve terminals contains mitochondria and a very large number of small vesicles (400 to 600 Å) apparently identical to the *synaptic vesicles* seen at axodendritic synapses in the nervous system. It has been suggested that these vesicles are the sites of storage of acetylcholine, but this remains speculative. The subneural sarcoplasm is unremarkable except for the abundance of its mitochondria. Histochemical studies demonstrate cholinesterase activity in the subneural apparatus of the motor end plate (Fig. 11-28). The major

part of this activity appears to be due specifically to acetylcholinesterase, which is localized in or near the sarcolemma lining the secondary clefts.

It is the prevailing view that when the nerve action potential reaches the terminal arborization at the motor end plate, *acetylcholine* is released. Diffusing across the synaptic cleft, this activates receptor sites in the postsynaptic membrane, increasing the permeability of the sarcolemma to ions. The resulting increase in ion flow generates an end plate potential, which, upon reaching threshold value, sets off a propagated wave of depolarization that spreads over the muscle fiber and into its interior via the T system, initiating contraction. The acetylcholine released is rapidly broken down by the acetylcholinesterase in the subneural apparatus thus limiting the duration of the response.

NEUROMUSCULAR SPINDLES. Skeletal muscle contains complex sensory organs called *muscle spindles*. These fusiform encapsulated structures consist of several modified striated muscle fibers and their associated nerve endings enclosed in a common sheath. The specialized muscle fibers in the interior of the organ, referred to as *intrafusal fibers*, number from a few to as many as 20, but there are usually about

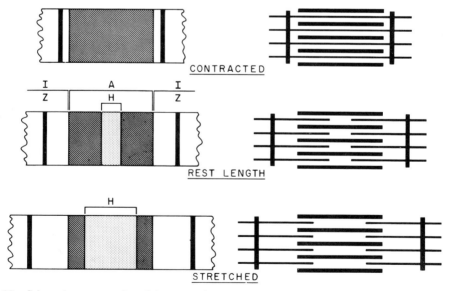

Figure 11-23. Schematic representation of the current interpretation of the changing appearance of the cross striations (*left*) in different phases of contraction, depending upon the degree of interdigitation of the sliding filaments (*right*). The A band is of constant length but the width of the H band is determined by the depth of penetration of the thin I filaments into the A band. In the contracted state the thin filaments slide more deeply into the A band, obliterating the H band. In stretched muscle the thin filaments are drawn out of the A band and the H band is widened.

six (Fig. 11-29). The fibers are 1 to 5 mm. long and attached at their ends to tendon or endomysium. For descriptive purposes they are subdivided into a central or *equatorial segment* and two long tapering *polar segments*. The equatorial segment can be further subdivided on the basis of its structural organization into three regions. The central portion is usually devoid of obvious cross striations and contains an accumulation of 40 to 50 spherical nuclei, which completely fill and often slightly distend the fiber. This region is referred to as the *nuclear bag*. Extending from it toward either pole is a myotube region, in which oval nuclei are aligned in a row in an axial core of sarcoplasm surrounded by a peripheral layer of cross striated myofibrils. In the slender polar segments the nuclei are scattered at irregular intervals along the axis of the fiber. The capsule closely invests the poles of the intrafusal fiber but diverges from its surface in the equatorial segment to enclose the *periaxial space,* a fluid filled cavity up to 200 μ in diameter that surrounds the nuclear bag and myotube regions. It has been reported that this space is continuous with the lymphatic system, but this does not seem to have been confirmed.

A special kind of nerve ending is associated with each of the three regions of the intrafusal fiber. One or both polar ends are supplied by small efferent myelinated fibers provided with motor end plates similar to those found on ordinary extrafusal muscle fibers. The sensory endings supplied by large myelinated afferent fibers are confined to the equatorial segment. The primary sensory ending is associated mainly with the nuclear bag region but may extend onto the adjacent myotube region. The endings consist of a complex system of half rings and spirals around the fiber (Fig. 11-30). Secondary sensory endings may also be present in the myotube regions. The details of innervation vary greatly from species to species.

The spindles scattered through skeletal muscles appear to function like miniature strain gauges, sensing the degree of tension in the muscle. The motor innervation of the polar regions of the intrafusal fibers maintains the nuclear bag region under sufficient tension for its stretch receptor endings to be close to their threshold. A further stretch of the equatorial region results in discharge of the spindle afferent fiber, and the frequency of its discharge is proportional to the tension exerted on the intrafusal fiber.

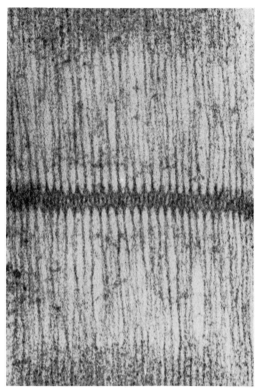

Figure 11-24. High magnification electron micrograph of a Z band from rabbit psoas, showing the offset arrangement of the I filaments approaching the Z band from opposite sides. At the I-Z junction the filaments appear to thicken and to divide into diverging Z filaments. There are varying interpretations of the fine structure of this band. (Courtesy of M. Reedy.)

CARDIAC MUSCLE

The vertebrate heart consists of striated muscle fibers that differ in several respects from those of skeletal muscle. (1) The fibers are not syncytial, as was formerly thought, but are made up of separate cellular units joined end to end by special surface specializations, *intercalated disks,* that run transversely across the fiber. (2) The fibers are not simple cylindrical units but they bifurcate and connect with adjacent fibers to form a complex three dimensional network. (3) The elongated nuclei of the cellular units are usually situated deep in the interior of the fiber instead of immediately beneath the sarcolemma. The principal physiological points of difference between cardiac and skeletal muscle are the spontaneous nature of the beat of cardiac muscle and its rhythmical contraction, which is ordinarily not subject to voluntary control.

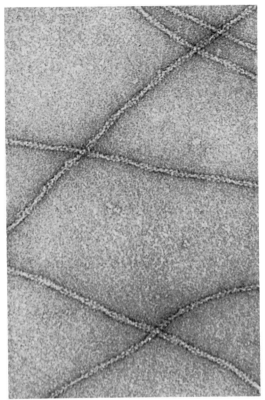

Figure 11-25. A preparation of purified F-actin embedded in a thin film of uranyl acetate. The resulting negative staining brings out considerable detail. In many of the filaments the double helical structure can be seen. ×250,000. (Courtesy of H. Huxley.)

THE CYTOLOGY OF CARDIAC MUSCLE. The thin sarcolemma of cardiac muscle is similar to that of skeletal muscle, but the sarcoplasm is relatively more abundant and its mitochondria are much more numerous. The longitudinal striation of the fibers is quite obvious with the light microscope owing to the subdivision of the contractile material into fascicles by rows of mitochondria in the interfibrillar sarcoplasm. The pattern of cross striation of the myofibrils and the designation of the A, I, M, H and Z bands is identical to that of skeletal muscle. The myofibrils diverge around the centrally placed nucleus to outline a fusiform axial region of sarcoplasm rich in mitochondria. Near one pole of the nucleus is a small Golgi complex. In the conical regions of sarcoplasm extending in either direction from the nucleus there are often a few droplets of lipid and, in older animals, deposits of lipofuscin pigment. In old humans this pigment

may come to constitute as much as 20 per cent of the dry weight of the myocardium. In small animal species lipid droplets are plentiful and occur in the interfibrillar sarcoplasm throughout the fiber, often being located between the ends of the mitochondria. The sarcoplasm of cardiac muscle is richer in glycogen than is that of skeletal muscle.

At fairly regular intervals along the length of the fibers the intercalated disks appear as heavy transverse lines (Fig. 11-31). These are relatively inconspicuous in hematoxylin and eosin but are clearly revealed in iron-hematoxylin or phosphotungstic acid–hematoxylin preparations. The disk may extend uninterruptedly across the full width of the fiber but more often is divided into segments that are offset longitudinally so as to give the disk a steplike configuration. In the repeating pattern of cross striations, the intercalated disks invariably occur at the level of the I bands. They were formerly interpreted as local contraction bands or specializations for intracellular conduction but are now known to be devices for maintaining firm cohesion of the successive cellular units of the myocardium and for transmitting the tension of myofibrils along the axis of the fiber from one cellular unit to the next.

THE SUBMICROSCOPIC STRUCTURE OF THE SARCOPLASM. In electron micrographs, cardiac muscle bears a superficial resemblance to skeletal muscle. Its contractile substance is composed of two sets of myofilaments, thick and thin, in the same interdigitating relationship. In longitudinal section the tubules of the sarcoplasmic reticulum and rows of mitochondria appear to subdivide the contractile

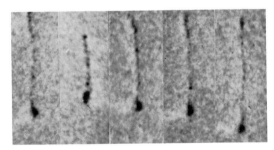

Figure 11-26. Several myosin molecules from shadowed preparations, demonstrating the "head and tail" structure with the knoblike head end corresponding to the heavy meromyosin fraction and to the laterally projecting spines on the myosin filaments. The average length of the molecules is about 1600 Å. (Micrograph courtesy of H. Huxley.)

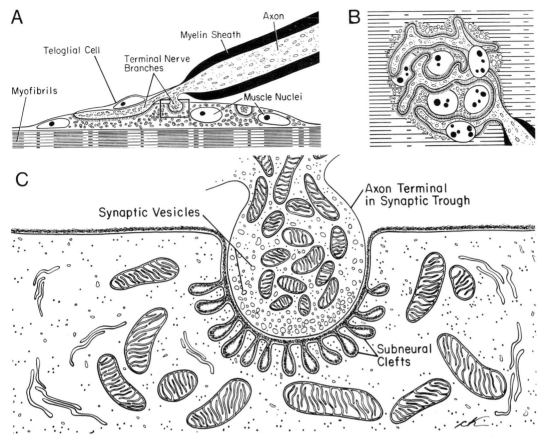

Figure 11-27. Schematic representations of the motor end plate as seen by light and electron microscopy. *A,* End plate as seen in histological sections in the long axis of the muscle fiber. *B,* As seen in surface view with the light microscope. *C,* As seen in an electron micrograph of an area such as that in the rectangle on *A.* (Modified after R. Couteaux.)

material into myofibrils of variable width. However, upon close examination of transverse sections (Figs. 11-32 and 11-33), it becomes evident that the myofilaments are not organized in discrete myofibrils as they are in skeletal muscle. In cross sections the circular profiles of the sarcotubules are aligned in rows that partially demarcate polygonal or irregular areas of myofilaments, but these are usually confluent over some fraction of their perimeter with adjacent areas of myofilaments. Mitochondria often appear completely surrounded by myofilaments (Fig. 11-33). Thus the contractile substance of cardiac muscle forms a continuum that can be thought of as a large cylindrical mass of parallel myofilaments incompletely subdivided into irregular fascicles by deep incisures and by fusiform or lenticular clefts of sarcoplasm that are occupied by mitochondria and the other organelles essential to the contractile mechanism.

The confluent nature of the contractile mass is not peculiar to cardiac muscle but is also found in certain relatively slow, *tonic* skeletal muscles, particularly in amphibia. The German term *Felderstruktur* has been adopted to describe this pattern of organization of the myofilaments, and the term *Fibrillenstruktur* is applied to the pattern of separate myofibrils that is typical of fast, *twitch* muscles.

The large mitochondria of cardiac muscle have very numerous closely spaced cristae that often exhibit a periodic angulation of their membranes, giving them a zig-zag configuration. As a rule the mitochondria are about the length of one sarcomere ($2.5\ \mu$) but may occasionally be 7 or $8\ \mu$ long. Spherical lipid droplets are often located between the ends of the mitochondria (Fig. 11-34). Glycogen occurs in the form of 300 to 400 Å dense granules crowded into the interstices among the mitochondria. The bulk of the glycogen is located

A

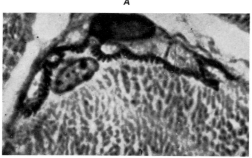

B

Figure 11-28. Photomicrograph of motor end plates on the intercostal muscle of the hedgehog, stained by the acetylthiocholine method for cholinesterase. *A,* Cut perpendicular to the long axis of the muscle fiber; the synaptic grooves or gutters of the subneural apparatus are visible. × 3300. *B,* The branching pattern of the motor end plate in surface view. × 1500. (Courtesy of R. Couteaux.)

in the interfibrillar sarcoplasm, but particles may also be found aligned in rows between the myofilaments (Fig. 11-35). They are particularly numerous in the I band and occur more sparsely in the H band. Both the glycogen and the lipid may be used as energy sources for the contractile activity of the myocardium.

THE T SYSTEM AND THE SARCOPLASMIC RETICULUM. The tubular invaginations of the sarcolemma that comprise the T system of cardiac muscle are larger than the corresponding intermediate element of the triads in skeletal muscle. These tubules, representing inward extensions of the extracellular space, are located at the level of the Z lines instead of at the A-I junction and penetrate to the center of the muscle fiber (compare Figs. 11-20 and 11-36). They are lined by a protein-polysaccharide boundary layer (external lamina) continuous with the layer that coats the sarcolemma (Fig. 11-37). Apparently no point in a cardiac muscle fiber is more than 2 to 3 μ from the extracellular space, either at the outer sur-

face of the fiber or in one of the transverse tubular invaginations. In addition to playing a role in the coupling of excitation to contraction, these channels no doubt provide important additional surface for the exchange of metabolites between cardiac muscle and the extracellular space.

The sarcoplasmic reticulum is not as highly developed as in skeletal muscle. It consists of a simple plexiform arrangement of

A

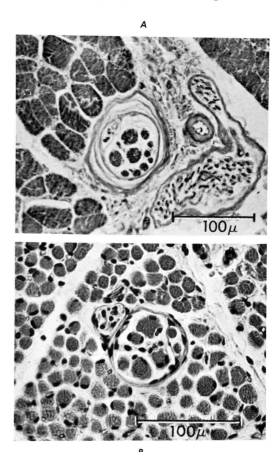

B

Figure 11-29. *A,* Photomicrograph of a muscle spindle in the lumbrical muscle of a human hand. The equator of the spindle is seen with its laminated capsule and large periaxial space. There are nine intrafusal muscle fibers; three of these are nuclear bag fibers. The other six small muscle fibers, lying in a group, are nuclear chain fibers. A blood vessel and several nerves are also seen. Transverse section. Holmes' silver method. *B,* Muscle spindle in human extrinsic eye muscle. Seven of the muscle fibers are surrounded by a thin capsule and there is a small nerve trunk attached. The muscle spindles are usually smaller than those in the limb muscles and have no nuclear bag fibers in man. Transverse section. Hematoxylin and eosin. (Both photomicrographs courtesy of S. Cooper.)

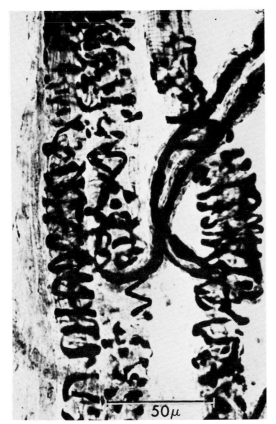

Figure 11-30. Primary nerve ending of a muscle spindle in a cat's plantaris muscle. Two branches of an afferent nerve fiber supply the ending, consisting of two large spirals around the muscle fibers at their nuclear bag regions. Teased gold chloride preparation. (Courtesy of S. Cooper.)

tubular elements occupying slender clefts within the mass of myofilaments. There are no continuous transverse elements of the reticulum itself comparable to the terminal cisternae of the triads in skeletal muscle. Instead small terminal expansions of the reticulum here and there are closely applied to the membrane of the T tubes (Fig. 11-37). Similar contacts are made between small flattened expansions of the reticulum and the sarcolemma at the outer surface of the fiber. The total surface area of the many small sites of apposition of the reticulum to the sarcolemma of cardiac muscle is quite great but would seem to be considerably smaller than the area of contact between the terminal cisternae and intermediate elements of the triads in skeletal muscle. It is noteworthy, too, that the T tubules in cardiac muscle occur only over the Z lines at the ends of

the sarcomeres, whereas in mammalian skeletal muscle there are two triads located at the A-I junctions of each sarcomere. The functional significance of this difference in location of the T system is not fully understood.

THE INTERCALATED DISKS.   On the transverse portions of the intercalated disks, the opposing ends of the cardiac muscle cells have a deeply sculptured surface (Fig. 11-38). A complex pattern of ridges and papillary projections on each cell fit into corresponding grooves and pits in the other cell to form an elaborately interdigitated junction (Figs. 11-38, 11-39, and 11-40). The entire junctional surface of both cells is specialized in various ways for maintaining cell to cell cohesion, and one can distinguish areas that are similar in their fine structure to the *macula adherens* (desmosome), *zonula adherens,* and *zonula occludens* of epithelial

Figure 11-31. Longitudinal section of human cardiac muscle, showing intercalated disks. Sublimate fixation; stained in thiazin red and toluidine blue. × about 450. (Slightly modified from H. Heidenhain.)

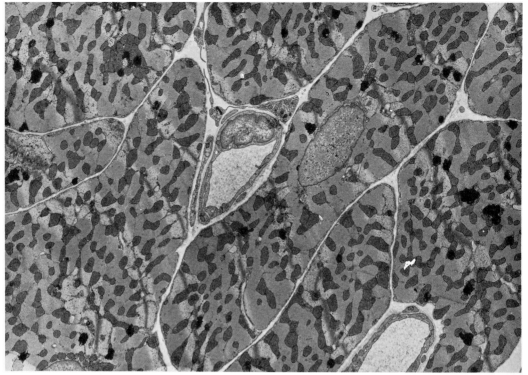

Figure 11-32. Low power electron micrograph of a cross section of cardiac muscle. Notice the central location of the nucleus in one of the fibers and the relatively large proportion of the cross sectional area that is occupied by the mitochondria. The black spots are lipid droplets in the sarcoplasm. Two capillaries are also included in this field. Cat papillary muscle. × 4500.

junctions (see p. 86). However, in the mosaic of different types of surface specialization that comprise the intercalated disk, only the *maculae adherents* or desmosomes are typical with respect to their shape. The others are not beltlike, as implied by the term *zonula*, but are moderately extensive areas of irregular and variable outline. Therefore, more appropriately descriptive terms would be *fascia adherens* and *macula* or *fascia occludens*, depending upon their area.

In longitudinal sections, the opposing cell membranes at the intercalated disk can be identified as two parallel dense lines that follow a sinuous course separated for the most part by a 200 Å intercellular cleft. At desmosomes, the inner leaf of each of the opposing unit membranes is reinforced by a thin layer in which the myofilaments of the adjacent I bands terminate. At irregular intervals along the transverse portion of the disk there are small tight junctions or maculae occludentes, where the outer layers of the opposing membranes appear to have fused, obliterating the intercellular gap. There is no fibrous layer or condensation of the adjacent sarcoplasm associated with these close junctions.

In addition to the small maculae occludentes that occur here and there in the transverse portions of the intercalated disks, there are more extensive areas of close membrane contact, *fasciae occludentes*, or the longitudinal portions of the steplike cell to cell junctions where overlapping processes of successive cells are joined side to side (Fig. 11-40). Considerable emphasis is placed upon these junctional specializations where the intercellular space is obliterated because it is believed that they are areas of low electrical resistance that permit the rapid spread of excitation from cell to cell throughout the heart and thus enable the myocardium to behave as though it were a syncytium. The other specializations of the transverse portions of the intercalated disks, where the membranes are not in such close apposition, evidently have a mechanical significance, being mainly concerned with maintaining cell to cell cohesion and transmitting the pull of one contractile unit to the next along the axis of the muscle fibers.

Our understanding of the nature of the forces that bind cells together is still very incomplete, but it is known that calcium ions play an important role. If the beating, isolated heart of an experimental animal is perfused for some time with a calcium free medium, the heart will soon cease beating. If it is then fixed and examined in thin sections, the individual cells of the muscle fibers are found to have come apart at the intercalated disks (Fig. 11-41*A* and *B*). At high magnification it can be ascertained that the membranes, for the most part, are intact and separation has taken place by opening up of the intercellular space. But at the close junctions where the membranes are apparently in intimate apposition the two elements are unable to separate in calcium-free medium, and one or the other of the cells is denuded of its membrane when the ends of the cells are pulled apart in the agonal contractions of the muscle.

SPECIALIZED CONDUCTING TISSUE OF THE HEART. In addition to those cells of the myocardium whose primary function is contraction, there is a specialized system made up of modified muscle cells whose function is to generate the stimulus for the heart beat and to conduct the impulse to the various parts of the myocardium in such a way as to ensure the contraction of the atria and ventricles in the proper succession so that the heart acts as an effective pump. This system consists of the *sinoatrial node* (node of Keith and Flack), the *atrioventricular node* (node of Tarawa) and the *atrioventricular bundle* (bundle of His). The sinoatrial node is located beneath the epicardium at the junction of the superior vena cava and the right atrium. The atrioventricular node is found beneath the endocardium in the lower part of the interatrial septum between the attachment of the septal leaf of the tricuspid valve and the opening of the coronary sinus. The common atrioventricular bundle originates from the anterior portion of the node and

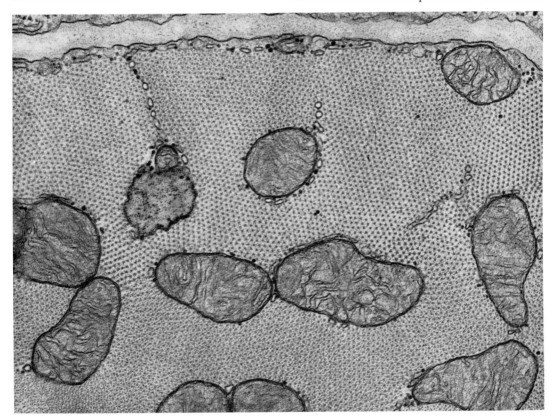

Figure 11-33. Electron micrograph of a small peripheral area of a cardiac muscle fiber in cross section. The cut ends of the myofilaments, seen here, are not associated in discrete myofibrils with clearly defined limits, but instead form a more or less continuous field interrupted by mitochondria. × 44,000.

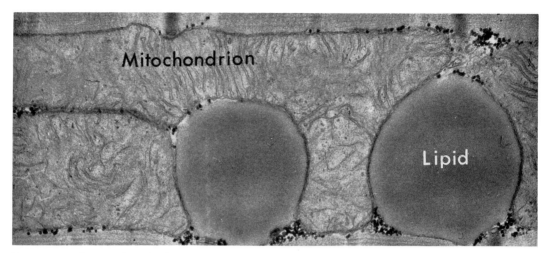

Figure 11-34. Between the ends of the mitochondria that occupy the narrow clefts among the myofilaments are numerous lipid droplets. These can apparently be utilized as an energy source. Cat papillary muscle. × 35,000.

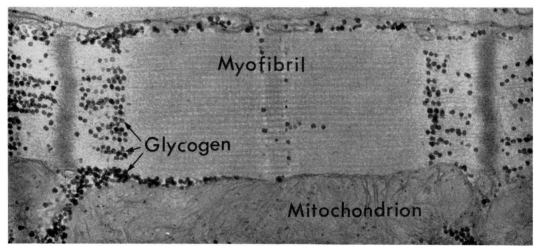

Figure 11-35. Glycogen is abundant in the interfibrillar sarcoplasm of cardiac muscle, where it occurs as small dense granules of uniform size. As shown in this electron micrograph it also may be found between the myofilaments, particularly in the I band region and occasionally in the H band. Cat right ventricular papillary muscle. × 51,000.

Myofibrils

Sarcolemma

Contact of
reticulum with
T-tubules

Transverse tubule

Sarcoplasmic
reticulum

Mitochondrion

Mitochondrion

T-tubule

T-tubule
(sarcolemmal
invagination)

colardK

Contact of reticulum
with T-tubule

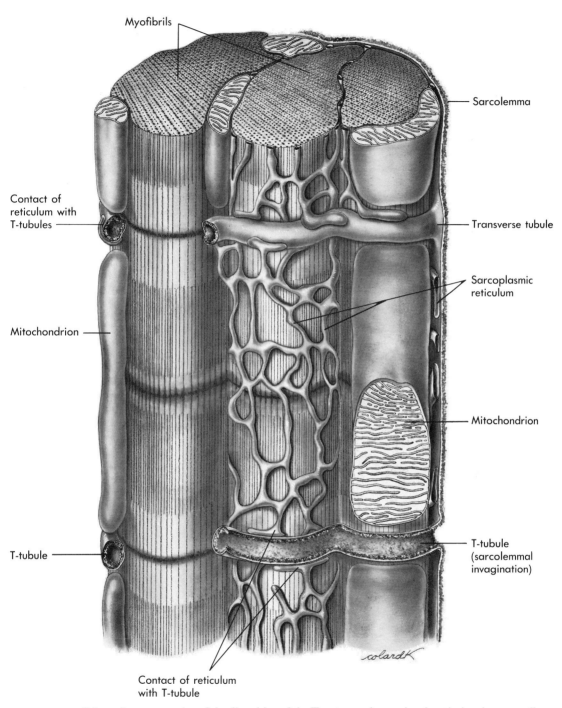

Figure 11-36. Schematic representation of the disposition of the T system and sarcoplasmic reticulum in mammalian cardiac muscle. The transverse tubules are much larger than those of skeletal muscle. The relatively simple sarcoplasmic reticulum has no terminal cisternae and therefore no triads. Instead, small expansions of its tubules end in close apposition to the sarcolemma, either at the surface of the fiber or its inward extension in the T tubules. (After D. W. Fawcett and S. McNutt. Drawing by Sylvia Colard Keene.)

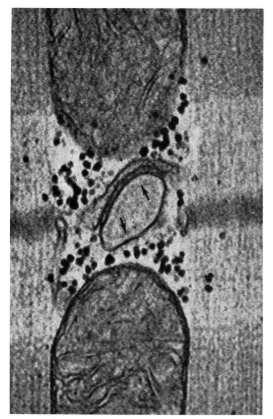

Figure 11-37. Longitudinal section of a small area of a cardiac muscle fiber illustrating a T tubule cut transversely and a tubule of the reticulum in close apposition to it. The T tubule is lined with a layer of protein-polysaccharide (at arrows) like that coating the sarcolemma at the surface of the fiber. The dense granules in the neighboring sarcoplasm are glycogen. × 70,000.

ations. In the mammal no connection between the sinoatrial node and the atrioventricular node via specialized conduction tissue has yet been convincingly demonstrated. The nodal fibers appear to be continuous with ordinary atrial muscle fibers. The node is richly innervated by both the sympathetic and parasympathetic divisions of the autonomic nervous system. Peripheral ganglia of the parasympathetic division are closely associated with the nodal tissue.

In cardiac muscle, which is characterized by the ability to beat rhythmically without nervous or other external stimuli, the cells with the most rapid inherent rhythm establish the rate of beating of the rest of the myocardium. In warm-blooded animals the fibers of the sinoatrial node have the most rapid rhythm, and this node is therefore referred to as the "pacemaker" of the heart. The evidence for this resides in the fact that the electrical events associated with each beat begin at the sinoatrial node and travel from there over the atria. Warming or cooling the node increases or decreases, respectively, the rate of the heart beat. Although the heart will normally beat at a rate determined by the inherent rhythm of its pacemaker, this rate can be modified by the

enters the fibrous portion of the interventricular septum, where it soon divides into right and left bundles that are ultimately distributed to the right and left ventricles. Each of these bundles or trunks ramifies beneath the endocardium of its respective chamber to form an extensive plexus, from which fine fibers penetrate the myocardium to come into intimate contact with the ordinary contractile fibers.

The specialized cells of the nodal tissue are distinctly smaller than ordinary cardiac muscle fibers and are arranged in a network embedded in an abundant and rather dense connective tissue. In sections, the slender fusiform nodal cells coursing in various directions among the collagen bundles may be difficult to distinguish from the associated fibroblasts, but careful examination reveals their cross stri-

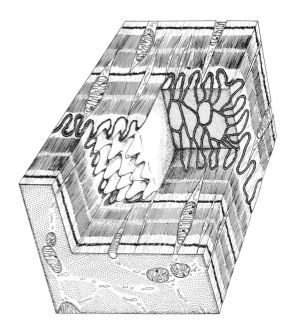

Figure 11-38. Diagrammatic representation of the relation of heart muscle cells at the intercalated disk. (From J. Marshall, *in* Bard's Medical Physiology, C. V. Mosby Co., 1961. Redrawn and slightly modified from Poche and Lindner.)

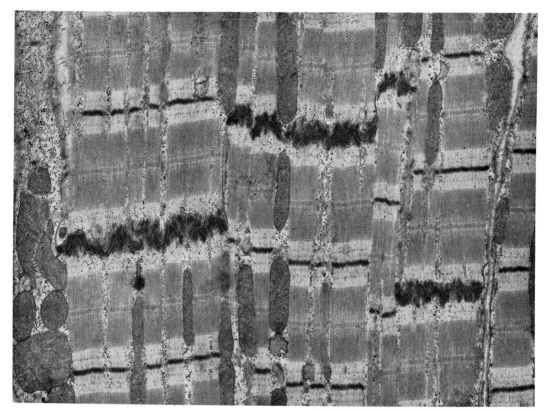

Figure 11-39. Low power electron micrograph of cardiac muscle in longitudinal section, showing a typical steplike intercalated disk. The transverse portions are highly interdigitated and characterized by an abundance of dense material at the insertions of the myofilaments into the end of the cell. The longitudinal portions of the cell boundary are smooth, unspecialized, and difficult to see at this magnification. × 12,000.

autonomic nervous system. Parasympathetic (vagal) stimulation brings about a slowing of the heart and sympathetic stimulation accelerates it.

The fibers of the atrioventricular node are small, like those of the sinoatrial node. The fibers of the atrioventricular bundle are similar at their origin, but more distally in the right and left bundle branches they become much larger than ordinary cardiac muscle fibers and take on a highly distinctive appearance. These are the so-called *Purkinje fibers* (Fig. 11-42). They have one or two nuclei situated in a clear central mass of sarcoplasm that is rich in mitochondria and glycogen.

The myofibrils are relatively sparse and displaced to the periphery, and they are less consistent in their orientation than are those of ordinary muscle fibers. The Purkinje fibers of ungulates reach very large size, and for this reason these have been more extensively studied than those of other mammals, but they do not seem to differ in any other important respect (Fig. 11-43*A* and *B*). Typical intercalated disks are seldom seen in the conducting tissue. At their ends the Purkinje fibers are said to lose their specific cytological features and to become continuous with the ordinary muscle fibers of the myocardium.

In electron micrographs the cytoplasmic matrix of the Purkinje cells is of relatively low density and contains numerous, randomly oriented mitochondria (Figs. 11-45 and 11-46). The myofilaments do not form a continuous contractile mass but are arranged in separate myofibrils that are relatively few in number. Although their prevailing orientation is parallel to the long axis of the cell, they are very poorly ordered compared to those of ordinary cardiac muscle.

The cells have variable and unusual shapes, one often partially surrounding another or sending a large process into a deep recess in the adjoining cell (Fig. 11-46). As a

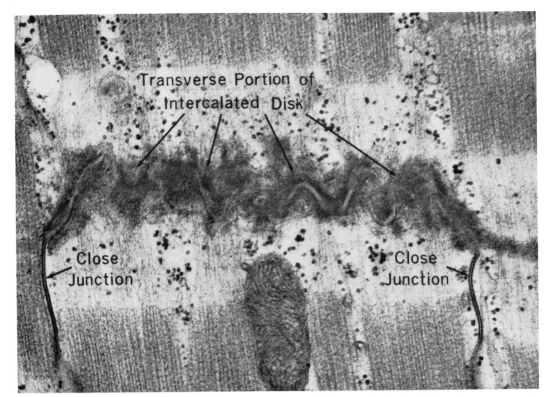

Figure 11-40. Electron micrograph showing an appreciable intercellular space in the interdigitated transverse portion of the intercalated disk. In the longitudinal portion at either side the intercellular space is obliterated and the membranes are in apposition. Such close junctions are believed to be low resistance connections between the cells of the myocardium. × 38,000.

consequence of their irregular shape the cells are in extensive contact with one another. No typical intercalated disks are found, but numerous *maculae adherentes* (*desmosomes*) are distributed at irregular intervals along the cell boundaries. There are also areas of closer apposition corresponding to the *close junctions* or *fasciae occludentes* of ordinary cardiac muscle. Surprisingly, these do not appear to be as numerous or as extensive as in the unspecialized fibers of the myocardium, and the morphological basis for the more rapid conduction in the atrioventricular bundle is not evident. Disease of the conduction system results in asynchrony in the beating of the ventricles or disorders in the timing of the contraction of the atria and ventricles that result in impaired efficiency of the heart.

NERVES TO THE MYOCARDIUM. Although the initiation of the heart beat is not dependent upon the nervous system, the heart is richly innervated. The parasympathetic (vagus) and sympathetic divisions of the autonomic nervous system form extensive plexuses at the base of the heart. Ganglion cells and numerous nerve fibers have been described in the wall of the right atrium, particularly in the region of the sinoatrial and atrioventricular nodes. Stimulation of the vagus slows the heart, and release of norepinephrine from sympathetic nerve endings accelerates it. It is commonly assumed that the autonomic nervous system acts indirectly upon the myocardium by modifying the inherent rhythm of the pacemaker. This view is supported by physiological experiment and by light and electron microscopic observations establishing the presence of large numbers of unmyelinated nerve fibers close to the specialized cells of the nodal and conduction systems. (Fig. 11-45). In addition, however, a surprising number of unmyelinated fibers are also found in close relation to the ordinary cardiac fibers of the atrium and ventricles. Although it is difficult to determine to which division of the autonomic nervous system these belong, some at least contain granulated vesicles and therefore appear to be sympathetic. Release of catecholamine from these endings apparently exerts a direct effect upon the cadiac muscle.

Neither in ordinary cardiac muscle nor in the conduction tissue do the nerve fibers form specialized endings comparable to the myoneural junctions of skeletal muscle. Slender axons merely pass near the surface of the cardiac muscle cells. That these are functional endings and not merely passing axons is inferred from the fact that their axoplasm often contains large numbers of small vesicles identical to those found at other nerve endings and at synapses in the central nervous system.

HISTOGENESIS OF MUSCULAR TISSUE

Smooth Muscular Tissue. Smooth muscle cells arise from the mesenchyme. In those places where a layer of smooth muscle

will later develop, the mesenchymal cells begin to stretch out, the nuclei become elongated, and myofilaments appear in the cytoplasm. In blood vessels, which at first consist only of endothelium, mesenchyme cells become arranged at regular intervals along the outside of the tube. They stretch out transversely, multiply by mitosis, and produce myofilaments within their cytoplasm. Then these *myoblasts* come in contact with one another laterally and a continuous layer of smooth muscle is produced.

The reticular fibers between the muscle cells are probably produced by the same cells —the developing smooth muscle cells functioning as both myoblasts and fibroblasts.

It is claimed that some of the new smooth muscle cells that develop in the uterus during pregnancy arise from the undifferentiated connective tissue cells in this tissue. In a virgin

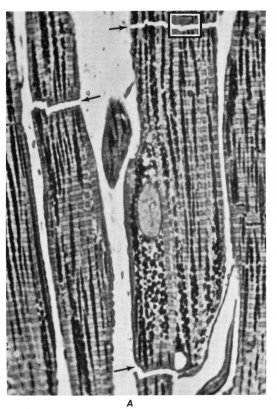
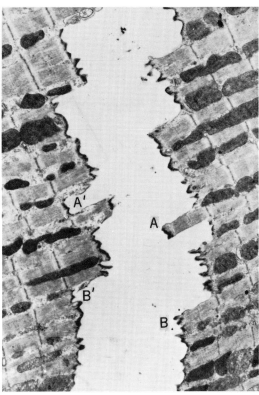

A   B

Figure 11-41. *A,* Photomicrograph of cardiac muscle from an isolated heart that had been perfused with calcium free Krebs' solution until it stopped beating. Notice that the muscle cells have come apart at the intercalated disks (see at arrows). × 1100. *B,* Electron micrograph of an area such as that enclosed in the rectangle at the top of *A,* showing the separated ends of two cardiac muscle cells. Notice the close conformation of the two surfaces: A fits into A′, B into B′, etc. The separation occurs between the membranes except at the close junctions; there, the membrane pulls off one of the cells. × 5000. (Micrographs courtesy of A. Muir.)

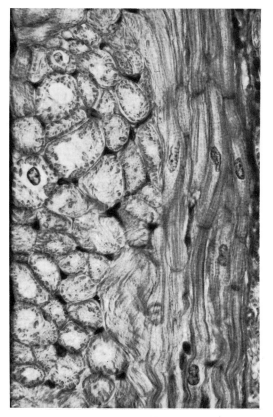

Figure 11-42. Photomicrograph of the specialized conduction tissue of the human atrioventricular bundle. The large Purkinje fibers seen in cross section at the left of the figure can be compared with the smaller unspecialized heart muscle cut longitudinally at the right side of the figure. × 650.

rabbit, after injection of the female sex hormone, there is mitotic proliferation of the smooth muscle cells of the uterus. The smooth muscle elements (myoepithelial cells) in certain glands arise from the same epithelium as the glandular elements themselves.

STRIATED MUSCULAR TISSUE. The striated muscular tissue arises in vertebrates from the mesoderm and in particular from its somites, except in the head, where it develops directly from mesenchyme. Those cells that give rise to the muscle tissue are called *myoblasts.* Within the myotome they are regular and cylindrical, but soon they become spindle-shaped and arrange themselves into parallel bundles. At the same time they multiply rapidly by mitosis. Within the myoblasts, myofibrils appear and gradually develop the characteristic cross striations.

There are several explanations of how the

large, multinucleated, skeletal muscle fibers arise from the myoblasts: (1) Each muscular fiber is a syncytium resulting from fusion of many separate cells. (2) Each myoblast grows markedly in length, and the rapid multiplication of the nuclei by mitosis is not accompanied by division of cytoplasm, so that a multinuclear cell is produced. (3) Both methods of development occur. General agreement on this question has not been reached, but electron microscope studies of the developing myotomes of amphibian larvae strongly favor the first of these three alternatives. The myoblasts have large nuclei with prominent nucleoli and abundant cytoplasm rich in ribosomes and containing scattered myofilaments. The endoplasmic reticulum is poorly developed. These cells can be found in the process of fusing with each other or with muscle fibers in more advanced stages of differentiation. As development progresses, the thick and thin filaments become associated to form myofilaments. Thereafter, new filaments are added to the lateral surfaces and distal ends of existing myofibrils (Hay).

In the further development of the muscular tissue the separate fibers increase in thickness and length, and their number increases through transformation of new myoblasts. The increase in number of fibers in the sartorius muscle stops when the human fetus is 130 to 170 mm. long. The future growth of the muscle depends only on the continued increase in the size of the fibers already present.

The nuclei are believed by some investigators to increase in number by mitosis during the gradual growth of the muscle fiber. In mammals the nuclei at first are in the center and the fibrils occupy the periphery of the fiber. In later stages the nuclei move toward the periphery, so that the central parts become occupied by myofibrils.

Contractility begins in the embryonic muscular elements about the time or shortly before the first myofibrils arise in their protoplasm. This contractility, at first slight and slow, gradually increases with the increase in number of myofibrils and their arrangement in bundles. The appearance of voluntary movements is connected with the development of the nervous motor tracts that lead from the spinal cord to the myotomes.

CARDIAC MUSCULAR TISSUE. Cardiac muscle in the embryo forms from the splanchnopleure adjoining the endothelium of the heart primordium. At first a layer of loosely connected cuboidal cells, this part of the splanchnopleure becomes stratified. The processes of its star-shaped cells adhere to one another by special desmosome-like attachments that later develop into intercalated disks as the processes shorten and thicken and the forcefulness of contraction increases. The cells multiply energetically by mitosis. The cytoplasm contains many elongated mitochondria, often in groups. Electron micrographic study of embryonic cardiac muscle shows fine bundles of myofilaments developing in the myoblasts; the first cross striations are Z bands.

The *Purkinje fibers* develop from the same primary stellate reticulum as the cardiac muscle fibers. They soon become distinguishable from the remaining myocardium. A few myofibrils are irregularly distributed at their periphery.

Toward the end of the embryonic period,

cardiac muscular tissue is well differentiated. It is clear that the cellular units increase at first by mitosis, but the manner in which the fibers of the myocardium increase in number is poorly understood.

REGENERATION OF MUSCULAR TISSUE

SMOOTH MUSCLE. In the vicinity of injured regions in the walls of the intestine or stomach, mitosis has been observed in the smooth muscle cells. But this capacity for regeneration is small, and great defects in smooth muscle heal by scar formation. Whether smooth muscle cells in the adult organism may be formed anew from fibroblasts has not been established; it is practically certain that they can develop from the perivascular mesenchymal cells.

STRIATED MUSCLE. During intense activity, the skeletal muscles increase in volume by enlargement of the existing fibers through

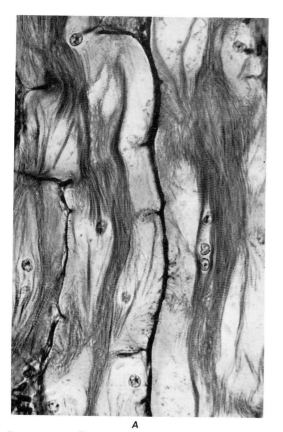

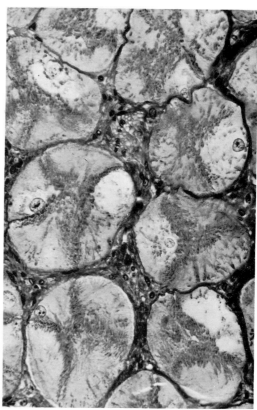

A B

Figure 11-43. Photomicrographs of the very large Purkinje fibers in the moderator band of the bovine heart. In *A* the fibers are cut longitudinally and in *B* transversely. In both, it is evident that the myofibrils occupy only a small part of the sarcoplasm. The large clear areas are rich in glycogen. × 600.

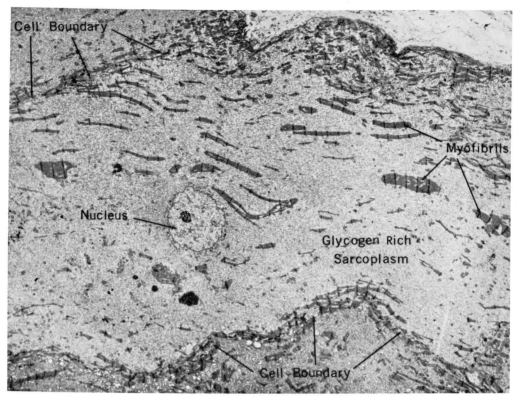

Figure 11-44. Electron micrograph of a Purkinje fiber from a steer heart. Myofibrils in these modified muscle cells are widely scattered in an abundant sarcoplasm rich in glycogen. × 1600. (After J. Rhodin; labeling added.)

an increase in the amount of sarcoplasm and not in the number of fibrils.

The regenerative capacity of the striated muscular tissue of higher vertebrates does not always lead to the formation of functioning fibers. After destruction of muscle fibers, regeneration always starts from existing fibers. The most successful regeneration takes place when the nuclei with the surrounding sarcoplasm remain alive. These become separate cells called *myoblasts.* The ends of the fibers become thicker and grow out toward the place of injury as muscular buds. The sarcoblasts hypertrophy, multiply, digest the degenerating fibers, and fuse in groups. Inside the reticulum of the old fibers they form new fibers in which striated fibrils appear. In such a regenerative process in vitally stained animals, the myoblasts can be easily distinguished from the macrophages that have penetrated the fiber. A large defect in the muscular tissue is replaced by a connective tissue scar. Connection with motor nerve fibers is necessary for the maintenance of the normal structure of

skeletal muscle as well as for its successful regeneration.

CARDIAC MUSCLE. In various pathological conditions in the adult organism, an increase in volume of the cardiac muscle may take place. This probably depends on the increase in thickness and length of the existing fibers. The regenerative capacity of cardiac muscle tissue is insignificant and healing takes place by the formation of scar tissue.

REFERENCES

SMOOTH MUSCLE

Bozler, E.: Smooth muscle. *In* Rodahl, K., and S. M. Horvath, eds.: Muscle as a Tissue. New York, McGraw-Hill Book Co., 1962, p. 20.

Choi, J. K.: Fine structure of smooth muscle of chicken gizzard. Proc. 5th Internat. Congr. Electron Microscopy. New York, Academic Press, 1962.

Csapo, A.: Molecular structure and function of smooth muscle. *In* Bourne, G. H., ed.: Structure and Function of Muscle. New York, Academic Press, 1960, Vol. I, p. 229.

Dewey, M. M., and L. Barr: Intercellular connection between smooth muscle cells: The nexus. Science *137*:670, 1962.

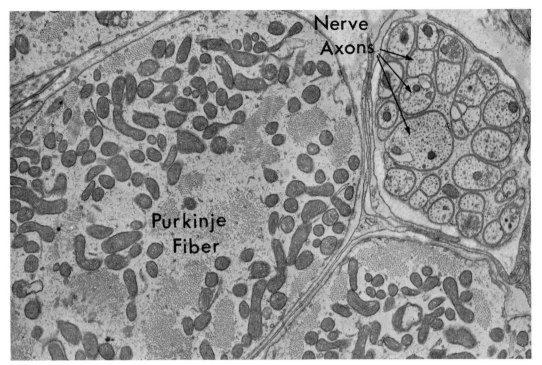

Figure 11-45. Electron micrograph of adjacent areas of two Purkinje fibers and an accompanying nerve, in the atrioventricular bundle of the cat heart. The mitochondria are abundant and pleomorphic; the loosely organized myofilaments occur only in scattered bundles. × 12,000.

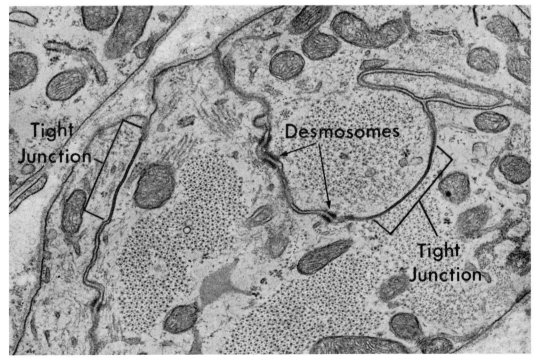

Figure 11-46. Electron micrograph of the cell junctions in the atrioventricular bundle. The cells of the conduction tissue are irregular in shape and have an extensive area of cell to cell apposition, on which are numerous desmosomes and occasional close junctions (fasciae occludentes). × 22,000. (Courtesy of D. Feldman.)

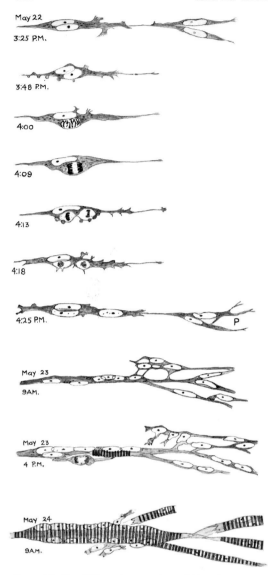

Figure 11-47. Differentiation of myoblasts into cross-striated muscle fibers as seen in living regenerating zone, following removal of the tip of a tadpole's tail. One of a pair of closely associated myoblasts was watched throughout its nuclear division. The next day many nuclei were present. At 4 P.M., the first faint cross striations were visible. The following day many cross striations were in evidence in all fibers. (Redrawn after Speidel.)

Hanson, J.: Structure of the smooth muscle fibres in the body wall of the earthworm. J. Biophys. & Biochem. Cytol., *3:*111, 1957.

Harman, J. W., M. T. O'Hegarty, and C. K. Byrnes: The ultrastructure of human smooth muscle. I. Studies of cell surface and connections in normal and achalasic esophageal smooth muscle. Exp. & Mol. Path., *1:*204, 1962.

Lane, B. P.: Alterations in cytological detail of intestinal smooth muscle cells in various stages of contraction. J. Cell Biol., *27:*199, 1965.

Lane, B. P., and J. A. G. Rhodin: Cellular interrelationships and electrical activity in two types of smooth muscle. J. Ultrastruct. Res., *10:*470, 1964.

Lane, B. P., and J. A. G. Rhodin: Fine structure of the lamina muscularis mucosae. J. Ultrastruct. Res., *10:*489, 1964.

Needham, D. M., and C. F. Shoenberg: Proteins of the contractile mechanism of mammalian smooth muscle and their possible location in the cell. Proc. Roy. Soc. Lond., Series B, *160:*517, 1964.

Prosser, C. L., J. Burnstock, and J. Rahn: Conduction in smooth muscle. Comparative structural properties. Am. J. Physiol., *199:*545, 1960.

Rhodin, J. A. G.: Fine structure of vascular walls in mammals with special reference to smooth muscle component. Physiol. Rev., *42:*49, 1962.

CARDIAC MUSCLE

Bompiani, G. D., Ch. Rouiller, and P. Y. Hatt: Le tissu de conduction du coeur chez le rat étudé au microscope electronique. Arch. Mal. Coeur des Vais, *52:*1257, 1959.

Fawcett, D. W., and C. C. Selby: Observations on the fine structure of the turtle atrium. J. Biophys. & Biochem. Cytol., *4:*63, 1958.

Hirsch, E. F., and A. M. Borghard-Erdle: The innervation of the heart. Arch. Path., *72:*100, 1962.

Jamieson, J. D., and G. E. Palade: Specific granules in atrial muscle cells. J. Cell Biol., *23:*151, 1964.

Karrer, H. E.: The striated musculature of blood vessels. II. Cell interconnections and cell surface. J. Biophys. & Biochem. Cytol., *8:*135, 1960.

Muir, A. R.: Electron microscope study of the embryology of the intercalated disc in the heart of the rabbit. J. Biophys. & Biochem. Cytol., *3:*193, 1957.

Muir, A. R.: Further observations on the cellular structure of cardiac muscle. Journal of Anatomy (London). Proc. Anat. Soc. Gt. Brit. and Ireland, 1963, p. 642.

Nelson, D. A., and E. S. Benson: On the structural continuities of the transverse tubular system of rabbit and human myocardial cells. J. Cell Biol., *16:*297, 1963.

Rhodin, J. A., P. Missier, and L. C. Reid: The structure of the specialized impulse-conducting system of the steer heart. Circulation, *24:*349, 1961.

Rostgaard, J., and O. Behnke: Fine structural localization of adenine nucleoside phosphatase activity in the sarcoplasmic reticulum and T-system of the rat myocardium. J. Ultrastruct. Res., *12:*579, 1965.

Simpson, F. O., and S. J. Oertelis: Relationship of the sarcoplasmic reticulum to the sarcolemma in sheep cardiac muscle. Nature, *189:*758, 1961.

Sjostrand, F. S., E. Andersson-Cedergren, and M. M. Dewey: The ultrastructure of the intercalated discs of frog, mouse, and guinea pig cardiac muscle. J. Ultrastruct. Res., *1:*271, 1958.

Stenger, R. J., and D. Spiro: The ultrastructure of mammalian cardiac muscle. J. Biophys. & Biochem. Cytol., *9:*325, 1961.

Truex, R. C.: Comparative anatomy and functional considerations of the cardiac conduction system. *In* de Carvalho, A. P., de Mello, W. C., and Hoffman, B. F., eds.: The Specialized Tissues of the Heart. Amsterdam, Elsevier Publishing Co., 1961, p. 22.

Truex, R. C., and W. M. Copenhaver: Histology of the moderator band in man and other mammals, with special reference to the conduction system. Am. J. Anat., *80:*173, 1947.

Truex, R. C., and M. A. Smythe: Recent observations on the human cardiac conduction system with special considerations of the atrioventricular node and bundle. *In* Electrophysiology of the Heart. New York, Pergamon Press, 1964, p. 177.

SKELETAL MUSCLE

Andersson-Cedergren, E.: Ultrastructure of motor end plate and sarcoplasmic components of mouse skeletal muscle fiber as revealed by three dimensional reconstructions from serial sections. J. Ultrastruct. Res., Suppl. 1, 1959, p. 1.

Barker, D.: The innervation of the muscle spindle. Quart. J. Micr. Sci., *89:*143, 1948.

Bennett, H. S.: Modern concepts of structure of striated muscle. Am. J. Phys. Med., *34:*46, 1955.

Bennett, H. S.: The structure of striated muscle as seen by the electron microscope. *In* Bourne, G. H., ed.: Structure and Function of Muscle. New York, Academic Press, 1960, Vol. I, p. 137.

Bourne, G. H., ed.: The Structure and Function of Muscle. 3 Vols. New York, Academic Press, 1960.

Constantin, L. L., C. Franzini-Armstrong, and R. J. Podolsky: Localization of calcium accumulating structures in striated muscle. Science, *147:*158, 1965.

Cooper, S.: Muscle spindles and other muscle receptors. *In* Bourne, G. H., ed.: Structure and Function of Muscle. New York, Academic Press, 1960, Vol. I, p. 381.

Couteaux, R.: Motor end plate structure. *In* Bourne, G. H., ed.: Structure and Function of Muscle. New York, Academic Press, 1960, Vol. I, p. 337.

Davies, R. E.: A molecular theory of muscle contraction: Calcium dependent contractions with H bond formation plus ATP-dependent extensions of part of the myosin-actin cross-bridges. Nature, *199:*1068, 1963.

Denny-Brown, D. E.: The histological features of striped muscle in relation to its functional activity. Proc. Roy. Soc. Lond., Series B, *104:*371, 1929.

Ebashi, S., and F. Lipmann: Adenosine triphosphate-linked concentration of calcium ions in a particulate fraction of rabbit muscle. J. Cell Biol., *14:*502, 1962.

Endo, M.: Entry of a dye into the sarcotubular system of muscle. Nature, *202:*1115, 1964.

Franzini-Armstrong, C.: Sarcolemmal invaginations and the T-system in skeletal muscle fibers. J. Cell Biol., *19:*24A, 1963.

Franzini-Armstrong, C., and K. R. Porter: The Z disc of skeletal muscle. Zeitschr. f. Zellforsch., *61:*661, 1964.

Hanson, J., and H. E. Huxley: The structural basis of contraction in striated muscle. *In* Fibrous Proteins and Their Biological Significance. Symposia of the Society of Experimental Biology, No. IX. New York, Academic Press, 1955, p. 228.

Hanson, J., and L. Lowy: The structure of actin filaments and the origin of the axial periodicity in the I-substance of vertebrate striated muscle. Proc. Roy. Soc. Lond., Series B, *160:*449, 1964.

Hanson, J., and L. Lowy: Molecular basis of contractility in muscle. Brit. Med. Bull., *21:*264, 1965.

Hasselback, W.: Relaxation and the sarcotubular calcium pump. Federation Proc., *23:*909, 1964.

Hay, E. D.: The fine structure of differentiating muscle in salamander tail. Zeitschr. f. Zellforsch., *59:*6, 1963.

Holtzer, H., J. M. Marshall, Jr., and H. Finck: An analysis of myogenesis by the use of fluorescent antimyosin. J. Biophys. & Biochem. Cytol., *3:*705, 1957.

Huxley, A. F., and R. E. Taylor: Local activation of striated muscle fibers. J. Physiol. (London), *144:*426, 1958.

Huxley, H. E.: Muscle cells. *In* Brachet, J., and A. E. Mirsky, eds.: The Cell; Biochemistry, Physiology, Morphology. New York, Academic Press, 1960, Vol. 4, p. 365.

Huxley, H. E.: Electron microscopic studies on the structure of natural and synthetic protein filaments from striated muscle. J. Mol. Biol., *7:*281, 1963.

Huxley, H. E.: Evidence for continuity between the central elements of the triads and extracellular space in frog sartorius muscle. Nature, *202:*1067, 1964.

Huxley, H. E., and J. Hanson: The molecular basis of contraction in cross-striated muscles. *In* Bourne, G. H., ed.: Structure and Function of Muscle. New York, Academic Press, 1960, Vol. I, p. 183.

Lockhart, R. D., and W. Brandt: Notes upon length of striated muscle fibre. J. Anat., *72:*470, 1938.

Merrillees, N. C. R.: The fine structure of muscle spindles in the lumbrical muscles of the rat. J. Biophys. & Biochem. Cytol., *7:*725, 1960.

Peachey, L. D.: The sarcoplasmic reticulum and transverse tubules of the frog's sartorius. J. Cell Biol., *25:*209, 1965.

Peachey, L. D., and K. R. Porter: Intracellular impulse conduction in muscle cells. Science, *129:*721, 1959.

Porter, K. R.: The sarcoplasmic reticulum, its recent history and present status. J. Biophys. & Biochem. Cytol., *10:*Suppl. 219, 1961.

Porter, K. R., and G. E. Palade: Studies on the endoplasmic reticulum. III. Its form and distribution in striated muscle cells. J. Biophys. & Biochem. Cytol., *3:*269, 1957.

Smith. D. S.: The structure of insect fibrillar flight muscle. J. Biophys. & Biochem. Cytol., *10:*Suppl. 123, 1961.

Uihara, Y., and K. Hama: Some observations on the fine structure of the frog muscle spindle. I. On the sensory terminals and motor endings of the muscle spindle. J. Electron Microscopy, *14:*34, 1965.

Zacks, S. I.: The Motor Endplate. Philadelphia, W. B. Saunders Co., 1964.

CHAPTER TWELVE

The Nervous Tissue

The nervous system comprises the entire mass of nervous tissue in the body. The essential function of nervous tissue is *communication,* and this depends upon special signaling properties of the nerve cells and their long processes. These properties are based upon two fundamental attributes of protoplasm: the capacity to react to various physical and chemical agents and the ability to transmit the resulting excitation from one locality to another. The first quality is called *irritability* and the second *conductivity.*

In signaling the reception of a stimulus from the external or internal environment, various forms of energy are transduced into electrical energy by a specialized cellular structure, a receptor. Patterns of electrical messages, or nerve impulses, are transmitted from receptors to nervous centers, where they evoke, in other cells, more complex patterns of signals that result in appropriate sensations or motor responses. By these means the organism reacts to the events in the world in which it lives and coordinates the functions of its organs so that the integrity of the body is maintained. In addition, the nervous system provides the structural and chemical basis of conscious experience. It furnishes the mechanism for behavior and its regulation and for the maintenance of the unity of the personality.

The *central nervous system (neuraxis)* consists of the brain and spinal cord and contains the *nerve cells* or *neurons* and a variety of supportive cells called collectively the *neuroglia.* Within the central nervous system, nerve impulses carried to it from all parts of the body over the long processes of the nerve cells, called *axons,* come together and are integrated with other nerve impulses resulting from stimuli coming from outside the body. The *peripheral nervous system* is made up of all nervous tissue outside of the brain and spinal cord and serves to keep the other tissues of the body in communication with the central nervous system. The functions of all parts of the organism are thus integrated by a central clearing house that controls the activity of the individual as a whole.

The sensory, integrative, and motor functions of the nerve cells depend mainly upon their properties of irritability and conductivity. In addition, however, some nerve cells possess secretory capabilities. These extend the influence of those cells by endowing them with some of the properties of the endocrine system, which carries out its integrative function by means of the blood borne chemical agents called *hormones.*

In the evolution of the nervous system of higher organisms, it is believed that certain cells of primitive Metazoa developed to a high degree their fundamental properties of irritability and conductivity, and by virtue of their greater efficiency in responding and signaling gradually constituted a rudimentary nervous system. By further specialization, some of the nerve cells developed the capacity to react to special kinds of exogenous stimuli. These cells, with the corresponding accessory structures distributed throughout the body or near its surface, gave rise to three systems of sensory receptors: the *exteroceptive system,* concerned with receiving impulses from the surface of the body; the *interoceptive system,* responsive to impulses from the internal organs; and the *proprioceptive system,* receiving excitations from the muscles, tendons, and joints.

Other nerve cells became connected with the peripheral *effector organs,* such as the muscles, forming with them *neuromotor* systems. Still other nerve cells, collected in a large central mass, assumed the role of correlators and integrators. These receive and select, combine, distribute, inhibit, or otherwise modify the excitations arising from the receptors and in turn exercise the appropriate influence on the effector organs.

NEURONS

The cells within the nervous system that are primarily involved in carrying out its special function are the *neurons.* Each has a cell body or *soma* consisting of a *nucleus* and the surrounding cytoplasm, often called the *perikaryon.* Typically the cytoplasm is drawn out into several short radiating processes called *dendrites* and into a single long process called the *axis cylinder* or axon (Fig. 12-1). The axon, which may attain a great length, often emits branches or *axon collaterals* along its course and at its terminus may exhibit additional fine ramifications.

The size, shape, and other peculiarities of the cell body of a neuron and the number and mode of branching of its processes are all subject to variation, which results in a great many morphologically distinguishable kinds of nerve cells. It is assumed that functional specializations are correlated with this morphological diversity. The neurons are anatomically and functionally related to other cells by their processes. These are in contact with other nerve cells, or with epithelial, muscular, or glandular cells. At the points of contact between nerve cells, called *synapses,* functional influences are transmitted, usually by chemical mediators, from one cell to another in one direction only (p. 339).

The nervous system is composed of countless neurons that are morphologically and trophically independent but functionally interrelated at synapses. This fundamental generalization is known as the *neuron doctrine.* It is in essence a restatement of the cell theory as it applies to the nervous system. The neuron doctrine implies that the nervous system is entirely cellular; that its cells are distinctive as to morphological type and functional characteristics; and that its cells are not in protoplasmic continuity but are juxtaposed without a significant amount of intervening extracellular substance. Observations with the electron microscope have corroborated these central assumptions of the neuron doctrine and have demonstrated that the nervous system is basically a highly specialized epithelium. In its definitive organization, the nervous system thus reflects its phylogenetic and ontogenetic origin from the ectodermal epithelial layer of the body. In common with other epithelia, nervous tissue exhibits characteristic cell to cell contacts other than synapses.

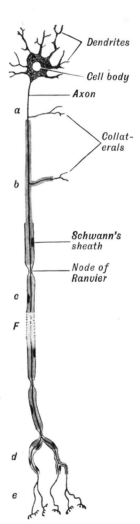

Figure 12-1. Diagram of a peripheral motor neuron (Type I of Golgi). *a,* Naked axon; *b,* axon invested only with myelin; *c,* axon covered with both myelin and Schwann's sheath; *F,* broken lines indicating great extent of the fiber; *d,* telodendria covered only with Schwann's sheath; *e,* the naked axon endings.

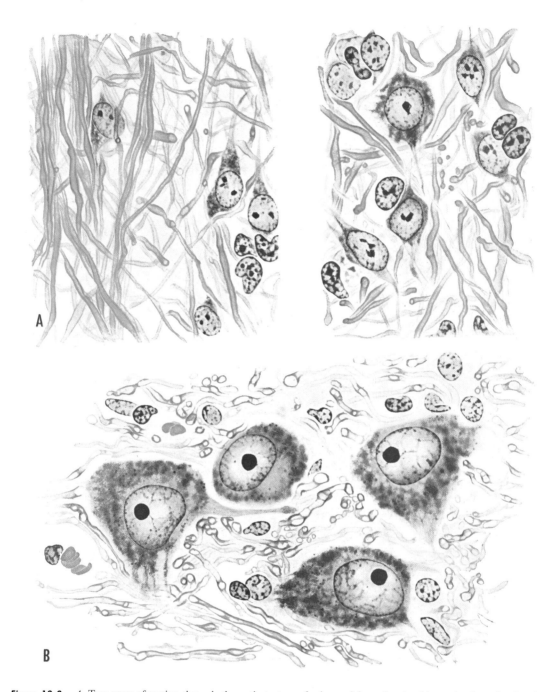

Figure 12-2. *A,* Two areas of section through the optic tectum of a leopard frog, showing blue-stained myelin sheaths and the nerve cell bodies. The small dark nuclei are supporting cells. *B,* Section from pons of man, showing myelin sheaths, nerve cell bodies, and glial cells. *A,* From a frozen section fixed in formalin; *B,* Paraffin section after post-mortem formalin fixation. Klüver and Barrera staining methods for cells and myelin sheaths. × 1100. (Drawn by Esther Bohlman.)

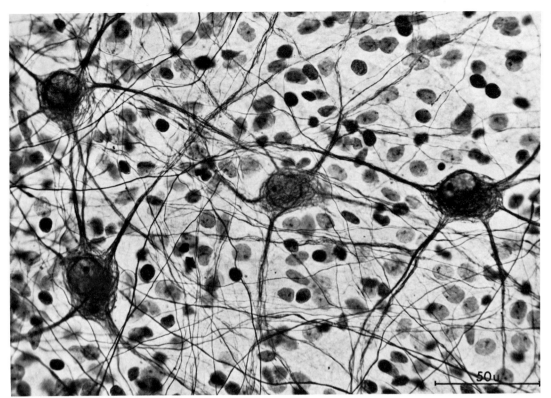

Figure 12-3. In tissue cultures of the nervous system, the three dimensional configuration of the intact neurons can be seen to better advantage than in sections. Shown here are multipolar neurons from the deep nuclei of the rat cerebellum in a 12 day culture. Notice the neurofibrils in the cell bodies. Holmes stain. (From W. Hild, Zeitschr. f. Zellforsch., *69*:155, 1966.)

These are generally described as appositional or junctional complexes and consist of local specializations of the surfaces of adjacent cells. Their probable function is to maintain the position of the nerve cells and to stabilize those spatial relations of their processes that are essential to the signaling function of the nervous system.

The wide variety of neurons and neuroglial components of nervous tissue possess correspondingly varied staining characteristics. Indeed, to study the many cytological features of the neuron alone, several different staining methods must be used. And to achieve a comprehensive view of the organization of nervous tissue with the light microscope, one must synthesize impressions gained from studying tissue prepared with an ensemble of selective staining techniques. On the other hand, electron microscopy has the advantage of presenting in the same preparation a view of the nervous tissue with all its parts visible in their proper spatial relations. This approach suffers,

however, from the serious limitations that only very small areas can be examined and that the exceedingly thin sections used provide little information about the three dimensional configuration of the components. However, the combined use of light and electron microscopy permits the student and investigator to obtain a far more detailed and accurate appraisal of the organization of the nervous system than either method used alone.

The Structure of the Neuron

The nerve cell, or neuron, is usually large and may be quite complex in its shape. The volume of cytoplasm in its processes is often greater than in its perikaryon. The nerve cell body in the central nervous system is generally *multipolar;* that is to say, it has several processes. The outline of the perikaryon is typically angular or polygonal, with a slight concavity of the cytoplasmic surfaces between sites of emergence of the processes at

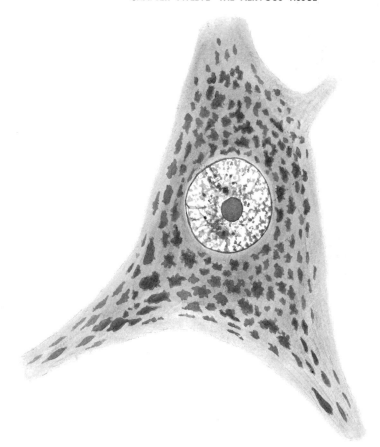

Figure 12-4. Motor cell from the gray substance of the ventral horn of the spinal cord of a cat, showing granular chromophilic substance. Axon hillock at upper right. × 670. (After A. A. Maximow.)

the corners of the cell (Figs. 12-3 and 12-6). The motor neurons throughout the neuraxis and the pyramidal cells of the cerebral cortex are two of many examples of the angular form of nerve cell bodies. The cell bodies in the dorsal root ganglia, on the other hand, are rounded and have only one process projecting from the cell body, and they are therefore said to be *unipolar* (Fig. 12-12). Whatever its shape may be, the neuron has a number of distinctive cytological characteristics.

THE NUCLEUS. The nucleus is large, pale, spherical or slightly ovoid, and usually centrally placed within the perikaryon. In most cases there is a single conspicuous nucleolus, and very fine and uniformly dispersed particles of chromatin. Because of the uniform dispersion of the chromatin, the nuclei of nerve cells, stained with basic dyes, appear rather empty and pale and are commonly described as "vesicular." In smaller

nerve cells the concentration of chromatin may be somewhat greater and the vesicular character of the nucleus less obvious. In man but not in all mammals, the sex chromatin body of females is prominent and located either near the nucleolus or at the periphery of the nucleus. Although neurons usually contain a single nucleus, binucleate cells are sometimes encountered in autonomic ganglia. In electron micrographs, the nuclear envelope and its pores and the fine structure of the nucleolus and karyoplasm are not signficantly different from the corresponding features in other cells. In general, however, little attention has been directed to the fine structure of the nucleus of neurons.

THE PERIKARYON. The cytoplasmic matrix, or *neuroplasm,* of the nerve cell is crowded with filamentous, membranous, and granular organelles arranged more or less concentrically around the nucleus. These organelles as identified by light microscopy are neurofibrils, chromophilic substance or Nissl bodies, Golgi apparatus, mitochondria, a centrosome, and various inclusions. The neuroplasm extends into the cell processes and in the axon is called *axoplasm*. Although any one of the selective stains for light microscopic identification of a particular organelle leaves many of the other organelles unstained, electron micrographs reveal all of the organelles at once.

Neurofibrils. The neurofibrils are best developed in large neurons, but they have been demonstrated in almost every variety of nerve cell (Fig. 12-3). When impregnated with silver, they appear as slender interlacing threads passing through the cytoplasm of the perikaryon from one dendrite into another or into the axon. They can be followed into the finest terminal ramifications of all the processes. In electron micrographs, it is evident that neurofibrils seen with the light microscope are formed by aggregations of slender *neurofilaments*, about 100 Å in diameter, that are seen coursing through the cytoplasm. In the dendrites and axon, these filaments usually are arranged parallel to the long axis of the process. At high magnification, they appear as fine tubules with a dense wall about 30 Å thick and a clear center. It has been suggested that the neurofilaments may be composed of helically organized protein threads. Similar filaments extracted from the giant nerve axon

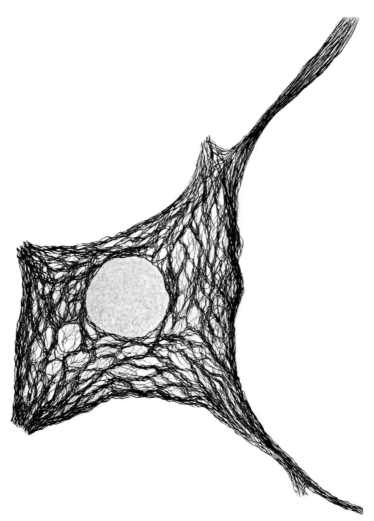

Figure 12-5. Motor cell from the gray substance of the ventral horn of the spinal cord of a rabbit. The net of neurofibrils in the perikaryon continues into the processes; the nucleus appears as a pale disk. Bielschowsky method. × 500. (After A. A. Maximow.)

of the squid have been characterized chemically as a single protein.

Chromophilic Substance. The chromophilic substance or Nissl bodies (Figs. 12-4 and 12-6) stand out clearly in the cytoplasm of neurons stained with basic dyes and show important changes in some pathological conditions. They are visible in living neurons examined with the phase contrast microscope but are best demonstrated by staining fixed cells with such basic aniline dyes as toluidine blue, thionine, or cresyl violet. Thus stained, the bodies appear as deeply basophilic masses or blocks in the perikaryon. The study of Nissl substance in living cells with phase contrast or by the freeze-drying method establishes that its clumped pattern in histological sections accurately reflects its distribution in life. By use of ultraviolet microscopy and ribonuclear digestion, it has been shown that one of the principal constituents of the Nissl substance is ribonucleoprotein.

In electron micrographs the Nissl bodies are found to consist of aggregations of cisternae of rough surfaced or granular endoplasmic reticulum in ordered parallel array (Fig. 12-7). Ribosomes are attached to the outer surface of the membranes, as in the basophilic regions of other cell types. They are arranged on the membranes in loops, rows, and spirals. They also occur in clusters or rosettes in the neuroplasm between cisternae. The Nissl bodies, like the basophilic substance of pancreatic and hepatic cells, represent the sites of synthesis of the protein.

Nissl substance or endoplasmic reticulum is abundant throughout the neuroplasm, including the dendrites, where it appears under the electron microscope as anastomosing slender tubules and short cisternae. Sites of dendritic branching are frequently occupied by small Nissl bodies—that is, parallel arrays of cisternae. They are usually absent from the most peripheral region of the perikaryon. They are also lacking in the area of the perikaryon where the axis cylinder originates (the *axon hillock*), as well as from the axis cylinder itself.

The form, size, and distribution of the Nissl bodies vary considerably in different types of neurons. As a rule, they are coarser and more abundant in large neurons, especially motor neurons, and small and scarce in

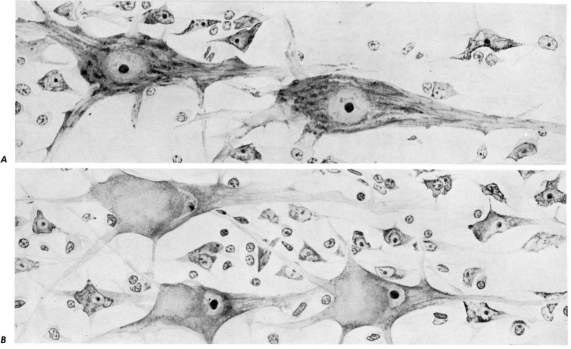

Figure 12-6. *A*, Normal cells of motor cortex of macaque; *B*, chromatolysis in similar cells after hemisection of the cervical spinal cord. Stained after Nissl-Lenhossek. (Courtesy of S. Polyak.)

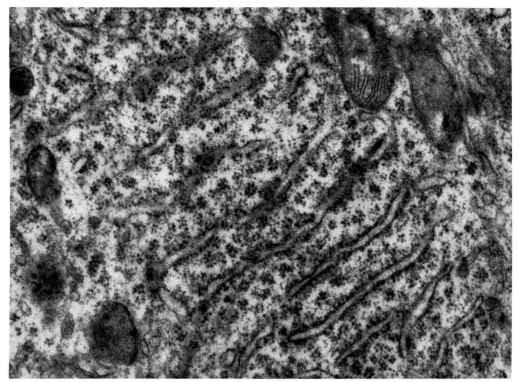

Figure 12-7. Electron micrograph of a Nissl body in a Purkinje cell of the rat brain. It is composed of parallel cisternae of the endoplasmic reticulum and particles of ribonucleoprotein. Some of the particles are intimately related to the membranes of the reticulum, but many others occur individually or in conspicuous clumps in the cytoplasmic matrix between the cisternal elements. Osmium fixation. × 42,000. (Courtesy of S. L. Palay.)

small neurons. Obvious exceptions are encountered, however. The ganglion cells of the dorsal roots of spinal nerves may attain large size yet typically display a uniform distribution of very fine Nissl bodies. Under different physiological conditions, such as rest and fatigue, the Nissl bodies are said to change their appearance. In pathological states, they may disappear. Their dissolution, called *chromatolysis,* may follow direct injury either to the cell body or to the axon anywhere along its course (Fig. 12-6B). If caused by injury to the axon, the chromatolysis is called *axonal reaction.*

Golgi Apparatus. The intracellular reticular apparatus of Golgi is present in all nerve cells and when selectively stained for light microscopy appears as a network of irregular, wavy strands, coarser than the neurofibrillar network. Under the electron microscope, the Golgi network appears as multiple clusters of closely apposed, flattened cisternae arranged in stacks and surrounded by multitudes of small vesicles. The ends of the

cisternae are frequently dilated; they may be continuous with branching tubules extending into the surrounding neuroplasm. In low-power electron micrographs, the distribution of the seemingly isolated arrays of Golgi membranes is found to correspond to the image obtained with the light microscope. The Golgi complex is arranged in an arc or a complete circle roughly parallel to the nuclear envelope and situated approximately halfway between it and the surface membrane of the perikaryon. The correspondence of these arrays of smooth membranes in electron micrographs and the dense Golgi strands in cytological preparations has been further documented by application of a histochemical reaction for the enzyme, thiamine pyrophosphatase. This procedure yields a reaction product that is concentrated in the agranular cisternae of this organelle and is coextensive with the Golgi apparatus as classically delineated by optical methods.

The areas of typical *Golgi membranes* are interconnected by smooth surfaced tubular elements, often interpreted as *agranular endo-*

plasmic reticulum. These in turn are often continuous with tubules or cisternae of the *granular reticulum.* Thus no sharp limits can be assigned to these three types of membrane limited structures that are usually designated by different names. Some workers prefer to regard them simply as local or regional differentiations of a single organelle.

Mitochondria. The rodlike or filamentous mitochondria are scattered everywhere, intermingling with the Nissl bodies and neurofibrils. They are generally smaller than those of non-nervous tissues, varying from 1.0 to 0.1 μ in diameter with a predominance of slender forms close to the lower limit of the range. They can be demonstrated in fresh nerve cells by supravital staining. Their number varies from a few to many. They are especially numerous in axon endings (Fig. 12-38). The fine structure resembles that of mitochondria in other cells but displays two peculiarities of unknown significance. The first is that their cristae are not consistently transverse but often run

parallel to the long axis of the mitochondrion. The second is that the dense granules that usually appear in the inner mitochondrial chamber are either absent or very infrequent.

Centrosome. The spherical centrosome contains a pair of centrioles and is characteristic of the immature, multiplying neuroblasts during the early stages of embryonic development. In adult neurons of vertebrates, a typical centrosome is seldom observed in light microscopic preparations. In electron micrographs, however, a centrosome is frequently encountered. In view of the fact that mature neurons do not undergo cell division, the role of this organelle in the adult nerve cell is unknown.

Inclusions. In addition to the organelles already described, there are inclusions in the nerve cells that are of more restricted occurrence. Pigment granules are frequently encountered. The coarse, dark brown or black granules are undoubtedly melanin. These are found only in neurons in certain areas: the substantia nigra of the midbrain, the locus coeruleus in the floor of the fourth ventricle, the dorsal motor nucleus of the vagus nerve, and in the spinal and sympathetic ganglia. The physiological significance of melanin pigment in these sites is unknown. Of more general occurrence, especially in man, are golden brown lipochrome pigment granules termed *lipofuscin.* They are probably a harmless byproduct of normal metabolic activity, which accumulates within the neuroplasm. In favor of this interpretation is the fact that there is a gradual progressive increase in the amount of lipofuscin with advancing age, until indeed it may displace the nucleus and organelles far over to one side of the neuron. Lipid is encountered in the form of droplets in the cytoplasm of the nerve cells and may represent either normal metabolic reserve material or a product of pathological metabolism. Glycogen is found in embryonic neurons, as well as in embryonic neuroglial cells and in embryonic cells of the ependyma and chorioid plexus, but it is not present in a histochemically demonstrable quantity in adult nervous tissue. Iron-containing granular deposits are found in the nerve cells of the substantia nigra, the globus pallidus, and elsewhere. Their number increases as the individual grows older.

Processes. The cytoplasmic processes of the nerve cells are their most remarkable features. In almost all of the many varieties of

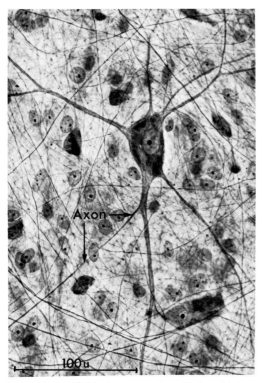

Figure 12-8. Multipolar neuron in a 29 day old tissue culture of rat brain stem. The axon in this cell does not spring from the cell body but from one of the larger dendrites. Bodian stain. (From W. Hild, Zeitschr. f. Zellforsch., *69:*155, 1966.)

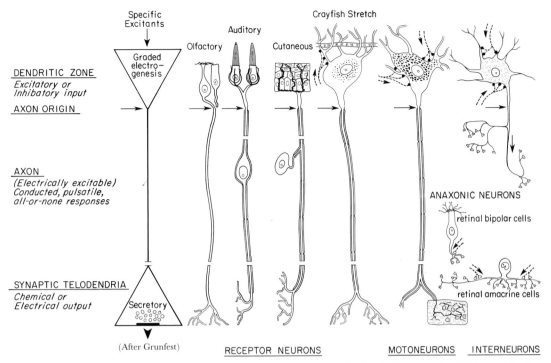

Figure 12-9. The traditional selection of the mammalian motoneuron as the "typical neuron" has led to a misleading emphasis upon the cell body as the focal point for analysis of neuron structure in functional terms—it being commonly assumed that dendrites must conduct toward and axons away from the cell body. The diagram presented here illustrates several variations in the position of the cell body in a number of receptor and effector neurons. A more important consideration in terms of function is the site of origin of the impulse. The location of the perikaryon in the neuron is not critical for the electrochemical functions of response generation, conduction, and synaptic transmission. The neuroplasm in the interior of the perikaryon is concerned primarily with the outgrowth and maintenance of the axon and dendrites and metabolic functions other than membrane activity. (After D. Bodian.)

neurons there are two kinds: the dendrites and the axon.

The *dendrites* provide most of the receptive surface of the neuron. They may be direct extensions of the perikaryon (Fig. 12-8), or they may be remote arborizations, as in the peripheral branches of a sensory ganglion cell, in which case a length of typical axis cylinder is interposed. Dendrites usually contain Nissl bodies and mitochondria. A neuron usually has several main dendrites. More rarely there is only one (Fig. 12-9). Where the dendrites emerge from the cell body they are thick, tapering gradually along their length toward the ends. In the majority of neurons the dendrites are relatively short and are confined to the immediate vicinity of the cell body. Each dendrite may divide into primary, secondary, tertiary, and higher orders of branches. These are of highly variable shapes and sizes, and are distributed in the most diverse ways (Figs. 12-10 and 12-11). The number and length of the

dendrites appear to bear little relation to the size of the perikaryon, but their pattern of branches is typical for each variety of neuron. As seen in Golgi preparations, the surface of many dendrites is covered with a great number of minute, thorny *spines* or *gemmules*. These spines and other similar terminal twigs often serve as sites of synaptic contact (Figs. 12-38 and 12-40).

In addition to Nissl bodies and mitochondria, dendrites contain long, straight, and parallel tubules or canaliculi about 200 Å in diameter, which appear to correspond to the microtubules found in many cells outside of the nervous system. In cross section these "neurotubules" appear as small circles with a thick wall (60 Å) and a clear center. Neurofilaments, already described as the subunits of the classical neurofibrils and the basis for the argyrophilia of the axon and perikaryon, are also encountered in small numbers in the dendrites. The neurotubules and neurofila-

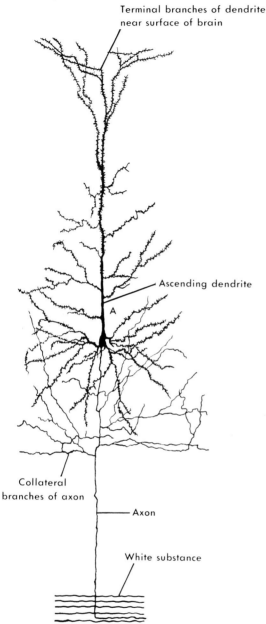

Terminal branches of dendrite near surface of brain

Ascending dendrite

A

Collateral branches of axon

Axon

White substance

Figure 12-10. Pyramidal neuron (Type I of Golgi) from cerebral cortex of rabbit. The axon gives off numerous collateral branches close to the cell body (seen just below *A*). The axon then enters the white substance, within which it extends for a long distance. Only a small part of the axon is included in the drawing. Golgi method. (After Ramón y Cajal.)

ments, as well as the larger tubular elements of the endoplasmic reticulum, become progressively more scanty toward the ends of the dendrites. In contrast, mitochondria remain relatively constant in number per unit length and may actually appear increased as they are confined in the finer dendritic ramifications.

Through their synapses with the axon endings of functionally related neurons, the dendrites receive nerve impulses from other neurons. The number of impulses and the number of the sources from which they are received may be very great. In a Purkinje cell of the cerebellar cortex in man (Fig. 12-11), the number of terminals upon the dendritic tree from one type of cell alone may be as many as 200,000. It is obvious that the system of dendrites plays a crucial role in the ability of the neuron to integrate information received from its multitude of inputs. The nerve impulses received excite or inhibit electrical activity in the localized regions of the dendrite membrane and thus continuously shift the neuron toward or away from its threshold for signaling a nerve impulse. Although the nerve impulse or action potential, carried by the axon, behaves in an "all-or-nothing" fashion, the integrative capacity of the dendrites depends upon graded changes in electrical potential.

The *axon* or *axis cylinder* differs considerably from the dendrites. While there are usually several dendrites, there is only one axon to each neuron. This cell process often arises from a small conical elevation on the perikaryon, devoid of Nissl bodies, called the *axon hillock*. The axon does not contain Nissl bodies and usually is thinner and much longer than the dendrites of the same neuron.* The axoplasm contains longitudinally oriented tubules of the endoplasmic reticulum, long and extremely slender mitochondria, neurotubules (microtubules) similar to those in dendrites, and many neurofilaments.

The axons of many nerve cells are readily identified by the presence of a prominent sheath of material called myelin, which is highly refractile in the fresh condition and which blackens in tissue fixed in osmium. Strictly speaking, the myelin sheath of the axis

---

* When the dendritic branches are included in a comparison of axonal and dendritic length, however, there is usually a much greater total length of dendritic "cable."

cylinder is not part of the neuron. Its presence or absence exerts an important influence on the physiological properties of the neuron. Because it is associated only with axons, it provides a dependable criterion for their recognition except for those of neurons devoid of a myelin sheath. In electron micrographs unmyelinated axons and dendrites of large caliber can usually be distinguished by the much greater number of neurofilaments in the axon. The smaller processes are more difficult to distinguish, because the neurofilaments upon which the identification largely depends are less numerous in the smaller axons.

Along its course the axon may or may not emit collateral branches. Unlike the branches of dendrites, which diverge at an acute angle, axonal branches tend to depart at right angles. In certain instances a neuron may display an extensive system of axon collaterals, which individually ramify into ever finer branches. In such cases the total length of axonal "cable" may approach or even exceed that of the dendrites and can extend the sphere of immediate functional influence of the neuron to a very great number of other neurons. Axon collaterals from many neurons of this kind may combine to form a fibrous plexus of incredible complexity, enveloping the perikarya of other nerve cells.

The chief arborization is at the end of the main branch and is called the *axon ending* (also *telodendron*). It is composed of primary, secondary, and other branches and buds, varying greatly in number, shape, and distribution. Often its branches are assembled into networks that surround the body of the related neuron in the form of a basket, or they may twist around the dendrites of the latter in the manner of a clinging vine. In simpler cases one or two twigs of an axon ending just touch the surface of a dendrite or the body of another related neuron (Fig. 12-37).

An axon arising from the cell body, as described, receives excitatory or inhibitory influences from the dendrites of the neuron. The perikaryon also offers a large area of electrically excitable membrane upon which additional influences from the axon terminals of other neurons can be received and integrated. In many instances, it provides a strategic receptive zone for inhibitory signals, which may act to thwart excitations accumulating in the dendritic tree. Frequently, however, an axon may arise from the stem of a principal dendrite

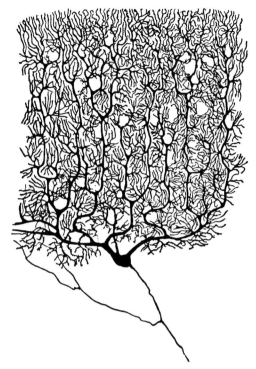

Figure 12-11. Purkinje cell of the cerebellum. Golgi method. (After Ramón y Cajal.)

rather than from the cell body. In such instances influences may be exerted directly from dendrite to axon of the same cell (Fig. 12-8). The pseudounipolar neuron of the craniospinal ganglia is another type of nerve cell that exhibits direct transmission of a nerve impulse from the peripheral to the central branches of its long, single, T-shaped process. The perikaryon of this particular neuron, off the path of nervous transmission and devoid of synaptic contacts derived from other neurons, may be considered chiefly of trophic significance.

Through its ending, the axon transmits nerve impulses to other neurons or to effector cells such as muscle fibers and gland cells. The response of the effector cells is always excitatory, but that of other neurons may be either excitatory or inhibitory. There are many types of axon endings (Fig. 12-37), and indeed the same axon may terminate in several different ways and be synaptically connected with several different neurons.

Some dendrites and axons may have special attributes. In general, dendrites display brief local changes in electrical potential to impulses received at their surface membrane.

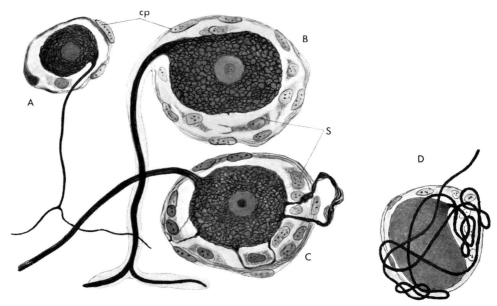

Figure 12-12. Three cells from the nodose ganglion of the vagus nerve of man. *A* and *B,* Cells with **T**-shaped dividing processes; *C,* cell with looped processes; *D,* cell of spinal ganglion of man, showing typical tangle of proximal part of axon (initial glomerulus); *cp,* capsule; *S,* satellites. Reduced silver nitrate method. (Redrawn after Ramón y Cajal.)

Certain neurons with very long dendrites, however, exhibit the property of propagated dendritic electrical potentials. These propagated potentials are very similar to the nerve impulse transmitted by the axon, usually called the *action potential.* They appear to summate and to convey quickly to the perikaryon weak and fleeting excitations received in a remote region of the neuron. In the peripheral sensory neurons of the craniospinal ganglia, the afferent (incoming) fiber in the adult has the histological and conducting properties of the axon, although it derives from the distal process of a bipolar neuron in the embryo that conducts impulses toward the cell body and may, at that time, properly be considered a dendrite.

A very important development in our knowledge of nerve cells is the concept that the nerve cell body is continuously forming new cytoplasm, which flows down the nerve cell processes at a rate of about 1 mm. per day. According to Weiss and Hiscoe, "The perpetual growth of the neuron presumably serves to replace catabolized protoplasmic systems, especially proteins, which cannot be synthesized in the peripheral cytoplasm." Autoradiographic studies with labeled amino acids have demonstrated the synthesis of protein by the endoplasmic reticulum (Nissl substance) of the perikaryon and its progressive transport down the axon.

Distribution, Forms, and Varieties of Neurons

The core of the central nervous system, in which the cell bodies of the neurons, their dendrites, and proximal portions of the axis cylinders are located, is called the *gray matter.* Clusters of nerve cell bodies in the gray matter are called *nuclei* (not to be confused with nuclei in the cytological sense) and represent functional aggregates of neurons. Surrounding the gray matter in more or less concentric fashion is a zone devoid of nerve cell bodies. This zone contains axis cylinders of neurons whose cell bodies are located either in the gray matter of the central nervous system or in ganglia outside the central nervous system. This zone is known as the *white matter* because the axis cylinders here are invested by *myelin,* which has a glistening white appearance in the fresh state. Bundles of myelinated fibers in the white matter are known as *tracts* and are functional groupings of nerve fibers resembling cables. In the cerebral hemispheres and the cerebellum, additional gray matter or *cortex* is located peripheral to the white matter and its nerve cell bodies are arranged in distinct layers.

Depending on the number, length, thickness, and mode of branching of the processes, and also on the shape, size, and position of the cell body, and on the synaptic relationships, a great variety of neurons can be distinguished in the central nervous system. In general, the neurons may have axons of considerable length that leave the place of their origin in the gray matter, traverse the white matter, and terminate at some distance in another part of the gray substance. Or they may join in the formation of craniospinal nerves, leaving the central nervous system and ending in the periphery. Such nerve cells with long axons are termed *Golgi Type I* neurons (Figs. 12-1 and 12-10). To this type belong all the neurons that contribute to formation of the peripheral nerves and the neurons whose axons form long fiber tracts of the brain and spinal cord. In other neurons the axon is relatively short and does not leave the confines of the gray matter where its cell body lies. These nerve cells with short axons are *Golgi Type II* neurons, and they are especially numerous in the cerebral and cerebellar cortex and in the retina.

The shape of the perikaryon is variable: it may be spherical, ovoid, pyriform, fusiform, or polyhedral. The absolute size of the cell body similarly varies between extreme limits, from dwarf neurons of 4 μ diameter (smaller than an erythrocyte) to giants approaching 150 μ. The giant pyramidal cells of Betz in the mammalian cerebral cortex and the paired Mauthner neurons in the medulla oblongata of certain fishes and amphibians are examples of exceptionally large neurons, and, could they be isolated from the surrounding tissue, they would be visible to the naked eye.

True *unipolar* neurons are rare except in the early embryonic stage. In *bipolar* neurons each cell has one main dendrite and one axon projecting from opposite ends of the fusiform cell body. Typical bipolar neurons are found in the retina (Fig. 12-41), in the vestibular and cochlear ganglia, and in the olfactory nasal epithelium. In vertebrate embryos all neurons of the craniospinal ganglia are at first bipolar, but during further development they undergo changes through which the opposing processes are brought together and combined into a single process. This process does not represent a simple axon and because of this fact, these neurons are properly called *pseudounipolar*. During embryonic stages, the perikaryon of such neurons is progressively set apart from the region of the fusion of the two initial processes. In the adult form, the cell body is globular or pear-shaped; a single process arises and divides like the letter **T** into a peripheral branch (morphologically an axon) directed to the periphery, and a central branch traveling in a sensory or posterior nerve root to terminate in the central nervous system. The single process may be relatively short, as shown in Figure 12-12*A*, and *B*, or it may run a considerable distance before bifurcating, sometimes enveloping the cell body of origin in a complex tangle (Fig. 12-12*D*). Although unipolar, these neurons are physiologically bipolar. Except in the smallest examples the initial single process and both peripheral and central branches are myelinated. The perikaryon of a pseudounipolar

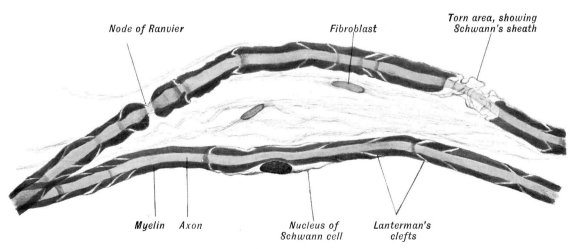

Figure 12-13. Two myelinated fibers of the sciatic nerve of a frog; treated with osmium tetroxide and picrocarmine and teased. × 330. (After A. A. Maximow.)

neuron is ensheathed by two cellular capsules. The inner is made up of small, flat, epithelium-like *satellite cells* continuous with similar cells (Schwann cells) enveloping the peripheral process. The satellite cells possess a relationship to the ganglion cells similar to that of one of the neuroglial cell types (oligodendrocytes) to the nerve cells in the central nervous system. Satellite cells, however, differ in structure and embryonic origin from neuroglial cells. The outer capsule of pseudounipolar neurons is vascular connective tissue, which extends along the cellular process and becomes continuous with the endoneurium of the nerve fiber.

In the multipolar neurons, which represent the great majority of neurons, shape is determined by the number and arrangement of the dendrites (Fig. 12-3). *Stellate* or *star-shaped neurons* include the motor nerve cells of the ventral gray matter of the spinal cord and of the motor nuclei of the brain stem. *Pyramidal neurons* constitute one of the characteristic elements of the cerebral cortex (Fig. 12-10).

Of remarkable shape are the graceful *Purkinje's cells* of the cerebellar cortex (Fig. 12-11). One or two thick dendrites covered with a multitude of tiny spines arise from the upper end of the cell body. These branch repeatedly to form a large dendritic arborization, which is oriented in one plane and is shaped like a fan turned at a right angle to the longitudinal axis of the cerebellar convolution in which it lies. The axon enters the white matter beneath the cortex, and hence the Purkinje cell is classed as a Golgi Type I neuron. Synaptic terminals upon the dendrites and body of the Purkinje cell are notable for their number (several hundred thousand per cell) and their specificity of site and mode of ending upon the postsynaptic surface.

Many more varieties of neurons are found

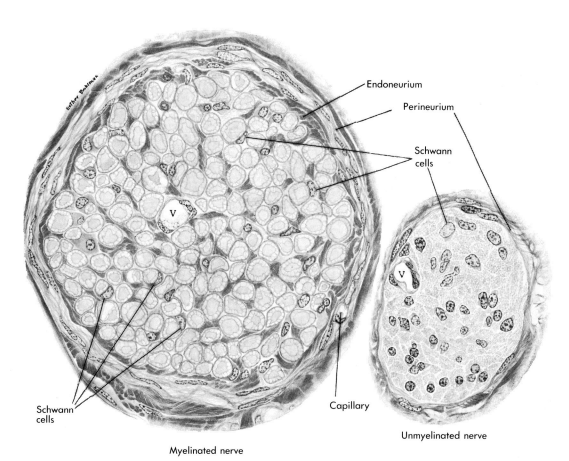

Figure 12-14. Drawings of myelinated and unmyelinated nerves of *Macacus rhesus*. As a result of fixation by perfusion with Zenker-formol, the vessels *V* are empty. × 700.

in the cerebral and cerebellar cortices. Among these are diminutive *granule cells.* In these a few short dendrites radiate in all directions, while the axon and its axon collaterals are confined either to the immediate neighborhood of the cell or at least within the cortical gray matter. Such neurons qualify as Golgi's Type II. Other neurons encountered in the reticular formation of the brain stem possess large, variously shaped perikarya and have extensive but poorly branched dendrites. Great attention has been accorded these neurons in recent years because their morphology and synaptic relationships suggest important integrative functions. The extensive dendrites frequently overlap in complex fashion and receive an impressively heterogeneous input from axons and axon collaterals derived from many sources. The typically long axon emitted by these neurons may distribute impulses through ascending and descending branches to a considerable portion of the length of the neuraxis and ramify into rich collateral plexuses at different levels. At first glance, such sprawling neurons convey an impression of disorder in the extreme, yet they are encountered in the core of the brain stem, upon which the delicate and exquisite control of homeostatic mechanisms depends.

The few examples described give an incomplete picture of the wealth of different kinds of neurons. A great many more have been discovered by numerous investigators, especially by Ramón y Cajal and his pupils. Recent studies, in which the electron microscope and chrome-silver method of Golgi have played complementary roles, have further refined the knowledge of neuronal types. It is apparent that each ganglion, nucleus, or cortical area is composed of (1) a characteristic variety of neurons in differing proportions, each type of cell designed to meet its special functional requirements, and (2) a complex and highly ordered meshwork of dendritic, axonal, and glial processes whose fine structure and relationships are adapted to provide a framework for a particular form of organized activity. The term frequently used to designate this feltwork of processes is *neuropil.* The details of its dense entanglements cannot be resolved in silver preparations and have only begun to be appreciated with the advent of the electron microscope. The neuropil is of great importance in the communication function of nervous tissue in that it provides an enormous area for synaptic contact and functional interaction between the processes of nerve cells. It has been estimated that well over half the cytoplasmic bulk of neurons lies in the neuropil. The great variety of neurons and of the neuropil results in a striking degree of regional heterogeneity in nervous tissue.

The number of nerve cells in the entire nervous system is astronomical, being estimated at 14 billion in man. The tremendous increase in this number in the course of evolution has involved chiefly the integrator cells or *interneurons* of the central nervous system. The number of *sensory neurons* and associated receptors has also increased, especially in the retina, but to a much lesser extent. The number of *motor neurons,* which exert control over the effector organs, has remained relatively small and in man probably does not exceed two million. The term *final common pathway* is employed to designate the motor neurons by which nerve impulses from a variety of central sources are transmitted to a muscle or gland in the periphery.

THE NERVE FIBER

The *nerve fiber* is composed of an axon and certain coverings or sheaths that are of ectodermal origin. All peripheral nerve fibers are enclosed by a sheath composed of Schwann cells, which form an investment for the axis cylinder from its beginning at a craniospinal nerve root or in a ganglion almost to its peripheral termination. All of the larger peripheral fibers are also enveloped in a *myelin sheath,* within the *sheath of Schwann.* The smallest axons of peripheral nerves are likewise ensheathed by Schwann cells but lack a myelin sheath. It is common practice, therefore, to designate nerves as myelinated or unmyelinated. Fresh myelinated fibers appear as homogeneous, glistening tubes. It is this refractile property of myelin that is responsible for the white color of fiber masses of the brain and spinal cord, and of numerous peripheral nerves. In stained preparations, the appearance of various constituents of the nerve fiber differs according to the technique applied. With methylene blue vital staining and with silver methods, the axon is stained blue, brown, or black, the myelin remaining unstained. Unmyelinated fibers, which are often difficult to observe by routine histological methods, are well demonstrated by these special techniques. Weigert's method or osmium tetroxide darkens the myelin, leav-

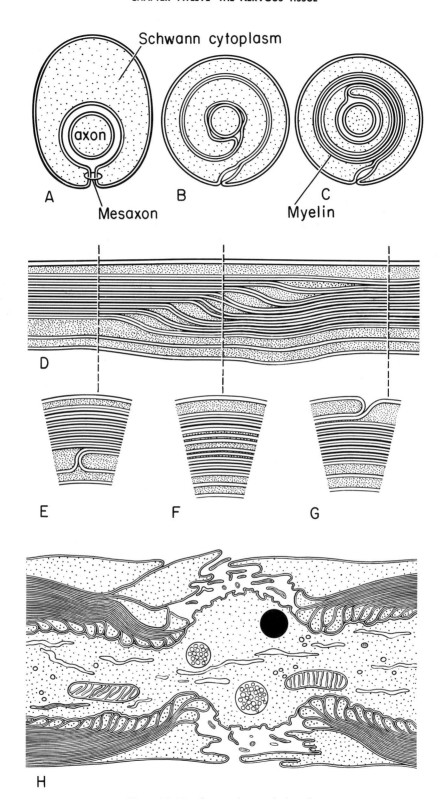

Figure 12-15. *See opposite page for legend.*

ing the axon colorless or light gray (Fig. 12-13). Myelin sheaths are stained blue-green by the Klüver-Barrera method (Fig. 12-2).

THE SHEATH OF SCHWANN. This sheath of flattened cells, sometimes called the *neurilemmal sheath,* forms a thin sleeve around the myelin, which, in turn, surrounds the axon. The Schwann cells, like the neurons, are of ectodermal origin and can be considered as neuroglial elements that have left the central nervous system and become adapted to the special conditions of the peripheral nervous system. In embryonic life as the axons grow outward, the cells of Schwann accompany them and migrate from branch to branch until they form complete neurilemmal sheaths. In the adult their nuclei are flattened and a small Golgi apparatus and a few mitochondria can be demonstrated in their attenuated cytoplasm. The myelin and the Schwann sheaths appear distinct with the light microscope and were formerly considered to be separate structures. It has been found with the electron microscope, however, that the myelin is actually part of the Schwann cell, consisting of spirally wrapped layers of its surface membrane (see below). The outer membrane of the Schwann cell and the protein-polysaccharide boundary layer on its outer aspect were resolved with the light microscope as a single layer, which has traditionally been called the *neurilemma.* As originally employed, the term *axolemma* referred to the inner membrane of the Schwann cell, but the term is now commonly applied to the plasmalemma of the axon. The sheath of Schwann and the myelin are interrupted at regular intervals by structures called *nodes of Ranvier* (Fig. 12-13). These mark the points of discontinuity between successive Schwann cells along the length of the fiber. At these points the axon is partially uncovered, being only incompletely enclosed by a complex arrangement of Schwann cell

processes (Fig. 12-15). The myelinated nerve fibers thus have individual neurilemmal sheaths, which are divided into segments. Each internodal segment between two consecutive nodes of Ranvier is composed of a Schwann cell with its contained myelin lamellae.

The internodal segments are shorter in the terminal portion of the fiber. The length varies in different nerve fibers and in different animals from about 200 to over 1000 μ. The longer and thicker the fibers, the longer the segments. If the peripheral nerve fiber gives off collateral branches, this takes place at a node of Ranvier.

In fixed preparations of the peripheral nerves the myelin of each segment appears to be interrupted by oblique discontinuities, the *incisures* or *clefts of Schmidt-Lanterman,* several to each Schwann segment (Fig. 12-13). These cone-shaped indentations or clefts may be seen in teased fresh or osmicated nerves. They represent areas of local separation of the spirally wrapped myelin lamellae, which are nevertheless continuous across the incisures. The regions between the separated lamellae consist of Schwann cell cytoplasm continuous with that forming the outer sleeve of the nerve fiber on the one hand and a thin, inconstant layer of cytoplasm next to the axon. (Fig. 12-15).

The exact relationship of the Schwann sheath to the unmyelinated nerves cannot be visualized with the light microscope, but in electron micrographs it is evident that multiple axons, up to a dozen or more, may occupy deep recesses in the surface of the same Schwann cell (Fig. 12-20). The plasmalemma of the Schwann cell is closely applied to the axon and, as a rule, completely surrounds it. At some point around the periphery of each axon, however, the Schwann cell membrane is reflected off to form the *mesaxon,* a pair of parallel membranes marking the line of edge

Figure 12-15. *A, B,* and *C,* Diagrams illustrating the development of nerve myelin. *A,* Earliest stage: axon enveloped by a relatively large Schwann cell. *B,* Intermediate stage: unit membranes of mesaxon (*M*) and to some extent of axon have come together, line of contact representing future *intraperiod* line of myelin. *C,* Later stage: a few layers of compact myelin have formed by contact of cytoplasmic surfaces of mesaxon loops to make *major dense line* of myelin. (Redrawn from Robertson, Prog. in Biophys., *10:*349, 1960.) *D, E, F,* and *G,* Diagrams of a Schmidt-Lanterman cleft. *D,* Cleft in longitudinal section. Schwann cell cytoplasm stippled, basement lamella not shown. *E, F,* and *G,* Appearance of cleft in transverse section at respective points. (Redrawn from Robertson, Molecular Biology. New York, Academic Press, 1960.) *H,* Diagram of a node of Ranvier, showing gap between membranes of nodal processes of Schwann cells and axon membrane over unmyelinated part of node. Tubular components of endoplasmic reticulum, mitochondria, multivesicular bodies, and a lipid droplet are represented within axoplasm. OsO₄ fixation. (Redrawn from Robertson, Prog. in Biophys., *10:*344, 1960.)

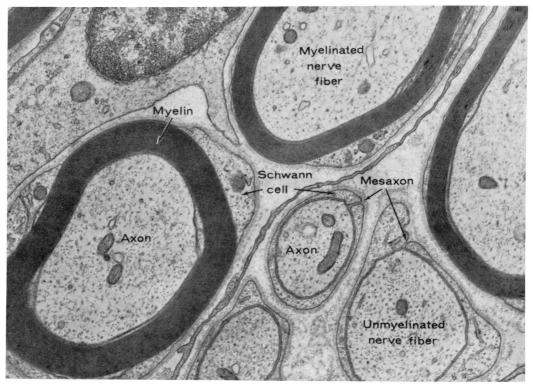

Figure 12-16. Electron micrograph of a small area of a mixed nerve, showing myelinated and unmyelinated nerve fibers. × 18,000.

to edge contact of the encircling sheath cell (Figs. 12-16 and 12-20).

Schwann's cells are indispensable for the life and function of the axons of the peripheral nerve fibers. In regeneration, the new axon always grows out of the central stump, which remains continuous with the cell body of the neuron, and spreads along the pathways formed by Schwann's cells. In tissue cultures, Schwann cells may transform into phagocytic cells.

THE MYELIN SHEATH. Before the advent of biological electron microscopy, Schmitt, Bear, and Palmer, on the basis of x-ray diffraction analysis, described the myelin sheath as "being composed of concentrically wrapped layers of mixed lipides alternating with thin, possibly unimolecular, layers of neurokeratinogenic protein material. Within the layers, the lipide molecules are oriented with paraffin chains extending radially and with polar groups in the aqueous interfaces, loosely bonded to those of the protein .... The specific structure of the sheath is relatively insensitive to the action of temperature, electrolytes, and detergents." In general, electron microscopic studies have supported this interpretation of the molecular organization of myelin and have shown additionally that the alternating layers of mixed lipids and proteins are in fact successive layers of the plasma membrane of the Schwann cell wrapped spirally about the axon.

In electron micrographs at high magnification compact myelin consists of a series of light and dark lines in a pattern repeating at about 120 Å (Figs. 12-17 and 12-18). The dark line bounding the repeating unit is called the *major dense line* and is about 30 Å thick; it represents the apposition of the inner (cytoplasmic) surfaces of the unit membrane of the Schwann cell. Between each major dense line is a less dense *intraperiod line,* which represents the union of the outer surfaces of the Schwann cell unit membrane (Fig. 12-15).

Where the laminated myelin sheath is interrupted at each node of Ranvier, the axon is surrounded loosely by a collar of minute finger-like processes of the two adjoining Schwann cells. A distinct gap, however, is

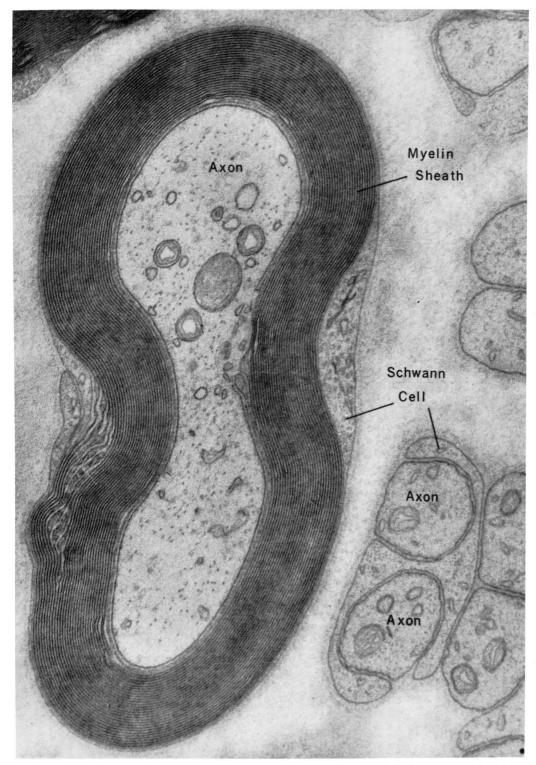

Figure 12-17. Electron micrograph of a small area of a guinea pig sciatic nerve, including a cross section of a myelinated nerve (at the left) and several unmyelinated axons (at the right) partially enveloped by a Schwann cell process. × 50,000. (Courtesy of H. Webster.)

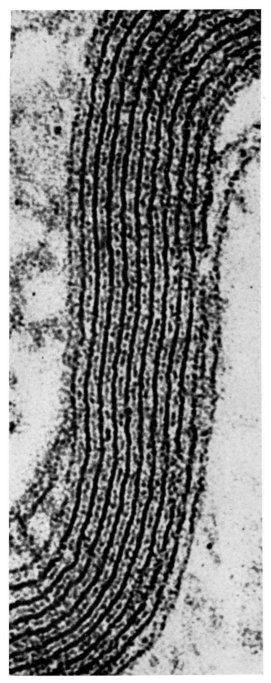

Figure 12-18. Electron micrograph of a section of myelin sheath at very high magnification, showing alternation of the uniformly spaced dense lamellae with the less dense intermediate layers. × 460,000. (Courtesy of H. Fernández-Morán.)

found between all of the membranes in this unmyelinated part of the node (Fig. 12-15). This gap is of probable significance in relation to current flow between axoplasm and the exterior during propagation of the action potential.

In electron micrographs of myelinating peripheral nerves successive stages can be found in the development of the sheath from a double-layered infolding of the Schwann cell membrane. The mechanism of formation of the spiral, consisting of a few to 50 or more turns around the axon, is still unsettled.

It has been suggested that during myelinization, the spiral disposition of the myelin lamellae is established by rotation of the sheath cells with respect to the axon (Fig. 12-15). It is difficult, however, to imagine how such movements could be initiated or controlled so as to result in formation of the precisely uniform laminated structure observed. Studies by Robertson strongly indicate that the myelin spiral does not develop because of any sort of corkscrew rotation during growth. If this were the mechanism, the direction of spiral for a particular axon would probably be the same in all its myelin segments, and such is not the case. Robertson's findings suggest that it is the Schwann cell alone that actively produces the spiral and that there seems to be no interaction between individual Schwann cells as far as the direction of spiral production is concerned. It is likely that formation of new membrane substance at the free edge or base of the original infolding of the satellite cell membrane can result in extension of the fold in a spiral fashion around the axon without any significant change in the relative position of the neuron and its satellite cells. It is clear that much remains to be learned concerning the morphogenesis of myelin, but whatever the morphogenetic process, the result is that the axon becomes surrounded by a many-layered sheath. The measurements across lamellae indicate a thickness of about 130 to 180 Å.

Many nerve fibers in the brain and spinal cord, especially those of the white subcortical substance, have myelin sheaths but lack Schwann cells. In myelinated fibers of the central nervous system certain of the neuroglial cells (oligodendroglia) play a role corresponding to that of the neurilemmal cells in the peripheral nervous system. Nodes of Ranvier occur in the central nervous system, but

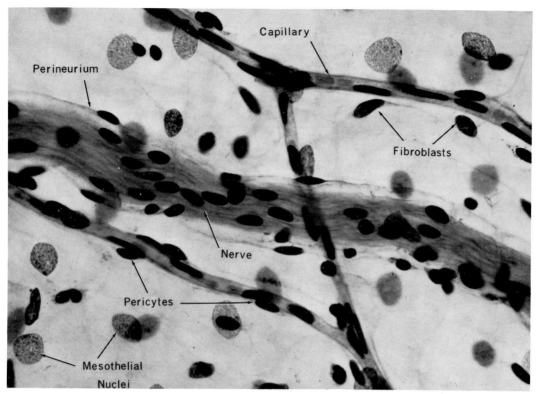

Figure 12-19. A whole mount of a small nerve in a thin spread of rat mesentery, showing the longitudinally oriented connective cells of the perineurium, and the nuclei of the Schwann cells in the interior of the nerve. May-Grünwald-Giemsa stain. × 500.

Schmidt-Lanterman clefts have not been seen.

In ontogenesis myelin appears relatively late, and the process of myelinization ends some time after birth. Different fiber systems or tracts of the brain and spinal cord become myelinated at different times.

Physiological Properties of the Nerve Fiber. The nerve fiber is essentially a highly irritable conductor. During the conduction of a nerve impulse the activity of one portion of the axon serves as a stimulus activating the next portion, and thus the impulse is propagated along its length in a rapidly moving wave. The rate of conduction is faster in large axons than in small ones. As the nerve fiber becomes active, it changes its electric potential, the outside of each active portion becoming negative relative to resting portions. Action currents then flow between active and resting regions.

Studies on giant nerve fibers of squid demonstrate that changes in the permeability of the axon membrane, permitting sodium ions to enter the axon and potassium ions to migrate from it, are of great importance in conduction. When artificially stimulated, the nerve fiber increases its metabolism. The electrical changes in active nerves and the accompanying chemical reactions are discussed in detail in textbooks of physiology.

There are seven characteristic features of the activity of the nerve fiber or axon. (1) Like all living substance, it has *irritability*, the ability to respond to various stimulating agents, and, in addition, the property of *conductivity*, the ability to transmit impulses from point to point. (2) To act as a transmitter, the nerve fiber must be anatomically continuous and physiologically in an appropriate condition. (3) After the passing of the impulse the fiber remains unexcitable for a short time ("refractory period"). (4) The axon can conduct an impulse with equal ease in the normal direction and in the opposite, *antidromic*, direction. (5) The impulse normally remains confined to the stimulated axon, spreading only along it and its branches to the synapses. (6) The impulse traveling along an axon can be weakened temporarily or blocked by the local action of heat, cold, pressure, or electric current, and by many drugs (anesthetics, narcotics). (7) Any stimulation intense enough to cause the axon to respond calls forth the maximum discharge of which the axon is capable ("all-or-nothing law").

The properties of axons, as listed, differ profoundly in several respects from those of the gray matter of the brain, the spinal cord, and the ganglia.

Nerve Fibers as Constituents of Peripheral Nerves, Brain, and Spinal Cord. In their course outside of the central nervous system, nerve fibers of varying thickness (1, 2 and up to 30 μ) are associated in fascicles and held together by connective tissue to form nerve trunks. The outer layer of the latter, the *epineurium,* is made up of connective tissue cells and of collagenous fibers, mainly arranged longitudinally (Fig. 12-14). Fat cells may also be found here. Each of the smaller fascicles of a nerve is in turn enclosed in dense, concentric layers of connective tissue, called *perineurium.* From this, fine longitudinally arranged strands of collagenous fibers, fibroblasts, and fixed macrophages pass into the spaces between the individual nerve fibers. These constitute the *endoneurium.* Where the nerve trunks divide into branches, the connective tissue sheaths become thinner. The smaller branches show no epineurium, and here the perineurium cannot be distinguished from the endoneurium, being reduced to a thin, fibrillar layer covered with flat connective tissue cells resembling endothelial cells. Delicate reticular fibrils around each nerve fiber form the tenuous endoneural or *connective tissue sheath of Key and Retzius.* This sheath is also known as the sheath of Henle, although he called it neurilemma. Blood vessels are embedded in the epineurium and perineurium and more rarely are found in the thicker layers of endoneurium.

It has become customary to classify

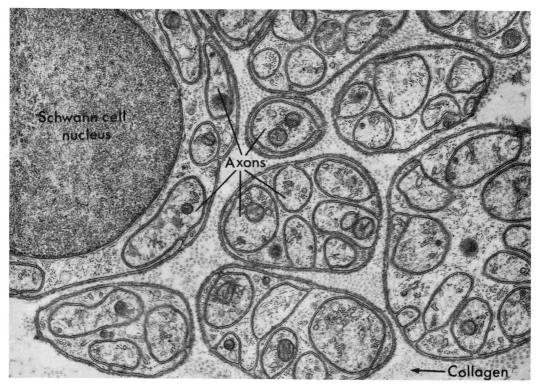

Figure 12-20.　Electron micrograph of a small area of an unmyelinated nerve from the rat mesentery, showing multiple axons associated with the cross sectional profile of each Schwann cell. Between these fascicles of unmyelinated axons are unit fibrils of collagen of the endoneurium. × 25,000.

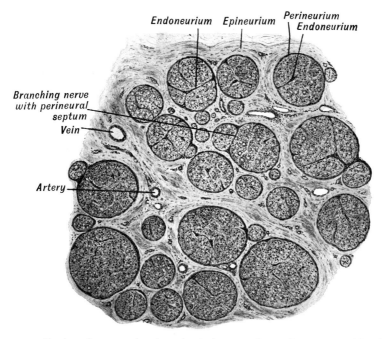

Figure 12-21.   Portion of cross section through sciatic nerve of a newborn. × 42. (After Schaffer.)

nerve fibers according to their diameter, because the speed of impulse transmission and the size of the action potential vary with the diameter of the fiber. Fiber diameters cover a wide and continuous range from large myelinated to small unmyelinated fibers. In peripheral nerves the fibers fall into three distinct groups according to their diameter. The large fibers of group A, conducting at 15 to 100 meters per second, include motor and some sensory fibers. The fibers of group B conduct at 3 to 14 meters per second and include mainly visceral sensory fibers. The C group consists of small unmyelinated fibers conducting at 0.5 to 2 meters per second, and carrying autonomic and some sensory impulses.

The following rule on the *functional characters of the nerve fibers* generally holds good: the motor nerve fibers of the skeletal muscles are thick and heavily myelinated; those of the visceral smooth muscles are thin and lightly myelinated or without myelin; those of tactile sensibility are of medium size and moderately myelinated; those of pain and taste are thinner, with less myelin or none at all, and those of the olfactory nerve are always unmyelinated. Such histologically defined fiber aggregates are therefore functional systems: somatic motor, visceral motor, tactile, gustatory, olfactory, and so forth.

A particularly clear segregation of functionally different nerve fibers is found in the *spinal roots*. In general, each segmental spinal nerve contains in its ventral root motor fibers of several types: (1) some, coarse and heavily myelinated, destined to innervate ordinary skeletal muscle fibers; (2) others, small and myelinated, going to intrafusal muscle fibers (see p. 284); and (3) visceral motor fibers, thinner and more lightly myelinated, belonging to the autonomic nervous system. The dorsal root of each segmental spinal nerve contains cutaneous fibers of several types, such as those of deep sensibility; sensory fibers from muscles and tendons; and afferent fibers of visceral sensibility. More than half of the dorsal root fibers are very small axons, and most of these are distributed with the cutaneous rami. The relative numbers of myelinated and unmyelinated fibers vary widely in different spinal segments and in the same segment in different mammalian species. In the mixed trunks peripheral to the spinal ganglia, the fibers of the motor and sensory roots mingle, and to those are added sympathetic fibers from the communicant rami. In routine preparations of mixed trunks stained with

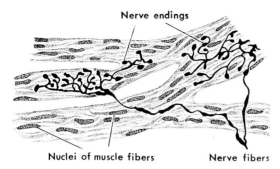

Nerve endings

Nuclei of muscle fibers   Nerve fibers

Figure 12-22. Smooth muscle spindles in small bronchial muscle bands of an 8 month old child. Intravital methylene blue and borax carmine. Camera lucida. × 356. (Redrawn and slightly modified from Larsell and Dow.)

hematoxylin and eosin or another survey method, many lipid constituents of myelin are dissolved out. There remains only a loosely arranged protein network traditionally called *neurokeratin.* A faintly stained axis cylinder may usually be seen in the center of the neuro-keratin network. In such preparations, the myelinated fibers of various sizes are readily identified by the clear zones of unstained myelin surrounding the darkly stained axons. The unmyelinated fibers tend to assemble in small fascicles. Some of these are sensory fibers from the spinal ganglia; others are postganglionic sympathetic fibers.

In the central nervous system, in the brain and spinal cord, numerous nerve fibers are also segregated into functional systems. Such, especially, are the *afferent* (incoming) and *efferent* (outgoing) pathways (the spinocerebellar, spinothalamic, corticobulbar, corticospinal, and many other fiber tracts whose origins and terminations are indicated by similar binomial nomenclature). Each of these has a special function, partly well known, partly still obscure.

Peripheral Nerve Endings

Each peripheral nerve fiber, whether sensory, motor, or secretory, sooner or later terminates in some peripheral organ with one or several terminal arborizations. Some nerve fibers ramify as free endings among the non-nervous tissue cells; others are attached to these by means of specialized terminations. The nerve fibers ending in *receptors* are analogous to dendrites; those with *motor* or *secretory* endings are analogous to axons, and their terminations are equivalent to axon endings. In general, the structure of the nerve ending is adapted to increase the surface of contact between the neuron and its related non-nervous element. The chemical-physical changes which mediate the transfer of the various "sensory" stimuli from, or the efferent impulses to, a peripheral non-nervous organ have been the subject of intensive investigation. Depending upon the tissue being studied, three groups of nerve terminations can be distinguished: (1) endings in muscle, (2) endings in epithelium, and (3) endings in connective tissue.

NERVE ENDINGS IN SMOOTH AND CARDIAC MUSCLE. These belong to the unmyelinated fibers. From complicated plexuses, thin nerve fibers are given off and eventually come in contact with or in proximity to the surface of the muscle cells (Fig. 12-22). Some of these, the *visceral motor endings,* terminate here by means of one, two, or more terminal swellings. The *visceral sensory fibers* ramify in the connective tissue between the smooth muscle bundles or are in contact with the muscle fibers themselves. In cardiac muscle the tissue is permeated by a multitude of thin fibers passing between the muscle trabeculae. They appear to end near the surface of the muscle fibers but form no specialized contacts with them.

TERMINATIONS OF MYELINATED SOMATIC MOTOR NERVE FIBERS ON STRIATED MUSCLES (MOTOR PLATES). These have a more complex structure than those of smooth and cardiac muscle. The motor end-plate has already been described in Chapter 11, and need only be reviewed here briefly.

Each motor nerve fiber branches to supply many muscle fibers. The motor neuron together with the muscle fibers it innervates is called a *motor unit.* The myelin sheath ends as a terminal branch of the nerve fiber nears the muscle fiber. The outer process of Schwann cell cytoplasm continues beyond the termination of the myelin and covers the surfaces of the axonal branch. At the junction of the nerve with the muscle fiber there is a local accumulation of sarcoplasm rich in mitochondria and muscle nuclei. This is the *motor end-plate* (Fig. 12-23). The terminal branches of the nerve fiber ramify upon its surface and occupy grooves or troughs in its surface (see Fig. 11-27). Within the expanded axon terminal are numerous mitochondria and *synapic vesicles,* 200 to 400 Å in diameter.

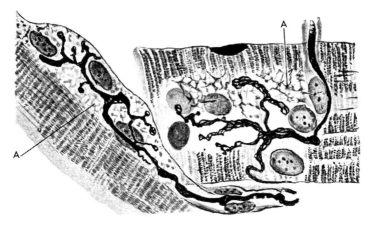

Figure 12-23. Motor end-plate from the tongue of a rabbit, showing the "periterminal net" (*A*) of the end-plate. (Redrawn after Ramón y Cajal.)

The neurofilaments and canaliculi found within the axon do not continue into the terminal. The apposed membranes of the axon and of the muscle fiber do not touch but are separated at all points by a glycoprotein layer continuous with the boundary layer investing the Schwann cell and the sarcolemma. This layer extends into the trough and narrow "gutters" formed by infolding of the sarcolemma of the end-plate. The gap between the surfaces of the axon and muscle fiber varies in width up to 500 Å.

SENSORY NERVE ENDINGS IN STRIATED MUSCLES. These are always present in considerable numbers. Some are located in the muscular tissue, others on tendons or at muscle-tendon junctions. Some terminations are simple, others complex. The interstitial terminations are distributed in the connective tissue; the epilemmal terminations are in close contact with the muscle fibers. The interstitial terminations may be simple naked branches of the axons or encapsulated structures. The epilemmal endings likewise may be simple: one or more tortuous axons, after shedding their myelin sheath at approximately the middle of a muscle fiber, envelop the sarcolemma in continuous circular and spiral twists. Their varicose twigs terminate with nodular swellings (Fig. 12-24). More complicated are the neuromuscular spindles, found only in higher vertebrates (Figs. 12-25 and 12-26). They are narrow, long (0.75 to 7 mm. or more) structures slightly thickened in the middle, arranged parallel to the bundles of ordinary muscle fibers, and situated mainly near the junction of muscles with tendons. Each spindle, enveloped by a connective tissue capsule, consists of one or several long striated muscle fibers, the intrafusal fibers. Near the middle of each fiber the striations are replaced by a collection of nuclei, the *nuclear bag*. In another type of intrafusal fiber, a longitudinal array of nuclei, or *nuclear chain*, is found. Each spindle is approached by two types of thick sensory nerve fibers. Their axons, covered with

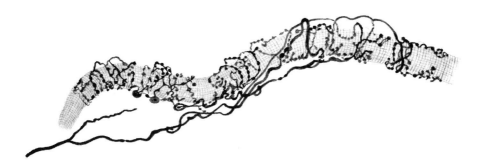

Figure 12-24. Sensory nerve ending enveloping a fiber of an ocular muscle. (Redrawn after Dogiel.)

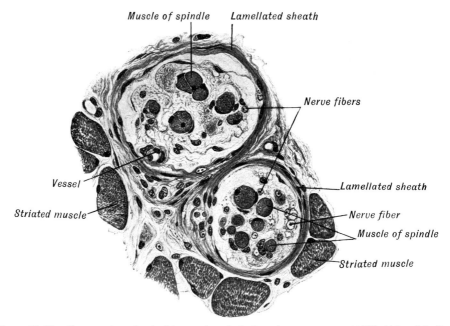

Muscle of spindle   *Lamellated sheath*

Nerve fibers

Vessel

Striated muscle

Lamellated sheath

Nerve fiber

Muscle of spindle

Striated muscle

Figure 12-25.   Cross section of a double muscle spindle from human tongue. × 380. (After Schaffer.)

a thin layer of Schwann cell cytoplasm, end in two ways. *Annulospiral endings,* the primary muscle receptors, surround the noncontractile nuclear bag. This receptor signals an increase in muscle length by generating nerve impulses at a higher frequency. The intrafusal muscle fibers are attached in parallel with the other muscle fibers and are stretched whenever the muscle is stretched. Annulospiral endings, therefore, function as stretch receptors. Heightened activity of the receptors exerts an excitatory effect upon the motor neurons to the same muscle by a direct reflex connection in the central nervous system. A secondary group of receptors, *flower-spray endings,* occurs on the contractile portions of the intrafusal muscle fibers. The function of these receptors is not yet clear.

Neuromuscular spindles are also supplied by thin motor nerves, *gamma fibers,* which emanate from small *gamma motor neurons* in the central nervous system. (The large motor neurons which send axons to the main muscle fibers are called *alpha motor neurons.*) The gamma fibers terminate on the intrafusal muscle fibers with typical motor end-plates. These motor fibers effect contraction and shortening of the intrafusal fibers. These contractions do not contribute significantly to the tension produced by the muscle but serve instead to stretch the noncontractile nuclear

bag where the annulospiral endings are located. Such stretching causes the receptor to discharge more rapidly; hence the function of the gamma fibers is to regulate the sensitivity of the muscle spindle to stretch. The muscle fibers of the spindles are distinguished by their thinness, abundant sarcoplasm, and peripheral nuclei; in this they resemble the so-called "red muscle fibers."

SENSORY NERVE ENDINGS IN TENDONS. These are of several kinds and are also either simple or encapsulated. In simple forms, the naked nerve fibers and their branches spread over the surface of the somewhat changed tendon fibers in small treelike figures of different types (Fig. 12-27). These simple types of endings in tendons and fascia probably give rise to pain sensation. Composite forms, the *Golgi tendon organs,* are located at the junction of muscle fibers and in their tendons. They resemble neuromuscular spindles and are sometimes called *neurotendinal spindles.* In contrast with neuromuscular spindles, which are arranged in parallel with the other muscle fibers, the Golgi tendon organs are placed in series with the contractile elements. These receptors respond to increase in tension; a heightened activity of the receptors exerts an inhibitory effect, through the interneurons of the central nervous system, upon the alpha motor neurons of the same muscle.

The physiological significance of the sensory endings in muscles and tendons has been clarified greatly in recent years, as has their morphology. These receptors participate in postural and phasic adjustments of skeletal musculature. Intimate and complex connections in the central nervous system relate their activity to the alpha and gamma motor neurons. This activity, however, must not be described as "muscle sense" or "position sense," the awareness of the position of the body parts in space. This sensation appears mediated by receptors located in joints.

NERVE ENDINGS IN EPITHELIAL TISSUE. These are of both receptor and effector types. Histologically, then can be distinguished only in rare instances. The terminations in the epithelial layers of the skin and mucous membranes are regarded as sensory receptors, those in the epithelial glands partly as secretory, partly as sensory. The terminations of the cochlear and vestibular nerves are undoubtedly sensory in their function. The nervous terminations in glands (lacrimal, salivary, kidneys, and so on) are all unmyelinated sympathetic fibers forming dense nets on the outer surface of the basement lamina, with branches penetrating the latter and often forming a second network on its inner surface. They end between the glandular cells.

Free Sensory Epithelial Endings. These are found in the epithelium of the cornea (Fig. 12-33), in the epithelium of the mucous membrane of the respiratory passages and oral cavity, and in the skin, and they are especially abundant where sensitiveness is highly developed. In the epidermis these branches do not penetrate farther than the granular layer. Nerve endings in hair follicles are important tactile organs. There are two sets of free nerve endings—an outer one circularly arranged in the middle layer of the dermal sheath, the other consisting of fibers running parallel to the hair shaft and terminating in the outer root sheath.

NERVE ENDINGS IN CONNECTIVE TISSUE. These are numerous and of many forms, particularly in the dermis, under the epithelium and mesothelium of the mucous and serous membranes, around the joints, in the endocardium, and elsewhere. The terminations of the somatic cerebrospinal nerve fibers in the connective tissue are either free or encapsulated endings, or are connected with special tactile cells of epithelial origin. More complex

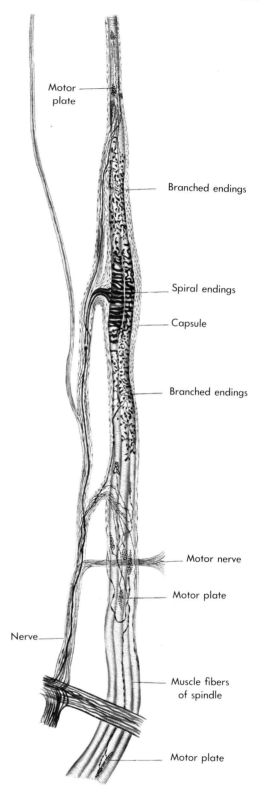

Figure 12-26. Neuromuscular spindle of a cat, showing nerve endings. (Redrawn after Ruffini.)

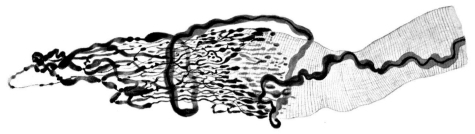

Figure 12-27. Sensory nervous apparatus, consisting of palisade-like terminal branches, located at the junction of a muscle fiber with a tendon. (Redrawn after Dogiel.)

endings are in the skin and hypodermis, in mucous and serous membranes, endocardium, cornea, sclera, periosteum, and elsewhere. Nonencapsulated nerve glomeruli are frequent in the papillary layer of the skin, in the connective tissue of the mucous membranes (such as that of the urinary bladder), and in the pericardium, endocardium, and periosteum. In these the terminal branches of the nerve fibers form spherical or elongated structures resembling glomeruli.

ENCAPSULATED TERMINAL SENSORY APPARATUS. In these there is a special connective tissue capsule of varying thickness surrounding the actual nerve endings. The capsule attains its greatest thickness in the *corpuscles of Vater-Pacini* (Fig. 12-31). Terminations of this type are found in the deeper layers of the skin, under the mucous membranes, in the conjunctiva, cornea, heart, mesentery, and pancreas, and in loose connective tissue in general. These structures are of considerable size (1 to 4 by 2 mm.), and they are white. Each corpuscle is supplied with one or more thick myelinated fibers, which lose their myelin upon entering the corpuscle. Their endoneural sheaths are continuous with the capsule. Of the same type are the so-called *genital corpuscles,* found in the skin of the external genital organs and of the nipple (Fig. 12-32*A*). Meissner's corpuscles (Figs. 12-28 to 12-30) are found in the connective tissue of the skin of the palms, soles, and tips of the fingers and toes. They are elongated, pear-shaped, or elliptical formations with rounded ends, located in the cutaneous papillae, with the long axis vertical to the surface. Their size varies (40 to 100 by 30 to 60 μ). The *corpuscles of Golgi-Mazzoni* or the *terminal bulbs of Krause* are similar in structure to the corpuscles of Vater-Pacini but are smaller and simpler in construction.

VISCERAL NERVOUS SYSTEM

All motor neurons of the central and peripheral nervous system primarily concerned with the regulation of visceral activities form the *autonomic* portion of the *visceral nervous system.* Not included under the term *autonomic* are the *visceral sensory neurons,* or interoceptive system, which form the afferent side of visceral arcs.

The autonomic nervous system includes numerous small ganglia. Some of these, the *vertebral ganglia,* form a chain, the *sympathetic trunk,* on either side of the spinal column; the sympathetic trunk is connected proximally with the ventral roots of the spinal nerves. Additional ganglia are found at some distance from the central nervous system in certain nerve plexuses (*collateral* or *prevertebral ganglia*) or in the walls of organs (*terminal ganglia*). The autonomic ganglia contain motor nerve cell bodies, which relay impulses originating in the brain and spinal cord to smooth muscle and glands by way of the *visceral* or *splanchnic* nerves (Fig. 12-34). Fibers of some motor neurons in the sympathetic trunk join those in the peripheral nerves and run to the sweat glands and arrector pili muscles. Whatever the destination, the activity of the autonomic nervous system is mediated by *two* motor neurons placed in series, the first of which lies either in a nucleus of the brain stem or in a special territory of the spinal gray matter and the second in a ganglion. This is in contrast to the peripheral nervous system, where only one motor neuron transmits impulses to the effector organ. The autonomic system consists of *sympathetic (thoracolumbar)* and *parasympathetic (craniosacral)* divisions; it influences the intrinsic activity of cardiac muscle and supplies nerve fibers to the smooth muscle in the viscera, salivary and sweat glands, blood vessels, and other structures. This also contrasts with the peripheral nervous system, which innervates striated skeletal muscle. Despite these few special features, however, the distinction of an autonomic nervous system is justifiable only in terms of convenience. Its components and functions are inextricably bound up with the rest of the nervous system and do not in any respect possess autonomy.

The sympathetic trunks and their ganglia, as well as the collateral ganglia, are the chief avenues of communication for the thoracolumbar outflow between the central nervous system and the viscera. Each sympathetic trunk contains ganglia at the level of exit of most of the spinal nerves. The *communicating branches* (rami communicantes) pass between the trunk and the spinal nerves.

The cell bodies of the sympathetic neurons are segregated in the intermediolateral gray column of the thoracic and upper lumbar spinal cord. Their axons pass out of the cord into the ventral roots and through the white communicating branches, to end either in a vertebral ganglion of the sympathetic trunk or in a prevertebral ganglion. Most of these axons, the *preganglionic fibers,* with thin myelin sheaths, terminate in a sympathetic ganglion. Here they effect synaptic junction with secondary visceral motor neurons, whose axons—the mostly unmyelinated *postganglionic fibers*— transmit the impulse to visceral muscles or glands. Some postganglionic fibers travel to internal viscera over sympathetic nerves, such as the cardiac or splanchnic nerves; others extend from vertebral ganglia through gray communicating branches and spinal nerves to visceral structures of the body wall and extremities. Among the latter are the *vasomotor* fibers going chiefly to arteriolar muscles, the *pilomotor* fibers to the small muscles of the hair follicles, and the *sudomotor* fibers to the sweat glands.

The craniosacral division of the autonomic system has preganglionic neurons situated in the brain and spinal cord. Axons of the cranial component emerge from the brain in the oculomotor, facial, glossopharyngeal, and vagus nerves, to synapse with terminal ganglia innervating the head and trunk. From the second, third, and fourth sacral segments of the spinal cord, axons leave via ventral roots and sacral nerves to reach postganglionic

neurons in terminal ganglia associated with pelvic viscera.

Postganglionic neurons that lie wholly within the peripheral autonomic system may exercise a local regulatory control over the viscera to which they are related. These local adjusters are subject to control by the visceral centers of the central nervous system.

Distributed with both divisions of the autonomic nervous system, the peripheral processes of the visceral sensory neurons extend from the viscera through communicating branches, or through cranial or sacral nerves to sensory ganglia. Their cell bodies are morphologically indistinguishable from those of the somatic sensory neurons, with which they are mingled in craniospinal ganglia.

AUTONOMIC NERVE CELLS. The cell bodies of the preganglionic visceral efferent neurons are small, spindle-shaped elements in the intermediolateral gray column. Their perikarya are not studded with a multitude of synaptic endings or terminal boutons as are the large nerve cell bodies of somatic motor

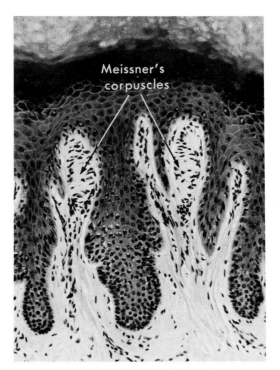

Figure 12-28. Photomicrograph of palmar digital epidermis showing Meissner's corpuscles in two neighboring dermal papillae. Hematoxylin and eosin. × 200.

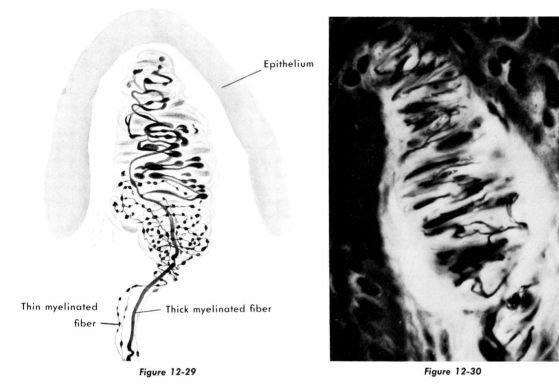

Epithelium

Thin myelinated fiber   Thick myelinated fiber

Figure 12-29.   **Figure 12-30.**

Figure 12-29. Meissner's corpuscle of a dermal papilla of a human finger. Methylene blue. (Redrawn after Dogiel.)
Figure 12-30. Meissner's corpuscle of an 11 year old girl. Silver stain. (Courtesy of N. Cauna.)

neurons. Instead, a relatively small number of axodendritic endings are found.

The postganglionic neurons of the craniosacral visceral nervous system lie, as a rule, close to the viscera innervated. The preganglionic fibers, accordingly, are relatively long—as in the vagus nerve—and the postganglionic fibers are short. On the other hand, most of the synapses of the thoracolumbar system are in the ganglia of the sympathetic chains or trunks; therefore their postganglionic fibers are relatively longer.

The nervous elements of the sympathetic ganglia are generally small and have such diverse shapes and structure that some maintain that no morphological classification is practicable. The cells are generally multipolar, with the dendrites and axon sometimes being clearly distinguishable but in other cases showing no obvious difference. Preganglionic fibers often synapse with the dendrites of the ganglion cell in dense glomeruli. For a typical example, see the description of the postganglionic neurons of the intestine (p. 577).

The cell body may be surrounded by a capsule of satellite cells, which, like those of the craniospinal ganglia, are ectodermal ele-

ments related to the cells of Schwann in the nerve sheaths. In the outlying sympathetic ganglia these capsules may be absent, but the cells of Schwann accompany the peripheral sympathetic fibers everywhere.

NEUROGLIA

The number of nerve cells within the central nervous system, although enormous, is exceeded by the number of non-neural supportive cells called the *neuroglial cells* or *neuroglia* ("nerve glue"). The term neuroglia is applied to the following interstitial tissues: the *ependyma*, which lines the ventricles of the brain and spinal cord; *neuroglial cells* and their processes, which mingle with the neurons in the central nervous system and in the retina; and the *satellite* or *capsular cells* of the peripheral ganglia. The *cells of Schwann* of the peripheral nerves may be considered equivalent to peripheral neuroglia.

EPENDYMA. In the early embryonic stages of the brain and spinal cord the wall of the neural tube is a simple epithelium (Fig. 12-46). Certain thin, non-nervous parts of the brain retain this structure throughout adult life, as for example, the epithelial layer of the choroid plexus (Figs. 12-49 and 12-50). In most other parts of the neural tube, the wall is greatly thickened by the differentiation and multiplication within it of neurons and neuroglial elements. The lining of the inner surface of the wall enclosing the ventricular cavities always retains an epithelial character. This lining membrane, the adult ependyma, is composed of the inner ends of the persisting epithelial cells, with their nuclei and some of their cytoplasm, and such derivatives of the primitive embryonic epithelium as remain in connection with it.

The embryonic ependyma is ciliated, and in some parts of the ventricular lining the cilia may persist into adult life. In the mature brain, the broad bases of ependymal cells taper to long, threadlike processes that may branch and that are lost among other elements of the brain. In a few places, where the nervous wall is thin, as in the ventral fissure of the spinal cord, some ependymal cells span the entire distance between the ventricular and external surfaces. All of them do so in the early embryonic stages. In these cases the ependymal cells form a dense *internal limiting membrane* at the ventricular end.

At the external surface, under the *pia mater,* the ependymal threads and bars expand into pedicles that fuse into a thin, smooth, dense membrane, the *external limiting membrane* of the central nervous system. Similar membranes are formed around the blood vessels.

NEUROGLIA PROPER, OR GLIA. In any section of the central nervous system prepared by ordinary histological methods, small nuclei are seen scattered among the nerve cells and their processes (Fig. 12-2). The cytoplasm and long processes of these neuroglial elements are revealed by special histological techniques.

Three types of neuroglia are distinguished: *astrocytes, oligodendrocytes,* and *microglia.* The first two, called *macroglia,* are undoubtedly of ectodermal origin, as are the nerve cells proper. The third, or *microglia,* originates from mesodermal cells of the pia mater, which migrate into the central nervous system along the blood vessels.

The *astrocytes* are of two varieties. The first is the *protoplasmic astrocyte,* with a larger nucleus than in oligodendrocytes and microglia and with relatively abundant granular cytoplasm and numerous, rather thick processes (Fig. 12-35*A*). Many of the processes

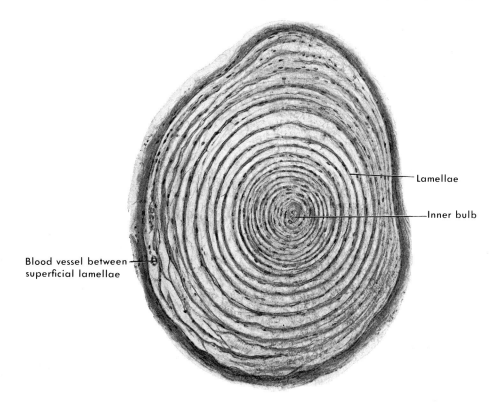

Figure 12-31. Cross section of corpuscle of Vater-Pacini, from dermis of the sole of a human foot. × 110. (After Schaffer.)

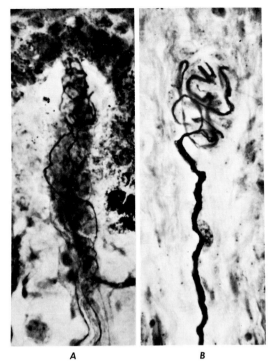

A   B

Figure 12-32. *A*, Genital corpuscle from the glans penis of a 23 year old man. Silver preparation. × 800. (Courtesy of N. Cauna.) *B*, Lingual corpuscle from a filiform papilla on the tongue of a 21 year old woman. Silver stain. × 600. (From N. Cauna, Anat. Rec., *124*:77, 1956.)

of these cells are attached to the blood vessels and to the pia mater by means of expanded pedicles. In other cases, the body of the cell lies directly on the wall of the blood vessel or on the inner surface of the pia. Some of the smaller cells of this variety lie close to the bodies of the neurons and represent one type of *satellite cell*.

The other variety is the *fibrous astrocyte* (Fig. 12-35*B*), distinguished from the first by long, relatively thin, smooth, and infrequently branched expansions. Embedded within the cytoplasm of their bodies and expansions are fibrillar structures or neuroglial fibers. It is evident from electron micrographs that the neuroglial fibers of light microscopy result from aggregation of the slender filaments that are present in great profusion in the cytoplasm of these cells. These cells also are often attached to the blood vessels by means of their processes. The protoplasmic astrocytes are found chiefly in the gray substance and the fibrous astrocytes in the white substance of the brain, insinuated

between the fascicles of nerve fibers. Mixed or *plasmatofibrous astrocytes* are occasionally encountered at the boundary between the gray and white substance; those of their processes that spread into the gray substance have a protoplasmic character, whereas those that pass into the white substance are fibrous.

The *oligodendrocytes*, or *oligodendroglia* (Fig. 12-35*D*), are closely akin to the astrocytes, which they resemble in many respects. They are smaller and have smaller nuclei, although there are many transitional forms. The name is derived from the fact that their few and slender processes have few branches. No true neuroglial fibers are related to them. They seem to be in an especially intimate relationship with the nerve fibers, along which they are frequently found in rows or columns. Although it is difficult to demonstrate the connection of the oligodendrocyte with the myelin sheath in the adult, studies on the developing nervous system have convinced most investigators that this cell forms myelin in the central nervous system. Thus it is regarded as the homologue of the neurilemmal cells of Schwann. In the gray substance those oligodendrocytes that adjoin the nerve cells proper are the principal type of satellite cell. In tissue cultures the oligodendrocytes have been shown to exhibit rhythmic pulsatile movements (Pomerat). The significance of this behavior in relation to their

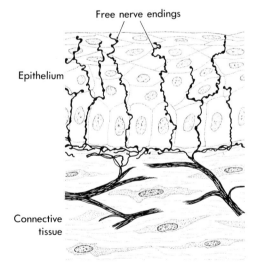

Free nerve endings

Epithelium

Connective tissue

Figure 12-33. Free nerve endings in the epithelium of rabbit cornea. The connective tissue is of the corneal substance proper. Impregnation with gold chloride. (Redrawn and slightly modified from Ramón y Cajal.)

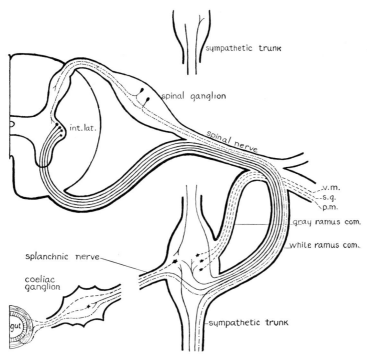

Figure 12-34. Diagram of relations of sympathetic trunk to spinal cord and spinal nerves. Visceral sensory fibers are drawn in dot-and-dash lines, preganglionic fibers in continuous lines, and postganglionic fibers in broken lines. For clearness the rami communicantes are drawn more widely separated from the spinal ganglion than is natural. *Int. lat.,* Intermediolateral gray column of the spinal cord, containing cells whose axons form preganglionic fibers; *p.m.,* pilomotor postganglionic fiber; *s.g.,* postganglionic fiber for sweat glands; *v.m.,* vasomotor postganglionic fiber. (From Herrick's Introduction to Neurology.)

normal function in the brain is not known. The criteria for identification of the several types of macroglia in electron micrographs have only been partially established.

In the *microglia* (Fig. 12-35*C*), the nucleus is small but deeply stained and surrounded by scanty protoplasm. The few expansions are rather short and, unlike the more or less straight expansions of the astrocytes, are twisted in various ways. Also, the processes and the body do not appear smooth, but are covered with a considerable number of tiny pointed twigs or "spines." The microglial cells are scattered everywhere throughout the brain and spinal cord.

The neuroglia of the adult central nervous system is of ectodermal origin. Exceptions are the microglia, which are mesodermal. In the mature brain and spinal cord the neuroglial tissue as a whole forms an extremely complicated supporting framework of cells and their expansions, in which the nerve cells and their processes are suspended. Like the nerve cells, the supporting neuroglial cells do not form a syncytium, as assumed by some;

they, too, retain their individuality. In the chambers of a complex labyrinth made up of glial cells, the nerve cells and their processes are individually encapsulated and thus insulated from one another. An interesting and probably highly significant fact revealed by electron microscopy is that wherever nerve cell bodies and their processes are not in synaptic contact with another neuron, they are generally enveloped by the cell bodies or processes of neuroglial cells. The distribution of these neuroglial processes appears not to be random nor merely to fulfill the requirements of mechanical support and nutrition of the neurons. It was proposed early in this century, by Ramón y Cajal, that neuroglial processes are always disposed so as to prevent contact between processes of nerve cells at sites other than those appropriate to their specific signaling function. On the basis of electron microscopic observations Palay has renewed this hypothesis and clearly documented that each neuron has a characteristic pattern of neuroglial investment, which is complementary to the specific pattern of its synaptic connections. It appears

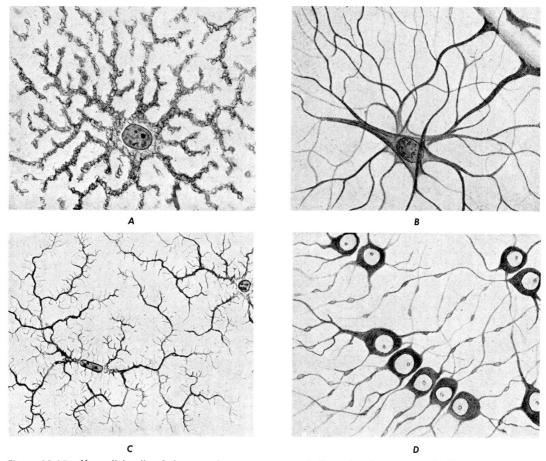

Figure 12-35. Neuroglial cells of the central nervous system. *A,* Protoplasmic astrocyte; *B,* fibrous astrocyte; *C,* microglia; *D,* oligodendroglia. (After del Rio-Hortega.)

that only at the synapses are the neuroglial barriers interrupted and only here is a direct contact between the neurons possible. Thus, by isolating and individualizing the many diverse pathways that may converge upon a given neuron, the neuroglial cells may play an essential role in the communications function of the nervous system.

The neuroglia appears also to be an important mediator for the normal metabolism of the neurons, although little is known in this respect. More is known about the activity of the neuroglia in pathological processes. Whenever the neurons are affected by a local or distant pathological process, the surrounding neuroglial elements always react in some way. They are actively involved in the degeneration and regeneration of the nerve fibers, in vascular disorders, and in various infectious processes, and they are the chief source of tumors of the central nervous system. In particular,

the microglial cells assume a great variety of forms, with active migration and phagocytosis.

SYNAPSE AND THE RELATIONSHIPS OF NEURONS

Essentially, the nervous system is composed of complex chains of neurons so arranged as to permit transmission of excitation from one neuron to another in one direction only. The site of impulse transmission from neuron to neuron is called a *synapse.* Physiologically it is of the utmost importance, for functional polarization is established here and not along the nerve fiber, where conduction in either direction is possible.

Anatomically, the synapse has traditionally been described as a place of contact between two neurons; it may be from axon to dendrite, from axon to perikaryon, or, more rarely, from axon to axon. The number of synapses on a neuron varies enormously. Some neurons, such as the granule cell of the cerebellum, have only a few. A motor neuron may possess as many as 1800 synapses. A Purkinje cell of the cerebellum may have several hundred thousand endings upon its dendrites alone. The forms of the synapses also vary in the extreme (Fig. 12-37). Usually they are tiny swellings at the tips of the axon endings, but the terminal twigs may form bouquets or loose baskets and the like, adhering to the body or dendrites of another nerve cell. Each variety of neuron is distinguished by its own form of synaptic terminations, some having endings of several kinds.

In electron micrographs showing synaptic endings in the central nervous system (Figs. 12-38 to 12-40) the axons are expanded into rounded terminal boutons close to the dendrites or perikarya of other neurons. Neurofilaments are absent in these endings, but they typically contain a cluster of mitochondria and a very large number of small vesicles 200 to 650 Å in diameter, commonly called *synaptic vesicles*. These are believed to arise by budding from the ends of the slender canaliculi that are present in the axon. They are frequently found to be aggregated very near the presynaptic surface. The pre- and postsynaptic surface membranes are separated by a narrow extracellular cleft about 200 Å wide. Along the synaptic surface there are local thickenings of the apposing membranes and a subjacent condensation of the cytoplasm (Fig. 12-39). These structures bear a superficial resemblance to the desmosomes that help to maintain cohesion of epithelial cells.

The absence of cytoplasmic continuity between neurons forms the basis for the neuron doctrine, which maintains that each mature nerve cell represents a cellular unit anatomically separate from, and trophically independent of, other neurons. The claim of cytoplasmic continuity between neurons of the intestinal autonomic plexus has not been verified with the electron microscope and is no longer accepted.

The processes of a neuron are dependent on the cell body and its nucleus. When cut off, the processes die. New processes may, however, grow out from the perikaryon. The body and nucleus of the nerve cell are the trophic center of the entire neuron. If one nerve cell suffers irreparable injury, adjoining nerve cells are not necessarily affected. An exception, the so-called *transneuronal degeneration,* sometimes occurs in pathways where certain neurons are almost totally dependent on other neurons as sources of nerve impulses, as is the case in the visual system.

Transmission of the nervous impulse from one neuron to another or to another effector ending is known to involve the passage of a *transmitter substance* across the intervening synaptic cleft. Of particular interest is acetylcholine, which is found in the central nervous system as well as in peripheral autonomic ganglia and motor end-plates. Its specific destructor, acetylcholinesterase, has been found in the plexiform layers of the cerebral cortex, which are rich in synapses. The full significance of these findings is not known. It is clear that there are other transmitter substances at central synapses. One which has been identified is gamma-aminobutyric acid (GABA). In addition, at certain synapses in which the apposing cell surfaces are in especially intimate contact, electrical energy is the chief agent of transmission instead of a chemical mediator.

EXAMPLES OF INTERRELATIONSHIPS OF NEURONS. Except in the primate retina, where one-to-one synapses are found, almost every neuron is connected with several or many other neurons. With the aid of the Golgi impregnation and other methods, several dif-

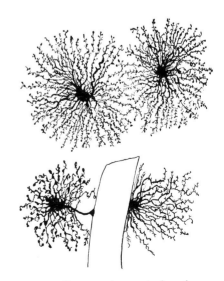

Figure 12-36.   Short-rayed astrocytes from the gray matter of the brain of an adult man; the two lower ones are connected with the walls of a blood vessel by their processes. Golgi method. (After Ramón y Cajal.)

ferent types of relationships between neurons have been shown to be present. These vary from extremely complex relationships involving the processes of hundreds of cells to relatively simple configurations. It will suffice here to give examples of a few extreme categories. For instance, attached to the body and dendrites of many large motor cells of the anterior gray columns of the spinal cord are many hundreds of synaptic boutons of axons from neurons in the cerebral cortex, medullary nuclei, and elsewhere in the spinal cord. The spinal motor cells serve, accordingly, as the final common pathway by which the nervous impulses from a variety of sources are transmitted to effector organs. A clear instance of this is found in the giant Mauthner cells in the medulla oblongata of fishes (Fig. 12-37). In the retina the *d*-bipolar neurons serve as a common pathway for impulses from both rods and cones. The reverse arrangement is shown in Figure 12-41*C*, where one retinal cone is in contact with three neurons (*d, f,* and *h*).

In the frequent arrangements in which a few neurons are related to a large group of neurons, the reaction is not commensurate with the initial stimulus but is determined by the number and kinds of reacting interneurons, often arranged in chains effecting inhibition or facilitation of the impulse. Thus, in a spinal reflex arc (Fig. 12-42) the excitation of a few peripheral sensory elements may activate a great number of motor neurons, and the total response or effect may many times exceed the energy that initiated it.

These glimpses of the intricate connections between neurons, coupled with their enormous numbers (it is estimated that there are 9,200,000,000 neurons in the cerebral cortex alone) and their extreme variability in the various parts of the nervous system, may provide some indication of the complexity of neural structure and function.

The details of the complex organization of the central nervous system are beyond the scope of this book and must be sought in text-

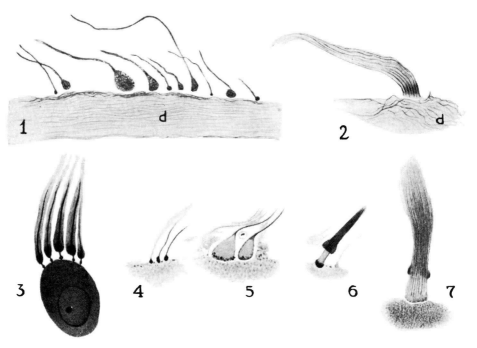

Figure 12-37. Types of nerve fiber endings in the vertebrate central nervous system. *1,* End-feet of Held of unmyelinated nerve fibers ending on dendrite of another neuron (*d*). *2,* Club ending of Bartelmez, which ends abruptly on dendrite of another neuron (*d*). *3,* Fine myelinated fibers ending on nerve cell by means of tiny "end-feet." *4,* Similar endings of unmyelinated fibers on dendrite of another nerve cell. *5,* Large "end-feet" on dendrite of another nerve cell. Note granular mitochondria at terminal surfaces of the "end-feet." *6* and *7,* Clublike endings of myelinated fibers ending on dendrites of other cells. Neurofibrils in dendrite of *7* are cut transversely and appear as fine dots. *1* and *2* stained for neurofibrils with reduced silver. *3* to *7* fixed by injecting Zenker-formol into blood vessels of living animal; silver followed by Mallory-azan stain. All from the brain of the goldfish. × 1440. (From the color plate of Bodian, 1937. Drawn by Miss Agnes Nixon.)

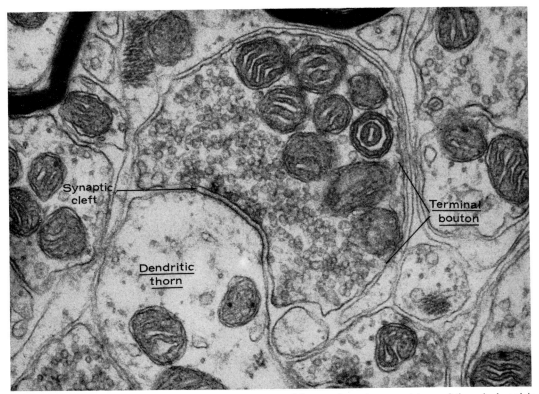

Figure 12-38. Tip of a dendritic thorn, capped by a terminal bouton from the ventral horn of the spinal cord in a rat. The typical features of synapses—mitochondria, clustered vesicles, and the cleft—are well shown. The terminal is enclosed within a thin astrocytic process. × about 60,000. (Courtesy of S. L. Palay.)

books of neuroanatomy. It may be instructive, however, to include photomicrographs of three different parts of the nervous system. Figure 12-43, of the spinal cord, illustrates the external position of the great masses of myelinated fibers in relation to the relatively small amount of gray matter containing the nerve cell bodies. Figures 12-44 and 12-45 show gray matter outside the white in cerebral cortex and cerebellum. The white matter of the cerebral hemispheres, the numerous tracts of the brain stem and spinal cord, and practically all peripheral nerves are chiefly or entirely made up of myelinated or unmyelinated axons. These elements serve, accordingly, to transmit nerve impulses from parts of the body to the central nervous system, or vice versa, or from one part of the brain or cord to another part. There is no evidence that any modification of the nerve impulse occurs in nerves or tracts.

The situation is reversed in the gray matter, in which nerve cell bodies are mingled with unmyelinated and some myelinated fibers. A microscopic preparation of such an area shows the bodies of the cells arranged in a certain order, usually in layers. The space between the cellular layers, and also between the individual cells, is filled with innumerable axons and dendrites, and also with neuroglia and blood vessels. Nerve processes usually are without myelin sheaths, which accounts for the gray appearance of these parts in fresh condition. Here innumerable reciprocal contacts between the various types of neurons make possible an endless variety of mutual influences. It is here that incoming impulses are selected, combined, and divided, and the resulting impulses sent back to the effector organs. Recent findings that axons originating in the motor cerebral cortex end in relation to sensory as well as motor neurons provide a possible explanation for intensification of stimuli and the phenomenon of attention.

When stained with routine methods, the region between cell bodies has a punctate or stippled appearance and corresponds to the *neuropil* described above. In the cerebellar and cerebral cortices and in the retina certain lay-

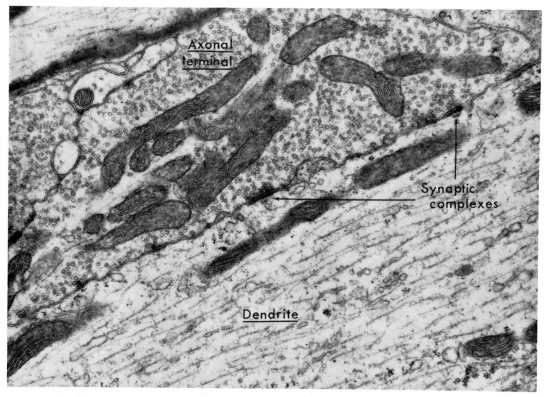

Figure 12-39. Large axonal terminal forming synapses upon a dendrite in the lateral vestibular nucleus of a rat. Several synaptic complexes are shown. × about 26,000. (Courtesy of C. Sotelo and S. L. Palay.)

ers are composed almost exclusively of naked neuronal or neuroglial processes. Huge numbers of synaptic contacts take place in such synaptic fields.

The pattern of the cells and fibers (cytoarchitecture) in the gray matter varies in detail from place to place. Every subcortical nucleus, peripheral ganglion, and locality of the cerebral cortex has architectural features of its own. Thus, the cortex in the precentral convolution of the primate brain, which coincides with the so-called *motor area*, differs from that of the postcentral convolution, where the combined *somatosensory function* is represented, and from all other parts of the cerebral cortex. One of the important cortical regions having a characteristic cytoarchitecture is the *visual area* along the calcarine fissure of the occipital lobe. Another, in the sylvian fossa, is the *auditory area*. Careful attempts to correlate cytoarchitectonic and functional findings have, however, failed up to the present time.

The properties of gray matter differ from those of the nerve fiber in several respects. A monosynaptic reflex arc serves as an example. It is composed of a sensory (afferent) and a motor (efferent) neuron connected in the central nervous system, together with the corresponding peripheral receptor and effector organs. Such a mechanism has several functional characteristics. (1) It fatigues rapidly in contrast to the simple nerve fiber, which is exhausted slowly—or never, in the case of myelinated fibers. (2) The reflex is blocked in the central nervous system by a fraction of the amount of a drug that is needed to block the peripheral nerve fiber. (3) The direction of the signal is always from the sensory fiber to the motor or secretory fiber, indicating the functional polarity of the gray matter, termed *irreversibility* or *irreciprocal conduction*. (4) The response varies greatly with respect to the latent period and the intensity, depending on the condition of the central nervous system. (5) The latent period is much longer than in the nerve fiber, and there may be an *after-discharge;* that is, the response may continue for some time after the stimulus ceases. (6) Although one or a few stimuli may have no effect, an effect may result from numerous stimuli applied in sequence, which indicates *summation*. (7) Certain nerves are capable of decreasing or stopping the reflex response induced by the stimulation of other nerves through the mechanism of *central inhibition*. (8) The rhythm of the response in a reflex is usually slower than that of the applied stimulus (Sherrington). The mechanisms underlying these phenomena are still only partially understood and are beyond the scope of this chapter; the student should consult a current textbook of neurophysiology for discussion of these properties.

Bewildering though nervous tissue may seem at first, correlated anatomical and physiological studies provide compelling evidence that the nervous system is by no means a random tangle of neurons and neuroglial cells and their processes. Neurons appear not to be redundant but instead display remarkable structural and functional individuality. Morphologically the individuality is expressed in the connections established between particular cells and in the number, type, and location of synaptic terminals upon different parts of the same cell. It has been demonstrated physiologically that particular neurons among the astronomical numbers comprising, for example, the visual area of the cerebral cortex respond to, or are inhibited by, highly specific modes of visual stimuli presented to the retina. Other principles of organization of the nervous system cannot be appreciated fully until the student has undertaken a study of neuroanatomy. Among these are the concepts that the central nervous system is subdivided into a series of interdependent cellular ensembles for analysis and control; that the patterns of connections often permit the reciprocal interactions necessary for modulation of both incoming and outgoing impulses; and finally, that the cellular units of the central nervous system at all levels from the motor neuron to the cell of the cerebral cortex are designed for integrative action.

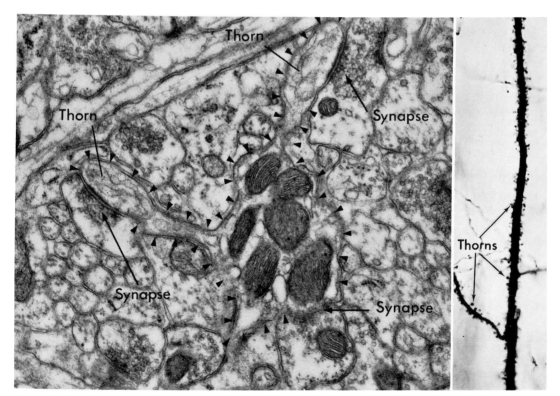

Figure 12-40.   Transverse section across a spiny branchlet of a Purkinje cell dendrite in the cerebellar cortex of a rat. The surface membrane of the spiny branchlet is outlined by arrow heads. Two thorns are shown in synaptic contact with terminals of parallel fibers. × about 35,000. (Courtesy of S. L. Palay; inset courtesy of D. K. Morest.)

DEVELOPMENT OF THE NEURONS AND OF THE NERVOUS TISSUE

The neurons of the nervous system develop from embryonic ectoderm. Also of ectodermal origin are the neuroglial cells (except for the mesodermal microglia), the Schwann cells of peripheral nerves and the corresponding satellite cells in peripheral ganglia, and certain elements of the meninges.

In early embryonic stages the future central nervous system separates by folding from the primitive ectoderm to form the *neural tube.* At the time the neural folds meet, some cells leave the junctional region bilaterally to form cellular bands between the neural tube and the prospective epidermis. These bands, the *neural crests,* soon become segmented and are the precursors of the craniospinal and sympathetic ganglia, adrenal medulla, and melanocytes. Schwann cells are also generally regarded as derivatives of the neural crests. Autoradiographic studies with tritiated thymidine, however, show that some (possibly all) Schwann cells originate in the neural tube.

The early neural tube is a type of pseudostratified epithelium in which all cells reach the lumen (Fig. 12-46). Autoradiographic and electron microscopic studies demonstrate a single type of epithelial cell, called a primitive ependymal cell or *matrix cell.* During proliferation, the nuclei of matrix cells undergo a cyclical change of position in the *matrix layer* (Fig. 12-47); nuclei of premitotic cells lie deep, progressively approaching the lumen during prophase. Karyokinesis occurs only at the luminal surface, whereupon the daughter nuclei move again to deeper positions. With further development of the neural tube, *neuroblasts* (immature, migratory neurons incapable of further division) derived from matrix cells migrate peripherally to form the *mantle layer* (future gray matter). A *marginal layer* (future white matter) is subsequently formed external to the mantle layer by the axons of the differentiating neuroblasts. Neuroglial cells in general originate later from the matrix layer and, unlike typical neuroblasts, continue to divide after migration to the mantle and marginal layers. In certain regions of the brain, cells are pro-

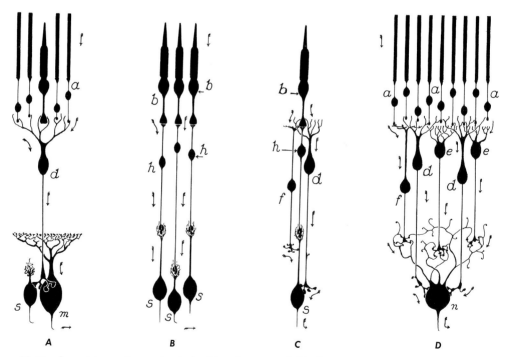

A   **B**   **C**   **D**

Figure 12-41. Several types of synaptic relationships of neurons. *A,* Bipolar neuron (*d*) serving as a common pathway for both rods and cones (*a*). *B,* Isolated conduction, or one-to-one relationship of neurons (*b, h, s*). *C,* Single excitation (in *b*) is transferred to each of the three related neurons (varieties *d, f, h*). *D,* Excitations from a number of rods (*a*) pass through intermediary neurons (*d, e, f*) to a single large neuron (*n*). Examples from the primate retina (see Fig. 32-25). (Courtesy of S. Polyak.)

duced that retain proliferative ability after origin in the matrix layer, and these give rise to additional neurons. Such a secondary germinal matrix is found in the development of the cerebellum. A transient layer is formed on the external surface of the embryonic cortex by cells that migrate from the matrix layer of the underlying brain stem. Proliferation in this external layer produces neuroblasts that descend into the cerebellar cortex. Other cerebellar neurons and most neurons of the cerebral cortex arise directly from the matrix layer and traverse mantle and marginal layers to reach their destinations. Autoradiographic studies demonstrate that proliferation of neurons by the matrix zone is a rigorously timed and highly ordered process, followed by active migration and frequent intermingling of neuroblasts as they proceed to their final positions.

The sensory neurons of the craniospinal nerves arise in the neural crests. The peripheral processes grow outward and become typical axons of the sensory nerve fibers. The dendritic region of these neurons is the receptive zone at the periphery; here, the axon develops a variable pattern of branches, which may or may not be encapsulated. The central processes enter the central nervous system as the axons of dorsal roots and establish connections with interneurons or motor neurons (Fig. 12-42). The cell bodies of the somatic and visceral motor neurons remain within the brain or spinal cord; their axons grow out as ventral roots of the peripheral nerves and terminate in muscles or autonomic ganglia.

The protoplasm of a growing axon shows ameboid movements and insinuates itself between other tissue elements by positive outgrowth (Fig. 12-48). At its advancing tip a bulbous enlargement, or "growth cone," thrusts slender, spinelike projections between obstructing cells and fibers. The features of neuronal development seen in fixed and stained material were confirmed by observations on living nerves in tissue culture and by studies of growing nerves in the transparent tail of the living frog tadpole. Axons of neuroblasts grow into the intercellular spaces as slender, protoplasmic strands. In peripheral nerve fibers all newly formed axons are at first devoid of Schwann and myelin sheaths. The earliest myelin appears near the Schwann cell nucleus, from which locality it spreads proximally and distally.

The forces that direct the course of devel-

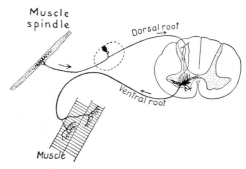

Figure 12-42. Diagram illustrating simple spinal reflex arc, consisting of a sensory neuron connected with a receptor ending and a motor neuron connected with a muscle. Physiological connection between the two neurons is effected within the spinal cord. (Modified from van Gehuchten.)

opment of the complex nervous tissue of vertebrates are largely unknown. The importance of an oriented microstructure (micellar orientation and aggregation) as a guide, along whose channels developing axons spread, has been confirmed. There has been no confirmation, however, of the concept of "neurobiotaxis," which assumes that differences in electric potential between dendrites and axons account for migration of nerve cell bodies in the direction of the source from which their stimuli come. No clear-cut effects of electric currents have been seen on either the rate or direction of the growth of nerves. Chemotactic influences upon growing axons have been demonstrated clearly in the optic nerve. Regenerating optic nerve fibers from different parts of the goldfish retina unerringly reach their former terminations in the optic lobes of the midbrain, even after surgical cross-union of medial and lateral optic tracts. There is evidence for refined chemoaffinities of growing axons in other regions of the central nervous system, but the role of chemotactic influences on the growth of peripheral nerves remains controversial. There is also evidence to show that the periphery affects the development of the central nervous system in many ways after contact has been established between the two regions. These effects are both quantitative and qualitative; they act to regulate the number and size of neurons in specific regions of the neuraxis and to influence the pattern of their connections. Another important finding has been the discovery of specific nerve growth factors, identified as proteins, which exert powerful effects upon the generation, growth, and maintenance of specific types of nerve cells.

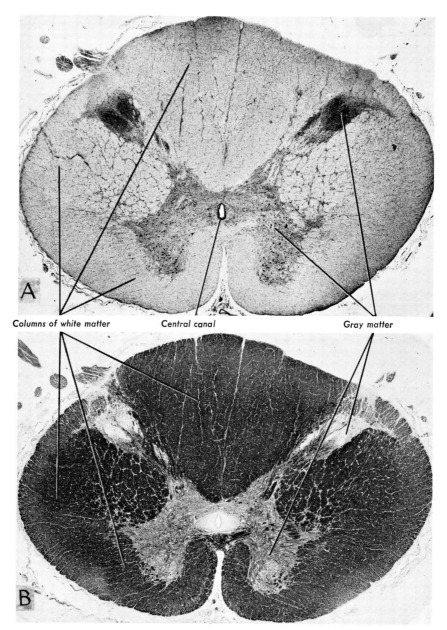

Columns of white matter   Central canal   Gray matter

Figure 12-43. Sections through human upper cervical spinal cord stained with thionine (*A*) to show cells, and with the Weigert-Weil method (*B*) to show myelinated fibers. Note the external arrangement of the fibers (white matter) and the central, cruciate area containing the cell bodies (gray matter). The ventral surface is below. A portion of the dorsal root is seen in the upper left. × 12. (Courtesy of P. Bailey.)

CONNECTIVE TISSUE, CHOROID PLEXUS, VENTRICLES, AND THE MENINGES OF THE CENTRAL NERVOUS SYSTEM

In addition to the neurons and the supporting neuroglia, which are both of ectodermal origin, the brain and the spinal cord everywhere contain blood vessels derived from mesenchyme. The membranes enveloping the brain and spinal cord are likewise composed chiefly of connective tissue. There are three such membranes. The outermost, the *dura mater* or *pachymeninx*, is dense and firm. Both of the inner membranes, the *pia mater*, which is innermost, and the *arachnoid membrane*, which is intermediate, are composed of much looser connective tissue and are called *leptomeninges*.

DURA MATER. The dura of the spinal cord and that of the brain differ in their relationships to the surrounding bones. The inner surface of the vertebral canal is lined by its own periosteum, and a separate cylindrical dural membrane loosely encloses the cord. The rather wide *epidural space*, between the periosteum and the dura, contains much loose connective and fatty tissue, and the epidural venous plexus. The dura is firmly connected to the spinal cord on each side by a series of denticulate ligaments. The inner surface of the spinal dura is lined with squamous cells. Its collagenous bundles run for the most part longitudinally, and the elastic fibers are less prominent than in the cerebral dura.

The dura mater of the brain at the beginning of its embryonic development also has two layers, but in the adult these are closely joined. Both consist of loose connective tissue with elongated fibroblasts. The outer layer adheres to the skull rather loosely except at the sutures and the base of the skull. It functions as periosteum, is looser and richer in cells than the inner layer, and contains many blood vessels; its thick collagenous fibers are arranged in bundles. The inner layer is thinner, with finer fibers forming an almost continuous sheet. Its fibers run from the frontal region backward and upward, being oriented opposite to those of the outer layer. The inner surface of the dura is smooth and covered with a layer of squamous mesothelial cells.

ARACHNOID. The leptomeninges of the brain and spinal cord are similar in structure. The arachnoid is a thin, netlike membrane devoid of blood vessels, resembling the transparent parts of the omentum. Its outer surface is smooth, but from its inner surface runs a multitude of thin, branching threads and ribbon-like strands, attached to the pia. The tissue on macroscopic examination has a cobweb-like appearance. The arachnoid membrane bridges over the sulci and the fissures on the surface of the brain and the spinal cord, forming *subarachnoid spaces* of various extent within these sulci.

PIA MATER. This inner membrane is a thin connective tissue net that closely adheres to the surface of the brain and the spinal cord. It contains a large number of blood vessels, from which most of the blood of the underlying nervous tissue is supplied. Attached to the pia are the inner fibrous strands of the arachnoid, and these two membranes are so intimately related that their histological structure can best be described together. In fact, these two membranes are often treated as one, the *pia-arachnoid*.

The main elements of both the arachnoid and the pia are interlacing collagenous bundles surrounded by fine elastic networks. In the spinal pia an outer longitudinal and an inner circular layer can be distinguished. Among the cells are fibroblasts and fixed macrophages; these are especially numerous along the blood vessels in the pia. They correspond in their properties to the macrophages of the other parts of the body. They store vital dyes injected directly into the subarachnoid space. In inflammation, they are transformed into large, free macrophages or epithelioid cells. In man they often contain considerable amounts of a yellow pigment that sometimes reacts positively to tests for iron.

Along the blood vessels of the pia mater are scattered single mast cells and small groups of lymphocytes. In certain pathological conditions the latter increase enormously in number and may become transformed into plasma cells. The tissue of the leptomeninges, especially along the blood vessels of the pia, also contains many embryonic mesenchymal elements. In the pia mater, particularly on the ventral surface of the medulla oblongata, a varying number of melanocytes can be found.

The outer and the inner surfaces of the arachnoid, the trabeculae, and the outer surface of the pia are covered with a layer of squamous mesenchymal epithelial cells. Although some investigators describe their rounding off, mobilization, and transformation into free macrophages under the influence of

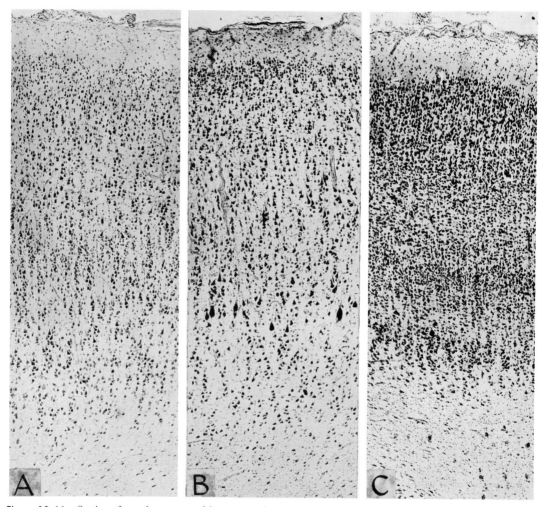

Figure 12-44. Sections from three areas of human cerebral cortex, showing distribution of nerve bodies (*A*) in the temporal eulaminate (associational) cortex, (*B*) in the precentral agranular cortex (motor area), and (*C*) in the occipital koniocortex (striate visual cortex). Much stress has been laid on minute differences in lamination of the nerve cells and fibers in these and other areas of the cortex, but there is now a tendency to minimize some of these differences. × 53. (Courtesy of P. Bailey.)

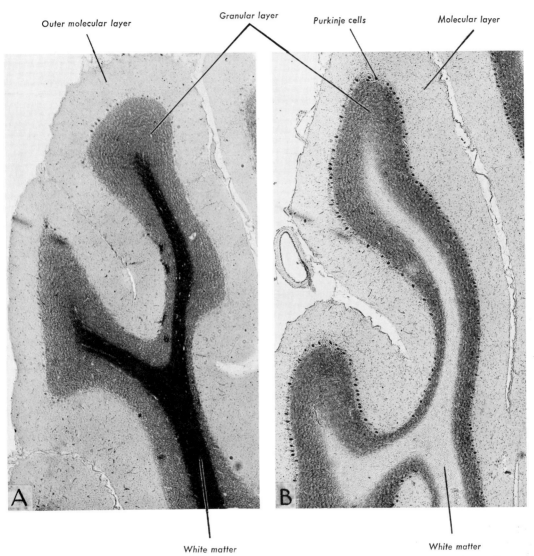

Figure 12-45. Sections of human cerebellar folia stained with the Weigert-Weil method (*A*) for myelinated fibers and with thionine (*B*) for cells. Note the central disposition of the white matter with its myelinated fibers, which stain black with Weigert-Weil and pale with thionine; the outer molecular layer (pale gray), with scattered neurons and the large Purkinje cells, and the intermediate, or granular, layer, composed of cells and fibers. × 32. (Courtesy of P. Bailey.)

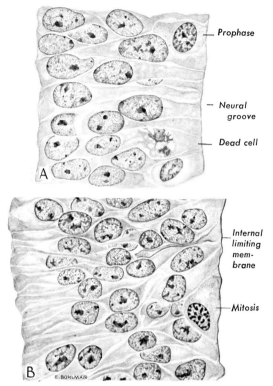

Figure 12-46. *A,* Portion of neural fold just caudal to the posterior neuropore of an 18 somite human embryo (about 24 days old). It is a pseudostratified epithelium with cell boundaries clearly defined. The internal limiting membrane is developing, but the external one has not appeared. As in most rapidly growing tissues, there is an occasional degenerating cell. × 845. *B,* Part of lateral wall of neural tube in the region of the medulla oblongata from a 26 somite human embryo (about 4 weeks old). The cells are much longer and more irregular than in *A,* but it is occasionally possible to follow one through the entire thickness of the wall. Cell boundaries indicate that the original epithelial condition persists. Both external and internal limiting membranes are present. × 845. (Courtesy of G. W. Bartelmez.)

inflammatory stimuli, others trace the origin of macrophages exclusively to fixed macrophages. This question requires further study.

During development of the meninges two zones may be distinguished: an outer zone of condensation of mesenchyme, which gives rise to periosteum, dura, and membranous arachnoid; and an inner zone, which becomes pia. Between these two zones the mesenchyme remains loose and later forms spongy tissue permeating the subarachnoid spaces.

NERVES OF THE MENINGES. The dura and pia mater are richly supplied with nerves.

All vessels of the pia and of the choroid plexus are surrounded by extensive nervous plexuses in the adventitia, from which fine fibrils penetrate the media. These nerves have their origin in the carotid and vertebral plexuses and in certain cranial nerves, and belong to the sympathetic system. Sensory, nonencapsulated nerve terminations, and even single nerve cells, are also present on the adventitia of the blood vessels.

The cerebral dura contains, besides the nerves of the vessels, numerous sensory nerve endings in its connective tissue. The connective tissue of the cerebral pia contains extensive nervous plexuses. They are especially abundant in the tela choroidea of the third ventricle. The fibers end either in large, pear-shaped or bulbous swellings or in skeins and convolutions similar to those of the corpuscles of Meissner. In the spinal pia the vessels receive their nerves from the plexuses following the larger blood vessels to the cord. Afferent nerve endings are also present, but are very unevenly distributed.

Both myelinated and unmyelinated nerve fibers accompany the blood vessels into the substance of the spinal cord and the brain, ending on the muscle cells of the vessels. These come from similar nerves of the pial vessels, and the two nervous plexuses are continuous.

MENINGEAL SPACES. Between the dura mater and the arachnoid, the subdural space is comparable to a serous cavity. It contains a minimum of fluid and in reality is scarcely more than a potential space. Between the outer sheet of arachnoid and the pia, the subarachnoid space is traversed by cobwebby connective tissue trabeculae. It is independent of the subdural space and contains a large amount of fluid. At the summits of the convolutions it is narrow, but in the sulci it is wide and deep. The subarachnoid space is especially wide throughout the length of the spinal cord. In the brain it is greatly enlarged in a few places termed "cisterns," where the arachnoid is widely separated from the pia and the trabeculae are rare or absent. The most important of the cisterns lies above the medulla oblongata and below the posterior border of the cerebellum (cisterna cerebellomedullaris, or cisterna magna). The fourth ventricle communicates with this cistern through three openings in the tela choroidea: a medial foramen of Magendie, and the two lateral foramina of Luschka.

VENTRICLES. The central nervous system begins its development as a neural tube with a wide cavity throughout its length, and it preserves its character as a hollow organ throughout life. The central canal or ventricle of the spinal cord in the adult is minute, or it may be obliterated. It does not seem to perform any important function. But in the normal adult the ventricular cavities of the brain always form a continuous channel for flow of cerebrospinal fluid throughout its length. If any part of this channel is occluded by disease so as to prevent free circulation of its fluids, an increased intracerebral pressure develops, with resulting hydrocephalus or other serious pathological consequences.

The ventricular cavity is dilated in four regions: the two lateral ventricles in the cerebral hemispheres, the third ventricle in the thalamic region, and the fourth ventricle in the medulla oblongata and pons. Choroid plexuses develop in these four regions, and most of the ventricular fluid is derived from the blood vessels of these plexuses.

CHOROID PLEXUS. There are four places where the wall of the brain retains its embryonic character as a thin, non-nervous epithelium. This part of the brain wall is the *lamina epithelialis*. The pia mater which covers it is extremely vascular and otherwise modified to form a choroid plexus. The lamina epithelialis is closely joined to the choroid plexus, and the whole is called the *tela choroidea* or, less exactly, *choroid plexus*.

These choroid plexuses are found in the roof of the third and fourth ventricles and in a part of the wall of the two lateral ventricles. In each case the tela choroidea is much folded and invaginated into the ventricle, so that the free surface exposed to the ventricular fluid is large, with tortuous vessels and a rich capillary net.

The epithelium early acquires a peculiar structure, different from that of the ependymal cells lining the ventricles. In embryonic stages it contains glycogen and carries cilia. In the adult its cells are cuboidal and are arranged in a single, regular layer. Each contains a large, round nucleus and a varying number of rod-shaped mitochondria.

On the free surface the cells have a specialized border that bears some resemblance to a brush border. In electron micrographs, however, it is seen to be made up of long microvilli that are quite irregular in their orientation. They are often somewhat expanded at their tips (Fig. 12-51). Although this may possibly be an artifact of fixation, microvilli of other cell types fixed similarly do not have this appearance.

In animals repeatedly injected intravenously with vital dyes, such as trypan blue, the epithelium of the choroid plexus stores large amounts of the dye. Also in the perivascular connective tissue core of the plexus are many fixed macrophages, which store large amounts of dye.

On the boundary between adjacent epithelial cells in electron micrographs there is a juxtaluminal junctional complex that appears to seal the intercellular space. The capillaries beneath the epithelium are unlike those elsewhere in the brain in that they are thin walled and have fenestrations or pores closed by thin diaphragms. The junctions between the endothelial cells also appear to be more permeable. Following intravenous injection in mice the protein peroxidase can be shown to cross the capillary walls and enter the stromal space. It moves between the epithelial cells but is stopped near the lumen by the junctional complex (Brightman).

CEREBROSPINAL FLUID. The central nervous system is surrounded by cerebrospinal fluid and suspended in it as in a water bath. This fluid protects it from concussions and

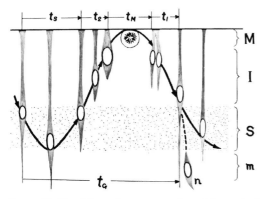

Figure 12-47. Schematic representation of intermitotic migrations of matrix cell nucleus. *M*, Zone of mitosis; *I*, intermediate zone; *S*, zone of DNA synthesis; *m*, mantle layer; *n*, young neuroblast; t_s, DNA synthetic period (S); t_2, premitotic period (G_2); t_M, mitotic period (M); t_1, postmitotic period (G_1); and t_G, generation time. Zones *M, I,* and *S* constitute the matrix layer. The neuroblast is differentiated from the matrix cell at time t_1, traverses the *S*-zone quickly without synthesizing DNA, and migrates into the mantle layer (*m*). (From Fujita, J. Comp. Neurol., *120*:37, 1963 and *122*:311, 1964.)

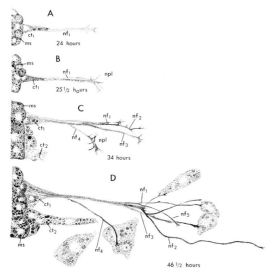

Figure 12-48. Stages in the outgrowth of nerve fibers in a culture of embryonic frog spinal cord. *A*, 24 hours after explanation, an apparently single fiber (nf_1) has grown out from a cell (ct_1) that projects from a mass of cells (ms). *B*, The same fiber, 1½ hours later, appeared clearly double, *C*, 8½ hours later, four distinct fibers (nf_1–nf_4) were visible. Another cell, ct_2, had begun to emigrate from the cell mass. *D*, 12½ hours later, more processes have developed; nf_5 was thought to be possibly a branch of nf_1. (Redrawn and slightly modified from R. G. Harrison.)

mechanical injuries and is important for its metabolism. The subarachnoid spaces are in free communication, so that cerebrospinal fluid may pass through them from end to end of the central nervous system. The amount of the fluid is variable, estimated as 80 to 100 ml., or even as much as 150 ml. It is limpid and slightly viscous and has a low specific gravity (1.004 to 1.008). It contains traces of proteins, small quantities of inorganic salt and dextrose, and few lymphocytes (about 2 or 3, and not more than 10, in 1 cu. mm.). It resembles the aqueous humor of the eye more closely than it does any other fluid of the body.

The cerebrospinal fluid is constantly renewed. It circulates slowly through the brain ventricles and through the meshes of the subarachnoid spaces. If these spaces are opened to the outside by injury, large amounts of fluid steadily drain off—200 ml. or more in a day. The sources of this fluid are primarily the blood vessels of the choroid plexus, the pia mater, and the brain substance. From the brain substance the flow is outward into the subarachnoid spaces; from the choroid plexus

it is inward into the ventricles. Fluid may be added to the ventricles in a few other places, notably in the area postrema at the lower end of the fourth ventricle. The ependymal surfaces in general do not seem to discharge fluid into the ventricles. On the other hand, the absorption of fluid from the ventricles into neighboring veins takes place through the ventricular walls. The plexuses are wholly secretory, not resorptive, in function. They are the chief source of the cerebrospinal fluid. The chief channel of discharge of ventricular fluid outward into the subarachnoid spaces is through specially modified localities of the membranous roof of the fourth ventricle.

The flow of ventricular fluid normally passes from the lateral ventricles of the cerebral hemispheres, where it is derived chiefly from the lateral choroid plexuses, through the foramina of Monro into the third ventricle. Here fluid is added from the choroid plexus of the third ventricle and the augmented flow passes through the aqueduct of Sylvius into the fourth ventricle, where more fluid is added from the choroid plexus of that ventricle. From there the fluid passes into the cerebellomedullary cistern, and from here it diffuses in all directions through the subarachnoid spaces. Some of it is said to get into the extracranial lymphatics by way of the perineural spaces within the sheaths of the cranial nerve roots, part reaching the nasal cavity along the perineural sheaths of the olfactory nerve filaments. Around the spinal nerve roots there is an arrangement of the dural veins and sinuses adapted for the passage of cerebrospinal fluid directly into the venous blood, rather than into the lymphatic vessels. A small part of the cerebrospinal fluid may enter the lymphatics or the veins by the routes just mentioned, but most of it passes directly into the big endocranial venous sinuses through the arachnoid villi.

ARACHNOID VILLI. The large endocranial venous sinuses are entirely enclosed by thick walls of dura mater except in definite places, chiefly in the sagittal sinus of the falx, where the dura is perforated by numerous protrusions of the arachnoid membrane, through each of which a finger-like evagination of the arachnoid mesothelium is thrust into the lumen of the sinus. This is an arachnoid villus. Its cavity, which contains a small amount of loose arachnoid tissue, is in free communication with the subarachnoid spaces, so that here the fluid of these spaces is separated from the blood of the sinus only by the thin mesothelial membrane.

These villi have been found in dogs, cats, monkeys, and human infants and adults. In man, with advancing age, they are enlarged, and in this condition they have long been known as *pacchionian corpuscles,* or *granulations.*

The arachnoid villi provide the main pathway for the outflow of cerebrospinal fluid directly into the venous circulation. This flow is rapid. Dyes and other chemicals injected into the subarachnoid spaces can be detected in the bloodstream in 10 to 30 seconds, and after only 30 minutes they can be found in the lymphatics.

BLOOD VESSELS OF THE CENTRAL NERVOUS SYSTEM. The arteries reach the spinal cord with the ventral and dorsal nerve roots (anterior and posterior radicular arteries) and form a dense arterial network in the spinal pia mater. Here several longitudinal arterial pathways can be distinguished (spinal arterial tracts). The most important among them is the anterior arterial tract; it gives off a multitude of small branches (central arteries), which enter the ventral medial fissure and penetrate to the right and left into the medial part of the anterior gray columns. They supply the major part of the gray substance with blood. Numerous smaller branches of the pial arterial net, the peripheral arteries, penetrate the white

substance of the cord along its entire circumference. The capillary nets in the white substance are loose and have meshes that are drawn out longitudinally. The capillaries of the gray substance are much more numerous and dense. The course of the veins does not correspond with that of the arteries. Numerous venous branches emerge from the periphery of the cord and from the ventral median fissure and form a diffuse plexus in the pia; this is especially prominent on the dorsal surface of the cord. From this plexus the blood is led away by veins accompanying the ventral and dorsal roots.

The arterial supply of the brain is derived almost entirely from the carotids and the large arteries at its base, chiefly the basilar artery and the circle of Willis. Most of the arteries from these large vessels pass upward in the pia mater, from which smaller vessels dip into the brain substance. These vessels, after penetrating the brain, are commonly supposed to be functional end arteries, with few anastomoses from one to another through vessels large enough to be effective in establishing a collateral circulation.

As in the spinal cord, the capillary net in the cerebral white matter is relatively meager, with elongated meshes; in the gray matter the net has a closer mesh. It is assumed that the density of capillaries is a crude indication of the rate of metabolism of the tissue supplied

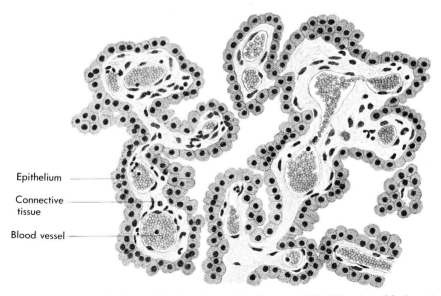

Epithelium

Connective tissue

Blood vessel

Figure 12-49. Choroid plexus of the fourth ventricle of man. × 190. (After A. A. Maximow.)

by it. On this assumption, it is clear that the metabolism of the gray substance is much more active than that of the white.

The linear extent of capillaries per unit volume of brain substance has been measured in a number of representative parts of the central nervous substance in various animals. In the rat, parts of both white and gray matter differ in vascularity, all the gray being more vascular than the white. The motor nuclei are less vascular than the sensory nuclei and correlation centers.

There are no lymphatics in the central nervous system. Fluid that passes out from the capillaries seeps through the tissue and is not collected in lymphatic vessels, as in most other parts of the body. The blood vessels that penetrate from the pia mater are surrounded by perivascular spaces, which open freely at the brain surface into the subarachnoid spaces. Thus the cerebrospinal fluid, derived from the blood, is drained from the brain tissue outward toward the meninges without at any time being enclosed in definite lymphatic vessels.

When certain vital dyes, pigments, or metals are present in circulating blood of adult animals, the tissues of the central nervous system remain colorless except for the choroid plexus and certain subependymal areas. In these regions, most dyes and pigments are found within extravascular cells. From such experiments the concept has been developed of a barrier between the blood and the nervous tissue. There are several views as to the location of the *blood-brain* or *hematoencephalic barrier;* some maintain that the capillary endothelium is less permeable than in the rest of the body; others believe that the layer formed by end processes of neuroglial cells on vessel walls excludes certain substances; still others designate the specialized subependymal areas as the barrier. Wislocki and Leduc suggest that the blood-brain barrier is composed of a succession of thresholds which have to be crossed, including the structures named above.

In young animals given intravenous dye injections, however, there can be found a distinct, although small, storage of the dye in the cells in different places of the brain stem,

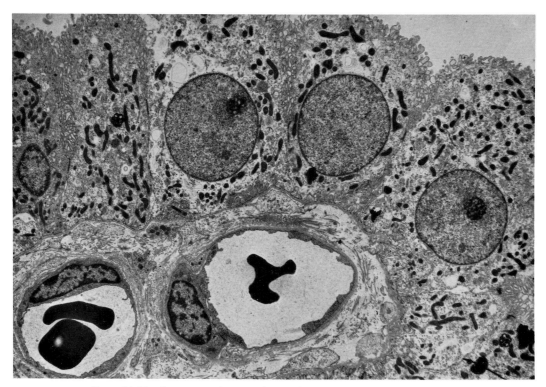

Figure 12-50. Low power electron micrograph of cat choroid plexus. × 4000.

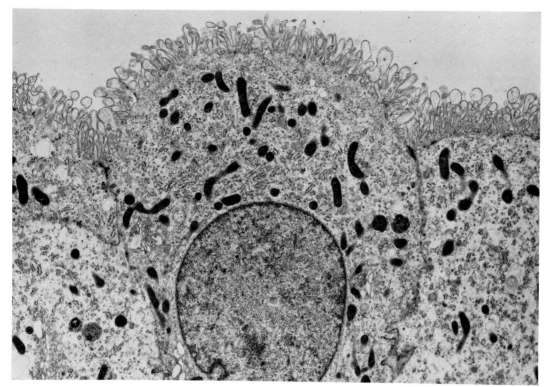

Figure 12-51. Electron micrograph at higher magnification, illustrating the unusual free border of bulbous or clavate microvilli. × 7200.

so that the apparent impermeability of the walls of the blood vessels develops gradually.

The choroid plexus is often considered separately as the blood–cerebrospinal fluid barrier.

REFERENCES

Adrian, E. D.: The Mechanism of Nervous Action; Electrical Studies of the Neuron. Philadelphia, University of Pennsylvania Press, 1933.

Ångevine, J. B.: Time of neuron origin in the hippocampal region. An autoradiographic study in the mouse. Exper. Neurol., Supp. 2, 1965.

Ariëns Kappers, C. U., G. C. Huber, and E. C. Crosby: The Comparative Anatomy of the Nervous System of Vertebrates, Including Man. New York, Macmillan, 1936, Vols. I and II.

Bailey, P., and G. von Bonin: The Isocortex of Man. Urbana, University of Illinois Press, 1951.

Bartelmez, G. W., and N. L. Hoerr: The vestibular club endings in Ameiurus; further evidence on the morphology of the synapse. J. Comp. Neurol., 57:401, 1933.

Bethe, A., G. Bergmann, G. Embden, and A. Ellinger: Handb. l. norm. u. pathol. Physiol. Berlin, Julius Springer, 1927–31, Vols. 1, 9, 10, 11, and 12.

Bodian, D.: Cytological aspects of synaptic function. Physiol. Rev., 22:146, 1942.

Bodian, D.: The generalized vertebrate neuron. Science, 137:323, 1962.

Bodian, D.: An electron microscopic study of the monkey spinal cord. Bull. Johns Hopkins Hosp., 114:13, 1964.

Boyd, I. A.: The structure and innervation of the nuclear bag muscle fiber system and the nuclear chain muscle fiber system in mammalian muscle spindles. Philos. Trans. Roy. Soc. B, 245:81, 1962.

Brightman, M. W.: The intracerebral movement of proteins injected into blood and cerebrospinal fluid of mice. Anat. Rec. 157:219, 1967 (abstract).

Cauna, N.: Structure of digital touch corpuscles. Acta Anat., 32:1, 1958.

Cauna, N., and G. Mannan: The structure of human digital pacinian corpuscles (corpuscula lamellosa) and its functional significance. J. Anat. (Lond.), 92:1, 1958.

Causey, G.: The Cell of Schwann. Edinburgh and London, E. & S. Livingstone, Ltd., 1960.

Cole, K. S.: Ions, potentials and the nerve impulse. Lecture and Review Series, No. 53–7, Naval Med. Research Inst., 1953, p. 89.

Coombs, J. S., J. C. Eccles, and P. Fatt: Several papers on electrical properties of neurons. J. Physiol., 130:291, 1955.

Davis, H.: Some principles of sensory receptor action. Physiol. Rev., 41:391, 1961.

Davison, P. F., and E. W. Taylor: Physical-chemical studies of proteins of squid nerve axoplasm, with special reference to the axon fibrous protein. J. Gen. Physiol., 43:801, 1960.

Deitch, A. D., and M. J. Moses: The Nissl substance of living and fixed spinal ganglion cells. II. An ultraviolet absorption study. J. Biophys. & Biochem. Cytol., 3:449, 1957.

Deitch, A. D., and M. R. Murray: The Nissl substance of living and fixed spinal ganglion cells. I. A phase contrast study. J. Biophys. & Biochem. Cytol., 2:433, 1956.

Dempsey, E. W., and G. B. Wislocki: An electron microscopic study of the blood-brain barrier in the rat, employing silver nitrate as a vital stain. J. Biophys. & Biochem. Cytol., 1:245, 1955.

De Robertis, E. D. P., and H. S. Bennett: Some features of the submicroscopic morphology of synapses in frog and earthworm. J. Biophys. & Biochem. Cytol., 1:47, 1955.

Eccles, J. C.: The Physiology of Nerve Cells. Baltimore, Johns Hopkins Press, 1957.

von Economo, C.: The Cytoarchitectonics of the Human Cerebral Cortex. New York, Oxford University Press, 1929.

Elliott, K. A. C., I. H. Page, and J. H. Quastel: Neurochemistry; The Chemical Dynamics of Brain and Nerve. Springfield, Ill., Charles C Thomas, 1955.

Fernández-Morán, H.: The Submicroscopic Structure of Nerve Fibers. *In* Butler, J. A. V., and J. T. Randall, eds.: Progress in Biophysics. New York, Academic Press, 1954, vol. 4, p. 112.

Fernández-Morán, H.: Low-Temperature Electron Microscopy and X-Ray Diffraction Studies of Lipoprotein Components in Lamellar Systems. Annual Meeting, Association for Research in Nervous and Mental Disease, Albert Einstein College of Medicine, New York. December 1960.

Fernández-Morán, H., and J. B. Finean: Electron microscope and low-angle x-ray diffraction studies of the nerve myelin sheath. J. Biophys. & Biochem. Cytol., *3:*725, 1957.

Field, J., H. W. Magoun, and V. E. Hall (eds.): Handbook of Physiology. Section 1: Neurophysiology. 3 vols. Washington, American Physiological Society, 1959–1961.

Finean, J. B.: Chemical Ultrastructure in Living Tissues. Springfield, Ill., Charles C Thomas, 1961.

Flexner, L. B.: Events associated with the development of nerve and hepatic cells. Ann. N. Y. Acad. Sci., *60:*986, 1955.

Fox, C. A., and J. W. Barnard: A quantitative study of the Purkinje cell dendritic branchlets and their relations to afferent fibers. J. Anat., *91:*299, 1957.

Fujita, S.: Analysis of neuron differentiation in the central nervous system by tritiated thymidine autoradiography. J. Comp. Neurol., *112:*311, 1964.

Furshpan, E. J.: "Electrical transmission" at an excitatory synapse in a vertebrate brain. Science, *144:*878, 1964.

Gasser, H. S.: Properties of dorsal root unmedullated fibers on the two sides of the ganglion. J. Gen. Physiol., *38:*709, 1955.

Gerard, R. W.: Metabolism and Function in the Nervous System. *In* Elliott, K. A. C., I. H. Page, and J. H. Quastel, eds.: Neurochemistry. Springfield, Ill., Charles C Thomas, 1955, p. 458.

Geren, B. B.: The formation from the Schwann cell surface of myelin in peripheral nerves of chick embryos. Exper. Cell Res., *7:*558, 1954.

Geren, B. B.: Structural studies of the formation of the myelin sheath in peripheral nerve fibers. *In* Rudnick, D., ed.: Cellular Mechanisms in Differentiation and Growth. Princeton, Princeton University Press, 1956, p. 213.

Gersh, I., and D. Bodian: Some chemical mechanisms in chromatolysis. J. Cell. & Comp. Physiol., *21:*253, 1943.

Glees, P.: Neuroglia; Morphology and Function. Springfield, Ill., Charles C Thomas, 1955.

Glimstedt, G., and G. Wohlfort: Electron microscope studies on peripheral nerve regeneration. Lunds Universitets Arsskrift, *56:*1, 1960.

Granit, R.: Receptors and Sensory Perception; a Discussion of Aims, Means, and Results of Electrophysiological Research into the Process of Reception. New Haven, Yale University Press, 1955.

Gray, E. G., and R. W. Guillery: The basis for silver staining of synapses of the mammalian spinal cord: A light and electron microscope study. J. Physiol., *157:*581, 1961.

Gray, E. G., and R. W. Guillery: Synaptic morphology in the normal and degenerating nervous system. Int. Rev. Cytol., *19:*41, 1962.

Guth, L.: Regeneration in the mammalian peripheral nervous system. Physiol. Rev., *36:*441, 1956.

Harrison, R. G.: Observations of the living developing nerve fiber. Anat. Rec., *1:*116, 1908.

Harrison, R. G.: The outgrowth of the nerve fiber as a mode of protoplasmic movement. J. Exper. Zool., *9:*787, 1910.

Hartmann, J. F.: An electron optical study of sections of central nervous system. J. Comp. Neurol., *99:*201, 1953.

Hartmann, J. F.: Electron microscopy of motor nerve cells following section of axones. Anat. Rec., *118:*19, 1954.

Herndon, R. M.: The fine structure of the Purkinje cell. J. Cell Biol., *18:*167, 1963.

Herrick, C. J.: An Introduction to Neurology. 5th ed. Philadelphia, W. B. Saunders Co., 1931.

Herrick, C. J.: The Brain of the Tiger Salamander. Chicago, University of Chicago Press, 1948.

Herrick, C. J.: The Evolution of Human Nature. Austin, University of Texas Press, 1956.

Hild, W.: Das Neuron. *In* von Möllendorff, W., and W. Bargmann, eds.: Handbuch der mikroskopischen Anatomie des Menschen. Berlin, Springer Verlag, 1959, Vol. 4, part 4, p. 1.

Hines, M.: Studies in the innervation of skeletal muscle. J. Comp. Neurol., *56:*105, 1932.

Hinsey, J.: The innervation of skeletal muscle. Physiol. Rev., *14:*514, 1934.

Hodgkin, A. L., and B. Katz: The effect of sodium ions on the electrical activity of the giant axon of the squid. J. Physiol., *108:*37, 1949.

Hogue, M. J.: A study of adult human brain cells grown in tissue cultures. Am. J. Anat., *93:*397, 1953.

Huxley, A. F., and R. Stämpfli: Effect of sodium and potassium on resting and action potentials of single myelinated nerve. J. Physiol., *112:*496, 1951.

Hydén, H.: The Neuron. *In* Brachet, J., and A. E. Mirsky, eds.: The Cell; Biochemistry, Physiology, Morphology. New York, Academic Press, Vol. 4, p. 215.

Katz, B.: Mechanisms of Synaptic Transmission, and Nature of the Nerve Impulse. *In* Oncley, J. L., *et al.*, eds.: Biophysical Science—A Study Program. New York, John Wiley & Sons, 1959, pp. 254 and 466.

Klüver, H., and E. Barrera: A method for the combined staining of cells and fibers in the nervous system. J. Neuropath. & Exper. Neurol., *12:*400, 1953.

Kuntz, A.: The Autonomic Nervous System. 4th ed. Philadelphia, Lea & Febiger, 1953.

Lehmann, H. J.: Die Nervenfaser. *In* von Möllendorff, W., and W. Bargmann, eds.: Handbuch der mikroskopischen Anatomie des Menschen. Berlin, Springer Verlag, 1959, Vol. 4, part 4, p. 515.

Levi-Montalcini, R.: Events in the developing nervous system. *In* Purpura, D., and J. Schadé, eds.: Progress in Brain Research. Amsterdam, Elsevier Publishing Co., 1964, Vol. 4, p. 1.

Lorente de Nó, R.: Transmission of impulses through cranial motor nuclei. J. Neurophysiol., *2:*402, 1939.

Lorente de Nó, R.: On the existence of a gradient of sensitivity to the lack of sodium in the spinal roots of the bullfrog. Studies of the Rockefeller Institute for Medical Research, *144:*352, 1952.

Luse, S. A.: Electron microscopic observations of the central nervous system. J. Biophys. & Biochem. Cytol., *2:*531, 1956.

Luse, S. A.: Formation of myelin in the central nervous system of mice and rats, as studied with the electron microscope. J. Biophys. & Biochem. Cytol., *2:*777, 1956.

Maxfield, M.: Axoplasmic proteins of the squid giant nerve fiber with particular reference to the fibrous protein. J. Gen. Physiol., *37:* 201, 1953.

Ortiz-Picón, J. M.: The neuroglia of the sensory ganglia. Anat. Rec., *121:*513, 1955.

Palay, S. L.: The Fine Structure of the Neurohypophysis. *In* Waelsch, H., ed.: Ultrastructure and Cellular Chemistry of Neural Tissue. New York, Paul B. Hoeber, Inc., 1957, p. 31.

Palay, S. L.: The structural basis for neural action. *In* Brazier, M. A. B., ed.: Brain Function. Berkeley, University of California Press, 1963, Vol. II, p. 69.

Palay, S. L., and G. E. Palade: The fine structure of neurons. J. Biophys. & Biochem. Cytol., *1:*69, 1955.

Penfield, W., ed.: Cytology and Cellular Pathology of the Nervous System. New York, Paul B. Hoeber, Inc., 1932, Vols. 1, 2, and 3.

Penfield, W.: Neuroglia: Normal and Pathological. *In* Cytology and Cellular Pathology of the Nervous System. New York, Paul B. Hoeber, Inc., 1932, vol. 2, p. 421.

Peterson, E. R., and M. R. Murray: Myelin sheath formation in cultures of avian spinal ganglia. Am. J. Anat., *96:*319, 1955.

Polyak, S.: The Main Afferent Fiber Systems. Berkeley, University of California Press, 1932.

Polyak, S.: The Retina. Chicago, University of Chicago Press, 1941.

Polyak, S.: Vertebrate Visual System. Chicago, University of Chicago Press, 1957.

Pomerat, C. M.: Dynamic neurogliology. Texas Rep. Biol. Med., *10:*885, 1952.

Pope, A.: Application of quantitative histochemical methods to the study of the nervous system. J. Neuropath. & Exper. Neurol., *14:*39, 1955.

Ramón y Cajal, S.: Histologie du système nerveux de l'homme et des vertébrés. Paris, A. Maloine, 1909.

Ramón y Cajal, S.: Degeneration and Regeneration of the Nervous System. London, Oxford University Press, 1928.

Ranson, S. W., and S. L. Clark: The Anatomy of the Nervous System. 10th ed. Philadelphia, W. B. Saunders Co., 1959.

Rasmussen, A. T.: The Principal Nervous Pathways; Neurological Charts and Schemas, with Explanatory Notes. 4th ed. New York, Macmillan Co., 1952.

Reiser, K. A.: Die Nervenzelle. *In* von Möllendorff, W., and W. Bargmann, eds.: Handbuch der mikroskopischen Anatomie des Menschen. Berlin, Springer Verlag, 1959, Vol. 4, part 4, p. 185.

Rhines, R.: Ultraviolet irradiation of small portions of nerve cell processes in tissue culture. Exper. Neurol., *1:*569, 1959.

Robertson, J. D.: The ultrastructure of adult vertebrate peripheral myelinated nerve fibers in relation to myelinogenesis. J. Biophys. & Biochem. Cytol., *1:*271, 1955.

Robertson, J. D.: The ultrastructure of Schmidt-Lanterman clefts and related shearing defects of the myelin sheath. J. Biophys. & Biochem. Cytol., *4:*39, 1958.

Rodriguez, L. A.: Experiments on the histologic locus of the hemato-encephalic barrier. J. Comp. Neurol., *102:*27, 1955.

Ruch, T. C., H. D. Patton, J. W. Woodbury, and A. L. Towe: Neurophysiology. 2nd ed. Philadelphia, W. B. Saunders Co., 1965.

Sauer, F. C.: Mitosis in the neural tube. J. Comp. Neurol., *62:*377, 1935.

Schaltenbrand, G.: Plexus und Meningen. *In* von Möllendorff, W., and W. Bargmann, eds.: Handbuch der mikroskopischen Anatomie des Menschen. Berlin, Springer Verlag, 1955. Vol. 4, part 2, p. 1.

Scharrer, E., and B. Scharrer: Neurosekretion. *In* von Möllendorff, W., and W. Bargmann, eds.: Handbuch der mikroskopischen Anatomie des Menschen. Berlin, Springer Verlag, 1954. Vol. 6, part 5, p. 953.

Schmitt, F. O.: The structure of the axon filaments of the giant nerve fibers of Loligo and Myxicola. J. Exper. Zool., *113:*499, 1950.

Schmitt, F. O.: Molecular Organization of the Nerve Fiber. *In* Oncley, J. L., *et al.,* eds.: Biophysical Science—A Study Program. New York, John Wiley & Sons, 1959, p. 455.

Schmitt, F. O., R. S. Bear, and K. J. Palmer: X-ray diffraction studies on the structure of the nerve myelin sheath. J. Cell. & Comp. Physiol., *18:*31, 1941.

Sherrington, C. S.: The Integrative Action of the Nervous System. New Haven, Yale University Press, 1906.

Sholl, D. A.: The Organization of the Cerebral Cortex. New York, John Wiley & Sons, 1956.

Speidel, C. C.: Studies of living nerves. VII. Growth adjustments of cutaneous terminal arborizations. J. Comp. Neurol., *76:*57, 1942.

Sperry, R. W.: Neuronal Specificity. *In* Weiss, P., ed.: Genetic Neurology; Problems of the Development, Growth, and Regeneration of the Nervous System and of Its Functions. Chicago, University of Chicago Press, 1950, p. 232.

Sperry, R. W.: Cerebral organization and behavior. Science, *133:* 1749, 1961.

Sperry, R. W.: Chemoaffinity in the orderly growth of nerve fiber patterns and connections. Proc. Nat. Acad. Sci., *50:*703, 1963.

Tobias, J. M.: Further studies on the nature of the excitable system in nerve. J. Gen. Physiol., *43:*57, 1960.

Tobias, J. M., and S. H. Bryant: An isolated giant axon preparation from the lobster nerve cord. J. Cell. & Comp. Physiol., *46:*163, 1955.

Uzman, B. G., and G. Nogueira-Graf: Electron microscope studies of the formation of nodes of Ranvier in mouse sciatic nerves. J. Biophys. & Biochem. Cytol., *3:*589, 1957.

Van Breemen, V. L., and C. D. Clemente: Silver deposition in the central nervous system and the hematoencephalic barrier studied with the electron microscope. J. Biophys. & Biochem. Cytol., *1:*161, 1955.

Waelsch, H., ed.: Biochemistry of the Developing Nervous System. New York, Academic Press, 1955.

Weddell, G., E. Palmer, and W. Pallie: Nerve endings in mammalian skin. Biol. Rev., *30:*159, 1955.

Weed, L. H.: Certain anatomical and physiological aspects of the meninges and cerebrospinal fluid. Brain, *58:*383, 1935.

Weiss, P., ed.: Genetic Neurology; Problems of the Development, Growth, and Regeneration of the Nervous System and Its Functions. Chicago, University of Chicago Press, 1950.

Weiss, P., and M. W. Cavanaugh: Further evidence of perpetual growth of nerve fibers; recovery of fiber diameter after the release of prolonged constrictions. J. Exper. Zool., *142:*461, 1959.

Weiss, P., and H. B. Hiscoe: Experiments on the mechanism of nerve growth. J. Exper. Zool., *107:*315, 1948.

Weston, J. A.: A radioautographic analysis of the migration and localization of trunk neural crest cells in the chick. Develop. Biol., *6:*279, 1963.

Windle, W. F.: Regeneration of axons in the vertebrate central nervous system. Physiol. Rev., *36:*427, 1956.

Wislocki, G. B., and E. H. Leduc: Vital staining of the hemato-encephalic barrier by silver nitrate and trypan blue, and cytological comparisons of neurohypophysis, pineal body, area postrema, intercolumnar tubercle and supraoptic crest. J. Comp. Neurol., *96:*371, 1952.

Young, J. Z.: Functional repair of nervous tissue. Physiol. Rev., *22:* 318, 1942.

CHAPTER THIRTEEN

Blood Vascular System

All but the simplest multicellular animals require a mechanism to distribute oxygen, nutritive materials, and hormones to the tissues and to collect from them carbon dioxide and other products of tissue metabolism and to transmit these to the excretory organs. In vertebrates this important function is carried out by the *blood vascular system,* which consists of a muscular pump, the *heart,* and two continuous systems of tubular vessels. One of these, the *pulmonary circulation,* carries blood to and from the lungs; the other, the *systemic circulation,* distributes to and collects from all of the other tissues and organs of the body. In both of these circulations the blood pumped from the heart passes successively through *large arteries, small arteries, arterioles, capillaries, venules, small veins,* and *large veins,* and back to the heart. The actual exchange between the blood and the inspired air or between the blood and the tissues takes place in the minute thin-walled capillaries and venules. In most organs the network of capillaries of the blood vascular system is paralleled by a plexus of capillaries belonging to the lymphatic system. These are described in Chapter 14.

CAPILLARIES

The endothelium, the main component of the wall of a capillary, is the living layer common to all parts of the vascular system including the heart. The endothelial cells, although they differ from fibroblasts in shape, have many similar cytological characteristics. The elongated or oval nucleus is flattened and contains an inconspicuous nucleolus and fine chromatin particles. The cells are elongated in the direction of the axis of the capillary and have tapering ends. In capillaries of greater diameter they are shorter and broader, and in the lung their outlines are irregularly scalloped. In the smallest capillaries, a single endothelial cell may extend around the entire circumference of the vessel, whereas in capillaries of medium size, two or three curved cells extend around the lumen.

The caliber of the capillaries in various parts of the body varies within relatively narrow limits and is related to the size of the red blood corpuscles. In man it averages about $8\,\mu$. In an organ or tissue that is in a state of minimal functional activity, a considerable number of the capillaries may be narrowed, so that little blood circulates through them. When the organ begins to function actively, these capillaries open up and blood circulates through them. This variability in caliber should be borne in mind, and it should be realized that in tissues fixed by immersion the capillaries appear narrower than in the living animal, while in those fixed by perfusion they are often distended beyond their normal physiological limits. Intravascular injection of silver nitrate and subsequent exposure to light results in deposition of silver along the cell boundaries. In the majority of capillaries, it is possible to show by this means that the walls consist of separate endothelial cells whose boundaries stand out as sharply stained black lines. This staining reaction was long interpreted as being due to deposition of metallic silver in an abundant "intercellular cement." Along the cell boundaries and at the sites of their junction, lenticular or angular blackened regions were seen, and these were thought to be openings in the walls called *stigmata* or *stomata*. Electron microscopy has shown that the endothelial cells, like the cells of other epithelia, are in close apposition with no appreciable amount of intercellular substance. It is also evident that there are no intercellular gaps and that the so-called stomata described earlier were artifacts.

The capillaries originate from the embryonic connective tissue. They penetrate between the parenchymal elements of various organs and tissues, accompanied along their entire course by occasional connective tissue cells and thin collagenous or reticular fibers that closely adjoin the endothelium. Whether the capillary endothelium possessed a "basement membrane" was a subject of debate among light microscopists, but this has now been settled by the demonstration in electron micrographs of a thin glycoprotein basal lamina similar in all respects to that underlying other epithelia.

The capillaries are, as a rule, accompanied by fixed macrophages and undifferentiated mesenchymal cells and rarely by scattered nerve cells, which can be identified by the use of special staining methods. The pericapillary mesenchymal cells are clearly demonstrable in whole mounts of the thin serous membranes (Fig. 13-3). In certain sites the pericapillary cells are of quite different nature. For example, along the capillaries of the nictitating membrane of the frog's eye are peculiar cells with long branching processes that surround the capillary wall (Rouget cells). These cells have been seen to contract under electrical stimulation and hence are considered by some to be of the nature of smooth muscle cells, but they lack the birefringent myofilaments characteristic of smooth muscle. Other cells have been described in very close association with the endothelium but without

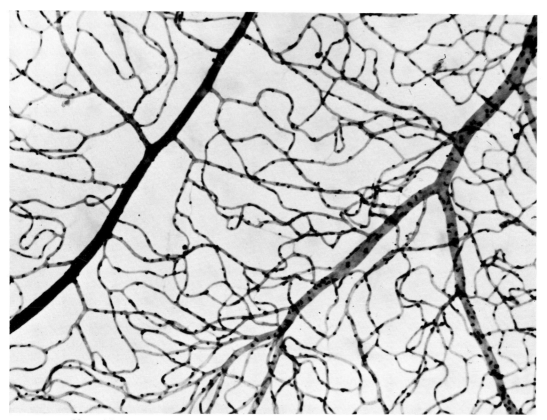

Figure 13-1. Normal human retinal blood vessels. These have been isolated by tryptic digestion of the neural and receptor elements, leaving behind only the vessels. At the left is an arteriole, at the right is a venule, and between is a network of capillaries of very uniform caliber. × 100. (Courtesy of T. Kuwabara.)

demonstrated contractility. Whether these are the same as or different from the cells described by Rouget is not clear, and it is now customary to describe all such cells as *pericytes* without attributing to them a special role in regulation of the caliber of the vessel (Fig. 13-4). Microdissection studies have shown that the endothelial cells themselves may contract after direct mechanical stimulation, and therefore it may be unnecessary to ascribe variations in the size of the lumen of a capillary to special cells in its wall.

The Fine Structure of the Capillary Wall

CONTINUOUS CAPILLARIES. The endothelial cell is thickened in the region of the

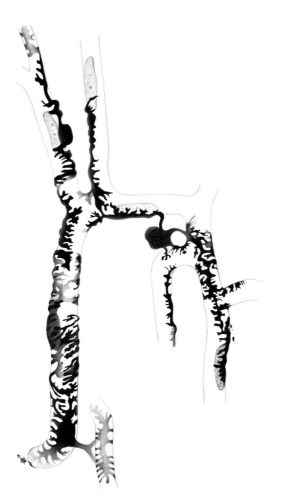

Figure 13-2. Arterial capillaries from the heart of a 43 year old man, showing four polymorphous perivascular cells. The arrow points toward the artery. Chrome-silver impregnation. × 1000. (Redrawn after Zimmermann.)

nucleus but may be extremely attenuated elsewhere. The cytoplasm near the nucleus contains a small Golgi apparatus, a pair of centrioles, and a few profiles of granular endoplasmic reticulum. Most of the cell's complement of mitochondria are near the nucleus, but occasional ones may be found in the thin peripheral parts of the cell. Cytoplasmic filaments 40 to 60 Å thick are present. One of the most conspicuous and characteristic features of most capillaries is the presence of many small vesicles 600 to 700 Å in diameter. These are so numerous in the capillaries of the rat myocardium that they are said to occupy one third of the cell volume (Fig. 13-8). They seem to arise from a large number of saccular invaginations (caveolae) of the plasma membrane opening onto the luminal and basal surfaces of the endothelial cells by narrow orifices 300 to 400 Å in diameter (Fig. 13-9). At the junctions of endothelial cells, the membranes of adjoining cells approach to within a few hundred angstroms but, for the most part, remain distinctly separate. Over limited areas of the interface, however, the trilaminar unit membranes approach much closer, and after some methods of specimen preparation, they may appear to fuse in a five layered junction (Muir and Peters). In certain capillaries typical desmosomes also occur, but these are rarely if ever found in mammals. The areas of close apposition of membranes have been interpreted by some investigators as beltlike *tight junctions* (zonulae occludentes) extending entirely around the cell. For technical reasons, it has not been possible to establish their continuity around the cell beyond question. This is an important point, for it has a bearing upon interpretation of the pathway of exchange across the capillary wall.

The endothelial cell junction may be interdigitated or relatively straight. At its luminal end the margin of one or both cells may be prolonged into a narrow fold or flaplike structure protruding into the capillary lumen (Fig. 13-8, 13-9). It has been suggested that these are active and under certain conditions may be involved in pinocytosis, but their true functional significance is by no means clear.

Although light microscopists described the presence of an *endocapillary layer* lining the endothelium of capillaries, no layer of a thickness that would be visible with the light microscope has been seen in electron micrographs. At high magnification, however, there

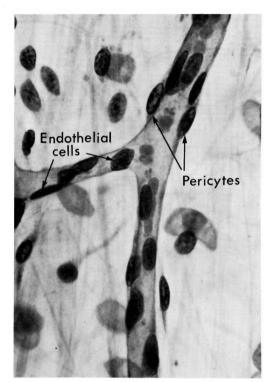

Figure 13-3. Photomicrograph of an intact capillary in a whole mount of rat mesentery. The nuclei of the flattened endothelial cells lining the capillary can be distinguished from those of the pericytes, which bulge outward. May-Grünwald-Giemsa stain. × 475.

does seem to be a thin layer of filamentous or granular appearance attached to or part of the outer leaflet of the plasma membrane.

The endothelial tube of the capillary is supported on its outside by a thin continuous *basal lamina* (basement membrane) similar in all respects to that of other epithelia. There is good evidence that it is a product of the endothelial cells. Where pericytes or their processes are found around the circumference, this layer splits to enclose them. The principal component of the capillary basal lamina is evidently collagen in a form not exhibiting cross striations. Typical cross striated reticular fibers may, however, be closely associated with its outer surface.

While conforming in most respects to the general description just given, the capillaries of the brain and retina differ in two important features. First, the number of vesicular invaginations and free vesicles in the endothelial cells is quite low, and secondly, the cell boundaries have true zonulae occludentes or tight junctions, in contrast to muscle capillaries, in

which the membranes make a close approach in certain areas but do not actually fuse and obliterate the intercellular space.

FENESTRATED CAPILLARIES. Capillaries of the kind just described are found in smooth, skeletal, and cardiac muscle and in various other tissues. Having an uninterrupted endothelium 0.2 μ or more in thickness and a continuous basement lamina, they are sometimes called *continuous capillaries* to distinguish them from *fenestrated capillaries,* found in the renal glomeruli, endocrine glands, intestinal villi, and elsewhere. The latter type is characterized by the presence of extremely attenuated areas of endothelium, often as thin as 500 Å and penetrated by circular fenestrae or pores 800 to 1000 Å in diameter (Figs. 13-6 and 13-10). Actually the perforations are only apparent, for they are usually closed by a very thin diaphragm with a slight central thickening. The diaphragm does not seem to be formed by the

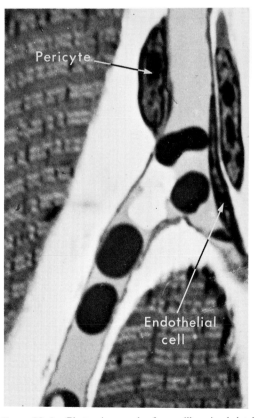

Figure 13-4. Photomicrograph of a capillary in skeletal muscle cut longitudinally. The nuclei of a pericyte, an endothelial cell, and a fibroblast can be distinguished. Several erythrocytes in the lumen give an indication of its dimensions. × 1800. (Courtesy of J. Venable.)

apposition of the two cell membranes, for it is usually thinner than a single unit membrane. The basement lamina is continuous across the fenestrations on the outside of the capillary. Where the fenestrae are present, they are often very regularly arranged with a center to center spacing of about 1300 Å, but in any given cross section, the areas exhibiting these fenestrae make up only a fraction of the circumference of the vessel. The cell to cell junctions usually occur in the thicker areas of the endothelium and are not significantly different from those of continuous capillaries.

The fenestrated capillaries are not the same everywhere. The fenestrae vary in size, number, and distribution. Although the matter is not entirely settled, it is the consensus that those of the renal glomeruli are exceptional in that they are not closed by diaphragms. The glomerular capillaries also have a basal lamina that is as much as three times as thick as in other capillaries.

SINUSOIDS. As originally defined by Minot (1900), sinusoids are vascular channels of generally large irregular caliber and with a very tenuous connective tissue layer between the vascular wall and the parenchyma of the organ. They develop embryologically by ingrowth of the parenchyma (as in the liver) into a large, thin-walled blood sinus. This mode of development is to be contrasted to that of true capillaries, which branch dichotomously and grow in length by addition of vasoformative cells at the ends of the vessel. Sinusoids are characteristic of the circulation of the liver, spleen, bone marrow, and certain endocrine glands, such as the adrenal and pituitary. The cells in some of these are phagocytic and thus belong to the reticuloendothelial system; in others they are not. Electron microscopy brings out a number of other differences among them.

In the *discontinuous sinusoids* of the liver of most species, the lining cells meet and overlap in typical endothelial junctions in some areas, while in other areas there are large gaps between cells (see Chapter 27). A basal lamina is discontinuous or entirely lacking. In certain

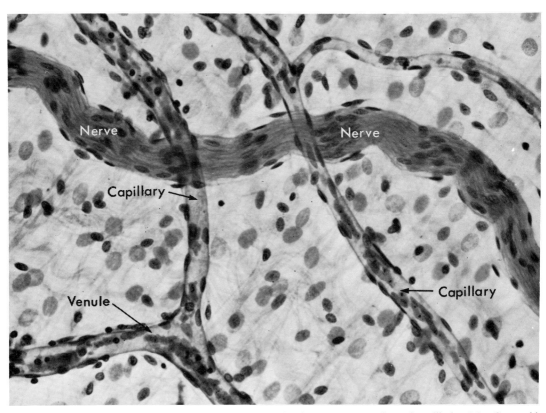

Figure 13-5. Photomicrograph of a thin spread mesentery showing a nerve, venule, and capillaries. May-Grünwald-Giemsa stain. × 300.

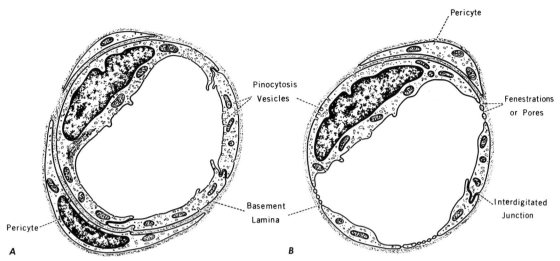

Figure 13-6. Schematic representation of the two commonest types of capillaries. *A,* The continuous or muscle type with an uninterrupted endothelium. *B,* The fenestrated type, in which the endothelium varies in thickness and the thinnest areas have small pores closed by an exceedingly thin membranous diaphragm. (After D. W. Fawcett, in J. L. Orbison and D. Smith, eds.: Peripheral Blood Vessels. Baltimore, Williams & Wilkins, 1962.)

species, the sinusoids of the liver are said to have a continuous lining and a basal lamina. The sinusoids of the spleen and bone marrow have peculiarities of their own, described elsewhere. In the *fenestrated sinusoids* of the pituitary and adrenal cortex, the cells are not phagocytic; there are no intercellular gaps; the basal lamina is continuous, but the thin endothelium exhibits pores closed by diaphragms as in the fenestrated capillaries.

In summary, it may be said that at the light microscope level few differences were discernible in the smallest blood vessels of the various tissues and organs, and it was commonly assumed that all capillaries were much the same. It has been one of the important contributions of the electron microscope to have demonstrated that there are a number of different kinds of vessels structurally adapted to the physiological requirements of the particular region—continuous capillaries without zonulae occludentes, continuous capillaries with tight junctions, fenestrated capillaries, continuous sinusoids, fenestrated sinusoids, and other variants of these major types. We turn now to a consideration of the functional significance of these different structural arrangements.

Histophysiology of Exchange Across the Capillary Wall

The vascular system carries nutrients, hormones, and gaseous metabolites required by the cells throughout the body, and it takes up the products and byproducts of their metabolism for distribution or excretion. One of the most important concerns of physiologists, therefore, is the mechanism of exchange of substances across their walls—*capillary permeability.* The capillaries present an enormous surface for interchange of substances with the tissues. The interchange appears to take place without significant transformation of energy, and the endothelium seems to exhibit many of the characteristics of an inert porous membrane, permeable to water and crystalloids but relatively impermeable to large molecules. Calculations based upon experiments with the continuous capillaries of skeletal muscle have indicated that the observed rates of exchange could be accounted for by postulating uniform circular pores of 30 Å radius and a length of $0.3\ \mu$, corresponding to the thickness of the endothelium. These pores need have a frequency of occurrence of only $3 \times 10^9/\text{cm.}^2$ and hence it was felt that they need not traverse the cells themselves but might be confined to the slender intercellular clefts (Pappenheimer).

Palade interpreted the numerous vesicles at the surface and within the endothelium as a submicroscopic form of *pinocytosis,* or drinking by cells, and proposed that the endothelial cells are active in capillary exchange, taking into these vesicles small quantities of fluid, transporting it across the cell, and discharging it to the perivascular space. Experiments using

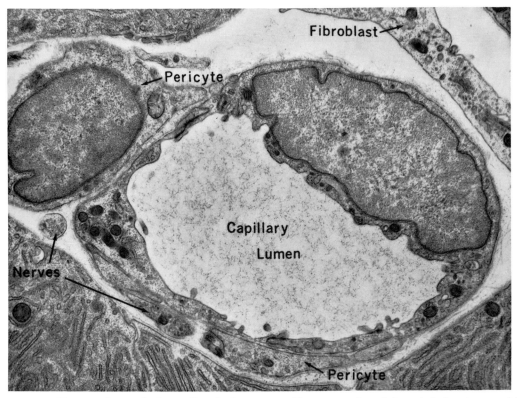

Figure 13-7. Electron micrograph of a capillary in the pancreas. The outer surface of the endothelium is covered by a thin amorphous basement lamina and numerous small fibrils of collagen. An adventitial cell or pericyte is seen at the upper left and one of its processes is closely applied to the endothelium at the lower part of the figure. The small nerves accompanying the capillary are destined to innervate the neighboring acinar cells. × 13,500.

as tracers such electron opaque particulate materials as ferritin have provided some support for this thesis by showing that the particles can enter the vesicles and that they do emerge on the outside of the capillary (Fig. 13-11). The labeled vesicles are relatively few, however, and the results of these experiments leave many in doubt as to whether this mechanism could account for either the selectivity of the process or the considerable volume of material transported per unit time.

Use of the enzyme *peroxidase,* a protein with a molecular weight of about 40,000, as an ultramicroscopic tracer has confirmed that rapid uptake and transendothelial transport by micropinocytosis vesicles does occur, but the label is also found along the entire length of the intercellular clefts in muscle capillaries. The presence of the label between cells is interpreted to mean that passage can also take place through the intercellular small pore system postulated by the physiologists (Karnovsky).

The intravenous injection of dyes that readily escape from peripheral capillaries fails to stain all but a few small areas of the brain. This has given rise to the concept of a special *blood-brain barrier.* Whether this permeability barrier depends upon the special relations of the perivascular astrocytic foot processes or is located in the walls of the capillaries has long been debated. Application of the peroxidase tracer method to this problem has now shown that the junctions between endothelial cells of brain capillaries do not permit intercellular passage of the label. Although rare micropinocytosis vesicles were found to take up peroxidase, there was no evidence of its discharge on the abluminal side of the endothelium. Thus the paucity of micropinocytosis vesicles in brain capillaries and the presence of true zonulae occludentes on their endothelial junctions appear to account for their much lower permeability compared to muscle capillaries (Reese and Karnovsky).

In fenestrated capillaries, exchange is

evidently facilitated by the presence of the fenestrae, even though these are closed by a thin diaphragm. In the glomerular capillaries, where this closure seems to be lacking, fluid passes out of the vessels a hundred times more rapidly than in the continuous muscle capillaries. In discontinuous sinusoids, such as those in the liver, there is of course no barrier to the escape of particles smaller than cells, and the composition of the fluid in the perivascular space is essentially the same as that of plasma.

ARTERIES

Blood is carried from the heart to the capillary networks in the tissues and organs by arteries. These comprise an extensive system of tubular structures beginning with the aorta and pulmonary artery, which emerge from the left and right sides of the heart respectively. As they course away from the heart these vessels branch repeatedly and thus give rise to large numbers of arteries of progressively diminish-

ing caliber. Although the diameter of the individual arterial branches steadily decreases as a result of their dichotomous branching, the sum of the cross sections of all the branches gradually increases, and the rate of blood flow diminishes as the capillaries are approached. There is a further marked expansion of the total cross sectional area of the vascular system at the level of the capillaries. As a consequence, flow through the capillaries is quite slow, thus allowing ample time for efficient exchange with the tissues. It should be borne in mind that it is only at the level of the capillaries and small venules that the vessel walls are thin enough to permit the exchange that is the essential function of the circulation. At any given moment less than 10 per cent of the blood volume is in the capillaries and over 90 per cent is on its way to or from them. In all the rest of the vascular system, which is concerned with the propulsion and distribution of the blood, the endothelium is reinforced by networks of elastic fibers, smooth muscle cells, fibroblasts, and collagenous fibers. These sev-

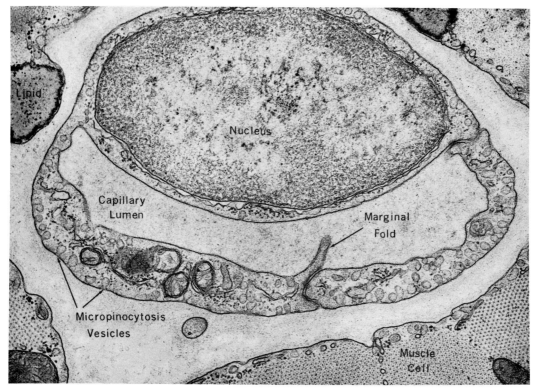

Figure 13-8. Electron micrograph of a capillary from cardiac muscle, illustrating a continuous endothelium, with a typical marginal fold at the cell to cell junction. There are numerous micropinocytosis vesicles, principally on the external surface of the endothelium. × 28,000. (After D. W. Fawcett, J. Histochem. & Cytochem., *13*:75, 1965.)

eral components of the vessel walls vary in their proportions and in their arrangement in different segments of the system.

The walls of the large *elastic* or *conducting arteries* (aorta, innominate, subclavian, common carotid, and pulmonary) contain fenestrated sheets and bands of elastin. The wall of the largest of these vessels may be distinctly yellow in the fresh condition because of the predominance of elastic elements. Continuing peripherally from the elastic arteries are the *muscular* or *distributing arteries*. This category includes the majority of the vessels in the arterial system. The smallest arteries, 0.3 mm. and less in diameter, are called *arterioles*. Some authors distinguish *precapillary arterioles* in the transition from arterioles to capillaries, but the limits and morphological characteristics of this class of vessels are rather poorly defined.

Three layers can be distinguished in the walls of all arteries: (1) an inner coat, the *tunica intima*, whose structural elements are, for the most part, oriented longitudinally; (2) an intermediate coat, the *tunica media*, which is the thickest layer of the wall and has its components disposed circumferentially; and (3) an outer coat, the *tunica adventitia*, most of whose elements run parallel to the long axis of the vessel. The fibrous and cellular elements of this layer gradually merge with those of the loose connective tissue that accompanies every blood vessel. The boundary between the tunica intima and tunica media is formed by the *internal elastic membrane* (elastica interna), which is particularly noticeable in arteries of medium caliber. Between the tunica media and the tunica adventitia, a thinner *external elastic membrane* (elastica externa) can be found in many cases.

ARTERIOLES AND SMALL ARTERIES. The *tunica intima* of the smallest arterioles consists only of endothelium and is surrounded by a media consisting of a single layer of smooth muscle cells (Figs. 13-13 and 13-14). In larger arterioles the intima includes an internal elastic membrane, which appears as a thin bright line immediately beneath the endothelium. In cross sections it usually has a scalloped appear-

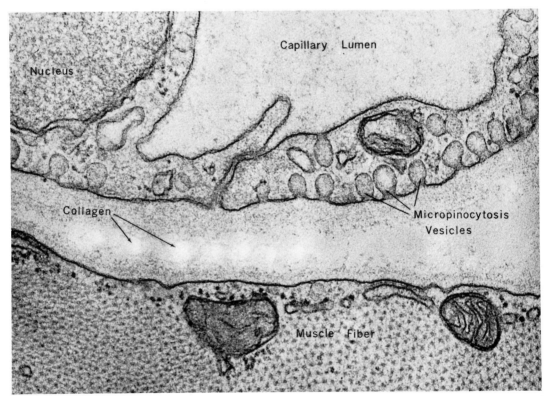

Figure 13-9. Electron micrograph of capillary endothelium, illustrating the small vesicular inpocketings of the luminal and basal surfaces that are characteristic of the type of capillaries found in muscle. × 75,000. (After D. W. Fawcett, J. Histochem. & Cytochem., *13*:75, 1965.)

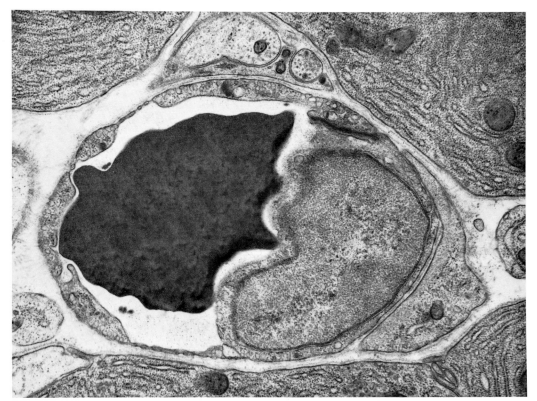

Figure 13-10. Electron micrograph of a fenestrated capillary in bat pancreas. The dark object in the lumen is an erythrocyte deformed by contact with the irregular surface of the endothelium. At the upper and lower left are extremely attenuated areas of endothelium that are penetrated by large pores 600 to 800 Å in diameter. Such fenestrations of the capillary endothelium are common in a number of organs. × 13,000.

ance because the agonal contraction of the muscle in the media throws it into longitudinal folds.

The *tunica media* of small arteries is composed of smooth muscle cells 15 to 20 μ in length. When seen in surface view they are always oriented transversely to the long axis of the vessel, and in cross sections they are disposed circumferentially. The number of layers of muscle cells depends upon the caliber of the artery (Fig. 13-15).

The *tunica adventitia* approximately equals the tunica media in thickness; it is a layer of loose connective tissue with longitudinally oriented collagenous and elastic fibers and a few fibroblasts. It merges with the surrounding connective tissue. The small arteries lack a definite external elastic membrane.

In electron micrographs of small arterioles, the continuous endothelium is found to be supported by a typical basal lamina and occasional small bundles of collagen fibrils. In vessels having an elastica interna, the endo-thelium and its basal lamina are closely applied to it (Fig. 13-15). The elastin in vessels of small caliber is in the form of longitudinally oriented bars separated by long slitlike fenestrations. In larger vessels this layer becomes much thicker and is a more nearly continuous sheet but retains occasional, very narrow fenestrations. A new cytoplasmic component has been described in the endothelial cells of small arteries. It is a rod-shaped structure 0.1 μ in diameter and 3 μ in length and consists of a bundle of fine tubules embedded in a dense matrix and enclosed in a closely fitting membrane. In addition, the endoplasmic reticulum of the endothelial cells often is distended with dense, finely granular material. The significance of these features of arterial endothelium has not been determined (Weibel and Palade).

MUSCULAR ARTERIES OF MEDIUM CALIBER. This is the most numerous class of arteries. Beneath the endothelium in the smaller arteries of this group is the elastica interna (Figs. 13-16 and 13-18). The basal

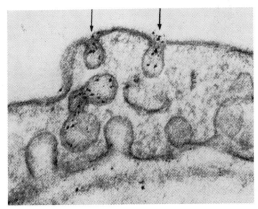

Figure 13-11. Electron micrograph of capillary endothelium, illustrating uptake of particulate matter (saccharated iron oxide) from the lumen by pinocytosis vesicles and its transport across the cell. Although such a mechanism exists, its quantitative importance in capillary exchange is questioned by many. × 100,000. (After M. A. Jennings, V. T. Marchesi, and S. H. Florey, Proc. Roy. Soc. B., *156*:14, 1962.)

surfaces of the endothelial cells closely conform to all of the irregularities of contour in the elastica and send slender processes through its fenestrations to establish contact with the underlying smooth muscle cells of the media. It is believed that these discontinuities in the elastica may be essential for the sustenance of the avascular media by permitting diffusion of metabolites from the lumen. The scalloped internal elastic membrane is very well developed, and because of its low affinity for osmium it appears in electron micrographs as a sinuous light layer stippled with pointlike profiles of fibrils within the substance of the elastin (Fig. 13-20).

The tunica media of muscular arteries consists almost exclusively of smooth muscle cells arranged in concentric layers. The muscle cells are surrounded and separated from one another by a moderately thick layer of glycoprotein analogous to the basal lamina of epithelia. This stains deeply with the periodic acid–Schiff reaction and generally appears amorphous in electron micrographs of low magnification (Fig. 13-15). Embedded within this abundant interstitial material are small bundles of collagen fibrils corresponding to the network of reticular fibers seen surrounding individual muscle fibers in silver stained preparations viewed with the light microscope. Loose networks of thin elastic fibers also course circumferentially in the media and can

be recognized as dark wavy lines among the smooth muscle cells in preparations stained with aldehyde-fuchsin or resorcin-fuchsin (Fig. 13-19). In electron micrographs they appear as unstained elongated profiles of irregular outline. The elastica externa may appear in photomicrographs as a continuous layer at the junction of the media and adventitia (Fig. 13-19), but in election micrographs of cross sections it is an interrupted row of irregular strands of elastin considerably thinner than the elastica interna (Fig. 13-21). In contracted vessels, portions of smooth muscle cells occupy the discontinuities in the elastica externa sometimes bulging into the adventitia. Closely applied to the elastica on its outer aspect are numerous small fascicles of unmyelinated nerve axons, some containing collections of mitochondria and numerous synaptic vesicles. The nerves do not ordinarily penetrate into the media and ramify among the smooth muscle cells but appear to terminate at the elastica externa (Fig. 13-21). The neural stimulation of the muscle cells may then result from diffusion of the transmitter substance through this layer, and depolarization of the peripheral muscle cells may be propagated throughout the media via low-resistance cell to cell contacts between muscle cells.

The tunica adventitia of arteries of this type is sometimes thicker than the media (Fig. 13-19), and consists of fibroblasts, strands of elastin, and bundles of collagen oriented longitudinally or tangentially. These continue into the surrounding connective tissue without a clearly defined boundary. The loose consistency of the tunica adventitia and predominant longitudinal orientation of its components permits the continual changes in the diameter of the vessel but limits the amount of retraction that takes place when the artery is cut.

LARGE ELASTIC ARTERIES. The resistant elastic wall of a vessel such as the aorta is quite thick, but in proportion to the size of the lumen it is thinner than the wall of muscular arteries.

The tunica intima in adult man is about 127 μ in thickness (Fig. 13-22). Its endothelium differs from that of smaller arteries in that the cells tend to be polygonal rather than elongated in the axis of the vessel. The thin subjacent layer contains a few fibroblasts and thin interlacing bundles of collagen fibrils. Occasional wandering cells may be present. The next deeper layer of the intima consists of many branching elastic fibers that fuse into sheets in certain areas. Among these elastic fibers are a few collagenous fibers, fibroblasts, and small bundles of smooth muscle cells. Externally these elastic fibers join a fenestrated elastic membrane corresponding in location to the elastica interna of smaller vessels. In large elastic arteries, however, this is not a single well defined sheet marking the junction of intima and media but is merely the first of many similar elastic membranes found throughout the thickness of the media. Thus in these very large vessels the tunica intima is poorly demarcated from the tunica media.

The tunica media consists largely of elastic tissue. In the human aorta it appears in the form of 50 to 65 concentric fenestrated elastic membranes 2.5 μ thick and 6 to 18 μ apart. The successive membranes are frequently connected by elastic fibers or bands. In the spaces between elastic membranes are thin layers of connective tissue with thin collagenous and elastic fibers, fibroblasts, and smooth muscle cells (Fig. 13-24). The smooth muscle cells, particularly in the inner layers of the tunica media of the aorta, are flattened, branched elements with irregular outlines and serrated edges; they have characteristic rodlike nuclei. Most of them are arranged circularly. These smooth muscle cells are closely surrounded by collagenous fibers, which bind them to the elastic membranes. Between these various structures is an appreciable amount of metachromatic amorphous ground substance. The basophilia and metachromasia of this ground substance is believed to be due to the presence of chondroitin sulfate.

The tunica adventitia in arteries of large caliber is relatively thin. It cannot be sharply distinguished from the surrounding connective tissue. The most external of the fenestrated

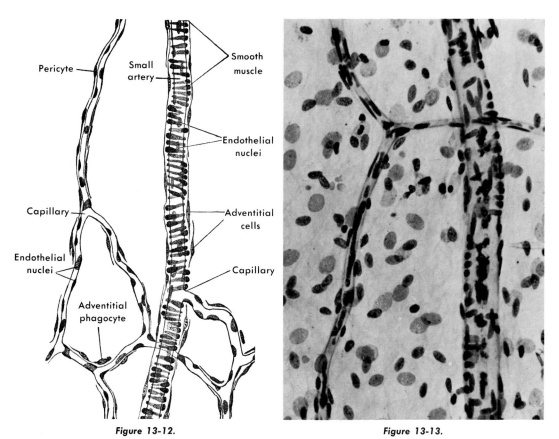

Figure 13-12.

Figure 13-13.

Figure 13-12. Small artery and capillaries from mesentery of a rabbit. $\times$ 187. (After A. A. Maximow.)

Figure 13-13. Photomicrograph of an arteriole and capillary comparable to those drawn in Figure 13-12. Notice in the arteriole the rows of nuclei of the circumferentially oriented smooth muscle cells. Their elongated form is not evident here because they are seen in optical section. $\times$ 250.

membranes of the tunica media serves as an external elastic membrane, from which numerous elastic fibers project. There is a gradual transition from the tunica adventitia into the surrounding loose connective tissue with its fat cells.

The walls of large arteries and veins are evidently too thick to be nourished by diffusion from its lumen alone. They are provided with small arteries, the *vasa vasorum*, derived either from branches of the main vessel or from neighboring arteries. These break up into a capillary plexus in the deeper layers of the tunica adventitia. As a rule they do not penetrate deeply into the media of arteries, but in veins they may extend nearly to the intima.

Transitions Between Arteries of Different Types

In the gradual transition from one type of artery to another it is sometimes difficult to classify the intermediate region. Some arteries of rather small caliber (popliteal, tibial) have walls that suggest large arteries, while some large arteries (external iliac) have walls like those of medium-sized arteries. The transitional regions between elastic and muscular arteries are often designated *arteries of mixed type*. Such are the external carotid, axillary, and common iliac arteries. Their walls contain, in the tunica media, islands of smooth muscle fibers that interrupt the elastic membranes in many places.

Where arteries of mixed or elastic type pass suddenly into arteries of the muscular type, short regions of transition occur; in these regions the vessels are called *arteries of hybrid type*. The visceral arteries that arise from the abdominal aorta (Fig. 13-17) are examples of such vessels. In them, for a varying distance, the tunica media may consist of two different layers—the internal is muscular and the external is composed of typical elastic membranes.

SPECIAL TYPES OF ARTERIES. In the tunica media of the arteries of the lower limbs, the muscular tissue is more highly developed than it is in the arteries of the upper limbs.

The arteries of the skull, which are protected from external pressure or tension, have

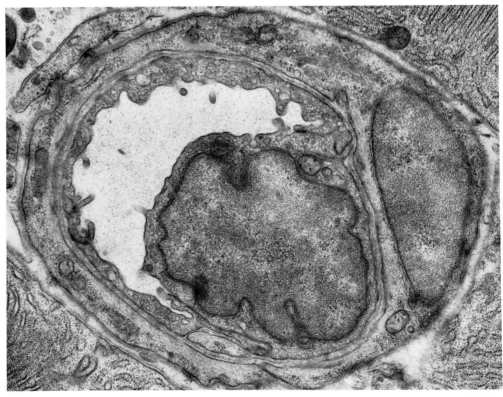

Figure 13-14. Electron micrograph of a very small arteriole in which the endothelium is completely encircled by one smooth muscle cell. × 12,000.

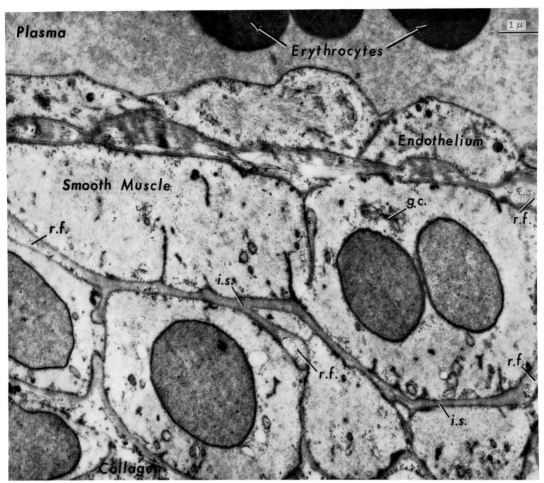

Figure 13-15. Electron micrograph of cross section of smooth muscle cells in the wall of a human arteriole. The myofilaments of smooth muscle cells are exceedingly fine and are barely perceptible here. *g.c.*, Golgi complex; *i.s.*, interstitial substance; *r.f.*, reticular fibrils, which are half the diameter of the fibrils in the collagenous bundle. Buffered osmic acid fixation.

a thin wall and a well developed elastica interna. In the tunica media the elastic fibers are almost entirely absent.

The *umbilical artery* has an atypical, special structure. Its intima consists only of endothelium and lacks an internal elastic layer. The tunica media contains a small number of elastic fibers and two thick muscular layers, which are sharply separated. The inner layer is composed of longitudinally directed fibers; in many places these form longitudinal protrusions into both the lumen and the outer circular muscular layer. The extra-abdominal portion of the umbilical artery is provided with numerous oval swellings; in these regions the wall becomes thin and consists almost exclusively of circularly arranged muscle.

PHYSIOLOGICAL SIGNIFICANCE OF THE STRUCTURE OF ARTERIES. Because the movement of the blood in the arteries is caused by contractions of the heart, it is rhythmical or pulsatile. If the walls of the arteries were inflexible, the flow of blood into the capillaries would be intermittent. But because the large arteries near the heart have expansible elastic walls, only part of the force of contraction of the heart goes to advancing the column of blood in the vessels; the rest goes to expanding the walls of the elastic arteries. The potential energy accumulated in the stretching of the walls of these vessels during contraction of the heart (systole) is dissipated in elastic recoil of the vessel wall during the period when the heart is inactive (diastole). This release of tension in the arterial wall serves as an auxiliary pump, forcing the blood forward during diastole. Thus, near the heart the flow of blood is intermittent, but in the periphery it is continuous, and it is the elasticity of the walls of the larger conducting vessels that makes it possible to have a continuous flow with an intermittent pump.

Contractions and relaxations of the muscular arteries influence the distribution of blood to various tissues and organs, and variations in the peripheral resistance to flow affect the blood pressure. The contraction and dilation of the muscular arteries is regulated by the *vasoconstrictor* and *vasodilator* nerves of the autonomic nervous system, which terminate in the vessel walls at the outer margin of the media.

The muscular tissue of the arterial wall is normally in a state of partial contraction referred to as the *tone*, which changes with pressure in the system and variations in activity of the various tissues.

CHANGES IN THE ARTERIES WITH AGE. The arterial blood vessels reach their mature form only in adult life. During the fourth month of embryonic life in man, the arteries acquire their three main layers. From this time the wall of the vessels changes gradually.

In the aorta of a four month human embryo, the intima consists only of the endothelium and of one rather thick elastic membrane, the elastica interna. The media consists of several layers of circular smooth muscles, between which are flat networks of elastic fibers. The adventitia is thicker than the media and consists of embryonic connective tissue.

At the end of embryonic life the internal elastic membrane becomes thicker, while the networks of elastic fibers in the media turn into thick elastic membranes. The muscular elements have increased slightly in number but are still inconspicuous. The adventitia by this time has become smaller.

After birth the number and thickness of the elastic membranes in the media of the aorta gradually increase. By now they are much like the elastica interna. In the intima, between the endothelium and the elastica interna, an elastic muscular layer appears. It arises in part by a splitting of the elastica interna and in part by the new formation of collagenous and elastic fibers, and it gradually increases in thickness. At about the age of 25, these layers are completely differentiated.

The medium-sized muscular arteries, such as the brachial, even in the middle of embryonic life have an intima composed of an endothelium and an elastica interna, a media of circular smooth muscles, and an adventitia. The latter has a pronounced elastica

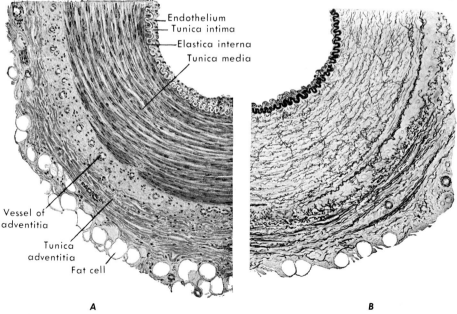

Endothelium
Tunica intima
Elastica interna
Tunica media

Vessel of adventitia

Tunica adventitia

Fat cell

A   B

Figure 13-16.   Sectors of two cross sections of the volar digital artery of man; *A,* stained with hematoxylin and eosin; *B,* stained with orcein to show elastic tissue. × 80. (Slightly modified from Schaffer.)

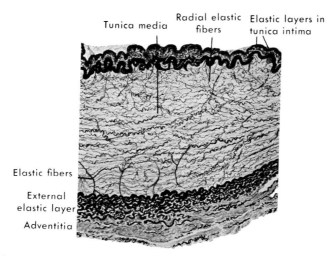

Tunica media   Radial elastic   Elastic layers in
                    fibers   tunica intima

Elastic fibers

External
elastic layer

Adventitia

Figure 13-17. Portion of cross section of mesenteric artery of man. Orcein stain. × 110. (After Schaffer.)

externa surrounded by a connective tissue layer rich in elastic fibers. Toward the end of the embryonic period the greatly thickened media consists only of circular muscle bounded by the external and internal elastic membranes. After birth, in the arteries of muscular type, in addition to the thickening of the wall as a whole, a connective tissue layer gradually develops between the endothelium and the elastica interna.

The heart and arteries are always active mechanically and seem to wear out more than any other system or organs. Indeed, the final differentiation of the structure of the wall frequently cannot be sharply separated from the regressive changes that develop gradually with age and lead to *arteriosclerosis* or "hardening of the arteries." Some authors view these alterations as physiological, others as a pathological process. In general, arteriosclerosis is a pathological process when its degree of development in a given vessel is beyond the norm for this vessel at a particular age. The arteries of elastic type, particularly the aorta, show much greater changes with age than do the arteries of muscular type. The small arteries, under physiological conditions, participate in this process relatively little. The type of pathological change is different in the different types of vessels. The large vessels, particularly the aorta, are subject to *atherosclerosis,* a patchy irregular thickening with deposition of lipid in the intima, followed by degenerative changes. In the medium-sized arteries of muscular type, the main changes are degeneration and cal-

cification in the tunica media, but there may also be thickening of the intima, splitting of the elastica interna, and considerable new formation of collagenous and elastic fibers.

VEINS

The blood is carried from the capillary networks toward the heart by the veins. In progressing toward the heart, they gradually increase in caliber, while their walls become thicker. The veins usually accompany their corresponding arteries (Fig. 13-25). The veins are more numerous than the arteries and their caliber is larger, so that the venous system has a much greater capacity than the arterial. The walls of the veins are always thinner, more supple, and less elastic than those of the arteries. Hence in sections, the veins, unless fixed in distention, are usually collapsed, and their lumen is irregular and slitlike.

One can frequently distinguish three types: veins of small, medium-sized, and large caliber. This subdivision is often unsatisfactory, for the caliber and structure of the wall cannot always be correlated. Individual veins show much greater variations than do the arteries, and the same vein may show great differences in different parts.

Most authors distinguish three layers in the walls of the veins: tunica intima, tunica media, and tunica adventitia. But the boundaries of these layers are frequently indistinct, and in certain veins these coats, particularly the tunica media, cannot be distinguished. The

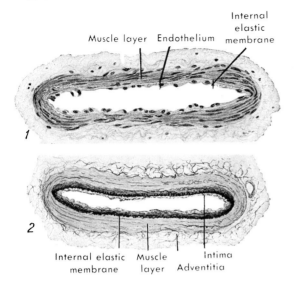

Figure 13-18. Cross section of central artery of human retina: *1*, stained with hematoxylin and eosin; *2*, stained with orcein. × 160. (After Schaffer.)

muscular and elastic tissue is not nearly as well developed in the veins as in the arteries, while the connective tissue is much more prominent.

VEINS OF SMALL CALIBER. When several capillaries unite, they first form a tube about 20 μ in diameter. This consists of a layer of endothelium surrounded by a thin layer of longitudinally directed collagenous fibers and fibroblasts (Fig. 13-26). When the caliber has increased to about 45 μ, partially differentiated smooth muscle cells appear between the endothelium and the connective tissue. These cells are at first some distance apart. Farther along they become arranged closer and closer together. In veins with a diameter of 200 μ these elements form a continuous layer and have a typical long spindle shape. In still larger veins thin networks of elastic fibers appear. The tunica intima consists only of endothelium, and one or several layers of smooth muscle cells form the media. The tunica adventitia consists of scattered fibroblasts and thin elastic collagenous fibers. Most of these fibrous elements run longitudinally, and some penetrate among the muscle cells of the tunica media.

There is reason to believe that not all of the exchange between the blood and the tissues takes place in the capillaries. The venules appear to play a role in this and are particularly important in the changes associated with inflammation. The walls of venules up to about

50 μ in diameter closely resemble those of capillaries when examined in electron micrographs. They are, however, more permeable to intravenously injected dyes. The early observations with vital dyes and light microscopy have now been extended by electron microscopic studies (Majno). When particulate markers are injected intravascularly the particles are usually not found in the walls of the capillaries but in somewhat larger vessels having more than one cell layer and interpreted as venules. This same category of vessels is also most susceptible to histamine, serotonin, and other substances known to increase vascular permeability (Fig. 13-27). If one of these substances is injected locally in an animal that has been injected intravenously with a particulate marker, it induces the appearance of small intercellular gaps in the endothelium. The particles, held back by the basal lamina, accumulate in the gaps, thus marking the vessels and permitting identification of the sites of increased permeability. Although occasional leaks can be found in capillaries, the vast majority are in small venules. There seems to be a gradient of permeability from the arterial to the venous side, which reaches a maximum in the venules and then diminishes abruptly in vessels of larger size.

VEINS OF MEDIUM CALIBER. The veins of medium caliber (2 to 9 mm.) include the cutaneous and deeper veins of the extremities distal to the brachial and the popliteal, and the veins of the viscera and head with the exception of the main trunks. In the *tunica intima* of these veins the endothelial cells in surface view are polygons with highly irregular outlines. Sometimes the tunica intima also contains an inconspicuous connective tissue layer with a few cells and thin elastic fibers. Externally, it is sometimes bounded by a network of elastic fibers. Because the tunica intima is frequently feebly developed, some authors consider the inner and middle coats as forming one layer.

The *tunica media* is much thinner than in the arteries and consists mainly of circular smooth muscle fibers separated by many longitudinal collagenous fibers and a few fibroblasts (Fig. 13-28).

The *tunica adventitia* is usually much thicker than the media and consists of loose connective tissue with thick longitudinal collagenous bundles and elastic networks. In the layers adjacent to the media, it often contains a number of longitudinal smooth muscle bundles.

VEINS OF LARGE CALIBER. The *tunica intima* has the same structure as in the medium-sized veins. In some of the larger trunks its connective tissue layer is of considerable thickness (45 to 68 μ).

The *tunica media*, in general, is poorly developed and is sometimes absent. Its structure is the same as in the veins of medium caliber. The *tunica adventitia* makes up the greater part of the venous wall and is usually several times as thick as the tunica media. It consists of loose connective tissue containing thick elastic fibers and mainly longitudinal collagenous fibers. In the layer adjacent to the tunica media or, if the latter is absent, to the tunica intima, the tunica adventitia contains prominent longitudinal layers of smooth muscle and elastic networks. This is the structure of the inferior vena cava and of the portal, splenic, superior mesenteric, external iliac, renal, and azygos veins.

SPECIAL TYPES OF VEINS. There are longitudinal or circumferential smooth muscle fibers in the subendothelial connective tissue layer of the tunica intima of the iliac, femoral, popliteal, saphenous, cephalic, basilar, umbilical, and other veins. In certain veins the longitudinal orientation is also noticed in the innermost muscular layers of the tunica media.

In a considerable portion of the inferior vena cava, the tunica media is absent and the well developed longitudinal muscle bundles of the tunica adventitia are directly adjacent to the intima. In the pulmonary veins the media is well developed with circular muscle and is like an artery in this respect. Smooth muscle is particularly prominent in all the layers of walls of the veins in the pregnant uterus.

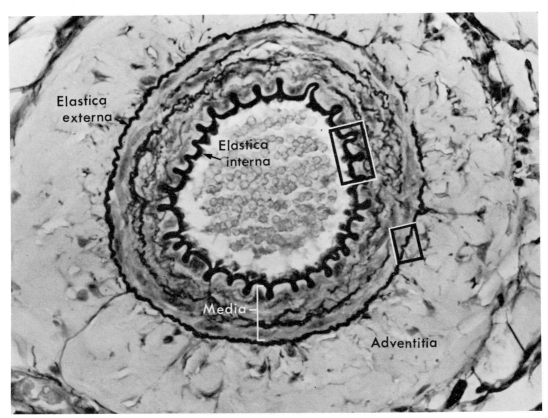

Figure 13-19. Photomicrograph of a muscular artery from the rat, showing the media, adventitia, elastica interna, elastica externa, and scattered elastic fibers in the media. Areas similar to those enclosed in the rectangles are illustrated in Figures 13-20 and 13-21. Aldehyde-fuchsin stain. × 250.

Certain veins are entirely devoid of smooth muscle tissue and consequently of a tunica media. In this group belong the veins of the maternal part of the placenta, the spinal pia mater, the retina, and the bones, as well as the sinuses of the dura mater, the majority of the cerebral veins, and the veins of the nailbed and the trabeculae of the spleen. The last two are simply channels lined by endothelium with a fibrous connective tissue covering.

The adventitia of the vena cava and particularly of the pulmonary vein is provided for a considerable distance with a layer of cardiac muscle fibers arranged in a ring with a few longitudinal fibers where these vessels enter the heart. In the rat, the pulmonary veins up to their radicles contain much cardiac muscle in the tunica media.

VALVES OF THE VEINS. Many veins of medium caliber, particularly those of the extremities, are provided with *valves* that prevent the blood from flowing away from the heart. These are semilunar pockets on the internal surface of the wall, directed with their free edges in the direction of the blood flow (Fig. 13-29). In man they are usually arranged in pairs, one opposite the other. Between the valve and the wall of the vein there is the so-called *sinus of the valve;* in this place the wall of the blood vessel is usually thin and distended.

The valve is a thin connective tissue membrane; on the side toward the lumen of the vessel, it contains a network of elastic fibers continuous with those of the tunica intima of the vein. The wall of the vein is thinner in the region of the sinus of a valve, and its intimal and medial tunics contain only longitudinal smooth muscle fibers; these do not enter into the substance of the valve in man.

Both surfaces of the valve are covered by endothelium, which is reflected from the internal surface of the intima. The endothelial cells lining the surface toward the lumen of

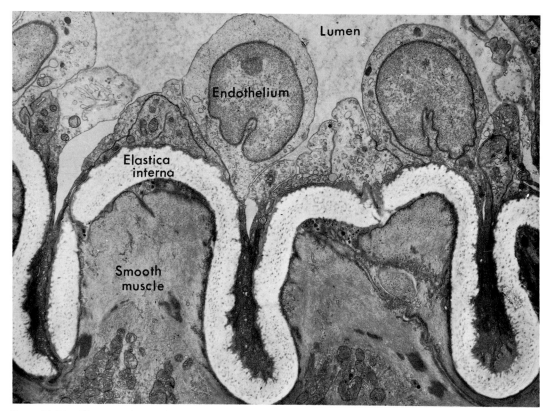

Figure 13-20. Electron micrograph of a small area of the wall of a small muscular artery (see upper box in Figure 13-19). The elastica interna is scalloped because of agonal contraction of the vessel wall. It is penetrated at intervals by slender fenestrations, through which processes extend from the endothelial cells to contact the smooth muscle cells of the media. × 10,000.

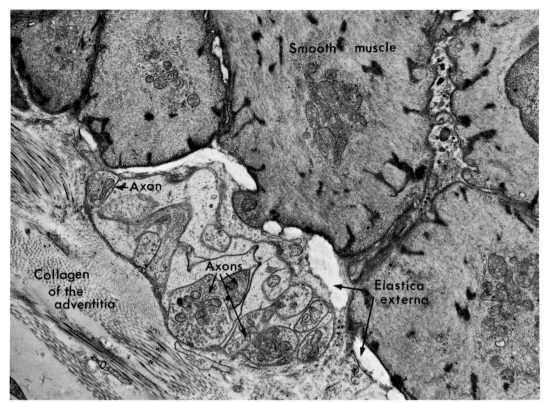

Figure 13-21. Electron micrograph of junctional zone between the media and adventitia of a small muscular artery (see lower box in Figure 13-19). The smooth muscle layer is limited on its outer aspect by a discontinuous elastica externa. Closely applied to this are numerous small nerves, some of whose axons contain many synaptic vesicles. × 10,000.

the vessel are elongated in the axis of the vessel; those that line the surface of the valve facing the sinus are elongated transversely.

PORTAL SYSTEMS OF VESSELS. As a general rule, a capillary network connects the terminal ramifications between the arteries and veins, and the transition occurs gradually. In many organs and tissues, however, modifications of this vascular plan are adapted to the special functions of the particular tissues.

An arrangement of vessels wherein blood is collected from one set of capillaries and passes through a larger vessel or vessels to a second set of capillaries before it returns to the systemic circulation is called a *portal system*. The *portal vein* of the mammalian liver arises from the capillary networks of the abdominal viscera, enters the liver, and ramifies into a network of sinusoids that penetrate the organ and are then gathered into the hepatic vein.

In certain cases an artery may also ramify into a number of capillaries, which are then collected into a larger vessel of the original type. An example of this is found in the arterioles that give rise to the glomeruli of the kidney; the afferent artery suddenly breaks up into a mass of contorted capillaries, which do not empty into veins but coalesce to form the efferent artery; this goes on to break up into another set of capillaries around the kidney tubules.

ARTERIOVENOUS ANASTOMOSES. In many parts of the body the terminal ramifications of arteries are connected with veins, not only by capillaries, but also by direct arteriovenous anastomoses. They usually arise as side branches from terminal arterioles and run directly to small venules. Their walls are muscular, remarkably thick for the caliber of the vessel, and richly supplied with vasomotor nerves. Observation of living vessels has shown that they contract markedly on stimulation of the sympathetic nerves (Clark). When the arteriovenous anastomosis is contracted, blood

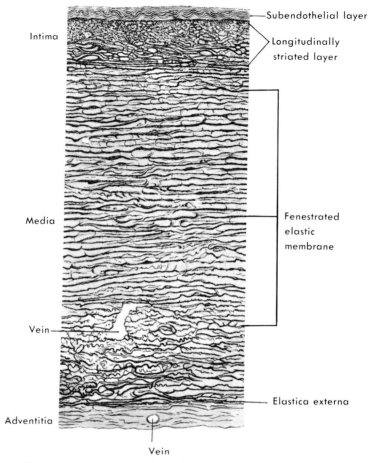

Figure 13-22. Longitudinal section through posterior wall of human descending aorta. Elastic tissue is black; the other elements are not shown clearly. Elastic fiber stain. × 85. (After Kölliker and von Ebner.)

passes along the arteriole into the capillary network; when it relaxes, blood bypasses the capillaries and goes directly into a thin-walled venule. The arteriovenous anastomoses are therefore considered important mechanisms for regulating the supply of blood to many tissues.

In addition to these simple direct communications, Masson has described highly organized connections between arteries and veins that occur as part of a specific organ, the *glomus,* found in the nailbed, the pads of the fingers and toes, and the ears. The afferent arteriole enters the connective tissue capsule of the glomus, loses its internal elastic membrane, and develops a heavy epithelioid muscle coat and narrow lumen. The arteriovenous anastomosis of the glomus may be branched and convoluted, and it is richly innervated by sympathetic and myelinated nerves. The anastomosis empties into a short, thin-walled vein with a wide lumen, which drains into a periglomic vein and then into the ordinary veins of the skin.

In addition to helping regulate the flow of blood in the extremities, it is claimed that the glomus is concerned with temperature regulation and conservation of heat.

COCCYGEAL BODY. This organ, sometimes erroneously included in the paraganglia, does not contain chromaffin cells. It is situated in front of the apex of the coccyx and measures 2.5 mm. in diameter. It consists of numerous arteriovenous anastomoses embedded in a dense fibrous matrix. The smooth muscle cells have undergone extensive "epithelioid" change. An internal secretion has not been demonstrated in this organ.

THE HEART

The heart is a thick, muscular, rhythmically contracting portion of the vascular system. It lies in the pericardial cavity within the mediastinum. It is about 12 cm. long, 9 cm. wide, and 6 cm. in its anteroposterior diameter. It consists of four main chambers: a right and left *atrium* and a right and left *ventricle*. The superior and the inferior vena cava bring the venous blood from the body to the right atrium, from which it passes to the right ventricle. From here the blood is forced through the lungs, where it is aerated, and it is then brought to the left atrium. From there it passes to the left ventricle and is distributed throughout the body by the aorta and its branches. The orifices between the atria and the ventricles are closed by the tricuspid and the mitral valves on the right and left sides, respectively. The openings to the pulmonary artery and the aorta, from the right and left ventricles, respectively, are closed by the semilunar valves.

The wall of the heart, in both the atria and the ventricles, consists of three main layers: the internal, or *endocardium;* the intermediate, or *myocardium;* and the external, or *epicardium.* The internal layer is in immediate contact with the blood; the myocardium is the contractile layer; and the epicardium is the visceral layer of the *pericardium,* a serous membrane that forms the pericardial sac, in which the heart lies.

Most authors believe that the endocardium is homologous with the tunica intima of the blood vessels, the myocardium with the tunica media, and the epicardium with the tunica adventitia.

ENDOCARDIUM. The endocardium is lined with ordinary endothelium, which is continuous with that of the blood vessels entering and leaving the heart. This endothelium consists of rounded or polygonal cells. Directly under the endothelium in most places is a thin *subendothelial layer;* it contains collagenous and a few elastic fibers and fibroblasts. External to this layer is a thick layer of connective tissue, which comprises the main mass of the endocardium and contains great numbers of elastic elements (Fig. 13-30). Bundles of smooth mus-

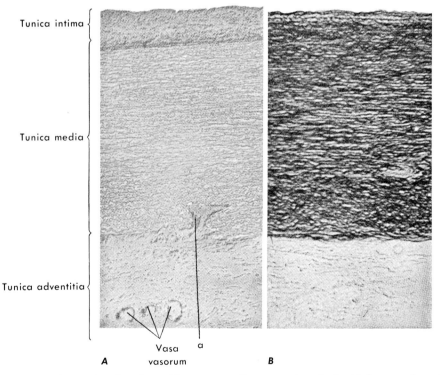

Tunica intima {

Tunica media {

Tunica adventitia {

Vasa   a
A   vasorum   **B**

Figure 13-23. Photomicrographs of sections of human ascending aorta: *A,* stained with hematoxylin and eosin; *B,* stained with resorcin-fuchsin for elastic fibers. Vasa vasorum penetrate the tunica media at *a.* About × 50. (After von Herrath and Abramow.)

cle fibers are found in varying numbers in this layer, particularly on the interventricular septum.

A *subendocardial layer,* absent from the papillary muscles and the chordae tendineae, consists of loose connective tissue that binds the endocardium to the myocardium and is directly continuous with the interstitial tissue of the latter. It contains blood vessels, nerves, and branches of the conduction system of the heart. In the spaces between the muscular bundles of the atria, the connective tissue of the endocardium continues into that of the epicardium, and the elastic networks of the two layers intermingle.

MYOCARDIUM. The minute structure of the cardiac muscle has been described in Chapter 11. In the embryos of the higher vertebrates the myocardial fibers form a spongy network. In the adult stage, however, they are bound by connective tissue into a compact mass. This condensation of the myocardium progresses from the epicardium toward the endocardium. Many embryonic muscle fascicles remain in a more or less isolated condition on the internal surface of the walls of the ventricular cavities. These muscle fiber bundles are covered with endocardium and are called *trabeculae carneae.*

Elastic elements are scarce in the myo-

cardium of the ventricles of adult mammals, except in the tunica adventitia of the larger blood vessels of these chambers. In the myocardium of the atria, however, there are networks of elastic fibers, which run everywhere between the muscle fibers and are directly connected with similar networks in the endocardium and epicardium. They are also continuous with the elastic networks in the walls of the large veins. A large part of the interstitial connective tissue of the cardiac muscle consists of extensive networks of reticular fibrils.

EPICARDIUM. The epicardium is covered on its free surface by a single layer of mesothelial cells. Beneath the mesothelium is a thin layer of connective tissue with flat networks of elastic fibers, blood vessels, and many nervous elements. About the adventitia of the coronary vessels there is a loose layer of considerable thickness, which contains much adipose tissue.

The parietal layer of the pericardium is a serous membrane of the usual type—a flat layer of connective tissue that contains elastic networks, collagenous fibers, fibroblasts, fixed macrophages, and a covering layer of mesothelial cells. Removal of the parietal pericardium in cats results in thickening of the epicardium and enlargement of the heart.

CARDIAC SKELETON. The central sup-

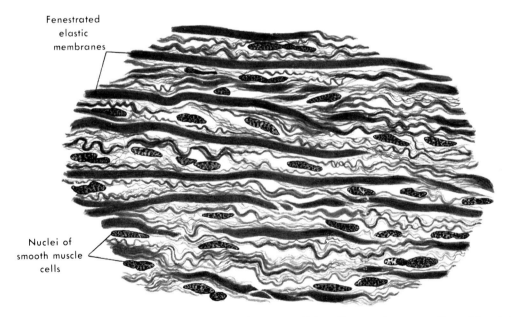

Fenestrated
elastic
membranes

Nuclei of
smooth muscle
cells

Figure 13-24. Cross section from media of the aorta of a 5 year old boy. Between the cross sections of fenestrated elastic membranes are wavy bundles of collagenous fibers. Orcein and hematoxylin. × 500. (After A. A. Maximow.)

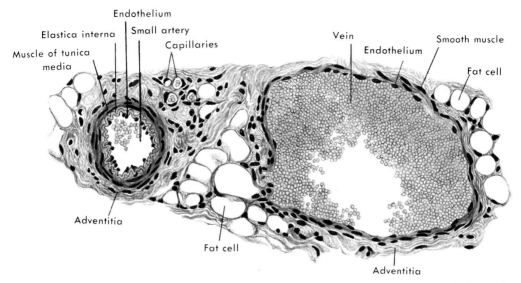

Endothelium
Elastica interna   Small artery
Muscle of tunica   Capillaries
media   Vein   Smooth muscle
                                               Endothelium   Fat cell
Adventitia   Adventitia
Fat cell

Figure 13-25. Cross section through a small artery and its accompanying vein from the submucosa of a human intestine. × 187. (After A. A. Maximow.)

porting structure of the heart, to which most of the muscle fibers are attached and with which the valves are connected, is the *cardiac skeleton*. It has a complicated form and consists mainly of dense connective tissue; its main parts are the *septum membranaceum,* the *trigona fibrosa,* and the *annuli fibrosi* of the atrioventricular and arterial foramina.

In man the fibrous rings around the atrioventricular foramina consist mainly of dense connective tissue, which contains some fat and thin elastic fibers. The structure of the septum membranaceum suggests that of an aponeurosis, with its more regular distribution of collagenous bundles in layers. The connective tissue of the trigona fibrosa contains islands of chondroid tissue. The cells of the latter are globular, as in cartilage. The interstitial substance stains deeply with basic aniline dyes and hematoxylin, and is penetrated by collagenous fibers but practically no elastic fibers. In aged persons the tissue of the cardiac skeleton may become calcified in places and sometimes even ossified.

There are important differences in the histological structure of the cardiac skeleton among different animals, and even in persons of different ages. In some cases it is a simple, dense connective tissue with a few elastic fibers and is directly continuous with the interstitial tissue of the myocardium; in other cases it approaches cartilage in its structure (horse and pig); in the dog it forms true hyaline cartilage, and in the ox it contains bone. These tissue types may be located in islands side by side; one type may merge into another.

CARDIAC VALVES. Each *atrioventricular valve* consists of a plate of connective tissue, which begins at the annulus fibrosus and is reinforced by thin ligamentous strands. It is covered on the atrial and ventricular sides by a layer of endocardium. At the free edge of the valve these three layers blend (Fig. 13-31).

The ground plate consists mainly of dense chondroid tissue with small spindle-shaped or rounded cells and a basophilic, fibrillated interstitial substance. The endocardial layer is thicker on the atrial side. Here the subendothelial layer has a small amount of chondroid tissue and rests upon a connective tissue layer, which contains many elastic fiber networks and some smooth muscles. In the vicinity of the annulus fibrosus the subendocardial layer is quite loose, and the musculature of the atrium penetrates far into it. On the ventricular side the endocardial layer has a similar structure but is much thinner. In many places the chordae tendineae enter it, and at the base of the valves are some muscle fibers from the ventricle.

The *aortic* and *pulmonic valves* have the same general structure as the atrioventricular valves. In the middle of the valve are plates of chondroid tissue with collagenous and thin

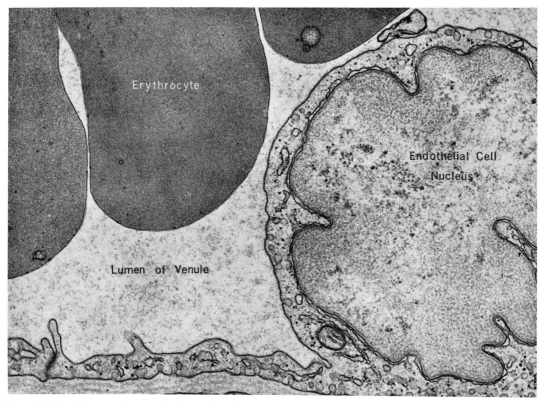

Figure 13-26. Electron micrograph of a portion of the wall of a small venule from the myocardium. The thin continuous endothelium is essentially the same as that of a capillary. The nuclear region of the endothelial cell bulges into the lumen. × 25,000.

elastic fibers. At the root of the valve these all continue into the annulus fibrosus of the arterial foramen, and at the middle of the free edge they form the *noduli Arantii*.

On the arterial side this plate is covered with a thick, uneven endocardium consisting of connective tissue with coarse, collagenous bundles and a few elastic fibers, and a thin subendothelial layer with an elastic network and a peripheral endothelium. On the ventricular side the central plate is covered with a thick endocardium composed of a connective tissue layer with longitudinal collagenous and elastic fibers and two connective tissue layers not sharply distinct; one of these contains longitudinal and the other transverse elastic fibers; the covering is endothelium. There is also a dense network of particularly thick elastic fibers that suggest the elastica interna of arteries.

Impulse Conducting System

In the adult mammalian heart, the motor impulse arises in the part of the heart that develops from the embryonic sinus venosus, an area where the superior vena cava enters the right atrium. There is a specialized mechanism by which the contraction spreads to the atria and then to the ventricles.

An impulse beginning at the *sinoatrial node,* which is the pacemaker of the heart, activates the atrial musculature and is conducted to the atrioventricular node. A continuous tract of atypical muscle fibers extends from this node to the ventricles, sending branches to the papillary muscles and other portions of the myocardium. This system thus serves to originate and transmit the contractile impulse. The microscopic and submicroscopic structure of this specialized conduction tissue has been described in Chapter 11.

This system of conduction fibers, even up to the terminal ramifications in the ventricles, is covered with a connective tissue membrane, which separates it from the remaining muscular mass of the heart.

At the boundary between the right atrium and the superior vena cava, in the region of the sulcus terminalis, is the sinoatrial node, 1 cm. in length and 3 to 5 mm. in width. Although not sharply outlined, it can be seen with the naked eye. It consists of a dense network of interwoven Purkinje fibers.

The atrioventricular node is a flat, white structure about 6 mm. long and 2 to 3 mm. wide; it is located in the posterior lower part of the interatrial septum below the posterior leaf of the aortic valve. The node consists of Purkinje fibers, which form a tangled dense network whose meshes are filled with connective tissue. These fibers pass into (or between) the usual myocardial fibers, so that the boundary of the node is indistinct. Toward the ventricles the substance of the node converges abruptly into a shaft about 1 cm. long, the atrioventricular bundle. It is located in the dense connective tissue of the trigonum fibrosum dextrum and continues into the septum membranaceum, where it divides into two branches.

The first branch, a cylindrical bundle 1 to 2 mm. thick, runs downward along the posterior circumference of the membranous septum and is located in part directly under the endocardium of the right ventricle. It proceeds along the interventricular septum and splits into many branches, which spread along the entire internal surface of the right ventricle and along the papillary muscles of the trabeculae carneae and disappear in the substance of the myocardium.

The left branch is a wide, flat band that comes forward under the endocardium of the left ventricle in the upper portion of the interventricular septum, under the anterior edge of the posterior cusps of the aortic valve. It divides into two main branches at the border between the upper and middle thirds of the septum; then it separates, as in the right ventricle, into numerous anastomosing thin threads, which are lost to view in the myocardium.

BLOOD VESSELS OF THE HEART. The blood supply to the heart is carried by the coronary arteries, usually two in number, which arise in the aortic sinuses. They are distributed to the capillaries of the myocardium. The blood from the capillaries is collected by the cardiac veins, most of which empty by way of the coronary sinus into the right atrium. A few small cardiac veins empty directly into the right atrium.

In the coronary arteries of the human heart, the tunica media, which is limited on both sides by the usual internal and external elastic membranes, is divided by a thick fenestrated membrane into an inner and an external layer.

In ordinary preparations it is difficult to see blood vessels in the cardiac valves. Most

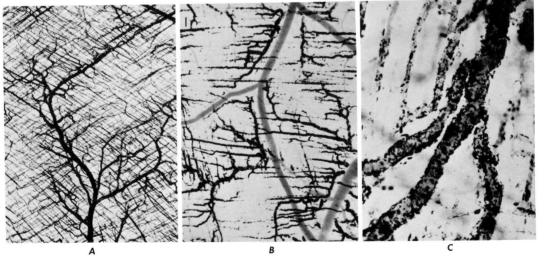

A   B   C

Figure 13-27. Photomicrographs illustrating the greater permeability of venules induced by serotonin. *A,* Cremaster of the normal rat injected with carbon to demonstrate the entire vascular system. *B,* Vascular labeling resulting from leakage of opaque particles from the vessels after local injection of serotonin. The black vessels are venules; the permeability of the many small capillaries visible in *A* has not been enhanced by this treatment. *C,* Higher magnification of a venule after seven days, showing intracellular mass of particulate matter in the vascular wall. (From Majno, G., G. E. Palade, and G. I. Schoefl, J. Biophys. & Biochem. Cytol., *11*:607, 1961.)

authorities now believe that normal valves are practically devoid of vessels, those that have been demonstrated being the result of chronic inflammatory processes (endocarditis).

There are a few vessels in the chordae tendineae; they run for the most part under the endothelium and arise from the vessels of the papillary muscles.

The conduction system and, particularly, both of its nodes are abundantly supplied with blood from special, rather constant branches of the coronary arteries.

LYMPHATIC VESSELS OF THE HEART. Three groups of lymphatic vessels are described in the heart: (1) large lymphatic vessels, which lie in the grooves of the heart together with the blood vessels; they are connected with the lymphatic nodes beneath the loop of the aorta and at the bifurcation of the trachea; (2) the lymphatic vessels of the epicardial connective tissue; and (3) lymphatic vessels of the myocardium and the endocardium.

In the subepicardial connective tissue, ordinary flat networks of lymphatic capillaries may be demonstrated easily. These are connected with large efferent lymphatic capillaries and vessels.

Within the subendothelial connective

tissue there is an even larger network of typical lymphatic capillaries; the larger vessels have valves. Lymphatic capillaries have been described in the atrioventricular and semilunar valves.

This lymphatic network in the endocardium used to be confused with the netlike ramifications of the sinoventricular system, for both structures may be demonstrated by the same injection method. But the conducting system forms much wider meshes, and its cross bars are thicker and coarser than those of the lymphatic network.

The myocardium is penetrated by an abundant lymphatic network, which is everywhere connected with the subendocardial one and also continues into the pericardial network. Muscular fibers are surrounded by lymphatic capillaries longitudinally oriented along their surface. These are connected by means of cross and tangential anastomoses and closely adjoin the blood capillaries, which run approximately in the same direction.

NERVES OF THE HEART. The numerous nerves of the heart belong in part to the vagus nerve and in part to the sympathetic nerves. For a detailed description, see Kuntz (1953).

Some nerve endings in the heart are ap-

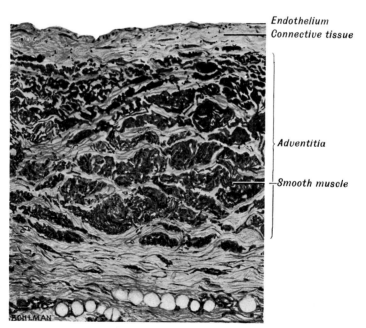

Endothelium
Connective tissue

Adventitia

Smooth muscle

Figure 13-28. Low-power view of a cross section of the wall of human vena cava. Note the muscular adventitia. (Drawn by E. Bohlman.)

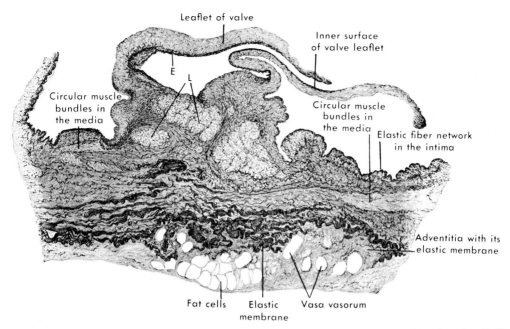

Leaflet of valve

Inner surface
of valve leaflet

E
L

Circular muscle
bundles in
the media

Circular muscle
bundles in
the media

Elastic fiber network
in the intima

Adventitia with its
elastic membrane

Fat cells   Elastic   Vasa vasorum
membrane

Figure 13-29. From cross section of femoral vein of man. The section passes through the origin of a valve. *E*, Elastic fiber network in the intima on the inner surface of the valve leaflet; *L*, longitudinal muscles of the base of the valve. Acid orcein stain. × 70. (After Schaffer.)

parently of effector type, while other endings are of receptor or sensory character. Nonidez (1937) has given detailed descriptions of the nerve endings in the large arteries, near the heart, which are affected by changes in pressure in these vessels.

CAROTID AND AORTIC BODIES. These structures used to be erroneously included with the paraganglia. They do not contain chromaffin cells and have not been shown to have an internal secretion. The carotid and aortic bodies are similar in structure and presumably in function.

The carotid bodies are flattened, inconspicuous structures at the bifurcation of each common carotid artery. They contain irregular masses of pale-staining epithelium-like cells with pale nuclei closely applied to the endothelium of sinuses. The epithelioid cells are richly supplied with nerve endings apparently specialized to receive chemical stimuli (hence the name *chemoreceptors*) indicating a fall in pH, a rise in carbon dioxide, or a decrease in oxygen content of the circulating blood. Hollinshead found a degranulation of the epithelioid cells when the oxygen tension was reduced to lethal levels. He believes that the granules "are directly concerned with the initiation of chemoreceptor reflexes." The specific nerves from

the carotid body reach the central nervous system by the sinus branch of the glossopharyngeal nerve.

The aortic body on the right side lies between the angle of the subclavian and the carotid, while on the left it is found above the aorta mesial to the origin of the subclavian, in each case occurring where the aortic nerve reaches the externa of the artery on which it ends (Nonidez, 1935). The structure of these bodies is identical with that of the carotid bodies. The impulses from the aortic bodies are carried by the aortic nerve (depressor nerve of the vagus).

The carotid body arises from the mesenchyme of the third branchial cleft artery and from the glossopharyngeal nerve. It is believed that the aortic bodies have a similar origin from the fourth branchial cleft artery and the vagus nerve.

CHROMAFFIN CELLS. In the connective tissue between the aorta and pulmonary artery, approximately at the level of the semilunar valves, and also within the subepicardial connective tissue in the sulcus coronarius, mainly along the left coronary artery, are scattered small islands of chromaffin cells, similar to the elements of the medullary substance of the adrenal glands. They are in close connection with nerve networks and ganglion cells. They are more highly developed in the newborn than in adults.

HISTOGENESIS OF THE BLOOD VESSELS AND OF THE HEART

BLOOD VESSELS. The blood vessels and the heart first appear as a layer of endothelial cells. In mammals the first vessels are laid down in the area vasculosa, where they develop from the mesenchymal cells. In the embryo proper, the blood vessels and the heart appear later; at first they are devoid of blood cells and are empty.

In the spaces between the germ layers, groups of mesenchymal cells flatten around spaces filled with fluid, which are thus surrounded by a thin endothelial wall. In this way, in given places in the body, the primordia of the heart and the main blood vessels, such as the aorta and the cardinal and umbilical veins, are laid down. These originally independent primordia then rapidly unite with one another and with the vessels of the area vasculosa, after which the blood circulation is established. The endothelial cells in these first stages are merely mesenchymal cells adjusted to the new and special function of bounding the blood vessel lumen. The idea that the vascular system in the embryo proper arises as an ingrowth of vessels from the area vasculosa has been rejected by most observers.

After the closed blood vascular system has developed and the circulation begun, new blood vessels always arise by "budding" from pre-existing blood vessels.

The new formation of blood vessels by budding may be studied in sections of young embryos or in the living condition in the margin of the tail in larval amphibians, the mesentery of newborn mammals, or the thin layer of inflamed tissue that grows between two coverslips introduced under the skin of an animal. A method has been devised for the continued observation of such chambers in the living rabbit for weeks and even months (Clark and Clark, Sandison).

In the process of budding, a protrusion appears on the wall of the capillary and is directed into the surrounding tissues. From the beginning it often appears to be a simple, hollow expansion of the endothelial wall; in other cases it is at first a solid accumulation of endothelial cytoplasm. This *vascular bud* or sprout enlarges, elongates, and assumes many shapes. Most frequently it appears as a pointed cylinder. It always becomes hollow and thus represents a local outpouching of the blood vessel into which blood cells penetrate.

An endothelial bud may encounter another bud and fuse with its end, or its lateral wall may come into contact with another bud or another capillary. A lumen appears within the fused endothelial protoplasm and unites the two capillaries. In this way a new mesh is formed in the capillary network, and

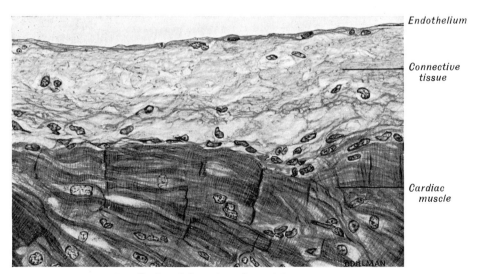

Figure 13-30. Section of the endocardium of the ventricle of man. × 265.

blood begins to circulate in it. Later, new buds may arise from the newly formed vessels.

The developing vascular buds are often accompanied by undifferentiated cells, phagocytes, and fibroblasts, stretched parallel to the long axis of the buds; sometimes there are also wandering cells.

The most probable explanation for the origin of the capillary bud is that the increase of metabolism within the tissue causes an increase in circulation of substances through the endothelium and thereby induces the growth of the endothelium in the direction of this current.

Arteries and veins of all types are always laid down at first as ordinary capillaries. The primary endothelial tube expands and thickens as new elements, uniting with the outside of the wall, differentiate in several directions. These elements originate from the surrounding mesenchyme in the embryo, and form cells with mesenchymal potencies along the capillaries in the adult. They play an important part in the formation of new arteries and veins from capillaries, as well as in the formation of large vessels from smaller ones in the development of a "collateral circulation" of the blood. The mesenchymal cells outside the endothelium become young smooth muscle cells, and myofibrils differentiate in their cytoplasm. Soon more layers of smooth muscle fibers join the first layer; these arise in part by the addition of new mesenchymal cells. In addition, networks of reticular fibers appear and form sheaths around the smooth muscle cells.

The factors that cause the larger arteries and veins to develop into more or less constant shapes in definite places and in definite directions are not completely determined. It is probable that in the earliest embryonic stages the formation of the vessels takes place through forces of heredity, while in the later stages the shape and growth of the blood vessels are determined by local chemical and hemodynamic factors.

THE HEART. The heart at the beginning of the circulation is a tube with a double wall: the internal endothelial layer, from which the endocardium develops, and the external myoepicardial layer. The latter consists of several layers of cells with indistinctly outlined boundaries. In the beginning (human embryo of 3 mm. length) the distance between the two layers of the wall is rather great, and the space is filled with a gelatinous intercellular sub-

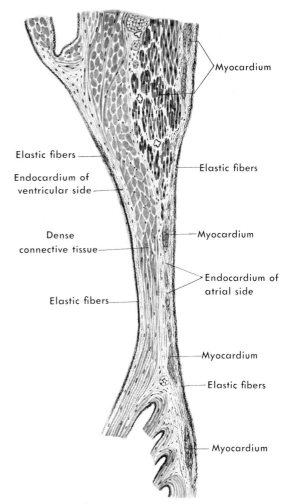

Figure 13-31. Cross section through mitral valve of man. Atrial surface on the right, ventricular on the left. In the upper left is the attachment of the aortic valve; on the left, below, is the passage of chordae tendineae into the valve. Low magnification. (After Sato.)

stance that is penetrated by long protoplasmic processes passing from the endothelium to the myoepicardial layer.

In a human embryo 3.5 mm. in length, beginning with the sinus venosus and passing over to the atrium and the ventricle, this mucoid tissue disappears, and the endothelium closely adjoins the myocardial layer. But in the vicinity of the opening that connects the atrium with the ventricle and in the bulbus, this tissue remains. In this way, cushion-like thickenings of the endocardium are formed, consisting of a mucoid connective tissue. The myocardium differentiates at the same time into an external peripheral layer of flat cells, the primordium of the serous membrane of the epicardium, and into the internal, thicker layer of irregular cells united by intercellular bridges.

The endocardial cushion-like thickenings play an important role in the formation of partitions that separate the primary single cavity of the heart into compartments, and they are particularly important in the formation of the valves.

In the earlier stages of development the myocardium is continuous from the atria to the ventricles. But later, from the epicardium, along the course of the atrioventricular ridge, a transverse band of embryonic connective tissue develops that completely encircles the heart. It cuts into the myocardium from the exterior and entirely separates the muscle of the atria from that of the ventricles, save for the connection between them created by the atypical fibers of the conduction system.

REFERENCES

Altschul, R.: Endothelium. New York, Macmillan Co., 1954.

Bennett, H. S., J. H. Luft, and J. C. Hampton: Morphological classification of vertebrate blood capillaries. Am. J. Physiol., *196*:381, 1959.

Bloch, E. H.: Microscopic observations of the circulating blood in the bulbar conjunctiva in man in health and disease. Ergeb. Anat. Entwickl., *35*:1, 1956.

Boyd, J. D.: The development of the human carotid body. Cargenie Contributions to Embryol., *26*:1, 1937.

Burton, A. C.: Relation of structure to function of the tissues of the wall of the blood-vessels. Physiol. Rev., *34*:619, 1954.

Clark, E. R., and E. L. Clark: Microscopic observations on the extraendothelial cells of living mammalian blood vessels. Am. J. Anat., *66*:1, 1940.

Dobbing, J.: The blood-brain barrier. Physiol. Rev., *41*:130, 1961.

Ebert, J. D., R. A. Tolman, A. M. Mun, and J. F. Albright: Patterns of synthesis in differentiation; the molecular basis of the first heart beats. Ann. N.Y. Acad. Sci., *60*:968, 1955.

Farquhar, M.: Fine structure and function in capillaries of the anterior pituitary gland. Angiology, *12*:270, 1961.

Fawcett, D. W.: Comparative observations on the fine structure of blood capillaries. *In* Peripheral Vessels. Internat. Acad. Pathol., Monograph No. 4. Baltimore, Williams & Wilkins, 1963.

Florey, H.: Exchange of substances between the blood and tissues. Nature, *192*: 908, 1961.

Florey, Lord: The endothelial cell. Brit. M. J., *2*:487, 1966.

Goss, C. M.: The physiology of the embryonic mammalian heart before circulation. Am. J. Physiol., *137*:146, 1942.

Harper, W. F.: The blood supply of human heart valves. Brit. M. J., *2*:305, 1941.

Heath, D., J. W. DuShane, E. H. Wood, and J. E. Edwards: The structure of the pulmonary trunk at different ages and in cases of pulmonary hypertension and pulmonary stenosis. J. Path. & Bact., *77*:443, 1959.

Heath, D., and J. E. Edwards: Configuration of elastic tissue of pulmonary trunk in idiopathic pulmonary hypertension. Circulation, *21*:59, 1960.

Hogan, M. J., and L. Feeney: The ultrastructure of retinal blood vessels. I. The large vessels. J. Ultrastruct. Res., *9*:10, 1963.

Hollinshead, W. H.: Effects of anoxia upon carotid body morphology. Anat. Rec., *92*:255, 1945.

Jennings, M. A., V. T. Marchesi, and H. Florey: The transport of particles across the walls of small blood vessels. Proc. Roy. Soc. B., *156*:14, 1962.

Karnovsky, M. J.: Vesicular transport of exogenous peroxidase across capillary endothelium into the T-system of muscle. J. Cell Biol., *27*:49A, 1965.

Karnovsky, M. J., and R. S. Cotran: The intercellular passage of exogenous peroxidase across endothelium and mesothelium. Anat. Rec., *154*:365, 1966.

Karrer, H. E., and J. Cox: Electron microscopy study of developing chick embryo aorta. J. Ultrastruct. Res., *4*:420, 1960.

Keech, M. K.: Electron microscope study of the normal rat aorta. J. Biophys. & Biochem. Cytol., *7*:533, 1960.

Knisely, M. H., L. Warner, and F. Harding: Antemortem settling. Angiology, *11*:535, 1960.

Kurtz, S. M., and J. D. Feldman: Experimental studies on the formation of the glomerular basement membrane. J. Ultrastruct. Res., *6*:19, 1962.

Landis, E. M., and J. R. Pappenheimer: Exchange of substances through the capillary walls. *In* Hamilton, W. F., and P. Dow, eds.: Handbook of Physiology. Washington, American Physiological Society, 1963, Section 2, Vol. II, p. 961.

Luft, J. H.: The fine structure of the vascular wall. *In* Jones, R. J., ed.: Evolution of the Atherosclerotic Plaque. Chicago, University of Chicago Press, 1963, p. 3.

Luft, J. H.: The ultrastructural basis of capillary permeability. *In* Zweifach, B. W. L. Grant, and R. T. McCluskey, eds.: The Inflammatory Process. New York, Academic Press, 1965, p. 121.

Lutz, B. R., C. P. Fulton, and R. P. Akers: The neuromotor mechanism of the small blood vessels in membranes of the frog (*Rana pipiens*) and the hamster (*Mesocricetus auratus*) with reference to the normal and pathological conditions of blood flow. Exper. Med. Surg., *8*:258, 1950.

Majno, G.: Ultrastructure of the vascular membrane. *In* Hamilton, W. F., and P. Dow, eds.: Handbook of Physiology. Washington, American Physiological Society, 1965, Section 2, Vol. III, p. 2293.

Majno, G., and G. E. Palade: Studies on inflammation. I. The effect of histamine and serotonin on vascular permeability: An electron microscopy study. J. Biophys. & Biochem. Cytol., *11*:607, 1961.

Movat, H. Z., and N. V. P. Pernando: The fine structure of the terminal vascular bed. I. Small arteries with an internal elastic lamina. Exp. & Mol. Path., *2*:549, 1963.

Movat, H. Z., and N. V. P. Pernando: The fine structure of the terminal vascular bed. IV. The venules and their perivascular cells. Exp. & Mol. Path., *3*:98, 1964.

Nonidez, J. F.: The aortic (depressor) nerve and its associated epithelioid body, the glomus aorticum. Am. J. Anat., *57*:259, 1935.

Nonidez, J. F.: Identification of the receptor areas in the venae cavae and pulmonary veins which initiate reflex cardiac acceleration (Bainbridge's reflex). Am. J. Anat., *61*:203, 1937.

Palade, G. E.: Transport in quanta across the endothelium of blood capillaries. Anat. Rec., *136*:254, 1960.

Palade, G. E.: Blood capillaries of the heart and other organs. Circulation, *24*:368, 1961.

Palade, G. E., and R. R. Bruns: Structure and function in normal muscle capillaries. *In* Siperstein, M. D., A. R. Colwell, and K. Meyer, eds.: Small Blood Vessel Involvement in Diabetes Mellitus. Baltimore Garamond/Pridemark, 1964.

Pappenheimer, J. R.: Passage of molecules through capillary walls. Physiol. Rev., *33*:387, 1953.

Patten, B. M., and T. C. Kramer: The initiation of contraction in the embryonic chick heart. Am. J. Anat., *53*:349, 1933.

Pease, D. C., and W. J. Paule: Electron microscopy of elastic arteries, The thoracic aorta of the rat. J. Ultrastruct. Res., *3*:469, 1960.

Pease, D. C., and S. Molinari: Electron microscopy of muscular arteries: Pial vessels of the cat and monkey. J. Ultrastruct. Res., *3*:447, 1960.

Reese, T. S., and M. J. Karnovsky: Fine structural localization of a blood-brain barrier for exogenous peroxidase. J. Cell Biol. (in press).

Reynolds, S. R. M., and B. W. Zweifach: The Microcirculation; A Symposium on Factors Influencing Exchange of Substances Across Capillary Wall. Urbana, University of Illinois Press, 1959.

Rhodin, J. A. G.: Fine structure of the vascular wall in mammals. Physiol. Rev., *42* (Suppl. 5):48, 1962.

Rhodin, J. A. G.: The diaphragm of capillary endothelial fenestrations. J. Ultrastruct. Res., *6:*171, 1962.

Rhodin, J. A. G., P. del Missier, and L. C. Reid: The structure of the specialized impulse-conducting system of the steer heart. Circulation, *24:*349, 1961.

Sabin, F. R.: Studies on the origin of blood vessels and of red blood corpuscles as seen in the living blastoderm of chicks during the second day of incubation. Carnegie Contributions to Embryol., *9:*213, 1920.

Sandison, J. C.: Contraction of blood vessels and observations on the circulation in the transparent chamber in the rabbit's ear. Anat. Rec., *54:*105, 1932.

Schmidt, C. F., and J. H. Comroe, Jr.: Functions of the carotid and aortic bodies. Physiol. Rev., *20:*115, 1940.

Speidel, E., and A. Lazarow: Chemical composition of glomerular basement membrane material in diabetes. Diabetes, *12:*355, 1963.

Weibel, E. R., and G. E. Palade: New cytoplasmic components in arterial endothelia. J. Cell Biol., *23:*101, 1964.

Weidenreich, F.: Allgemeine Morphologie des Gefäss-systems. Handb. d. vergleich. Anat., *6:*375, 1933.

Zimmermann, K. W.: Der feinere Bau der Blutkapillaren. Zeitschr. f. Anat. u. Entwicklungs., *68:*29, 1923.

CHAPTER FOURTEEN

Lymphatic System

An exchange of water, nutritive materials (including proteins and other solutes in the blood), and oxygen proceeds continuously between the blood within the capillaries and the tissue fluid bathing the cells of the various tissues. Most of the waste products of metabolism are returned to the blood capillaries and venules. In the higher vertebrates, vessels of the closed lymphatic system return some of the tissue fluids to the general circulation by a roundabout route.

The lymphatic system is composed of *lymphatic vessels* and *lymphatic organs.* The smallest vessels, the *lymphatic capillaries,* are thin-walled, blindly ending tubes, which form a dense network in most of the tissues of the body. They collect tissue fluid, which is called *lymph* as soon as it enters these capillaries. The lymphatic capillaries unite to form larger vessels, the largest of which empty into veins. The lymphatic system thus differs from the blood vascular system in that it is not a closed vascular ring. The lymphatic organs are located along the course of the lymphatic vessels and contribute various-sized lymphocytes to the lymph passing through them. The lymph of the finest lymphatic radicles is almost devoid of cells.

Connected with the lymphatic system are the serous cavities, the spaces surrounding the meninges, the chambers of the eye, Tenon's cavity around the eyeball, the cavity of the internal ear, the ventricles of the brain, and the central canal of the spinal cord. The liquids in these cavities are different from the lymph and have a different physiological significance, although the liquid in the serous cavities is much like lymph. Despite the differences in the fluids, injected colloidal solutions and particulate matter may penetrate from these cavities into the lymphatic vessels, and vice versa.

LYMPHATIC VESSELS

LYMPHATIC CAPILLARIES. Lymphatic capillaries are thin-walled, tubular structures that have a slightly greater caliber than blood capillaries. Unlike the latter, which usually have a regular cylindrical form, they have irregular shapes and are constricted in some places and dilated in others. They branch abundantly and anastomose freely. Dilatations occur frequently where several capillaries join. The lymphatic networks are often located beside networks of blood capillaries, but are always independent of them. As a general rule, the lymphatic networks are farther from the surface of the skin or mucous membranes than are the blood capillary networks.

The lymphatic networks are distinguished from the blood capillaries by ending blindly in rounded or swollen ends. This is best seen in the mucous membrane of the small intestine, where a network of lymphatic capillaries or a single, blindly ending vessel, the *central lacteal*, extends in the lamina propria up to the end of the villus (Fig. 14-1). The lymphatic capillaries form expanded networks of considerable size around the solitary and aggregated lymphatic nodules of the intestine, and in the thyroid and mammary glands.

The wall of a lymphatic capillary is formed by a single layer of flat endothelial cells; these are slightly larger and thinner than those of the blood capillaries. Hence, in sections of collapsed lymphatic capillaries, only the endothelial nuclei can be seen, and these cannot be distinguished from the nuclei of the surrounding fibroblasts. The lymphatic capillaries abut directly against the surrounding tissues and are not provided with a layer of pericytes as are the blood capillaries.

LARGER LYMPHATIC VESSELS. The lymph passes from the capillary networks into lymphatic vessels that have slightly thicker walls, and are provided with valves. These vessels are covered by thin, collagenous bundles, elastic fibers, and a few smooth muscle cells, arranged tangentially or transversely to the vessel. Those lymphatic vessels with a diameter greater than 0.2 mm. have thicker walls, in which three layers, corresponding to the inner, medial, and adventitial coats of arteries and veins, can be distinguished. The boundaries between these layers are often indistinct, so that the division is somewhat artificial. The tunica intima consists of endothelium and a thin layer of longitudinal, interlacing elastic fibers. The tunica media is composed of several layers of mainly circular and a few tangential smooth muscle fibers and several thin elastic fibers. The tunica adventitia is the thickest layer and consists of interlacing collagenous and elastic fibers, and smooth muscle bundles. The elastic fibers of the tunica adventitia continue into those of the surrounding connective tissue.

VALVES. The valves of the lymphatic vessels always occur in pairs placed on opposite sides of the vessel, with their free edges pointing in the direction of the lymph flow. The valves are often unable to withstand the pressure of a retrograde injection.

As in the veins, the valves of the lymphatic vessels are folds of the tunica intima. They have a thin connective tissue base and are covered on both sides by a layer of endothelium continuous with that of the rest of the vessel. Although valves are not present in all lymphatic vessels, when they occur they are usually much closer together than those in the veins. Proximal to each pair of valves, the lymphatic vessel is more or less expanded, and the wall in these places has several prominent layers of smooth muscles in its media. It is believed that in some species the contractions of these muscles may help move the lymph along the vessel.

LARGE LYMPHATIC VESSELS; THORACIC DUCT. The lymphatic vessels unite with other similar vessels and become larger and larger,

while their walls become thicker. They form networks that often surround blood vessels. These are very prominent about the mesenteric vessels of some mammals.

Finally, all the lymphatics come together and form two main trunks—the *right lymphatic duct* and the *thoracic duct.* The former is the smaller; it carries the lymph from the upper right portion of the body and usually opens into the right innominate vein, at the site where it originates from union of the right internal jugular and subclavian veins. The thoracic duct carries the lymph from all the remaining parts of the body (including the digestive system) and opens into the point of junction of the left internal jugular and subclavian veins. Both ducts are provided with valves where they enter the veins.

The wall of the thoracic duct differs from that of the great veins by the greater development of the muscles in the tunica media and by a less distinct division into three layers.

The tunica intima consists of the endothelial lining and several thin layers of collagenous and elastic fibers; the latter condense into a layer similar to an internal elastic membrane near the junction with the tunica media. The transverse smooth muscle bundles in the tunica media are penetrated by elastic fibers coming from the elastica interna. The tunica adventitia is composed of longitudinal collagenous fibers, interlacing elastic fibers, and a few longitudinal smooth muscle bundles. The

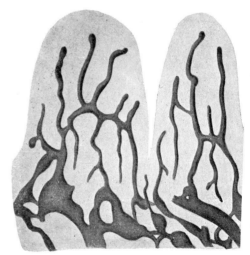

Figure 14-1. Lymphatic capillaries (lacteals), filled with Berlin blue, in the villi of the intestine of a rat. (Redrawn after Ranvier.)

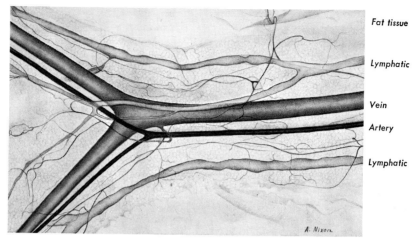

Fat tissue

Lymphatic

Vein

Artery

Lymphatic

A. Nixon.

Figure 14-2. Vital injection of lymphatic vessels with alpha–azurine F.G. and of the blood vessels with colloidal mercuric sulfide. Mesentery of rabbit. × about 20.

tunica adventitia gradually merges into the surrounding loose connective tissue.

BLOOD VESSELS OF LYMPHATICS. The wall of the thoracic duct is provided with many blood vessels that extend into the outer layer of the middle tunic; these vessels are similar to the vasa vasorum of the larger blood vessels. The narrow, thin-walled lymphatic vessels are often accompanied by a small artery and vein running parallel to them. Capillaries arise from the arteriole and encircle the lymphatic vessels or form regular networks on their surfaces.

NERVES OF LYMPHATICS. Both the large thoracic duct and the smaller lymphatic vessels are abundantly supplied with nerves. In both adventitial and medial coats, some of the fibers terminate in sensory endings. The other fibers are motor nerves for the smooth muscles, as in the blood vessels.

PASSAGE OF LYMPH FROM THE TISSUES INTO THE LYMPHATICS. With injection methods it has been shown that the lumen of lymphatics does not communicate directly with the "tissue spaces." The so-called "stomata" seen in silver nitrate preparations are undoubtedly artifacts. As the lymphatics form a closed, endothelium lined system of tubes, the tissue fluid must pass through the endothelial cytoplasm or through the narrow intercellular clefts between endothelial cells to reach the lumen of the lymphatics. In inflammation the permeability of the local lymphatics to certain dyes is increased.

LYMPHATIC ORGANS

Closely connected with the lymphatic vessels are collections of *lymphatic tissue* aggregated into the *lymphatic organs*. The lymphatic tissue has been discussed in Chapter 6. The solitary and aggregated lymphatic nodules of the gastrointestinal, respiratory, and genitourinary systems will be described with the respective systems. Here only the lymph nodes will be considered.

Lymph Nodes

A lymph node is a large accumulation of lymphatic tissue organized as a definite lymphatic organ. Such nodes are always located along the course of lymphatic vessels, whose contents pass through the nodes on their way to the thoracic or right lymphatic ducts. Lymph nodes are scattered in large numbers, usually in groups, throughout the prevertebral region, in the mesentery, and in the loose connective tissue of the axilla and groin. They are flat, well defined bodies varying from 1 to 25 mm. in diameter. Their form is rounded or kidney-shaped, and their surface is somewhat rough. Usually there is a slight indentation, the *hilus*, on one side of the node, where blood vessels enter and leave the organ. Lymphatic vessels enter the node at many places over its convex surface; they leave it only at the hilus.

STROMA. The lymph node is covered by a *capsule* of dense collagenous fibers with a few fibroblasts and, particularly on its inner surface, networks of thin elastic fibers. A few smooth muscle cells are also found in the capsule about the points of entry and exit of the afferent and efferent lymph vessels. At the *hilus* the capsule is greatly thickened. *Trabeculae* of dense collagenous connective tissue arise from the capsule and penetrate the organ. Toward the hilus they become highly branched and finally fuse with the collagenous tissue of the hilus. Near the capsule, they divide the interior of the lymph node into roughly round areas, sometimes called ampullae or alveoli. As the trabeculae are frequently interrupted, adjacent ampullae connect with each other. The capsule, the hilus, and the trabeculae constitute the collagenous framework of the lymph node.

Suspended within this collagenous framework is the *reticular framework.* The reticular fibers are frequently continuous with fibers of the collagenous framework. The reticular fibers penetrate all parts of the node and form a network of varying density in different locations. The loosely meshed areas constitute the *sinuses,* through which the lymph percolates. Such loosely meshed areas occur under the capsule and along the trabeculae, where they are called subcapsular and trabecular sinuses, respectively. The *cellular stroma* of the lymph node is made up of the primitive reticular cells and the fixed macrophages. These are associated with the reticular fibers. The primitive reticular cells or the fixed macrophages (or perhaps both) form the reticular fibers. Typical fibroblasts are found only in the collagenous framework. In the meshes of the stroma are the free cells, mostly lymphocytes of various sizes. Plasma cells often occur, especially in the rat. A few hematogenous eosinophilic leukocytes can be found in most lymph nodes. The sinuses, particularly of the medulla, contain free macrophages, even under normal conditions. Usually there are fewer free cells in the sinuses than in the tissue, because the cells are swept away by the flowing lymph.

CORTEX AND MEDULLA. The sectioned surface of a lymph node under low magnification shows the organ divided into an outer cortical and an inner medullary part. The difference in appearance between the cortex and medulla consists mainly in differences in arrangement of the lymphatic tissue in the two zones. The cortex occupies the surface of the organ, with the exception of the hilus, and consists primarily of dense lymphatic tissue, which continues into the medulla as medullary cords. As mentioned before, a rim of loose lymphatic tissue is present under the capsule and bordering the trabeculae. The cortex contains lymphatic nodules about 1 mm. in diameter. The nodules are temporary structures (see p. 179), expressing the cytogenetic and defense func-

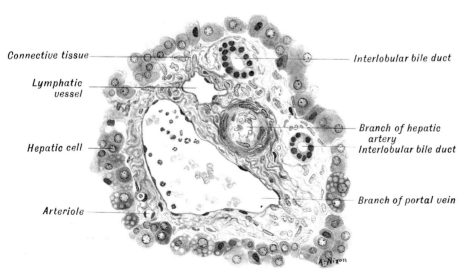

Connective tissue
Lymphatic vessel
Hepatic cell
Arteriole

Interlobular bile duct
Branch of hepatic artery
Interlobular bile duct
Branch of portal vein

Figure 14-3. Section of periportal area of a human liver. × 480.

tions of the lymphatic tissue, which depend on age, condition or nutrition of the organism, and the like. They may develop and disappear, to reappear again at the same or another place. The number and size of the nodules fluctuate remarkably. In the embryo and in the first months after birth they lack the central "germinal" or "reactive" areas. With the growth and development of the organism these centers appear and then become more numerous and larger. With advancing age they become less conspicuous and smaller, and in old age and in various diseases they may disappear.

The medulla consists of the same cytological constituents as the cortex. It is not sharply separated from the cortex and usually occupies the inner portion of the node radiating from the hilus. The medullary cords are dense lymphatic tissue and rarely contain nodules. The cords branch and anastomose freely with one another. Near the hilus they terminate with free ends, or, more frequently, they form loops that continue into other cords. The cords are accompanied and surrounded by the medullary sinuses, which separate them from the trabeculae and are continuations and amplifications of the cortical sinuses. The substance of the sinuses is also composed of lymphatic tissue, but its meshes are so wide that they constitute relatively broad channels for the passage of lymph.

Lymphatic Vessels and Sinuses

The afferent vessels that supply lymph to the node are provided with valves that open toward the node (Fig. 14-7). These afferent vessels approach the convex surface of the node, pierce its capsule, and open into the subcapsular sinus. From here the lymph passes through the looser parts of the lymphatic tissue, the sinuses, of both the cortex and medulla, and then into the efferent lymphatic vessels at the hilus.

Unlike the tubular, endothelium lined blood vascular and lymphatic *vessels*, the lymphatic *sinuses* are irregular, tortuous spaces within the lymphatic tissue. Their walls are

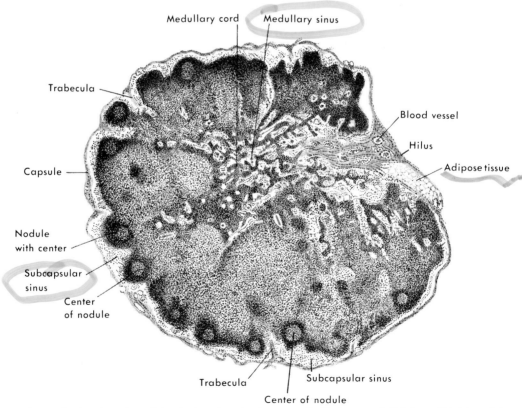

Figure 14-4. Section through small jugular lymph node of man. × 18. (Redrawn and slightly modified from Sobotta.)

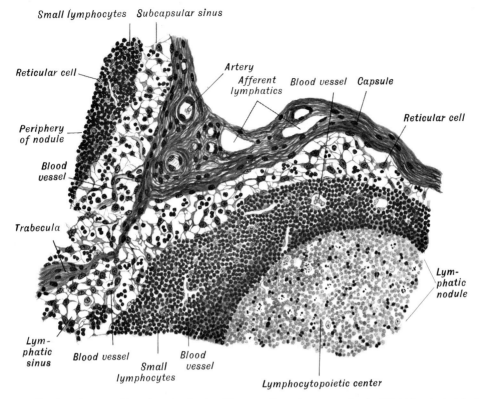

Figure 14-5. Portion of cortex of lymph node of a dog. Hematoxylin-eosin-azure stain. × 187. (After A. A. Maximow.)

formed of reticular cells and fixed macrophages supported by the reticular fibers. As a continuous stream of lymph flows through the sinuses, lymphocytes are swept into the efferent lymphatic vessels, and new lymphocytes enter the sinuses by their own ameboid movement.

The sinuses of the medullary substance at first pass over into a network of twisted tubes which penetrate the thickened portion of the capsule at the hilus and then continue into the efferent vessels, which conduct the lymph away. These are wider and less numerous than the afferent vessels and are provided with valves that open away from the node. The arrangement of the valves in the afferent and efferent vessels thus permits a flow of lymph in only one direction through the node.

The margins of the endothelial cells in the lymphatic vessels can be outlined by treatment with silver nitrate. The outlines of the reticular cells that form the walls of the lymphatic sinuses may sometimes be demonstrated by this means only when they are so closely packed as to simulate endothelial cells.

Variations in Structure of Lymph Nodes

The described arrangement of the constituents of a typical lymph node is realized in but few instances, for the lymph nodes show great variations in structure, depending on the animal species as well as on the location of the node and its state of activity. None of these deviations, however, affect the fundamental structure.

In large nodes the trabeculae are prominent; in small nodes they are thin and frequently interrupted. Nodes deep in the body, as in the peritoneal cavity, are also distinguished by the poor development of their trabeculae as contrasted with the more peripheral nodes.

In some cases a hilus may be absent, while in others it may be so highly developed that its connective tissue may penetrate far into the node and divide it completely. In the ox the trabecular system is so well developed that the ampullae of the cortex are completely separated. When the trabecular system is poorly

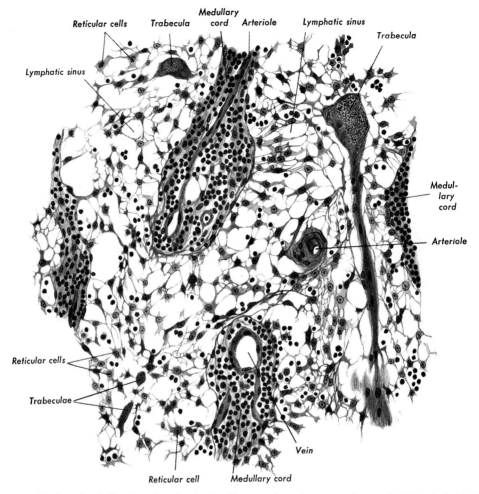

Figure 14-6. Portion of medulla of lymph node of a dog. Hematoxylin-eosin-azure stain. × 187. (After A. A. Maximow.)

developed, as in man, the nodules of the cortical substance and the sinuses may lose their sharp outlines and often fuse into a continuous, diffuse mass of lymphatic tissue, in which there are occasional looser strips or passages along which the lymph flows. Such areas, when filled with macrophages, have been called "interfollicular tissue." The term should be discarded, because the only tissue in the node is lymphatic tissue.

The relative amounts of cortical and medullary substance and their mutual arrangement vary within wide limits. The nodes of the abdominal cavity are especially rich in medullary substance. In those cases in which the cortical substance predominates, the nodules may be arranged in several layers. Sometimes the cortical substance may surround the me-

dulla completely; in other cases the medullary substance may be adjacent to the capsule for long distances. In some cases the medulla and cortex may accumulate at opposite poles of the node, while in the pig the cortical substance with its nodules is collected in the central portion of the node, and the medullary cords with their wide sinuses may occupy only small portions of the periphery.

BLOOD VESSELS. Almost all the blood vessels destined for the lymph node enter it through the hilus; only occasional small ones enter through the capsule. The larger arterial and venous branches pass along the trabeculae, while the smaller ones pass along the axis of the medullary cords toward the cortex. The capillaries form particularly dense networks in the peripheral layers of the medullary cords and of the nodules. In the latter they form radially arranged meshes. In the cortex, they have a thickened endothelium, so that in cross section they often appear as though lined by cuboidal epithelium. Large numbers of small lymphocytes are present and pass through this endothelium into the blood. There is substantial evidence that most of these lymphocytes are migrating from the venules into the lymph node. This movement is an important part of the fourth circulation (p. 128).

NERVES. Nerves enter the hilus of the node with the blood vessels, forming perivascular networks. In the trabeculae and in the medullary cords, independent nervous networks may be noticed. But in the nodules nerves are present only along the vessels and are probably of vasomotor type.

HEMAL NODES. Even in normal lymph nodes varying numbers of erythrocytes are found. These have either entered the lymph from the afferent vessels or have come from the

blood vessels of the node. Some of them pass with lymph into the efferent vessels, but most of them are engulfed by the fixed macrophages. Some nodes, however, are characterized by their great content of erythrocytes. Macroscopically, such organs are called *hemal nodes*. They are most numerous and well defined in the ruminants (sheep); they probably do not occur in man.

They vary from the size of a hardly noticeable granule to that of a pea or larger, and are scattered near large blood vessels in the retropleural and retroperitoneal tissues along the vertebral column from the neck to the pelvic inlet. They are also found near the kidneys and spleen, where they are believed by some to be accessory spleens.

Each node is covered by a dense capsule loosely connected with the surrounding tissue. At the hilus a small artery and a large vein enter and leave. The nodes are devoid of lymphatics. The hemal nodes are "filters" of lym-

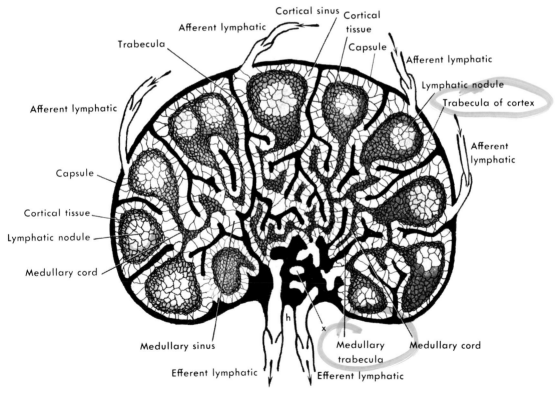

Figure 14-7. Diagram of lymph node, showing afferent and efferent lymphatic vessels with valves; arrows indicate the direction of lymph flow. The cortical trabeculae originate in the capsule and divide the cortex into ampullae. The medullary trabeculae are continuous with those in the cortex. *x*, Lymphatic vessels in the dense connective tissues in the hilus, *h*. The blood vessels are not shown.

phatic tissue, situated in the course of blood vessels, and their structure is closer to that of the spleen than of lymph nodes. In the pig a special type of hemolymphatic node occupies a position halfway between the ordinary lymph node and the typical hemal node. It has blood as well as lymphatic vessels, and the contents of both types of vessels mix in the sinuses. It is possible that even in adult animals a simple lymph node may change into a hemal node, and vice versa. The functions of the hemal nodes are probably like those of the spleen.

Function of Lymph Nodes

Although they share this function with all the other accumulations of lymphatic tissue in the body, the lymph nodes are the most active structures for the formation of the lymphocytes, except, perhaps, for the thymus. The stimuli for lymphocyte production are probably brought to the lymph nodes by both lymphatic and arterial vessels. Although great numbers of lymphocytes are produced in certain infections and the lymphatic leukemias, the actual stimuli for lymphocytopoiesis in these conditions, as well as in physiological states, are unknown. As the lymph nodes are composed essentially of lymphocytes and phagocytes, it is obvious that their main functions depend on these cells. The functions of these cells are discussed in Chapters 6 and 8.

In some pathological conditions, *extramedullary myelopoiesis* occurs, and the nodes become the sites of formation of granular leukocytes.

Because of the phagocytic activity of the reticular cells, particularly in the sinuses, the nodes serve as filters in which various particles, arising locally or brought with the lymph from other regions of the body, are taken up and often destroyed. Even in normal conditions, erythrophagocytosis can be seen in the sinuses of lymph nodes. This process is much more prominent when great numbers of erythrocytes are brought to the nodes as a result of hemorrhage into the nearby tissues. Particles of coal dust inhaled into the lungs finally enter the bronchial lymph nodes, where they are taken up by the reticular cells and often accumulate in such quantities that the organ becomes black. Pathogenic bacteria brought to the lymph nodes are frequently ingested and sometimes destroyed by the macrophages. Just like all the other tissues and organs containing many macrophages and lymphoid cells, the lymph nodes elaborate *antibodies*.

HISTOGENESIS

In the mammalian embryo the lymphatic system is laid down much later than the blood vascular system. The lymphatic vessels arise first, and the lymphatic organs develop in connection with them somewhat later.

LYMPHATIC VESSELS.   Although there are many unsettled details in the question of the mode of development of the lymphatic system,

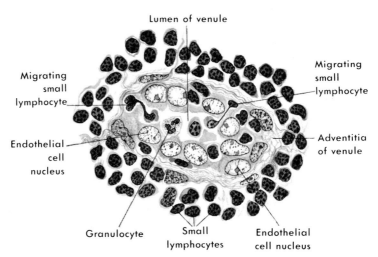

Figure 14-8. Extensive migration of small lymphocytes through the cuboidal, epithelium-like endothelium of a post capillary venule in the lymphoid tissue of the human palatine tonsil. Such migration of lymphocytes is currently believed to be important in the "fourth circulation" (see page 128). After A. A. Maximow.

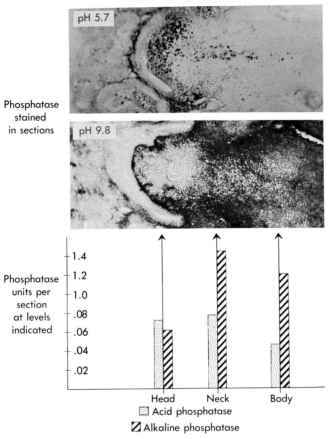

Phosphatase stained in sections

pH 5.7

pH 9.8

Phosphatase units per section at levels indicated

1.4
1.2
1.0
.08
.06
.04
.02

Head   Neck   Body
▦ Acid phosphatase
▨ Alkaline phosphatase

Figure 14-9. Quantitative analyses of amounts of acid and alkaline phosphatase made on sections taken at the levels indicated in rabbit appendix. The qualitative distribution of the enzymes in the lymphatic tissue is shown in the photomicrographs made with the methods of Gomori. (After Doyle.)

most observers believe that the primordia of the lymphatic sacs and vessels arise independently of the veins, although often close to them, as isolated small clefts in the mesenchyme, which are filled with tissue fluid and surrounded by mesenchymal cells. The latter, owing to the pressure exerted by the fluid, acquire a flattened appearance and the character of endothelium. These spaces gradually fuse, forming in certain places large cavities, the *lymphatic sacs,* as well as vessels of more or less cylindrical shape. The sacs later communicate with the adjacent veins.

The vessels elongate rapidly in all directions owing to a continued addition of new cavities arising in the mesenchyme. The presence of blood in the early lymphatic vessels is explained as being due in part to a flow of blood from the veins and in part to the appearance of local hemopoietic islands in the mesenchyme together with the lymph sacs. These

blood cells become included in the latter and are carried with the lymph into the veins.

After a certain stage the further development of the lymphatic system takes place mainly by budding of the endothelium of existing lymphatic vessels. These outgrowths may be observed directly in the tail of living amphibian larvae and in chambers in the rabbit's ear. They correspond closely with the outgrowths from blood vessels (p. 386).

As in the blood vascular system, the developing lymphatic system does not retain all the parts laid down in the beginning; its constituents continue to change and become reconstructed. The main parts of the primary lymphatic system, the *sacs,* spread irregularly in various directions, and change their form; they develop in part into networks of lymphatic vessels and in part into complexes of lymphatic nodes. The student is referred to Zimmermann's monograph.

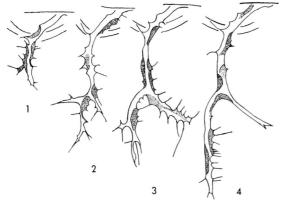

Figure 14-10. Successive stages (*1–4*) during three days of growth of bud of a lymphatic capillary of frog tadpole. × 180. (Redrawn after E. R. Clark.)

VALVES. Valves appear in the lymphatic vessels several weeks before they develop in the blood vessels. They appear first in the lymphatics near the jugular sacs and the upper part of the thoracic duct, then in the lymph vessels of the appendages, and finally in the remainder of the thoracic duct. They consist of a connective tissue base and a covering of endothelium.

LYMPH NODES. The development of the lymph nodes begins after the formation of the primary lymphatic vascular system. The earliest or primary nodes develop by a transformation of the lymphatic sacs. Each sac disappears as such and separates into a group of connected networks of lymphatic vessels that become nodes of various sizes; portions of the primary cisterna chyli and of the jugular sacs remain as cavities. As the sacs are at first the centers of development of the lymphatic vessels in a given region of the body, all the lymph collected from that region is finally carried into the corresponding group of deep primary nodes, such as the deep jugular nodes, retroperitoneal nodes, and so on. The secondary nodes, such as the popliteal, the inguinal, and the like, appear later along the course of lymphatic vessels; many smaller nodes are apparently formed after birth.

The transformation into a primary node is carried out by an invagination, into the lumen of the sac, of the surrounding mesenchyme, which grows through the sac in thick or thin bars. The mesenchyme forming the bars or partitions between the cavities at first does not contain wandering cells.

According to the newer investigations, the lymphatic sinuses arise as irregular, blind

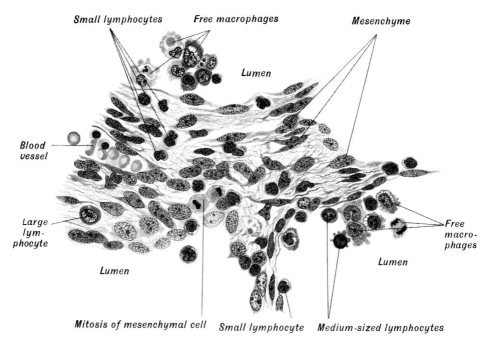

Figure 14-11. Primordium of lymph node in the wall of cervical lymph sac of a 37-mm. human embryo. Lumen of the sac is divided into cavernous spaces by partitions of mesenchyme. Eosin-azure stain. × about 400. (After A. A. Maximow.)

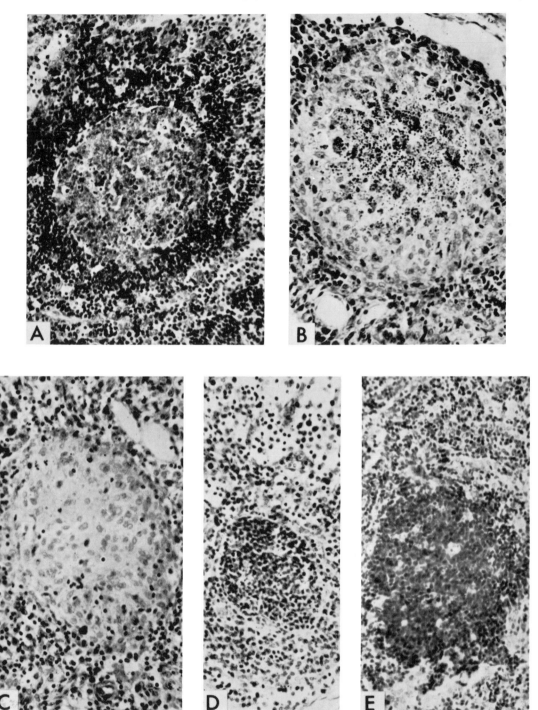

Figure 14-12. Four stages in degeneration and beginning regeneration of lymphatic tissue of mesenteric lymph nodes after total body irradiation with 800 R of 200 kV x-rays. *A,* From untreated rabbit, shows an active germinal center sharply demarcated from its corona of small lymphocytes extending into dense diffuse lymphatic tissue. *B,* 17 hours after irradiation, all the lymphocytes in the nodule have been destroyed and many of those at its periphery are also degenerating. Most of the debris is within macrophages, especially in the center of the nodule. *C,* 24 hours after irradiation, the center consists of reticular cells and the debris of a few lymphocytes. *D,* 21 days after irradiation, a new germinal center is developing. *E,* 31 days after irradiation, there is a larger focus of intense formation of lymphocytes in a new nodule and repopulation of the diffuse tissue with lymphocytes. × 245. (After DeBruyn.)

and anastomosing spaces, lined from the beginning by flattened mesenchymal cells; only later do they come in contact with the endothelium lined afferent and efferent vessels.

The primary node is a common primordium for the lymphatic tissue of the cortex and medulla, from which the medullary substance arises first. The true cortical substance appears much later as the medullary cords on the periphery of the node gradually develop club-shaped thickenings that bulge into the marginal sinus. The development of the lymphatic nodules is completed late, in the majority of cases after birth.

The lymphocytes develop in situ by the isolation and rounding up of mesenchymal elements and later through their own multiplication (Chapter 8). They accumulate mainly in the marginal sinus and are carried away by the lymph stream. Among these cells, the small ones always predominate at first, but large lymphocytes and macrophages also occur. Granulocytes and megakaryocytes appear temporarily with the lymphocytes, but soon disappear. The mesenchymal elements, which did not transform into lymphoid cells, either remain as undifferentiated elements (primitive reticular cells) or give rise to the fixed macrophages of the stroma. Fibers appear rather late in the stroma of lymphatic tissue.

REGENERATIVE CAPACITY OF
THE LYMPHATIC SYSTEM

When the adult human body is incised or otherwise injured, lymphatic vessels, and sometimes lymphatic organs, are injured. Regeneration of the vessels begins in the lymphatic capillaries and proceeds by vascular budding. In some cases, however, for reasons not known, regeneration of the lymphatic vessels does not take place.

The tissue of the lymphatic nodes responds to local injury at first by the rounding up of reticular cells and their transformation into macrophages, which multiply by mitosis. The lymphocytes, which at first are unchanged, then begin to multiply and hypertrophy into exudate mononuclear cells. But this attempt at regeneration is limited, and healing is usually brought about by the development of ordinary scar tissue.

After excision in young rabbits, lymph nodes may regenerate from local cells. With advancing age, such regenerative ability decreases markedly.

Lymphocytes are exceedingly sensitive to ionizing radiations. Figure 14-12 shows the dramatic sequence of changes reflecting the destructive effects of x-rays on the lymphocytes of lymphatic tissue and the regeneration which follows. The reticular cells, in contrast, are relatively radioresistant and show no changes at this level of irradiation.

REFERENCES

Caffery, R. W., N. B. Everett, and W. O. Rieke: Radioautographic studies of reticular and blast cells in the hemopoietic tissues of the rat. Anat. Rec., *155:*41, 1966.

Clark, E. R., and E. L. Clark: Further observations on living lymphatic vessels in the transparent chamber in the rabbit's ear—their relation to the tissue spaces. Am. J. Anat., *52:*263, 1933.

Clark, S. L., Jr.: The reticulum of lymph nodes in mice studied with the electron microscope. Am. J. Anat., *110:*217, 1962.

Conway, E. A.: Cyclic changes in lymphatic nodules. Anat. Rec., *69:*487, 1937.

Dougherty, T. F., M. L. Berliner, G. L. Schneebell, and D. L. Berliner: Hormonal control of lymphatic structure and function. *In* Bierman, H. R., ed.: Leukopoiesis in Health and Disease. Ann. N.Y. Acad. Sci., *113:*511, 1964.

Downey, H.: The structure and origin of the lymph sinuses of mammalian lymph nodes and their relations to endothelium and reticulum. Haematologica, *3:*31, 1922.

Downey, H., ed.: Handbook of Hematology. New York, Paul B. Hoeber, Inc., 1938.

Doyle, W. L.: The distribution of phosphatases in the rabbit appendix after x-irradiation. Am. J. Anat., *87:*79, 1950.

Gowans, J. L., and E. J. Knight: The route of re-circulation of lymphocytes in the rat. Proc. Roy. Soc. B., *159:*257, 1964.

Kampmeier, O.: The genetic history of the valves in the lymphatic system of man. Am. J. Anat., *40:*413, 1928.

Klein, J. J., A. L. Goldstein, and A. White: Enhancement of in vitro incorporation of labeled precursors into DNA and total protein of mouse lymph nodes after administration of thymic extracts. Proc. Nat. Acad. Sci., *53:*812, 1965.

Landis, E. M., and J. R. Pappenheimer: Exchange of substances through the capillary walls. *In* Hamilton, W. F., and P. Dow, eds.: Handbook of Physiology. Washington, American Physiological Society, 1963. Section 2, Vol. II, p. 961.

Latta, J.: The histogenesis of dense lymphatic tissue of the intestine (Lepus); a contribution to the knowledge of the development of lymphatic tissue and blood-cell formation. Am. J. Anat., *20:*159, 1921.

Marchesi, V. T., and J. L. Gowans: The migration of lymphocytes through the endothelium of venules in lymph nodes: An electron microscope study. Proc. Roy. Soc. B., *159:*283, 1963.

McClure, C. W. F.: The endothelial problem. Am. J. Anat., *22:*219, 1921.

McMaster, P. D., ed.: Lymph. Ann. N.Y. Acad. Sci., *46:*679, 1946.

Meyerson, H. S.: The physiologic importance of lymph. *In* Hamilton, W. F., and P. Dow, eds.: Handbook of Physiology. Washington, American Physiological Society, 1963, Section 2, Vol. II, p. 1035.

Micklem, H., C. Ford, E. Evans, and J. Gray: Interrelationships of myeloid and lymphoid cells: Studies with chromosome-marked cells transfused into lethally irradiated mice. Proc. Roy. Soc. B. *165:*78, 1966.

Yoffey, J. M.: The lymphocyte. Annual Rev. Med., *15:*125, 1964.

Yoffey, J. M., and F. C. Courtice: Lymphatics, Lymph and Lymphoid Tissue. Cambridge, Harvard University Press, 1956.

Zimmermann, A. A.: Origin and development of the lymphatic system in the opossum. Illinois Medical and Dental Monographs, *3:*Nos. 1 and 2, 1940.

CHAPTER FIFTEEN

The Spleen

The spleen, one of the blood cell forming and destroying organs, contains a large amount of lymphatic tissue and plays important roles in the metabolism and defense mechanisms of the body. But unlike those collections of lymphatic tissue that are interposed in the lymph stream, the spleen is in the bloodstream. There is a peculiar type of blood vessel that allows the circulating blood to come into contact with the macrophages of this organ, so that the spleen acts in many respects as a filter for the blood; this property becomes greatly accentuated in some immune reactions.

The spleen, much like the lymph node, has a collagenous framework within which is suspended a reticular framework. As in the lymph nodes, the collagenous framework consists of a *capsule,* thickened at the hilus of the organ, where it is attached to folds of the peritoneum and where arteries enter and veins leave the viscus. Branching and anastomosing continuations of the capsule, called *trabeculae,* penetrate the organ and form part of its framework.

The reticular framework fills the spaces between the capsule, hilus, and trabeculae, and forms, together with the cells present, the splenic tissue. This is composed of typical lymphatic tissue (*white pulp*) and an atypical lymphatic tissue (*red pulp*). The red pulp is a paste-like, dark red mass which can be scraped from the cut surface of the organ. On a freshly sectioned surface the white pulp is seen as irregular long or rounded gray areas, 0.2 to 0.7 mm. in diameter, scattered throughout the red pulp. These white areas are often called *malpighian bodies,* after the anatomist who first described

them. They consist of diffuse and nodular lymphatic tissue, which varies considerably in its finer structure from time to time. It is inadvisable to use the term "malpighian body," because it has been interpreted to mean different structures by various histologists.

The structure of the spleen and the relations between the red and white pulp depend on the distribution of the blood vessels and change markedly in certain infections, intoxications, and disturbances in blood cell formation (anemias, leukemia). The arteries are closely connected with the white pulp and the veins with the red pulp.

CAPSULE AND TRABECULAE. The capsule and the trabeculae of the spleen consist of dense connective tissue and a few smooth muscle cells. The collagenous fibers of the trabeculae are continuous with the reticular fibers of the pulp. Elastic fibers form a network between the collagenous bundles. In man, the network of the thickest elastic fibers is located in the deep layers of the capsule. The external surface of the capsule is covered by a layer of flattened mesothelium, which is part of the peritoneum.

In the trabeculae the elastic fibers are more numerous than in the capsule and sometimes replace most of the collagenous fibers. Muscle fibers are present in small groups (in man) or in long cords. Slow rhythmical changes in the volume of the organ are due to the smooth muscle in the capsule and trabeculae (in those species in which smooth muscle is prominent) and to the vascularly controlled changes in the amount of blood in the organ.

WHITE PULP. The white pulp (lym-

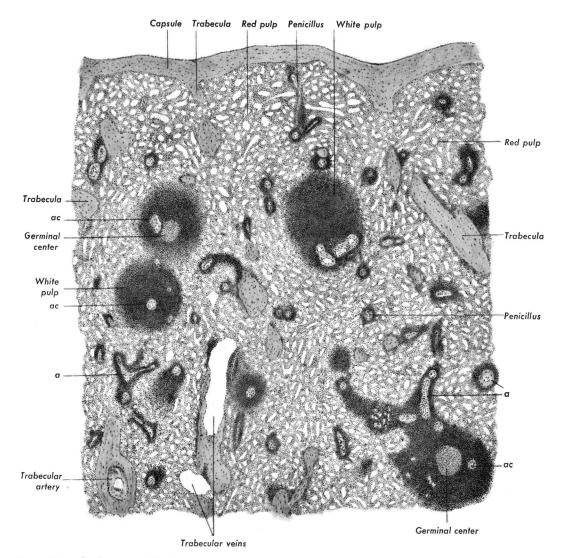

Figure 15-1. Section, perpendicular to capsule of human spleen. The arterial branches are covered with a thick layer of white pulp (lymphatic tissue) at *ac* and a thin layer at *a*. × 32. (After A. A. Maximow.)

phatic tissue) forms a sheath about the arteries. The stroma is a network of reticular fibers closely joined to the primitive reticular cells and phagocytic reticular cells or fixed macrophages (p. 177). As in all lymphatic tissue, the meshes of the framework are filled with free lymphocytes of various sizes, distributed to form diffuse and nodular lymphatic tissue. In the center of the lymphatic nodules of the spleen, as in the nodules of lymph nodes, the framework consists of thin, scattered threads, while at the periphery it is coarser and much denser. A few elastic fibers are interspersed among the reticular fibers of the white pulp close to the artery and its capillaries.

The absolute and relative amounts of dense and nodular lymphatic tissue vary continuously and reflect the reaction of the lymphatic tissue to various generalized stimuli. The lymphatic tissue of the spleen undergoes the same changes described on pages 179 to 181 for the lymphatic tissue in general. That is, diffuse lymphatic tissue may become nodular, and vice versa. The centers of the nodules undergo the same cyclic changes as described on page 179. The volume and number of the nodules decrease progressively with age. In myeloid leukemia the red pulp is greatly increased in amount (besides changing qualitatively), while the white pulp almost disappears. In lymphatic leukemia, on the contrary, the white pulp hypertrophies and the red pulp atrophies. The amount of lymphatic tissue is said to diminish during starvation. Lymphocytopoietic centers in the nodules appear and disappear in connection with the general condition of the organism. In the young they are numerous, while in the aged they are usually absent, especially in man. "Reaction centers" are common in certain infections and intoxications.

RED PULP. This tissue consists of the "venous sinuses" and the tissue filling the spaces between them, the "splenic cords" or "Billroth cords." The venous sinuses are discussed in the section on the veins of the spleen, of which they are a part. The splenic cords form a spongy network. Their tissue is a modified lymphatic tissue, which merges gradually into the tissue of the white pulp. Outside the latter, there is a band of tissue looser than the white pulp and containing some erythrocytes, but devoid of venous sinuses. It constitutes the so-called "marginal zone" of the periarterial lymphatic tissue.

A framework of reticular fibers forms the foundation of the red pulp. At the boundary between the white and the red pulp, it is evident that the fibers of the former continue into those of the latter. The collagenous fibers of the trabeculae continue directly into the reticular fibers of the red pulp. The fibrous stroma of the

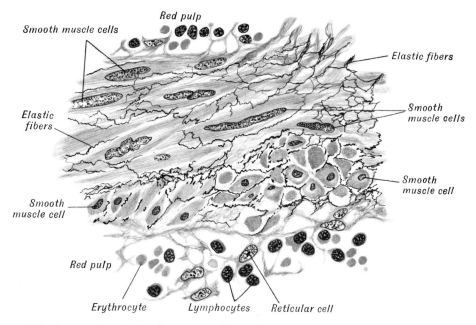

Figure 15-2. Portion of a trabecula from spleen of a cat. Elastic fiber stain. × 750. (After A. A. Maximow.)

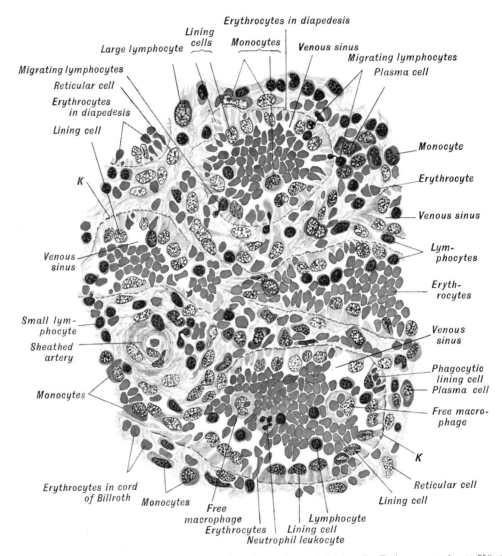

Figure 15-3. Red pulp of a human spleen. *K,* condensed cytoplasm of lining cells. Eosin-azure stain. × 750. (After A. A. Maximow.)

latter is accompanied by fixed macrophages and primitive reticular cells.

In the meshes of this framework are many lymphocytes, free macrophages, and all the elements of the circulating blood. The nongranular leukocytes are the most numerous of these free cells. Among them small, medium-sized, and large lymphocytes and monocytes are present in great numbers, intermingled without order. Various types of lymphocytes, which arise in the white pulp, spread by ameboid movement throughout the red pulp, where they continue to multiply.

The free macrophages are similar to those of the lymphatic tissue and are in close genetic relation with the fixed macrophages. They are round or irregularly shaped cells with large vesicular nuclei and much cytoplasm, which often contains engulfed particles, mainly erythrocytes in different stages of digestion, and yellow and brown granules, some of which give an iron reaction. Free macrophages can sometimes be found in blood filling the venous sinuses.

In many mammals (mouse, guinea pig, and hedgehog) and in mammalian embryos the red pulp of the spleen contains various-sized groups of myelocytes, erythroblasts, megakaryocytes, and plasma cells, in addition to the hemocytoblasts. In adult man this tissue does not form myeloid cells under physiological conditions.

In infections, in some of the anemias and leukemias, in poisoning with certain blood-destroying agents, and in local inflammations of the organ, the splenic tissue undergoes a *myeloid metaplasia* (p. 207). Myelocytes, megakaryocytes, and erythroblasts develop within the red pulp; only myelocytes have been described as arising in the germinal centers. This indicates that both white and red pulp are composed primarily of the same lymphatic tissue, which also has myeloid potencies. The myeloid elements may develop from lymphocytes as well as from primitive reticular cells (p. 209). The old idea of an "antagonism" between the red and white pulp is untenable. *The red pulp is a modified lymphatic tissue heavily infiltrated with all the cells of the circulating blood.*

ARTERIES. The branches of the splenic artery enter the hilus and pass along the trabeculae, with which they branch repeatedly, becoming smaller in caliber. They are muscular arteries of medium caliber and have a loose

tunica adventitia surrounded by the dense connective tissue of the trabeculae.

When the arterial branches have reached a diameter of approximately 0.2 mm., they leave the trabeculae (Fig. 15-6). At this place the tunica adventitia is replaced by a cylindrical sheath of lymphatic tissue (the white pulp), which surrounds the arteries almost to the point where they break up into capillaries. In many places along the course of the arteries the lymphatic sheath contains lymphatic nodules. The artery, although called "central artery," practically never passes through the nodules and their centers.

Throughout its course within the white pulp, the artery gives off numerous capillaries, which supply the lymphatic tissue of the sheath. The endothelial wall of these capillaries is supported externally by a thick network of reticular fibers. These arterial capillaries pass into the red pulp; how they end is uncertain (p. 408). Plasma cells are found surrounding the arterial capillaries. As in the marrow, these cells are increased in conditions in which the plasma globulins are elevated or when the organism is responding to an antigenic stimulus by formation of antibodies.

The small arteries in the white pulp continue to branch and become thinner; on reaching a caliber of 40 to 50 μ they leave the lymphatic tissue and enter the red pulp. Here they branch into small, straight vessels called *penicilli*, which show three successive parts. The first portion is the longest (0.6 to 0.7 mm.) and is called the *artery of the pulp*, which rapidly becomes narrow and divides (the caliber now is about 10 μ). Each branch (0.15 to 0.25 mm. long) is provided with a characteristic spindle-shaped thickening of its wall, the *Schweigger-Seidel sheath*, but has a narrow lumen (6 to 8 μ)—the so-called *sheathed artery;* this portion may ramify into two or three branches. These—forming the third portion—are the shortest (60 to 90 μ, with a lumen up to 10 μ) and represent simple arterial capillaries (Fig. 15-6), which either do not divide or split into only two branches. Their terminations are unknown and will be discussed after the veins have been described.

The artery of pulp has a tunica media consisting of one layer of smooth muscles surrounded by a thin, discontinuous envelope of lymphatic tissue which contains a few elastic fibers. In man the Schweigger-Seidel sheaths are only slightly developed. The tunica media is lost, so that the sheath is external to the endothelium (Fig. 15-7). The sheath is a compact mass of concentrically arranged cells with elongated nuclei (probably reticular cells) and longitudinal fibers which continue into the reticular fibers of the red pulp. The arterial capillaries consist of the endothelium, supported externally by a few longitudinal fibers and elongated cells.

In the dog, hedgehog, and pig, and in lower vertebrates, the sheaths are thick, oval bodies; they may be seen in the red pulp with low magnification. Red corpuscles are always present in large or small numbers inside the sheath.

VEINS.   The veins of the spleen begin as networks of *venous sinuses,* which penetrate all the red pulp and are especially numerous outside the marginal zone surrounding the white pulp. These vessels are called *sinuses* because they have a wide (12 to 40 μ) irregular lumen, the size of which varies with the amount of blood in the organ. The sinuses, even when moderately expanded, occupy more space than the splenic cords between them.

Unlike the veins, the walls of the venous sinuses do not contain common vascular endothelium, but are lined by long, narrow cells arranged parallel to the long axis of the vessel. The middle of each of these rod-shaped cells is distended by a nucleus. These lining cells are fixed macrophages, identical in origin and properties with those of the adjacent splenic cords, although normally less actively phagocytic.

Outside these cells, the wall of the sinus is supported by a system of mainly circularly disposed, occasionally branching reticular fibers which continue into the reticular fibers of the splenic cords. The sinus wall is thus a network of longitudinal, rod-shaped fixed macrophages and circular reticular fibers. Some hold that the meshes of this framework are closed by a thin, homogeneous membrane or by the edges of the phagocytes. Others claim that the presence of such a membrane has not been proved and that the wall of the venous sinuses of the spleen is perforated by many permanent openings. The solution of this problem will do much to solve the riddle of the blood circulation in the spleen.

The venous sinuses empty into the veins of the pulp, whose wall consists of endothelium

supported externally by a condensed stroma of the red pulp and a few elastic fibers. These pulp veins coalesce to form the veins of the trabeculae. These vessels consist only of endothelium supported by the connective tissue of the trabeculae. The trabecular veins form the splenic veins, which leave the organ at the hilus and empty into the portal vein.

UNION OF THE ARTERIES WITH THE VEINS. In almost all the other organs of the body the connection between the arterial and venous systems is accomplished by a direct passage of the arterial capillaries into the venous, in which the endothelium retains its continuity and the vascular lumen is completely enclosed. In the spleen, however, the connection is different, and its details are still subject to dispute. There are three main theories as to how blood gets from the arteries to the venous sinuses. (1) The arterial capillaries open directly into the spaces between the reticular cells of the splenic cords, and the blood gradually filters into the venous sinuses—the "open" circulation theory. (2) The arterial capillaries communicate directly with the lumen of the venous sinuses—the "closed" circulation theory. (3) The compromise view holds that both types of circulation are present at the same time. One of the modifications of this theory is that a "closed" circulation in a contracted spleen may become an "open" circulation when the organ is distended (Fig. 15-8).

The opposing theories are based on the following observations: (1) There are always many erythrocytes scattered irregularly between the fixed cells in the splenic cords. As there is normally in most species no evidence of erythropoiesis in the cords, the conclusion is that the red blood cells have come from the circulating blood through gaps in the vascular connection between the arterioles and the venous sinuses. Those who maintain that the circulation is "closed" hold that the number of erythrocytes in the splenic cords is much smaller than it would be if the arterial capillaries opened directly into the pulp. They claim that if the capillaries were open the red pulp would be completely filled with blood, as in hemorrhages in the spleen.

(2) When the splenic arteries are injected even at low pressures with stained fluids, India ink, or avian erythrocytes, the foreign materials readily gain access to the spaces between the fixed cells of the splenic cords,

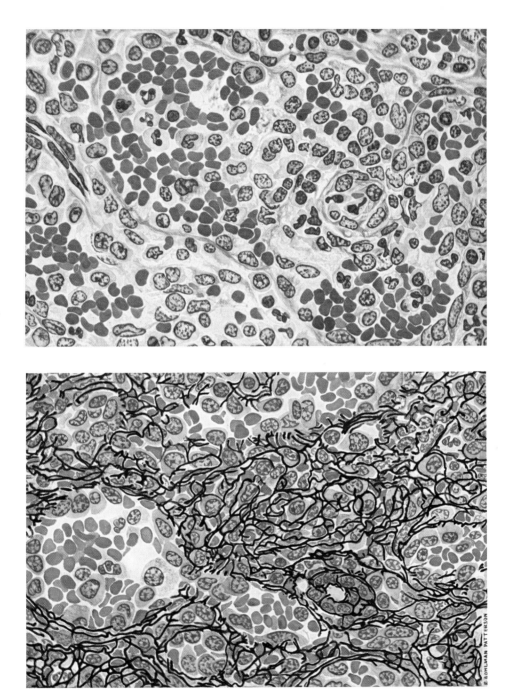

Figure 15-4. Portions of two sections from a human spleen, the upper stained with H + E, the lower with H + E after Bielschowsky impregnation for reticular fibers. × 600.

particularly in the red pulp immediately surrounding the white pulp. Only later do they reach the venous sinuses. When the splenic vein is injected, the venous sinuses and the meshes of the stroma can be filled easily, but the arteries cannot.

Those who hold for a closed circulation believe that this injection of the red pulp by foreign materials is artificial and results from the rupture of the delicate vascular walls.

(3) In every freshly fixed spleen, granulocytes, lymphocytes with greatly constricted nuclei, and erythrocytes can be found passing through the walls of the venous sinuses. It is difficult to reconcile this finding with either the "closed" or the "open" circulation theory, for these views hold that there are open connections between the sinuses and the arterial terminals or the meshes of the cords of Billroth, respectively. It is of course possible that such pictures are artifacts due to the collapse of the spleen when it is incised before being fixed.

The problem of circulation in the spleen would seem to be an ideal one for solution by direct observation of the living organ. Unfortunately, the technique available for this is difficult, and the few reports made on such studies are contradictory. According to one group, the circulation in the spleen is closed, there is a marked intermittence of circulation, there is extensive filtering of the liquid portion of the blood from the sinuses into the cords of Billroth, and diapedesis of erythrocytes from the sinuses occur normally and are especially noticeable when the animal is dying.

These conclusions are contradicted by another group, which finds that the circulation is open, that is, without preformed connections between the arterial and venous systems, so that the blood from the terminals of the arterial tree passes between the reticular cells (fixed macrophages) of the cords of Billroth and finds its way through openings into the sinuses. According to these observations, erythrocytes may be stored in the spaces between the reticular cells, and it is here that the separation of the blood cells from the plasma occurs. The channels in the cords of Billroth vary from time to time with the degree of engorgement of that part of the organ, so that a channel which previously had been a tortuous passage between reticular cells may appear as a direct communication to the lumen of a venous sinus when the spleen is contracted. From the foregoing it is obvious

that the manner of connection of arterioles and venules in the spleen requires further investigation.

If the splenic veins are tied for a few moments, and the splenic artery is then ligated and the entire organ fixed and sectioned, one can easily trace columns of erythrocytes from the meshes of the cords of Billroth into the venous sinuses. The pictures seen in spleens prepared by this old method correspond more closely with those seen in the living organ than do the usual preparations made by cutting thin slices from the fresh organ before fixation.

LYMPHATIC VESSELS AND NERVES. In man, lymphatic vessels are poorly developed and are found only in the capsule of the spleen and in the thickest trabeculae, particularly those in the vicinity of the hilus. In some mammals true lymphatic vessels follow the arteries of the white pulp to the hilus. Nervous networks, which originate from the celiac plexus and which consist almost entirely of nonmedullated fibers, accompany the splenic artery and penetrate into the hilus of the spleen. In the sheep and ox these nerves form trunks of considerable thickness. The nerve bundles mainly follow the ramifications of the arteries and form networks that can be followed up to the central arteries of the white pulp and even along the branches of the penicilli. The terminal branches usually end with button-like thickenings in the smooth muscles of the arteries and of the trabeculae. Apparently many branches penetrate into the red as well as the white pulp, but their endings here are not definitely established.

FUNCTIONS OF THE SPLEEN. The spleen is closely related to the lymphatic and hemal nodes and the bone marrow, and is an important hemopoietic organ. Lymphocytes are produced in it, mainly in the white pulp and in particular in its nodules. From the white pulp they migrate into the red pulp, where some of them perhaps become monocytes. Lymphocytes and monocytes actively enter the venous sinuses through the reticular wall.

Although in the embryo the spleen is a hemopoietic organ of some importance, the red corpuscles of the splenic tissue of the *normal adult man* are never formed in the white or the red pulp. In certain mammals (but not in man) some myelocytes and erythroblasts are found normally in the red pulp. Megakaryocytes occur regularly in the red pulp in rats and mice.

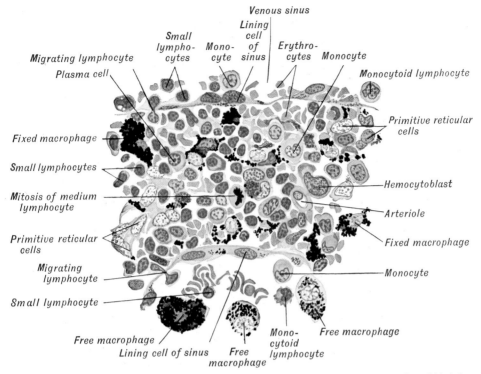

Figure 15-5. Cross section of cord of Billroth lying between two venous sinuses from spleen of a rabbit injected with lithium carmine and India ink. Hematoxylin-eosin-azure II. × 560. (After A. A. Maximow.)

In some pathological conditions, especially in *myeloid leukemia*, the red pulp of the spleen undergoes *myeloid metaplasia*. In this case a large number of erythroblasts, megakaryocytes, and myelocytes appear in the tissue, so that the red pulp acquires a structure suggesting that of red bone marrow.

After the removal of the spleen the number of lymphocytes in the blood increases (lymphocytosis); this is explained by an excessive compensation on the part of lymph nodes. Then, there is an increase in the number of eosinophilic leukocytes. Both of these phenomena soon disappear.

The spleen also acts as a store for red blood cells. From time to time large numbers of them are retained in the red pulp and then given up to the bloodstream as they are needed in the circulation.

The destruction of erythrocytes occurs in the spleen, with a varying intensity in different species, for they are phagocytosed by the macrophages in the splenic cords and sometimes by those lining the sinuses. Disintegrat-ing erythrocytes and granules of hemosiderin are often found in the cytoplasm of these phagocytes. After poisoning with substances which destroy the red blood cells (pyrogallol), the red pulp becomes filled with large macrophages containing the debris of erythrocytes. Destruction of erythrocytes may possibly proceed extracellularly, for particles of disintegrating erythrocytes have been described among the cells of the red pulp. After splenectomy the erytholytic function is carried out by the macrophages of the bone marrow, lymph nodes, and liver.

Closely connected with erythrocyte destruction by the spleen is its function in iron metabolism. The iron-containing component of hemoglobin is freed from the disintegrating erythrocytes and stored in the reticular cells of the spleen. This accumulated iron is again utilized in the formation of hemoglobin.

The spleen is thought by some to regulate the formation and destruction of erythrocytes by the production of a hormone which decreases the erythropoietic capacity of the bone

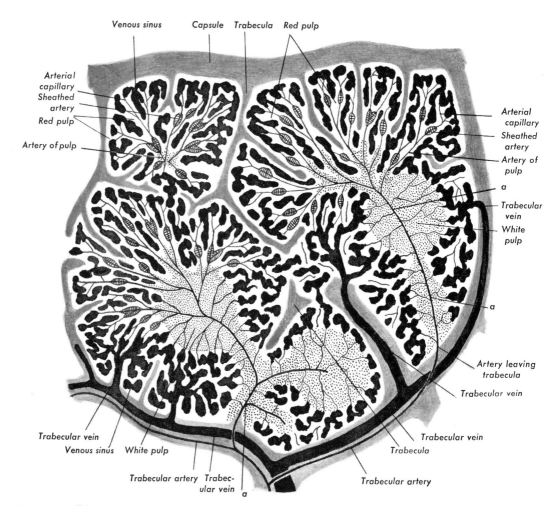

Figure 15-6. Diagram of lobules in the spleen. Two complete lobules (right and left) and portions of two others (above and below) are shown. *a,* arteries surrounded by lymphatic tissue (white pulp). (After A. A. Maximow.)

marrow. Others think that a hormone is produced by the spleen which inhibits the formation of leukocytes in the other hemopoietic organs.

Lead shielding of the spleen during total body irradiation with x-rays greatly increases survival, accelerates regeneration of the bone marrow, and protects the antibody producing mechanism. Lead shielding of lymphoid tissues other than spleen does not markedly increase survival or regeneration of the bone marrow but does protect against damage to the antibody forming mechanism. Furthermore, the degree of protection of antibody production is correlated with the amount of lymphoid tissue shielded rather than with the antibody forming activity of the tissue in the normal animal (Sussdorf and Draper).

The spleen possesses a combination of phagocytic, cytopoietic, and antibody forming activities which are of great importance in immunity to organisms or antigens which get into the blood (see review by Taliaferro). These functions are shared with the other filter organs, chiefly the liver and bone marrow, which contain macrophages strategically placed for contact with substances in the blood. The macrophages of the spleen are the most active individually, but the liver, because of its size, is the most important from the viewpoint of total phagocytic activity. In the cytopoiesis of phagocytes, the spleen is the most important in producing macrophages and the bone marrow in producing granulocytes. The spleen is initially the most active per unit weight in the formation of antibodies against antigens reaching the blood, but rapidly falls off in production as the bone marrow and various lymphoid tissues other than the spleen become active. The total amount of antibody formed by the bone marrow and possibly by various lymph nodes is eventually larger than that formed by the spleen. The liver, although it synthesizes serum globulins, forms very little antibody except when lymphatic tissue increases in the periportal spaces, as during long-continued infection or immunization.

A large amount of evidence indicates that antibodies are formed by the basophilic (pyroninophilic) hemocytoblasts (or lymphocytes) and especially the plasma cells to which they give rise. It should be noted that these large lymphoid cells also have the ability to turn into other types of blood and connective tissue cells

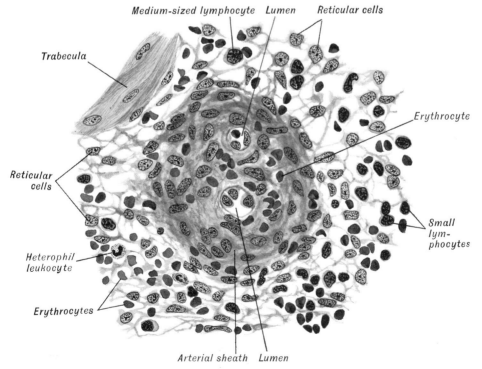

Figure 15-7. Cross section of sheathed artery which has divided into two lumens. Spleen of a dog. Eosin-azure stain. × 500. (After A. A. Maximow.)

(see p. 209). For further information on the relation of lymphoid cells to the formation of immune bodies, see the reviews cited below by Coons; Gowans and McGregor; Nossal; and Taliaferro.

In many animals, splenectomy is often followed by a recrudescence of a latent or low-grade infection, as is strikingly exemplified by Bartonella infections of rats, piroplasmosis of dogs and sheep, and malaria of monkeys. Similarly, splenectomy often temporarily depresses antibody formation. This effect is greatly enhanced if splenectomy is combined with so-called "blockade" by the intravenous injection of colloidal dyes or particulate matter.

As macrophages in contact with the bloodstream and antibody forming cells are not restricted to the spleen, it is not surprising that the effects of splenectomy largely disappear as splenic functions are assumed by other organs. This makes improbable the view of a few authors that the spleen has peculiar powers of defense in addition to those referable to its content of macrophages and lymphoid cells.

When the lipids in the blood are increased in amount, the reticular cells of the spleen, like the other macrophages of the body, have the capacity to remove the lipids from the blood and to store them. During this process these macrophages increase greatly in size, are filled with lipid droplets, and acquire a foamy ap-

pearance; this is observed in diabetic lipemia in man and in the experimental hypercholesterolemia of rabbits.

During digestion, the spleen increases in size. The reason for this is not known. Relations between the spleen and the various glands of internal secretion have not been established.

HISTOGENESIS AND REGENERATION OF THE SPLEEN. The primordium of the spleen appears, in human embryos of 8 to 9 mm., as a small thickening of the dorsal mesentery, consisting of a closely aggregated mass of energetically multiplying mesenchymal elements.

The mesenchymal cells which comprise this first primordium of the spleen multiply independently by mitosis, and the primordium grows. It has been supposed that it also increases in size by apposition of new cells from the mesothelium of the body cavity covering the primordium. After the embryo (pig) has reached a length of 15 mm., it receives no more cells from the mesothelium.

The elements of the primary mesenchymal primordium differentiate in two directions. Some remain connected with one another by means of processes and form the reticular framework of the white as well as the red pulp. Some of the mesenchymal elements soon become isolated from the rest and become free cells, located in the meshes of the framework. At first they all have the character of

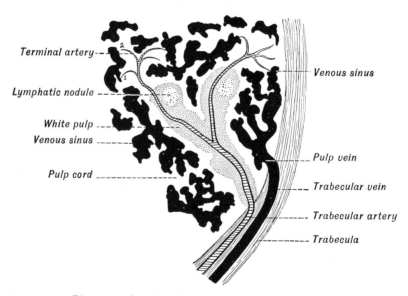

Figure 15-8. Diagram to show closed (1) and open (2) circulation through the spleen.

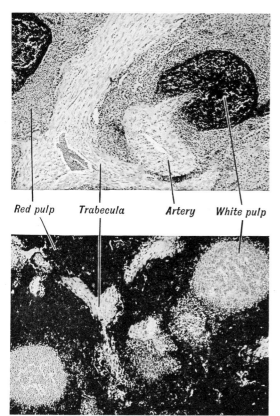

Red pulp   Trabecula   Artery   White pulp

Figure 15-9. Photomicrographs of sections of spleen of a dog, showing (upper figure) distribution of alkaline phosphatase as the black-stained material in the white pulp, and (lower figure) distribution of acid phosphatase as the black-stained material in the red pulp. The thick trabeculae are characteristic of the dog's spleen. × 30. (Courtesy of G. Gomori.)

basophilic wandering elements—that is, lymphocytes. Later on, they give origin to red corpuscles, granular myelocytes and leukocytes, and megakaryocytes, as well as more lymphocytes. In the lower vertebrates, up to the urodele amphibians, this erythropoietic function is retained throughout life in the spleen; in the higher vertebrates the myeloid function stops sooner or later and is replaced by an erythrolytic function, although the formation of lymphocytes persists throughout life.

In mammals (pig) the mesenchymal primordium contains a capillary vascular network connected with the afferent arteries and efferent veins. Meanwhile, irregular spaces, the precursors of the venous sinuses, appear (embryo pigs of 4 to 6 cm.) and become connected,

in 6 to 7 cm. embryos, with the afferent and efferent vessels.

The tissue of the embryonic mammalian spleen has at first a myeloid character and cannot be compared with either the red or the white pulp. At the end of fetal life (in the rat) the adventitia of the arteries begins to be infiltrated with large numbers of lymphocytes, and in this manner the white pulp originates; typical lymphatic nodules are found after birth. The myeloid elements, which had reached their maximum development three weeks after birth (in the rat), begin to disappear gradually, and the tissue of the spleen located between the accumulations of white pulp then may be called the red pulp.

When the spleen is removed, its functions are taken over by other organs, and the formation of a new spleen has never been observed, although a compensatory hypertrophy of the so-called "accessory spleens" has been described. Local injuries and wounds of the spleen are accompanied by a temporary myeloid metaplasia of the red pulp and heal with a simple scar. In the amphibians, particularly in larval stages, a certain degree of regeneration is possible, whereas in birds the spleen shows marked regenerative powers.

REFERENCES

Coons, A. H.: Some reactions of lymphoid tissues to stimulation by antigen. Harvey Lectures, 53:113, 1959.

Coons, A. H., E. H. Leduc, and J. M. Connolly: Studies on antibody production. I. A method for the histochemical demonstration of specific antibody and its application to a study of the hyperimmune rabbit. J. Exper. Med., 102:49, 1955.

Gowans, J. L., and D. D. McGregor: The immunological activities of lymphocytes. Progress in Allergy, 9:1, 1959.

Jacobson, L. O., E. K. Marks, M. J. Robson, E. Gaston, and R. E. Zirkle: The effect of spleen protection on mortality following x-irradiation. J. Lab. & Clin. Med., 34:1538, 1949.

Klemperer, P.: The Spleen. In Downey, H., ed.: Handbook of Hematology. New York, Paul B. Hoeber, Inc., 1938.

Knisely, M. H.: Spleen studies I. Microscopic observations of the circulatory system of living unstimulated mammalian spleens. Anat. Rec., 65:23, 1936.

Leduc, E. H., A. H. Coons, and J. M. Connolly: Studies on antibody production. II. The primary and secondary responses in the popliteal lymph node of the rabbit. J. Exper. Med., 102:61, 1955.

Lewis, O. J.: The blood vessels of the adult mammalian spleen. J. Anat., 91:245, 1957.

MacKenzie, D. W., Jr., A. O. Whipple, and M. P. Wintersteiner: Studies on the microscopic anatomy and physiology of living transilluminated mammalian spleens. Am. J. Anat., 68:397, 1941.

McMaster, P. D.: Antibody Formation. In Brachet, J., and A. E. Mirsky, eds.: The Cell; Biochemistry, Physiology, Morphology. New York, Academic Press, 1961, Vol. 5, p. 323.

Mollier, S.: Über den Bau der kapillaren Milzvenen (Milzsinus). Arch. f. Mikr. Anat., 76:608, 1911.

Nossal, G. J. V.: Genetic control of lymphopoiesis, plasma cell formation, and antibody production. Int. Rev. Exp. Path., 1:1, 1962.

‍‌‍

Nossal, G. J. V.: How cells make antibodies. Scientific American, *211*:106, Dec. 1964.

Nossal, G. J. V., A. Szenberg, G. L. Ada, and C. M. Austin: Single cell studies on 19S antibody production. J. Exper. Med., *119*:485, 1964.

Peck, H. M., and N. L. Hoerr: The intermediary circulation in the red pulp of the mouse spleen. Anat. Rec., *109*:447, 1951.

Robinson, W.: The vascular mechanism of the spleen. Am. J. Path., *2*:341, 1926.

Snook, T.: A comparative study of the vascular arrangements in mammalian spleens. Am. J. Anat., *87*:31, 1950.

Solnitzky, O.: The Schweigger-Seidel sheath (ellipsoid) of the spleen. Anat. Rec., *69*:55, 1937.

Sussdorf, D. H., and L. R. Draper: The primary hemolysin response in rabbits following shielding from X rays or X irradiation of the spleen, appendix, liver or hind legs. J. Infect. Dis., *99*:129, 1956.

Taliaferro, W. H.: Functions of the spleen in immunity. Am. J. Trop. Med., *3*:391, 1956.

Thiel, G. A., and H. Downey: The development of the mammalian spleen, with special reference to its hematopoietic activity. Am. J. Anat., *28*:279, 1921.

Weidenreich, F.: Das Gefässsystem der menschlichen Milz. Arch. f. Mikr. Anat., *58*:247, 1901.

Weiss, L.: An experimental study of the organization of the reticulo-endothelial system in the red pulp of the spleen. J. Anat., *93*:465, 1959.

CHAPTER SIXTEEN

The Thymus

The thymus is a lymphoepithelial organ that produces lymphocytes and, very probably, a hormone. Both of these functions are currently under active study and are discussed later in this chapter. In man and many mammals, the thymus is situated in the anterior mediastinum in close connection with the pericardium and the great veins at the base of the heart. The organ presents marked variations in its structure depending on the age and the condition of the organism as a whole.

In relation to body weight, the thymus is largest during embryonic life and childhood up to the period of puberty. After this it begins to involute, a process that proceeds gradually and continuously throughout life under normal conditions. This change in its structure is spoken of as *age involution*. During the course of some infectious and wasting diseases the normal slow involution may be greatly accelerated. This is called *accidental involution* and explains many contradictory reports on the size of the thymus, because the organ has no chance to regenerate in those persons who die as a result of severe infection. At birth the thymus weighs 12 to 15 gm.; it increases in weight to about 30 to 40 gm. at puberty, after which it begins to decrease, so that at 60 years it weighs only 10 to 15 gm. This decreasing size of the organ with aging and the involution after certain debilitating diseases do not seem to be functionally significant. According to some observers the residual endodermal epithelium of the thymus may be important in that it may be invoked to hypertrophy and become active again. Unexplained is the enormous overgrowth of the thymus in some cases of exophthalmic goiter and in myasthenia gravis.

The thymus begins in embryos as separate primordia on each side of the midline. In most species these become closely joined by connective tissue, although their parenchymas remain discrete. Exceptions to this among the common laboratory animals are guinea pigs and chickens, in which the thymus persists as separate organs in each side of the neck. The thymus is divided into a number of macroscopic lobules varying from 0.5 to 2 mm. in diameter. The lobules are separated from one another by connective tissue and are divided into a darkly staining, peripheral (cortical) area and a lighter staining, inner (medullary) portion (Fig. 16-1). In serial sections one can trace a continuity of the medullary tissue from one lobule to another. That is, the medulla consists of a central stalk from which arise projections of medullary tissue; these are almost completely surrounded by a zone of cortical tissue.

The difference between the cortex and the medulla is due to the proportion of lymphocytes to reticular cells in each. The cortex consists mainly of densely packed small lymphocytes with their dark nuclei and, between them, a relatively few reticular cells with pale-staining nuclei. In the medulla the reticular cells outnumber the few lymphocytes. As one proceeds from the cortex toward the medulla, the number of lymphocytes drops rather abruptly, but there is no sharp line of demarcation between the two zones. The medulla is more vascular than the cortex.

CELLS.   The principal cells of the thymus are *lymphocytes* and *epithelial reticular cells.* The latter have an oval nucleus, which is smooth contoured and contains one or two small nucleoli and finely dispersed, pale-staining chro-

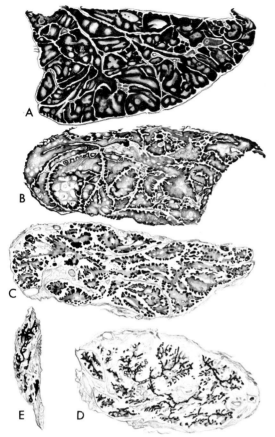

Figure 16-1. Sections of human thymuses, showing age and accidental involution. *A,* From a newborn (15 gm. gland); *B,* from a 7 year old boy (35 gm. gland); *C,* from a 17 year old boy (35.2 gm. gland), showing the beginning of age involution; *D,* from a 17 year old boy (8.8 gm. gland), high grade accidental involution, the dark parenchyma being surrounded by fat and connective tissue; *E,* from a 17 year old boy (1.65 gm. gland), extensive accidental involution. (Redrawn and slightly modified from Hammar, 1906.)

certain diseases of malnutrition in infants, they store large quantities of iron and lipid, and in Niemann-Pick disease they become distended with droplets of complex lipid.

In the embryo the epithelial nature of the reticular cells is quite obvious (Fig. 16-4), but as the organ becomes more and more heavily infiltrated with lymphocytes, the epithelial cells become greatly attenuated and difficult to distinguish from the macrophages, sometimes also called *phagocytic reticular cells.* In electron micrographs the cell types are easily identified. Thin processes of epithelial cells extend between the masses of lymphocytes and appear to form a more or less continuous peripheral boundary layer interposed between the lymphoid cells and the connective tissue of the interlobular septa (Fig. 16-6). The epithelial reticular cells are joined by typical desmosomes and their cytoplasm is made distinctive by the presence of conspicuous bundles of dense filaments. These are randomly oriented but often terminate in desmosomes at the cell surface like the tonofibrils of stratified squamous epithelium (Fig. 16-7). The cells contain inclusions of various kinds (Fig. 16-8). Some have been interpreted as secretion droplets or vacuoles; others are stainable with the acid phosphatase reaction and evidently correspond to lysosomes.

There has been considerable interest in the possibility that the interposition of a sheet of epithelial cell processes around the periphery of the lobules and between the lymphocytes and the perivascular connective tissue might constitute a blood-thymus barrier excluding certain substances. In electron microscope studies after intravenous injection of trypan blue and ^{125}I-labeled human albumin into mice, Clark found less of these substances in the thymus than in other lymphoid organs and concluded that there was a partial but not an absolute barrier to the penetration of antigens into the thymus.

The predominantly small thymic lymphocytes and the relatively few larger ones are morphologically identical with those of the lymphatic tissue as seen with the optical microscope. These thymic lymphocytes show the same susceptibility to x-ray injury as do other lymphocytes. Both are cytolyzed by sera obtained by the injection of thymus cells into rats, and both show the same types of ameboid motion. Transplants of the thymus consist only of epithelium if lymphocytes are prevented by

matin. In the cortex, their irregular cell outlines are deformed and obscured by the very numerous lymphocytes and are exceedingly difficult to discern with the light microscope. But in the medulla, where the lymphocytes are less numerous, the nature of the supporting cellular network can be studied to better advantage. The reticular cells of the thymus are, for the most part, of endodermal epithelial origin and are not to be equated with the phagocytic reticular cells of the bone marrow and spleen. Also present in the thymic reticulum are *macrophages* of mesenchymal origin, especially in the vicinity of blood vessels. The thymic epithelial cells in vitally stained animals do not take up the dyestuff. However, in mechanical means from migrating into them. A few small thymic lymphocytes have been described as developing into plasma cells and eosinophilic myelocytes in human embryos. In addition to lymphocytes and reticular cells, eosinophilic myelocytes and plasma cells occur not infrequently in the medulla. Exceptionally, the thymus may contain lymphatic nodules.

The epithelial nature of the great mass of reticular cells becomes prominent when the lymphocytes have been destroyed by x-rays and the epithelium condenses. It becomes even more evident in transplants and cultures of the thymus (Fig. 16-4). Certain tumors clearly of epithelial nature arise in this gland.

FIBERS. Most of the reticular fibers are concentrated around the blood vessels; there are none in the great masses of epithelial reticular cells. Further study of the fiber content of the organ, particularly during involution, is needed.

HASSALL'S BODIES. The medulla contains the bodies of Hassall, characteristic of the thymus. They are rounded epithelial structures which vary from 30 to over 100 μ in diameter and stain with acid dyes. They are composed of concentrically arranged cells, many of which show evidences of degeneration and hyalinization (Fig. 16-2). Epithelial reticular cells are connected at one or more places with the periphery of each Hassall body. The cells of the central part of a Hassall body may degenerate completely, allowing small cysts to develop in the center. In other cases calcium may be deposited in them.

INVOLUTION OF THE THYMUS. The clear-cut separation of the thymus into cortex and medulla obtains normally in the later embryonic periods and in childhood. Age involution begins as a gradual thinning out of the lymphoid cells of the cortex; at about four years the epithelial reticular cells become compressed and the area occupied by them is gradually replaced by adipose tissue, which is thought to arise in the interlobular connective tissue. The medulla begins to atrophy at pu-

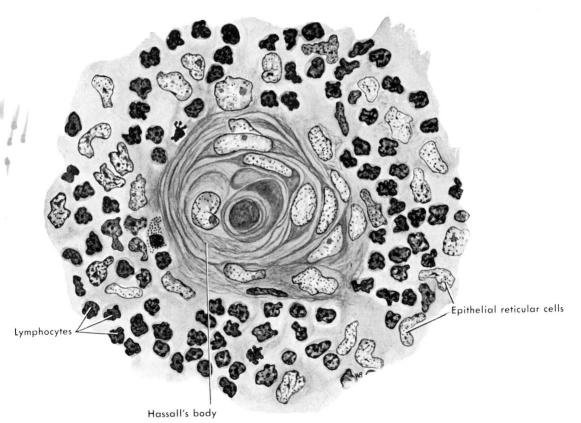

Lymphocytes

Epithelial reticular cells

Hassall's body

Figure 16-2. Portion of medulla of thymus of an 8 year old boy. An eosinophilic myelocyte is just outside the left-hand margin of Hassall's body. Eosin-azure stain. $\times$ 970.

berty. This process continues throughout life. The last elements to be replaced are the Hassall bodies, but even in very old persons there are scattered Hassall bodies surrounded by a few epithelial reticular cells and lymphocytes. This process of normal or age involution may be complicated by the rapid changes of "accidental involution" (Fig. 16-1).

VESSELS AND NERVES. The arteries supplying the thymus arise from the internal mammary and the inferior thyroid arteries and are first distributed to the cortical tissue. Large venules arise in the medulla and combine into larger veins which empty into the left innominate and thyroid veins. The lymphatics run mainly in the interlobular connective tissue and empty into the anterior mediastinal

and tracheobronchial lymph nodes. The thymus receives a few branches from the vagus and sympathetic nerves; these are probably mainly of vasomotor nature.

HISTOGENESIS. In man the thymus is an outgrowth of the third branchial pouch on each side of the median line; the fourth branchial pouch often gives rise to some thymic tissue. The primordium has a cleftlike lumen and a wall of several layers of cylindrical epithelium. The surrounding mesenchyme, in the earliest stages, contains lymphoid cells, which arise from mesenchymal cells. The epithelial bud proliferates, the lumen disappears, and anastomosing strands extend into the mesenchyme. The future lobules arise at the ends of these branches.

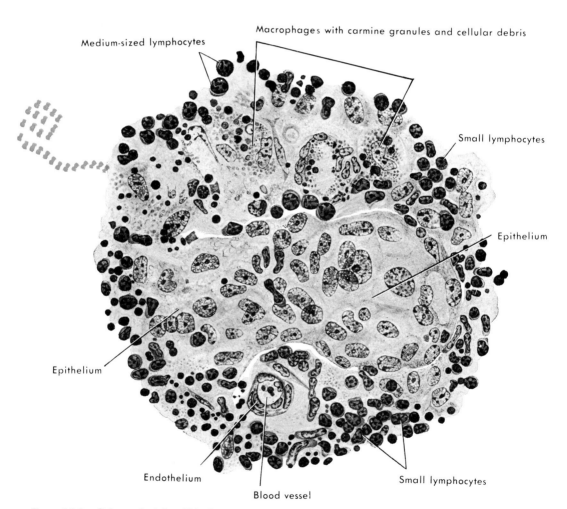

Medium-sized lymphocytes
Macrophages with carmine granules and cellular debris
Small lymphocytes
Epithelium
Epithelium
Endothelium
Blood vessel
Small lymphocytes

Figure 16-3. Culture of adult rabbit thymus, 24 hours in vitro, in a medium containing lithium carmine. The epithelial reticulum is contracting into a solid epithelial island which, in contrast to the macrophages, does not store lithium carmine and does not contain cellular debris. × 850. (After Popoff.)

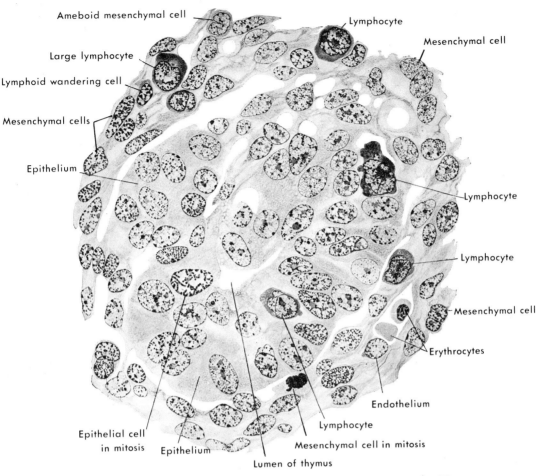

Ameboid mesenchymal cell
Lymphocyte
Mesenchymal cell
Large lymphocyte
Lymphoid wandering cell
Mesenchymal cells
Epithelium
Lymphocyte
Lymphocyte
Mesenchymal cell
Erythrocytes
Endothelium
Lymphocyte
Epithelial cell
in mitosis
Epithelium
Mesenchymal cell in mitosis
Lumen of thymus

Figure 16-4. Portion of cross section through the right thymus of a 14.5 mm rabbit embryo. The organ appears as an epithelial island surrounded by mesenchyme. × 900. (After A. A. Maximow.)

Although some early students of the histogenesis of the thymus believed that its lymphocytes arose from the endodermal epithelium of the organ, for five decades it was widely accepted that the lymphocytes were cells of mesenchymal origin that wandered into the epithelium and proliferated there. A few years ago this view was vigorously challenged when renewed histogenetic study and experiments with explants and transplants appeared to show that the thymic lymphocytes were of epithelial origin, in contrast to the other lymphocytes, which are of mesenchymal origin. However, the problem seems not to be solved to the satisfaction of all, for studies by Ackerman and Knouff on the hamster and by Smith on the mouse led to contradictory conclusions.

In an embryo of about 20 mm., thymic lymphocytes appear. Some of them are large,

others are small, and there are numerous transitions between the two types. The number of lymphocytes increases greatly, partly from immigration and in part through their own proliferation. The small lymphocyte type gradually predominates and the epithelium is converted into a reticular cell mass whose meshes are occupied by the lymphocytes and are penetrated here and there by blood vessels.

The definitive medulla arises late in the main stem and deeper portion of the lobules by hypertrophy of the epithelium, while most of the lymphocytes move from these areas or degenerate. Finally, the Hassall bodies arise.

In later stages of embryonic life a few of the lymphocytes turn into granulocytes, but much larger numbers wander into the blood and lymph streams. The thymus in the embryo is thus a blood cell forming organ, even though

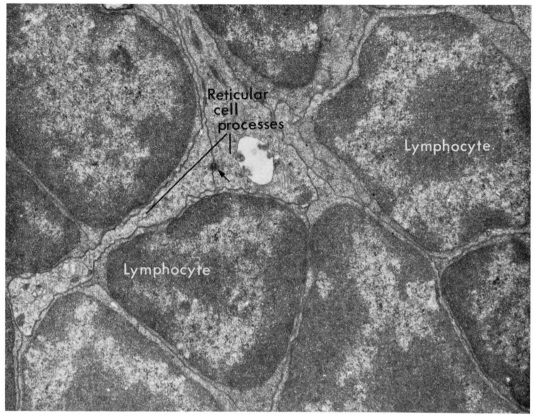

Figure 16-5. Electron micrograph from the cortex of a rat thymic lobule, showing among the crowded small lymphocytes two reticular cell processes joined by a desmosome (at arrow). × 14,000. (Courtesy of E. Raviola.)

few or no erythrocytes are produced in it. There are some points of similarity between the embryonic thymus and the embryonic liver. In both organs the epithelial cells are separated by mesenchymal cells and lymphocytes; in both the lymphocytes produce some granulocytes, although in the liver they also produce many megakaryocytes and vast numbers of erythrocytes as well.

Most investigators ascribe the regeneration of the small thymic lymphocytes (thymocytes) in transplants of the gland to immigration of lymphocytes.

Functions of the Thymus. As mentioned above, the thymus produces lymphocytes and a few plasma cells and myelocytes. In rat and opossum embryos it is the first organ to produce large numbers of small and medium-sized lymphocytes.

The thymus has been found to play some obscure roles in immune body formation. Al-

though the organ does not produce antibodies to circulating antigens, it does form specific antibodies to antigens injected into it. If the thymus is injured it will also produce specific antibodies to circulating antigen. In keeping with the fact that lymphoid cells are known to play a role in formation or storage of specific antibodies (p. 129), it has been suggested that lymphocytes first made in the thymus move to the spleen and lymph nodes, where they persist and multiply. From grafts of thymic cells with chromosome markers, there is some evidence that this can occur.

It has been known for several decades that removal of the thymus from young rats, mice, and rabbits causes a depletion of lymphocytes in the lymphatic tissue, lymph, and blood. It has also been known that the younger the animal, the more extensive were the effects of removal of the thymus. Much of the current interest in the functions of the thymus started with the experiments of Miller (in 1961) and others (Martinez et al. in 1962), who found that removal of this organ from newborn mice resulted, after a few months, in a wasting, gradually fatal disease with underdevelopment of the lymphocyte producing tissues and a decreased immunological competence. This was manifested by the failure of such mice to reject skin grafts from foreign donors, which intact mice would have rejected. In addition their ability to produce antibodies was decreased.

In comparison to the lymphatic tissue of animals raised in a normal environment, the lymphatic tissue of animals raised in an aseptic environment is not so well developed and shows no change after removal of the thymus. This has been interpreted as further evidence that the thymus plays a role in normal development of the immunological activities of lymphocytes and that the germ free animals

have not been subjected to the need for immunological competence to develop in the absence of infection with bacteria and viruses.

As mentioned in Chapter 8, the free stem cells (hemocytoblasts, lymphocytes) of the hemopoietic tissues, including the thymus, are exceedingly sensitive to ionizing radiations. Mice receiving lethal total body x-irradiation and a transfusion of bone marrow cells, distinguishable from host cells by marker chromosomes, showed repopulation of bone marrow and of the lymphocyte depleted thymus and spleen by the foreign cells. When the transfusion also contained lymphatic tissue lymphocytes, these were found in substantial numbers only in lymph nodes for a few weeks, after which they were progressively but not completely replaced by bone marrow derived cells. More details of these experiments are given in papers by Ford, Micklem, and coworkers.

In preliminary experiments with a few

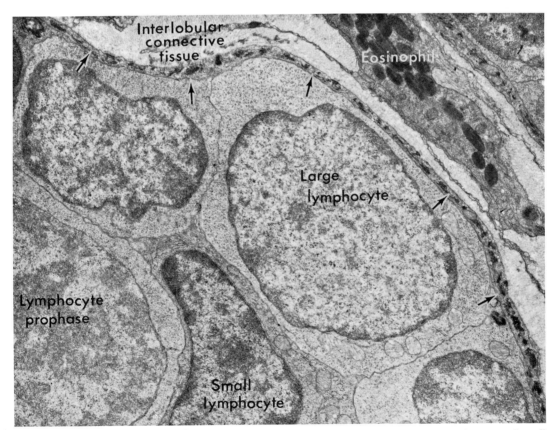

Figure 16-6. Electron micrograph of the periphery of a rat thymic lobule. Primitive large lymphocytes and small lymphocytes are seen in the superficial portion of the cortex. These are separated from the connective tissue of the interlobular septum by a continuous layer of attenuated processes of epithelial reticular cells, indicated here by the arrows. × 9600. (Courtesy of E. Raviola.)

pairs of parabiotic syngenetic mice with distinguishable marker chromosomes, it was found that there was an extensive exchange of cells in bone marrow, spleen, thymus, and lymph nodes between the two members of each pair. It was concluded by Harris et al. (1964) that their "demonstration of immigrant cells in the thymus does reveal a natural process, and that there is an afferent stream of flow into the thymus, of cells that are capable of becoming attached there and of undergoing mitosis. We do not know what these cells are or where they come from."

The change from a large organ during embryonic development, infancy, and childhood, into a gradually disappearing organ with the development of sexual maturity led many authors to ascribe an endocrine function to the thymus. The clearest evidence in favor of an internal secretion by the thymic epithelium comes from experiments with grafts of thymus in capsules made with minute pores, which permit the passage of substances in solution but are impenetrable to cells. In these grafts lymphocytes die but the epithelium does not. Most investigators interpret this to mean that such grafts prevent the development of changes characteristic of removal of the thymus. These grafts also permit the development of a virus induced disease, lymphocytic choriomeningitis, in thymectomized mice; this does not occur in the absence of a thymic factor stimulating the formation of lymphocytes. A few investigators, however, suspect the possibility of leaks in the chambers, which might permit the escape of lymphocytes from the graft, thus invalidating the conclusion that such changes are due to a hormone.

Other evidence of a possible thymic hormone has been seen in experiments by Klein et al., who found that injection of thymic tissue extracts into mice stimulated the production of lymphocytes, as measured by an increased incorporation of labeled precursors into DNA

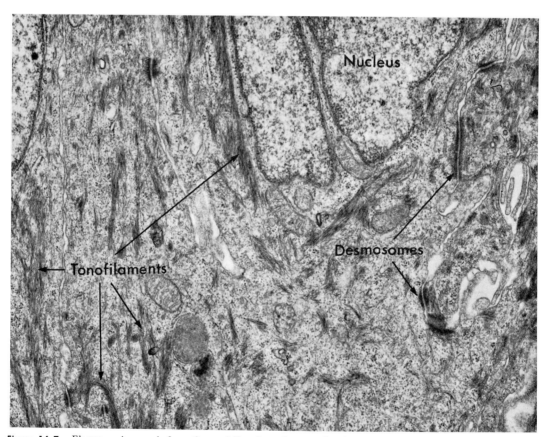

Figure 16-7. Electron micrograph from the medulla of rat thymus, showing portions of several reticular cells joined by desmosomes typical of epithelia and containing conspicuous bundles of tonofilaments. × 11,000. (Courtesy of E. Raviola.)

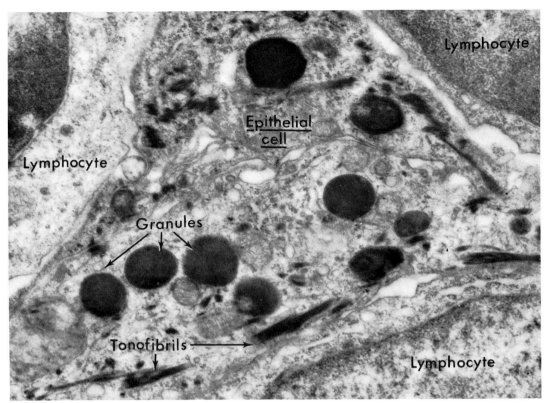

Figure 16-8. An electron micrograph of portions of a thymic epithelial cell and three neighboring lymphocytes. The epithelial cell is characterized by the presence of prominent tonofibrils and large dense granules, possibly secretory in nature. × 25,000. (Courtesy of S. Clark, Jr.)

and total protein of peripheral lymph nodes as well as a significant increase in weight.

Purified adrenocorticotropic hormone causes a striking reduction in the weight and size of the thymus in male rats. Repeated injection of horse gonadotropic hormone causes atrophy of the thymus, but this does not occur in castrated rats. On the contrary, castration causes hyperplasia of the involuted gland in the rat. Selye has found that fasting, toxins, and morphine cause a rapid atrophy of the thymus and enlargement of the adrenal cortex in rats, and that atrophy of the thymus does not take place in adrenalectomized rats.

EXPERIMENTAL LYMPHOSARCOMA AND LYMPHATIC LEUKEMIA (by H. S. Kaplan). Malignant neoplasms which are morphologically identical with human lymphosarcoma and lymphatic leukemia occur in fowl and in several mammalian species, of which mice are the most susceptible. The tumor cells usually resemble medium-sized to large lymphocytes, less often lymphoblasts or small lymphocytes,

and are occasionally pleomorphic (Dunn). In many inbred mouse strains, they tend to arise in the thymus gland, as cortical foci of immature cells which proliferate and gradually replace much or all of the cortex, permeate the medulla, and then penetrate the thymic capsule and disseminate to the mediastinal connective tissues, the lungs, the intra-abdominal viscera, the mesenteric, superficial, and retroperitoneal lymph nodes, and ultimately the bone marrow and peripheral blood. Incipient tumors may be detected in a preinvasive stage, when their rate of growth tends to be slow and their autonomy, as measured by capacity for progressive growth after isologous transplantation, appears at first to be distinctly limited, increasing during the life history of each tumor in its primary host.

These neoplasms may develop spontaneously, or in response to certain external agents: ionizing radiations, the hydrocarbon carcinogens, urethan, nitroquinoline oxides, and estrogens. Viruses have long been known to elicit leukemia in fowl. In strains of mice susceptible to "spontaneous" lymphatic leukemia, viruses have now been established as etiologic agents by the inoculation of cell-free filtrates of the leukemic tissues into newborn mice of ordinarily resistant strains (Gross). Cell-free extracts prepared from lymphoid tumors induced in other strains by radiation (Lieberman) or hydrocarbons (Irino) have also been shown to contain a leukemogenic virus (Kaplan, 1966). The target cell for the oncogenic action of the virus appears to be the immature lymphoblast of the thymic cortex, which is normally abundant only in the neonatal thymus (Axelrad; Kaplan, 1961, 1966). The external leukemogens apparently act (a) by releasing the otherwise innocuous virus from sites in which it has little or no oncogenic potential and (b) by causing thymic injury and regeneration, thus restoring to the adult thymus an abundant population of susceptible target cells (Kaplan, 1966). It appears, therefore, that such "latent" leukemogenic viruses are the real leukemogenic agents in many and perhaps in all mouse strains and that the external agents merely trigger a change in the host-virus relationship.

The development of these tumors in irradiated mice may be strikingly inhibited by normal isologous bone marrow, either shielded in situ or intravenously injected after irradiation (Kaplan et al., 1953). Marrow injection also promotes regeneration of the radiation-injured thymus gland. Tumor incidence is further conditioned by genetic, age, and nutritional factors (Law) and by the endocrine environment; it may be depressed by administration of thymus-involuting hormones or augmented by ablation of the endocrine glands which secrete thymocytic hormones (Kaplan et al., 1954), presumably by altering the relative numbers of susceptible target cells.

REFERENCES

The reports of these two symposia on the thymus will help to orient the student in this rapidly advancing field:

Defendi, V., and D. Metcalf, eds.: The Thymus. The Wistar Institute Symposium, Monograph No. 2. Philadelphia, The Wistar Institute Press, 1964.
Good, R. A., and A. E. Gabrielsen, eds.: The Thymus in Immunobiology. New York, Hoeber Medical Division, Harper & Row, 1964.

Ackerman, G. A., and R. A. Knouff: The epithelial origin of the lymphocytes in the thymus of the embryonic hamster. Anat. Rec., 152:35, 1965.

Auerbach, R.: Experimental analysis of the origin of cell types in the development of the mouse thymus. Develop. Biol., 3:336, 1961.
Auerbach, R.: On the function of the embryonic thymus. In Defendi, V., and D. Metcalf, eds.: The Thymus. The Wistar Institute Symposium, Monograph No. 2. Philadelphia, The Wistar Institute Press, 1964.
Azar, H. A.: Bacterial infection and wasting in neonatally thymectomized rats. Proc. Soc. Exper. Biol. & Med., 116:817, 1964.
Balner, H., and H. Dersjant: Early lymphatic regeneration in thymectomized radiation chimeras. Nature, 204:941, 1964.
Bargmann, W.: Der Thymus. In von Möllendorff, W., and W. Bargmann, eds.: Handbuch der mikroskopischen Anatomie des Menschen. Berlin, Julius Springer, 1943, Vol. 6, part 4, p. 1.
Billingham, R. E., and W. K. Silvers: Some biological differences between thymocytes and lymphoid cells. In Defendi, V., and D. Metcalf, eds.: The Thymus. The Wistar Institute Symposium, Monograph No. 2. Philadelphia, The Wistar Institute Press, 1964.
Burnet, F. M.: The immunological significance of the thymus: An extension of the clonal selection theory of immunity. Australasian Am. Med., 11:79, 1962.
Burnet, F. M.: The thymus gland. Scientific American, 207:50, 1962.
Clark, S. L., Jr.: The penetration of proteins and colloidal materials in the thymus from the bloodstream. In Defendi, V., and D. Metcalf, eds.: The Thymus. The Wistar Institute Symposium, Monograph No. 2. Philadelphia, The Wistar Institute Press, 1964.
Clark, S. L., Jr.: Electron microscopy of the thymus in mice of the strain 129/J. In Good, R. A., and A. E. Gabrielsen, eds.: The Thymus in Immunobiology. New York, Hoeber Medical Division, Harper & Row, 1964.
Davies, W. E., Jr., M. L. Tyan, and L. J. Cole: Homographs in thymectomized, irradiated mice: Responses to primary and secondary skin grafts. Science, 145:394, 1964.
East, J., and D. M. V. Parrott: Prevention of wasting in mice thymectomized at birth and their subsequent rejection of allogeneic leukemic cells. J. Nat. Cancer Inst., 33:637, 1964.
Ernström, U., and B. Larsson: Thymic and thoracic duct contributions to blood lymphocytes in normal and thyroxin-treated guinea-pigs. Acta Physiol. Scandinav., in press.
Fichtelius, K. E., and B. J. Bryant: On the fate of thymocytes. In Good, R. E., and A. E. Gabrielsen, eds.: The Thymus in Immunobiology. New York, Hoeber Medical Division, Harper & Row, 1964.
Ford, C. E., H. S. Micklem, E. P. Evans, J. G. Gray, and D. A. Ogden: The inflow of bone marrow cells to the thymus: Studies with part-body irradiated mice injected with chromosome-marked bone marrow and subjected to antigenic stimulation. Proc. 7th Internat. Transplantation Conf. Ann. N. Y. Acad. Sci., in press.
Friedman, N. B., E. J. Bomze, S. Rothman, and E. Grutz: The effect of local hormonal organ transplants and steroid hormone implants upon the thymus gland. In Bierman, H. R., ed.: Leukopoiesis in Health and Disease. Ann. N. Y. Acad. Sci., 113:511, 1964.
Gibbs, C. L., and N. V. Ricchiuti: Thymus: Role in resistance to polyoma virus oncogenesis. Science, 147:164, 1965.
Gowans, J. L., and D. D. McGregor: The immunological activities of lymphocytes. Progress in Allergy, 9:1, 1965.
Hammar, J.: Über Wachstum und Rückgang, über Standardisierung, Individualisierung und bauliche Individualtypen im Laufe des normalen Postfötallebens. Leipzig, Akademische Verlagsgesellschaft Leipzig, 1932.
Harris, L. E., C. E. Ford, D. W. H. Barnes, and E. P. Evans: Cellular traffic of the thymus: Experiments with chromosome markers. Nature, 201:884, 1964.
Kaplan, H. S., B. B. Hirsch, and M. B. Brown: Indirect induction of lymphomas in irradiated mice. IV. Genetic evidence of the origin of the tumor cells from thymic grafts. Cancer Res., 16:434, 1965.
Klein, J. J., A. L. Goldstein, and A. White: Enhancement of in vitro incorporation of labeled precursors into DNA and total protein of mouse lymph nodes after administration of thymic extracts. Proc. Nat. Acad. Sci., 53:812, 1965.
Law, L. W., T. B. Dunn, N. Trainin, and R. H. Levey: Studies of

thymic function. *In* Defendi, V., and D. Metcalf, eds.: The Thymus. The Wistar Institute Symposium, Monograph No. 2. Philadelphia, The Wistar Institute Press, 1964.

Lieberman, M., and H. S. Kaplan: Leukemogenic activity of filtrates from radiation-induced lymphoid tumors of mice. Science, *130:* 387, 1959.

Martinez, C., A. P. Dalmasso, and R. A. Good: Effect of thymectomy on development of immunological competence in mice. *In* Bierman, H. R., ed.: Leukopoiesis in Health and Disease. Ann. N. Y. Acad. Sci., *113:*933, 1964.

Metcalf, D.: The thymus and lymphopoiesis. *In* Good, R. A., and A. E. Gabrielsen, eds.: The Thymus in Immunobiology. New York, Hoeber Medical Division, Harper & Row, 1964.

Metcalf, D., and M. Brumby: The role of the thymus in the ontogeny of the immune system. J. Cell Physiol., *67*(Suppl. 1):149, 1966.

Micklem, C., C. E. Ford, E. P. Evans, and J. G. Gray: Interrelationships of myeloid and lymphoid cells: Studies with chromosome-marked cells transfused into lethally irradiated mice. Proc. Roy. Soc. B., *53:*812, 1966.

Miller, J. F. A. P.: The thymus and the development of immunologic responsiveness. Science, *144:*1544, 1964.

Miller, J. F. A. P.: Recovery of immunological responsiveness in thymectomized animals by thymus grafting. *In* Defendi, V., and D. Metcalf, eds.: The Thymus. The Wistar Institute Symposium, Monograph No. 2. Philadelphia, The Wistar Institute Press, 1964.

Miller, J. F. A. P., M. Block, D. T. Rowlands, Jr., and P. Kind: Effect of thymectomy on hematopoietic organs of the opossum "embryo." Proc. Soc. Exper. Biol. & Med., *118:*916, 1965.

Murray, R. G.: The thymus. *In* Bloom, W., ed.: Histopathology of Irradiation from External and Internal Sources. National Nuclear Energy Series. New York, McGraw-Hill Book Co., 1948, Vol. 22–I, chapter 9.

Murray, R. G.: Pure cultures of rabbit thymus epithelium. Am. J. Anat., *81:*369, 1965.

Murray, R. G., A. Murray, and A. Pizzo: The fine structure of the thymocytes of young rats. Anat. Rec., *151:*17, 1965.

Murray, R. G., and P. A. Wood: Studies of the fate of lymphocytes. III. The migration and metamorphosis of *in situ* labeled thymic lymphocytes. Anat. Rec., *150:*113, 1964.

Nagaya, H., and H. O. Sieker: Allograft survival: Effect of antiserums to thymus glands and lymphocytes. Science, *150:*1182, 1965.

Osoba, D.: Immune reactivity in mice thymectomized soon after birth: Normal response after pregnancy. Science, *147:*298, 1965.

Rieke, W. O.: Lymphocytes from thymectomized rats: Immunologic, proliferative, and metabolic properties. Science, *152:*535, 1966.

Sainte-Marie, G., and C. P. Leblond: Thymus cell population dynamics. *In* Good, R. A., and A. E. Gabrielsen, eds.: The Thymus in Immunobiology. New York, Hoeber Medical Division, Harper & Row, 1964.

Sherman, J. D., M. M. Adner, and W. Dameshek: Effect of thymectomy on the golden hamster (*Mesocricetus auratus*). II. Studies of the immune response in thymectomized and splenectomized non-waste animals. Blood, *23:*375, 1964.

Sherman, J. D., and W. Dameshek: Post-thymectomy wasting disease of the golden hamster. *In* Good, R. A., and A. E. Gabriel-

sen, eds.: The Thymus in Immunobiology. New York, Hoeber Medical Division, Harper & Row, 1964.

Siegler, R., J. Geldner, and M. A. Rick: Histogenesis of the thymic lymphoma induced by a murine leukemia virus. Canc. Res., *24:*444, 1964.

Smith, C.: Studies on the thymus of the mammal. XIV. Histology and histochemistry of embryonic and early postnatal thymuses of C57BL/6 and AKR strain mice. Am. J. Anat., *116:*611, 1965.

Symposium on differentiation and growth of hemoglobin- and immunoglobin-synthesizing cells. J. Cell. Physiol., *67:* Suppl. 1, 1966.

Tilney, N. L., E. J. Beattie, Jr., and S. G. Economou: The effect of neonatal thymectomy in the dog. J. Surg. Res., *5:*23, 1965.

Van Putten, L. M.: Thymectomy: Effect on secondary disease in radation chimeras. Science, *145:*935, 1964.

Vazquez, J. J.: Kinetics of proliferation of antibody forming cells. *In* Good, R. A., and A. E. Gabrielsen, eds.: The Thymus in Immunobiology. New York, Hoeber Medical Division, Harper & Row, 1964.

Wilson, R., K. Sjodin, and M. Bealmar: Thymus studies in germ-free (axenic) mice. *In* Defendi, V., and D. Metcalf, eds.: The Thymus. The Wistar Institute Symposium, Monograph No. 2, Philadelphia, The Wistar Institute Press, 1964.

Yoffey, J. M.: The lymphocyte. Ann. Rev. Med., *15:*125, 1964.

Experimental Lymphosarcoma and Lymphatic Leukemia

Axelrad, A. A., and H. C. Van der Gaag: Susceptibility to lymphoma induction by Gross' Passage A virus in C3Hf/Bi mice of different ages: Relation to thymic cell multiplication and differentiation. J. Nat. Cancer Inst., *28:*1065, 1962.

Dunn, T. B.: Normal and pathologic anatomy of the reticular tissue in laboratory mice, with a classification and discussion of neoplasms. J. Nat. Cancer Inst., *14:*1281, 1954.

Gross, L.: Mouse leukemia: An egg-borne virus disease. Acta haemat., *13:*13, 1955.

Irino, S., Z. Ota, T. Sezaki, M. Suzaki, and K. Hiraki: Cell-free transmission of 20-methylcholanthrene-induced RF mouse leukemia and electron miscroscopic demonstration of virus particles in its leukemic tissue. Gann, *54:*225, 1963.

Kaplan, H. S.: The role of cell differentiation as a determinant of susceptibility to virus carcinogenesis. Cancer Res., *2:*981, 1961.

Kaplan, H. S.: Interaction of occult leukaemogenic viruses with ionizing radiation and other external leukaemogenic agents in the induction of thymic lymphosarcoma in the mouse. *In* Wolstenholme, G. E. W., and R. Porter, eds.: Ciba Foundation Symposium on the Thymus. London, J. & A. Churchill, Ltd., 1966, p. 310.

Kaplan, H. S., M. B. Brown, and J. Pauli: Influence of bone marrow injections on involution and neoplasia of mouse thymus after systemic irradiation. J. Nat. Cancer Inst., *14:*303, 1953.

Kaplan, H. S., C. S. Nagareda, and M. B. Brown: Endocrine factors and radiation-induced lymphoid tumors of mice. Recent Progress in Hormone Research, *10:*293, 1954.

Law, L. W.: Recent advances in experimental leukemia research. Cancer Res., *14:*695, 1954.

Lieberman, M., and H. S. Kaplan: Leukemogenic activity of filtrates from radiation-induced lymphoid tumors of mice. Science, *130:*387, 1959.

CHAPTER SEVENTEEN

Hypophysis

The hypophysis or pituitary gland is an endocrine gland located at the base of the brain. It is about 1 cm. in length, 1 to 1.5 cm. in width, and about 0.5 cm. deep. It weighs about 0.5 gm. in men and slightly more in women. Despite its small size it is one of the most important organs in the body, producing at least nine hormones and having many reciprocal relations with other endocrine glands. It also has neural and vascular connections with the brain, to which it is attached by a slender stalk. By virtue of these connections, the hypophysis occupies a key position in the interplay of the nervous system and the endocrine system—the two great integrating systems of the body.

The hypophysis has two major subdivisions, the *neurohypophysis,* which develops as a process growing downward from the floor of the diencephalon, and the *adenohypophysis,* which originates in the embryo as a dorsal outpocketing of the roof of the mouth. There are three subdivisions of the adenohypophysis: the *pars distalis* or anterior lobe, the *pars infundibularis* (*pars tuberalis*) and the *pars intermedia.* The neurohypophysis is generally divided into three regions: the *median eminence,* a funnel-shaped extension of the tuber cinereum; the *infundibu-lar stalk;* and the *infundibular process.* The relations of these components are depicted in Figures 17-1, 17-2, and 17-3. In many species the pars intermedia is closely adherent to the infundibular process to form the so-called *posterior lobe,* separated by a cleft from the pars distalis or anterior lobe. In man the cleft is largely obliterated in late fetal and postnatal life, so that the anterior and posterior lobes are in continuity (Fig. 17-2). The subdivisions of the hypophysis and the accepted descriptive terminology are presented in tabular form below.

The hypophysis is lodged in a deep depression in the sphenoid bone, the *sella turcica,* and is covered by a tough diaphragm, the *diaphragma sellae.* This barrier between the sella turcica and the intracranial cavity is often incomplete, being penetrated by an opening 5 mm. or more in diameter around the hypophyseal stalk. Some of the pia-arachnoid membrane may extend through this opening and occupy the narrow space between the diaphragm and the connective tissue capsule of the gland. Elsewhere the dense collagenous capsule is separated from the perioteum of the sphenoid bone by a looser layer of connective tissue containing numerous veins. This layer

Divisions and Subdivisions of the Hypophysis

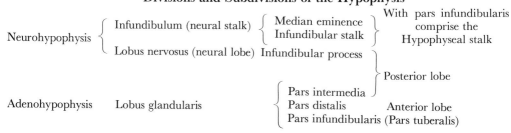

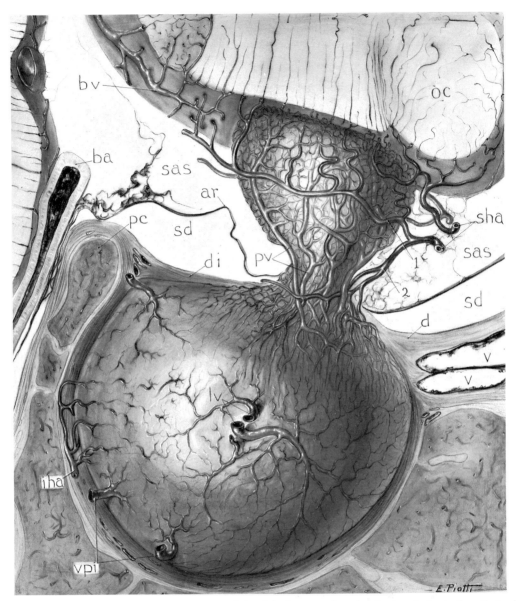

Figure 17-1. Schematic drawing of the hypophysis of an adult rhesus monkey, showing its relation to the sella turcica of the sphenoid bone. Also depicted are the superior and inferior hypophyseal arteries (*sha* and *iha*) and the important portal venules (*pv*) coursing down the infundibular stalk. The superior hypophyseal artery usually sends an ascending branch (*1*) to the proximal part of the infundibular stalk and median eminence and a descending branch (*2*) coursing distally. *ar*, Arachnoid membrane; *ba*, basilar artery; *bv*, basilar veins; *d*, dura; *di*, sellar diaphragm; *lv*, lateral hypophyseal veins; *oc*, optic chiasm; *pc*, posterior clinoid process; *sas*, subarachnoid space; *sd*, subdural space; *v*, dural vein; *vpi*, veins of the infundibular process. (After G. B. Wislocki, Proc. Assoc. Res. Nervous and Mental Diseases, *17*:48, 1936.)

appears to be separate from the pia-arachnoidal tissue. In mammals other than man, the diaphragm is commonly incomplete.

PARS DISTALIS

The pars distalis or anterior lobe is the largest subdivision of the hypophysis. It is composed of glandular cells arranged in irregular cords and clumps that vary in diameter from 20 to 180 μ in man. These are intimately related to an extensive system of thin-walled sinusoids of the blood vascular system. The anterior lobe is largely enclosed by a dense collagenous capsule. The stroma of the gland is not abundant, but some collagenous fibers, which accompany the superior hypophyseal arteries and the portal venules, penetrate the anterior lobe at the pole adjacent to the pars tuberalis and fan out bilaterally, extending about a third of the way into the gland. There they become continuous with reticular fibers that surround the cords of parenchymal cells and support the small arterial branches and the sinusoids. Although the endothelium lining the sinusoids has traditionally been regarded as phagocytic, like that of the spleen and liver, this has not been borne out by electron microscopy, and the sinusoids of the pituitary are no longer considered to be part of the reticuloendothelial system. The sinusoids at the periphery of the gland continue into collecting venules that join an extensive venous plexus in the capsule.

The glandular cells are classified as *chromophilic* or *chromophobic* cells on the basis of their avidity or lack of affinity for the dyes in routinely stained histological sections. The chromophilic cells were originally subdivided into *acidophilic cells* or *basophilic cells,* according to the tinctorial reactions of their specific granules in sections stained with eosin and alum-hematoxylin or with other combinations of an acid and a basic dye.

It is important to realize that the terms acidophilic and basophilic as used by the pituitary cytologist do not have the same connotation with respect to the chemistry of the cytoplasm that they generally have. The basophilia of the granules in the pituitary basophilic cell is not to be confused with that due to ribonucleoprotein in other glandular cells. In the naming of the pituitary cells, *acidophilic* and *basophilic* refer only to the staining affinities of the specific granules of the cells. Historically these terms were reasonable and adequate in that they served to distinguish two major classes of chromophilic cells at a time when there were only a few empirically developed staining combinations in routine use, and the great diversity of pituitary functions was not yet appreciated. As time has passed the number of hormones known to be secreted by the adenohypophysis has increased to seven. The

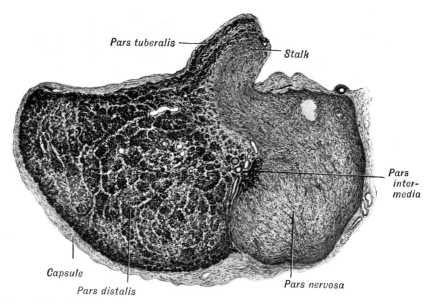

Figure 17-2. Sagittal section through hypophysis of a 45 year old man. $\times$ 16. (After Schaffer.)

effort to distinguish additional cell types to which synthesis of these hormones could be attributed led to the development of numerous staining methods. The terminological problem has been greatly aggravated by the fact that most of the staining procedures now considered most useful for the study of the adenohypophysis involve mixtures of acid dyes. With many of these methods, staining does not depend on the binding of a dye by a tissue component of opposite charge, and no conclusion as to the chemical nature of the granules can be drawn from their color in stained sections. The color of the specific granules may be red, orange, purple, or blue, depending on the combination of acid dyes used. With the trichrome staining methods, it has been necessary to establish the relation of the cell types to the traditional acidophilic, basophilic, and chromophobic categories by comparison of the same cells in consecutive sections stained with hematoxylin and eosin, or by reliance on their size, shape, distribution, and other structural characteristics.

Various systems of nomenclature based on Greek letter designations have been proposed to avoid the inconsistency involved in continued use of "acidophilic" and "basophilic," but none of these has gained widespread acceptance. The terminology now in general use is therefore a bizarre, and often confusing, mixture in which acidophilic, basophilic, and chromophobic are used to designate the major classes of cells in the adenohypophysis, and various Greek letters or adjectives referring to distinctive tinctorial reactions are used to identify specific cell types within these classes. The most meaningful and reproducible single staining method for identification of the cell types is the periodic acid–Schiff reaction, which serves as a group reaction for the granules of basophils—which can thus be distinguished by their content of glycoprotein. Electron microscopy has shown that the specific granules of the chromophilic cells differ in size, and by permitting their measurement has provided an additional valuable criterion for distinguishing the several types of cells.

ACIDOPHILS (ALPHA CELLS). These cells, 14 to 19 μ in diameter in the human, are rounded or ovoid and possess a well developed juxtanuclear Golgi apparatus and small rod-shaped mitochondria. They contain many refractile granules that are large enough to be resolved with the light microscope. In the

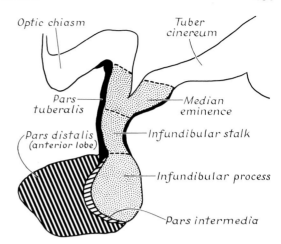

Figure 17-3. Diagram of midsagittal section of hypothalamus and hypophysis of man to show relations of major divisions and subdivisions of the gland to the hypothalamus. (Modified from Tilney.)

common laboratory rodents the granules are smaller and, being closely crowded together, may be difficult to resolve. In routine preparations they stain with eosin, and with the classical Mallory's trichrome stain they are colored red. The acidophils are believed to secrete *growth hormone* (somatotropin) and *prolactin* (mammotropin, LTH). The assignment of these hormones to the acidophils is based upon the association of human gigantism with acidophilic adenomas of the hypophysis and upon immunohistochemical staining and assay of centrifugally isolated granules. Fluorescein-labeled antibody to purified growth hormone is localized in the acidophils of the human pars distalis (Leznoff et al.). In differential centrifugation of homogenates of the anterior lobe the rapidly sedimenting granules, which are mainly acidophilic, have been shown to contain prolactin and somatotropin (Hymer and McShan).

In a number of mammalian species, two classes of acidophils can be distinguished—one staining preferentially with orange G and the other with azocarmine, erythrosin, or acid fuchsin. In the rat two kinds are also distinguishable in electron micrographs, mainly on the basis of granule size. In one the granules are abundant and 300 to 350 $m\mu$ in diameter, while in the other they are fewer and larger, ranging from 600 to 900 $m\mu$. The population of acidophils with the smaller granules is relatively stable, and this type is believed to be the source of growth hormone. The number

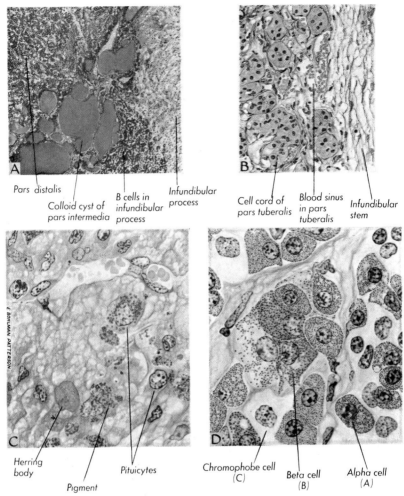

Pars distalis   B cells in   Infundibular   Cell cord of   Blood sinus
                   infundibular   process   pars tuberalis   in pars   Infundibular
        Colloid cyst of   process   tuberalis   stem
        pars intermedia

Herring   Chromophobe cell   Alpha cell
body   Pituicytes   (C)   Beta cell   (A)
        Pigment   (B)

Figure 17-4. Sections of human hypophysis. *A,* Pars intermedia and its relations to pars distalis and infundibular process. × 60. *B,* Cell cords of pars tuberalis, with numerous small blood vessels, and adjacent infundibular stem. × 275. *C,* Cells and intercellular substance of infundibular process. × 690. *D,* Cells of pars distalis. × 690. Zenker-formol, H + E.

of those having larger granules varies in relation to the reproductive cycle, increasing significantly during pregnancy and lactation. These are therefore believed to secrete prolactin.

BASOPHILS (BETA CELLS). These cells are round, oval, or angular and range from 15 to 25 μ in diameter. The nucleus resembles that of the acidophils but may have a coarser chromatin pattern. The mitochondria are small and the Golgi apparatus is some distance from the nucleus and often appears in negative image as a ring or loose network (Fig. 17-7B). The specific granules vary in size from species to species but are generally distinctly smaller than those of acidophils. In the rat

their maximum size is 150 mμ, and if diffusely distributed, they are not readily resolved by the light microscope. They are stained by hematoxylin, aniline blue, or resorcin-fuchsin, but, as stated, the most dependable method for their identification is the periodic acid–Schiff reaction.

Thyrotropic hormone (TSH), follicle stimulating hormone (FSH), and interstitial cell stimulating hormone (ICSH or LH) of the hypophysis are known to be glycoprotein in nature. It is therefore reasonable to attribute these hormones to the basophilic cells, which have PAS-positive granules. Moreover, basophilic granules exhibit the same solubility characteristics as those required to extract these hormones from fresh or acetone dried anterior lobe. Centrifugally isolated basophilic granules have been shown to contain thyrotropin and gonadotropins.

In most mammals two types of basophilic cells can be identified by their staining reactions and ultrastructural characteristics. One of these, the *beta basophil,* stains with aldehyde-fuchsin (Halmi); it is angular and its granules are only about 100 mµ in diameter and tend to congregate at the periphery of the cell. This cell type is presumed to produce thyrotropic hormone. The *delta basophil* does not stain with aldehyde-fuchsin. It is larger and rounded in contour, with a prominent Golgi complex, a well developed endoplasmic reticulum, and granules about 150 mµ in diameter. This cell type secretes gonadotropins. The same techniques are claimed to distinguish two types of delta basophil in some species—one for each gonadotropin.

CHROMOPHOBES.   The chromophobes are usually small and have relatively little cytoplasm but may rarely reach the dimensions of large acidophilic and basophilic cells. Their nuclear characteristics are similar to those of the chromophilic cells. They have a loosely organized Golgi apparatus and numerous mitochondria but are usually devoid of granules.

Because mitoses are relatively uncommon in the anterior lobe, it was formerly concluded that the observed shifts in proportions of the three major cell types were the result of transformations of one cell type to another. Investigations of these population changes led to numerous proposals for cell lineages based upon supposed morphological transition stages. The most widely accepted of these theories considered the chromophobes to be a reservoir of relatively undifferentiated cells capable of differentiating into the various types of chromophilic cells. It has become increasingly apparent that the cells classified as chromo-

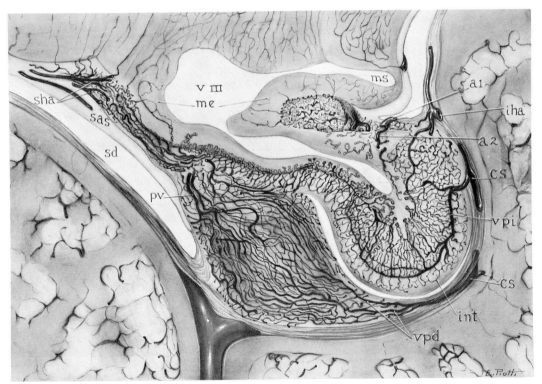

Figure 17-5. Drawing of a thick median sagittal section of a cat's hypophysis after injection of the blood vascular system with India ink. There are no communications with the hypothalamus except by capillaries. The main supply is by the superior hypophyseal and inferior hypophyseal arteries; the venous drainage is via systemic veins from the anterior lobe and from the neural lobe. Portal veins arising in capillaries in the median eminence and pars tuberalis are favorably situated to carry neurohumoral releasing factors from the median eminence of the hypothalamus to the pars distalis. (After G. B. Wislocki, Anat. Rec., *69:*361, 1937.)

phobes by light microscopy are not a homogeneous population. Some are evidently chromophils degranulated to the point that their specific nature is not detectable. It seems likely that there is a considerable degree of cytological specialization among the cells normally classified as chromophobes. For example, some have a Golgi apparatus characteristic of acidophils, while others resemble basophils. It is probable that many of the apparent chromophobes are already determined and are capable of differentiating only into a particular type of chromophil. True chromophobes in the sense of nonspecific stem cells are evidently much less numerous than they were formerly thought to be.

Blood Supply

The blood supply of the hypophysis is unusual and is intimately involved in the control of the secretory activity of the gland. Two *inferior hypophyseal* arteries from the internal carotid arborize within the capsule of

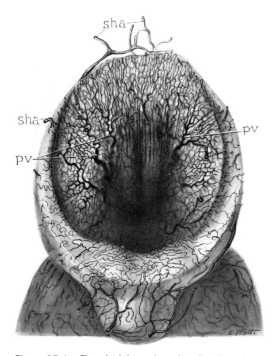

Figure 17-6. Detached hypophyseal stalk of cat hypophysis with the neural stalk dissected out, leaving intact the mantle of the pars tuberalis. Clearly illustrated is the rich plexus of capillary sinusoids draining into a number of venules of the hypophyseoportal system (*pv*) destined for the sinusoids of the anterior lobe. Branches of the superior hypophyseal artery (*sha*) are also shown. (After G. B. Wislocki, Anat. Rec., *69*:361, 1937.)

the gland, sending branches to the posterior lobe and to a lesser extent to the sinusoids of the anterior lobe. Several *superior hypophyseal* arteries arise from the internal carotid artery and posterior communicating artery of the circle of Willis and anastomose freely in the region of the median eminence of the hypothalamus and base of the pituitary stalk (Figs. 17-1 and 17-6). From these vessels capillaries comprising the so-called *primary plexus* extend into the median eminence and are then returned to the surface, where they are collected into veins that run downward around the hypophyseal stalk to supply the sinusoids of the adenohypophysis below. The venules connecting capillaries in the median eminence with the sinusoidal capillaries of the anterior lobe constitute the *hypophyseoportal* system. The venous drainage of the hypophysis is chiefly through vessels that run in the vascular layer of the capsule to the diaphragm of the sella turcica and thence into adjacent dural sinuses. Some venous blood may also enter sinuses in the sphenoid bone. There is strong circumstantial evidence indicating that neurohumoral substances released by nerves in the median eminence of the hypothalamus are carried in the blood via the hypophyseoportal system to the adenohypophysis, where they stimulate the cells to release their specific hormones (Fig. 17-15).

Histophysiology of the Pars Distalis

Surgical removal of the anterior lobe results in cessation of growth in young animals; atrophy of the adrenal cortex, thyroid, testis, and ovaries; and disturbances of carbohydrate, protein, and lipid metabolism. These profound and potentially fatal effects of hypophysectomy are the collective consequences of eliminating the source of the following hormones, which have been isolated in nearly pure form from the anterior lobe.

1. Growth Hormone (Somatotropin, STH). This is a protein hormone composed of about 200 amino acid residues and having a molecular weight of about 21,000. It plays an important part in the normal growth of the body. The cessation of growth that follows hypophysectomy is reversed by administration of this hormone, and gigantism may be produced experimentally by excessive doses. Dwarfism in certain strains of mice has been

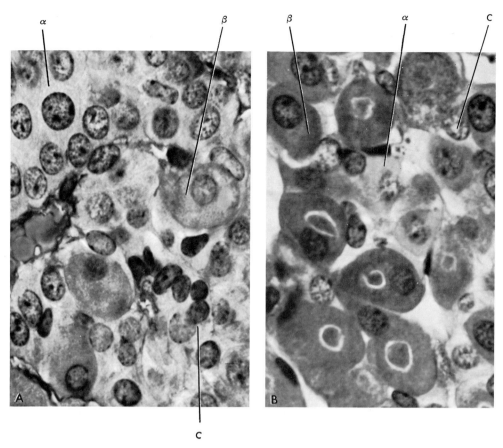

Figure 17-7. Photomicrographs of anterior lobe of hypophysis of adult rats. *A*, Normal female rat; *B*, Castrate female rat of same age. Hypertrophy of basophil cells (*β*), with enlargement of the Golgi complexes (here shown next to each nucleus as a negative image and appearing as a clear halo), and reduction in acidophil (*α*) and chromophobe (C) cells follow castration. Zenker-formol, Mallory-azan. × 1300. (Courtesy of I. Gersh.)

traced to a congenital defect in the development of the hypophysis. The hormone has a nearly specific growth effect on epiphyseal cartilage. Simultaneous administration of thyroid extracts augments the action of the growth hormone, while simultaneous administration of adrenocorticotropic hormone inhibits its action. Certain tumors of the anterior lobe cause *gigantism* in children by inducing continued growth in length of the bones. If such tumors arise after closure of the epiphyseal plate, they cause *acromegaly*, in which the bones become thicker, the hands and feet broader, the mandible heavier, and the calvaria thicker.

Somatotropin also plays a significant role in the metabolism of proteins, fats, and carbohydrates. It also appears to enhance the effectiveness of certain other hormones.

2. FOLLICLE STIMULATING HORMONE

(FSH). FSH is a water soluble glycoprotein of molecular weight in the range from 30,000 to 67,000. It has not yet been isolated in pure form. It promotes the growth of ovarian follicles in the female (Fig. 17-8) and stimulates the seminiferous tubules of the testis in the male. The atrophy of the sex organs that follows hypophysectomy is largely reversed by administration of this hormone, but for secretion of adequate amounts of estrogen by the follicles and complete restoration of spermatogenesis in the male, small doses of luteinizing hormone are also required.

3. LUTEINIZING HORMONE (LH OR ICSH). This glycoprotein hormone has a molecular weight of about 26,000. It reverses the involution of the interstitial cells of the ovary in hypophysectomized animals, but causes luteinization of follicles only after they have been ripened by prior treatment with

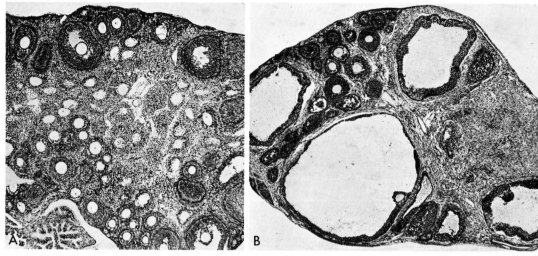

Figure 17-8. Photomicrographs of ovary of immature female rats. *A,* Normal immature female; *B,* Female rat of similar age, injected with follicle-stimulating hormone for three days. The hormone caused growth of the follicles and the appearance of a corpus luteum. × 38. (Courtesy of I. Gersh.)

follicle stimulating hormone. Luteinizing hormone activates the interstitial cells of the testis and stimulates their production of androgenic steroid hormones.

4. PROLACTIN (LACTOGENIC HORMONE). Prolactin is a protein hormone with a molecular weight of about 25,000. It has diverse functions in different species. In rodents and possibly other mammals it has a "luteotropic" effect—that is, it promotes the secretion of progesterone by the corpus luteum of the ovary. It is also involved in causing secretion of milk after the ducts and secretory portions of the mammary gland have been developed in response to ovarian hormones. There is evidence that it shares this function with STH, to which it is chemically related.

5. ADRENOCORTICOTROPIC HORMONE (ACTH, CORTICOTROPIN). This is a straight chained polypeptide with 39 amino acid residues and a molecular weight of about 4500. Its complete synthesis has been accomplished. Given to hypophysectomized animals, it repairs the atrophy of the adrenal cortex, particularly the zona fasciculata and reticularis, and stimulates the production of adrenal glucocorticoids.

6. THYROTROPIC HORMONE (TSH, THYROTROPIN). Thyrotropic hormone has not been purified, but it appears to be a glycoprotein of molecular weight in the range of 10,000 to 30,000. The atrophic thyroid of hypophysectomized animals is restored to normal by its administration. It stimulates hypertrophy of thyroid cells and promotes their secretion.

7. OTHER FUNCTIONS. A number of other functions have been attributed to the anterior lobe of the pituitary, but these are less well established than those enumerated above. Some of them may prove to be the result of combined action of two or more of the above hormones or may be mediated by effects on other endocrine glands.

The cell types believed to be responsible for secretion of these hormones have already been identified. Elaboration of somatotropin and prolactin are attributed to two morphologically distinct types of acidophil. The glycoprotein gonadotropic hormones FSH and LH are assigned to the PAS positive basophils. There is reason to believe that basophils that also stain with aldehyde-fuchsin are responsible for secretion of thyrotropin. In addition to the histochemical and biochemical evidence relating these hormones to the basophils, there is experimental evidence based upon the negative feedback mechanisms that operate in the regulation of hormone release.

Endocrine glands that are under the direct control of the anterior lobe hormones usually exert a reciprocal inhibiting effect upon hypophyseal function via the hypothalamus. Removal of the target organ therefore results in hypertrophy of those cells in the adenohypophysis responsible for elaboration of the corresponding tropic hormone. After castration, the rat hypophysis contains increased amounts of gonadotropic hormones, and at the same time the basophils become markedly enlarged and vacuolated in a characteristic way (*castration cells,* Fig. 17-7). Thyroidectomy also results in an increase in the percentage of basophils. These changes therefore constitute substantial additional evidence that basophils secrete both gonadotropins and thyrotropin.

Efforts to relate the production of adrenocorticotropic hormone to one of the specific cell types in the anterior lobe have thus far led to inconclusive results. Corticotropin appears to be somewhat more concentrated in the basophilic zone of the bovine pituitary, but it is not yet clear whether this hormone is produced by the same type of basophil that produces gonadotropin or by a separate specific cell type.

PARS INTERMEDIA

In many mammals the pars distalis is separated from the neurohypophysis by a cleft, lined on the juxtaneural side by a multilayered epithelium of basophilic cells comprising the pars intermedia. In the human embryo there is a distinct cleft and the pars intermedia is represented by a typical stratified epithelium adjacent to the infundibular process. The cleft may persist in young children and rarely in adults. In such cases the posterior wall consists of several layers of small basophilic cells forming a discrete pars intermedia. In the great majority of humans, however, the cleft becomes discontinuous in postnatal life and is represented in the adult by a zone of cysts (Rathke's cysts). These are often lined by ciliated epithelium and contain a colorless to yellow colloidal material that varies in consistency from a thin to a highly viscous fluid (Fig. 17-4*A*). With the disappearance of the cleft, the epithelium of the pars intermedia adjacent to the neural lobe becomes an inconspicuous, discontinuous layer, and its basophilic cells not infrequently extend some distance into the neural tissue of the infundibular process. Thus, the pars intermedia of man differs from that of most mammals in several respects: the cleft is rarely complete; cysts are of common occurrence; and the basophilic cells extend into the neural lobe, sometimes to a surprising degree. Whereas in

rodents such as the mouse the pars intermedia constitutes some 19 per cent of the hypophysis, it forms only 2 per cent in man. In the whale, porpoise, manatee, and some birds the intermediate lobe is entirely lacking.

The cells of the pars intermedia are polygonal or prismatic and are basophilic in their staining properties. At the light microscope level their nucleus and their cytoplasmic organelles are in no way unusual and resemble those of the basophils of the pars distalis. In the cytoplasm there are small granules (200 to 300 mμ), barely visible with the light microscope but clearly seen in electron micrographs. The granules are often polarized toward the basal lamina, they consist of glycoprotein and stain with the PAS reaction and with aldehyde-fuchsin or resorcin-fuchsin. The carbohydrate staining reactions of the granules in this instance are not correlated with the chemical nature of the hormone. The only hormone known to be secreted by the pars intermedia is *melanocyte stimulating hormone* (MSH), a simple polypeptide. It is possible, however, that in the cell it is bound to glycoprotein in the granules.

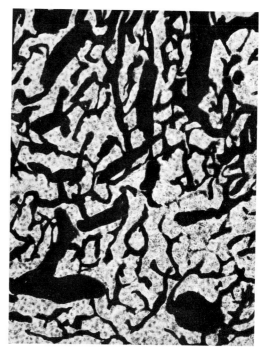

Figure 17-9. Photomicrograph of anterior lobe of hypophysis of monkey injected intravenously with India ink to show the irregular, richly anastomotic sinusoids. × 165. Compare with Figure 17-10, of infundibular process. (Courtesy of I. Gersh.)

In mammals generally the pars intermedia is rather poorly vascularized. In man, numerous anastomoses between the superior and inferior hypophyseal arteries traverse the pars intermedia and it receives some supply from a rich capillary network in the connective tissue layer that incompletely separates it from the neural lobe. This plexus is continuous with the capillary bed of the neural lobe but also has some connections with the sinusoids of the pars distalis.

Nerve fibers enter the pars intermedia from the neural lobe and ramify among its cells. These nerves, originating in the hypothalamus, appear to have a mainly inhibitory effect. In some mammalian species their interruption by stalk section results in hypertrophy of the intermedia. In amphibia, their interruption results in increased liberation of the hormone of the intermediate lobe. Neurosecretory material has been demonstrated in some of the nerves of the pars intermedia in amphibians and some mammals but has not been reported in man.

Histophysiology of the Pars Intermedia

Melanocyte stimulating hormone (MSH) of the hypophysis appears to be produced in the pars intermedia. The evidence for this is the demonstration that removal of the anterior and intermediate lobes of the hypophysis in frogs results in skin lightening, and when these lobes are then transplanted separately into tadpoles only the intermediate lobe transplants produce skin darkening (Allen). The pars intermedia is anatomically associated with the neural lobe and comes away with it when the anterior and posterior lobes are separated. Assays of the separated portions show 10 times more MSH activity in the posterior and intermediate lobe portion.

A highly basic melanocyte stimulating polypeptide was first isolated in pure form by Lee and Lerner from pig pituitary glands. This is now designated α-MSH. A slightly acidic polypeptide isolated by Benfey and Purvis from the same source is called β-MSH. These two forms of MSH have since been isolated from pituitaries of other species, including man. α-MSH contains 13 amino acids in a sequence that is identical to one portion of the molecule of adrenocorticotropic hormone (ACTH). β-MSH contains 18 amino acids, of which seven are in a sequence similar to part of the ACTH molecule. The common structure of certain regions of MSH and ACTH is believed to account for the fact that ACTH shows some melanocyte stimulating activity.

The effect of MSH upon pigmentation in amphibian skin is to cause dispersion of the melanin granules in chromatophores and consequent darkening of the skin. There is evidence that it also affects the synthesis of melanin. In mammals whose melanocytes are not subject to expansion and contraction, as are the melanophores of lower animals, the effect of the hormone appears to be on melanin production. The pigmentation that occurs in humans suffering from deterioration of the adrenal cortex (Addison's disease) is apparently due to the release by the hypophysis of excess ACTH and MSH, both of which have melanocyte stimulating properties. The dark-

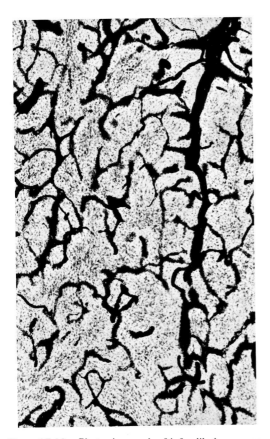

Figure 17-10. Photomicrograph of infundibular process of monkey injected intravenously with India ink to show the pattern of small blood vessels. The arterioles break up into a number of arching, interconnected capillaries. × 165. Compare with Figure 17-9, of anterior lobe. (Courtesy of I. Gersh.)

A

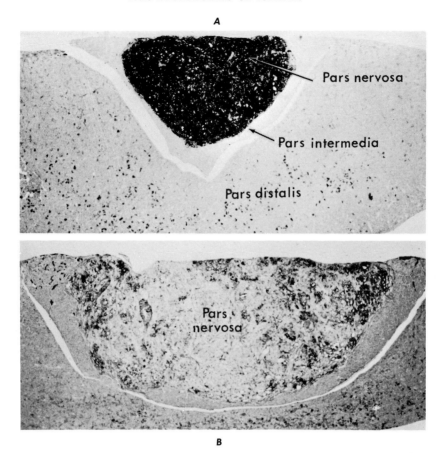

B

Figure 17-11. Photomicrograph of cross sections of rat hypophysis stained with paraldehyde-fuchsin. *A,* Hypophysis of a normal control rat showing abundant densely stained neurosecretory material in the neurohypophysis. *B,* Hypophysis of a rat of the Brattleboro strain with hypothalamic diabetes insipidus. The neurohypophysis is unusually large but contains very little neurosecretion (black). × 40. (After H. W. Sokol and H. Valtin, Endocrinol., *77:*692, 1965.)

ening of the skin during human pregnancy may also result from increased release of one or both of these hormones.

PARS INFUNDIBULARIS OR TUBERALIS

Like the pars intermedia, the pars tuberalis constitutes only a small part of the hypophysis. Both are adjacent to and continuous with the anterior lobe. The pars tuberalis is 25 to 60 μ thick and forms a sleeve around the stalk, the thickest portion being on its anterior surface (Fig. 17-3). It is frequently incomplete on the posterior surface of the stalk. The distinctive morphological characteristic of the pars tuberalis is the longitudinal arrangement of its cords of epithelial cells, which occupy the interstices between the longitudinally oriented blood vessels.

The pars tuberalis is the most highly vascularized subdivision of the hypophysis, because it is traversed by the major arterial supply for the anterior lobe and the hypothalamohypophyseal venous portal system. The pars tuberalis is separated from the infundibular stalk by a thin layer of connective tissue continuous with the pia. On the outside, the connective tissue is typical arachnoidal membrane. Between these, the blood vessels and groups of epithelial cells are supported by reticular fibers.

The epithelial cells of the pars tuberalis include undifferentiated cells and some small acidophilic and basophilic cells. The main component is a cuboidal-columnar cell, which may reach 12 to 18 μ in size and contains numerous small granules or sometimes fine colloid droplets. The mitochondria are short rods, and numerous small lipid droplets may be present. These are the only cells in the

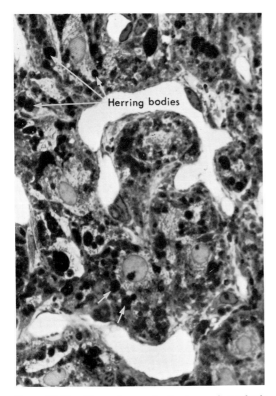

Figure 17-12. Photomicrograph of rat neurohypophysis fixed by perfusion. The large clear areas are capillaries. The dark rounded masses indicated by arrows are Herring bodies. In electron micrographs these are resolved as accumulations of neurosecretory material in dilatation of nerve axons. × 950. (Courtesy of P. Orkand and S. L. Palay.)

adult hypophysis containing large amounts of glycogen. The cells may be arranged to form a follicle-like structure. Islands, 50 to 70 μ in extent, of squamous epithelial cells may also be present. Despite the occurrence of a pars tuberalis in all vertebrates studied, the epithelial cells are not known to have any hormonal function.

NEUROHYPOPHYSIS

The median eminence of the tuber cinereum, the infundibular stalk, and infundibular process together comprise the neurohypophysis (Fig. 17-3). It consists of an intrinsic population of cells, the *pituicytes,* and the terminal portions of the axons of extrinsic secretory neurons, whose cell bodies are located in the hypothalamus. The bulk of its substance is made up of a large bundle of approximately 100,000 unmyelinated nerve fibers comprising

the *hypothalamo-hypophyseal tract.* It originates mainly from the *supraoptic nucleus* of the hypothalamus close to the optic chiasm, and from the *paraventricular nucleus* in the wall of the third ventricle, with minor contributions from other hypothalamic areas. The fibers from these sources converge upon the median eminence and course down the infundibular stalk into the infundibular process. There they do not terminate upon nerve cells or other effector cells but end blindly in intimate relation to the vessels of the rich capillary plexus of the neural lobe.

Throughout the neurohypophysis but particularly abundant in the infundibular process are spherical masses of highly variable size that stain deeply with the chrome alum-hematoxylin stain. These are the so-called *Herring bodies* (Fig. 17-9). They were originally misinterpreted as a product of the pars intermedia and were thought to be situated in the extracellular spaces but are now known to be local accumulations of neurosecretory material in the axoplasm of fibers of the hypothalamo-hypophyseal tract. Stainable neurosecretory material can be traced upward along the tract and can also be demonstrated in the cell bodies of the neurons in the hypothalamic nuclei. Electron microscope studies of these secretory neurons reveal cytological characteristics that are comparable to those of other protein secreting cells. Granular endoplasmic reticulum (Nissl substance) is abundant and is presumably the site of hormone synthesis. The hormone product, probably bound to some carrier protein, is segregated by the Golgi apparatus in membrane bounded electron-dense secretion granules 120 to 200 mμ in diameter. Granules of the same type are found in irregular accumulations along the length of axons destined for the neurohypophysis. In the neural lobe greatly dilated portions of axons are densely packed with granules. These undoubtedly correspond to the Herring bodies seen by light microscopy in sections stained with chrome alum-hematoxylin.

Surgical interruption of the hypophyseal stalk is followed by gradual disappearance of detectable hormone and of stainable neurosecretory substance in the infundibular process distal to the lesion, and by a concomitant accumulation of both in the stump proximal to the site of stalk section. From these observations it is concluded that the Herring bodies of light microscopy and the 120 to 200 mμ-dense granules seen in electron micrographs represent neurosecretory material that is formed in the cells of the supraoptic and paraventricular nuclei of the hypothalamus, transported along the nerve fibers, and stored in their terminals in the infundibular process.

Evidence for the association of the hormones with the stainable neurosecretory material and the electron-dense granules is of two kinds. Both stainable material and electron-dense granules disappear from the neurohypophysis under conditions of severe hormone depletion. Density gradient centrifugation of homogenates of neurohypophyseal tissue yields a fraction containing the neurosecretory granules that is very rich in hormone activity.

The terminal arborizations of the axons in the neural lobe abut the basement lamina lining perivascular spaces of variable thickness (Fig. 17-13). The endothelial cells forming the walls of the capillaries of the pars nervosa, like those of the pars distalis and other endocrine glands, are extremely attenuated and penetrated by circular fenestrations closed only by thin diaphragms. In addition to the dense neurosecretory granules the nerve endings contain aggregations of small ($\sim$ 400 Å) agranular vesicles similar to those found in synaptic terminals elsewhere in the nervous system. Secretion granules never appear free in the perivascular space and are probably not released from the nerve endings as such. It seems more likely that the hormones released from the granules in the nerve terminals traverse the perivascular space and the endothelium in molecular dispersion. The role of the small agranular vesicles in hormone release is unknown.

Distributed among the nerve fibers in the infundibular process are the *pituicytes*. In man they are highly variable in size and shape and commonly contain pigment granules that reduce silver directly or blacken with the meth-

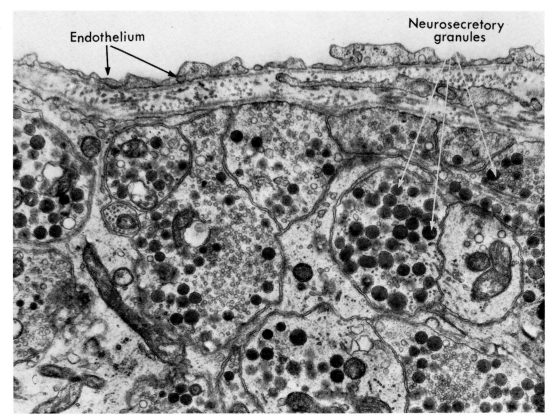

Figure 17-13. Electron micrograph of rat neurohypophysis, showing neurosecretory granules and small vesicles in the axoplasm of fibers of the hypothalamo-hypophyseal tract ending in close relation to a capillary. $\times$ 22,000. (Courtesy of P. Orkand and S. L. Palay.)

ods of Bielschowsky and Hortega. These cells were extensively studied by Gersh and by Romeis, who distinguished several types and believed that one or more of them secreted the hormones of the neurohypophysis. The pituicytes are no longer believed to have a secretory function. Electron microscopic studies have greatly clarified their nature. Their structural relation to the nerve fibers is similar to that of the neuroglial cells of the central nervous system. The cytoplasmic processes meander among clusters of preterminal secretory axons

CENTRAL NERVOUS SYSTEM

Afferent nervous pathway

Nucleus paraventricularis

Neural lobe of hypophysis

Oxytocin release

General circulation

Tactile stimuli

Myoepithelial cell

Nipple

MAMMARY GLAND

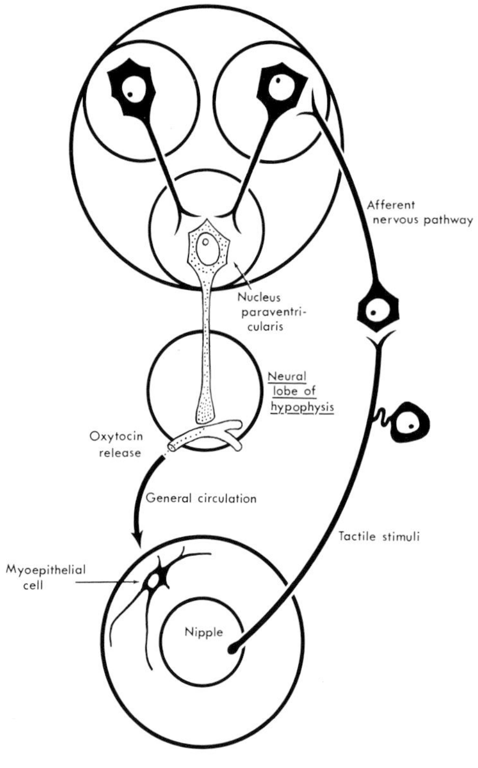

Figure 17-14. An example of a first order neuroendocrine system—the milk ejection reflex. Tactile stimuli evoked by suckling young are conducted from receptors in the nipple via afferent fibers to the central nervous system. These impulses compete with those from inhibitory centers for the final common pathway whose cell bodies are presumably in the nucleus paraventricularis. In the posterior pituitary, oxytocin is released into the systemic circulation, by which it reaches myoepithelial cells in the mammary glands, causing their contraction and ejection of milk. (After E. Scharrer, in Endocrines and the Central Nervous System. Baltimore, Williams & Wilkins, 1966.)

and often intimately envelop their granule-filled expansions (Herring bodies). Many processes of pituicytes end upon the perivascular space, along with the nerve terminals. It is not known whether their only function is supportive or whether they have some metabolic role in the secretion process.

Histophysiology of the Neurohypophysis

The neural lobe of the hypophysis is the site of storage and release of two closely related hormones, *oxytocin* and *vasopressin* (antidiuretic hormone, ADH). Both have been isolated in pure form, their structure has been determined, and they have been synthesized (du Vigneaud). They are cyclic polypeptides consisting of eight different amino acids. Oxytocin causes contraction of uterine smooth muscle during coitus and at the time of delivery, and contraction of myoepithelial cells in the alveoli of the mammary gland, thus mediating the *milk ejection reflex* in response to suckling in lactating animals (Fig. 17-14). Vasopressin raises the blood pressure by stimulating contraction of smooth muscle in the walls of small blood vessels, and conserves body water by promoting reabsorption of water in the distal convoluted tubules of the kidney. The antidiuretic effect of the hormone is physiologically more important than the pressor effect.

Humans with tumor or injury to the hypothalamus may develop *diabetes insipidus,* a condition in which the capacity of the kidney to concentrate the glomerular filtrate is lost. A very large volume of urine is eliminated (polyuria) and the patient, driven by thirst, drinks a large quantity of water (polydipsia). A similar condition can be produced in experimental animals by hypothalamic lesions that destroy the supraoptico-hypophyseal tracts. A strain of rats with hereditary diabetes insipidus is now available for experimental study (Sokol). These animals are apparently unable to synthesize vasopressin and have a daily water consumption of 80 per cent of their weight and a urine output of 70 per cent of their weight. Sections of their hypophysis stained with aldehyde-fuchsin reveal little or no staining of neurosecretory material and a conspicuous compensatory hypertrophy of the neurohypophysis (Fig. 17-11). The neurons of

CENTRAL NERVOUS SYSTEM

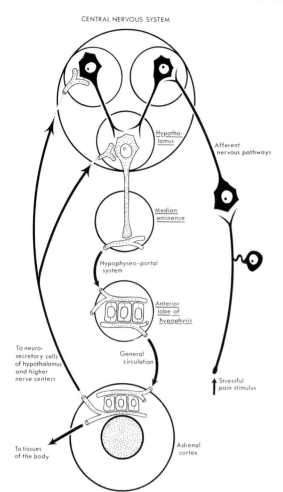

Figure 17-15. Diagram of some of the pathways involved in the control of glucocorticoid release by the adrenal. A stressful stimulus via afferent pathways reaches neurosecretory cells, whose axons end in the median eminence. There corticotropin-releasing factors are released. These are carried through hypothalamic-hypophyseal portal vessels to the anterior pituitary, which in turn releases ACTH into the general circulation. When ACTH acts on the adrenal cortex, glucocorticoids are released into the general circulation and reach all of the tissues, including hormone-sensitive neurosecretory cells in the hypothalamus and nerve centers of higher order. (After E. Scharrer, in Endocrines and the Central Nervous System. Baltimore, Williams & Wilkins, 1966.)

the supraoptic nucleus also show hypertrophy and contain very few neurosecretory granules.

REFERENCES

Allen, B. M.: Extirpation of the hypophysis and thyroid glands of *Rana pipiens*. Science, *44*:755, 1916.

Barer, R., H. Heller, and K. Lederis: The isolation, identification and properties of the hormonal granules of the neurohypophysis. Proc. Roy. Soc. B., *158*:388, 1963.

Barer, R., and K. Lederis: Ultrastructure of the rabbit neurohypophysis with special reference to the release of hormones. Zeitschr. f. Zellforsch., *75*:201, 1966.

Bargmann, W., A. Knoop, and A. Thiel: Elektronenmikroskopische Studie an der Neurohypophyse von *Tropidonotus natrix*. Zeitschr. f. Zellforsch., *47*:114, 1957.

Bargmann, W., and E. Scharrer: The site of origin of the hormones of the posterior pituitary. Am. Scientist, *39*:255, 1961.

Benfey, B. J., and J. L. Purvis: Purification and amino acid composition of melanophore-expanding hormone from hog pituitary gland. J. Amer. Chem. Soc., *77*:5167, 1955.

Bergland, R.: The surgical significance of the anatomical variations surrounding the pituitary. Anat. Rec., *157*:396, 1967.

Bodian, D.: Cytological aspects of neurosecretion in opossum neurohypophysis. Bull. Johns Hopkins Hosp., *113*:57, 1963.

Bodian, D.: Herring bodies and neuroapocrine secretion in the monkey. An electron microscopic study of the fate of the neurosecretory product. Bull. Johns Hopkins Hosp., *118*:282, 1966.

Bagdanove, E. M., and S. A. DiAngelo: The effects of hypothalamic lesions on goitrogenesis and pituitary TSH secretion in the propylthiouracil-treated guinea pig. Endocrinol., *64*:53, 1959.

Bogdanove, E. M., and N. S. Halmi: Effects of hypothalamic lesions and subsequent propylthiouracil treatment on pituitary structure and function in the rat. Endocrinol., *53*:274, 1953.

Burgers, A. C. J.: Melanophore-stimulating hormones in vertebrates. Ann. N. Y. Acad. Sci., *100*:669, 1963.

Dawson, A. B.: The demonstration by differential staining of two types of acidophile in the anterior pituitary gland of the rat. Anat. Rec., *120*:810, 1954.

du Vigneaud, V.: Trail of sulfur research from insulin to oxytocin. Science, *123*:967, 1956.

du Vigneaud, V., H. C. Lawler, and E. A. Popenoe: The synthesis of an oxtapeptide amide with the hormonal activity of ocytocin. J. Am. Chem. Soc., *75*:4879, 1953.

Everett, J. W., and C. H. Sawyer: Estimated duration of the spontaneous activation which causes release of ovulating hormone from the rat hypophysis. Endocrinol., *52*:83, 1953.

Farguhar, M. G.: Fine structure and function in capillaries of the anterior pituitary gland. Angiology, *12*:270, 1961.

Farquhar, M. G., and J. F. Rinehart: Cytologic alterations in the anterior pituitary gland following thyroidectomy; an electron microscope study. Endocrinol., *55*:857, 1954.

Furth, J.: Experimental pituitary tumors. In Pincus, G., ed.: Recent Progress in Hormone Research. New York, Academic Press, 1955, Vol. XI, p. 221.

Green, J. D.: The comparative anatomy of the portal vascular system and of the innervation of the hypophysis. In Harris, G. W., and B. T. Donovan, eds.: The Pituitary Gland. Berkeley, University of California Press, 1966, Vol. I, p. 127.

Green, J. D., and G. W. Harris: The neurovascular link between the neurohypophysis and adenohypophysis. J. Endocrinol., *5*:136, 1947.

Greep, R. O.: Architecture of the final common path to the adenohypophysis. Fertility and Sterility, *14*:153, 1963.

Halmi, N. S.: Two types of basophils in the rat pituitary; "thyrotrophs" and "gonadotrophs" vs. beta and delta cells. Endocrinol., *50*:140, 1952.

Harris, G. W.: Neural Control of the Pituitary Gland. London, Edward Arnold, Ltd., 1955.

Heller, H., ed.: The Neurohypophysis. New York, Academic Press, 1957.

Hume, D. M.: The neuroendocrine response to injury; present status of the problem. Ann. Surg., *138*:548, 1953.

Hunt, T. E.: Mitotic activity in the anterior hypophysis of female rats. Anat. Rec., *82*:263, 1942.

Hymer, W. C., and W. H. McShan: Isolation of rat pituitary granules and the study of their biochemical properties and hormonal activities. J. Cell Biol., *17*:67, 1963.

Lederis, J.: An electron microscopical study of the human neurohypophysis. Zeitschr. f. Zellforsch., *65*:847, 1965.

Lee, T. H., and A. B. Lerner: Isolation of melanocyte-stimulating hormone from hog pituitary gland. J. Biol. Chem., *221*:943, 1956.

Lerner, A. B., and J. S. McGuire: Effect of alpha- and beta-melano-
cyte stimulating hormones on skin colour in man. Nature, *189:*
176, 1961.

Lerner, A. B., and Y. Takahashi: Hormonal control of melanin
pigmentation. Rec. Prog. Hormone Res., *12:*203, 1956.

Leznoff, A., J. Fishman, L. Goodfriend, E. McGarry, J. Beck, and
B. Rose: Localization of fluorescent antibodies to human growth
hormone in human anterior pituitary glands. Proc. Soc. Exper.
Biol. & Med., *104:*232, 1960.

Midgley, A. R., Jr.: Immunofluorescent localization of human
pituitary leuteinizing hormone. Exper. Cell Res., *32:*606, 1963.

Nalbandov, A. V.: Reproductive Physiology. San Francisco, W. H.
Freeman & Co., 1958.

Palay, S. L.: The fine structure of the neurohypophysis. *In* Waelsch,
H., ed.: Progress in Neurobiology. II. Ultrastructure and Cellular Chemistry of Neural Tissue. New York, Paul B. Hoeber, Inc.,
1957, p. 31.

Peterson, R. R., and J. Weiss: Staining of the adenohypophysis with
acid and basic dyes. Endocrinol., *57:*96, 1955.

Pickford, M.: Neurohypophysis and kidney function. *In* Harris, G.
W., and B. T. Donovan, eds.: The Pituitary Gland. Berkeley,
University of California Press, 1966, Vol. 3, p. 374.

Purves, H. D.: Morphology of the hypophysis related to its function.
In Young, W. C., ed.: Sex and Internal Secretions. 2nd ed. Baltimore, Williams & Wilkins, 1961, Vol. I, p. 161.

Purves, H. D.: Cytology of the adenohypophysis. *In* Harris, G. W.,
and B. T. Donovan, eds.: The Pituitary Gland. Berkeley, University of California Press, 1966, Vol. 1, p. 147.

Rennels, E. G.: Two tinctorial types of gonadotrophs in the rat
hypophysis. Zeitschr. f. Zellforsch., *45:*464, 1957.

Rinehart, J. F., and M. G. Farquhar: The fine vascular organization
of the anterior pituitary gland; an electron microscopic study
with histochemical correlations. Anat. Rec., *121:*207, 1955.

Romeis, B.: Hypophyse. *In* von Möllendorff, W., and W. Bargmann,
eds.: Handbuch der mikroskopischen Anatomie des Menschen.
Berlin, Julius Springer, 1940, Vol. 6, part 3, p. 1.

Salazar, H., and R. R. Peterson: Morphologic observations concerning the release and transport of secretory products in the adenohypophysis. Am. J. Anat., *115:*199, 1964.

Sawyer, W. H.: Comparative physiology and pharmacology of the
neurohypophysis. Rec. Prog. Hormone Res., *17:*437, 1961.

Sawyer, W. H.: Vertebrate neurohypophyseal principles. Endocrinol., *75:*981, 1964.

Scharrer, E., and B. Scharrer: Hormones produced by neurosecretory cells. Rec. Prog. Hormone Res., *10:*183, 1954.

Scharrer, E., and B. Scharrer: Neurosekretion. *In* von Möllendorff,
W., and W. Bargmann, eds.: Handbuch der mikroskopischen
Anatomie des Menschen. Berlin, Springer Verlag, 1954, Vol. 6,
part 5, p. 953.

Simpson, M. E., C. W. Asling, and H. M. Evans: Some endocrine
influences on skeletal growth and differentiation. Yale J. Biol.
Med., *23:*1, 1950.

Simpson, M. E., H. M. Evans, and C. H. Li: The growth of hypophysectomized female rats following chronic treatment with pure
pituitary growth hormone. Growth, *13:*151, 1949.

Smith, P. E.: Hypophysectomy and replacement therapy in the rat.
Am. J. Anat., *45:*205, 1930.

Smith, R. W., Jr., Gaebler, O. H., and C. N. H. Long, eds.: The
Hypophyseal Growth Hormone, Nature and Actions. (Inter-
national symposium, sponsored by Henry Ford Hospital and
Edsel B. Ford Institute for Medical Research, Detroit.) New
York, Blakiston Division, McGraw-Hill Book Co., 1955.

Sokol, H. W., and H. Valtin: Morphology of the neurosecretory
system in rats homozygous and heterozygous for hypothalamic
diabetes insipidus (Brattleboro strain). Endocrinol., *77:*692,
1965.

Turner, C. D.: General Endocrinology. 4th ed. Philadelphia, W. B.
Saunders Co., 1966.

Wislocki, G. B.: The vascular supply of the hypophysis cerebri of
the rhesus monkey and man. Proc. Assoc. Res. Nervous Mental
Diseases, *17:*48, 1938.

CHAPTER EIGHTEEN

The Thyroid Gland

The thyroid gland is in the anterior part of the neck and weighs 25 to 40 gm. It consists of two *lateral lobes* connected by a narrow *isthmus,* which crosses the trachea just below the cricoid cartilage. In about one third of the persons examined, a *pyramidal lobe* extends upward from the isthmus near the left lobe.

The gland is enclosed in a connective tissue capsule that is continuous with the surrounding cervical fascia. This outer capsule is loosely connected on its deep surface to another layer of moderately dense connective tissue that is intimately adherent to the gland. This separation of the capsule into two layers creates a plane of cleavage between the two, which facilitates surgical removal of the gland.

The function of the thyroid is to elaborate, store, and release into the bloodstream *thyroid hormone,* which is concerned with the regulation of metabolic rate. The thyroid differs from other endocrine glands in that a mechanism for extracellular storage of its hormone is highly developed, whereas in other glands of internal secretion there are only rather limited provisions for intracellular storage.

MICROSCOPIC STRUCTURE. The gland is composed of spherical, cystlike follicles 0.02 to 0.9 mm. in diameter, lined with a simple epithelium and containing a gelatinous *colloid.* This represents the stored product of the secretory activity of the epithelium lining the follicle. In man there is great variability in the size of the follicles, but the small predominate over the large. In animals other than man the follicles are of more uniform size. In the rat and guinea pig those at the periphery of the gland are larger than those more centrally situated.

The follicles are surrounded by an extremely thin basement lamina, which usually is not resolved with the light microscope. With silver stains the follicles are seen to be enclosed by a delicate network of reticular fibers. A close meshed plexus of capillaries surrounds each follicle (Fig. 18-2). Between the capillary nets of adjacent follicles are the blind terminations of lymphatic vessels. Numerous nerve fibers accompany the blood vessels as they ramify among the follicles. These seem to terminate mainly along the vessels, but in some instances they appear to end in direct contact with the base of the thyroid epithelial cells. The nerves entering the thyroid are postganglionic sympathetic fibers originating in the middle and superior cervical ganglia. There are also preganglionic parasympathetic fibers, for ganglion cells may occasionally be encountered within the thyroid. The nerves to the thyroid are presumed to be mainly vasomotor, for transplanted thyroid tissue functions adequately, suggesting that an intact nerve supply is not necessary for secretion.

The epithelial cells vary in height but are commonly low cuboidal to squamous. In general, the epithelium tends to be squamous when the gland is underactive and columnar when it is overactive, but there are many exceptions, and an accurate assessment of the functional activity of the gland cannot be based upon histological examination alone.

The nucleus of the gland cell is spheroidal, centrally situated, poor in chromatin, and contains one or more nucleoli. The cytoplasm is basophilic; the mitochondria are thin rods and the Golgi apparatus is usually supranuclear. Lipid droplets are common, and clear

Figure 18-1. Surface view of human thyroid, slightly enlarged, showing the irregular shapes of the lobules and variations in the size of their component follicles. × about 5. (After Rienhoff.)

iodothyronine) and *triiodothyronine*, which when released into the blood, constitute the *thyroid hormone*. The presence of these compounds in the colloid has been demonstrated by microchemical analysis, by ultraviolet absorption spectrophotometry, and by the use of radioactive ^{131}I. The follicle cells are also believed, by some workers, to secrete into the colloid a protease that splits thyroglobulin into smaller molecules and liberates the biologically active iodinated derivatives of tyrosine, of which *thyroxine* (tetraiodothyronine) is the principal circulating hormone. Others believe that the proteases act within the thyroid cells upon thyroglobulin taken up from the lumen of the follicle.

In addition to the principal cells of the thyroid follicles, there is another smaller population of cells present both in the follicular epithelium and in the interfollicular spaces. These cells were described by Baber (1877) and Hürthle (1894) and studied in greater de-

droplets have been described by various workers and interpreted as globules of colloid. They stain with aniline blue and with the periodic acid–Schiff reaction in much the same way as the colloid in the lumen of the follicle. Granules of varying size, located mainly in the apical cytoplasm, give positive staining reactions for acid phosphatase and esterase and are therefore considered to be lysosomes.

The fresh colloid is optically homogeneous, except for occasional desquamated cells and rare macrophages. After fixation the colloid stains with either acid or basic dyes, and with the trichrome stains it is not uncommon for different follicles or even different areas of the colloid in the same follicle to be colored differently. Although physiological significance has been erroneously ascribed to this multiple staining, the varied patterns observed appear to be due to local differences in concentration of protein that depend upon the direction and rate of penetration of fixative into the tissue block (Mayer). The colloid stains intensely with the periodic acid–Schiff reaction, because the *thyroglobulin* secreted by the thyroid is a glycoprotein containing 2 to 4 per cent hexosamine, as well as galactose, mannose, fucose, and other carbohydrates. The thyroglobulin of the colloid also contains various iodinated amino acids. Among these are *thyroxine* (tetra-

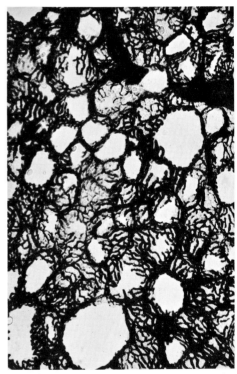

Figure 18-2. Photomicrograph of thyroid gland of monkey injected intravenously with India ink to show pattern of small blood vessels. The richly anastomotic baskets of capillaries intimately enclose the follicles. Some of these are sectioned through the midportion; others are observed from above or below this level. × 67. (Courtesy of I. Gersh.)

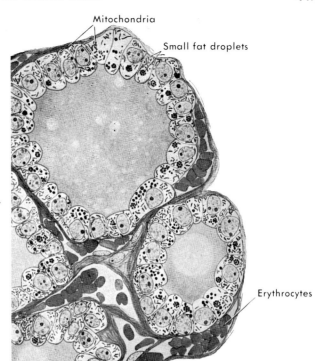

Mitochondria

Small fat droplets

Erythrocytes

Figure 18-3. Section through several follicles of human thyroid. Aniline-acid-fuchsin. (Courtesy of R. R. Bensley.)

tail by Nonidez (1931). They are commonly called parafollicular cells but are also referred to as "mitochondria-rich cells" or "C cells." The term "parafollicular cell" was introduced (by Nonidez) to designate these cells as opposed to other interfollicular cells, some of which may be persisting undifferentiated embryonal elements. Although many of the parafollicular cells are interfollicular in location, they arise from cells in the epithelium and gradually withdraw into the interfollicular spaces. They are often larger than the principal cells and in routine histological preparations are less deeply stained. In tissue impregnated by the silver nitrate method of Cajal, they contain brown to black cytoplasmic granules (Figs. 18-8 and 18-9). Although in the past these cells have been considered by some to be exhausted or degenerate follicular cells, more recent studies indicate that they are metabolically active cells having an enzyme pattern quite different from that of the principal cells. They are richer in mitochondria and have a higher level of α-glycerophosphate dehydrogenase. Recent evidence suggests that the parafollicular cells may produce the hormone *thyrocalcitonin.*

ULTRASTRUCTURE. In electron micrographs the follicles of the human thyroid are found to be composed of a single layer of low cuboidal to squamous cells around a homogeneous, moderately dense colloid. A thin, continuous basal lamina about 500 Å thick surrounds the entire follicle. In the interfollicular space are numerous capillaries of the fenestrated type, occasional fibroblasts, and small bundles of collagen fibrils. The follicle cells are joined laterally by typical junctional complexes, and the free surfaces bear a small number of short, irregularly oriented microvilli. In follicles with cuboidal epithelium, the microvilli are somewhat more numerous. The basal plasma membrane is smoothly contoured and not infolded. The relatively large nucleus is centrally placed and has an eccentric nucleolus. The mitochondria are relatively few and uniformly distributed. Their cristae are not especially numerous. The endoplasmic reticulum varies in its degree of development. In the flattened cells there are only a few elongated cisternal profiles, but in the cuboidal cells the reticulum is well developed. The Golgi apparatus is in the supranuclear or paranuclear position and is composed of flattened or dilated saccules, vacuoles, and small vesicles. Small vesicles similar to those of the Golgi apparatus

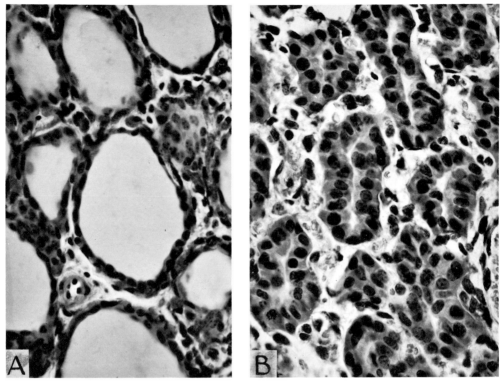

Figure 18-4. Photomicrographs of thyroid glands of guinea pigs, showing effects of repeated injections of extracts of anterior lobe containing thyrotropic hormone. *A*, Normal acini with low cuboidal epithelium and rich in colloid; *B*, treated, with acini consisting of columnar cells containing small amount of dilute colloid. Fixed by freezing and drying. Hematoxylin and eosin. × 350. (Courtesy of I. Gersh.)

are present in abundance throughout the cytoplasm. Multivesicular bodies are also common. Membrane limited dense bodies 0.5 to 0.6 μ in diameter are plentiful in the apical cytoplasm. These are believed to be lysosomes.

In humans suffering from hyperactive thyroids (thyrotoxicosis), the cells are taller, their microvilli more numerous, and the endoplasmic reticulum more extensive. The mitochondria are increased in number and more variable in shape, and their cristae are more numerous. The Golgi apparatus is enlarged and the number of lysosomes is increased (Heimann).

The parafollicular cells have not been thoroughly studied in electron micrographs. The matrix of their mitochondria is denser than in those of the principal cells. They contain relatively little granular endoplasmic reticulum but are filled with small membrane limited vesicles about 1500 Å in diameter. In some species these have a dense content and resemble secretory granules.

HISTOPHYSIOLOGY. By a mechanism that is still poorly understood the thyroid concentrates *iodine* to the extent of fifty to several hundred thousand times the concentration of this element in the blood plasma (Turner). The concentration of administered iodine is very rapid. Ten minutes after injection of inorganic iodide, 40 per cent of the circulating ion is concentrated in the gland. This reaction is partially inhibited by thiocyanates. Nearly all of the iodine is accumulated in the organic form as *mono-, di-,* and *triiodothyronine,* and *thyroxine* bound to thyroglobulin, the storage form of thyroid hormone. The site of iodination of thyroglobulin is still unsettled. The resolution of autoradiography with ^{125}I is not sufficient to establish conclusively whether the iodine is bound in the cells before secretion of thyroglobulin or after it reaches the lumen of the follicle. By use of ^{3}H leucine, however, it is possible to follow the intracellular pathway of secretion of the thyroglobulin. The label can first be detected over the granular reticulum, later over the Golgi region, and still later in the lumen of the follicle (Nadler, 1964).

The site of hydrolysis of thyroglobulin is also a subject of dispute. Although some contend that proteases are secreted into the colloid, the bulk of the evidence now seems to favor uptake of colloid by the cells, possibly by pinocytosis, with intracellular hydrolysis resulting from coalescence of lysosomes with the vacuoles containing thyroglobulin. Of the active hormone entering the blood, 90 per cent or more is thyroxine, but triiodothyronine has also been detected in the blood of normal and hyperthyroid individuals and is more active than thyroxine.

There is recent evidence that the thyroid produces a hormone other than thyroxine and triiodothyronine. Copp and his collaborators in 1962, perfusing the thyroid and parathyroid glands of the dog with hypercalcemic blood, demonstrated release of a factor tending to lower blood calcium levels. They attributed this factor to the parathyroids and called it "calcitonin." In 1963 Hirsch and his collaborators confirmed the existence of the hypocalcemic factor but demonstrated that it originated from the thyroid gland and proposed the name "thyrocalcitonin." Calcium lowering activity has been demonstrated in thyroid tissue from several species, including the dog, rat, rabbit, ox, pig, goat, sheep, birds, and man. Isolation and purification of the hormone have been carried out (chiefly from fresh pig thyroids) and it is now considered to be a single-chain polypeptide consisting of approximately 22 amino acids with a total molecular weight of about 3000. It is believed to lower the serum calcium level by suppressing the resorption of bone, thereby diminishing the return of calcium from the skeleton to the blood. The physiological significance of its activity is still under investigation and may vary from one species to another. It appears to counteract the effects of the parathyroid hormone and, by so doing, to contribute to the homeostatic regulation of the calcium ion concentration in the blood plasma.

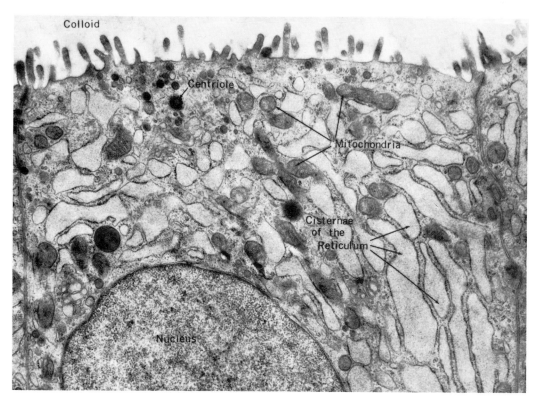

Figure 18-5. Electron micrograph of the apical half of an epithelial cell from a rat thyroid gland. The free surface of the cell is provided with microvilli that project into the colloid of the follicle. The endoplasmic reticulum is well developed and its cisternae are distended with an amorphous content of low density. Osmic acid fixation. × 13,000. (Courtesy of S. Wissig; labeling added.)

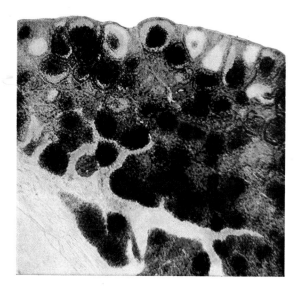

Figure 18-6. Low-power photomicrograph of auto-radiograph of thyroid gland of rat previously injected with ^{131}I. The blackened areas represent sites of deposition of the radioactive material. There is great variability in the content of the isotope in the several follicles. In a few places the epithelium is blackened. (Courtesy of C. P. Leblond, D. Findlay, and S. Gross.)

Secretion of thyrocalcitonin has been attributed to the parafollicular cells. Perfusion with hypercalcemic blood appears to cause increased secretion of the content of the small vesicles present in the cytoplasm of these cells. Fluorescent antibody staining suggests that other thyroid cells may contain the hormone in much lower concentration.

Control of the rate of release of the hormone *thyroxine* is thought to be mediated largely through other endocrine glands, particularly through the action of the *thyrotropic* hormone of the anterior lobe of the hypophysis (TSH). After hypophysectomy, the thyroid is no longer capable of accumulating significant amounts of ^{131}I, and only traces of thyroxine appear in the blood. The amount of discharge of hormone is normally adjusted by the levels of circulating hormone in the blood. An excess of thyroid hormone in the blood inhibits the secretion by the pituitary of *thyrotropic* hormone, which results in reduced thyroid activity. A reduction of thyroid hormone in the blood stimulates the secretion of thyrotropic hormone, resulting in increased thyroid activity. The accumulation of iodine from the blood, its conversion to the active principle, and its release into the circulation are all affected by thyrotropic hormone.

The secretion of thyrotropin by the hypophysis is in turn controlled by the central nervous system. There is now a considerable body of evidence indicating that nervous impulses reaching specific areas of the hypothalamus stimulate formation and liberation of specific releasing factors for gonadotropin, corticotropin, and thyrotropin. These are carried via the hypophyseal portal veins to the anterior lobe of the hypophysis, where they induce secretion of the appropriate tropic hormone. The release of thyrotropic hormone (TSH) is thus presumed to depend in part upon a thyrotropin releasing factor (TRF) formed in the hypothalamus. There is also evidence for a direct feedback mechanism, in which thyroxine acts directly upon the anterior hypophysis.

The most striking effect of thyroid secretion is its control of the *metabolic rate* of the body above a minimal value. When a deficiency of thyroid hormone occurs, the metabolic rate falls below normal; when there is an excess, the metabolic rate rises above normal. When *hypothyroidism* begins in infancy and persists, it leads to *cretinism*, a condition attended by stunting of physical and mental development. When hypofunction begins in adulthood and persists, it leads to *myxedema*, a disorder characterized by a sallow, puffy appearance, dry sparse hair, lethargy, and delayed cerebration. In both forms the basal metabolic rate is reduced, and in both the symptoms may be removed through timely oral administration of dried thyroid gland.

Thyroidectomy may duplicate many of the symptoms of thyroid deficiency in man, but in adults of certain species (monkey) the effects of thyroidectomy are detectable only with difficulty.

Hyperthyroidism occurs in persons suffering from *exophthalmic goiter* or toxic adenoma of the thyroid. In both conditions, follicles become enlarged, with papillary infoldings of the epithelium; the cells become columnar; the Golgi apparatus hypertrophies; mitochondria increase in number; and the follicular colloid decreases or may be absent (Fig. 18-4*B*). The increased basal metabolic rate and associated symptoms return temporarily toward normal after the administration of iodine or of certain "antithyroid" drugs, which are derivatives of thiourea.

Many of the symptoms of hyperthyroidism can be produced in other animals by the administration of an extract of the anterior lobe of the hypophysis containing thyrotropic hormone. The thyroid of animals treated adequately with this extract shows the same changes as those occurring in the gland in human hyperthyroidism. The marked morphological changes are not diagnostic of *hyperthyroidism*, for they can be duplicated exactly by the administration of antithyroid drugs, such as thiouracil, which result in *hypothyroidism*. However, these drugs, by preventing synthesis of thyroid hormone, result in enhanced release of thyrotropic hormone by the hypophysis. Thus, although increased cell height is apparently not diagnostic of hyperthyroidism, it can

be taken as a dependable indicator of excess circulating thyrotropin.

In two other conditions in man, the thyroid enlarges but the basal metabolic rate is normal: *simple goiter*, which may be due to iodine deficiency, and *nontoxic adenoma*.

Inasmuch as the primary effect of thyroid hormone is on the basal metabolic rate, it is not surprising that it influences carbohydrate metabolism and probably also fat and protein metabolism. It is important also in growth of the animal as a whole, especially through its effects on ossification centers and on the development of certain organs, particularly the genital organs and the thymus. It also influences the functioning of the nervous system. There are certain interrelations with the anterior pituitary gland; thyroidectomy results in hypertrophy of the anterior lobe of the hypophysis, with degranulation of the acidophilic cells and the appearance of characteristically altered basophilic cells called *thyroidectomy cells*. The thyroid hypertrophies during pregnancy.

PHYLOGENY. Iodine is found in all marine invertebrates as well as some algae. Diiodotyrosine has been identified in some and may reach high concentrations in certain *sponges*. Although there is no agreement on whether the hypobranchial groove in the floor of the pharynx of the protochordate *Amphioxus* is homologous with the thyroid gland, there seems to be more reason for homologizing the

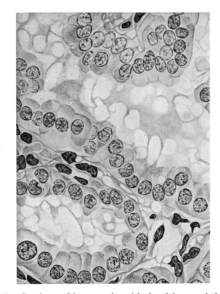
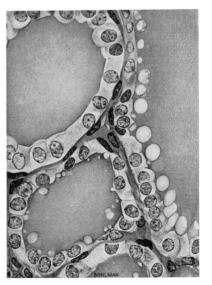

Figure 18-7. Sections of human thyroid gland in exophthalmic goiter (*A*) and in colloid goiter (*B*), from preparations of R. R. Bensley. Note the differences in height of the epithelium and the amount and depth of staining of the colloid in the two figures. Hematoxylin and eosin. × 570.

endostyle of the larval lamprey with the thyroid of higher vertebrates. The endostyle can concentrate iodine and synthesize thyroxine, but the organ is an elaborately shaped tubular sac and retains a duct to the pharynx. There is no evidence that the endostyle plays an endocrine role. The most primitive thyroid of reasonably typical structure is found in the adult lamprey. The thyroid is indisputably an endocrine gland in bony fish and is relatively uniform in its morphology in all higher animals. It is not of equal functional importance in all, however, for its effects on metabolism are largely limited to homeothermic animals.

HISTOGENESIS. In man, the primordium of the thyroid gland arises early (embryos of 1.37 mm.) as a medial ventral outgrowth of the endoderm, cranial to that of the trachea. The foramen cecum at the base of the tongue of the adult is a vestige of the point from which the diverticulum arose in the embryo. In man there does not seem to be a contribution to the thyroid gland from the fourth pharyngeal pouch.

At first the primordium is a hollow tube which grows caudally and thickens at its end. The connection between the tongue and the thyroid gland usually disappears in embryos of 4 to 7 mm., but it may persist either as a *thyroglossal duct* or as an eccentrically located irregular mass of thyroid tissue called the *pyramidal lobe.* The primordium then becomes a compact mass of epithelium, which later splits into ramifying plates and cords of epithelium about two cells thick.

The appearance of round or oval intercellular spaces 1 to 2 μ in diameter between pairs of adjoining cells is the first indication of follicle formation. This occurs at eight days of incubation in the chick (Hilfer; Fujita and Tanizawa); the time of its occurrence in the human embryo has not been definitely established. Microvilli project into these *primary follicles,* and there is often a single cilium on the epithelial cells. As a result of mitosis of the surrounding cells, coalescence of the lumens of neighboring primary follicles, and rearrangement of the cells, roughly spherical units are formed. These become separated as a consequence of the cellular rearrangement and the invasion of the epithelial cords by mesenchyme. Each of the *definitive follicles* formed in this way consists of a cavity lined by a single layer of epithelium. They are found in human

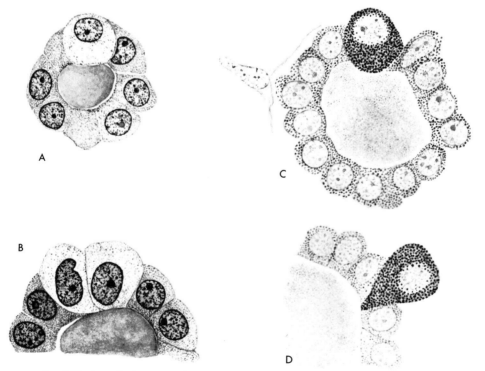

Figure 18-8. Parafollicular cells in thyroid follicles. *A* and *B,* Cat thyroid, Ehrlich's hematoxylin; *C* and *D,* Dog thyroid; 35 day old puppy. Cajal silver nitrate method. (After J. F. Nonidez, Am. J. Anat., *49:*479, 1932.)

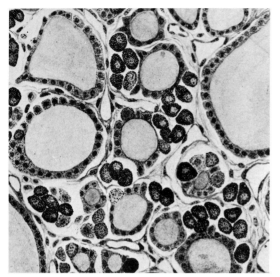

Figure 18-9. Drawing of an area occupied by small and medium-sized follicles in the thyroid of an adult dog. Numerous parafollicular cells are seen in clusters in the interfollicular spaces. Cajal stain. (After J. F. Nonidez, Anat. Rec., *53:*339, 1932.)

embryos of 24 mm. Colloid may be present before birth but does not become an important constituent of the follicles until after birth. In the pig, calf, and rat, thyroid activity appears at about the same time as the follicles begin to have stainable colloid. However, in amphibians the thyroid gland has some activity long before the cells appear "glandular" and before colloid is formed.

REFERENCES

Anast, C. S.: Thyrocalcitonin—A review. Clinical Orthopedics and Related Research, No. 47, p. 179, 1966.

Andros, G., and S. H. Wollman: Autoradiographic localization of iodine[125] in the thyroid epithelial cell. Proc. Soc. Exper. Biol. Med., *115:*775, 1964.

Baghdiantz, A., G. V. Foster, A. Edwards, M. A. Kumar, E. Slack, H. A. Soliman, and I. MacIntyre: Extraction and purification of calcitonin. Nature, *203:*1927, 1964.

Bargmann, W.: Schilddrüse. *In* von Möllendorff, W., and W. Bargmann, eds.: Handbuch der mikroskopischen Anatomie des Menschen, Berlin, Julius Springer, 1939, Vol. 6, part 2, p. 2.

Bogdanove, E. M.: Regulation of TSH secretion. Federation Proc., *21:*633, 1962.

Bussolati, G., and A. G. E. Pearse: Immunofluorescence localization of calcitonin in the C-cells of pig and dog's thyroid. J. Endocrinol., *37:*205, 1967.

Copp, D. H., E. C. Cameron, B. A. Cheney, A. G. F. Davidson, and K. G. Henze: Evidence for calcitonin—a new hormone from the parathyroid that lowers blood calcium. Endocrinol., *70:*637, 1962.

Dempsey, E. W., and R. R. Peterson: Electron microscopic observations on the thyroid glands of normal, hypophysectomized, cold-exposed and thiouracil-treated rats. Endocrinol., *56:*46, 1955.

Dempsey, E. W., and M. Singer: Observations on the chemical cytology of the thyroid gland at different functional stages. Endocrinol., *38:*270, 1946.

Ekholm, R.: Thyroid gland. *In* Kurtz, S. M., ed.: Electron Microscopic Anatomy. New York, Academic Press, 1964.

Falck, B., B. Larsen, C. v. Mecklenburg, C. Rosengren, and K. Svenaeus: On the presence of a second specific cell system in mammalian thyroid gland. Acta Physiol. Scandinav., *62:*491, 1964.

Foster, G. V., A. Baghdiantz, M. A. Kumar, E. Slack, H. A. Soliman, and I. MacIntyre: Thyroid origin of calcitonin. Nature, *202:* 1303, 1964.

Foster, G. V., I. MacIntyre, and A. G. E. Pearse: Calcitonin production and the mitochondrion-rich cells of the dog thyroid. Nature, *203:*1029, 1964.

Fujita, H., and Y. Tanizawa: Electron microscopic studies on the development of the thyroid gland of chick embryo. Zeitschr. f. Zellforsch., *125:*132, 1966.

Gersh, I., and R. F. Baker: Total protein and organic iodine in the colloid of individual follicles of the thyroid gland of the rat. J. Comp. Physiol., *21:*213, 1943.

Gittes, R. F., and G. L. Irvin: Thyroid and parathyroid roles in hypercalcemia: Evidence for a thyrocalcitonin releasing factor. Science, *148:*1737, 1965.

Grollman, A.: Essentials of Endocrinology. Philadelphia, J. B. Lippincott Co., 1947.

Gross, J., and R. Pitt-Rivers: 3:5:3'-Triiodothyronine. 1. Isolation from thyroid gland and synthesis. 2. Physiological activity. Biochem. J., *53:*645, 652, 1953.

Heimann, P.: Ultrastructure of the human thyroid. A study of normal thyroid, untreated and treated toxic goiter. Acta Endocrinol., *53*(Suppl. 110):5, 1966.

Hilfer, R. S.: Follicle formation in embryonic chick thyroid. I. Early morphogenesis. J. Morphol., *115:*135, 1964.

Hirsch, P. F., F. F. Gauthier, and P. L. Munson: Thyroid hypocalcemic principle and recurrent laryngeal nerve injury as factors affecting the response to parathyroidectomy in rats. Endocrinol., *73:*244, 1963.

Kumar, M. A., E. Slack, A. Edwards, H. A. Soliman, A. Baghdiantz, G. V. Foster, and I. MacIntyre: A biological assay for calcitonin. J. Endocrinol., *33:*469, 1965.

Hilfer, S. R.: Follicle formation in the embryonic chick thyroid. I. Early morphogenesis. J. Morphol., *115:*135, 1964.

Leblond, C. P., and J. Gross: Thyroglobulin formation in the thyroid follicle visualized by the "coated autograph" technique. Endocrinol., *43:*306, 1948.

MacIntyre, I., G. V. Foster, and M. A. Kumar: The thyroid origin of calcitonin. *In* Gaillard, P. J., R. V. Talmage, and A. M. Budy, eds.: The Parathyroid Glands: Ultrastructure, Secretion and Function. Chicago, University of Chicago Press, 1965.

Mayer, E.: Introduction to Dynamic Morphology. New York, Academic Press, 1963.

Nadler, N. J., S. K. Sarkar, and C. P. Leblond: Origin of intracellular colloid droplets in the rat thyroid. Endocrinol., *71:*120, 1962.

Nadler, N. J., B. A. Young, C. P. Leblond, and B. Mitmaker: Elaboration of thyroglobulin in the thyroid follicle. Endocrinol., *74:* 333, 1964.

Nonidez, J. F.: The origin of the parafollicular cell, a second epithelial component of the thyroid gland of the dog. Am. J. Anat., *49:*479, 1932.

Nonidez, J. F.: Further observations on the parafollicular cells of the mammalian thyroid. Anat. Rec., *53:*339, 1932.

Pearse, A. G. E.: The cytochemistry of the thyroid C cells and their relationship to calcitonin. Proc. Roy. Soc. B., *164:*478, 1966.

Pitt-Rivers, R.: Mode of action of antithyroid compounds. Physiol. Rev., *30:*194, 1950.

Pitt-Rivers, R., and W. R. Trotter, eds.: The Thyroid. London, Butterworths, 1964.

Turner, C. D.: General Endocrinology. 4th ed. Philadelphia, W. B. Saunders Co., 1966.

Welzel, B. K., S. S. Spicer, and S. H. Wollman: Changes in fine structure and acid phosphatase localization in rat thyroid cells following thyrotrophin administration. J. Cell Biol., *25:*593, 1965.

Wissig, S. L.: The anatomy of secretion in the follicular cells of the thyroid gland; the fine structure of the gland in the normal rat. J. Biophys. & Biochem. Cytol., *7:*419, 1960.

Wissig, S. L.: The anatomy of secretion in the follicular cells of the thyroid gland. II. The effect of acute thyrotrophic hormone stimulation on the secretory apparatus. J. Cell Biol., *16:*93, 1963.

[handwritten note: activity inhibits osteoclasts / responds to high Ca++ levels]

CHAPTER NINETEEN

Parathyroid Glands

The *parathyroid* glands are small, yellow-brown, oval bodies usually intimately connected with the posterior surface of the thyroid gland. In man there are usually four glands; accessory ones are common. Their total weight varies from 0.05 to 0.3 gm. They may range from 3 to 8 mm. in length, 2 to 5 mm. in width, and 0.5 to 2 mm. in thickness. Most of the glands are associated with the middle third of the thyroid, a smaller number with the inferior third. About 5 to 10 percent of the glands are associated with the thymus gland and may be deep in the anterior mediastinum. This association of the parathyroid glands with the thymus stems from their common origin from the same primordial structure in the embryo.

Most parathyroid glands lie in the capsule of the thyroid, but they may be embedded within the gland. In either case, the parathyroid glands are separated from the thyroid by a thin connective tissue capsule. The capsular connective tissue extends into the parathyroid gland, and it is via these trabeculae that the larger branches of blood vessels, nerves, and lymphatics enter. Between the gland cells is a framework of loose-meshed reticular fibers. These support the rich capillary network (Fig. 19-4) and the nerve fibers. The connective tissue stroma may contain numerous fat cells.

The parathyroid glands consist of densely packed groups of cells, which may form a compact mass or may be arranged as anastomosing cords, or less commonly as follicles with a small amount of colloidal material in the lumen. Two main types of epithelial cells have been described in man: *principal cells* and *oxyphilic cells* (Fig. 19-2).

THE PRINCIPAL CELLS (CHIEF CELLS).

The principal cells are polygonal and 7 to 10 μ in diameter, with a centrally placed vesicular nucleus and a pale, slightly acidophilic cytoplasm that tends to shrink during fixation. There is a small juxtanuclear Golgi apparatus and an average number of elongated mitochondria. Coarse granular deposits of fluorescent lipofuscin pigment are present, and when the cells are appropriately stained, a considerable amount of glycogen is found. In addition to these components, small granules have been described that stain with iron-hematoxylin and chrome alum-hematoxylin and exhibit argyrophilia with the Bodian stain. These have been interpreted by some investigators as secretory granules (Munger and Roth).

Electron microscopic studies reaffirm the presence of all of the components enumerated above and reveal, in addition, cisternal profiles of the granular endoplasmic reticulum, sometimes aggregated in conspicuous parallel arrays. The argyrophilic granules at this level of resolution have bizarre and irregular outlines, are limited by a membrane, and have a dense granular content. They appear to arise in the Golgi apparatus and tend to accumulate at the periphery of the cell. A single abortive cilium is often found projecting from the principal cell into the narrow intercellular space.

A second category of principal cells is distinguished at the electron microscope level. These have a smaller Golgi apparatus, few dense "secretory" granules, and large lakes of glycogen.

THE OXYPHILIC CELLS. The oxyphilic cells are greatly in the minority and occur singly or in small groups. They are distinctly larger than the principal cells. They have a small, darkly staining nucleus and a strongly acidophilic cytoplasm. When stained by the aniline-acid fuchsin method, they are found to have many more mitochondria than the principal cells. This is borne out in electron micrographs, which show a remarkable concentration of elongated mitochondria with numerous closely spaced cristae. In the interstices among the mitochondria are numerous glycogen particles, but these do not form large masses as they do in the less active form of the principal cell. The Golgi apparatus is inconspicuous and the endoplasmic reticulum sparse. The eosinophilic granulation described by light microscopists must be attributed to the abundant mitochondria, for granules resembling secretory granules are rarely encountered in electron micrographs.

Another type of cell, intermediate between the oxyphilic and principal cells, has been described. It has a fine granular cytoplasm, which stains faintly with acid dyes, and a nucleus that is smaller and stains darker than that of the principal cells. Also, "water-clear" cells and "dark oxyphilic" cells have been described, but it is not clear to what extent these latter types are to be attributed to vagaries of fixation.

The parathyroid glands show certain changes with increasing age: (1) an increase in the amount of connective tissue, including increased numbers of fat cells as well as mast cells; (2) the oxyphilic cells are said to appear at the age of 4½ to 7 years and to increase in number especially after puberty; (3) in the closely packed masses of gland cells, some cords and follicles appear in the 1 year old infant and they increase thereafter; colloid accumulation in the lumen of the follicles shows the same tendency.

When rats are given injections of a large dose of parathyroid extract, the cells of the parathyroid glands become smaller; the Golgi apparatus also becomes smaller and more compact. Both changes are suggestive of decreased functional activity. After two weeks the cells return to normal, both in size and in morphology of the Golgi apparatus, suggesting a resumption of normal secretory activity. During the hypertrophy of the parathyroid glands in rickets, the Golgi apparatus is described as undergoing changes that indicate great secretory activity in comparison with normal cells. It is not possible to extend these conclusions to the human gland, for it has yet to be clearly shown which cells in man are equivalent to those in laboratory animals.

HISTOPHYSIOLOGY. Parathyroid glands are essential for life. Their complete removal in most mammals is fatal. In their absence there is a precipitous lowering of the blood calcium, leading to violent contraction of skeletal muscle (tetany). The glands normally exercise their control over calcium metabolism by elaborating *parathyroid hormone*.

Although active extracts of bovine parathyroids have been available for some 40 years, there has recently been remarkable progress in

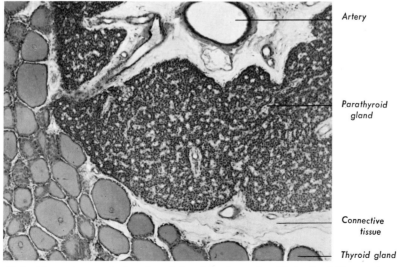

Artery

Parathyroid gland

Connective tissue

Thyroid gland

Figure 19-1. Photomicrograph of section of thyroid and parathyroid glands of *Macacus rhesus.* × 80.

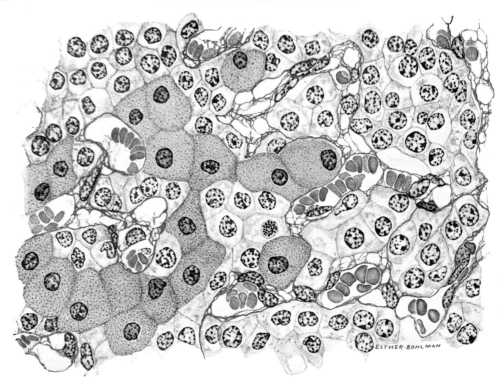

Figure 19-2. Section through human parathyroid gland showing the small principal cells, often vacuolated, and the large oxyphilic cells with fine purplish granules. Zenker-formol fixation. Mallory-azan stain. × 960.

purification of the active principle. Rasmussen and Craig isolated a homogeneous protein with an activity 200 times that of the earlier standard extract. The preparation behaves as a single substance in paper and column partition chromatography, ultracentrifugation, and countercurrent distribution, and appears to be the pure parathyroid hormone. It is a single unbranched polypeptide chain that contains no cystine and has a single N-terminal amino acid, alanine. Its molecular weight is about 9000.

The existence of a second hormone, called *calcitonin,* has been postulated by Copp and his coworkers. This is alleged to produce a transient lowering of the blood calcium level. This substance has now been found not to reside in the parathyroid but instead in the thyroid gland (Hirsch), and is now called *thyrocalcitonin.* Since all of the known functions of the gland have been reproduced by injection of the purified parathyroid hormone, there seems to be no evidence at present that the gland elaborates more than one hormone.

The principal function of the parathyroid glands is the regulation of the concentration of *calcium ions* in the fluids of the body. The glands respond to lowered plasma concentration of calcium by an increased output of the hormone, which acts upon the bone cells, mainly the osteoclasts, to bring about increased resorption of bone. This is another example of control of the function of an endocrine gland by a *negative feedback* mechanism—the change in the calcium ion concentration provides the stimulus regulating parathyroid activity.

Parathyroid hormone is also believed to influence the concentration of blood inorganic phosphate. Increased parathyroid activity reduces blood phosphate; decreased activity results in an increase. This effect is apparently attributable to inhibition of renal tubular reabsorption of phosphorus and increased loss of phosphate in the urine.

That the hormone acts directly upon bone can be shown by experiments in which parathyroids are grafted to sites where they are in direct contact with osseous tissue (Barnicot and Chang) (Fig. 19-3). Similar experiments can be carried out in organ cultures of parathyroids placed upon thin sheets of bone. In both of these examples the local high concentration

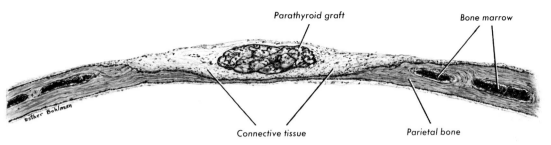

Esther Bohlman

Figure 19-3. Section of parietal bone of rat 14 days after autogenous transplantation of parathyroid gland. The bone beneath the graft has been nearly completely resorbed. × 50. From a preparation of H. Chang.

of parathyroid hormone causes an enhanced resorption of bone in the area adjacent to the gland (Gaillard, 1955).

Contrary to earlier suggestions, current evidence supports the view that in all of its peripheral effects, parathyroid hormone acts primarily upon cells. There is no evidence that it directly influences the solubility of bone mineral.

The parathyroid glands become large in rickets through an increase in the size and especially in the number of their cells. The hypertrophy is greater in low calcium than in low phosphate rickets. Hypertrophy is also observed in nephritis with uremia. It has been

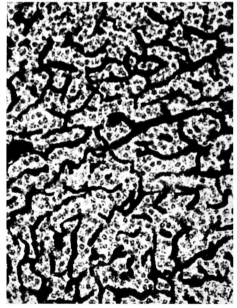

Figure 19-4. Photomicrograph of parathyroid gland of monkey injected intravenously with India ink to show the extensively anastomotic capillary network in intimate contact with the gland cells. × 165. (Courtesy of I. Gersh.)

shown to result from the experimental production of renal insufficiency and is associated with extensive bone changes (renal rickets, renal osteitis fibrosa) similar to those of primary hyperparathyroidism. It is probably a response to a lowered calcium ion concentration in the plasma resulting from phosphate retention. In birds deprived of sunlight, the parathyroid glands hypertrophy.

Tumor or hyperplasia of the parathyroids may lead to *hyperparathyroidism* associated with high plasma calcium, extensive bone resorption, and pathological calcification in soft tissues. Similar effects may be produced in susceptible animals by the administration of toxic doses of *parathyroid extract*.

Extirpation of the parathyroid glands or atrophy due to some pathological process is followed by *hypoparathyroidism,* characterized primarily by a decrease in the concentration of calcium in the plasma, and *tetany.* The symptoms may be alleviated by the administration of calcium, an extract of parathyroid glands, or calciferol, or by dietary control. *Latent tetany,* a condition that occurs in man, with low plasma calcium but without symptoms, may be produced experimentally in dogs.

REGENERATION. The parathyroids have insignificant powers of regeneration. The glands "take" readily in autotransplants and may be maintained successfully in tissue culture.

HISTOGENESIS. The parathyroid glands develop from thickenings of the third and fourth pharyngeal pouches on each side. The primordium on the third arch is close to the bud of the thymus. This proximity of origin of the two organs is a probable explanation of the frequent occurrence of aberrant parathyroid bodies in or near the thymus.

PHYLOGENESIS. Parathyroid glands are

absent from invertebrates and fishes and are found in all higher orders of vertebrates.

REFERENCES

Bargmann, W.: Die Epithelkörperchen. *In* von Möllendorff, W., and W. Bargmann, eds.: Handbuch der mikroskopischen Anatomie des Menschen. Berlin, Julius Springer, 1939, Vol. 6, part 2, p. 137.

Barnicot, N. A.: The local action of the parathyroid and other tissues on bone in intracerebral grafts. J. Anat., *82*:233, 1948.

Bensley, S. H.: The normal mode of secretion in the parathyroid gland of the dog. Anat. Rec., *98*:361, 1947.

Chang, H. Y.: Grafts of parathyroid and other tissues to bone. Anat. Rec., *111*:23, 1951.

Copp, D. H., E. C. Cameron, B. A. Cheney, A. G. F. Davidson, and K. G. Henze: Evidence for calcitonin—a new hormone from the parathyroid that lowers blood calcium. Endocrinol., *10*:638, 1962.

Davis, R., and A. C. Enders: Light and electron microscope studies on the parathyroid gland. *In* Greep, R. O., and R. V. Talmage, eds.: The Parathyroids. Springfield, Ill., Charles C Thomas, p. 76.

DeRobertis, E.: The cytology of the parathyroid gland of rats injected with parathyroid extract. Anat. Rec., *78*:473, 1940.

Gaillard, P. J.: Parathyroid gland tissue and bone *in vitro*. Exper. Cell Res., *3* (Suppl.):154, 1955.

Gaillard, P. J.: The influence of parathormone on the explanted radius of albino mouse embryos. J. Nederl. Akad. v. Wetensch., Amsterdam C, *63*:25, 1960.

Gaillard, P. J.: Parathyroid and bone in tissue culture. *In* Greep,
R. O., and R. V. Talmage, eds.: The Parathyroids. Springfield, Ill., Charles C Thomas, 1961, p. 20.

Grafflin, A. L.: Cytological evidence of secretory activity in the mammalian parathyroid. Endocrinol., *26*:857, 1940.

Greep, R. O.: Parathyroid glands. *In* The Parathyroids. Comparative Endocrinology. New York, Academic Press, 1963, Vol. I, p. 235.

Greep, R. O., and R. V. Talmage, eds.: The Parathyroids. Springfield, Ill., Charles C Thomas, 1961.

Lange, R.: Zur Histologie und Zytologie der Glandula parathyroidea des Menschen: Licht und elektronenmikroskopische Untersuchungen an Epithelkörperadenomen. Zeitschr. f. Zellforsch., *53*:765, 1961.

Munger, B. L., and S. I. Roth: The cytology of the normal parathyroid glands of man and Virginia deer: A light and electron microscopic study with morphologic evidence of secretory activity. J. Cell Biol., *16*:379, 1963.

Rasmussen, H.: Chemistry of parathyroid hormone. *In* Greep, R. O., and R. V. Talmage, eds.: The Parathyroids. Springfield, Ill., Charles C Thomas, 1961, p. 60.

Rasmussen, H., and L. C. Craig: Isolation and characterization of bovine parathyroid hormone. J. Biol. Chem., *236*:759, 1961.

Rosof, J. A.: An experimental study of the histology and cytology of the parathyroid glands in the albino rat. J. Exper. Zool., *68*:121, 1934.

Roth, S. I.: Pathology of the parathyroids in hyperparathyroidism with a discussion of recent advances in the anatomy and pathology of the parathyroid glands. Arch. Path., *73*:492, 1962.

Trier, J. S.: The fine structure of the parathyroid gland. J. Biophys. & Biochem. Cytol., *4*:13, 1958.

Turner, C. D.: General Endocrinology. 4th ed. Philadelphia, W. B. Saunders Co., 1966.

Weymouth, R. J., and B. L. Baker: The presence of argyrophilic granules in the parenchymal cells of the parathyroid glands. Anat. Rec., *119*:519, 1954.

CHAPTER TWENTY

Adrenal Glands and Paraganglia

The paired *adrenal* or *suprarenal* glands of man are roughly triangular, flattened organs embedded in the retroperitoneal adipose tissue at the cranial pole of each kidney. They measure approximately 5 by 3 by less than 1 cm. and together weigh about 15 gm. Both weight and size may vary considerably, depending upon the age and physiological condition of the individual. The cut surface of the transected gland presents a bright yellow *cortex* in its outer part, with a reddish brown inner zone adjacent to the thin, gray *medulla.*

The adrenal glands comprise two distinct endocrine organs that differ in their embryological origin, type of secretion, and function—the *interrenal tissue* and the *chromaffin tissue.* In mammals these are arranged as cortex and medulla respectively, but in other vertebrate classes they may be intermingled in a variety of patterns or may be entirely dissociated.

THE ADRENAL CORTEX

The cortex, which forms the bulk of the gland, has three distinguishable concentric zones—a thin, outer *zona glomerulosa* adjacent to the capsule; a thick middle layer, the *zona fasciculata;* and a moderately thick, inner *zona reticularis* contiguous with the medulla (Figs. 20-1 and 20-2). In man these comprise respectively 15 per cent, 78 per cent, and 7 per cent of the total cortical volume. The transition from one zone to another is gradual but may appear sharper in preparations injected to show the vascular pattern.

The zona glomerulosa consists of closely packed groups and arcades of columnar cells that are continuous with the cell columns of the zona fasciculata. The spherical nuclei stain deeply and contain one or two nucleoli. The cytoplasm is less abundant than in the cells of the other zones and is generally acidophilic but contains some basophilic material, which may be diffuse or disposed in clumps. Lipid droplets are small and relatively scarce in most species but may be numerous in others. Mitochondria are filamentous in the human but are usually spherical in rodents. The compact Golgi apparatus is juxtanuclear and in some animals may be polarized toward the nearest vascular channel.

At the electron microscopic level of resolution, the most characteristic feature of the cytoplasm is its well developed smooth surfaced endoplasmic reticulum, which forms an anastomosing network of tubules throughout the cell body. Profiles of granular endoplasmic reticulum are also present in limited numbers, and there are many polyribosomes free in the cytoplasmic matrix. There is nothing unusual in the organization of the Golgi complex or the centrioles that are associated with it. The mitochondria as a rule have lamellar cristae like those of most other organs. The plasma membrane is smoothly contoured over most of the cell body but may have a few folds or microvilli on the surface bordering on a perivascular space and at the junctions where several cells meet.

The zona fasciculata consists of polyhedral cells considerably larger than those of the glomerulosa and arranged in long cords disposed radially with respect to the medulla. The cords are usually one cell thick and separated by sinusoidal blood vessels. The nucleus is central, and binucleate cells are common. The cytoplasm is faintly basophilic or contains basophilic masses, particularly in the peripheral portion of the zone. The cells are crowded with lipid droplets in the fresh condition, but after treatment with the organic solvents used in preparation of routine histological sections, the cytoplasm is reduced to thin septa outlining clear vacuoles. In man, the zona glomerulosa may be absent in restricted areas of the cortex, and in such places the zona fasciculata is found immediately beneath the cortex, but this is not common. There may also be a thin transitional region between the zona glomerulosa and zona fasciculata which is relatively free of lipid droplets. Such a sudanophobic zona intermedia is particularly obvious in the rat adrenal.

When examined in electron micrographs, the nucleus is spherical and contains one or two nucleoli and small clumps of chromatin distributed around the periphery. The nuclear envelope has an obvious internal fibrous lamina. The smooth surfaced reticulum is even more elaborately developed than in the zona glomerulosa (Figs. 20-5 and 20-6). In man and other primates, parallel arrays of cisternae of the granular reticulum are also found, corresponding to the basophilic clumps seen with the light microscope (Fig. 20-4). These are less common in other species. The mitochondria appear to be less numerous and are more variable in size and shape than are those of the zona glomerulosa. Moreover, the cristae are usually vesicular invaginations of the inner membrane or vesicles free in the mitochondrial matrix. In some species they are long tortuous tubules. The Golgi apparatus is considerably larger in this zone. Lysosomes are found in the Golgi region of the cell and deposits of lipochrome pigment are often present, particularly in older individuals.

In the zona reticularis, the regular parallel arrangement of cell cords gives way to an anastomosing network. The transition from the fasciculata is gradual, the cells differing but little. The cytoplasm contains fewer lipid droplets. Toward the medulla there is a variable number of "light" and "dark" cells. The nuclei of the light cells are pale-staining; those of the dark cells are hyperchromatic and shrunken. The physiological significance of these differences in staining affinity is not known. In other organs this appearance is often a fixation artifact. It is so common in the zona reticularis, however, that some interpret these cells as degenerative. The cells of this zone, particularly the dark cells, contain large accumulations of lipofuscin pigment. Apart from the presence of light and dark cells and the greater amount of pigment, the cells of the zona reticularis resemble those of the fasciculata and, like them, have an abundance of agranular reticulum.

THE ADRENAL MEDULLA

The boundary between the zona reticularis and medulla is usually irregular in the human adult, with columns of cortical cells projecting some distance into the medulla. In other animals, the boundary may be quite sharp. The medulla is composed of irregular epithelioid cells arranged in rounded groups or short cords surrounded by blood capillaries and venules. When the tissue is fixed in a solution containing potassium bichromate, these cells are seen to be filled with fine brown granules. This is the *chromaffin reaction* and is thought to result from the oxidation and polymerization of the catecholamines *epinephrine* and *norepinephrine* contained within the granules of the cells. The medulla is colored green after treatment with ferric chloride—apparently for the same reason. There are other cells in the body that give a similar reaction, notably the argentaffin cells of the gastrointestinal tract and the mast cells, which are reactive because of their content of dopamine and 5-hydroxytryptamine. The chromaffin cells of the adrenal medulla, however, are derived from neuroectoderm, they secrete catecholamines, and they are innervated by preganglionic sympathetic fibers. Few other cells fulfill all three of these criteria.

In most species the application of a group of histochemical methods to the chromaffin cells permits the identification of two types of cells, one containing norepinephrine and the other epinephrine. The norepinephrine storing cells are autofluorescent, give argentaffin and iodate reactions, exhibit a low affinity for azocarmine, and give a negative acid phos-

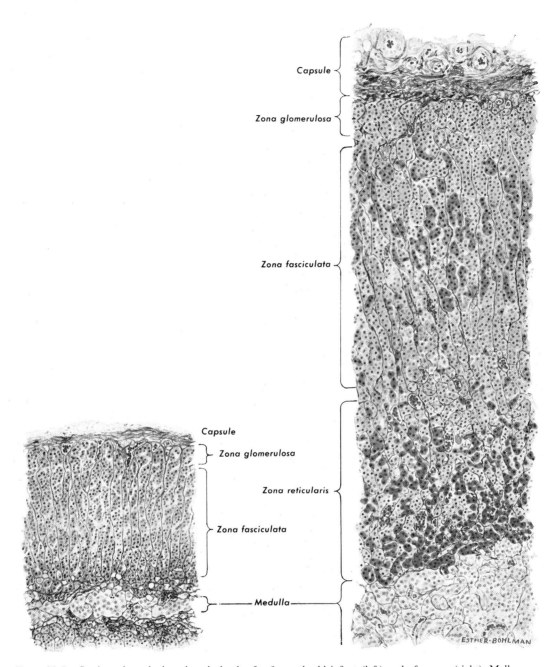

Figure 20-1.   Sections through the adrenal glands of a 6 month old infant (left) and of a man (right). Mallory-azan stain. × 110.

phatase reaction. The epinephrine storing cells have a high staining affinity for azocarmine and a positive acid phosphatase reaction, and are not fluorescent or reactive with iodate or silver.

In electron micrographs, the most prominent feature of these cells is the presence of large numbers of membrane bounded dense granules 50 to 350 mμ in diameter (Fig. 20-7). Two populations of cells are distinguishable on the basis of the character of their granules. Those that possess granules of very high electron density are believed to correspond to the norepinephrine storing cells, while the majority of the cells contain granules of lower density and are presumed to be the epinephrine storing cells. The mitochondria are not remarkable. The cisternae of the granular endoplasmic reticulum form small parallel arrays. The juxtanuclear Golgi apparatus frequently contains in its cisternae dense material interpreted as a precursor of the granules.

As in other endocrine glands, the mechanism of release of the hormone from the granules is not understood. Some workers contend that the granules are discharged into the extracellular space by a mechanism similar to the release of exocrine secretory products. Others insist that the chromaffin granules retain their integrity and that the catecholamine diffuses out or is actively transported from the granules and out of the cell.

In addition to the chromaffin cells, sympathetic ganglion cells occur singly or in small groups (Fig. 20-2).

BLOOD SUPPLY AND CONNECTIVE TISSUE OF THE ADRENAL

The adrenal is enclosed by a thick capsule of collagenous connective tissue that extends into the cortex to varying depths as trabeculae. Most of the rest of the supporting framework of the cortex consists of reticular fibers that lie between the capillaries and the cell cords and penetrate to some extent between the gland cells (Fig. 20-3). Reticular fibers also enclose the cell clusters in the medulla and support the capillaries, veins, and nerves. Collagenous fibers appear around the larger tributaries of the veins and merge with the capsular connective tissue.

The gland is richly supplied by a number of arteries that enter at various points around the periphery. Three principal groups are recognized. The *superior suprarenal arteries* arising from the inferior phrenic artery appear to be the major source, but in addition there are the *middle suprarenals* arising from the aorta and the *inferior suprarenals,* which are branches of the renal artery. Arteries from these several sources form a plexus in the capsule. The *cortical arteries* arise from this capsular plexus and distribute to the anastomosing network of sinusoids surrounding the cords of parenchymal cells in the cortex. The sinusoids of a given region converge in the zona reticularis upon a collecting vein at the corticomedullary junction. There is no venous system in the cortex.

Some major arterial branches from the capsule penetrate the connective tissue trabeculae and traverse the cortex, giving off few or no branches until they reach the medulla. In the medulla, they branch repeatedly to form the rich capillary net around the clumps and cords of chromaffin cells. The medulla thus has a dual blood supply—via the cortical sinusoids that anastomose with its capillary bed across the corticomedullary junction, and via the medullary arteries that course from the capsule directly to the medulla. The capillaries of the medulla empty into the same venous system that drains the cortex. The multiple venules ultimately join to form the large central veins of the medulla, which emerge from the gland as the *suprarenal vein.*

The cells lining the capillaries of the medulla are typical endothelium. The nature of the lining of the sinusoids in the cortex is still a subject of debate. These cells have been reported to take up colloidal vital dyes, such as lithium carmine and trypan blue, and on this basis they have been regarded as belonging to the reticuloendothelial system. More recent studies suggest that these substances simply adhere to the cell surface or that they are taken up by macrophages lying between the endothelium and the parenchymal cells. Electron microscopic observations have failed to reveal any evidence of phagocytosis by the endothelial cells of the sinusoids. Except in the regions occupied by the nucleus and cell center, the endothelium is extremely attenuated and interrupted at intervals by small circular pores or fenestrae closed only by a very thin diaphragm. There is a continuous basal lamina supported at intervals by small bundles of collagen fibrils corresponding to the reticulum of light microscopy.

LYMPHATICS AND NERVES

Lymphatics are limited to the capsule and its cortical trabeculae, and to the connective tissue around the large veins.

The rich nerve plexus in the capsule includes some sympathetic ganglion cells. Branches penetrate the cortex in the trabeculae and are distributed with few exceptions to the medulla. They end mainly in multiple terminations around individual cells of the medulla. The fibers are preganglionic.

HISTOPHYSIOLOGY OF THE ADRENAL CORTEX

The adrenal cortex is concerned with a wide variety of body functions, including maintenance of fluid and electrolyte balance, maintenance of carbohydrate balance, and maintenance of the normal function of certain cellular elements of the connective tissues. It is essential for life. Its removal or destruction in man leads to Addison's disease and ultimately to death unless the patient is given exogenous adrenal cortical hormones.

After ablation of the cortex there is excessive excretion of sodium in the urine, resulting in decreased plasma sodium concentration with corresponding decline of the plasma chloride and bicarbonate levels. The tissues are dehydrated and eventually concentration of the blood appears. Potassium, magnesium, urea, uric acid, and creatinine in the plasma are all lowered. Adrenalectomy also results in *hypoglycemia* (low blood sugar), with reduced glycogen stores in the liver and muscle. There appears to be a concomitant disturbance of protein and fat metabolism. Cortical deficiency also results in *hypotension* (low blood pressure), anorexia, diarrhea, vomiting, asthenia, lassitude, interference with normal sexual libido, and altered vascular "permeability." The functions disturbed by cortical deficiency are

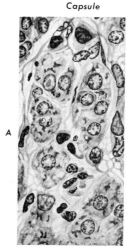

Capsule

Zona glomerulosa

A

Beginning of zona fasciculata

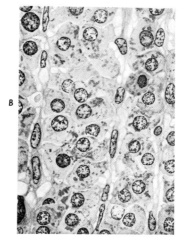

Zona fasciculata

B

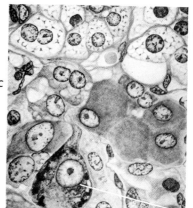

Zona reticularis

C

Chromaffin cells

Ganglion cell

Figure 20-2. Sections of the adrenal gland of a man. *A*, From the zona glomerulosa; *B*, from the zona fasciculata, showing columns of cells separated by collapsed sinusoids; *C*, showing the corticomedullary junction. The medullary portion contains a sympathetic ganglion cell with Nissl substance and several greenish brown stained chromaffin cells. The cells of the zona reticularis are highly vacuolated. Zenker-formol fixation. Hematoxylin-eosin-azure II. × 730. (Drawn by Miss Esther Bohlmann.)

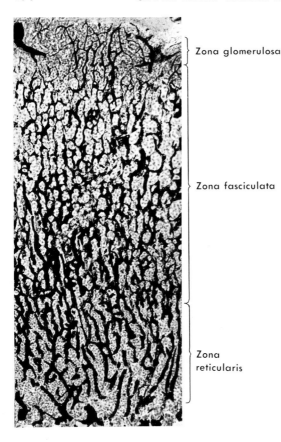

Zona glomerulosa

Zona fasciculata

Zona reticularis

Figure 20-3. Photomicrograph of adrenal cortex of monkey injected intravenously with India ink to show the vascular pattern. The arcuate sinusoids of the zona glomerulosa empty into the more longitudinally oriented sinusoids of the zona fasciculata. These are joined in the zona reticularis, where they flow into veins in the medulla. × 85. (Courtesy of I. Gersh.)

restored to normal by treatment with adrenal cortical extracts or the appropriate synthetic hormones.

The widely accepted zonal hypothesis of adrenal function holds that different functions can be ascribed to the morphologically recognizable zones. The zona glomerulosa secretes hormones concerned mainly with mineral metabolism, the *mineralocorticoids* (deoxycorticosterone and aldosterone), while the zona fasciculata and zona reticularis secrete the *glucocorticoids* (cortisone and cortisol), which participate in carbohydrate, protein, and fat metabolism. The concept of separate functions for the zona glomerulosa and the inner zones of the cortex is supported by much experimental evidence.

Hypophysectomy results in a marked atrophy of the zona fasciculata and zona reticularis but has little effect upon the zona glomerulosa. The atrophy of the inner zones can be prevented or reversed by injection of the adrenocorticotropic hormone (ACTH) of the anterior pituitary (Fig. 20-8). Conversely, administration of large doses of a glucocorticoid (cortisol) to an intact animal suppresses hypophyseal secretion of ACTH and permits the inner zones of the adrenal cortex to atrophy. Moreover, if increased demands are placed upon the homeostatic mechanisms for maintaining electrolyte balance, by giving an animal either a sodium deficient diet or one containing an excess of potassium, a selective hypertrophy of the zona glomerulosa results. Conversely, injection of large doses of the mineralocorticoids, deoxycorticosterone or aldosterone, results in atrophy of this zone.

Under normal conditions estrogens and androgens appear to be produced in very small amounts throughout the two inner zones of the cortex. In the pathological condition known as *adrenogenital syndrome*, which is characterized by high levels of circulating androgens, there is evidence that the zona reticularis is hypertrophied and may be responsible for the excessive secretion of androgenic steroids.

The metabolic effects of administration of glucocorticoids are numerous. Cortisol accelerates gluconeogenesis and the deposition of glycogen in the liver while at the same time suppressing peripheral utilization of glucose. It also results in release of fatty acids from adipose tissue. It causes destruction of lymphocytes, atrophy of lymphoid tissue, and suppression of the immune response. The decrease in circulating eosinophils caused by cortisol is used as a test for the capacity of the adrenal to respond to ACTH.

The mineralocorticoids are less diverse in their effects. Aldosterone promotes the resorption of sodium ions in the distal convoluted tubules of the nephron and causes a lowering of the sodium concentration in sweat, saliva, and intestinal secretions. The mechanisms by which it exerts these effects are still under study.

There appears to be some relation between the adrenal cortex and the sex glands. Adrenalectomy is followed by loss of libido in male rats, and abnormal estrus cycles or diestrus in females. Certain natural and synthetic estrogens exert adrenal steroid effects on metabolism. Removal of the adrenal interrupts

lactation. Whether these effects are mediated through the anterior lobe of the hypophysis, or to what extent, is not known.

Certain interrelations of the adrenal and thyroid glands are also indicated by several contradictory reports. In rabbits the adrenal glands hypertrophy, sometimes to two or three times the normal size, after removal of the thyroid. Sublethal adrenal injury results in hyperthermia and increased basal metabolic rate. The administration of thyroid powder may be followed by adrenal cortical hypertrophy.

CONTROL OF ADRENOCORTICAL FUNCTION. The cortex appears to respond by hyperfunction to a wide variety of stresses. The neural control of adrenal cortical function is believed to be mediated by a polypeptide produced in certain neurons of the hypothalamus and called *corticotropin releasing factor* (CRF). The precise location of the cells involved has not been determined, but they are thought to reside in the tuberal and median eminence of the hypothalamus between the rostral aspect

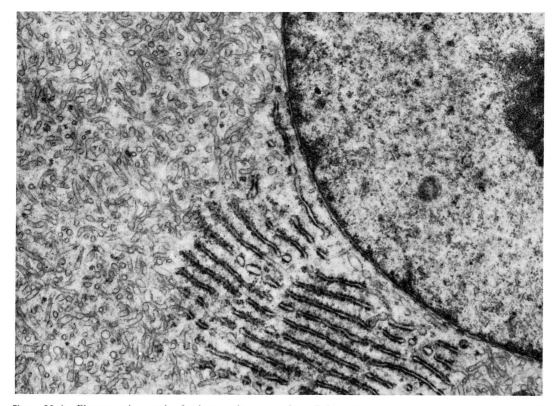

Figure 20-4. Electron micrograph of a juxtanuclear area of a cell from the adrenal cortex of a human fetus of 30 weeks. An array of parallel cisternae of granular endoplasmic reticulum is seen near the nucleus; the remainder of the field is occupied by tubular elements of an extensive agranular reticulum. ×20,000 (Courtesy of E. Yamada.)

of the infundibulum and the mammillary bodies. The rate of synthesis and release of CRF is modulated by nervous influences from other parts of the brain. Exposure to cold, for example, or severe anxiety ("stress") will result in increased secretion of CRF. The axons of the neurosecretory cells evidently release this substance into the hypothalamo-hypophyseal portal system. The cell type in the anterior pituitary that responds to blood borne CRF by secretion of adrenocorticotropic hormone (ACTH) is still not established with certainty, but in man, immunohistochemical and other evidence tends to implicate the basophils of the hypophysis as the *corticotropic cells.*

Adrenocorticotropic hormone is a polypeptide. Its amino acid sequence has been determined for several species including man. It stimulates the protein synthesis involved in growth of the adrenal cortex and stimulates the biosynthesis of steroids in the zona fasciculata and zona reticularis. The mechanism of action of ACTH is still controversial.

HISTOPHYSIOLOGY OF THE ADRENAL MEDULLA

The adrenal medulla is not essential for life. Animals that have had their adrenal medullas removed can survive under ordinary circumstances but are unable to respond normally to emergency situations. The hormones of the medulla, *epinephrine* and *norepinephrine,* are catecholamines and, unlike the steroid hormones of the cortex, they accumulate in high concentration in the cells. The granules appear to be the site of storage of catecholamines, for they can be released by exposure to hypotonic solutions. The two hormones are produced in different proportions depending upon the species. Aggressive and predatory animals tend to secrete large amounts of norepinephrine, whereas the more timid and placid species produce relatively little. Surprisingly the human adrenal secretes about ten times more epinephrine than norepinephrine.

Although the two hormones are very

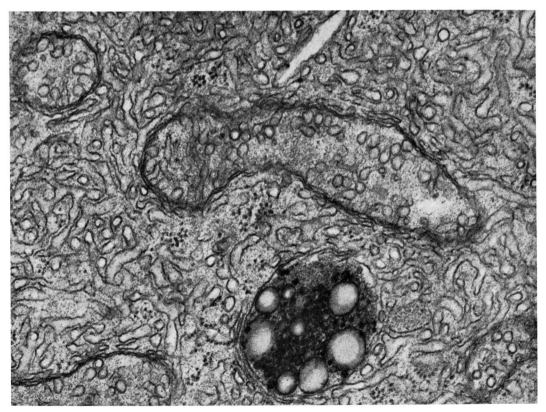

Figure 20-5. Electron micrograph of an area from an adult human adrenal cortical cell. A few free ribosomes are scattered among the tubular profiles of the smooth surfaced reticulum. Lipochrome pigment deposits like that in the lower part of the figure are very common in these cells. × 50,000. (Courtesy of J. Long.)

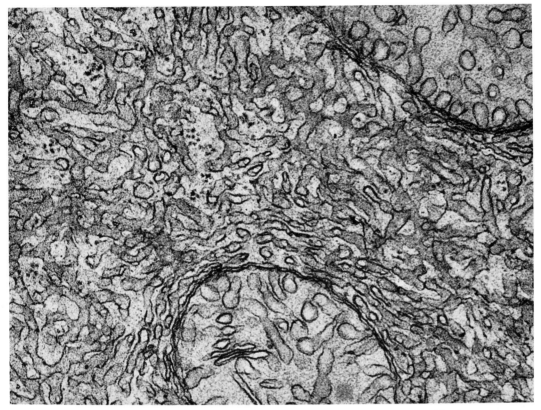

Figure 20-6. In an electron micrograph of an opossum adrenal cortical cell at higher magnification one can see a branching and anastomosing pattern of tubular elements of the elaborate agranular reticulum, which is characteristic of steroid secreting endocrine glands. Equally characteristic in these cells are the irregular tubular and vesicular cristae in the mitochondria, which appear here at the lower edge and at the upper right of the figure. × 66,000. (Courtesy of J. Long.)

closely related chemically, there are important qualitative and quantitative differences in their physiological effects. Epinephrine increases the heart rate and cardiac output without significantly increasing the blood pressure, and may increase the blood flow through some organs by as much as 100 per cent. It is effective on the cardiovascular system in very low concentrations. The denervated mammalian heart, for example, is accelerated by as little as 1 part epinephrine in 1.4 billion parts of fluid medium. Epinephrine also has a marked effect upon metabolism. It increases oxygen consumption and basal metabolic rate. It elevates the blood sugar level by mobilizing the carbohydrate stores of the liver, by promoting the conversion of muscle glycogen into lactic acid from which new carbohydrate can be made in the liver, and by causing the release of ACTH from the hypophysis, which, in turn, affects gluconeogenesis by stimulating secre-

tion of glucocorticoids from the adrenal cortex. The mobilization of glucose from the liver by epinephrine appears to result from its activation of the enzyme phosphorylase, which accelerates the first step in the breakdown of glycogen to glucose.

Norepinephrine has relatively little effect upon metabolism but causes a marked elevation of the blood pressure with very little effect upon heart rate or cardiac output. The effect of norepinephrine on the blood pressure is not due to an action upon the heart beat but is primarily a consequence of the vasoconstriction it brings about in the peripheral portion of the arterial system. Both epinephrine and norepinephrine cause lipolysis and release of unesterified fatty acid from adipose tissue isolated in vitro.

Norepinephrine is not confined to the adrenal medulla but is present in the brain and in most of the innervated peripheral tissues, where it is localized mainly in the sympathetic nerve endings. It has been established as the principal transmitter substance of adrenergic neurons. Thus it is a *neurohumor*. Neurohumors such as norepinephrine, acetylcholine, and serotonin are released by nerve cells, usually at their endings, and affect other neurons or muscles or glands. In general they act transiently and at very short range, being destroyed enzymatically before they reach effective concentrations in the circulation. The norepinephrine released into the bloodstream by the adrenal medulla is somewhat exceptional among neurohumors in that it does reach effective levels in the blood and acts at a distance. On the other hand, the *neurosecretory substances,* such as the oxytocin and vasopressin of the posterior lobe of the hypophysis, are long acting products of nerve cells that act at long range.

Although the adrenal medullary hormones are not essential for life, it appears that in times of stress they do help to maintain homeostasis and to prepare the organism to meet emergency situations. Epinephrine accomplishes this by elevating blood glucose, increasing cardiac output, and redistributing blood within the circulation to ensure continuing rapid flow to those organs vital for survival. Norepinephrine is less important in these emergency adjustments but, as the mediator of adrenergic nerve impulses throughout the body, it acts continuously on the blood vessels of the normal animal to maintain blood pressure.

Hyperfunction of the adrenal medulla in man occurs with certain rare tumors of the medulla or of extramedullary chromaffin tissues. In such cases there may be attacks of sweating, mydriasis, hypertension, and hyperglycemia, terminating suddenly in death. The paroxysmal hypertension (acute high blood pressure) of adrenal medullary tumors is decreased or abolished by intravenous administration of a series of compounds that have an epinephrine inhibiting action.

CONTROL OF ADRENAL MEDULLARY FUNCTION. The cells of the adrenal medulla are

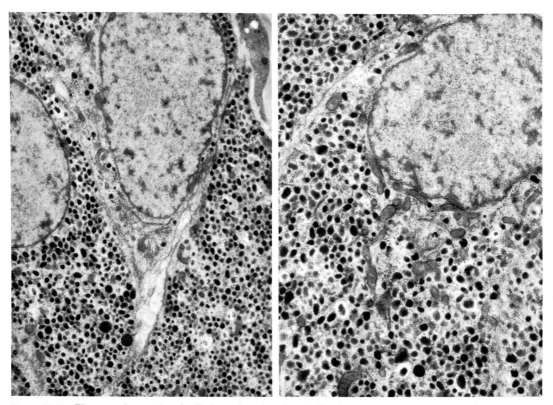

Figure 20-7. Electron micrographs of cells from the adrenal medulla of the cat, showing the abundant, membrane-limited, dense granules which are the sites of storage of catecholamines. × 9600 and × 13,600. (Courtesy of R. Yates.)

regarded as modified postganglionic neurons, and their secretory activity seems to be largely, if not entirely, under nervous control. Hormones of the medulla are increased in the blood of the adrenal veins after stimulation of the splanchnic nerves, and secretion is prevented by sectioning these nerves. Certain centers in the posterior hypothalamus are known to relay impulses to the adrenal medulla by way of the splanchnic nerves. In the intact animal, certain kinds of emotional stimuli are especially effective in releasing norepinephrine, and other kinds of stimuli, such as pain or hypoglycemia, promote the release of epinephrine. For this reason, it is believed that the cells producing epinephrine and those producing norepinephrine receive different innervation and secrete their hormones independently.

HISTOGENESIS OF THE ADRENAL GLANDS

The cortex develops from the coelomic mesoderm on the medial side of the urogenital ridge. Mesothelial cells near the cranial pole of the mesonephros in 8 to 10 mm. human fetuses proliferate and penetrate the subjacent, highly vascular mesenchyme. These cells ultimately form the *fetal cortex*. A second proliferation of the coelomic mesothelium taking place in 14 mm. fetuses later forms the definitive or *permanent cortex*. The adrenal gland in the fetus is relatively large, with the fetal zone comprising about 80 per cent of the cortex. The cells of this zone are large and stain intensely with eosin. After birth the fetal cortex undergoes a rapid degeneration and the permanent cortex enlarges. Associated with these changes is a 50 per cent decline in the absolute weight of the adrenal during the first few postnatal weeks.

The adrenal in the fetus is functional and under the control of ACTH secreted by the hypophysis. Anencephalic fetuses, which lack a normal hypophysis, have very small adrenal glands with no *fetal zone*. The physiological role of this zone during intrauterine life is not well understood. Progress in this area is hampered by the fact that none of the common laboratory animals has a comparable fetal zone. In the mouse, the so-called *X zone* differentiates postnatally and regresses at puberty in the male or at the time of the first pregnancy in the female. The hormonal factors controlling it appear to be different than those affecting the human fetal zone.

The medulla arises from the ectodermal neural crest tissue, which also gives rise to sympathetic ganglion cells. Strands of these sympathochromaffin cells migrate ventrally and penetrate the anlagen of the adrenal cortex on their medial side to take up a central position in the organ rudiment.

CELL RENEWAL AND REGENERATION IN THE ADRENAL CORTEX. There have long been divergent views as to the mode of growth and repair of the adrenal cortex. It was formerly believed that the cells arose either from fibroblast-like cells in the capsule or by division of the cells in the zona glomerulosa and that they gradually moved through the zona fasciculata and degenerated in the zona reticularis. The dark cells of this zone were interpreted as cells undergoing regressive changes. During their migration the cells were believed to go through one cycle of secretion.

The bulk of the evidence now seems to favor the view that, once formed, the cells of the glomerulosa and fasciculata do not move appreciably and that replacement and repair take place as a result of local mitotic activity. After injection of colchicine to arrest cell division at metaphase, mitotic figures are not confined to any one region but are found throughout the cortex, the majority being in the zona fasciculata. Autoradiographic studies after administration of tritiated thymidine have produced equivocal results but, on the whole, they provide little evidence of extensive cell migration.

In experimental animals the adrenal cortex has a considerable capacity for regeneration. If the gland is incised and all of the tissue in its interior removed, leaving behind only the capsule and a few adherent granulosal cells, the whole cortex will be regenerated. The medulla is not restored. Studies of the steroids elaborated during regeneration of the cortex show that an adequate level of secretion of mineralocorticoids is established early, although the secretion of glucocorticoids does not occur until one to two weeks later. Thus in the regenerating gland, cells functionally similar to those of the normal zona fasciculata and reticularis differentiate from cells of the zona glomerulosa.

PHYLOGENY OF THE ADRENAL GLAND. Chromaffin tissue which yields epinephrine-like activity is present in the central nervous system of leeches; it is present also in the mantles of certain molluscs. In cyclostomes and teleosts the *interrenal bodies* (which are homolo-

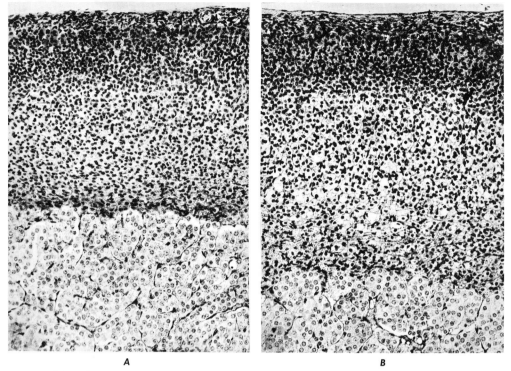

Figure 20-8. Photomicrographs of adrenal gland of rats, showing effects of injection of adrenocorticotropic hormone. *A,* Atrophic cortex of young hypophysectomized rat; *B,* hypophysectomized rat which had an injection for four days of purified adrenocorticotropic hormone. The hypertrophy of the zona fasciculata is most marked. Zenker-formol, hematoxylin and eosin. × 165. (Courtesy of I. Gersh.)

gous with the cortex) are separate from the discrete chromaffin bodies. In amphibians the two components are in juxtaposition, or they may be intermingled; in reptiles and birds they are commonly intermingled. The well known cortex and medulla relationship appears in mammals, in which this is the predominant form of organization.

THE PARAGANGLIA (CHROMAFFIN SYSTEM)

Under this term are grouped several widely scattered accumulations of cells that seem to have much in common with the medullary cells of the adrenal glands. These paraganglia include widespread, small accumulations of cells in the retroperitoneum—the organs of Zuckerkandl—and collections of similar cells in the kidney, ovary, liver, testis, and heart. The paraganglia all contain chromaffin cells, which are clear in the fresh condition or after preparation with most fixatives but stain positively with chromic and osmic acids and contain iron. They are usually ar-

ranged more or less as cords and have a rich blood supply.

It has not been proved that these paraganglia have an endocrine function. The assumption that they elaborate epinephrine, just like the chromaffin cells of the medulla of the adrenal, has not been established. Some authors include the medullary cells of the adrenal in this group and speak of them all as the chromaffin system. The advisability of this must be questioned until it has been shown that all the chromaffin organs have the same internal secretion.

REFERENCES

Bachman, R.: Die Nebenniere. *In* von Möllendorff, W., and W. Bargmann, eds.: Handbuch der mikroskopischen Anatomie des Menschen. Berlin, Springer Verlag, 1954, Vol. 6, part 5, p. 1.

Baulieu, E. E., and P. Robel, eds.: Aldosterone. Philadelphia, F. A. Davis Co., 1964.

Bennett, H. S.: Cytological manifestations of secretion in the adrenal medulla of the cat. Am. J. Anat., *69:*333, 1941.

Bush, I. E.: Chemical and biological factors in the activity of adrenocortical steroids. Pharmacol. Revs., *14:*317, 1962.

Coupland, R. E.: The Natural History of the Chromaffin Cell. London, Longmans, Green & Co., 1965

Currie, A. R., T. Symington, and J. K. Grant, eds.: The Human Adrenal Cortex. Baltimore, Williams & Wilkins Co., 1962.

Deane, H. W., ed.: The adrenocortical hormones: Their origin, chemistry, physiology and pharmacology. *In* Eichler, O., and A. Farah, eds.: Handbuch der Experimentellen Pharmakologie. Berlin, Springer Verlag, 1962, Vol. 14, part 1.

Ganong, W. F.: The central nervous system and the synthesis and release of adrenocorticotrophic hormone. *In* Nalbandov, A. V., ed.: Advances in Neuroendocrinology. Urbana, University of Illinois Press, 1963, p. 92.

Gorbman, A., and H. A. Bern: A Textbook of Comparative Endocrinology. New York, John Wiley & Sons, 1962.

Greep, R. O., and H. W. Deane: The cytology and cytochemistry of the adrenal cortex. Ann. N. Y. Acad. Sci., *50:*569, 1948.

Hartman, F. A., and K. A. Brownell: The Adrenal Gland. Philadelphia, Lea & Febiger, 1949.

Hartroft, P. M., and W. S. Hartroft: Studies on renal juxtaglomerular cells; correlation of the degree of granulation of juxtaglomerular cells with width of the zona glomerulosa of the adrenal cortex. J. Exper. Med., *102:*205, 1955.

Hechter, O., and I. D. K. Halkerston: On the action of mammalian hormones. *In* Pincus, G., K. V. Thimann, and E. B. Astwood, eds.: The Hormones: Physiology, Chemistry and Applications. New York, Academic Press, 1964, Vol. 5, p. 697.

Hechter, O., and G. Pincus: Genesis of the adrenocortical secretion. Physiol. Rev., *34:*459, 1954.

Hillarp, N. A., and B. Hökfelt: Cytological demonstration of noradrenaline in the suprarenal medulla under conditions of varied secretory activity. Endocrinol., *55:*255, 1954.

Hillarp, N. A., S. Lagerstedt, and B. Nilson: The isolation of a granular fraction from the suprarenal medulla, containing the sympathomimetic catechol amines. Acta Physiol. Scandinav., *29:*251, 1953.

Hoerr, N.: The cells of the suprarenal cortex in the guinea pig; their reaction to injury and their replacement. Am. J. Anat., *48:*139, 1931.

Ingle, D.: Current status of adrenocortical research. Am. Scientist, *47:*413, 1959.

Jones, I. C.: The Adrenal Cortex. London, Cambridge University Press, 1957.

Knigge, K. M.: The effect of acute starvation on the adrenal cortex of the hamster. Anat. Rec., *120:*555, 1954.

Lanman, J. T.: The fetal zone of the adrenal gland. Medicine, *32:*389, 1963.

Moon, H. D., ed.: The Adrenal Cortex. New York, Paul B. Hoeber, Inc., 1961.

Prunty, F. T. G., ed.: The Adrenal Cortex. Brit. Med. Bull., *18:*89, 1962.

Prunty, F. T. G.: Chemistry and Treatment of Adrenocortical Diseases. Springfield, Illinois, Charles C Thomas, 1964.

Selye, H.: Textbook of Endocrinology. 2nd ed. Montreal, Acta Endocrinologica, Inc., 1949.

Turner, C. D.: General Endocrinology. 4th ed. Philadelphia, W. B. Saunders Co., 1966.

Wolman, M.: Histochemistry of Lipids in Pathology. *In* Graumann, W., and K. Neumann, eds.: Handbuch der Histochemie. Stuttgart, Gustav Fischer Verlag, 1964, Vol. 5, part 2.

Yates, R. D.: A light and electron microscopic study correlating the chromaffin reaction and granule ultrastructure in the adrenal medulla of the Syrian hamster. Anat. Rec., *149:*237, 1964.

Yates, R. D., J. G. Wood, and D. Duncan: Phase and electron microscopic observations on two cell types in the adrenal medulla of the Syrian hamster. Tex. Rep. Biol. Med., *20:*494, 1962.

CHAPTER TWENTY-ONE

Pineal Body

The pineal body (conarium, epiphysis cerebri) of the human brain is a somewhat flattened, conical, gray body measuring 5 to 8 mm. in length, and 3 to 5 mm. in its greatest width. It lies above the diencephalic roof at the posterior extremity of the third ventricle. A small ependyma-lined recess of the third ventricle extends into a short stalk, which joins the pineal body to the diencephalic roof. The organ is invested by pia mater, from which connective tissue septa containing many blood vessels penetrate into the pineal tissue and surround its cords and follicles of epithelioid cells.

In sections stained with hematoxylin and eosin, the pineal body is seen to consist of cords of epithelioid cells with pale-staining cytoplasm and large nuclei that are often irregularly infolded or lobulated and have prominent nucleoli. These cells, making up the bulk of the organ, are the *pinealocytes* or *chief cells*. When appropriately stained, the cytoplasm is moderately basophilic. As described by del Rio-Hortega, who used silver impregnation methods, human pinealocytes are specific cells with long tortuous processes. These radiate from the follicles and cords toward the vascular connective tissue, where they end in bulbous swellings (Fig. 21-6). Such processes are seldom seen in routine preparations and are difficult to demonstrate by electron microscopy.

In electron micrographs the cytoplasm contains numerous free ribosomes and occasional short profiles of granular endoplasmic reticulum. Far more abundant are tubular and vesicular elements of an atypical agranular endoplasmic reticulum (Fig. 21-7). The Golgi apparatus is not particularly well developed or consistent in its location. Coated or alveolate vesicles are commonly associated with the Golgi, and some of these may have a dense content. Mitochondria are moderately abundant and not unusual in their structure. Centrioles are present, and the cells occasionally have a single flagellum. A distinctive feature of the cytoplasm is the presence of large numbers of microtubules. In the processes these may be aggregated in parallel bundles, but in the cell body they exhibit no consistent orientation. Lipid droplets, lipochrome pigment deposits, and structures resembling lysosomes are also present.

In addition there are *interstitial cells* between the clusters of pinealocytes and in the perivascular areas. Their nuclei are elongated and stain more deeply than those of the parenchymal cells. The cytoplasm is somewhat more basophilic and drawn out into long processes. In electron micrographs the granular endoplasmic reticulum is well represented, and free ribosomes are numerous. In addition, occasional deposits of glycogen are found. Rare microtubules are present, but they are overshadowed by a profusion of cytoplasmic filaments 50 to 60 Å in diameter and of indeterminate length. They may occur in large bundles or as single randomly oriented filaments.

Some workers consider the interstitial cells to be glial elements. The abundance of filaments in their cytoplasm is indeed reminiscent of the fine structure of astrocytes, but their identification as such has not yet gained general acceptance. The presence in rat pineal of stellate cells that stain strongly with the acid

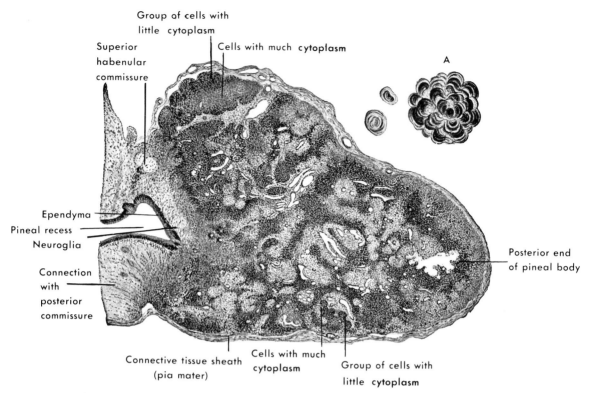

Figure 21-1. Median section through pineal body of a newborn child. Blood vessels empty. × 32. *A,* Acervulus (sand granule) from the pineal body of a 69 year old woman. × 160. (After Schaffer.)

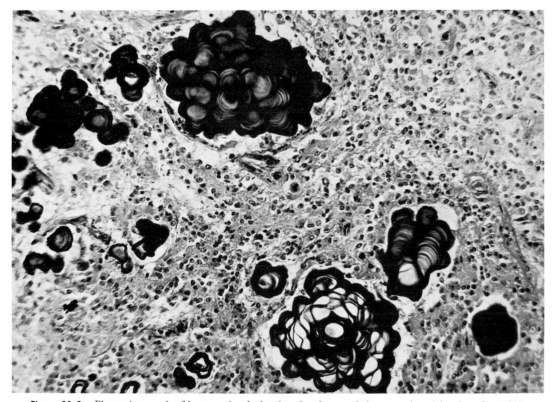

Figure 21-2. Photomicrograph of human pineal, showing the characteristic concretions (pineal sand). × 200.

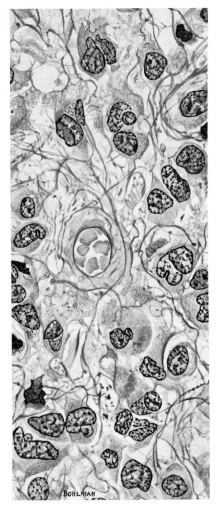

Figure 21-3. Section of pineal body of man stained with hematoxylin and eosin, showing irregularly shaped cells and their processes. Note the blood vessel in the center. Compare with Figure 21-6.

hematin method has been reported by Quay, but whether these represent a cell type distinct from interstitial cells is not yet clear.

The human pineal body often contains concretions called *corpora arenacea* or brain sand (Fig. 21-2). They are extracellular and are composed of a mineralized organic matrix that often has a concentric organization. The concretions consist mainly of calcium phosphates and carbonates. They increase in number with age, but their exact manner of formation and their significance are not known.

HISTOGENESIS. The pineal body first appears at about 36 days of gestation as a prominent thickening of the ependyma in the posterior part of the roof of the diencephalon. Cells migrate from this ependymal thickening to form a segregated mantle layer, whose cells tend to assume a follicular arrangement that is gradually transformed into the cordlike arrangement seen in later stages of development. By the end of the sixth month interstitial (neuroglial) and pineal parenchymal cells have differentiated.

It is generally believed that the pineal body increases in size until about 7 years of age. Involution is said to begin at this time and to continue to 14 years of age. It is manifested by the development of hyaline changes in both the septa and the lobules, and by increasing numbers of corpora arenacea.

INNERVATION. Nerves are found throughout the organ in silver impregnated specimens. As the nerve fibers penetrate into the organ their myelin sheaths terminate and the bare axons continue among the pinealocytes. Some of these contain many small vesicles in the size range of synaptic vesicles, suggesting that the nerves have functional endings in close relation to the parenchymal cells. The innervation appears to be exclusively via autonomic fibers originating in the superior cervical sympathetic ganglion.

PINEAL SYSTEM OF LOWER VERTEBRATES. In contrast to the single, relatively solid mass of tissue comprising the pineal body in adult mammals, the organs in most lower vertebrates remain saccular throughout life and are somewhat more complex. The pineal system may consist of a single pineal sac (the intracranial epiphysis), as in most fishes and tailed amphibians, or it may be double. In the latter case (primitive fishes, tailless amphibians, and lizards) a second, *parapineal* organ results either from elaboration of an anterior end vesicle of the epiphysis, or as a separate evagination from the diencephalic roof situated more anteriorly. In frogs, the parapineal component (the frontal organ) comes to lie subepidermally and is discernible externally on the median dorsal aspect of the head. It is connected with the intracranial epiphysis by a long pineal nerve. While many nerve fibers and their endings are readily demonstrable in pineal systems of lower vertebrates, no evidence exists suggesting that any are sympathetic.

Electron microscopic examination of adult saccular pineal systems reveals that, in most lower vertebrates, the principal cell type is an apparent photoreceptor. This cell closely

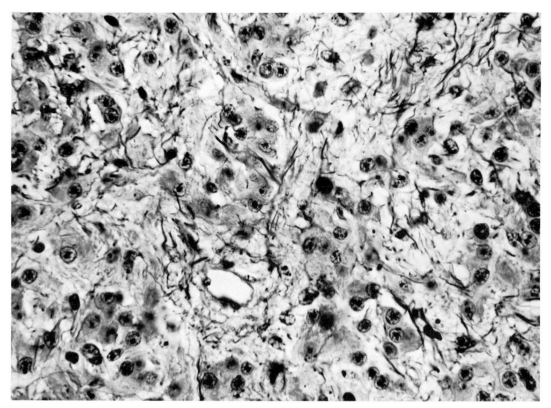

Figure 21-4. Photomicrograph of bovine pineal. The pinealocytes have large nuclei with prominent nucleoli. The outlines of the stellate cells are not easily distinguished. Many densely stained processes are visible in this preparation, but it is not possible to determine which belong to pinealocytes and which to interstitial cells. Iron hematoxylin stain. × 500. (Courtesy of E. Anderson.)

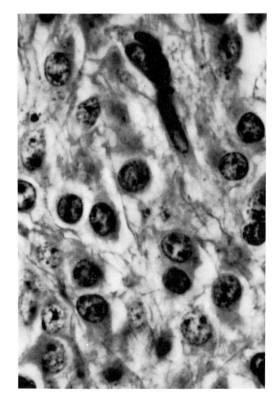

Figure 21-5. Histological section of sheep pineal. The pinealocyte nuclei are round or oval. The elongated nuclei in the upper part of the figure belong to interstitial glial cells. Heidenhain's iron-hematoxylin. × 700. (Courtesy of E. Anderson.)

resembles a retinal rod or cone, both in the form of the membranous lamellated modified flagellum that protrudes from the cell apex into the pineal lumen and in the presence of characteristic receptor synapses at the cell base. Physiological data indicate that, in these species, impulses course along pineal tracts to surrounding brain regions in response to darkness or to light of various wavelengths. The most elaborate pineal photoreceptor system seems to appear in certain lizards, such as the Tuatara *(Sphenodon)*, in which, in addition to a photoreceptor-type intracranial epiphysis,

Figure 21-6. Specifically impregnated section of the pineal body of a young boy, showing interlobular tissue (*C*) and vessel (*D*) with club-shaped processes of specific cells in its adventitia. Note parenchymatous cells and their claviform processes bordering on *C*. (After del Rio-Hortega.)

the parapineal component (or parietal "eye") is specialized to the extent of possessing a distinct lens and a retina composed of photoreceptor cells backed by supportive cells containing pigment. Photoreceptor cells have not been distinguished in mammalian pineal systems.

HISTOPHYSIOLOGY. Opinions regarding the function of the mammalian pineal body have been widely divergent, some considering it a functionless vestigial organ and others regarding it as an endocrine gland. Advances in recent years have brought a greater measure of agreement. Few would now insist that the pineal system of mammals and lower vertebrates is merely vestigial, but the physiological significance of its secretion and photoreception remains obscure.

The pineal has long been suspected of exerting an antigonadotropic effect. The principal basis for this was the clinical observation that boys with tumors that destroyed pineal parenchyma exhibited precocious puberty. Animal experimentation has, on the whole, substantiated this belief. Pinealectomy in young rats leads to enlargement of the reproductive organs and early onset of puberty. Injection of pineal extracts delays puberty and reduces ovarian weight. Other lines of evidence, none conclusive, have suggested relations to pituitary, adrenal, and thyroid function and a relation (possibly shared by the nearby subcommissural organ) to water and salt balance.

Application of isotopic techniques has provided clear evidence of a surprising degree of metabolic activity. The pineal body of rodents displays a rapid uptake and turnover of radioactive phosphorus and a high rate of amino acid incorporation. The organ contains detectable amounts of a 5-hydroxyindole compound, *melatonin*, that is synthesized from serotonin, which is present in abundance (Lerner). Both melatonin and the enzyme hydroxyindole-O-methyl transferase (HIOMT), responsible for its formation (Axelrod), are found exclusively in the pineal organ in white rats, but they are somewhat more widely distributed in the brain and retina of lower vertebrates possessing photoreceptor-type pineal systems.

Melatonin has been extracted primarily from mammalian pineal organs, but when applied in low concentrations to amphibian skin it causes marked aggregation of pigment

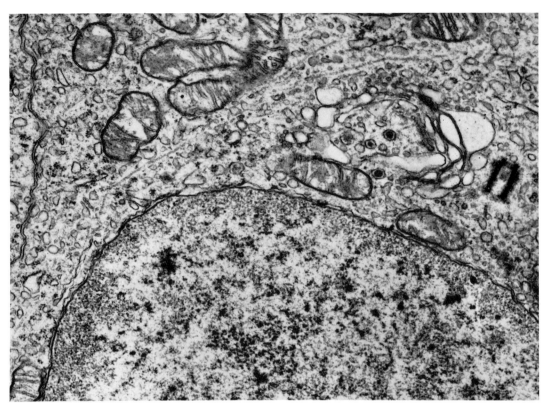

Figure 21-7. Electron micrograph of a juxtanuclear area of pinealocyte cytoplasm, showing a centriole and part of the Golgi complex with associated vesicles with dense osmiophilic content. The cytoplasm generally contains abundant small vesicles and numerous microtubules. × 30,000. (Courtesy of E. Anderson.)

granules in melanocytes and hence results in blanching. It has therefore been suggested that melatonin is an antagonist of the melanocyte stimulating hormone in the pigment regulation of lower vertebrates. No influence has been demonstrated on mammalian melanocytes. Some authors report, however, that melatonin seems to play an active role in the light-influenced reproductive cycles of rodents and birds. It is suggested that, in these forms, photic stimuli relayed from optic pathways to the pineal body via sympathetic nerves are translated by pineal activity into humoral gonadal control. Pineals from rats subjected to constant light weigh less and have smaller cells, exhibiting less basophilia and less lipid, than those from rats kept constantly in the dark (Roth). The activity of the specific enzyme for melatonin production (HIOMT) is also reduced in constant light. A diurnal rhythm of phosphorus uptake and serotonin content correlated with periods of daylight and darkness has also been reported. Extirpation of the superior cervical ganglion establishes that the responses to light are mediated by the autonomic nerves.

The physiology of the pineal is now a subject of intensive investigation. It appears that the pineal has a neuroendocrine function and that it participates in the regulation of the rhythmic activity of the endocrine system by elaborating specific methoxyindoles that serve as hormone-like mediators, but many of the details of its complex interrelationships have yet to be worked out.

REFERENCES

Anderson, E.: The anatomy of bovine and ovine pineals: Light and electron microscopic studies. J. Ultrastruct. Res., Suppl. 8, 1965.

Ariëns-Kappers, J., and J. P. Schadé, eds.: Structure and function of the epiphysis cerebri. *In* Progress in Brain Research. Amsterdam, Elsevier Publishing Co., 1965, Vol. 10.

Axelrod, J., and H. Weissbach: Purification and properties of hydroxyindole-O-methyl transferase. J. Biol. Chem., *236*:216, 1961.

Bargmann, W.: Die Epiphysis Cerebri. *In* von Möllendorff, W., and W. Bargmann, eds.: Handbuch der mikroskopischen Anatomie des Menschen. Berlin, Springer Verlag, 1943, Vol. 6, part 4, p. 309.

Fiske, V. M., J. Pound, and J. Putnam: Effect of light on the weight of the pineal organ in hypophysectomized, gonadectomized, adrenalectomized and thiouracil-fed rats. Endocrinol., *71:*130, 1962.

Kelly, D. E.: Pineal organs: Photoreception, secretion and development. Am. Scientist, *50:*597, 1962.

Kelly, D. E.: An ultrastructural analysis of the paraphysis cerebri in newts. Zeitschr. f. Zellforsch., *64:*778, 1964.

Kelly, D. E.: Circumventricular organs. *In* Haymaker, W., and R. D. Adams, eds.: Histology and Neuropathology of the Human Nervous System. Springfield, Ill., Charles C Thomas, 1966.

Kitay, J. I., and M. D. Altschule: The Pineal Gland; a Review of the Physiologic Literature. Cambridge, Harvard University Press, 1954.

Lerner, A. B., and J. D. Case: Pigment cell regulatory factors. J. Invest. Derm., *32:*221, 1959.

Quay, W. B.: Reduction of mammalian pineal weight and lipid during continuous light. Gen. Comp. Endocrinol., *1:*211, 1961.

Quay, W. B.: Experimental and cytological studies of pineal cells staining with acid hematin in the rat. Acta Morphol. Neerl. Scandinav., *5:*87, 1962.

Quay, W. B.: Circadian rhythm in rat serotonin and its modifica-

tions by estrous cycles and photoperiod. Gen. Comp. Endocrinol., *3:*473, 1963.

Quay, W. B.: Retinal and pineal hydroxyindole-O-methyl transferase activity in vertebrates. Life Sciences, *4:*983, 1965.

Roth, W. D.: Metabolic and morphologic studies on the rat pineal organ during puberty. *In* Ariëns-Kappens, J., and J. P. Schadé, eds.: Progress in Brain Research. Amsterdam, Elsevier Publishing Co., 1965, Vol. 10.

Roth, W. D., R. J. Wurtman, and M. D. Altschule: Morphologic changes in the pineal parenchymal cells of rats exposed to continuous light or darkness. Endocrinol., *71:*888, 1962.

Wolfe, D. E.: The epiphyseal cell: An electron microscopic study of intercellular relationships and intracellular morphology in the pineal body of the albino rat. *In* Ariëns-Kappens, J., and J. P. Schadé, eds.: Progress in Brain Research. Amsterdam, Elsevier Publishing Co., 1965, Vol. 10.

Wurtman, R. J.: Effects of light and visual stimuli on endocrine function. *In* Ganong, W. F., and L. Martini, eds.: Neuroendocrinology. New York, Academic Press, 1966.

Wurtman, R. J., W. D. Roth, M. D. Altschule, and J. J. Wurtman: Interactions of the pineal and exposure to continuous light on organ weights of female rats. Acta Endocrinol., *36:*617, 1961.

CHAPTER TWENTY-TWO

Skin

The skin covers the surface of the body and consists of two main layers, the surface epithelium, or *epidermis,* and the subjacent connective tissue layer, the *corium* or *dermis* (Figs. 22-1 and 22-2). Beneath the dermis is a looser connective tissue layer, the superficial fascia, or *hypodermis,* which in many places is largely transformed into subcutaneous adipose tissue. The hypodermis is loosely connected to underlying deep fascia, aponeurosis, or periosteum. The skin is continuous with several mucous membranes at *mucocutaneous junctions.* Such junctions are found at the lips, nares, eyelids, vulva, prepuce, and anus.

The skin is one of the largest of the organs, comprising some 16 per cent of the body weight. Its functions are several. It protects the organism from injury and desiccation; it receives stimuli from the environment; it excretes various substances; and, in warm-blooded animals, it takes part in thermoregulation and maintenance of the water balance. The subcutaneous adipose tissue has an important role in fat metabolism.

The specific functions of the skin depend largely upon the properties of the epidermis. This epithelium forms an uninterrupted cellular investment covering the entire outer surface of the body, but it is also locally specialized to form the various skin appendages: *hair, nails,* and *glands.* Its cells produce the fibrous protein *keratin,* which is essential to the protective function of the skin, and *melanin,* the pigment that protects against ultraviolet irradiation. The epidermis gives rise to two main types of glands, one of which produces the watery secretion *sweat* and the other the oily secretion *sebum.*

The free surface of the skin is not smooth but is marked by delicate grooves or flexure lines, which create patterns that vary from region to region. They are deeper on nonhairy areas, such as knees and elbows, palms and soles. The most familiar of the surface patterns are those responsible for the fingerprints. It is well known that the complicated patterns of ridges found on the fingers are subject to such marked variations that their impressions are a dependable means for identification of individuals. The same degree of variation holds for skin patterns in other regions, but these are less commonly used.

The interface of the epidermis and the dermis is also uneven. A pattern of ridges and grooves on the deep surface of the epidermis fits a complementary pattern of corrugations on the underlying dermis. The projections of the dermis have traditionally been described as *dermal papillae* and those of the epidermis as *epidermal ridges,* owing to their respective appearances in vertical sections of skin. As will be seen later, these terms are not always accurately descriptive of their three dimensional configuration as seen in whole mounts.

Although the boundary between the epithelial and the connective tissue portions of the skin is sharp, the fibrous elements of the dermis merge with those of the hypodermis, so that there is no clear-cut boundary between these layers.

THE EPIDERMIS

The epidermis is a stratified squamous epithelium composed of cells of two distinct lineages. Those comprising the bulk of the epithelium undergo keratinization and form the dead superficial layers of the skin. They are

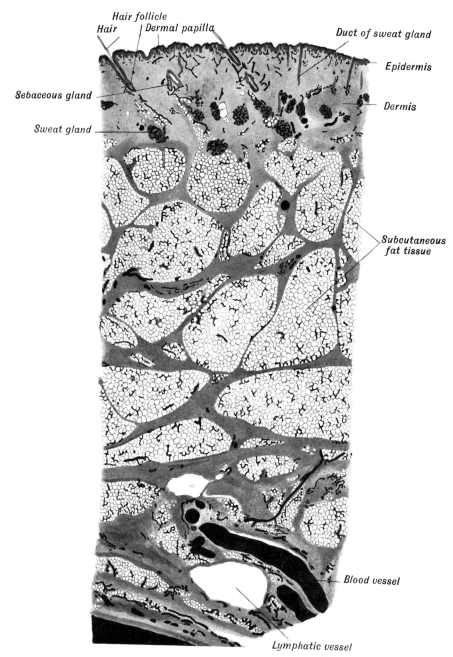

Figure 22-1. Section through human thigh perpendicular to the surface of the skin. Blood vessels are injected and appear black. Low magnification. (After A. A. Maximow.)

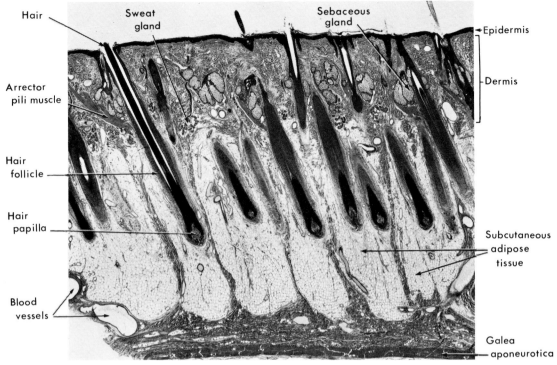

Hair
Sweat gland
Sebaceous gland
Epidermis
Dermis
Arrector pili muscle
Hair follicle
Hair papilla
Subcutaneous adipose tissue
Blood vessels
Galea aponeurotica

Figure 22-2. Section of the skin of the scalp. × 15. (Courtesy of H. Mizoguchi.)

derivatives of the ectoderm covering the embryo, and they constitute the *malpighian* or *keratinizing system*. In addition, there are cells in the deeper layers of the epidermis that do not keratinize but are capable of producing melanin. These are the melanocytes, which arise from the embryonic neural crest and invade the skin in the third to sixth month of intrauterine life. Collectively these cells comprise the *pigmentary system* of the skin.

The epidermis varies from 0.07 to 0.12 mm. in thickness over most of the body, but it may reach a thickness of 0.8 mm. on the palms and 1.4 mm. on the soles. In the fetus, these sites are already appreciably thicker than other areas of skin, but continuous friction or pressure in postnatal life may cause considerable additional thickening of the outer layer of the epidermis on exposed areas of the body surface.

The superficial keratinized cells of the skin are continually exfoliated from the surface and are replaced by cells that arise from mitotic activity in the basal layer of the epidermis. The cells produced there are displaced to successively higher levels by the generation of new cells below them. As they move upward, they elaborate keratin, which accumulates in

their interior until it largely replaces all metabolically active cytoplasm. The cell dies and its nucleus and other organelles disappear. It is finally shed as a flakelike, lifeless residue of a cell. This sequence of changes, referred to as the *cytomorphosis* of the malpighian cell, takes from 15 to 30 days, depending upon the region of the body and a number of other factors.

EPIDERMIS OF THE PALMS AND SOLES. The structural organization of the epidermis can be studied to advantage in those areas where it attains its greatest development—namely, the palm of the hand and the sole of the foot. In sections perpendicular to the surface, four layers can be distinguished (Figs. 22-3 and 22-4). The deepest of these is the *stratum malpighii*, which may be subdivided into the stratum germinativum (stratum basale), the layer of cells in contact with the dermis, and a layer of variable thickness above it called the stratum spinosum (prickle-cell layer). The next layer is the *stratum granulosum* or granular layer; then follow the *stratum lucidum* or clear layer and the *stratum corneum* or horny layer. The superficial keratinized portion of the epidermis consists of the stratum corneum and stratum lucidum.

The cells of the *stratum germinativum* adja-

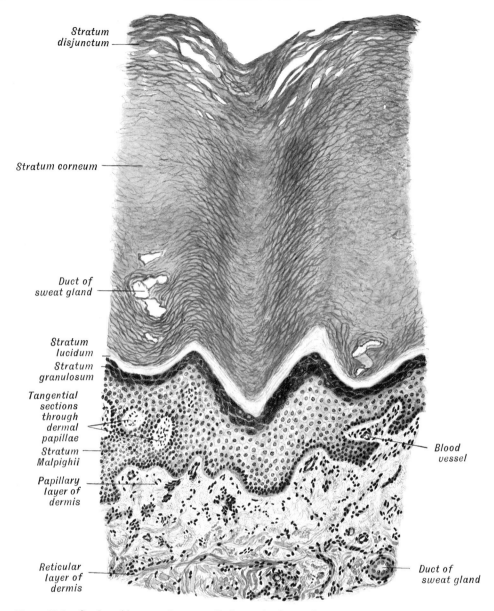

Stratum
disjunctum

Stratum corneum

Duct of
sweat gland

Stratum
lucidum

Stratum
granulosum

Tangential
sections
through
dermal
papillae

Stratum
Malpighii

Papillary
layer of
dermis

Reticular
layer of
dermis

Blood
vessel

Duct of
sweat gland

Figure 22-3.   Section of human sole perpendicular to the free surface. × 100. (After A. A. Maximow.)

cent to the dermis are cuboidal to columnar and have their cell axis perpendicular to the basal lamina (basement membrane). Mitotic figures are common in this layer but are by no means confined to it. As the cells move up into the stratum spinosum, they assume a flattened polyhedral form, with their long axis parallel to the surface and their nucleus somewhat elongated in this direction. All of the cells bear short processes or "spines" that are attached to similar projections from adjacent

cells. Because the cell membranes at the sites of end to end junction of these processes cannot be resolved with light microscopy, these structures were formerly called "intercellular bridges" in the belief that they represented open communications between the epidermal cells (Fig. 22-5). The term is no longer appropriate and should be abandoned, because it has been shown by electron microscopy that there is no protoplasmic continuity between the cells. Instead, the processes or "prickles"

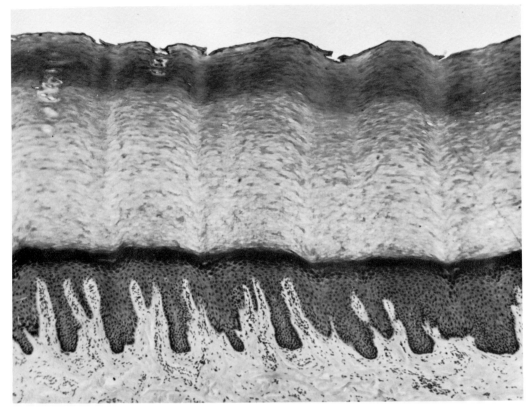

Figure 22-4. Skin of the human finger tip, illustrating a very thick stratum corneum. Hematoxylin and eosin. × 65.

simply meet end to end or side to side and are firmly attached by a well developed *desmosome,* which appeared in appropriately stained histological sections as a dense dot or granule in each "bridge" (Fig. 22-7). The cells of the malpighian layer are basophilic and show bundles of cytoplasmic fibrils called *tonofibrils.* These traverse the cytoplasm in various directions and extend into the cell processes to terminate in the desmosomes.

The *stratum granulosum* consists of three to five layers of flattened cells containing conspicuous granules of irregular shape that stain deeply with basic dyes. These are the *keratohyalin granules.* They are not to be confused with granules of melanin pigment, which are most abundant in the basal layers of the epidermis. The origin and chemical nature of the keratohyalin granules have not been clearly established, but they are believed to be intimately associated with the formation of keratin.

The *stratum lucidum* is formed of several layers of flattened, closely compacted, eosinophilic cells. It appears in section as a wavy clear stripe interposed between the stratum granulosum and stratum corneum. The nucleus of the cells has disappeared, but under favorable conditions refractile droplets of a substance called *eleidin* can be seen in the cytoplasm. Little more is known about eleidin or its relation to keratohyalin now than when it was described in 1879 by Ranvier.

The thick *stratum corneum* on the palms and soles consists of many layers of flat, cornified cells lacking a nucleus and with the cytoplasm replaced by keratin. The processes by which cells were joined in the spiny layer are no longer visible, and the lifeless cells are closely packed together without obvious interstices. In the most peripheral layers, where the dried horny cells are constantly being desquamated (stratum disjunctum), individual squamae or sheets of them may appear loosened and partially detached (Fig. 22-3).

The number of dividing cells in the mal-

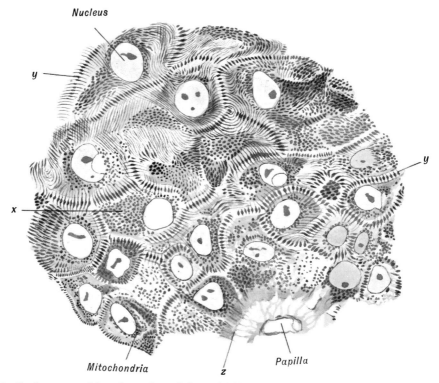

Nucleus

y

y

x

Mitochondria

z

Papilla

Figure 22-5. Section, tangential to the surface, of the malpighian layer of epidermis of human palm, showing fibrils and so-called "intercellular bridges" in cross section at *x* and in longitudinal section at *y*. The junction of the scalloped lower surface of the epithelial cells with the dermis is at *z*.

pighian layer corresponds to the intensity of desquamation of the stratum corneum in a given region. Contrary to the general view that mitosis in the skin occurs mainly in the most basal layer of cells, Thuringer found that in the skin of the scalp and prepuce only 12 per cent of the mitoses were in the basal layer, with 30 per cent in the lower third, 46 per cent in the middle third, and 12 per cent in the outer third of the spinous layer. In the palmar and plantar skin of the cat, he found mitoses slightly more numerous in the lower third of the spinous layers than in the basal layer. Both layers respond rapidly to mechanical stimulation of the skin, with increased numbers of mitoses.

EPIDERMIS OF THE BODY IN GENERAL. On the rest of the body the epidermis is much thinner and simpler in its structure (Figs. 22-11 and 22-12). The stratum malpighii and stratum corneum are always present, although the latter may be relatively thin. A granular layer consisting of two or three layers of cells is usually identifiable, but a definite stratum lucidum is seldom seen in the thinner epidermis of

the general body surface. The epidermis is entirely devoid of blood vessels; it is presumed to be nourished from capillaries in the underlying connective tissue by diffusion through tissue fluid, which occupies an extensive system of intercellular spaces of the malpighian layer. Human skin, unlike that of practically all other vertebrates, blisters after exposure to thermal and certain chemical stimuli, such as the vesicant gases. This reaction is apparently related to the many layers of cells in human epidermis.

FINE STRUCTURE OF THE EPIDERMIS AND THE PROCESS OF KERATINIZATION. In electron micrographs the cells of the malpighian layer are seen to be rich in free polyribosomes and to have occasional profiles of granular endoplasmic reticulum. The mitochondria are sparse and the Golgi apparatus poorly developed. The tonofibrils of light microscopy are resolved as bundles of 70 to 80 Å filaments called *tonofilaments*. In the basal layer of cells, these are loosely organized and randomly oriented, but in the spiny layer, they tend to be aggregated into conspicuous bundles (Fig. 22-7). In both layers the filaments converge upon the cell processes around the periphery and terminate in desmosomes where the processes of neighboring cells join.

In the uppermost cells of the stratum spinosum, there are numerous electron-dense spherical granules, 50 to 100 mμ in diameter (Odland). The exact nature of these granules is not known, but they gather at the uppermost cell surface. According to some authors they are secreted into the intercellular space, and their substance spreads upon the cell membrane, making it appreciably thicker than the lower surface (Matoltsy).

The cells of the granular layer differ from those of the spiny layer mainly in their more flattened shape and in the presence of irregular accumulations of dense material 1 to 5 μ in diameter, among and around the bundles of tonofilaments. These correspond to the keratohyalin granules of light microscopy (Figs. 22-8 and 22-17). Although at low power they appear homogeneous, it is found at higher magnification that the epidermal filaments extend into and mingle with the dense matrix of the keratohyalin granules.

Above the granular layer, the cells undergo an abrupt change. In the stratum lucidum, they are very much elongated and flattened, and although the cell outlines are still discernible, all of the cell organelles including the nuclei have disappeared. The cells of this layer and of the overlying stratum corneum may appear homogeneous, but at high magnification they are found to be completely filled with tightly packed 70 to 80 Å filaments embedded in an electron-dense matrix (Figs. 22-9 and 22-10). Keratohyalin granules are no longer visible as such, but some authors believe that the interfibrillar matrix of the keratinized cell is of the same nature and may derive from the keratohyalin granules. As the cells move upward in the epidermis and become more flattened, their spines are effaced but the desmosomes persist. Concurrent with the keratinization of the cells there is a marked change in the character of the desmosomes. Instead of two thickened regions of the opposing mem-

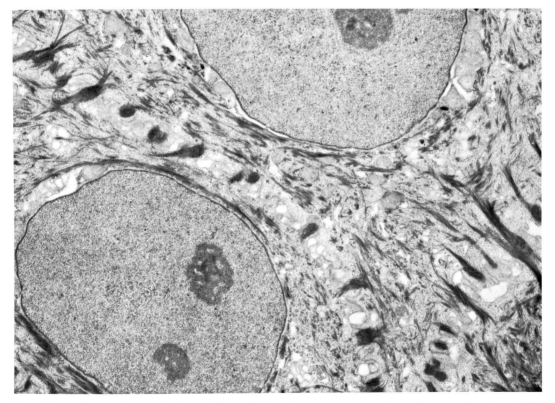

Figure 22-6.   Electron micrograph of parts of three cells from the stratum germinativum of human epidermis. × 12,000. (Courtesy of G. Odland.)

branes separated by a less dense intercellular cleft, the desmosome comes to be represented as a dense band of osmiophilic material that appears to be extracellular and to occupy the site of the intercellular cleft of the original desmosome (Fig. 22-10). The details of this transformation have not been worked out.

The Melanocyte System

The color of the skin is the resultant of three components. The tissue has an inherent yellowish color, attributable in part to *carotene.* The *oxyhemoglobin* in the underlying vascular bed imparts a reddish hue, and shades of brown to black are contributed by varying amounts of *melanin.* Of these three colored substances, only the melanin is produced in the skin. It is the product of specialized cells with elaborately branching processes called *melanocytes,* which are located in the malpighian layer of the epidermis or in the underlying connec-

tive tissue of the dermis. Although melanin granules are also found in the malpighian cells, they are formed only by the epidermal melanocytes, for these cells alone possess the enzyme tyrosinase that is necessary for synthesis of the pigment. The fully formed melanin granules are transferred from the melanocytes to the malpighian cells by an unusual form of activity sometimes referred to as *cytocrine* secretion. The melanocytes are commonly located at the dermoepidermal junction, with their pigment-containing processes extending for long distances upward into the interstices among the malpighian cells. They are not attached to the other cells by desmosomes, and in specimen preparation they may shrink away so that they are surrounded by a clear space. Because of their tendency to pass pigment to the malpighian cells, the melanocytes may actually contain less melanin than the neighboring epidermal cells, and their processes or dendrites are very difficult to identify in sec-

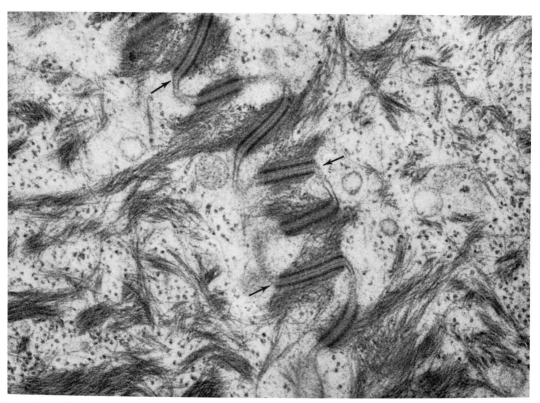

Figure 22-7.   Electron micrograph of portions of two adjoining epidermal cells. The junction of the two cells runs diagonally across the figure. Desmosomes attaching the apposed cell surfaces are indicated by the arrows. Bundles of epidermal filaments run in various directions in the cytoplasm and terminate in desmosomes. × 50,000. (Courtesy of G. Odland.)

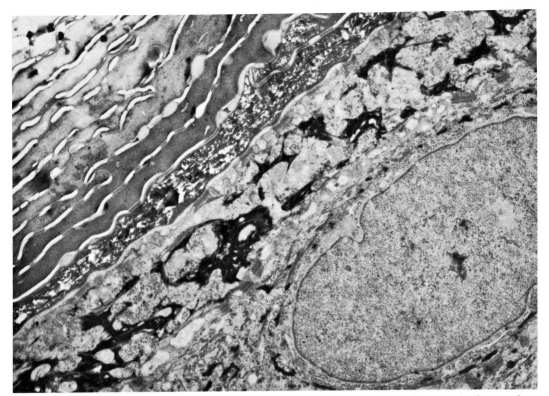

Figure 22-8. Electron micrograph of cells of the stratum granulosum, running diagonally across the figure and containing irregularly shaped keratohyalin granules. At the upper left are several cell layers of the stratum corneum. × 12,000. (Courtesy of G. Odland.)

tions stained with hematoxylin and eosin. They are best studied in whole mounts of separated epidermis that have been treated with 1, 3, 4-dihydroxyphenylalanine (DOPA) (Fig. 22-13). In such preparations, the melanocytes are blackened and appear as uniformly distributed, highly branched cells. The ratio of melanocytes to basal epidermal cells varies between 1 to 4 and 1 to 10, depending upon the region. The melanocytes in the cheek and forehead and in the genital, nasal, and oral epithelium are about twice as numerous as in other parts of the body surface. It is also of interest that the number of melanocytes is approximately the same in all human races; differences in color are attributable to differences in the amount of pigment that these cells produce (Fig. 22-14).

Melanin is formed on a specific cell particle, the *melanosome*. In man it is an elongated body with rounded ends, about 0.2 by 0.6 μ, with a fibrillar or lamellar internal structure exhibiting characteristic periodic density variations along its length in early stages of development (Fig. 22-15). This internal structure tends to be obscured by accumulation of dense melanin in the mature melanosome. The size, shape, and internal structure of the melanosomes vary with the animal species and are characteristic of particular genotypes within the same species. In man, however, melanosomes are uniformly elongated, except that in red-haired individuals they tend to be spherical.

Lack of melanin in the epidermis of some areas of the skin of animals may be due either to absence of melanocytes or, as in albinism, to the inability of the melanocytes to form pigmented melanosomes. In man, the entire integument normally possesses functioning melanocytes. Their activity is influenced by hormones and by factors in the physical environment. During pregnancy, the pigmentation of the areola of the nipples increases, and sometimes that of the cheeks and forehead as well. The phenomenon of *tanning* on exposure to sunlight results from an immediate biophysical darkening of the existing melanin

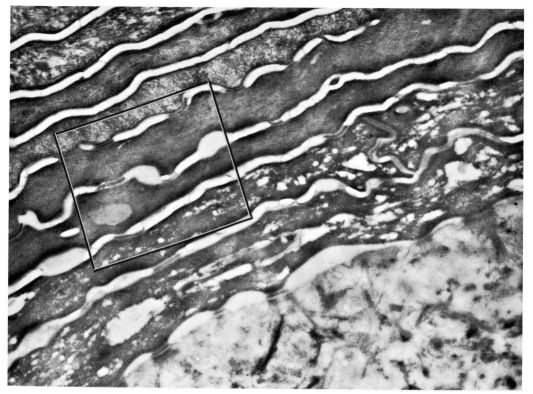

Figure 22-9. Electron micrograph showing (*lower right*) a portion of a cell of the granular layer and (*upper left*) several layers of flattened cells of the stratum corneum. The area enclosed in the rectangle is shown at higher magnification in Figure 22-10. Osmium fixation. × 22,500. (Courtesy of G. Odland.)

and, after a few days, an enhanced tyrosinase activity in the melanocytes that leads to the formation of new melanin. The pigmentation of the skin is believed to protect the underlying tissues against the potentially harmful effects of solar radiation.

Throughout the epidermis, but particularly in the upper layers of the stratum malpighii, there are peculiar cells described by Langerhans in 1868. In routine hematoxylin and eosin preparations, they have deep-staining nuclei surrounded by apparently clear cytoplasm. In sections stained by the gold chloride method, they are blackened and are revealed as stellate or dendritic cells (Fig. 22-18). Their slender processes penetrate the intercellular spaces among the prickle cells, but they themselves are devoid of desmosomes and of "intercellular bridges" to neighboring cells. The Langerhans cells have been variously interpreted. One of the most persistent views has been that they are effete epidermal melanocytes that have given up their melanin and

have lost the capacity to produce more (Masson). In favor of their relationship to melanocytes is their similar morphological appearance and several cytological and histochemical staining reactions that they have in common. Against their being degenerate or regressive forms is the fact that in the hyperplasia that follows ultraviolet irradiation of the epidermis, they exhibit a striking uptake of tritiated thymidine. Since the Langerhans cells are capable of active DNA synthesis they can no longer be regarded as worn out melanocytes (Giacometti and Montagna). Their appearance in electron micrographs also is that of a healthy active cell (Birbeck; Breathnach). The nucleus is highly irregular in outline and the cytoplasm is of relatively low density and lacks melanosomes and tonofilaments. A Golgi complex, mitochondria, and endoplasmic reticulum are present but unremarkable. The cytoplasm contains many small vesicles, rounded dense granules 0.3 μ in diameter, and peculiar rod-shaped, membrane limited structures that have not been found, to date, in other cell types. These are 150 to 500 mμ long and 40 mμ wide with a central linear density. Some of them seem to be in continuity with the cell membrane. Although the exact mode of formation and functional significance of these cells remain obscure, recent evidence suggests that despite their similar appearance they may not be related to the melanocytes.

Mucocutaneous Junctions

These are transitions between the mucous membranes and skin. Their epithelium is thicker than that of the adjacent skin and is more like that of the mucosa. They may have a thin, rudimentary, horny layer. Normally they do not contain sweat glands, hair follicles, hairs, or sebaceous glands, but are moistened by mucous glands situated within the body orifices. Since the horny layer is thin or may even be absent, the redness of the blood in the underlying capillaries shows through and gives the junction a red color.

THE DERMIS

The thickness of the dermis cannot be measured exactly, because it passes over into the subcutaneous layer without a sharp boundary. The average thickness is approximately 1 to 2 mm.; it is less on the eyelids and the prepuce (0.6 mm. or less) but reaches a thickness of 3 mm. or more on the soles and palms. On the ventral surface of the body and the appendages it is generally thinner than on the dorsal surface. It is thinner in women than in men.

The outer surface of the dermis in contact with the epidermis is usually uneven and is thrown up into papillae that project into the concavities between the ridges on the deep surface of the epidermis. This sculptured surface of the dermis is called the *papillary layer*, and the deeper main portion of the dermis is called the *reticular layer*. The two cannot be clearly separated.

The reticular layer consists of rather dense connective tissue. Its collagenous fibers

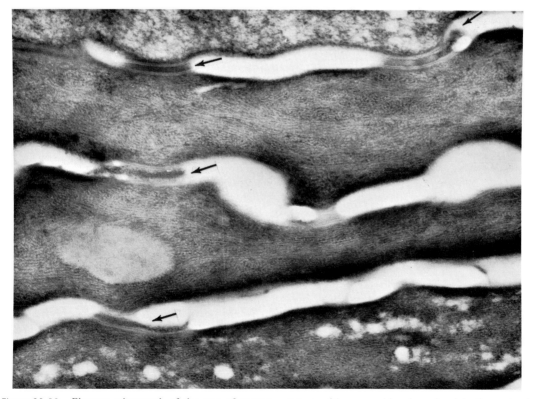

Figure 22-10. Electron micrograph of the area of stratum corneum of human epidermis enclosed in the rectangle on Figure 22-9. The cytoplasm of the flat keratinized cells appears devoid of organelles and seems to consist mainly of closely packed, fine filaments embedded in a rather dense matrix. The desmosomes, indicated by arrows, have an unusually thick, dense intermediate layer. The clear spaces between the cells are, in part, artifacts of specimen preparation. Osmium fixation. $\times$ 62,000. (Courtesy of G. Odland.)

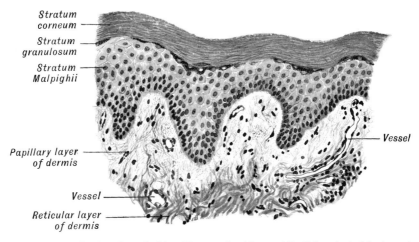

Stratum
corneum

Stratum
granulosum

Stratum
Malpighii

Vessel

Papillary layer
of dermis

Vessel

Reticular layer
of dermis

Figure 22-11. Section through skin of human shoulder. × 125. (After A. A. Maximow.)

form a feltwork with bundles running in various directions but, for the most part, more or less parallel to the surface. Occasional bundles are oriented almost perpendicular to the majority. The papillary layer and its papillae consist of looser connective tissue with much thinner collagenous bundles.

The elastic fibers of the dermis form abundant, thick networks between the collagenous bundles and are condensed about the hair follicles and the sebaceous and sweat glands. In the papillary layer they are much thinner and form a continuous fine network in the papillae beneath the epithelium. The cells of the dermis are more abundant in the papillary than in the reticular layer and are similar to those of the subcutaneous layer except for the relative paucity of fat cells.

Within the deep parts of the reticular layer in the areolae, penis, perineum, and scrotum, numerous smooth muscle cells form a loose plexus. Such portions of the skin become wrinkled during contraction of these muscles. Smooth muscles, the so-called *arrector pili* muscles, are also connected with the hairs (Figs. 22-20 and 22-21). In many places in the skin of the face, cross striated muscle fibers terminate in the dermis. These are the *muscles of facial expression* and are also responsible for the voluntary movement of the scalp. These represent vestiges, in man, of a more extensive subcutaneous layer of muscle that is present in many mammals and is called the *panniculus carnosus*. This layer is responsible for the voluntary movement of large segments of the integument, which can be observed when

animals attempt to dislodge insects from their skin or to shake dry when they emerge from the water. The absence of this layer over most of the body in man is disadvantageous in that, after wounds, the skin is likely to become immobile and bound down to the underlying structures because of shrinkage of scar tissue. Greater disfigurement results than in other mammals with more mobile skin.

At various levels of the dermis there are the hair follicles, sweat, and sebaceous glands, which are epidermal derivatives extending down into the dermis. There are also blood vessels, nerves, and many nerve endings.

HYPODERMIS. The subcutaneous layer consists of loose connective tissue and is a deeper continuation of the dermis. Its collagenous and elastic fibers are directly continuous with those of the dermis and run in all directions, mainly parallel to the surface of the skin. Where the skin is flexible or freely movable, these fibers are few, but where it is closely attached to the underlying parts, as on the soles and palms, they are thick and numerous.

Depending on the portion of the body and the nutrition of the organism, varying numbers of fat cells develop in the subcutaneous layer. These are also found in clusters in the deep layers of the dermis. The fatty tissue of the subcutaneous layer on the abdomen may reach a thickness of 3 cm. or more, but in the eyelids and on the penis the subcutaneous layer never contains fat cells.

The subcutaneous layer is penetrated everywhere by large blood vessels and nerve trunks and contains many nerve endings.

HAIRS

The hairs are slender keratinous filaments that develop from the matrix cells of follicular invaginations of the epidermal epithelium. They vary from several millimeters to over a meter in length and from 0.005 to 0.6 mm. in thickness. They are distributed in varying numbers (Fig. 22-34) and in variable thickness and length on the whole surface of the skin, except on the palms, the soles, the sides of fingers and toes, the side surfaces of the feet below the ankles, the lip, the glans penis, the prepuce, the clitoris, the labia minora, and the internal surface of the labia majora.

Each hair arises in a tubular invagination of the epidermis, the *hair follicle*, which extends down into the dermis, where it is surrounded by connective tissue (Figs. 22-2, 22-20, and 22-21). The active follicle has a bulbous terminal expansion with a concavity in its bottom occupied by a connective tissue *papilla* (Figs. 22-22 and 22-23). The papilla is covered by epithelial matrix cells of hair and root sheath. The cells on the dome of the convexity form the hair *root* which develops into the hair *shaft*. The free end of the shaft protrudes beyond the surface of the skin.

The hair is not a continuously growing organ but has phases of growth that alternate with periods of rest. The structure of the hair follicle varies markedly according to the stage of hair growth. In the resting hair (club hair), the follicle is relatively short and its epithelium is more or less similar to the surface epidermis, and the hair shaft is firmly anchored into the follicle by fine filaments of keratin that penetrate between the follicular cells. A cluster of dermal cells attached to the end of the follicular epithelium is the remnant of the dermal papilla of the growing hair and will again develop into a typical dermal papilla at the next period of hair generation (Figs. 22-21 and 22-23).

In a phase of growth the follicle elongates and the epithelium again surrounds the dermal papilla. The epithelial cells around the papilla (the matrix) differentiate into several types. (1) In certain types of coarse hairs, the central matrix cells on top of the convexity of the papilla develop into the *medulla* of the hair shaft. The cells are large and vacuolated and eventually keratinize. This central part of the hair shaft is not demonstrable in thinner hairs. (2) The next concentric layer of matrix cells keratinize and develop into the *cortex* of the hair, the main constituent of the shaft. Its cells are heavily keratinized and tightly compacted, and they carry most of the pigment of the hair. (3) Peripheral to the matrix cells of the cortex lie those of the *cuticle* of the hair. These cells of the outermost layer are the most heavily

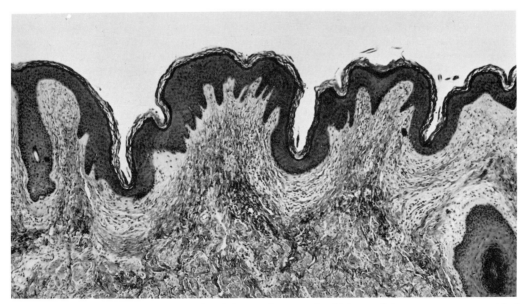

Figure 22-12. Photomicrograph of skin of the abdomen. Compare the thickness of the stratum corneum with that of the finger tip in Figure 22-4. × 60.

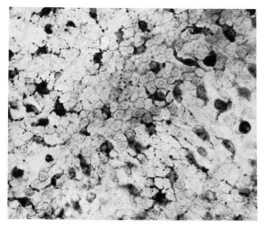

Figure 22-13. Photomicrograph of a whole mount of a sheet of epidermis from the thigh spread upon a slide and viewed from the under side to illustrate the melanocytes. The epidermis was separated from the dermis by treatment of the excised skin with trypsin. The epidermal sheet was then incubated in 1,3,4-dihydroxyphenylalanine (DOPA), which selectively stains the melanocytes. Notice their branching process. × 300. (Courtesy of G. Szabo.)

keratinized and their imbrication (overlapping) prevents matting of the erupted hairs. These three layers of cellular components all undergo keratinization in the so-called *kerato-genous zone* of the follicle, immediately above the dome of the dermal papilla, and form the solid hair shaft (Figs. 22-22 and 22-24).

The more peripheral concentric rows of matrix cells produce the *internal root sheath,* a transient structure surrounding the hair shaft below the level of the sebaceous glands, which is presumed to facilitate the movement of the growing hair shaft. It consists of three layers. The *cuticle of the internal root sheath,* like the cuticle of the hair, consists of overlapping thin scales with their free margins directed toward the bottom of the follicle. *Huxley's layer* consists of one to three layers of cornified cells and *Henle's layer* is a single layer of elongated cells closely adherent to the external sheath. These three layers form "trichohyalin" granules and keratinize, but they do not form a compact enduring structure, and they finally desquamate at the level of the opening of the sebaceous glands.

The outermost layer of the follicle, the *outer root sheath,* is basically similar to the unspecialized epidermal epithelium and is continuous with it above. At the neck of the papilla it is one layer of flat cells. It becomes two-layered at the level of the middle third of the papilla, and higher up it becomes stratified.

The glassy membrane, which is a part of the dermis, separates the epithelial from the connective tissue portion of the follicle. The latter portion is made up of two layers, a thin internal layer formed by circular fibers and an external, poorly outlined layer consisting of longitudinal collagenous and elastic fibers.

The hair matrix cells are analogous to the germinative cells of the epidermis insofar as the life cycle of each ends with formation of cornified cells. However, the epidermis produces a relatively soft keratinous material that is steadily shed in small invisible particles, whereas the product of the matrix cells, the hair, has a hard, cohesive, nonshedding, keratinous structure.

Since the hair is not perpendicular to the skin surface but inclined, it is very difficult to find a perfect longitudinal section of a follicle that displays these concentric layers well. The student will therefore have difficulty in identifying all of the structures described here. For this purpose the follicle needs to be reconstructed from serial sections.

It is well to bear in mind certain differences between the keratinizing epidermis and the keratinizing hair follicle. In the epidermis this process is general and continuous. In the case of the hair follicle it is intermittent and localized to a particular portion of the dermis —the dermal papilla having an inductive influence on the formation of the hair. If for any reason the dermal papilla is destroyed in postnatal life, no hair is formed. It is noteworthy, too, that there is a greater diversity of specialization and division of labor among the

SKIN AREA	TYPE OF POPULATION	AVERAGE NUMBER PER SQUARE MILLIMETER ± S. E. MEAN
Back	Caucasian	930 ± 140
Back	Negro	940 ± 60
Lip	Caucasian	1980 ± 200
Lip	Hindu	1820 ± 50
Thigh	Caucasian	1000 ± 70
Thigh	Negro	$997 \pm$
Thigh	Australian Aborigine	$742 \pm$
Trunk	Caucasian	890 ± 70
Trunk	Australian Aborigine	$816 \pm$

Figure 22-14. Comparison of melanocyte population in various human populations. (From M. A. Pathak, S. J. Sinesi, and G. Szabo, J. Invest. Derm., *45:*521, 1965.)

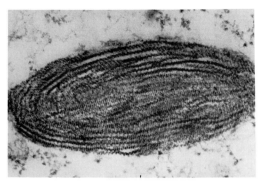

Figure 22-15. Electron micrograph of a developing human melanosome, showing the periodicity in its structural framework. When the melanosome is fully developed, its interior structure is obscured by the accumulated melanin. × 63,000. (Courtesy of A. Breathnach.)

characteristic differences in their granules and their mode of keratinization.

The pigmentation of the hair is attributable to epidermal melanocytes located over the tip of the dermal papilla, a site corresponding to their location in the base of the epidermis generally (Fig. 22-23A). These melanocytes donate their pigment to the cells of the hair matrix and cortex. The size and shape of the melanosomes in hair is similar to that of the skin, except that in red-haired humans the melanosomes are round instead of oval. The melanocytes of the hair follicle function only at the beginning of the growing phase of the hair cycle, the onset of hair growth usually being heralded by increased melanogenic activity. In later stages of the growing phase or in the resting hair, melanocytes cannot be distinguished in the follicle.

In young rodents, hair growth is synchronized and spreads over the body in a *wave pattern*. Later in life, however, this process gives way to a *mosaic pattern*, hair growth beginning

epidermal cells of the hair matrix with respect to their fate in the process of keratinization. In electron micrographs, the cells of the medulla, the cortex, and the internal and external root sheaths can all be distinguished by

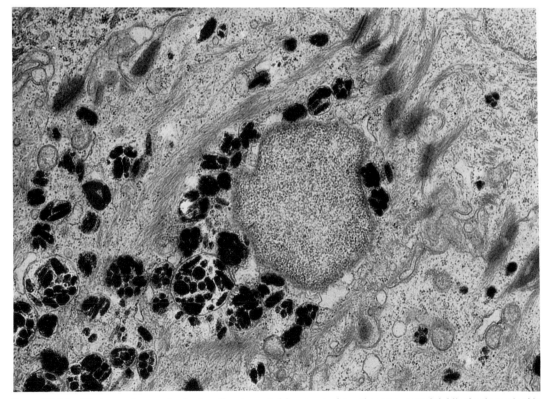

Figure 22-16. Electron micrograph of a heavily pigmented keratocyte from the stratum malpighii of guinea pig skin. Whereas the melanosomes of melanocytes occur singly, those of keratocytes are in clusters of varying size enclosed by a membrane. × 20,000. (Courtesy of G. Szabo.)

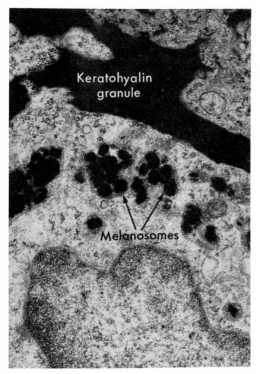

Figure 22-17. A micrograph of a portion of a cell from the stratum granulosum, showing dense keratohyalin granules and several clusters of melanosomes. × 8000. (Courtesy of G. Szabo.)

mented thick hairs. The same areas in the female, although they contain the same number of hair follicles, continue to produce fine hair. In other places, however, such as the axillae and the pubic regions, hair appears in both sexes at the onset of puberty. In males, there is often a characteristic regression of the scalp hair with age, which varies in degree according to genotype. In its extreme form, this male pattern of changing hair distribution progresses so far that all the hair follicles are lost or only a few are left and produce very fine hair.

One or more *sebaceous glands* are associated with each hair follicle. They discharge their secretory product through a short duct into the upper portion of the follicular canal.

A band of smooth muscle cells, the hair muscle or *arrector pili muscle,* is attached at one end to the papillary layer of the dermis and at the other to the connective tissue sheath of the hair follicle (Figs. 22-20 and 22-21). When this muscle contracts in response to cold, fear, anger, and the like, it moves the hair into a more vertical position while depressing the skin in the region of its attachment and elevating the region immediately around the hair. This is responsible for the erection of hairs in animals and for the so-called "goose flesh" in man.

in isolated islands here and there. In man the mosaic growth pattern prevails, and the duration of the growing and resting phases varies from one region to another. In the case of scalp hair the growing phase is very long (several years), whereas the resting phase is on the order of three months.

Among mammals the human is exceptional in that its skin is not furry. It is by no means hairless, however (see Fig. 22-34 for numbers of hair follicles per square centimeter). In accordance with its relative paucity of hairs, the human epidermis is generally thicker than that of other mammals. The architectural pattern of the dermoepidermal junction varies greatly from region to region. It is almost flat on the cheek, whereas deep ridges occur on the soles and palms (Fig. 22-19).

The human hairy coat also exhibits regional differences in the competence of the hair follicles to respond to male sex hormones. At the onset of puberty in males, the areas of the mustache and the beard produce strongly pig-

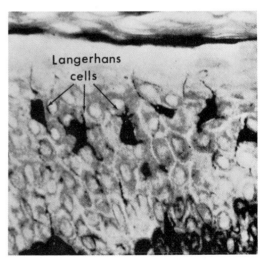

Figure 22-18. Section of human epidermis, showing gold impregnated Langerhans cells at a high level in the stratum malpighii. Gairn's gold chloride technique. × 610. (After A. S. Breathnach, Int. Rev. Cytol., *18*:1, 1965.)

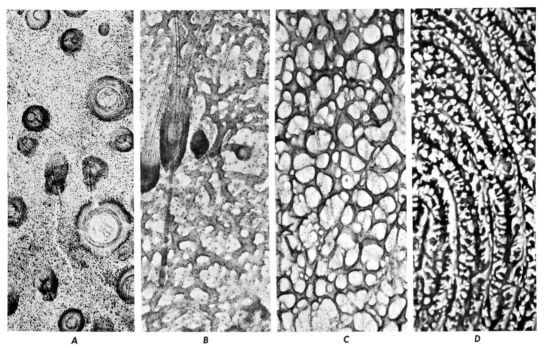

Figure 22-19. The pattern formed at a dermoepidermal junction shows marked regional variations. The figures shown here are views of the under surface of separated sheets of epidermis stained with carmine. The light areas are the depressions occupied in life by the dermal papillae. *A*, From the cheek; the under surface of the epidermis except for the hair follicles. *B*, From the back. *C*, The breast. *D*, The elaborate pattern of concavities occupied by the dermal papillae of a finger pad. (Courtesy of G. Szabo.)

NAILS

The nails are horny plates on the dorsal surfaces of the terminal phalanges of the fingers and toes. The surface of the skin covered by them is the *nail bed*. It is surrounded laterally and proximally by a fold of skin, the *nail wall*. The slit between the wall and the bed is the *nail groove*. The proximal edge of the *nail plate* is the *root* of the nail. The visible part of the nail plate, called the *body of the nail*, is surrounded by the nail wall. The distal portion, becoming free of the nail bed, extends forward and is gradually worn off or is cut off. The nail is semitransparent and permits the color of the underlying tissue, rich in blood vessels, to show through. Near the root, the nail has a whitish color. This crescentic portion, the *lunula*, is usually covered by the proximal portion of the nail fold.

The nail plate consists of closely compacted horny scales, the dead residues of cornified epithelial cells so arranged that in section the nail appears longitudinally striated. The *nail fold* has the structure of skin, with all its layers. Turning inward into the nail groove,

it loses its papillae, and the epidermis loses its horny, clear, and granular layers. Under the proximal fold, the horny layer spreads onto the free surface of the nail body as the *eponychium* (Fig. 22-26). The stratum lucidum and the stratum granulosum also reach far inside the groove but do not continue along the lower surface of the nail plate. On the surface of the nail bed only the malpighian layer of the epidermis is present.

In the nail bed the dermis is directly fused with the periosteum of the phalanx. The surface of the dermis under the proximal edge of the nail is provided with rather low papillae, but under the distal half of the lunula this surface is quite smooth. At the distal margin of the lunula, longitudinal, parallel ridges project instead of papillae. The boundary between the epithelium and the dermis of the nail bed is, therefore, scalloped in a perpendicular section (Fig. 22-27), whereas it is smooth in longitudinal sections. Beyond the free edge of the nail the dermal ridges are replaced by cylindrical papillae.

The epithelium of the nail bed distal to

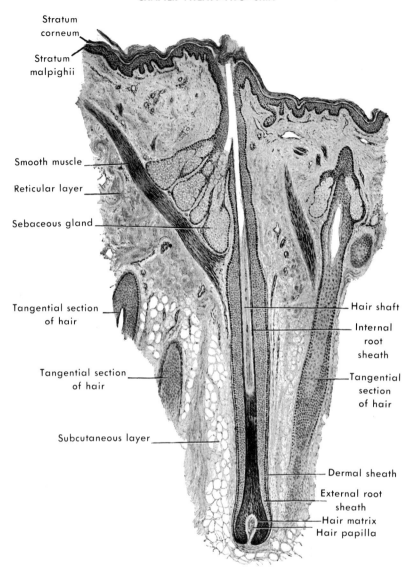

Stratum corneum

Stratum malpighii

Smooth muscle

Reticular layer

Sebaceous gland

Tangential section of hair

Tangential section of hair

Subcutaneous layer

Hair shaft

Internal root sheath

Tangential section of hair

Dermal sheath

External root sheath

Hair matrix

Hair papilla

Figure 22-20. Section of the scalp of a man, showing the root of a hair in longitudinal section. × 32. (After Schaffer.)

the lunula retains the typical structure of the malpighian layer. The epithelium is thicker between the ridges of the dermis than over them. The upper layer of cells, which touches the substance of the nail, is separated from it in places by an even line, while in others it is jagged. Under the free edge of the nail the usual horny layer again begins; it is thickened at this place and is called *hyponychium* (Fig. 22-26).

The epithelium that lines the proximal portion of the nail bed and corresponds roughly with the lunula is particularly thick; distally and upward it gradually passes over into the substance of the nail plate. Here the new formation of the nail substance proceeds; accordingly, this region of the epithelium is called the *nail matrix* (Fig. 22-27). The cells of the deepest layer are cylindrical, and mitoses can be observed frequently in them. Above these are 6 to 10 layers of polyhedral cells joined by 5 to 12 layers of more flattened cells. This entire mass is penetrated by parallel fibrils of a special "onychogenic" substance. On passing into the proximal edge of the nail plate, these cells cornify and become homogeneous.

As new formation of the nail takes place in the matrix, the nail moves forward. Most authors deny the participation of the epithelium of the other portions of the nail bed in the formation of the nail substance, believing that the nail simply glides forward over this region.

GLANDS

In man the glands of the skin include the sebaceous, sweat, and mammary glands. The last are described in Chapter 33.

SEBACEOUS GLANDS. The sebaceous glands are scattered over the surface of the skin (except in the palms, soles, and the sides of the feet where there are no hairs). They vary from 0.2 to 2 mm. in diameter. They lie in the dermis, and their excretory ducts open into the necks of hair follicles. When several glands are connected with one hair, they lie at the same level. On the lips, about the corners of the mouth, on the glans penis and the internal fold of the prepuce, on the labia minora, and on the mammary papilla, the sebaceous glands are independent of hairs and open directly on the surface of the skin. To this category also belong the *meibomian glands* of the eyelids. The sebaceous glands in mucocutaneous junctions are more superficial than those that are associated with hairs.

The secretory portions of the sebaceous glands are rounded sacs (alveoli). As a rule, several adjacent alveoli form a mass like a bunch of grapes, and all of them open into a short duct (Figs. 22-20 and 22-21). A simple branched gland results. Much less frequently, only one alveolus is present. In the meibomian glands of the eyelids there is one long, straight duct, from which a row of alveoli project.

The wall of the alveoli is formed by a basement lamina supported by a thin layer of fibrillar connective tissue. Along the internal surface is a single layer of thin cells with round nuclei. Toward the center of the alveoli a few cells keratinize, but most of them become larger and polyhedral, gradually fill with fat droplets, and resemble multilocular fat cells (Fig. 22-28). The nuclei gradually shrink and then disappear, and the cells break down into fatty detritus. This is the oily secretion of the gland, and it is secreted onto the hair and upon the surface of the epidermis. The ducts of sebaceous glands are lined by stratified squamous epithelium continuous with the external

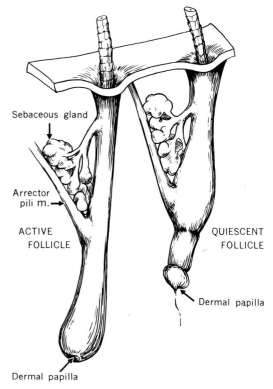

Figure 22-21. Diagrammatic representation of an actively growing and a quiescent hair follicle and the accessory structures. (Redrawn after W. Montagna, *in* Structure and Function of Skin. New York, Academic Press, 1956.)

root sheath of the hair and with the malpighian layer of the epidermis.

In sebaceous glands, the secretion results from the destruction of the epithelial cells and is, therefore, of the *holocrine* type. It is followed by a regenerative multiplication of epithelial elements. In the body of the gland, mitoses are rare in the cells lying on the basement lamina. They are numerous, however, in the cells close to the walls of the ducts, whence the new cells move into the secretory regions.

The so-called *preen glands* of certain aquatic birds are specialized sebaceous glands. They produce oily material that is spread with the beak over the surface of the feathers to make them impervious to water.

SWEAT GLANDS. The ordinary sweat glands (*eccrine type*) are distributed along the surface of the skin, with the exception of the margins of the lips, the glans penis, and the nail bed. They are simple, coiled, tubular glands; that is, the secretory portion is a simple tube

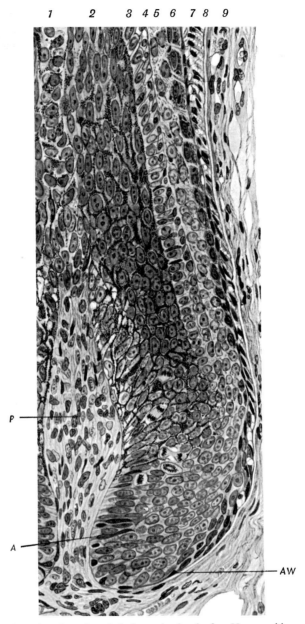

Figure 22-22. Longitudinal section through a hair from the head of a 22 year old man. *1*, Medulla; *2*, cortex; *3*, hair cuticle; *4*, inner sheath cuticle; *5*, Huxley's layer; *6*, Henle's layer; *7*, external root sheath; *8*, glassy membrane; *9*, connective tissue of the hair follicle; *A*, matrix; *AW*, external root sheath at the bulb; *P*, papilla. × 350. (After Hoepke.)

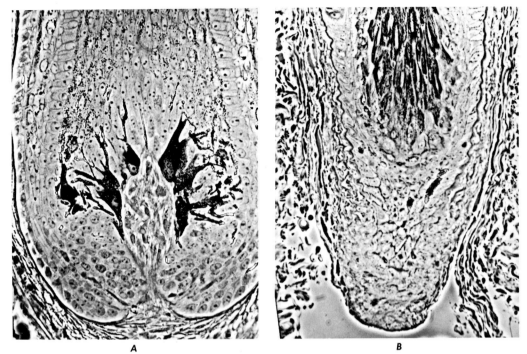

A   B

Figure 22-23. Unstained plastic sections of hair follicles. *A,* Active hair, showing large melanocytes and their processes contributing pigment to the hair. *B,* Inactive or club hair. × 200. (Courtesy of G. Szabo.)

convoluted in several unequal twists into a ball, and the duct is a narrow, unbranched tube (Figs. 22-29 and 22-30).

The bulk of the secretory portion is located in the dermis and measures 0.3 to 0.4 mm. in diameter. In the armpit and around the anus the secretory portions of some of the sweat glands may reach 3 to 5 mm. in diameter and are of *apocrine type.* They are connected with hair follicles and are located deep in the subcutaneous layer (Fig. 22-31).

The walls of the secretory portion rest on a thick basement lamina. Directly inside it are spindle-shaped and branching cells, 30 to 90 μ long, with their long axis tangential to that of the glandular tube. They have an elongated nucleus and myofilaments like those of smooth muscle (Fig. 22-32). It is supposed that, by contracting, these *myoepithelial cells* help to discharge the secretion. They are particularly numerous and highly developed in the large sweat glands of the axillary and perianal regions.

The truncated pyramidal cells that excrete sweat form a single layer upon the myoepithelial cells. At the base is a rather large round nucleus; the cytoplasm contains mito-

chondria and, near the lumen, a number of secretory vacuoles, varying with the functional state of the cell. Sometimes there are also fat droplets, glycogen, and pigment granules. Glycogen diminishes in active cells. Pigment appears in the secretion of certain sweat glands, as in the axilla. The free surfaces of the cells in the apocrine glands often show protrusions of protoplasm that are believed to separate and become a part of the secretion. Between these glandular cells are typical secretory capillaries. The caliber and the shape of the free lumen of the secretory portion fluctuate greatly with the functional state of the gland.

Two different cell types have been described in the secretory segment of human eccrine sweat glands, sometimes called "dark" or mucoid cells and "clear" cells. It was not apparent with the light microscope whether they were merely stages of the physiological activity of the same cell type. At the electron microscope level, the cells containing abundant ribosomes and numerous apical secretory vacuoles appear to correspond to the dark cells. Their shape is pyramidal, with the apical end being broader than the base. Protein-polysaccharide has been identified both in the

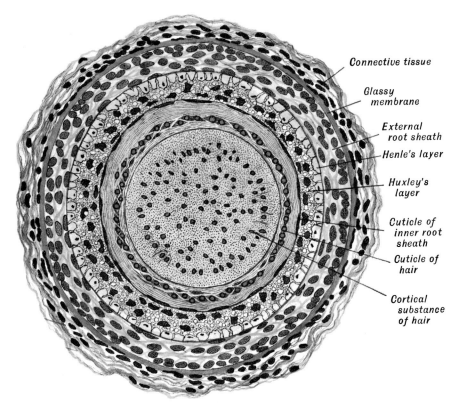

Connective tissue

Glassy membrane

External root sheath

Henle's layer

Huxley's layer

Cuticle of inner root sheath

Cuticle of hair

Cortical substance of hair

Figure 22-24.   Cross section through a hair follicle in the skin of a pig embryo, at the level where Henle's layer is completely cornified and Huxley's layer contains granules of trichohyalin. × 375.

secretory vacuoles and in the lumen (Munger). The clear cells are associated with the intercellular canaliculi. They have relatively few ribosomes but a considerable amount of glycogen. The endoplasmic reticulum is poorly developed. The basal plasma membranes, resting on the myoepithelial cells or basement lamina, are infolded in a complex manner. No secretory precursors are identified within their cytoplasm, but these cells are assumed to secrete into the intercellular canaliculi a product rich in water and various solutes.

The glandular tube, in passing over into the duct, suddenly becomes much narrower, and its lumen acquires a simple slitlike or starlike shape. The myoepithelial and glandular cells on the basement lamina are replaced by a double layer of cuboidal cells. The peripheral cells of the basal layer have comparatively large nuclei and rather abundant mitochondria (Fig. 22-33). The surface cells have large irregular nuclei and relatively little cytoplasm. The Golgi apparatus and other cytoplasmic membranes are poorly developed.

Immediately beneath the free surface, the cytoplasm is specialized, with a rather remarkable condensation of filaments constituting a terminal web which, in the past, has been erroneously referred to as a "cuticular border." This structure is lacking in the basal cells, which otherwise resemble the cells of the surface layer.

As the duct passes through the dermis toward the epidermis, it is slightly twisted and curved. In the epidermis the lumen of the excretory duct is a twisted intercellular channel surrounded by concentrically arranged epidermal cells which, in the malpighian layer, have fine, keratohyalin granules in their cytoplasm. On the palms and soles and on the palmar surface of the fingers, the rows of ducts open on the ridges with funnel-shaped openings that can be seen easily with a magnifying glass.

In certain parts of the skin the sweat glands have a peculiar arrangement and function. Such are the glands that produce *cerumen* in the external auditory meatus. They reach a considerable size and extend to the perichondrium. The secretory portions of the *cerumenous glands* branch, and the ducts, which sometimes also branch, may open together with the ducts of the adjacent sebaceous glands into the hair sacs of the fine hairs. In the terminal portions are highly developed smooth muscle cells; the glandular cells located upon them are particularly rich in pigment granules containing lipid.

Moll's glands of the margin of the eyelid are also a special kind of sweat gland, with terminal portions that do not form a ball but are irregularly twisted and provided with a wide lumen. The excretory ducts open onto the free surface or into the hair sacs of the eyelashes. The secretion of the sweat glands is not the same everywhere. True sweat, a transparent, watery liquid, is excreted mainly by the small sweat glands, while a thicker secretion of complex composition is produced by those of the axilla and about the anus. In women, the apocrine sweat glands of the axilla show periodic changes with the menstrual cycle. These changes consist mainly in enlarge-

ment of the epithelial cells and of the lumens of the glands in the premenstrual period, followed by regressive changes during the period of menstruation (Fig. 22-31).

The differences between the eccrine and apocrine sweat glands are as follows. The eccrine glands have no connections with hair follicles; they function throughout life, producing a watery secretion; and they are innervated by cholinergic nerves. The apocrine glands are connected with hair follicles; they begin to function at puberty, producing a more viscous secretion; and they are supplied by adrenergic nerves.

The eccrine glands do not function simultaneously or under the same conditions on all parts of the body. When the human body is exposed to excessive heat, sweating begins on the forehead and spreads to the face, and then to the rest of the body. Finally, the palms and the soles will show increased sweat production. Under nervous strain, however, palms and soles may start to sweat first.

It has been shown that the glandular portion of the eccrine sweat gland excretes more

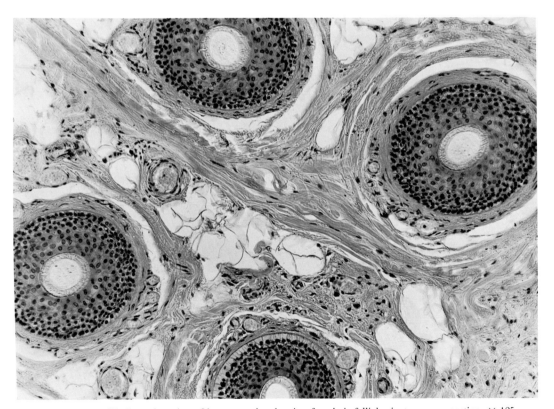

Figure 22-25. Horizontal section of human scalp, showing four hair follicles in transverse section. × 125.

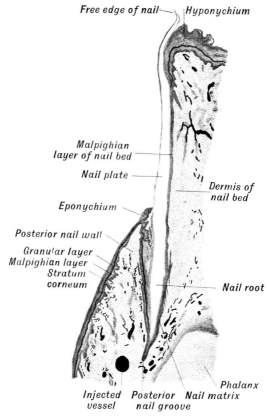

Figure 22-26.   Longitudinal section of the nail of a newborn infant. (After A. A. Maximow.)

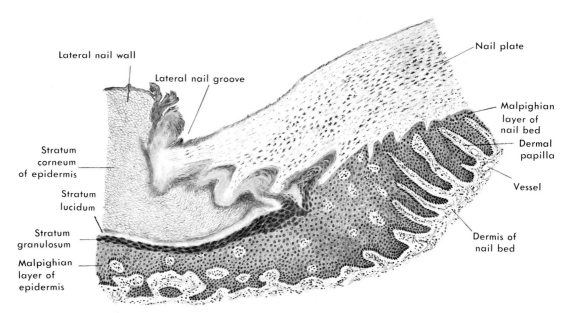

Figure 22-27.   Cross section of the lateral edge of a nail and its surrounding parts. (After A. A. Maximow.)

electrolytes than are finally found at the surface of the skin. It is assumed that an absorption of electrolytes takes place in the duct portion of the gland.

BLOOD AND LYMPHATIC VESSELS

The arteries that supply the skin are located in the subcutaneous layer. Their branches, reaching upward, form a network (rete cutaneum) parallel to the surface on the boundary line between the dermis and the hypodermis. From one side of this network, branches are given off that nourish the subcutaneous stratum with its fat cells, sweat glands, and the deeper portions of the hair follicles. From the other side of this network, vessels enter the dermis. At the boundary between the papillary and reticular layers they form the denser, subpapillary network or the rete subpapillare (Fig. 22-35). This gives off thin branches to the papillae. Each papilla has a single loop of capillary vessels with an ascending arterial and descending venous limb.

The veins that collect the blood from the capillaries in the papillae form the first network of thin veins immediately beneath the papillae. Then follow three flat networks of gradually enlarging veins on the boundary line between the papillary and reticular layers. In the middle section of the dermis and also at the boundary between the dermis and the subcutaneous tissue, the venous network is on the same level as the arterial rete cutaneum. Into this network the veins of the sebaceous and the sweat glands enter. From the deeper network the large, independent, subcutaneous veins pass, as well as the deep veins accompanying the arteries.

There are direct connections between the arterial and venous circulation in the skin without intervening capillary networks. These so-called "arteriovenous shunts" play a vital role in thermoregulation in the body.

Each hair follicle has its own blood vessels. It is supplied with blood from three sources: a special small artery that gives off a capillary network into the papilla; the rete subpapillare toward the sides of the hair sac; and several other small arteries that form a dense capillary network in the connective tissue layer of the follicle.

There is a dense network of capillaries

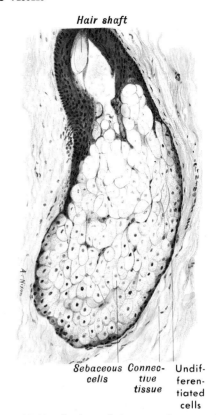

Hair shaft

Sebaceous cells   Connective tissue   Undifferentiated cells

Figure 22-28. Section of human sebaceous gland. × 120.

outside the basement lamina of the sebaceous and, particularly, of the sweat glands.

The skin is rich in lymphatic vessels. In the papillary layer they form a dense, flat meshwork of lymphatic capillaries. They begin in the papillae as networks or blind outgrowths, which are always deeper than the blood vessels. From this peripheral network, branches pass to the deeper network, which lies on the boundary between the dermis and the hypodermis; under the rete cutaneum it has much wider meshes, and its vessels are provided with valves. From the deeper network, large, subcutaneous lymphatic vessels originate and follow the blood vessels. Lymphatic vessels are not connected with the hairs or glands of the skin.

NERVES

The skin, with its accessories, serves as an organ for receiving impulses from the external environment. It is, accordingly, abundantly supplied with sensory nerves. In addition, it

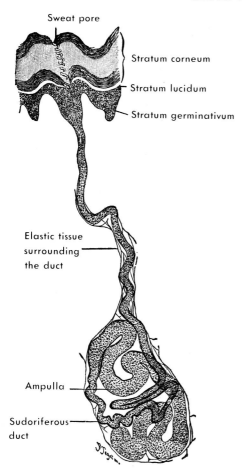

Sweat pore

Stratum corneum

Stratum lucidum

Stratum germinativum

Elastic tissue
surrounding
the duct

Ampulla

Sudoriferous
duct

Figure 22-29. Sweat gland from the palmar surface of an index finger. The drawing was based on study of sections and a teased preparation. × 45. (Slightly modified from von Brunn.)

contains nerves that supply the blood vessels, sweat glands, and arrector muscles.

In the subcutaneous stratum are rather thick nerve bundles that form networks composed mainly of myelinated and partly of non-myelinated fibers. The branches given off by this reticulum form, in the dermis, several new thin plexuses. Among them, the network on the boundary between the reticular and papillary layers stands out clearly, as does the subepithelial one.

In all the layers of the hypodermis, dermis, and epidermis are many different kinds of nerve endings, which are discussed in Chapter 12. Among them, the sensory endings are probably all connected with the craniospinal myelinated fibers; the nonmyelinated fibers lead to the blood vessels, smooth muscles, and glands. There are also free endings of unmyelinated sensory fibers in or close to the epidermis. The abundant nerves of the hair undoubtedly play an important part in the reception of tactile stimuli.

HISTOGENESIS OF THE SKIN AND ITS ACCESSORIES

The epidermis develops from the ectoderm, and the dermis arises from the mesenchyme. The *epidermis* in the human embryo, during the first two months, is a double layered epithelium. The basal layer, which lies on the mesenchyme, consists of cuboidal or cylindrical cells that multiply energetically. The peripheral layer consists of flat cells that are constantly formed anew from the elements of the

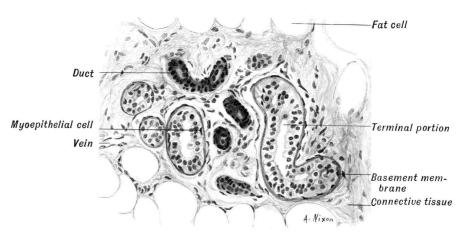

Fat cell

Duct

Myoepithelial cell

Vein

Terminal portion

Basement membrane

Connective tissue

A. Nixon

Figure 22-30. Section of human sweat gland. × 120.

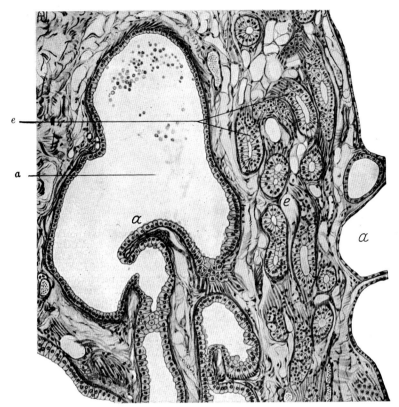

Figure 22-31. Axillary glands from a 37 year old woman during the premenstruum. *a,* Greatly enlarged glands that change with the menstrual cycle. *e,* Glands that do not change. Resorcin-fuchsin stain for elastic fibers. Preparation of Loescke. × 110. (After Hoepke.)

deeper layer. Beginning with the third month, the epidermis becomes triple layered. The new intermediate layer above the basal cells consists of polygonal cells, which increase in number and develop the surface projections formerly interpreted as intercellular bridges. At the end of the third month, in the peripheral portions of the intermediate layer, cornification begins and leads to the formation of the layers found in the adult. The horny scales are desquamated and form part of the vernix caseosa.

The irregularities on the lower surface of the epidermis arise at the end of the third month on the inner surfaces of the fingers, palms, and soles as parallel ridges protruding into the dermis. From the beginning they show a characteristic pattern, and from them sweat glands develop. Protruding longitudinal cushions corresponding to the ridges are formed on the external free surface of the epidermis.

The regional specificity of the epidermis has been the subject of detailed embryological study. It has been shown by Billingham and Silvers that the maintenance of the adult specificity of the epidermis depends on the dermis. When the dermis and epidermis are separated and epidermis from the ear is grown together with dermis from the sole, thick epidermis will develop. If a composite graft from sole epidermis is maintained with ear dermis, the originally thick epidermis becomes thinner and hair follicles develop. In the case of the tongue, however, the situation is different. There the epidermis remains tongue epidermis even when it is grown over dermis from the general body skin or the sole.

The *dermis* and *hypodermis* consist during the first six weeks of mesenchyme with wandering cells. From the second month on, the fibrillar interstitial substance appears, and elastic fibers follow. In still later stages, the mesen-

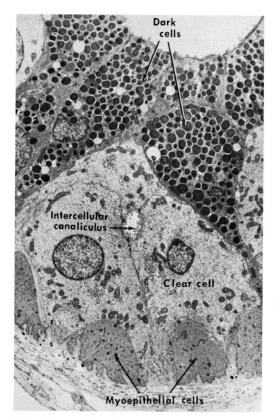

Figure 22-32. Electron micrograph of a sector of the secretory coil of a normal eccrine sweat gland. Muciginous, "dark" cells border the lumen, while "clear" serous cells are more deeply situated and surround intercellular canaliculi. The myoepithelial cells form an incomplete layer at the periphery of the tubule. × 3400. (Courtesy of R. E. Ellis.)

protrudes into the epithelial mass of the bulb (or germ). The epithelial cells at the surface of the connective tissue papilla represent the matrix of the future hair. The connective tissue that surrounds the bulb later forms the connective tissue portions of the hair follicle. On the surface of the epithelial hair bulb, two projections arise. The upper represents the primordium of the sebaceous gland; its central cells early undergo a fatty transformation. The lower protuberance becomes the insertion of the arrector pili muscle on the hair sac. In the mass of the epithelium that forms the hair primordium, a layer of rapidly cornifying cells differentiates into the layers of matrix, cortex, and inner and outer root sheaths. The shaft

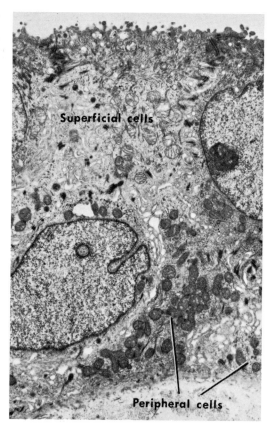

Figure 22-33. Electron micrograph of a portion of the wall of the coiled duct of an eccrine sweat gland. The luminal margin of the superficial cells contains a concentration of filaments formerly described as a "cuticular border." The peripheral cells have elaborately convoluted surfaces and contain many mitochondria. × 4000. (Courtesy of R. A. Ellis.)

chyme divides into a peripheral dense layer with a compact arrangement of its elements—the dermis—and the deep loose layer, the future subcutaneous layer. In the dermis, in turn, the peripheral papillary layer differentiates.

In man, *hair* first appears in the eyebrows and on the chin and upper lip, at the end of the second month. At first, in the deep layer of the epidermis, a group of cylindrical dividing cells appear. These grow into the underlying connective tissue and produce a gradually elongating epithelial cylinder (Fig. 22-36). This is the primordium of a hair follicle, the so-called "hair germ"; it is rounded and slightly flattened on its end. Under the latter an accumulation of condensed connective tissue appears early. From it the hair papilla forms and

AVERAGE NUMBERS, ± S. E. OF MEAN.		
HAIR FOLLICLES PER SQUARE CENTIMETER	SWEAT GLANDS PER SQUARE CENTIMETER	MELANOCYTES PER SQUARE MILLIMETER
Face	700±40	270±25	2120±90
Trunk	70±10	175±20	890±70
Arm	65±5	175±15	1160±40
Leg	55±5	130±10	1130±60
Average	330±20	212±15	1560±110

Figure 22-34. Regional anatomy of the human integument. (After G. Szabo.)

of the new hair elongates, owing to the multiplication of the cells of the matrix on the summit of the papilla, and perforates the top of the hollow cone of Henle's sheath. The tip of the hair moves upward, pierces the epidermis, and protrudes above the surface of the skin.

The development of the *nails* begins in the third month by the formation, on the back of the terminal phalanx of each finger, of a flat area, the *primary nail field,* which is surrounded by a fold of the skin. In the region of the nail the epithelium has three or four layers. The true nail substance is laid down during the fifth month, and without the participation of keratohyalin, in the portion of the nail bed near the proximal nail groove. Here the deep layer of the epidermis is transformed into the nail matrix, and its cells are penetrated by the fibrils of onychogenic substance; they become flat, adjoin one another closely, and give rise to the true nail plate. In the beginning it is still thin and is entirely buried in the epidermis of the nail field or bed. It gradually moves in the distal direction. The layers of epidermis that cover the plate eventually desquamate.

The development of the eccrine *sweat glands* in man proceeds independently of that of the hairs. The first primordia appear during the fifth month on the palms and soles and the lower surface of the fingers. At first they are similar to the primordia of the hairs. An epithelial shaft with a terminal thickening grows into the underlying connective tissue. But, unlike that around the hairs, the connective tissue here does not condense about the epithelium. The shaft gradually elongates and becomes cylindrical, and its lower portion curls in the form of a ball. Beginning in the seventh month, an irregular lumen forms in this lower

portion, which constitutes the secretory part; along the course of the future excretory duct another lumen develops and later unites with the first one. In the secretory portion, the epithelium around the lumen forms two layers, which differentiate into an external layer of myoepithelial elements and an internal layer of glandular cells.

New quantitative investigations have shown that in the embryo the density of the skin appendages, regardless of whether they are hair or eccrine glands, is originally the same. A large proportion of these appendages on the head, however, will become hairs and a large proportion of them on the rest of the body will become eccrine sweat glands. No hairs will be found on the palms and the soles. Due to the differential rate of growth of the body surface, the original uniform density changes because no new hair follicles or eccrine sweat glands form after the original population is established. These appendages subsequently become widely spaced in the trunk and in the extremities, which grow to a surface area about three times as great as the head. In wound

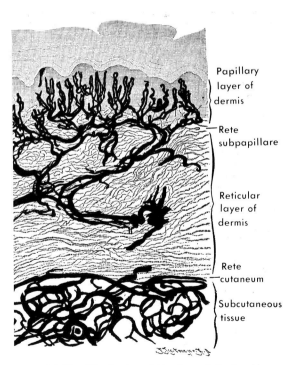

Papillary layer of dermis

Rete subpapillare

Reticular layer of dermis

Rete cutaneum

Subcutaneous tissue

Figure 22-35. Distribution of blood vessels in the skin. (Modified slightly from von Brunn.)

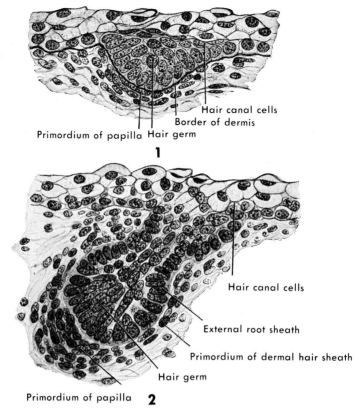

Figure 22-36. Two early hair primordia of the frontal skin of a three month embryo. *1,* First recognizable primordium and, *2,* at slightly later stage. × 740. (After Schaffer.)

healing, usually no new hair follicles are formed.

REFERENCES

Billingham, R. E.: Dendritic cells. J. Anat., *82:*93, 1948.

Billingham, R. E., and P. B. Medawar: A study of the branched cells of the mammalian epidermis with special reference to the fate of their division products. Philos. Trans. Roy. Soc. B, *237:*151, 1953.

Billingham, R. E., and W. K. Silvers: The melanocytes of mammals. Quart. Rev. Biol., *35:*1, 1960.

Billingham, R. E., and W. K. Silvers: The origin and conservation of epidermal specificites. N. Eng. J. Med., *268:*477, 539, 1963.

Birbeck, M. S. C., and E. H. Mercer: Electron microscopy of the human hair follicle. J. Biophys. & Biochem. Cytol., *3:*203, 1957.

Breathnach, A. S.: The cell of Langerhans. Int. Rev. Cytol., *18:*1, 1965.

Brody, I.: The keratinization of epidermal cells of normal guinea pig skin as revealed by electron microscopy. J. Ultrastruct. Res., *2:*482, 1959.

Chase, H. B.: Growth of the hair. Physiol. Rev., *34:*113, 1954.

Dole, V. P., and J. H. Thaysen: Variation in the functional power of human sweat glands. J. Exper. Med., *98:*129, 1953.

Drochmans, P.: On melanin granules. Int. Rev. Exp. Pathol., *2:*357, 1963.

Ellis, R. A.: Aging of the human male scalp. *In* Montagna, W., and R. A. Ellis, eds.: The Biology of Hair Growth. New York, Academic Press, 1958, p. 469.

Ellis, R. A.: Vascular patterns of the skin. *In* Montagna, W., and R. A. Ellis, eds.: Advances in Biology of the Skin. New York, Pergamon Press, 1961, Vol. 2, p. 20.

Felsher, Z.: Studies on the adherence of the epidermis to the corium. J. Invest. Derm., *8:*35, 1947.

Fitzpatrick, T. B., P. Brunet, and A. Kukita: The nature of hair pigment. *In* Montagna, W., and R. A. Ellis, eds.: The Biology of Hair Growth. New York, Academic Press, 1958, p. 255.

Fitzpatrick, T. B., and G. Szabo: The melanocyte: Cytology and cytochemistry. J. Invest. Derm., *32:*197, 1959.

Giacometti, L.: The anatomy of the human scalp. *In* Montagna, W., and R. A. Ellis, eds.: Advances in Biology of the Skin. New York, Pergamon Press, 1965, Vol. 6, p. 97.

Giacometti, L., and W. Montagna: Langerhans cells: Uptake of tritiated thymidine. Science, *157:*439, 1967.

Hibbs, R. G.: The fine structure of human eccrine sweat glands. Am. J. Anat., *103:*201, 1958.

Hoepke, H.: Die Haut. *In* von Möllendorff, W., and W. Bargmann, eds.: Handbuch der mikroskopischen Anatomie des Menschen. Berlin, Julius Springer, 1927, Vol. 3, part 1, p. 1.

Masson, P.: Les glomus cutanés de l'homme. Bull. Soc. franç. Dermat. et Syph., *42:*1174, 1935.

Matoltsy, A. G.: Chemistry of keratinization. *In* Montagna, W., and R. A. Ellis, eds.: The Biology of Hair Growth. New York, Academic Press, 1958, p. 135.

Matoltsy, A. G.: Membrane-coating granules of the epidermis. J. Ultrastruct. Res., *15:*510, 1966.

Matoltsy, A. G., and P. F. Parakkal: Membrane-coating granules of keratinizing epithelia. J. Cell Biol., *24:*297, 1965.

Medawar, P. B.: The micro-anatomy of the mammalian epidermis. Quart. J. Micr. Sci., *94:*481, 1953.

Mercer, E. H.: Keratin and Keratinization. An Essay in Molecular Biology. New York, Pergamon Press, 1961.

Montagna, W., H. B. Chase, and W. C. Lobitz: Histology and cytochemistry of human skin. IV. The eccrine sweat glands. J. Invest. Derm., *20:*415, 1953.

Montagna, W.: The Structure and Function of Skin. New York, Academic Press, 1956.

Munger, B. L.: The ultrastructure and histophysiology of human eccrine sweat glands. J. Biophys. & Biochem. Cytol., *11:*385, 1961.

Munger, B. L., and S. W. Brusilow: An electron microscopy study of eccrine sweat glands of the cat foot and toe pads. J. Biophys. & Biochem. Cytol., *11:*403, 1961.

Odland, G. F.: The fine structure of cutaneous capillaries. *In* Montagna, W., and R. A. Ellis, eds.: Advances in Biology of the Skin. New York, Pergamon Press, 1961, Vol. 2, p. 57.

Odland, G. F.: Tonofilaments and keratohyalin. *In* Montagna, W., and W. C. Lobitz, Jr., eds.: The Epidermis. New York, Academic Press, 1964, p. 237.

Pinkus, F.: Histologie der Haut. *In* Handbuch der Haut- und Geschlechtskrankheiten. Berlin, Julius Springer, 1927, Vol. 1, part 1, p. 77.

Quevedo, W. C., G. Szabo, J. Virks, and S. J. Sinesi: Melanocyte populations in UV-irradiated human skin. J. Invest. Derm., *45:* 295, 1965.

Rawles: M. E.: Origin of pigment cells from the neural crest in the mouse embryo. Physiol. Zool., *20:*248, 1947.

Rawles, M. E.: Skin and its derivatives. *In* Willier, B. J., P. A. Weiss, and V. Hamburger, eds.: Analysis of Development. Philadelphia, W. B. Saunders Co., 1955, p. 499.

Roth, S. I., and W. H. Clark, Jr.: Ultrastructural evidence related to the mechanism of keratin synthesis. *In* Montagna, W., and W. C. Lobitz, Jr., eds.: The Epidermis. New York, Academic Press, 1964, p. 303.

Rothman, S.: Physiology and Biochemistry of the Skin. Chicago, University of Chicago Press, 1954.

Seiji, M., T. B. Fitzpatrick, R. T. Simpson, and M. S. C. Birbeck: Chemical composition and terminology of specialized organelles (melanosomes and melanin granules) in mammalian melanocytes. Nature, *197:*1082, 1963.

Southwood, W. F. W.: The thickness of the skin. Plast. and Reconstr. Surg., *15:*423, 1955.

Szabo, G.: Quantitative histological investigations on the melanocyte system of the human epidermis. *In* Gordon, M., ed.: Pigment Cell Biology. New York, Academic Press, 1959, p. 99.

Szabo, G.: Current state of pigment research with special reference to the macromolecular aspects. *In* Lyne, A. G., and B. F. Short, eds.: Biology of the Skin and Hair Growth. Sydney, Angus and Robertson, 1965, p. 705.

Thuringer, J. M.: The mitotic index of the palmar and plantar epidermis in response to stimulation. J. Invest. Derm., *2:*313, 1939.

Zimmermann, A. A., and T. Cornbleet: The development of epidermal pigmentation in the Negro fetus. J. Invest. Derm., *11:* 383, 1948.

CHAPTER TWENTY-THREE

Oral Cavity and Associated Structures

GENERAL REMARKS ON THE DIGESTIVE SYSTEM

The digestive system is a long, tortuous tube, which begins with the lips and ends with the anus. On its way through this tract the food undergoes mechanical and chemical changes. It is minced and ground by the teeth and is forwarded through the tube by the contraction of its muscular walls, while it is digested by the secretions of the various parts of the alimentary tract and its auxiliary glands. A part of the digested food is absorbed through the walls of the intestine and passes into the blood, which carries it to the tissues of the organism. The undigested residue is eliminated as feces.

The digestive tract consists of the mouth, pharynx, esophagus, stomach, small intestine, large intestine, and rectum. The functional condition of one segment causes certain functional changes in the following segments. Thus the regular sequence of the processes necessary for the digestion of food is assured.

In the embryo the endoderm is transformed into the epithelial structures of the alimentary canal. The visceral mesoderm gives rise to its connective and muscular tissues. In the adult the inner surface of the wall of the digestive tube is lined by a *mucous membrane* consisting of a superficial layer of epithelium and a layer of connective tissue, the *lamina propria*. The wall of the digestive tube contains smooth muscles, which form the *muscularis externa* (Fig. 23-1).

In most parts of the digestive tube the outer limit of the mucous membrane is marked by a thin muscular layer, the *muscularis mucosae*. Between it and the *muscularis externa* is a layer of loose connective tissue, the *submucosa*. Where the muscularis mucosae is absent, there is a gradual transition from the lamina propria to the submucosa.

The mucous membrane of the developing gastrointestinal tract forms numerous outgrowths, which increase the surface area of the epithelium. It is also provided with many invaginations, the *glands* or *crypts*, lined by epithelium. Some of them elaborate digestive juices, which split the food into its simple chemical constituents, and others produce mucus to lubricate the surface of the membrane. Some of the glands remain confined to the thickness of the mucous membrane; others grow to such an extent that they become separate organs, connected by long ducts with the epithelial surface from which they originated. In the oral cavity, esophagus, and rectum, the wall of the digestive tube is surrounded by a layer of dense connective tissue, which attaches it to the neighboring organs. The outer surface of the stomach and intestines, suspended in the peritoneal cavity by the mesenteries, is covered with a serous membrane that permits these viscera to move freely in the cavity. The wall of the digestive tube is richly provided with blood vessels that bring nutritive materials and oxygen, as well as the raw materials necessary for the secretory activity. These vessels also carry away from the mucous membrane a large part of the absorbed products of digestion; the remainder of the absorbed products enter the lymphatics of the intestines. The wall of the digestive tract contains an intricate system of sympathetic nervous ganglia and plexuses, which are concerned with the control of the movements of the tube.

THE ORAL CAVITY

The epithelium of the mucous membrane in the mouth is stratified squamous, like that of the skin. However, in man, under physiological conditions, it does not undergo complete cornification. The nuclei of the cells of the superficial layers shrink and degenerate, but do not disappear, and the cell bodies do not reach the same degree of flatness as in the epidermis. These superficial cells are shed in large quantities and are found in the saliva. In some places they contain granules of keratohyalin. In the cells of the middle and superficial layers there is usually some glycogen. In

many animals the epithelium of the oral cavity undergoes extensive cornification.

The *lamina propria,* in most places, projects into concavities in the deep surface of the epithelium in papillae similar to those of the skin. Their structure is, however, more delicate, and the collagenous and elastic fibers are thinner than in the dermis. In the posterior region of the oral cavity the lamina propria contains many lymphocytes, which are often found migrating into and through the epithelium. The arrangement of the blood vessels is similar to that in the skin. There is a deep submucous plexus of large vessels, from which arise branches that form a second plexus in the lamina propria, which in turn sends small branches into the papillae. The lymphatics also show an arrangement similar to that in the skin, and begin with blind capillary outgrowths in the papillae.

The *oral mucous membrane* is very sensitive

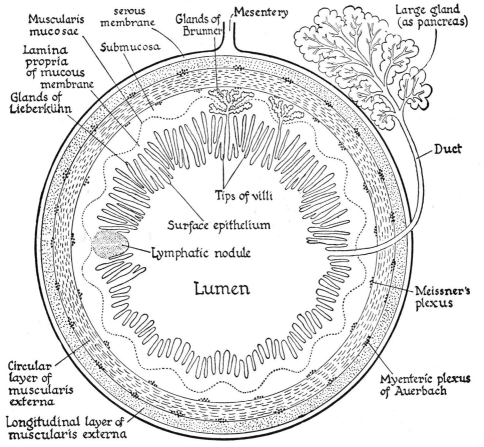

Figure 23-1. Diagram of cross section of intestinal tract. In the upper half of the drawing the mucous membrane is depicted with glands and villi as in the small intestine; in the lower half it contains only glands as in the colon.

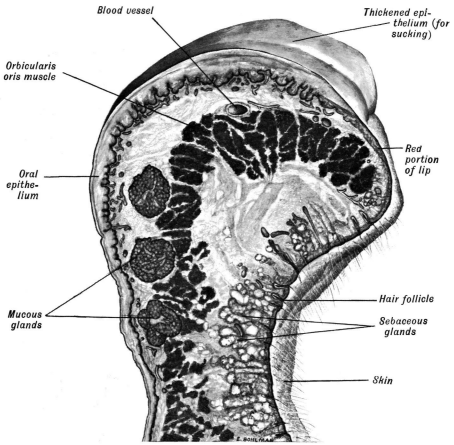

Figure 23-2. Camera lucida drawing of sagittal section through lip of a newborn infant. Stained with hematoxylin.
× 10.

and is provided with many nerve endings belonging to the sensory branches of the trigeminal nerve. On that portion covering the tongue it also contains the specific end-organs of the sense of taste. In most places under the lamina propria, especially in the cheeks and on the soft palate, there is a fat containing, loose *submucosa,* into which the dense connective tissue of the mucosa gradually merges. In places with a well developed submucosa the mucous membrane can be easily lifted into folds. In those places against which the food is crushed and rubbed, as on the hard palate, there is no submucosa, and the mucous membrane is firmly bound to the underlying periosteum or muscle.

The inner zone of the lip margin in the newborn is considerably thickened and provided with many high papillae and numerous sebaceous glands not associated with hairs. These structural features seem to facilitate the process of sucking.

The *soft palate* consists of layers of striated muscle and fibrous tissue covered with mucous membrane. On the oral surface the latter has the structure typical of the oral cavity—a stratified squamous epithelium, with high papillae, and glands of the pure mucous type. The glands are surrounded by adipose tissue and are scattered in a loose submucous layer separated from the lamina propria by dense elastic networks. This oral type of mucous membrane also covers the posterior margin of the soft palate and continues onto the nasal surface. On this surface, at varying distances from its posterior margin, the stratified epithelium is replaced by pseudostratified, ciliated columnar epithelium, which rests on a thickened basement lamina. The lamina propria contains small glands of the mixed type, but no adipose tissue, and it is infiltrated with lymphocytes. A dense layer of elastic fibers is found between the glands and the underlying muscle. A submucosa is not present.

THE TONGUE

The tongue consists of interlacing bundles of striated muscle that run in three planes and cross one another at right angles. The muscular mass is covered by a tightly adherent mucous membrane. The dense lamina propria is continuous with the interstitial connective tissue of the muscle. A submucous layer is present only on the under surface. The lower surface of the tongue is smooth. The dorsal surface is covered in its anterior part by a multitude of small excrescences—the *papillae* —whereas in its posterior part it presents only irregular bulges of larger size. The boundary line between the two regions is **V**-shaped, with the opening of the angle directed forward (Fig. 23-3). The principal gustatory region of the tongue is along this line. At the apex of the angle is a small invagination, the *foramen caecum*. It is the rudiment of the thyroglossal duct, which in early embryonic stages connects the thyroid gland primordium with the epithelium of the oral cavity.

PAPILLAE. Three types of papillae are present on the body of the tongue: the filiform, the fungiform, and the circumvallate. The *filiform papillae* are arranged in more or less distinct rows diverging to the right and left from the middle line and parallel to the **V**-shaped gustatory region. The *fungiform papillae* are scattered singly among the filiform and are especially numerous near the tip of the tongue. The *circumvallate papillae,* numbering only 10 to 12 in man, are arranged along the diverging arms of the **V**-shaped gustatory region (Fig. 23-3).

The filiform papillae are 2 to 3 mm. long. Their connective tissue core is beset with secondary papillae with pointed ends. The epithelium covering these connective tissue outgrowths also forms short papillae, which taper into pointed processes (Fig. 23-4). In man the superficial squamous cells are transformed into hard scales containing shrunken nuclei. The axial parts of the scales at the point of the papilla are connected with its solid axial strand, and their lower edges project from the surface of the papilla like the branches of a fir tree. When digestion is disturbed in illness, the normal shedding of these scales is delayed. They then accumulate, in layers mixed with bacteria, on the surface of the tongue, which thus is covered with a gray film—the "coated" tongue.

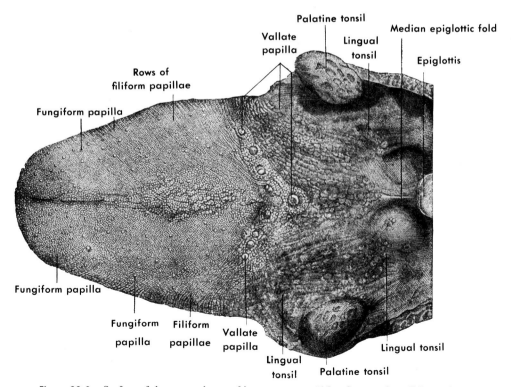

Figure 23-3. Surface of dorsum and root of human tongue. (After Sappey, from Schumacher.)

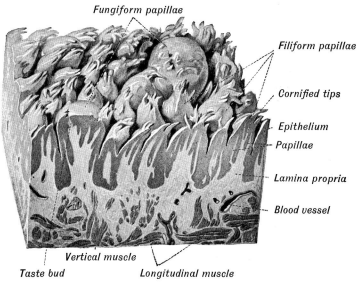

Figure 23-4. Surface of dorsum of tongue, drawn from a combined study with the binocular microscope and of sections. The anterior cut surface corresponds with the long axis of the tongue—the tip of the tongue being to the reader's left. × 16. (After Braus.)

The *fungiform papillae* have a short, slightly constricted stalk and a slightly flattened hemispherical upper part. The connective tissue core forms secondary papillae that project into recesses in the underside of the epithelium, which has a smooth free surface (Fig. 23-4). On many of the fungiform papillae the epithelium associated with the secondary papillae contains taste buds. Because the core is rich in blood vessels, the fungiform papillae have a marked red color.

The *circumvallate papillae* are sunk into the surface of the mucous membrane, and each is surrounded by a deep, circular furrow. The connective tissue core forms secondary papillae only on the upper surface. The covering epithelium is smooth, while that of the lateral surfaces of the papillae contains many taste buds (Figs. 23-6 and 23-7). In a vertical section, 10 to 12 of them can be seen on the lateral surface of the papilla. A few may be present in the outer wall of the groove surrounding the papilla. The number of taste buds in a single papilla is subject to great variations, but it has been estimated to average 250.

Connected with the circumvallate papillae are glands of the serous type (*glands of von Ebner*), whose bodies are embedded deep in the underlying muscular tissue and whose excretory ducts open into the bottom of the furrow.

On the lateral surface of the posterior part of the tongue are the paired *foliate papillae*. In man they are rudimentary, but in many animals they represent the main peripheral organ of taste. The fully developed foliate papillae in the rabbit are oval bulgings on the mucous membrane, consisting of alternating parallel ridges and grooves. The epithelium of the sides of the ridges contains many taste buds. Small serous glands open into the bottom of the furrows.

Taste buds are also found on the glossopalatine arch, on the soft palate, on the posterior surface of the epiglottis, and on the posterior wall of the pharynx as far down as the inferior edge of the cricoid cartilage.

The bulgings on the root of the tongue are caused by lymphatic nodules, the *lingual tonsils* and *follicles* (Fig. 23-3). On the free surface of each lingual tonsil a small opening leads into a deep invagination, the *crypt*, lined with stratified squamous epithelium. The crypt is surrounded by lymphatic tissue. Innumerable lymphocytes infiltrate the epithelium and assemble in the lumen of the crypt, where they degenerate and form masses of detritus with the desquamated epithelial cells and bacteria. The lingual tonsils are often associated with mucous glands embedded in the underlying muscle tissue. The ducts of the latter open into the crypt or onto the free surface.

TASTE BUDS.   The taste buds are seen in

sections under low power as pale, oval bodies in the darker-stained epithelium. Their long axis averages 72 μ. They extend from the basement lamina almost to the surface. The epithelium over each taste bud is pierced by a small opening—the *outer taste pore* (Figs. 23-8 and 23-10).

Two cell types are usually distinguished among the constituents of a taste bud: the *supporting cells* and the *neuroepithelial taste cells*. The first are spindle-shaped, and their ends surround a small opening, the *inner taste pore,* which leads into a pitlike excavation. The taste cells distributed between the supporting cells vary from 4 to 20 per taste bud. They have a slender, rod-shaped form, with a nucleus in the middle, and on the free surface short *taste hairs,* which project freely into the lumen of the pit.

There are only four fundamental taste sensations: sweet, bitter, acid, and salty. It has been shown by the application of substances to individual fungiform papillae that they differ widely in their receptive properties. Some do not give any taste sensations, while others give sensations of one or more taste qualities. No structural differences in the various taste buds have been found, in spite of the differences in sensation mediated. There is, moreover, a general chemical sensitivity in regions of the mouth where there are no taste buds.

NERVES. The anterior two thirds of the tongue is innervated by the lingual nerve, which contains fibers of general sensibility from the fifth cranial nerve (trigeminal) and fibers of gustatory sensibility from the seventh cranial nerve (facialis). The latter enter the lingual nerve from the chorda tympani. The posterior third of the tongue is innervated by the glossopharyngeal nerve for both general and gustatory sensibility. Taste buds of the epiglottis and lower pharynx are innervated by the vagus. These nerve fibers are lightly myelinated. They branch profusely under the basement lamina, lose their myelin, and form a subepithelial plexus, from which fibers penetrate the epithelium. Some terminate as *intergemmal fibers* by free arborization between the taste buds. Others, the *perigemmal fibers,* closely envelop the taste buds; and still others, the *intragemmal fibers,* penetrate the taste buds and end with small terminal enlargements in intimate contact with the taste cells. The functional significance of these different nerve endings is unknown.

GLANDS OF THE ORAL CAVITY

GENERAL DESCRIPTION. Numerous *salivary glands* open into the oral cavity. Many of them are small glands in the mucosa or submucosa and are named according to their location. They seem to secrete continuously and furnish a liquid, the *saliva,* which moistens the oral mucous membrane. In addition, there are three pairs of large glands, which constitute the salivary glands proper. They are the *parotid,* the *mandibular (submaxillary),* and the *sublingual* glands. They secrete only when me-

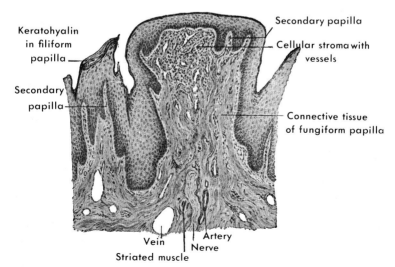

Figure 23-5. Perpendicular section through a fungiform papilla. × 46. (After Schaffer, from Schumacher.)

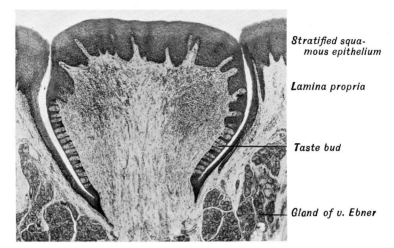

Stratified squa-
mous epithelium

Lamina propria

Taste bud

Gland of v. Ebner

Figure 23-6. Section through circumvallate papilla of *Macacus rhesus.* Photomicrograph. × 42.

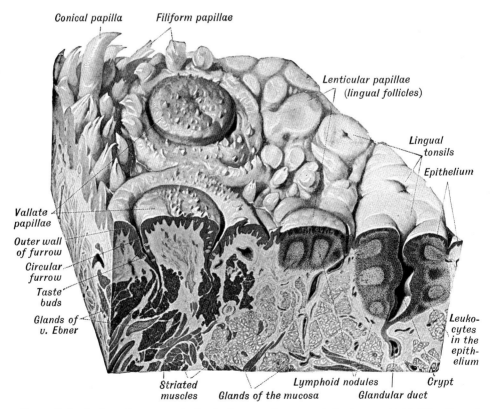

Conical papilla

Filiform papillae

Lenticular papillae
(lingual follicles)

Lingual
tonsils

Epithelium

Vallate
papillae

Outer wall
of furrow

Circular
furrow

Taste
buds

Glands of
v. Ebner

Leuko-
cytes
in the
epith-
elium

Striated
muscles

Glands of the mucosa

Lymphoid nodules

Glandular duct

Crypt

Figure 23-7. Surface of tongue at the border between the root and the dorsum. × 16. (After Braus.)

chanical, thermal, or chemical stimuli act upon the nerve endings in the oral mucous membrane, or as the result of certain psychic or olfactory stimuli. The saliva secreted by the large glands is abundant and helps prepare the food for digestion in the stomach and intestine.

The *saliva* collected from the oral cavity is a mixture of the secretions of the various salivary glands. It is a viscous, colorless, opalescent liquid which contains water, mucin, some proteins, mineral salts, and an enzyme, *ptyalin,* which splits starch into smaller water soluble carbohydrates. Saliva always contains desquamated squamous epithelial cells and *salivary corpuscles.* Most of the latter originate in the follicles of the tongue and in the tonsils, and are degenerating lymphocytes or granulocytes.

The quality of the saliva collected from the oral cavity varies, depending upon the degree of participation of the various salivary glands in its formation. But even the secretion of one gland may change considerably with variations in the stimuli acting upon the oral mucous membrane, as, for instance, with different kinds of food.

The salivary glands may be classified in three categories according to the type of their secretory cells. The glands containing only *mucous* cells elaborate a viscid secretion that consists almost exclusively of mucin. In glands with only *serous* cells, the secretion is a watery liquid that lacks mucus but contains salts, proteins, and the enzyme ptyalin. In the *mixed glands,* containing serous and mucous cells, the secretion is a viscid liquid containing mucin, salts, and ptyalin.

All glands of the oral cavity have a system of branching ducts. The secretory portions of the pure mucous glands are usually long, branching tubules. In the pure serous and mixed glands the secretory portions vary from simple oval to tubuloacinar forms with irregular outpocketings.

The initial intralobular ducts are thin, branched tubules called the *necks,* or *intercalated ducts.* Branches of the next larger order, also located in the interior of the smallest lobules, have a vertically striated epithelium; these segments are called *striated ducts,* Then follow the larger branches. Among them lobular, interlobular, and primary ducts may be distinguished in the large glands.

MUCOUS CELLS. In the pure mucous glands the cells are arranged in a layer against

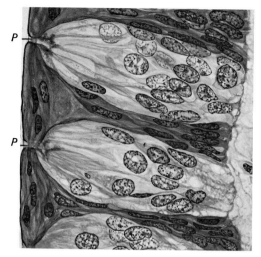

Figure 23-8. Two taste buds from side of circumvallate papilla of *Macacus rhesus,* showing outer taste pores at *P.* (Drawn by Miss E. Bohlman.)

the basement lamina and have an irregularly cuboidal form. In fresh condition their cytoplasm contains many pale droplets of *mucigen,* the antecedent of mucin. In fixed and stained sections the droplets of mucigen are usually destroyed, so that the cell body appears clear and contains only a loose network of cytoplasm and precipitated mucigen. This network stains red with mucicarmine, or metachromatically with thionine, like mucin. The nucleus is at the base of the cell and usually appears angular and compressed by the accumulation of mucigen. Between the droplets of mucigen a few mitochondria and fragments of a Golgi net can be found. The free surface of the mucous cells is usually provided with a network of terminal bars. Secretory canaliculi are absent. Usually the lumen of the terminal portions of the glands is large and filled with masses of mucin.

When the secretion has been discharged, the cell collapses, and only a few granules of mucigen may remain near its free surface. The nucleus rises from the base of the cell and becomes round. In this depleted condition the mucous cells may be mistaken for serous cells, but the absence of secretory capillaries always distinguishes mucous from serous glands. The demonstration of these capillaries, however, requires special staining methods. Under physiological conditions, the mucous cells rarely discharge all of their granules.

The most reliable criterion for separating mucous and serous cells is the positive staining of mucus in the former. The staining reactions of the mucin elaborated by different mucous cells are not the same, even in the same gland. The cells, as a rule, do not show any signs of degeneration and apparently recover completely from discharge of their secretion. Mitoses have occasionally been observed in them.

SEROUS CELLS. These cells are roughly cuboidal and surround a small tubular lumen. In an unfixed resting gland they contain a multitude of highly refractile *secretion granules* in an otherwise homogeneous cytoplasm. The secretory granules accumulate between the nucleus and the free surface. After the gland has secreted for a certain time, the serous cells diminish in size and their few remaining granules are confined to the apical cytoplasm of the cells. In nonphysiological extremes of induced secretory activity all the granules may disappear. Inasmuch as the serous cells are probably the source of ptyalin, the granules are to be looked upon as zymogen granules, the antecedents of the enzyme.

In cells crowded with secretion the nu-

cleus is spherical, small, and darkly staining. It occupies a position at the base of the cell and may show irregular indentations. With special cytological methods the cytoplasm can be shown to contain rod-shaped mitochondria and a supranuclear Golgi apparatus in addition to the secretory granules. At the base of the cell and extending upward around the nucleus is an accumulation of chromophilic substance, with the staining properties of ribonucleoprotein. Its arrangement in parallel lamellae sometimes results in a vertical striation of the base of the cell. By appropriate techniques mitochondria can be demonstrated between the lamellae. The serous cells often contain fat droplets or deposits of glycogen. On their free surfaces the serous cells may have a few microvilli visible in electron micrographs. Between their lateral surfaces, particularly at the corners of the prismatic cells, there are always secretory capillaries.

The serous cells of the different glands of the mouth are not functionally identical, although they have a similar structure. They are

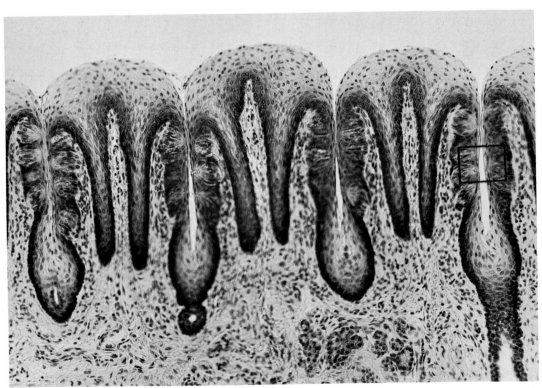

Figure 23-9 Photomicrograph of the foliate papillae of a rabbit, showing the alternating ridges and deep clefts with numerous taste buds on either side of the cleft. × 150. An area such as that enclosed in the rectangle is shown at higher magnification in Figure 23-10.

combined into one group and given a general name, because histological methods are not able to demonstrate differences in the nature of their secretory products. In some instances their secretory granules give a more or less distinct staining reaction with mucicarmine; such cells are called "mucoserous" or "muco-abuminous."

CELLS IN THE MIXED GLANDS. The relative numbers of the two kinds of granular cells in the mixed glands vary within wide limits. In some cases the serous cells are far more numerous than the mucous cells, whereas in other cases the reverse is true. In still other instances both cell types are present in about equal numbers. The mucous and serous cells line different parts of the terminal secretory portion of the gland. In those mixed glands in which the serous cells predominate, some of the terminal portions may be exclusively serous (Fig. 23-13). In others a part of the secretory portion is lined with mucous and a part with serous cells. In sections the mucous portions can usually be recognized by the clear empty appearance of their cytoplasm, but they are identified more certainly by their color after specific staining of the mucus.

As a rule, the mucous cells are located nearer the ducts, while the serous cells are confined to the blind end of the terminal secretory portion. It is quite probable that the mucous cells in mixed glands arise through the differentiation of the cells in the smallest ducts. Sometimes single mucous cells are scattered between the unspecialized cells of the neck of the gland. In other cases the part of the neck directly adjoining the terminal portion is lined exclusively with mucous cells. If the mucous transformation affects all the cells in the neck, this part of the duct ceases to exist as such. If the mucous cells are not numerous, the secretory portion of the gland will show an irregular mixture of the pale mucous and dark serous cells.

If the mucous cells predominate, the serous cells are displaced to the blind ends of the terminal portion or into saccular out-pockets. Here they form small groups, which in sections appear as darkly staining crescents (*demilunes of Giannuzzi*) surrounding the ends of the tubules of mucous cells (Figs. 23-11 and 23-13). In them the serous cells are small and flattened and often seem to be entirely separated from the lumen by the large mucous cells. However, there are always secretory

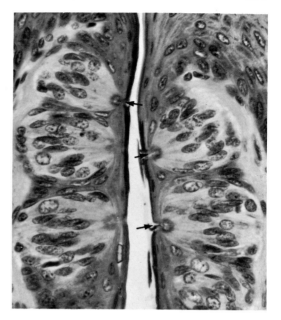

Figure 23-10. Photomicrograph of taste buds from the foliate papillae of a rabbit. × 450. See Figure 23-9 for location. The arrows indicate the taste pores.

capillaries, which conduct the secretion through clefts between the mucous cells into the lumen (Fig. 23-11).

BASAL (BASKET) CELLS. In all the glands of the oral cavity the epithelium in the terminal portion, as well as in the ducts, is provided with basal cells. They lie between the glandular cells and the basement lamina and appear as slender spindle-shaped elements. Usually only their nuclei can be discerned. When seen from the surface, they exhibit a stellate cell body with processes containing darkly staining fibrils (Fig. 23-15).

The basal cells are presumed to be contractile and to facilitate the movement of the secretion into the ducts. They are sometimes called "myoepithelial cells" and resemble the myoepithelial cells of the sweat glands and mammary gland.

DUCTS OF THE GLANDS. The necks of the glands of the oral cavity are of variable length and have a low cuboidal epithelium. Between the lining cells and the basement lamina are scattered basal cells. The epithelium of the necks often shows varying degrees of transformation to mucous cells.

In the columnar epithelium of the striated segments of the ducts the lower parts of the cell bodies show a parallel striation, attribut-

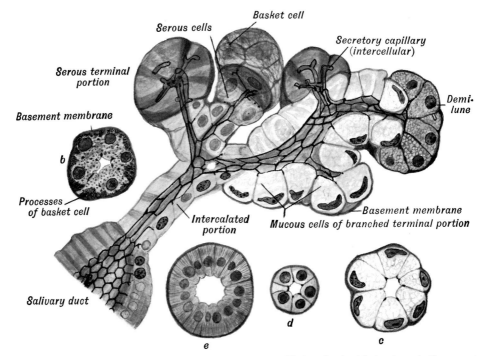

Figure 23-11. Reconstruction of a terminal portion of a submandibular gland with its duct. *b,* Cross section of a purely serous terminal portion, showing basal lamellae; *c,* cross section through a purely mucous terminal portion; *d,* cross section through an intercalated portion; *e,* cross section through a salivary duct. (Redrawn and modified after a reconstruction by Vierling, from Braus.)

able to vertical orientation of mitochondria in slender compartments formed by infolding of the basal cell membrane. The numerous infoldings of the basal surface of the cells in the striated ducts are not resolved with the light microscope but are visible with the electron microscope, as they are in other epithelia where there is rapid transport of water and ions (Fig. 23-14).

In the larger ducts the epithelium is columnar and pseudostratified, and occasionally contains goblet cells. Nearing the opening on the mucous membrane, it becomes stratified for a short distance and is then succeeded by stratified squamous epithelium.

CLASSIFICATION OF ORAL GLANDS BY LOCATION. The glands of the oral cavity may be classified on the basis of their location, as in the following outline:

A. Glands that open into the vestibule of the mouth:
   1. Parotid gland, with a duct opening into the vestibule
   2. Labial glands, scattered in the mucous membrane of the upper and lower lips
   3. Buccal glands, a continuation of the labial glands in the mucous membrane of the cheek

B. Glands that open on the floor of the oral cavity, between the tongue and the mandible:
   1. Submandibular (submaxillary) gland—a large gland with a duct opening at the side of the frenulum of the tongue
   2. Sublingual glands, situated deep to the mucous membrane of the tongue at the side of the frenulum. Among them:
      (a) The large sublingual gland with its duct opening into the duct of the submandibular gland
      (b) Several small glands varying in number and size. Their ducts open in many places along a fold of the mucous membrane, called the plica sublingualis. At the posterior end of this group are the small glossopalatine glands

C. Glands of the tongue:
   1. Anterior lingual gland (gland of Blandin or Nuhn), situated at the side of the median line near the apex of the tongue
   2. Posterior lingual glands:

(a) Serous or gustatory glands (of von Ebner) connected with the circumvallate papillae and opening into the circumvallate groove

(b) Mucous glands of the root of the tongue

D. Glands of the palate

In the various mammals the glands of the oral cavity show great structural differences. The descriptions given in the following paragraphs hold only for man.

The *parotid* is a nearly pure serous gland. The necks are long and may branch several times. Their cells almost never undergo mucous transformation in the adult. In the parotid gland of the newborn, however, the glandular cells often give a distinct staining reaction for mucus with mucicarmine. The striated tubules are fairly numerous.

In the *submandibular gland* the majority of the secretory portions are purely serous, while some are mucous with serous cells in the blind ends. Typical demilunes are rare. In some persons many of the serous cells show a slight mucoid reaction. The mucous cells are smaller than in the sublingual or the pure mucous glands. Some of the necks are short; others are long and branching. The striated tubules are numerous and long, and have many branches.

The *sublingual glands* are mixed glands with a markedly varying structure in their different parts. The mucous cells are far more numerous than in the mandibular gland, while the serous cells are in the minority and have a pronounced mucoserous character. For the most part they are arranged in thick demilunes, and the isthmuses are extremely variable in length. Many undergo a complete mucous transformation, so that the terminal portions abut directly on the striated tubules. The striated tubules are scarce and short, and are sometimes represented by small groups of irregular, striated cells in the epithelium of the interlobular ducts.

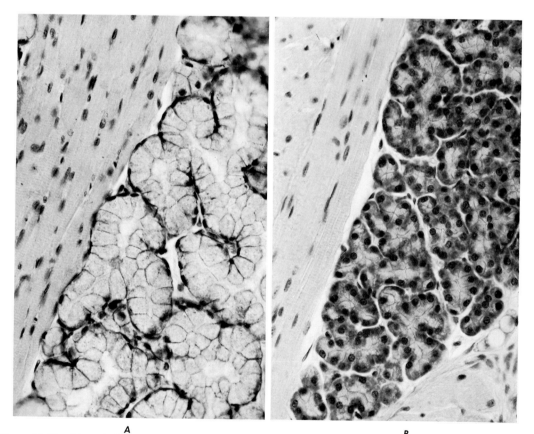

A   B

Figure 23-12. Lingual glands, situated among the bundles of striated muscle in rabbit tongue. *A,* Mucous glands. *B,* Serous glands. × 300.

In the *posterior lingual glands* the long secretory portions are branching and occasionally anastomosing tubules. They contain only serous cells, which sometimes show a slight reaction for mucus. These glands are rarely of mixed character. The system of ducts is poorly developed; isthmuses and short tubes are absent. These glands form a thin, serous secretion, which is found mainly in the furrows of the circumvallate papillae and evidently serves to wash out the taste buds.

The *glossopalatine glands* are pure mucous glands.

The *anterior lingual gland*, in its posterior part, consists of mixed branched tubules, which contain mucous cells and, on their blind ends, thin demilunes of seromucinous cells. The anterior part contains secretory tubules with seromucinous cells only.

The *labial* and *buccal glands* are of the mixed type. The secretory portion sometimes contains only seromucinous cells, but in most cases the latter are confined to the blind end, while the rest is lined with mucous cells. Some of the secretory parts may contain only mucous cells. Since the necks are short and branch but little, the mucous secretory portions often pass directly into striated ducts.

The *glands of the root of the tongue* and the *palatine glands* are of the pure mucous variety. Short isthmuses have been found in the latter group.

INTERSTITIAL CONNECTIVE TISSUE; BLOOD AND LYMPHATIC VESSELS. In the interstitial reticular connective tissue of the salivary glands are fibroblasts and macrophages, with fat cells scattered singly or in small groups. Plasma cells are of common occurrence and, occasionally, small lymphocytes are also found. The larger blood vessels follow the larger ducts. Loose capillary networks surround the ducts and the terminal portions. The lymph vessels are said to be scarce.

NERVES. Each salivary gland is provided with sensory nerve endings and two kinds of efferent secretory nerves, parasympathetic and sympathetic. The parasympathetic preganglionic fibers for the submandibular and sublingual glands run in the chorda tympani nerve to the submaxillary ganglion. The sympathetic preganglionic fibers go to the superior cervical ganglion. From here the postganglionic fibers follow along the carotid artery. The vasodilators are believed to be included in the chorda tympani, the vasoconstrictors in the sympathetic nerves.

The parotid gland receives its secretory fibers from the glossopharyngeal nerve. In the interstitial tissue, along the course of its blood vessels, are found plexuses of myelinated (preganglionic and sensory) and nonmyelinated fibers, and groups of sympathetic multipolar nerve cells close to the larger ducts. On the outer surface of the terminal portions, nonmyelinated fibers form a network that sends small branches through the basement lamina. These branches form a second network, from which branches penetrate between the glandular cells, ramify, and end on the surfaces of the glandular cells with small, terminal thickenings.

Stimulation of the parasympathetic nerves of the submandibular gland causes the secretion of an abundant thin saliva, rich in water and salts but poor in organic substances. Stimulation of the sympathetic nerve, on the contrary, yields a small quantity of thick sa-

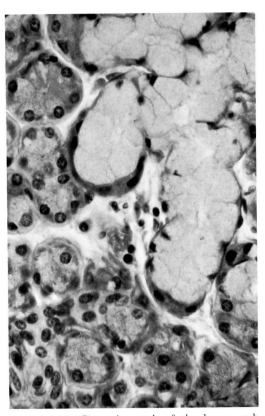

Figure 23-13. Photomicrograph of the human submandibular gland, a mixed gland, showing serous acini at the lower left and at the upper right mucous acini with serous demilunes. × 475.

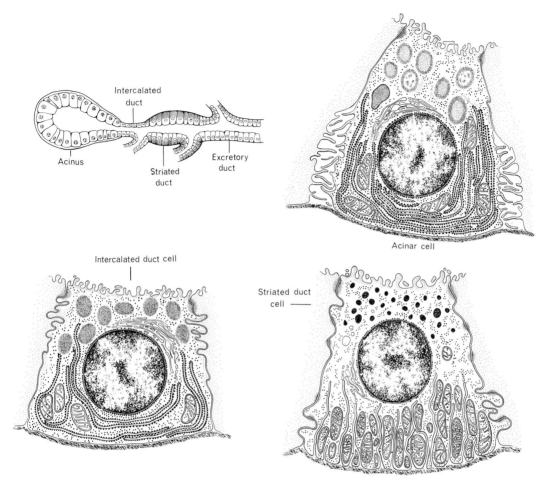

Acinar cell

Intercalated duct cell

Striated duct cell

Intercalated duct

Acinus

Striated duct

Excretory duct

Figure 23-14. Diagrammatic representation of the fine structural characteristics of the various cell types in the mouse submandibular gland. (Redrawn after U. Rutberg.)

liva, with a high content of organic substances. The mechanism of the action of the nerves upon the glandular cells and the role of the vasodilators in the secretion are not known. The presence of different kinds of nerve endings has not been proved. It is even doubtful whether the secretory fibers in the chorda tympani and in the sympathetic nerve are of different nature.

After sectioning of the chorda tympani nerve in the dog, the so-called "paralytic" secretion in the corresponding submandibular and retrolingual glands occurs. This secretion is accompanied by intense degeneration and atrophy of the gland cells, especially of the mucous elements in the retrolingual gland.

HISTOGENESIS OF THE GLANDS OF THE ORAL CAVITY. Each gland arises at a certain time of fetal life, through the growth of a solid epithelial bud from the lining of the embryonic oral cavity into the subjacent mesenchyme. The large glands, such as the submandibular and the parotid, appear in embryos of 6 and 8 weeks, respectively; the smaller ones appear

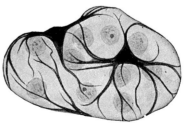

Figure 23-15. Branching basal (basket or myoepithelial) cells with dark fibrils; from an albuminous terminal portion of a human submaxillary gland. Iron-hematoxylin stain. Oil immersion. (after Zimmermann.)

a   *b*

Figure 23-16. Cross sections of two isthmuses from a human submaxillary gland, each showing three basal cells. *a,* Thin and, *b,* thicker canal belonging to purely serous terminal portions. In *b* a fixed connective tissue cell is adhering to the basement lamina. (After Zimmermann.)

later. The epithelial bud grows and ramifies into an arborescent structure with club-shaped ends. It consists of undifferentiated polyhedral or cuboidal epithelial cells with many mitoses. Gradually a lumen appears in the older parts of the primordium, and this canalization proceeds distally but does not reach the terminal branches as long as these continue to grow and to form additional buds. When the lumen reaches the terminal bud, the latter ceases to grow, and specific differentiation and enlargement of its cells occur. Mucigen appears in the mucous cells and zymogen granules in the serous ones. The histogenetic development of the glands continues after birth.

TONSILS

The aperture through which the oral cavity communicates with the pharynx is called the *fauces.* In this region the mucous membrane of the digestive tract contains accumulations of lymphatic tissue. In addition to small infiltrations of lymphocytes, which may occur anywhere in this part of the mucous membrane, there are well outlined organs of lymphatic tissue. The surface epithelium invaginates into them, and they are called "tonsils." The lingual tonsils have been described (p. 514).

Between the glossopalatine and the pharyngopalatine arches are the *palatine tonsils,* two prominent, oval accumulations of lymphatic tissue in the connective tissue beneath the mucous membrane. The overlying epithelium invaginates to form 10 to 20 deep tonsillar *crypts.* The stratified squamous epithelium of the free surface overlies a thin layer of fibrous connective tissue with papillae. The crypts almost reach the connective tissue *capsule* and are of simple or branching form (Fig. 23-17). The nodules with their prominent centers

are embedded in a diffuse mass of dense lymphatic tissue 1 to 2 mm. thick, and are usually arranged in a single layer under the epithelium. The crypts with their surrounding sheaths of lymphatic tissue are partially separated from one another by thin partitions of loose connective tissue which invaginate from the capsule. In this connective tissue there are always lymphocytes of various sizes, and mast and plasma cells. The presence of large numbers of heterophilic leukocytes is indicative of inflammation. A mild degree of inflammation of the tonsils is very common. Frequently there are islands of cartilage or bone, which probably indicate a pathological process. In the deeper portion of the crypts, the limit between the epithelium and the lymphatic tissue is effaced in most places by an intense infiltration of the epithelium with lymphocytes. The epithelial cells are pushed aside and disfigured, so that sometimes only a few recognizable epithelial cells remain on the surface. Heterophilic leukocytes are always present in small numbers (Fig. 23-18). Plasma cells are common here.

The lymphocytes that pass through the

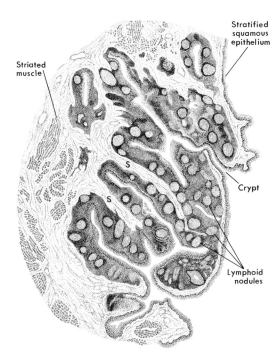

Striated muscle

Stratified squamous epithelium

S

S

Crypt

Lymphoid nodules

Figure 23-17. Section through palatine tonsil of man, showing crypts penetrating the tonsil from the free surface and connective tissue septa (*S*) penetrating the lymphoid tissue from beneath. × 6. (Redrawn and modified from Sobotta.)

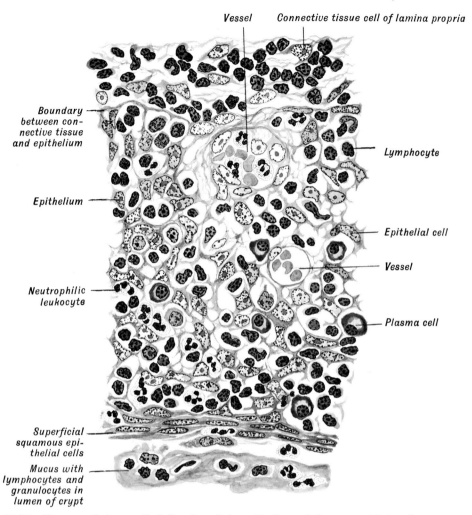

Vessel   Connective tissue cell of lamina propria

Boundary between con-nective tissue and epithelium

Epithelium

Neutrophilic leukocyte

Superficial squamous epi-thelial cells

Mucus with lymphocytes and granulocytes in lumen of crypt

Lymphocyte

Epithelial cell

Vessel

Plasma cell

Figure 23-18. Human palatine tonsil; infiltration of the epithelium of the crypt with lymphocytes, neutrophilic (heterophilic) granular leukocytes, and plasma cells. Hematoxylin-eosin-azure stain. × 520. (After A. A. Maximow.)

epithelium are found in the saliva as the *salivary corpuscles.* They appear here usually as degenerating vesicular elements with a more or less constricted nucleus surrounded by a clear vesicle containing granules that show brownian movement. The salivary corpuscles that originate from heterophilic leukocytes are recognized by the remnants of the granules and their polymorphous nucleus.

The lumen of the crypts may contain large accumulations of living and degenerated lymphocytes mixed with desquamated squamous epithelial cells, granular detritus, and microorganisms. These masses may increase in size and form cheesy plugs, which are gradually eliminated. If they remain for a long time, they may calcify. The microorganisms are sometimes the cause of inflammation and

suppuration; they may be responsible for some general infections.

Many small glands are connected with the palatine tonsils. Their bodies are outside the capsule, and their ducts open for the most part on the free surface. Openings into the crypts seem rare.

In the roof (fornix) and posterior wall of the nasal part of the pharynx is the unpaired *pharyngeal tonsil.* In this region the mucous membrane shows numerous folds but no crypts. The epithelium on the surface of this tonsil is the same as in the rest of the respiratory passages—pseudostratified, ciliated columnar epithelium with many goblet cells. Small patches of stratified squamous epithelium are common, however. The epithelium is abundantly infiltrated with lymphocytes, especially on the crests of the folds. A 2 mm. thick layer of diffuse and nodular lymphatic tissue is found under the epithelium and participates in the formation of the folds. The lymphoid tissue of the tonsil is separated from the surrounding parts by a thin capsule, which contains many elastic networks and sends thin partitions into the core of the folds. Outside the capsule are small glands of mixed character. Their ducts—often markedly dilated— traverse the lymphatic tissue and empty into the furrows or on the free surface of the folds.

Other small accumulations of lymphatic tissue occur in the mucous membrane of the pharynx, especially around the orifices of the eustachian tube behind the pharyngopalatine arches, and in the posterior wall.

Unlike the lymph nodes, the tonsils do not have lymphatic sinuses, and lymph is not filtered through them. However, plexuses of blindly ending lymph capillaries surround their outer surface.

The tonsils generally reach their maximal devlopment in childhood. The involution of the palatine tonsils begins about the age of 15 or earlier, while the follicles of the root of the tongue persist longer. The pharyngeal tonsil is usually found in an atrophic condition in the adult, with its ciliated epithelium largely replaced by stratified squamous epithelium.

The participation of the tonsils in the new formation of lymphocytes is the only function that can definitely be ascribed to them. It is generally believed, but not proved, that infil-tration of the tonsillar epithelium with lymphocytes has something to do with the protection of the organism against the penetration of noxious agents and especially invasion by microorganisms. Pathogenic bacteria have been found in the lymphatic tissue of the tonsils and in the nodules of the intestine, and this is apparently a normal phenomenon. It has been suggested that the bacteria penetrating the lymphatic tissue are made less virulent, and that they then act as antigens stimulating the production of antibodies. On the other hand, the tonsils and the nodules of the intestine have been shown to constitute the portals of entry for pathogenic microorganisms, and general infections have been traced from them.

HISTOGENESIS. The palatine tonsils develop from the rudiments of the dorsal part of the second gill pouch. During the fourth month of fetal life the epithelium extends solid outgrowths into the subjacent connective tissue; these later become hollow. Around these epithelial growths, lymphatic tissue gradually develops through isolation and mobilization of mesenchyme cells, which are transformed into lymphocytes, while the cells that remain fixed furnish the reticular framework.

THE PHARYNX

The posterior continuation of the oral cavity is the pharynx. In this section of the digestive tract the respiratory passage and the pathway for the food merge and cross. The

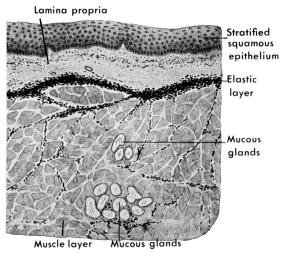

Lamina propria

Stratified squamous epithelium

Elastic layer

Mucous glands

Muscle layer   Mucous glands

Figure 23-19. Cross section through posterior wall of pharynx of human adult. Resorcin-fuchsin and hematoxylin stains. × 50. (After Schumacher.)

Opening of
duct of
mucous glands

Leukocytes
around orifice
of gland

Muscle
fibers

Stratified
squamous epithelium

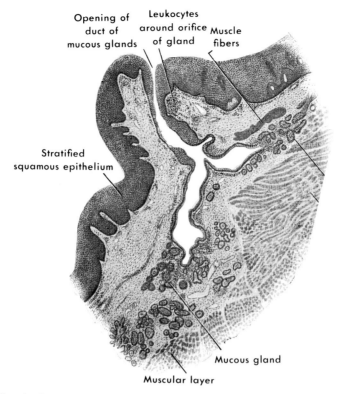

Mucous gland

Muscular layer

Figure 23-20. Longitudinal section of wall of the pharynx of an 11 year old girl. × 27. (After Schaffer.)

upper part of the pharynx is the *nasal,* the middle the *oral,* and the lower the *laryngeal* portion. In the upper part its structure resembles that of the respiratory system, while in the lower part it corresponds more closely to the general plan of the digestive tube.

Instead of a muscularis mucosae, the mucous membrane is provided with a thick, dense, elastic layer. A loose submucous layer is well developed only in the lateral wall of the nasal part of the pharynx and where the pharynx continues into the esophagus; here the elastic layer becomes thinner. In all other places the mucous membrane is directly adjacent to the muscular wall, which consists of an inner longitudinal and an outer oblique or circular layer of striated muscle. The elastic layer fuses with the interstitial tissue of the muscle and sends strands of elastic fibers between the muscular bundles. In the fornix it is fused with the periosteum of the base of the skull.

The lamina propria mucosae consists of dense connective tissue containing fine elastic networks. Those areas covered with stratified squamous epithelium are provided with small papillae. In the area covered with pseudostratified ciliated columnar epithelium there are no papillae.

The two lower sections of the pharynx and a part of the nasal region have stratified squamous epithelium. Toward the roof (fornix) of the pharynx its epithelium first becomes stratified columnar ciliated, with many goblet cells. On the lateral sides of the nasopharynx this ciliated epithelium continues downward beyond the aperture of the eustachian tube. With age the ciliated epithelium may be replaced by stratified squamous epithelium over large areas.

Glands of a pure mucous type are found in those places lined with stratified squamous epithelium. They are always located under the elastic layer, sometimes deep in the muscle. Glands of mixed type, similar to those of the dorsal surface of the soft palate, are confined to the regions covered with ciliated epithelium.

REFERENCES

Arey, L. B.: On the development, morphology and interpretation of a system of crypt analogues in the pharyngeal tonsil. Am. J. Anat., *80:*203, 1947.

Atkinson, W. B., F. Wilson, and S. Coates: The nature of the sexual dimorphism of the submandibular gland of the mouse. Endocrinol., *65*:114, 1959.

Beidler, L. M., and R. L. Smallman: Renewal of cells within taste buds. J. Cell Biol., *27*:263, 1965.

Farbman, A. I.: Fine structure of the taste bud. J. Ultrastruct. Res., *12*:328, 1965.

Gray, E. G., and K. C. Watkins: Electron microscopy of taste buds of the rat. Zeitschr. f. Zellforsch., *66*:583, 1965.

Jacoby, F., and C. R. Leeson: The post-natal development of the rat submaxillary gland. J. Anat., *93*:201, 1959.

Kolmer, W.: Geschmacksorgan. *In* von Möllendorff, W., and W. Bargmann, eds.: Handbuch der mikroskopischen Anatomie des Menschen. Berlin, Julius Springer, 1927, Vol. 3, part 1, p. 154.

Lacassagne, A.: Dimorphisme sexuel de la glande sous-maxillaire chez la souris. Compt. rend. soc. biol., *133*:180, 1940.

Langley, J. N.: On the changes in serous glands during secretion. J. Physiol., *2*:261, 1880.

Levi-Montalcini, R., and S. Cohen: Effects of the extract of the mouse submaxillary salivary glands on the sympathetic system of mammals. Ann. N.Y. Acad. Sci., *85*:324, 1960.

Maximow, A. A.: Beiträge zur Histologie und Physiologie der Speicheldrüsen. Arch. f. mikr. Anat., *58*:1, 1901.

Murray, R. G., and A. Murray: The fine structure of the taste buds of Rhesus and Cynomalgus monkeys. Anat. Rec., *138*:211, 1960.

Nemetschek-Gansler, H., and H. Ferner: Über die Ultrastruktur des Gesmacksknospen. Zeitschr. f. Zellforsch., *63*:155, 1964.

Oakley, B., and R. M. Benjamin: Neural mechanisms of taste. Physiol. Rev., *46*:173, 1966.

Parks, H. F.: Morphological study of the extrusion of secretory materials by the parotid glands of mouse and rat. J. Ultrastruct. Res., *6*:449, 1962.

Pischinger, A.: Beiträge zur Kenntnis des Speicheldrüsen besonders der Glandula sublingualis und submaxillaris des Menschen. Zeitschr. f. mikr. Anat. u. Forsch., *1*:437, 1924.

Rauch, S.: Die Speicheldrüsen des Menschen. Stuttgart, George Thieme Verlag, 1959.

Rawinson, H. E.: The changes in the cells of the striated ducts of the cat's submaxillary gland after autonomic stimulation and nerve section. Anat. Rec., *63*:295, 1935.

Rutberg, V.: Ultrastructure and secretory mechanism of the parotid gland. Acta odontol. Scandinav., *19*:Suppl. 30, 1961.

Schumacher, S.: Die Mundhöhle (p. 1), Die Zunge (p. 35), Der Schlundkopf (p. 290). *In* von Möllendorff, W., and W. Bargmann, eds.: Handbuch der mikroskopischen Anatomie des Menschen. Berlin, Julius Springer, 1927, Vol. 5, part 1.

Shackleford, J., and C. E. Klapper: Structure and carbohydrate histochemistry of mammalian salivary glands. Am. J. Anat., *111*:25, 1962.

Spicer, S. S., and L. Warren: The histochemistry of sialic acid containing mucoproteins. J. Histochem. & Cytochem., *8*:135, 1960.

Zimmermann, K. W.: Die Speicheldrüsen der Mundhöhle und die Bauchspeicheldrüse. *In* von Möllendorff, W., and W. Bargmann, eds.: Handbuch der mikroskopischen Anatomie des Menschen. Berlin, Julius Springer, 1927, Vol. 5, part 1, p. 61.

CHAPTER TWENTY-FOUR

The Teeth

The teeth are derivatives of the oral mucous membrane. They may be considered modified papillae whose surface is covered by a thick layer of calcified substance originating in part from epithelium and in part from connective tissue. The most primitive type of teeth, in which the character of cutaneous papillae is quite evident, is found in the placoid scales in the integument of elasmobranch fish. Similar structures develop in many parallel rows in the mucous membrane of the oral cavity of the bony fishes, where they are subject to continuous renewal during life.

Two sets of teeth have to be distinguished in man and most mammals. The first set forms the *primary* or *deciduous teeth* of childhood. Their eruption starts about the seventh month after birth, and they are shed between the sixth and the thirteenth year. They are gradually replaced by the *permanent teeth*. The microscopic structure of both kinds of teeth is basically similar, but the permanent tooth reaches a higher development. Each of the various types of teeth in each set has a different form adapted to its specific functions; that is, the incisors are adapted for biting and the molars for crushing and grinding the food.

All teeth consist of two portions, the *crown*, projecting above the gingiva (gum), and the tapering *root*, which fits into a socket, the *alveolus*, in the maxillary or mandibular bone. Where the crown and the root meet is sometimes called the *neck*. The lower molars have two, the upper molars three, roots. The tooth contains a small cavity which roughly corresponds in its shape with the outer form of the tooth. It is called the *pulp cavity* and continues downward into each root as a narrow canal that communicates with the *periodontal membrane* through one or more openings at the apex of the root.

The hard portions of a tooth consist of three different tissues: *dentin, enamel,* and *cementum*. The bulk of the tooth is formed by the *dentin*, or ivory, which surrounds the pulp cavity. It is thickest in the crown and tapers down to the points of the roots. Its outer surface is covered, in the region of the crown, by a layer of *enamel*, which reaches its greatest thickness on the exposed part of the crown and thins down toward the neck. In the region of the root the dentin is covered by a thin layer of *cementum*, which leaves the opening of the canal free. The edge of the enamel meets the cementum at the neck of the tooth.

The soft parts associated with the tooth are the *pulp*, which fills the pulp cavity; the *periodontal membrane*, which connects the cementum-covered surface of the root with the bone of the alveolus; and the *gingiva*, that portion of the oral mucous membrane surrounding the tooth. In young persons the gingiva is attached to the enamel; with increasing age it gradually recedes from the enamel, so that in old people it is attached to the cementum.

DENTIN. The dentin is yellowish and semitransparent in fresh condition. When dried, it acquires a silken sheen. It is harder than compact bone, although it resembles bone in its structure, chemical nature, and development.

As in bone, the substance of macerated dentin consists of an organic (28 per cent) and an inorganic (72 per cent) part. Upon decalcification in acids, the organic part remains and the substance of the tooth becomes soft.

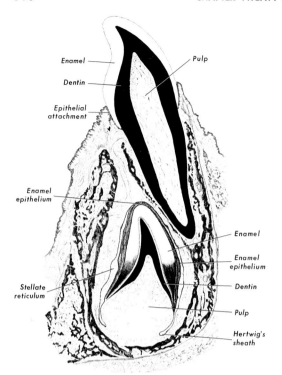

Figure 24-1. Diagram of deciduous tooth and the tooth germ (*below*) of its corresponding permanent tooth. Note the surrounding alveolar bone. × 5. (Redrawn from a photograph by B. Orban.)

Upon incineration, only the inorganic material remains. The inorganic material is much the same as in bone, except that it is denser and less soluble. The organic part, like other collagen rich tissues, contains a glycoprotein and dissolves in boiling water, yielding a solution of gelatin.

In a ground section passing through the axis of a macerated tooth, the dentin has a radially striated appearance. This is attributable to the presence of innumerable minute canals, the *dentinal tubules,* which radiate from the pulp cavity toward the periphery and penetrate every part of the dentin. In the innermost part of the dentin, near the pulp, their diameter is 3 to 4 μ; in the outer portions they become narrower. In their outward course from the pulp cavity most of the tubules describe an **S**-shaped curve. The tubules branch and, especially in the outer layers of dentin, frequently form loop-shaped anastomoses.

The layer of dentin immediately surrounding each tubule, as a *sheath of Neumann,*

differs from the rest of the dentin in its high refringence and distinct staining in decalcified specimens.

Between the dentinal tubules are systems of collagenous fibrils arranged in bundles 2 to 4 μ thick and kept together by a cementing substance, containing glycoprotein; they correspond to the collagenous fibrils of bone. The course of the fibrillar bundles is, in general, parallel to the long axis of the tooth and perpendicular to the dentinal tubules. They also run obliquely and around the tubules. In the

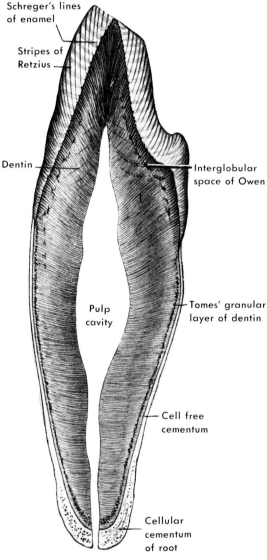

Figure 24-2. Longitudinal ground section of human cuspid. The top of the crown has been abraded. × 7. (After von Ebner, from Schaffer.)

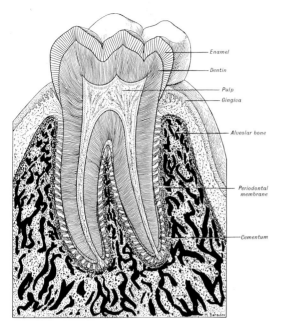

Figure 24-3. Diagram of sagital section of adult human lower first permanent molar. (Courtesy of I. Schour.)

crown they are tangential to the free surface. The fibrils in the adjacent layers form angles of varying degrees—more acute in the outermost portions of the dentin, and wider in the proximity of the pulp cavity. Some investigators distinguish a peripheral layer, the *cover* or *mantle dentin* characterized by a branching pattern of dentinal tubules, and a thicker inner layer, the *circumpulpar dentin,* with thinner, straighter tubules.

The calcification of the developing dentin is not always complete and uniform. The deposits of calcium salts which appear during development in the organic ground substance have the form of spheres, which gradually gain in size and finally fuse. In incompletely calcified regions, between the calcified spheres, there remain angular "interglobular" spaces which contain only the organic matrix of the dentin. The dentinal tubules continue without interruption through the spheres and interglobular spaces. In a macerated tooth from which all organic parts have disappeared, the tubules as well as the interglobular spaces are filled with air and appear dark in transmitted light. In many normal human teeth there are layers of large interglobular spaces in the deeper parts of the enamel covered dentin of the crown, forming the *contour lines of Owen.*

Immediately under the dentinocemental junction in the root there is always a layer of small interglobular spaces, the *granular layer of Tomes* (Fig. 24-2).

In sections through a decalcified tooth fixed with its soft parts, each dentinal tubule contains a slender protoplasmic process, *Tomes' fiber,* which in life probably completely fills the lumen of the tubule, but which in fixed preparations appears shrunken. When the tubules are seen in cross section, each small oval contains a dark dot (Fig. 24-4). These fibers of Tomes are processes of the *odontoblasts,* the cells that give rise to the dentin and remain in an epithelioid layer on the wall of the pulp cavity, sending their protoplasmic processes into the dentinal tubules. Dentin continues to be formed very slowly throughout life, and the pulp cavity is therefore progressively narrowed with advancing age.

The dentin is sensitive to touch, to cold, to acid containing foods, and the like. Only occasional nerve fibers penetrate the dentin and extend for short distances. It has been suggested that the fibers of Tomes may transmit the sensory stimulation to the pulp, which contains many nerves.

With the aid of radioactive phosphorus it has been shown that there is an active interchange of calcium and phosphorus between dentin and enamel on the one hand and the blood on the other. The interchange persists on a diminished scale via the dentinocemental junction in teeth in which the pulp cavity has been filled.

In bone the cells are evenly distributed in the hard intercellular substance and send their processes out in all directions, whereas in den-

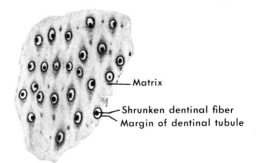

Figure 24-4. Tangential section though the root of a molar of an ape. The margin of the dentinal tubule is also called the sheath of Neumann. × 740. (After Schaffer.)

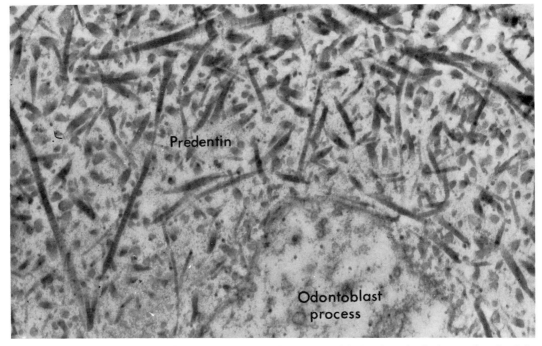

Figure 24-5. Electron micrograph of the tip of an odontoblast process (*below*) and predentin from molar of a 2 day old mouse. Cross striations are visible in some of the collagenous fibrils. Osmium fixation; section stained with phosphotungstic acid. × 38,500. (Courtesy of J. Yaeger and E. Swartz.)

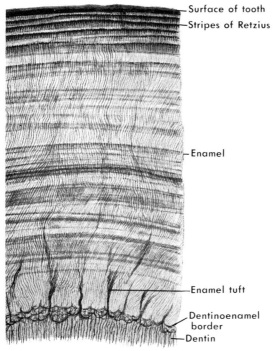

Figure 24-6. Portion of a ground cross section of crown of a human cuspid. × 80. (After Schaffer.)

tin the cells remain on the surface of the intercellular substance and only send their single processes into it. Although the odontoblasts undoubtedly play a role in the nutrition of the dentin, the latter does not become necrotic after the removal of the pulp.

In old age the dentinal tubules are often obliterated through calcification. The dentin then becomes more transparent. When the dentin is denuded because of extensive abrasion of the enamel of crown, or when the outside of the tooth is irritated, a production of new or "secondary" dentin of irregular structure may often be observed on the wall of the pulp cavity. This may be so extensive as to fill the cavity completely.

ENAMEL. This product of epithelial origin is the hardest substance found in the body; it gives sparks with steel. It is bluish white and transparent in thin-ground sections. When fully developed, enamel consists almost entirely of calcium salts in the form of large apatite crystals, while only 3 per cent of it is organic substance. The protein matrix of enamel has been isolated, and oriented samples have been subjected to x-ray diffraction analysis by Glimcher and coworkers. The protein was found to be in the cross-β configuration. Complete amino acid analysis revealed that between one fourth and one fifth of the amino acid residue is proline. The protein, accordingly, cannot be either keratin, as usually thought, or collagen. After decalcification of a fully developed tooth the enamel, as a rule, is completely dissolved.

As seen with the light microscope, the enamel consists of thin rods or prisms that stand upright on the surface of the dentin, usually with a pronounced inclination toward the crown. They are kept together by a small amount of cement substance. Every rod runs through the whole thickness of the enamel layer. This, however, cannot be seen in sections of the enamel, because the rods are twisted and soon pass out of the plane of section. The substance of a rod in its longitudinal section seems homogeneous in a ground preparation. But after acid acts upon such a section, a distinct cross striation appears in the rods; this indicates that the calcification probably proceeds layer by layer.

Studies with the electron microscope show that the *enamel rods* or *prisms* and the interprismatic substance are both composed of apatite crystals and organic material. The relations of the crystals in the prisms and in the interprismatic substance are clearly shown in Figures 24-9, 24-10, and 24-11.

In the human tooth most of the rods in cross section have the form of fluted semicircles. The convex surfaces of all rods face the dentin, and their cross sections have a scalelike appearance (Fig. 24-7).

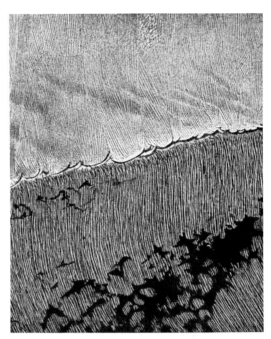

Figure 24-8. Dentinoenamel junction of a tooth of a man; ground section. The enamel prisms appear as a fine, wavy striation. The interglobular spaces in the dentin are black (air filled). Between these lacunae are the dentinal tubules. $\times$ 80. (After Braus.)

This form and arrangement are explained by calcification beginning earlier on the side of the rods that lies nearest the dentin. This inner, harder side is supposed to press into the softer side of the adjacent rod, compressing it and leaving one or two groovelike impressions.

The exact course of the enamel rods is extremely complicated and seems to be perfectly adapted to the mechanical requirements of the grinding and crushing of food. Starting from the dentin, the rods run perpendicular to the surface; in the middle zone of the enamel they bend spirally, and in the outer zone they again assume a direction perpendicular to the surface. In addition, the rods show numerous small, wavy curves. On the lateral surfaces of the crown the rods are arranged in zones that encircle the tooth in horizontal planes. The bends of the rods in two neighboring zones cross one another. In axial, longitudinal, ground sections, the crossing of groups of rods appears in reflected light as light and dark lines, more or less perpendicular to the surface—the *lines of Schreger* (Fig. 24-2).

In a cross section of the crown the enamel

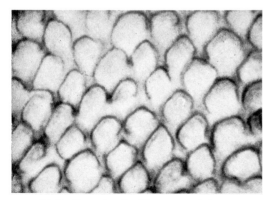

Figure 24-7. Enamel rods of human tooth in cross section. The dark lines are the cementing substance between the pale rods. Photomicrograph. High magnification. (Courtesy of B. Orban.)

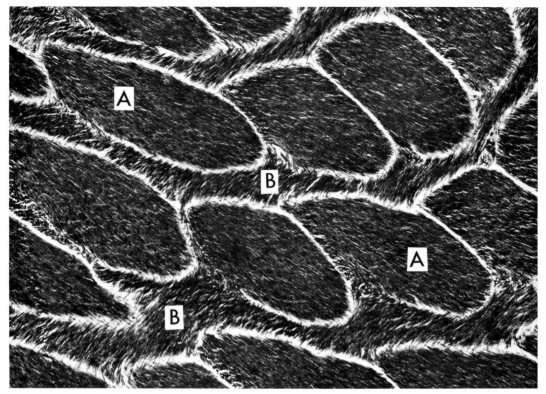

Figure 24-9.   Slightly oblique section of undecalcified calf enamel, showing the roughly ovoid enamel prisms (*A*) and the interprismatic substance (B). Note the remarkable orientation of the apatite crystals within the individual prisms, and the different orientation of the crystals in the interprismatic substance. Note, also, the clear areas that define the prisms. Embedded in methacrylate and sectioned with the diamond knife. Osmium fixation. × 18,000. (Courtesy of E. J. Daniel and M. J. Glimcher.)

shows concentric lines, which are brown in transmitted light and colorless in reflected light. In longitudinal, axial sections they are seen to run obliquely inward from the surface and toward the root. They are called the *lines of Retzius* and are connected with the circular striation on the surface of the crown.

The free surface of the enamel is covered by two thin layers. The inner, about a micron thick, appears to be the final product of the activity of the enamel forming ameloblasts before they disappear. The outer is a calcified layer of collagenous tissue 2 to 10 μ thick, which is most easily demonstrated on un-erupted teeth. It is continuous with the cementum covering the root and is similar in composition and histological structure. This layer is tenaciously adherent to the tooth and is distinct from the connective tissue of the gingiva. It may persist for some time after eruption of the tooth (Levine *et al.*).

In an axial section of the tooth the line

of junction between the dentin and the enamel (*dentinoenamel junction*) is uneven and scalloped. Pointed or spindle-shaped processes of dentin penetrate the enamel and are separated from one another by excavations. Some dentinal tubules penetrate a short distance into the enamel and end blindly. The spindle-shaped processes of the dentinal matrix penetrating a short distance into the enamel are called *enamel spindles*.

Local disturbances of the enamel during development cause the so-called *enamel lamellae* and *tufts*. These lamellae are organic material extending from the surface of the enamel toward and sometimes into the dentin. The tufts extend from the dentinoenamel junction into the enamel for one third of its thickness. The tuftlike shape, however, is an optical illusion, due to the projection, into one plane, of fibers lying in different planes. They are groups of poorly calcified, twisted enamel rods with abundant cementing substance between them.

CEMENTUM. The cementum covering most of the root is coarsely fibrillated bone substance. Near the apex *cementocytes* are embedded in it. Canaliculi, haversian systems, and blood vessels are normally absent. The layer of cementum increases in thickness with age, especially near the end of the root, and then haversian systems with blood vessels may appear. Coarse collagenous bundles from the periodontal membrane penetrate the cementum. These fibers, corresponding to Sharpey's fibers of other bone, remain uncalcified and in ground sections of a macerated tooth appear as empty canals.

Unlike the dentin, which may remain unchanged even after the destruction of the pulp and the odontoblasts and after the "filling" of the pulp cavity, the cementum readily undergoes necrosis when the periodontal membrane is destroyed, and it may be resorbed by the surrounding connective tissue. On the other hand, new layers of cementum may be deposited on the surface of the root. This deposition is called *cementum hyperplasia* when it becomes excessive and is considered to be a reaction to irritation.

PULP. The pulp of the tooth occupies the pulp cavity and is the connective tissue that formed the dental papilla during embryonic development. In the adult tooth it has an abundant, gelatinous, metachromatic ground substance similar to that of mucoid tissue. It contains a multitude of thin collagenous fibrils running in all directions and not aggregated into bundles. The spindle- or star-shaped cells suggest embryonic mesenchymal elements; macrophages and lymphoid cells are also present. The cells of the pulp adjacent to the dentin are large, columnar, and arranged in the fashion of an epithelium. These are called *odontoblasts*. They send one or more slender *odontoblastic processes*, or fibers of Tomes, into the dentinal tubules.

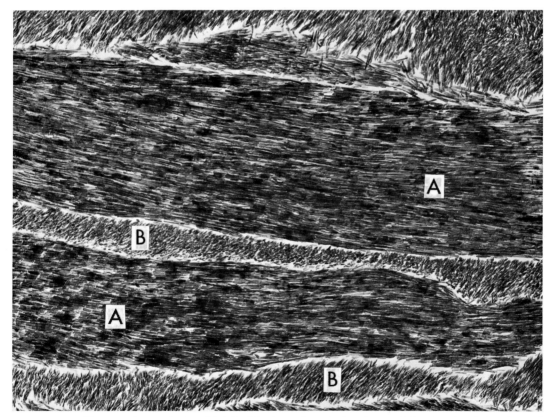

Figure 24-10. Electron micrograph of undecalcified bovine embryonic dental enamel showing two of the prisms (*A*) in predominantly longitudinal section. The long axis of the crystals (corresponding to the C-axis of the apatite lattice) is relatively parallel to the long axis of the prisms. The crystals in the interprismatic areas (*B*) have a distinctly different orientation. Osmium fixation. × 25,000. (Courtesy of E. J. Daniel and M. J. Glimcher.)

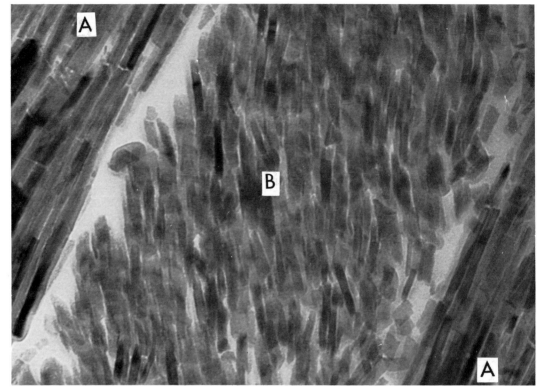

Figure 24-11.   *See opposite page for legend.*

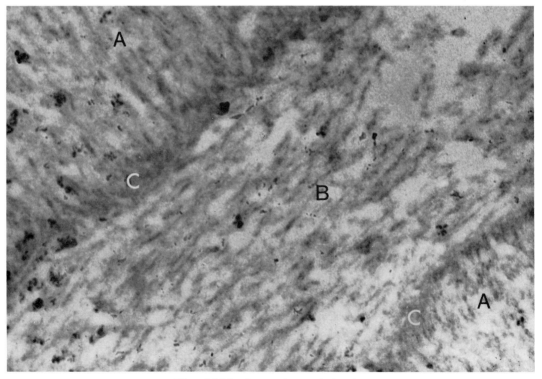

Figure 24-12.   *See opposite page for legend.*

The pulp continues into the narrow canal of the root, where it surrounds the blood vessels and nerves, and continues through the openings in the root apex into the periodontal membrane. The pulp contains many blood vessels. Small arteries enter each root, accompanied by veins. The arteries give rise to a dense network of wide capillaries whose loops come into close relation with the layer of the odontoblasts and then continue into the veins, which occupy a more central position in the pulp. True lymphatic capillaries have been found by some investigators. Numerous bundles of myelinated nerve fibers, which arise from small cells in the gasserian ganglion, enter the pulp cavity through the canals of the root. They form a plexus in the pulp, from which arises a finer plexus of nonmyelinated fibers in the peripheral layers. Nerve endings have been described between the odontoblasts.

PERIODONTAL MEMBRANE. The periodontal membrane, which also serves as periosteum to the alveolar bone, furnishes a firm connection between the root and the bone. It differs from the usual periosteum by the absence of elastic fibers. It consists, in part, of thick collagenous bundles, Sharpey's fibers that run from the alveolar wall into the cementum. The orientation of the fibers varies at different levels in the alveolus. From root tip to neck they are designated as *apical, oblique, horizontal,* and *alveolar crest fibers,* describing their direction or their attachments. The horizontal fibers at the neck of the tooth are especially prominent and firmly attached to the cementum. The fiber bundles of the periodontal membrane have a slightly wavy course; when the tooth is not functioning, they are re-

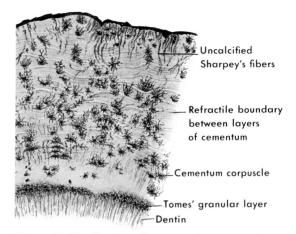

Figure 24-13. Portion of a ground cross section through the lower part of a root of a macerated human tooth. Air has filled the lacunae. × 80. (After Schaffer.)

laxed and permit it to move slightly on the application of stress.

Scattered in many places in the periodontal membrane, especially near the surface of the cementum, there are blood and lymph vessels and nerves embedded in a small amount of loose connective tissue, and small islands of epithelium. These islands are vestiges of the epithelial sheath of Hertwig. The epithelial rests frequently degenerate and undergo calcification, giving rise to the *cementicles.*

THE GINGIVA (GUM). The gingiva is that part of the mucous membrane that is firmly connected with the periosteum at the crest of the alveolar bone. It is also linked to the surface of the tooth by the *epithelial attachment of Gottlieb,* which gradually recedes with advancing age, moving toward the apex of the

Figure 24-11. Higher magnification of an area of bovine dental enamel similar to that shown in Figure 24-9, showing longitudinally oriented prismatic crystals (*A*) with the interprismatic crystals (*B*) oriented approximately 30 degrees to the direction of the crystals within the prism. Osmium fixation. × 100,000. (Courtesy of E. J. Daniel and M. J. Glimcher.)

Figure 24-12. Oblique section of decalcified bovine dental enamel. This was prepared by sectioning calcified enamel and then decalcifying it on the grid with phosphotungstic acid and a chelating agent (ethylene-diaminetetracetic acid). This procedure preserves the orientation of the organic matrix in relation to that of the crystals as seen in the electron microscope before decalcification. The orientation of the enamel protein filaments easily distinguishes the prisms (*A*) and the interprismatic area (*B*). The inorganic crystals were similarly oriented. The borders (*C*) surrounding the enamel prisms have a relatively heavy concentration of organic matrix corresponding to the clear areas seen in the fully calcified sections (as Fig. 24-9). The micrographs in this figure and Figure 24-11 show that the organic material and the inorganic constituents are similarly oriented, much like the apatite crystals and collagen in bone. Osmium fixation. × 100,000. (Courtesy of E. J. Daniel and M. J. Glimcher.)

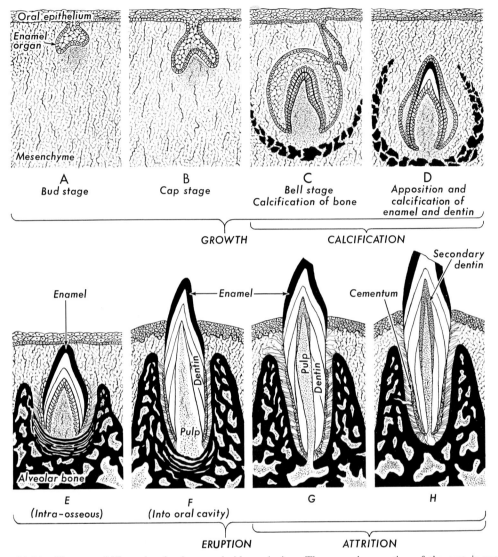

Enamel organ

Oral epithelium

Mesenchyme

A
Bud stage

B
Cap stage

C
Bell stage
Calcification of bone

D
Apposition and
calcification of
enamel and dentin

GROWTH   CALCIFICATION

Secondary
dentin

Enamel

Enamel

Cementum

Dentin

Pulp

Pulp

Dentin

Alveolar bone

E
(Intra-osseous)

F
(Into oral cavity)

G

H

ERUPTION   ATTRITION

Figure 24-24. Diagram of life cycle of a human deciduous incisor. The normal resorption of the root is not indicated. Enamel and bone are drawn in black. (Redrawn and modified from Schour and Massler.)

tooth. The gingiva generally has high papillae but the epithelial attachment is devoid of papillae except when chronically inflamed. Between the epithelium and the enamel there is a small furrow surrounding the crown, the *gingival crevice*.

HISTOGENESIS OF THE TEETH. The enamel is a product of the ectodermal epithelium. All the other parts are derivatives of the connective tissue.

In human embryos of the fifth week the ectodermal epithelium lining the oral cavity presents a thickening along the edge of the future upper and lower jaws. The thickening consists of two solid epithelial ridges which extend into the subjacent mesenchyme. Of these, the labial ridge later splits and forms the space between lip and alveolar process of the jaw. The lingual ridge, nearer the tongue, produces teeth and is called the *dental lamina*. According to most investigators, both ridges are independent from the beginning.

The edge of the dental lamina extends into the connective tissue of the jaw and shows at several points budlike thickenings that are the primordia of the teeth, the *tooth germs*.

There are ten tooth germs in each jaw, one for each deciduous tooth. In each germ a group of epithelial cells becomes conspicuous as the *enamel knot,* a temporary structure that later disappears. The cells of the mesenchyme under the enamel knot aggregate in a dense group to form the primordium of the papilla. The dental lamina then extends beyond the last deciduous tooth germ and slowly forms germs of the permanent molars, which are not proceeded by corresponding deciduous teeth.

Beginning with the tenth to twelfth week, the remainder of the dental lamina again produces solid epithelial buds—the *germs for the permanent teeth*—one on the lingual side of each deciduous germ. After the formation of the permanent tooth germs the dental lamina disappears. The germs of the permanent teeth undergo the same transformations as do those of the deciduous teeth.

The papilla enlarges and invaginates the base of the epithelial tooth germ (Fig. 24-15). The latter, while still connected by an epithelial strand with the dental lamina, becomes bell-shaped and caps the convex surface of the papilla. From now on it is called the *enamel organ,* because in its further development it produces the enamel. Both the papilla and the enamel organ gradually gain in height, and the latter soon acquires approximately the shape of the future tooth.

A concentric layer of connective tissue, the *dental sac,* develops around the tooth primordium and interrupts its epithelial connection with the oral cavity. Around the sac, and at a certain distance from it, the bone of the jaw develops.

The peripheral cells of the enamel organ are arranged in a regular, radial fashion. On the convex surface the cells of the outer enamel epithelium remain small and cuboidal. On the invaginated base the cells of the inner enamel epithelium become tall and regular. They play a major role in the elaboration of the enamel and are called *ameloblasts* or *gonoblasts.* Their attachments are provided with a system of terminal bars. In the interior of the enamel organ a clear liquid accumulates between the cell bodies, which remain connected by long processes. The epithelium thus acquires a reticular appearance like that of connective tissue and forms the *stellate reticulum* (enamel pulp).

When the formation of the hard tooth

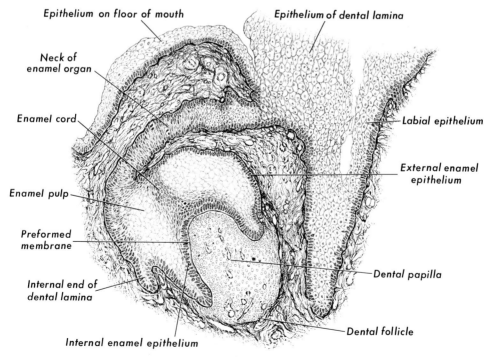

Figure 24-15. Primordium of the right lower central incisor of a human fetus of 91 days, in sagittal section. Collagenous fibers black. Mallory's connective tissue stain. × 80. (Redrawn and modified from Schaffer.)

substances begins (embryos of about 20 weeks), the mesenchyme of the papilla contains numerous blood vessels and a few reticular fibrils between its cells. The cells adjacent to the layer of ameloblasts become transformed into odontoblasts (Fig. 24-16).

The dentin first appears as a thick limiting line between ameloblasts and odontoblasts, sometimes called the *membrana preformata.* Some believe that the odontoblasts form the dentin; others believe that they do not form it, but are probably concerned in its nourishment and possibly with the deposition of calcium in it. In any event, just before the dentin is formed, the odontoblasts develop large amounts of glycoprotein, which is probably related to the ground substance.

The layer of dentin extends down the slopes of the dental papillae. It gradually grows thicker and is transformed into a solid cap of dentin by the apposition of new layers on its concave surface. As the odontoblasts recede from the dentin, thin processes of their cytoplasm remain in the mass of deposited dentin as the dentinal fibers.

When the dentin first appears, it is a soft fibrillar substance—the *predentin* (Fig. 24-5). The fibrils are continuations of the fibrils of the papilla. They are argyrophilic and are generally called *Korff's fibers.* They enter the dentin, spread out fanlike, and change into the collagenous, fibrillated matrix of the dentin (Fig. 24-18).

In dentin formation, calcification follows closely the deposition of the fibrillar soft substance. During the whole process, however, there is always a thin layer of uncalcified dentin adjacent to the odontoblasts.

The process of dentin formation is much the same as the formation of bone. Almost im-

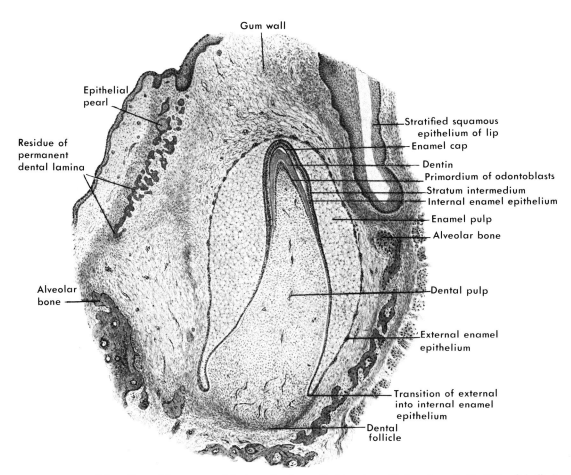

Figure 24-16.   Primordium of lower central incisor of a 5 month fetus, in sagittal section.   × 30. (After Schaffer.)

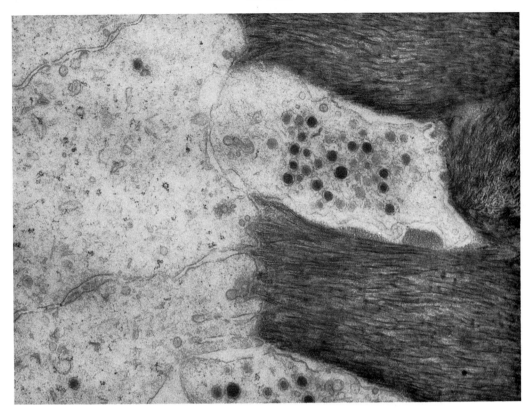

Figure 24-17. Electron micrograph of developing enamel of the rat incisor. The enamel appears to consist of highly ordered slender crystallites embedded in a dense matrix. The apical portions of the ameloblasts at the left of the figure project into indentations of the irregular surface of the enamel but their cytoplasm is covered at all points by the cell membrane. Thus, contrary to the traditional interpretation, the enamel matrix is not continuous with the cytoplasm of the ameloblast but is extracellular. × 24,000. (Courtesy of M. Watson.)

mediately after the appearance of the first calcified dentin on the convexity of the papilla, the ameloblasts begin the elaboration of enamel. It is deposited layer by layer on the surface of the calcifying dentin.

The ameloblasts grow into tall and regular columnar cells provided with the usual cell organelles. The attached part of the cell contains granular material which stains brown with osmic acid. In vitally stained animals this part stores the dyes in granular form. On the slopes of the papilla the height of the ameloblasts decreases, and at the base of the papilla they continue into the outer enamel epithelium.

As the mass of enamel increases, the ameloblasts recede. It was formerly believed that the enamel matrix was a specialization of the apical cytoplasm of the ameloblast and therefore intracellular, and that the calcified enamel prisms were essentially prolongations of the columnar cells. A distinct cell membrane has now been observed in electron micrographs between the cytoplasm and the calcified matrix (Fig. 24-18). The ameloblasts contain highly organized cisternae of granular endoplasmic reticulum—a fine structural feature commonly found in secretory cells. Small spherical masses of dense material are found in the apical cytoplasm, and a substance of similar appearance is found extracellularly between the cell and the calcifying enamel. It seems reasonable to conclude from these findings that the ameloblasts elaborate enamel matrix which calcifies extracellularly.

Calcification starts at the periphery of each prism and proceeds toward its interior. When the cementing substance finally calcifies, so little organic material remains that the enamel is completely dissolved in decalcification. Complete calcification is not reached until late, and for a long time dyes and other

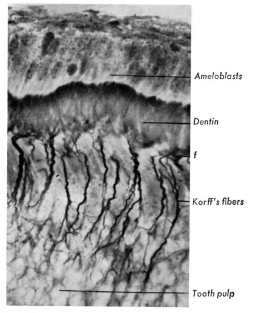

Figure 24-18. Continuation of Korff's fibers of the pulp into the matrix of the dentin at *f*. Photomicrograph. × 700. (Courtesy of B. Orban.)

Labels (Figure 24-18): Ameloblasts · Dentin · *f* · Korff's fibers · Tooth pulp

substances may penetrate the partly calcified enamel. That the calcification is seldom absolutely uniform has been mentioned. One of the most striking causes of hypocalcification is parathyroid dysfunction.

Schour (1936) studied the rate of deposition of enamel, with sodium fluoride, and of dentin, with vital injections of alizarin. He found that the daily thickening of dentin is about 4 μ and that unusual increments (*neonatal lines*) appear in the enamel and dentin formed in the deciduous teeth at the time of birth.

When the definitive thickness and extent of the enamel are reached in the neck region of the tooth, the ameloblasts become small cuboidal cells and then atrophy. Before they disappear, they elaborate the inner cuticle of the enamel, which covers the ends of the rods.

At the end of the enamel organ, the outer and inner enamel epithelium form a fold, the *epithelial sheath of Hertwig.* The *development of the root* begins shortly before the eruption of the tooth, continues after the crown has emerged

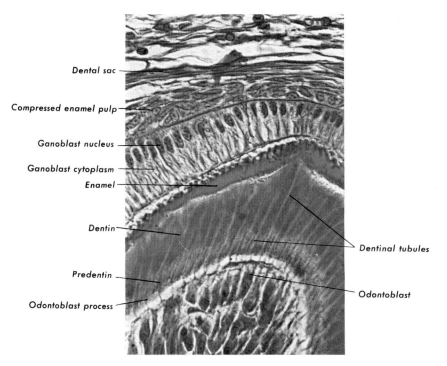

Labels (Figure 24-19): Dental sac · Compressed enamel pulp · Ganoblast nucleus · Ganoblast cytoplasm · Enamel · Dentin · Predentin · Odontoblast process · Dentinal tubules · Odontoblast

Figure 24-19. Section of primordium of incisor of a 5 month human fetus, showing formation of enamel and dentin. Mallory-azan stain. × 500. (After von Herrath and Abramow.)

from within the mucous membrane, and is not completed until much later. The epithelial sheath disappears when the root is completely developed.

When the germ of the permanent tooth begins to develop, its growth pressure causes resorption, first of the bony partition between the two teeth, then of the root, and eventually even of a part of the enamel of the deciduous tooth. Osteoclasts are prominent in this process of destruction just as in the resorption of bone. The crown of the permanent tooth moving upward gradually takes the place of the crown of the former deciduous tooth.

REFERENCES

Becks, H., D. A. Collins, M. E. Simpson, and H. M. Evans: Changes in the central incisors of hypophysectomized female rats after different postoperative periods. Arch. Path., *41:*457, 1946.

Bélanger, L. F.: Autoradiographic visualization of the entry and transit of S^{35} methionine and cystine in the soft and hard tissues of the growing rat. Anat. Rec., *124:*555, 1956.

Bevelander, G., and H. Nakahara: The formation and mineralization of dentin. Anat. Rec., *156:*303, 1966.

Engel, M. B.: Glycogen and carbohydrate-protein complex in developing teeth of the rat. J. Dent. Res., *27:*681, 1948.

Greulich, R. C., and C. P. Leblond: Radioautographic visualization of the formation and fate of the organic matrix of dentin. J. Dent. Res., *33:*859, 1954.

Glimcher, M. J., L. C. Bonar, and E. J. Daniel: The molecular structure of the protein matrix of bovine dental enamel. J. Molec. Biol., *3:*541, 1961.

Glimcher, M. J., V. A. Friberg, and P. T. Levine: The identification and characterization of a calcified layer of coronal cementum in erupted bovine teeth. J. Ultrastruct. Res., *10:*76, 1964.

Glimcher, M. J., P. T. Levine, and L. C. Bonar: Morphological and biochemical considerations in structural studies of the organic matrix of enamel. J. Ultrastruct. Res., *13:*281, 1965.

Glimcher, M. J., G. Mechanic, L. C. Bonar, and E. J. Daniel: The amino acid composition of the organic matrix of decalcified fetal bovine dental enamel. J. Biol. Chem., *236:*3210, 1961.

Greep, R. O. (ed.): Recent advances in the study of the structure, composition and growth of mineralized tissues. Ann. N. Y. Acad. Sci., *60:*541, 1955.

Hoffman, M. M., and I. Schour: Quantitative studies in the development of the rat molar; alveolar bone, cementum, and eruption (from birth to 500 days). Am. J. Orthodont., *26:*854, 1940.

Hoffman, R. L.: Formation of periodontal tissues around subcutaneously transplanted hamster molars. J. Dent. Res., *39:*781, 1960.

Lehner, J., and H. Plenk: Die Zähne. *In* von Möllendorff, W., and W. Bargmann, eds.: Handbuch der mikroskopischen Anatomie des Menschen. Berlin, Julius Springer, 1936, Vol. 5, part 3, p. 449.

Levine, P. T., M. J. Glimcher, and L. C. Bonar: Collagenous layer covering the crown enamel of unerupted permanent human teeth. Science, *146:*1676, 1964.

Pannese, E.: Ultrastructure of the enamel organ. Int. Rev. Exp. Path., *3:*169, 1964.

Saunders, J. B. de C. M., J. Nuckolls, and H. E. Frisbie: Amelogensis; a histologic study of the development, formation and calcification of the enamel in the molar tooth of the rat. J. Am. Coll. Dentists, *9:*107, 1942.

Schour, I.: The Teeth. *In* Cowdry, E. V., ed.: Special Cytology. 2nd ed. New York, Paul B. Hoeber, Inc., 1932, Vol. 1, p. 67.

Schour, I.: The neonatal line in the enamel and dentin of the human deciduous teeth and first permanent molar. J. Am. Dent. A., *23:*1946, 1936.

Schour, I., (ed.): Noyes' Oral Histology and Embryology. 8th ed. Philadelphia, Lea & Febiger, 1960.

Schour, I., and Massler, M.: The effects of dietary deficiencies upon the oral structures. Physiol. Rev., *25:*442, 1945.

Sicher, H., (ed.): Orban's Oral Histology and Embryology. 5th ed. St. Louis, C. V. Mosby, 1962.

Sognnaes, R. F.: Microstructure and histochemical characteristics of the mineralized tissues. Ann. N. Y. Acad. Sci., *60:*545, 1955.

Stahl, S. S., J. P. Weinmann, I. Schour, and A. M. Budy: The effect of estrogen on the alveolar bone and teeth of mice and rats. Anat. Rec., *107:*21, 1950.

Watson, M. L.: The extracellular nature of enamel in the rat. J. Biophys. & Biochem. Cytol., *7:*489, 1960.

Watson, M. L., and Avery, J. K.: The development of the hamster lower incisor as observed by electron microscopy. Am. J. Anat., *95:*109, 1954.

Weidenreich, F.: Über den Bau und die Entwicklung des Zahnbeines in der Reihe der Wirbeltiere. Zeitschr. f. Anat. u. Entwicklungs., *76:*218, 1925.

Wislocki, G. B., and Sognnaes, R. F.: Histochemical reactions of normal teeth. Am. J. Anat., *87:*239, 1950.

Wolbach, S. B., and Howe, P. R.: The incisor teeth of albino rats and guinea-pigs in vitamin A deficiency and repair. Am. J. Path., *9:*275, 1933.

CHAPTER TWENTY-FIVE

The Esophagus and Stomach

The *esophagus* is a muscular tube that conveys food rapidly from the pharynx to the stomach. Its wall includes all the layers characteristic of the digestive tube in general (Fig. 25-1). The mucous membrane is 500 to 800 μ thick. The stratified squamous epithelium (Fig. 25-2) continues from the pharynx into the esophagus. At the junction of the esophagus with the cardia of the stomach, there is an abrupt transition from stratified squamous to simple columnar epithelium (Fig. 25-3). On macroscopic examination, the boundary line between the smooth, white mucous membrane of the esophagus and the pink surface of the gastric mucosa appears as a jagged line.

In man the flattened cells of the superficial layers of the epithelium contain a small number of keratohyalin granules but do not undergo true cornification. The lamina propria consists of loose connective tissue with relatively thin collagenous fibers and networks of fine elastic fibers. Besides the usual connective tissue cells, numerous lymphocytes are scattered throughout the tissue. Small lymphatic nodules are found around the ducts of the esophageal mucous glands.

At the level of the cricoid cartilage the elastic layer of the pharynx is succeeded by the *muscularis mucosae*, which consists of longitudinal smooth muscle fibers and thin elastic networks. Near the stomach the muscularis mucosae attains a thickness of 200 to 400 μ.

The dense connective tissue of the *submucous layer* consists of collagenous and elastic fibers and small infiltrations of lymphocytes

about the glands. The submucous layer, together with the muscularis mucosae, forms numerous longitudinal folds, which result in the irregular form of the lumen in cross section (Fig. 25-1). During the swallowing of food these folds are smoothed out. This is made possible by the elasticity of the connective tissue that forms the submucous layer.

The *muscularis externa* of the human esophagus is 0.5 to 2.2 mm. thick. In the upper quarter of the esophagus both its outer and inner layers consist of striated muscle. In the second quarter, bundles of smooth muscles begin gradually to replace the striated muscle, and in the lower third only smooth muscle is found. The relations between the two types of muscular tissue are subject to individual variations. The two layers of the muscularis externa are not regularly circular and longitudinal, respectively: in the inner layer there are many spiral, elliptical, or oblique bundles. The longitudinal muscular bundles of the outer layer are also irregularly arranged in many places.

The outer surface of the esophagus is connected with the surrounding parts by a layer of loose connective tissue called the *tunica adventitia*.

GLANDS OF THE ESOPHAGUS. Two kinds of small glands occur in the esophagus: *esophageal glands proper* and *esophageal cardiac glands*. The esophageal glands proper are unevenly distributed, small, compound glands with richly branched tubuloalveolar secretory portions containing only mucous cells (Fig. 25-4B). They are located in the submucous layer

(Fig. 25-4*A*) and can just be recognized with the naked eye as elongated white spots. The branches of the smallest ducts are short and fuse into a cystically dilated main duct, which pierces the muscularis mucosae and opens through a small orifice. The epithelium in the smallest ducts is low columnar; in the enlarged main duct stratified squamous epithelium is found. The mucous glands often give rise to cysts of the mucous membrane.

The *esophageal cardiac glands* closely resemble the cardiac glands of the stomach. Two groups of them can be distinguished: one is in the upper part of the esophagus at the level between the cricoid cartilage and the fifth tracheal cartilage; the other is in the lower part of the esophagus near the cardia. They show great individual variation and sometimes are entirely absent.

Unlike the esophageal glands proper, they are always confined to the lamina propria mucosae. Their terminal portions are branched and curled tubules that contain columnar or cuboidal cells with a pale granular cytoplasm, which sometimes seems to give the mucin

reaction; secretory canaliculi are present. The smallest ducts drain into a large duct, which is sometimes cystically dilated and always opens on the tip of a papilla. Its columnar epithelium often gives a distinct reaction for mucin and more or less resembles the mucous epithelium of the gastric foveolae.

In the regions of esophageal mucous membrane that contain the upper and lower groups of cardiac glands, the stratified squamous epithelium may be supplanted in places by a simple columnar epithelium of the same aspect as in the gastric pits. Such patches suggest erosions—that is, places denuded of epithelium. Sometimes the patches lined with mucous gastric epithelium are of considerable size and are provided with pitlike invaginations and even with tubular glands like those of the fundus; they may even contain typical zymogenic and parietal cells.

The number and development of the cardiac glands as well as of the islands of gastric mucosa in the esophagus are subject to great individual variation. According to some investigators, the presence of this ectopic

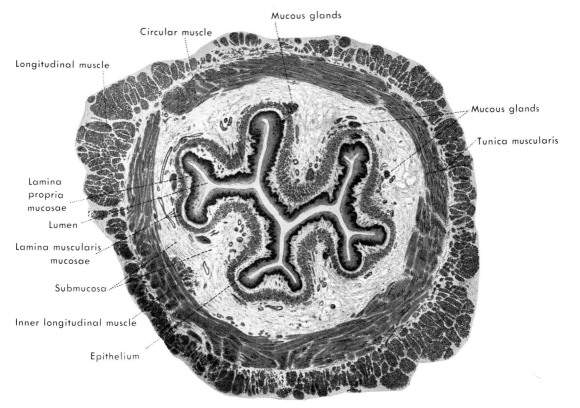

Figure 25-1. Cross section from the middle third of the esophagus of a 28 year old man. × 8. (After Sobotta.)

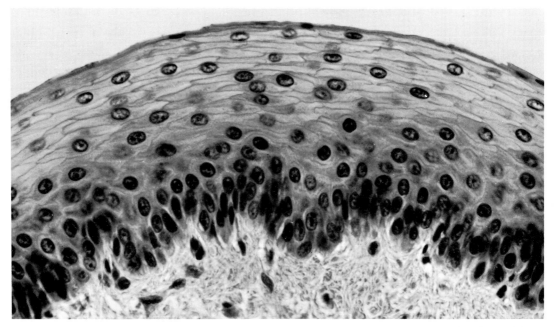

Figure 25-2. Esophageal stratified squamous epithelium of a rhesus monkey. Hematoxylin and eosin. × 500.

gastric epithelium may be of some importance in relation to the origin of diverticula, cysts, ulcers, and carcinomas of the esophagus.

In many mammals, especially those that consume coarse vegetable food (rodents, ruminants, and the horse), the stratified squamous epithelium of the esophagus undergoes cornification. The esophageal glands are present in most of the mammals, but instead of being purely mucous, as in man, they have a mixed character. In some species no glands are found (rodents, horse, cat).

HISTOGENESIS. The histogenesis of the epithelium of the esophagus in man presents certain peculiarities, which are especially important in connection with the question of metaplasia—that is, the transformation of one epithelial type into another. At first the endodermal layer is a simple, low columnar epithelium. It then becomes two layered, and in the ninth week the superficial cells become ciliated. In the eleventh week, rounded elements containing glycogen appear between the ciliated cells, soon outnumber them, and later are transformed into squamous cells. Finally, all the ciliated cells disappear, and the epithelium becomes stratified squamous. In embryos of the other mammals the epithelium does not seem to contain any ciliated cells.

STOMACH

The stomach is an organ concerned with both storage and digestion of food. In man, storage is a less important part of its function than in herbivores and particularly in ruminants. In the human stomach the solid food is reduced to a fluid by virtue of the contraction of its muscular wall and the admixture of food with the secretions of the glands of its mucous membrane. The contents of the upper part of the stomach may remain solid for some time after a meal, while those of the more distal region are reduced to a pulplike fluid mass, the *chyme*. When the chyme has attained the necessary softness, it is transferred to the intestine in small portions. Thus the function of the stomach is in part mechanical and in part chemical.

The cavity of the empty stomach in its living condition is not of much larger caliber than is the intestine. The opening from the esophagus into the stomach is called the *cardia*. To the left of the cardia the wall of the stomach forms a dome-shaped bulge, the *fundus*. The right concave and left convex margins are called the *lesser* and *greater curvatures*. The region of transition of the stomach into the duodenum is called the *pylorus*. The wall of the stomach consists of the usual layers of the digestive tube:

mucosa, submucosa, muscularis, and adventitia.

The mucous membrane of the stomach during life is grayish pink, except for paler zones at the pylorus and cardia. The surface of the filled stomach is stretched evenly. In the empty, contracted stomach the mucosa forms numerous longitudinal folds or rugae (Fig. 25-6). This is possible because of the loose consistency of the submucosal layer and the action of the muscularis mucosae. Another much finer and more constant system of elevations is brought about by furrows, which subdivide the surface of the mucous membrane into small, slightly bulging gastric areas 1 to 6 mm. in diameter. With a magnifying lens the surface of each area is seen to be further subdivided by tiny grooves into irregularly convoluted ridges. In a perpendicular section through the mucous membrane the transected furrows appear as invaginations, the so-called *gastric pits* or *foveolae gastricae.*

The entire thickness of the mucous membrane in all parts of the stomach is occupied by a multitude of glands, which open into the bottom of the gastric pits (Fig. 25-5). The epithelium that lines the gastric pits and covers the free surface of the mucosa between them is uniformly of the same structure. On the basis of differences in the glands, however, three regions are distinguished in the stomach. The first, which forms a narrow (5 to 30 mm.) ring-shaped area around the cardia, is called the *cardiac area* and contains the *cardiac glands.* The second zone comprises the *fundus and proximal two thirds* of the stomach and contains the gastric glands proper, or the *glands of the fundus,* also called *oxyntic glands.* The third part, the pyloric region, occupies the distal ninth of the stomach and extends farther along the lesser curvature than along the greater; it is characterized by the presence of *pyloric glands.* These zones are not sharply delimited, and along the borderline the glands of one region mingle to a certain extent with those of the region adjoining. According to some authors, between the second and third zones is a narrow strip, some millimeters in width, occupied by a fourth type of gland, the *intermediate glands.* In the dog, the animal widely used for physiological ex-

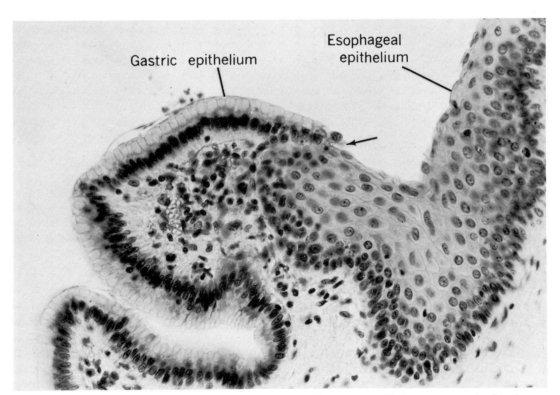

Figure 25-3. Esophagogastric junction. Notice the abrupt transition from stratified squamous to simple columnar epithelium (at arrow). Hematoxylin and eosin. × 375.

perimentation, this intermediate zone is unusually well developed, reaching a width of 1 to 1.8 cm.

In other mammals the subdivisions of the stomach are much more sharply pronounced and are marked by deep constrictions that separate the organ into chambers. The stratified squamous epithelium of the esophagus is sometimes cornified and may invade a smaller or larger part of the stomach. This esophageal portion, as a rule, has a few or no glands. In the ruminants the three first chambers—the rumen, the reticulum, and the omasum (or psalterium)—are all of esophageal nature; only in the fourth portion, the abomasum, are gastric glands found, and only here does digestion occur. In the monotremes and marsupials the whole stomach is esophageal in character, and the stratified squamous epithelium reaches as far as the glands of Brunner. In the pig the second, or cardiac, region, with mucus-secreting gastric epithelium and cardiac glands, is

highly developed; the third and physiologically the most important portion is the region of the corpus or fundus; the fourth portion is the pyloric region.

SURFACE EPITHELIUM. The gastric pits and the ridges between them are lined by a tall (20 to 40 μ) columnar epithelium. At the cardia it begins abruptly under the overlying edge of the stratified squamous epithelium of the esophagus (Fig. 25-3). In the pylorus it is replaced by the intestinal epithelium. The entire supranuclear portion of the cells on the free surface is occupied by granules of a peculiar type of mucigen. In sections in which the granules have not been preserved or fail to stain, the supranuclear region of the cell appears clear or highly vacuolated. After proper fixation the mucigen can be stained with mucicarmine and the periodic acid–Schiff reaction. With certain other dyes that normally stain mucus, the surface mucous cells are unstained. Upon release, the granules give

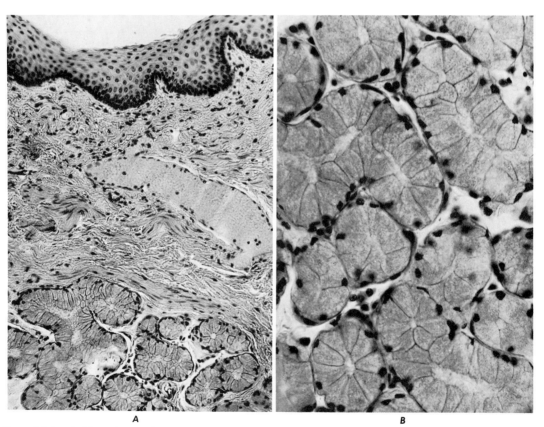

A   B

Figure 25-4. *A,* Photomicrograph of esophageal wall, showing the lumen and lining epithelium and the esophageal glands in the submucosa. × 120. *B,* Esophageal glands at higher magnification, illustrating the dark pyknotic appearing nuclei displaced to the base of the cell by the accumulated mucigen in the apical region. × 300.

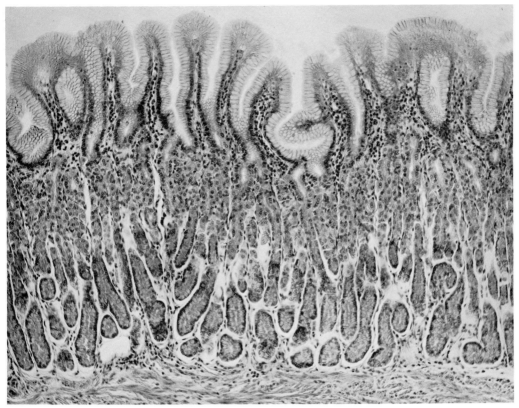

Figure 25-5.   Photomicrograph of the gastric mucosa of a macaque, showing the gastric glands opening into the gastric pits, or foveolae. Hematoxylin and eosin. × 120.

rise to the layer of mucus that lubricates the surface of the mucosa. This mucus, unlike that secreted by glands of the oral cavity, is not precipitated by acetic acid. A diplosome can be demonstrated near the free surface and there is a supranuclear or paranuclear Golgi complex. In preparations in which the granules are preserved and stained, it is evident that, in the cells of the foveolae, they become progressively less abundant at deeper levels, and in the bottom of the pits they form only a thin layer immediately beneath the cell surface. Cells of this kind continue into the neck of the glands.

Under physiological conditions the surface cells are continuously desquamated and perish. The population of surface mucous cells is renewed about every three days. Signs of regeneration are seen only in the deeper part of the foveolae and in the necks of the glands, where mitoses are frequent in the less differentiated cells that contain but a small number of mucigen granules under their free surface. The newly formed cells are slowly pushed

upward through growth pressure and replace those lost at the surface.

In electron micrographs the surface mucous cells have short microvilli on their free surfaces and the plasmalemma has a coating of fine filamentous material. The mucigen granules are spherical, ovoid, or discoid and are, for the most part dense and homogeneous. Some may have a dense core and a less dense periphery. The Golgi complex is well developed, the endoplasmic reticulum is sparse, and the mitochondria are in no way unusual (Figs. 25-8 and 25-9).

GASTRIC GLANDS.   These glands, which are the most important contributors to the secretion of the gastric juice, are simple, branched tubular glands. They are closely packed together and oriented perpendicular to the surface of the mucosa, and they extend through its entire thickness of 0.3 to 1.5 mm. In sections, from one to several open through a slight constriction or neck into the bottom of each foveola. The diameter of the gland is 30

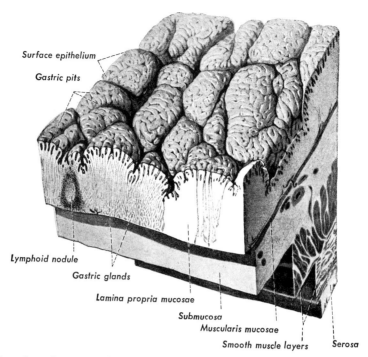

Surface epithelium

Gastric pits

Lymphoid nodule

Gastric glands

Lamina propria mucosae

Submucosa

Muscularis mucosae

Smooth muscle layers   Serosa

Figure 25-6. Surface of gastric mucosa of a man; drawn with a binocular microscope. The cut surfaces are slightly diagrammatic. At the left, the normal distribution of the gastric glands; to the right, only a few are indicated. Glands, gray; gastric pits, black. × 17. (After Braus.)

to 50 μ, but the lumen is narrow. The blind ends are slightly thickened and coiled, and sometimes divide into two or three branches. They reach almost to the muscularis mucosae. The number of these glands is estimated at 35,000,000.

There are four types of cells in these glands. Many different names have been proposed for them, so that the nomenclature is rarely the same in any two descriptions. The four types are: (1) *chief* or *zymogenic cells;* (2) *parietal* or *oxyntic cells;* (3) *mucous neck cells;* and (4) *argentaffin cells.* Mitotic activity is largely confined to cells in the necks of the glands, and it is probable that the zymogenic, parietal, and other cell types develop from relatively undifferentiated cells in this region.

Chief or Zymogenic Cells. The zymogenic cells are arranged in a simple layer on the inner surface of the basement lamina and line the lumen in the lower half or third of the glandular tubule. After death they begin to disintegrate almost immediately, so that adequate preservation is difficult to achieve, although if there is no acid in the stomach, they may remain for some time. In fresh condition, especially after a period of fasting, the cells are

full of coarse, refractile granules. After intense secretory activity the cells are smaller and contain but few granules near their surface. The granules are believed to contain pepsinogen, the antecedent of the enzyme pepsin. Only certain osmic sublimate and formalin mixtures preserve the granules; in most cases they dissolve, and the fixed cytoplasm shows a vacuolated structure. The spherical nucleus does not show any unusual features. In the basal part of the cell the cytoplasm contains mitochondria and radially striated accumulations of ergastoplasm or chromophilic substance.

In electron micrographs, the zymogenic cells are found to be cuboidal or low columnar in form, and they bear short, irregularly oriented microvilli on their free surfaces (Fig. 25-10). Their fine structure resembles that of the pancreatic acinar cells and other cell types secreting protein enzymes. The apical cytoplasm contains large, round or oval granules of relatively low density. A well developed Golgi complex is located in the supranuclear region. Tubular and cisternal profiles of granular endoplasmic reticulum are found throughout the cytoplasm but are particularly concentrated near the cell base (Fig. 25-12). The abundance of ribosomes, both on the membranes of the reticulum and free in the cytoplasmic matrix, is evidently responsible for the basophilia of these cells in histological sections.

Parietal Cells (Oxyntic Cells). Among the zymogenic cells are single parietal cells. They are large spheroidal or pyramidal cells and occupy a peripheral position with their tapering apical ends wedged between the zymogenic cells. Sometimes they bulge on the outer surfaces of the glands, especially after prolonged secretory activity, when the zymogenic cells are small.

Each parietal cell usually contains a single large round nucleus, but sometimes two or even more nuclei are present in one cell. The cytoplasm stains deeply with eosin, phloxine, and other acid aniline dyes. The cell contains a diplosome and very numerous, short,

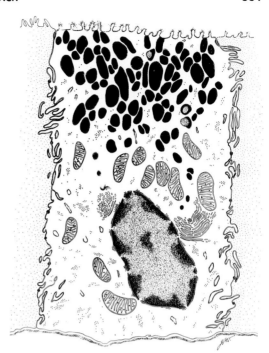

Figure 25-8. Diagrammatic representation of the fine structure of the surface mucous cell. (After S. Ito and R. J. Winchester, J. Cell Biol., *16:*541, 1963.)

rod-shaped or spherical mitochondria, but there are no secretory granules. The most typical feature of a parietal cell is the secretory canaliculus, which appears to occupy an intracellular position, forming a loose network around the nucleus and opening at the cell apex into the lumen of the gastric gland. The parietal cells do not seem to undergo any marked morphological changes with the various stages of functional activity.

The electron microscope shows that the free surface of a parietal cell is invaginated to form the extensive secretory canaliculus that penetrates the cell body and is lined with very numerous, long microvilli that partially occlude the lumen (Fig. 25-13). The plasma membrane appears to lack the external filamentous coating of protein-polysaccharide found on other cells of the gastric mucosa. Although the apex of the pyramidal cell is narrow, the cell has a very large area of free surface exposed to the lumen of the secretory canaliculus. The boundaries between the parietal cells and the adjacent zymogenic or mucous cells are relatively straight and possess typical terminal bars and desmosomes. The cytoplasm is filled with an extraordinary num-

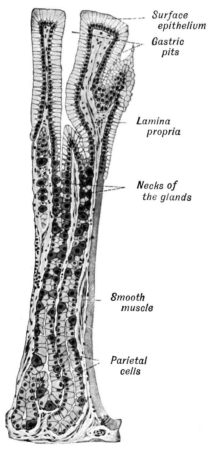

Surface epithelium

Gastric pits

Lamina propria

Necks of the glands

Smooth muscle

Parietal cells

Figure 25-7. Fundic glands of human stomach. Zymogenic cells light gray; parietal cells dark gray. × 130. (After Braus.)

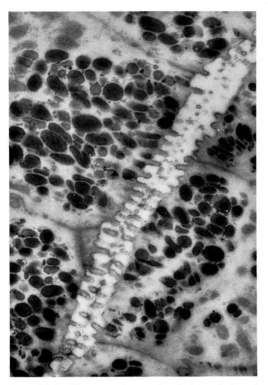

Figure 25-9. Electron micrograph of the apical ends of surface mucous cells of the bat gastric mucosa. The short microvilli have a coating of fine filaments and the apical cytoplasm contains mucinogen granules of varying shape. Osmic acid fixation. × 16,700. (Courtesy of S. Ito and R. J. Winchester.)

ber of plump, closely packed mitochondria having an elaborate internal membrane structure and numerous dense granules in the intercristal matrix (Fig. 25-12). The cytoplasm near the secretory canaliculus is permeated by an extensive system of minute tubules that appear to communicate with the cell surface. These have been considered to be a form of agranular endoplasmic reticulum, but because of their continuity with the surface, it may be more accurate to describe them as tubular invaginations of the cell membrane. Profiles of granular reticulum and free ribosomes are very few. There are no secretory granules. The Golgi complex is often located between the nucleus and the cell base, in contrast to the supranuclear position that it occupies in most epithelial cells.

Mucous Neck Cells. These are relatively few in number and are lodged between the parietal cells in the neck of the glands. Deeper in the glands they are abruptly succeeded by the zymogenic cells. In fresh, unstained preparations they are filled with pale transparent granules. These cells are easily overlooked or mistaken for zymogenic cells in preparations in which mucus is either not preserved or is unstained. In sections stained with the periodic acid–Schiff reaction, mucicarmine, or mucihematein, the granules that fill the apical cytoplasm are deeply colored. There is evidence that the mucus secreted by these cells is somewhat different from that of the surface mucous cells.

The mucous neck cells appear to be deformed by neighboring cells and tend to be irregular in shape, some having a wide base and narrow apex, others a broad apex and narrow base. The nuclei are at the bases of the cells and are often somewhat flattened.

Where the necks of the glands open into the narrow bottoms of the foveolae, the mucous neck cells appear to be connected with the surface epithelium by a series of gradual transitional forms. As mitoses are not found in the mucous neck cells of the adult, it is probable that the new cells arise through a gradual transformation of the undifferentiated epithelium in the bottom of the foveolae and in the neck regions of the glands.

In many gastric glands the mucous neck cells advance far toward the bottom and are sometimes scattered singly between the zymogenic cells. This is especially prominent in the glands near the pyloric region. According to some, the glands of the narrow intermediate zone may contain only mucous neck and parietal cells, and be devoid of zymogenic cells.

Under the electron microscope the luminal surfaces of the columnar mucous neck cells are studded with short microvilli that have a fuzzy appearance owing to the presence of a coating of exceedingly thin filaments that project from their limiting membrane. The lateral surfaces of neighboring cells are attached by small desmosomes and are interdigitated, particularly toward the base of the cell. The apical region of the cell contains numerous dense granules of spheroid, ovoid, or discoid form. Rod-shaped mitochondria of the usual internal structure are scattered through the cytoplasm. There is a sizable supranuclear Golgi complex. Membranous profiles of endoplasmic reticulum are present in small numbers.

Argentaffin Cells. Argentaffin or enterochromaffin cells, like those in the intestine, are moderately abundant in the fundic glands and are less frequent in the pyloric glands. These cells are scattered singly, between the basement lamina and the zymogenic cells, and have a rounded or somewhat flattened form. Their cytoplasm is filled with small granules which can be stained with silver or chromium salts. Two groups can be distinguished, the true "argentaffin cells" in which the specific granules reduce silver salts without special pretreatment and the so-called "argyrophilic cells," which require exposure to a reducing substance before their granules will react with silver. The basis for this difference and the relations of the two groups are poorly understood.

In electron micrographs, the nucleus is deeply infolded and there is a small Golgi complex and a few cisternal profiles of granular reticulum (Fig. 25-15). The appearance of the granules varies from cell to cell. In some they are very dense and spherical and enclosed in a loose fitting membrane; in others, the membrane is more closely applied to a granule that

is of lower density. Occasional argentaffin cells extend to the surface of the epithelium, but this is relatively uncommon. The argentaffin or enterochromaffin cells are sites of synthesis and storage of 5-hydroxytryptamine.

PYLORIC GLANDS. In the pyloric region the foveolae are deeper than elsewhere in the stomach, extending down into the mucous membrane for half its thickness. They have more branches than in the body of the stomach. The glands here are also of the simple, branched tubular type, but the lumen is larger and the tubules are coiled, so that in perpendicular sections they are seldom seen as longitudinal structures (Fig. 25-16). The pyloric glands contain only one type of cell, whose pale cytoplasm shows an indistinct granulation. Secretory capillaries have been described between the cells. The nucleus is often flattened against the base of the cell. In sections stained with hematoxylin and eosin, they are difficult to distinguish from mucous neck cells or the cells of the glands of Brunner in the duodenum. Some investigators believe that the pyloric

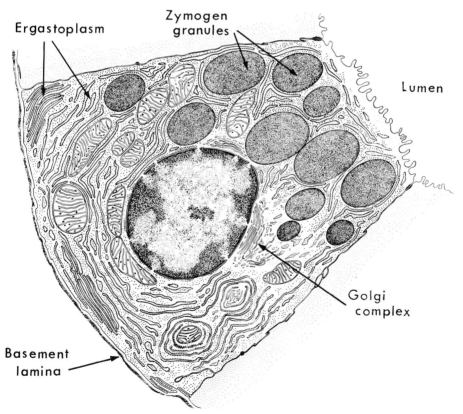

Figure 25-10. Diagram of the chief or zymogenic cell as seen with the electron microscope. (After S. Ito and R. J. Winchester, J. Cell Biol., *16*:541, 1963.)

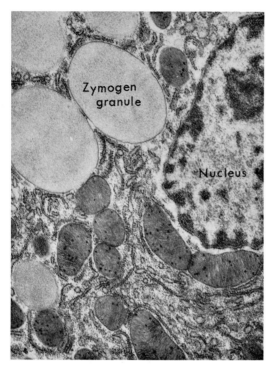

Figure 25-11. Electron micrograph of the apical portion of a gastric zymogenic cell of the bat, showing several pale zymogen granules, numerous mitochondria, and abundant ergastoplasm. Osmic acid fixation. × 17,000. (Courtesy of S. Ito and R. J. Winchester.)

glandular cells are identical with the mucous neck cells, for both give similar staining reactions for mucus. Cresyl violet, and the Giemsa mixture of dyes, however, seem to stain them in a specific way. In the human stomach, the pyloric glands in the region of the sphincter may contain parietal cells. Argentaffin cells have also been described in the pyloric glands.

CARDIAC GLANDS. These glands, found in the immediate vicinity of the esophageal orifice, are compound tubular glands that open directly into the gastric pits. They are composed of mucous cells that are histologically quite similar to the mucous cells of the pyloric glands or the mucous neck cells of the gastric glands proper. A few argentaffin cells are found among the mucous cells.

LAMINA PROPRIA. Connective tissue of the lamina propria occupies the narrow spaces between the glands and the muscularis mucosae and forms larger accumulations only between the necks of the glands and between the foveolae. It consists of a delicate network of

collagenous and reticular fibrils and is almost devoid of elastic elements. In addition to oval pale nuclei, which seem to belong to fibroblasts, the meshes of the fibrous network contain numerous small lymphocytes and some plasma cells, eosinophilic leukocytes, and mast cells. Sometimes, lymphoid cells with coarsely granular acidophilic inclusions, called Russell's bodies, are found between the epithelial cells of the glands. These may develop under physiological conditions but are more common in pathological states. In the lamina propria, especially in the pyloric region, strands of smooth muscle may be found, and small accumulations of lymphatic tissue occur normally.

OTHER LAYERS OF THE STOMACH WALL. The muscularis mucosae consists of an inner circular and an outer longitudinal layer of smooth muscle. In some places there is an additional outer circular layer. Strands of smooth muscle cells extend from the inner layer between the glands toward the surface. The contraction of these strands compresses the mu-

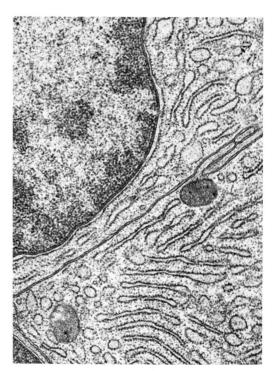

Figure 25-12. Electron micrograph of basal region of a gastric zymogenic cell, showing an extensive development of granular endoplasmic reticulum as in other protein secreting cells. × 18,000. (Courtesy of S. Ito.)

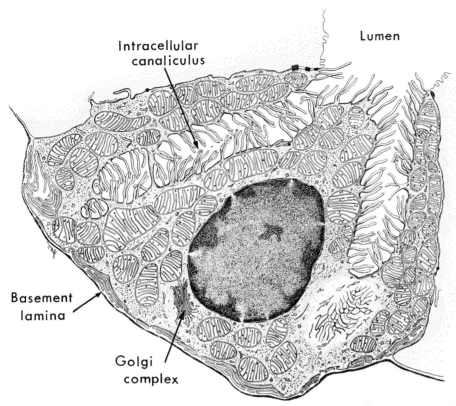

Figure 25-13. Diagram of the ultrastructure of a gastric parietal cell, illustrating its abundant mitochondria, sparse reticulum, and prominent "intracellular" canaliculus. (After S. Ito and R. J. Winchester, J. Cell Biol., *16*:541, 1963.)

cous membrane and probably facilitates the emptying of the glands.

The *submucous layer* consists of dense connective tissue that contains some fat cells and is rich in mast cells, lymphoid wandering cells, and eosinophilic leukocytes. This layer contains the large blood and lymph vessels and venous plexuses.

The *muscularis externa* consists of three layers—an outer layer, mainly longitudinal, a middle circular, and an inner oblique. The outermost layer is a continuation of the longitudinal fibers of the esophagus. The muscle fibers maintain their longitudinal course only along the two curvatures, while on the anterior and posterior surfaces of the stomach they gradually become oriented toward the greater curvature. In the pyloric region the longitudinal fibers are assembled in a layer that continues into the corresponding layer of the intestinal wall. The middle layer is the most continuous and the most regularly organized of the three. In the pylorus it forms a thick, circular sphincter that helps control the evac-

uation of the stomach. The emptying of the stomach depends primarily on the contraction of the gastric musculature.

The work of all the parts of the muscular coat just described is regulated with marked precision. The wall of the stomach adapts itself to the volume of its contents without alteration in the pressure in its cavity.

The serous membrane, the outermost layer of the stomach wall, is a thin layer of loose connective tissue overlying the muscularis externa and covered on its outer aspect with mesothelium. It is continuous with the serous covering of the large and small omentum.

Histophysiology of the Stomach

The quantity of gastric juice secreted by the human stomach during 24 hours is estimated at 1000 to 1500 ml. It is a clear colorless liquid that, in addition to mucin, water, and salts, contains 0.4 to 0.5 per cent hydrochloric acid, as well as the enzymes *pepsin* and *rennin*. The most remarkable aspect of gastric function is its capacity to elaborate a secretion whose pH is less than 2. Physiological and histological evidence supports the view that the parietal cells are the source of the hydrochloric acid of the gastric juice, although the exact mechanism of formation of the acid is unknown. It is suggested that the parietal cell secretes, into the canaliculi, a fluid rich in sodium chloride and that sodium is then actively absorbed by the membrane in exchange for active secretion of hydrogen ions. Sodium chloride in the extracellular fluid is thus replaced by hydrochloric acid. The gastric mucosa is rich in carbonic anhydrase, which promotes formation of carbonic acid. The hydrogen ions replacing the extracellular sodium in acid secretion are presumed to come from carbonic acid.

It is generally believed that pepsin is secreted by the zymogenic cells and that the contents of their granules are transformed into active pepsin only when acted upon by the hydrochloric acid. Pepsin is a highly active proteolytic enzyme only at very low pH. The hydrochloric acid secretion is therefore essential for protein digestion. Microchemical analyses show that the more numerous the zymogenic cells in a given location, the higher the pepsin content (Holter). Injection of histamine causes the secretion of large amounts of acid gastric juice low in pepsin, while stimulation of the vagus nerve results in a great increase in the pepsin content of the juice. This has been shown to be accompanied by an extensive depletion of zymogen granules.

The gastric secretion also contains the enzyme rennin, which promotes the coagulation and digestion of milk in suckling animals. This enzyme, too, has been attributed to the zymogenic cells.

The so-called *gastric intrinsic factor*, which acts upon vitamin B_{12} in such a way as to facilitate its absorption, is also believed to be produced by the gastric zymogenic cell. In the

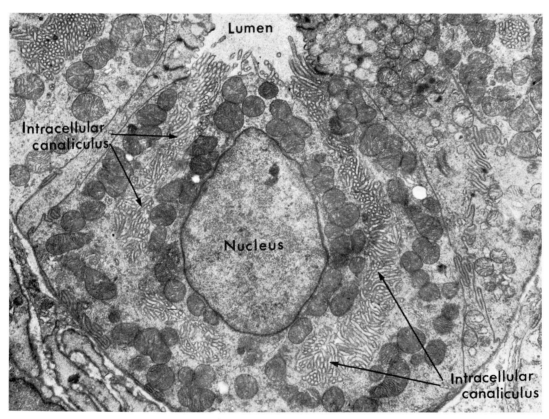

Figure 25-14. Electron micrograph of a parietal cell of bat gastric mucosa. The extensive secretory canaliculus within the limits of the cell is filled by large numbers of irregularly oriented microvilli. × 10,000. (Courtesy of S. Ito.)

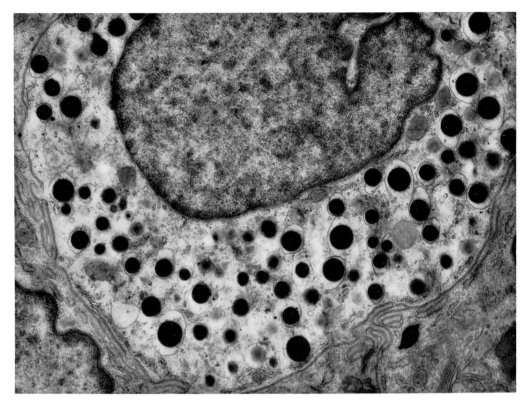

Figure 25-15. Electron micrograph of an argentaffin cell among the chief cells in a gastric gland from bat stomach. The argentaffin cell contains numerous dense spherical granules, each enclosed by a loose fitting membrane. Osmic acid fixation. × 14,000. (Courtesy of S. Ito and R. J. Winchester.)

absence of vitamin B_{12}, the maturation of erythrocytes in the bone marrow is impaired and *pernicious anemia* results. Therefore the intrinsic factor is sometimes called the *gastric antipernicious anemia factor*.

The mucous neck cells and the surface epithelium secrete *mucus*. The gastric mucus forms a layer on the surface of the mucous membrane, which is supposed by some to protect it against autodigestion by delaying the diffusion of pepsin and hydrochloric acid and by inhibiting the action of pepsin. It may also combine with the acid, for the mucosa is neutral during periods of inactivity. According to another opinion, autodigestion in life is prevented by an antienzyme elaborated by the mucous membrane. Immediately after death autodigestion begins.

Histogenesis of the Gastric Mucosa

In the young embryo the stomach is lined by a layer of pseudostratified columnar epithelium of uniform height. In embryos of 22.8

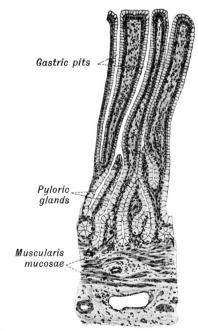

Figure 25-16. Pyloric glands from human stomach. Slightly diagrammatic. × 75. (After Braus.)

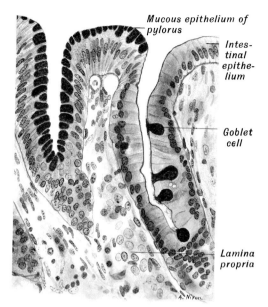

Figure 25-17. Section through junction of the pyloric and duodenal epithelia of an 8 year old child. Stained with hematoxylin, and for mucus with mucicarmine. × 220.

mm., groups of tall and low cells alternate, so that small pits arise, although the basement membrane remains even. In later stages (42 mm.), the pits begin to extend into the underlying mesenchyme, while the tall cells between them begin to elaborate mucus. At the bottom of the crypts in embryos of 90 mm., solid buds of granular cells appear—the primordia of the glands. In the 120 mm. stage, the glandular primordia establish two kinds of cells. Some of them stain intensely with eosin and are accumulated at the blind ends; these are the future parietal cells. Others remain pale—the future zymogenic cells.

At birth the length of the glands is half the thickness of the mucosa. Their number gradually increases, partly through division of the blind ends of the tubes, partly through the formation of new buds of undifferentiated cells. The pyloric and cardiac glands seem to arise from the very beginning as structures different from the gastric glands.

CELL RENEWAL AND REGENERATION IN THE ADULT STOMACH. The superficial portions of the gastric mucosa have a rapid rate of renewal. Studies on laboratory animals, by means of colchicine blockage of mitosis and autoradiography with tritiated thymidine, indicate that the surface mucous cells are renewed in about three days and the mucous

neck cells in about one week (Stevens and Leblond). Although the human gastric mucosa cannot be studied in this way, it is probable that its rate of replacement is also quite rapid. Mitotic activity is largely confined to the surface mucous cells in the depths of the foveolae and the mucous neck cells in the necks of the glands (Fig. 25-18). The epithelial cells exfoliated at the surface are replaced by upward migration from this region of mitotic activity. The mucous neck cells do not appear to migrate, but they may be extruded from time to time directly into the gland lumen.

There is some evidence that parietal cells and zymogenic cells can be replaced by differentiation from mucous neck cells, but most autoradiographic studies have indicated that these cell types are relatively long lived and are renewed only very slowly.

After injury, the gastric mucosa is regenerated in a sequence of events reminiscent of its development in embryonic life. Relatively undifferentiated mucous cells at the margins of

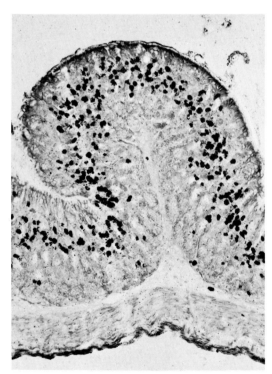

Figure 25-18. Autoradiograph of the gastric mucosa of a mouse given three injections of tritiated thymidine over a 12 hour period preceding fixation of the tissue. The distribution of the black deposits of silver demonstrates that the principal site of mitoses is in the neck region of the gastric glands. × 110. (Courtesy of A. J. Ladman.)

the wound proliferate to form an epithelial sheet that migrates over the defect. The epithelium then invaginates to form gastric pits and glands. Certain of the cells differentiate into cells resembling mucous neck cells, and these appear to differentiate into parietal and zymogenic cells.

REFERENCES

Baker, B. L.: Cell replacement in the stomach. Gastroenterology, 46:202, 1964.

Bensley, R. R.: The structure of the mammalian gastric glands. Quart. J. Micr. Sci., 41:361, 1898.

Bensley, R. R.: The cardiac glands of mammals. Am. J. Anat., 2:105, 1902.

Bertalanffy, F. D.: Cell renewal in the gastrointestinal tract of man. Gastroenterology, 43:472, 1963.

Boas, A., and T. H. Wilson: Cellular localization of gastric intrinsic factor in the rat. Am. J. Physiol., 206:783, 1963.

Davenport, H. W.: Physiology of the Digestive Tract. Chicago, Year Book Medical Publishers, 1961, pp. 85–102.

Dawson, A. B.: Argentophile and argentaffin cells in the gastric mucosa of the rat. Anat. Rec., 100:319, 1948.

Heinz, E., and K. H. Öbrink: Acid formation and acidity control in the stomach. Physiol. Rev., 34:643, 1954.

Helander, H. F.: Ultrastructure of fundus glands of the mouse gastric mucosa. J. Ultrastruct. Res., (Suppl. 4):1, 1962.

Hoedemarker, P. J., J. Abels, J. J. Wachters, A. Arends, and N. O. Nieweg: Investigations about the site of production of Castle's gastric intrinsic factor. Lab. Invest., 13:1394, 1964.

Holter, H., and K. Linderstrøm-Lang: Beiträge zur enzymatischen Histochemie; die Verteilung des Pepsins in der Schleimhaut des Schweinemagens. Zeitschr. f. physiol. Chem., 226:149, 1934.

Hunt, T. E., and E. A. Hunt: Radioautographic study of prolifera-

tion in the stomach of the rat using thymidine-H^3 and compound 48/80. Anat. Rec., 142:505, 1962.

Ito, S.: The endoplasmic reticulum of gastric parietal cells. J. Biophys. & Biochem. Cytol., 11:333, 1961.

Ito, S.: Anatomic structure of the gastric mucosa. In Code, C. F., and M. I. Grossman, eds.: Handbook of Physiology. Washington, American Physiological Society. (In press.)

Ito, S., and R. J. Winchester: The fine structure of the gastric mucosa in the bat. J. Cell Biol., 16:541, 1963.

Kammeraad, A.: The development of the gastrointestinal tract of the rat. I. Histogenesis of the epithelium of the stomach, small intestine and pancreas. J. Morphol., 70:323, 1942.

Landboe-Christensen, E.: Extent of the pylorus zone in the human stomach. Acta Path. et Microbiol. Scandinav., Suppl. 54:671, 1944.

Leblond, C. P., and B. E. Walker: Renewal of cell populations. Physiol. Rev., 36:255, 1956.

Lillibridge, C. B.: The fine structure of normal human gastric mucosa. Gastroenterology, 47:269, 1964.

Lipkin, M., P. Sherlock, and B. Bell: Cell proliferation kinetics in the gastrointestinal tract of man. II. Cell renewal in stomach, ileum, colon, and rectum. Gastroenterology, 45:721, 1963.

MacDonald, W. C., J. S. Trier, and N. B. Everett: Cell proliferation and migration in the stomach, duodenum and rectum of man. Gastroenterology, 46:403, 1964.

Plenk, H.: Der Magen. In von Möllendorff, W., and W. Bargmann, eds.: Handbuch der mikroskopischen Anatomie des Menschen. Berlin, Julius Springer, 1932, Vol. 5, part 2, p. 1.

Salenius, P.: On the ontogenesis of the gastric epithelial cells. Acta Anat., 50 (Suppl. 46):1, 1962.

Sedar, A. W.: The fine structure of the oxyntic cell in relation to functional activity of the stomach. Ann. N. Y. Acad. Sci., 99:9, 1962.

Sedar, A. W., and M. H. F. Friedman: Correlation of the gastric parietal cell with functional activity of the stomach. J. Biophys. & Biochem. Cytol., 11:349, 1961.

Stevens, C. E., and C. P. Leblond: Renewal of the mucous cells in the gastric mucosa of the rat. Anat. Rec., 115:231, 1953.

Wolf, S.: The Stomach. New York, Oxford University Press, 1965.

CHAPTER TWENTY-SIX

Intestines

THE SMALL INTESTINE

The small intestine is the portion of the alimentary tract between the stomach and the large intestine. It is a tubular viscus about 7 m. long, divisible grossly into three segments, the *duodenum,* the *jejunum,* and the *ileum.* The duodenum is about 25 cm. long and largely retroperitoneal, being closely attached to the dorsal wall of the abdomen. The remainder of the small intestine is suspended from the dorsal wall by a mesentery and is freely movable. The proximal portion of the mesenteric small intestine is the jejunum, usually occupying the upper left portion of the abdominal cavity, and the distal portion, in the lower abdomen, is the ileum. Although there are minor gross and microscopic differences between these three segments, they have the same basic organization, and the transitions between them are gradual. The general description that follows will apply to all and specific regional differences will be pointed out where they apply.

The principal functions of the small intestine are: to move forward the chyme that it receives from the stomach; to continue its digestion with special juices secreted by its own intrinsic glands and its accessory glands; and to absorb into the blood and lymph vessels in its mucosa the nutrient materials released by digestion.

SURFACE AMPLIFICATIONS OF THE MUCOUS MEMBRANE. The luminal surface of the small intestine is greatly increased by the formation of grossly visible circular folds, the *plicae circulares* or *valves of Kerckring* (Fig. 26-1), and by countless finger-like processes of microscopic dimensions, the *intestinal villi.*

The plicae circulares are permanent cres-

centic folds involving both the mucosa and submucosa and extending half to two thirds of the way around the circumference of the lumen. The larger ones may be as much as 5 cm. in length, 8 mm. in height, and about 3 mm. in thickness. They are absent in the first portion of the duodenum, beginning 2 to 5 cm. from the pylorus and reaching their greatest development in the distal half of the duodenum and the proximal portion of the jejunum. Beyond this point they gradually diminish in size and number and are seldom found beyond the middle of the ileum.

The villi are outgrowths of the mucous membrane and have a length of 0.5 to 1.5 mm. Their length is reduced by distention of the intestine. They cover the entire surface of the mucosa and give it a characteristic velvety appearance. Their number varies from 10 to 40 per square millimeter. In the duodenum they are broad, leaflike structures arranged with their long dimension in the transverse direction. In the ileum they gradually become more finger-like.

Many villi are bifid at their tips, especially in the infant. By dividing in this way the villi are believed to increase in number during the growth of the intestine. Between the bases of the villi are the openings of innumerable intestinal glands or *crypts of Lieberkühn* (Fig. 26-2). These are simple tubes, 320 to 450 μ long, which penetrate the thickness of the mucous membrane and reach almost to the muscularis mucosae (Fig. 26-3). The spaces between them, occupied by the cellular connective tissue of the lamina propria, are wider than those between the glands in the stomach.

EPITHELIUM. The epithelium covering the free surface of the mucous membrane is simple columnar. Three types of cells can be distinguished: columnar *absorptive cells, goblet cells,* and *argentaffin cells.*

The absorptive cells have a columnar prismatic form and a height of 22 to 26 μ. The free surface is specialized to form a striated border. Beneath this border is a clear layer that is usually free of organelles and inclusions. This layer, called the *terminal web,* may exhibit birefringence with the polarizing microscope and can be selectively stained by a method involving the use of tannic acid, phosphomolybdic acid, and amido black (Leblond et al.). Filamentous mitochondria are abundant in the apical cytoplasm beneath the terminal web. The Golgi apparatus occupies a supranuclear position. Smaller numbers of shorter mitochondria are found in the basal cytoplasm.

The bases of the cells rest upon a thin basal lamina (basement membrane), which is evidently firmly attached to the connective tissue fibers of the lamina propria, for the epithelium successfully withstands the forces arising from movements of the villi and the mechanical action of the food passing over it. After fixation the epithelium often appears detached from the stroma at the tip of the villi, and a cavity is seen between the two tissues. This space is probably an artifact, caused by the agonal contraction of the smooth muscles in the core of the villi. It should be borne in mind, however, that the epithelial cells arise from division of relatively undifferentiated cells in the crypts and then move up along the sides of the villi. The oldest cells are constantly being cast off at the tips. The apparent looseness of the epithelium at the ends of the villi may be related in part to this process of desquamation of cells in the continual renovation of the epithelium that results in complete replacement of the cell population every seven or eight days. The large number of degenerating epithelial cells that are shed and the lymphocytes that emigrate through the epithelium contribute to the bulk of the feces.

In electron micrographs, the striated border of the epithelial cell is found to be made up of countless, closely packed, parallel, cylindrical processes called *microvilli* (Fig. 26-6). These are 1 to 1.4 μ in length and about 80 mμ in diameter. Each is enclosed in an extension of the plasmalemma, which has the usual trilaminar unit membrane structure but whose outer leaflet bears a nap of delicate branching filaments (about 30 Å) that give the membrane a fuzzy appearance (Ito). These filaments are longer and more numerous at the tips of the microvilli than on the sides (Figs. 26-8 and 26-9). The intermingling of the filamentous excrescences on the microvillous tips results in a continuous surface layer on the striated border, which varies from 0.1 to 0.5 μ in thickness, depending upon the species (Fig. 26-7). This enteric surface coat has the staining properties

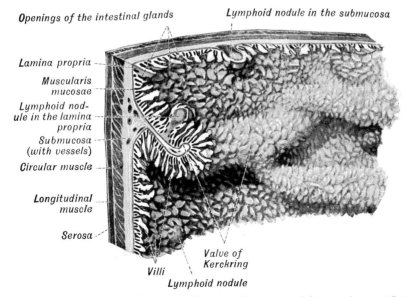

Openings of the intestinal glands   Lymphoid nodule in the submucosa

Lamina propria

Muscularis mucosae

Lymphoid nodule in the lamina propria

Submucosa (with vessels)

Circular muscle

Longitudinal muscle

Serosa

Villi

Value of Kerckring

Lymphoid nodule

Figure 26-1. Portion of small intestine; drawn with binocular microscope and from sections. × 17. (After Braus.)

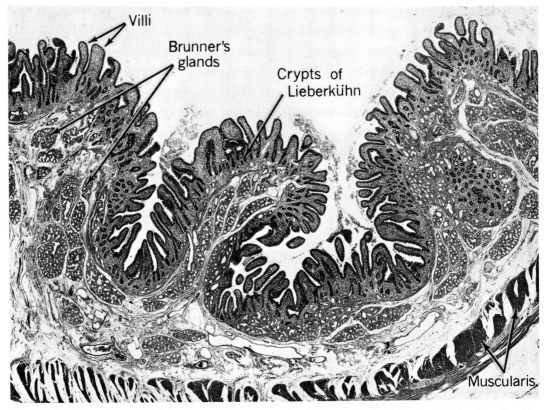

Figure 26-2. Photomicrograph of duodenum from a man who had committed suicide by drinking formalin. The mucosa is unusually well preserved; the muscularis shows considerable shrinkage. × 20. (Courtesy of Dr. H. Mizoguchi.)

of an acid protein-polysaccharide (muco-polysaccharide) and is extremely resistant to proteolytic and mucolytic agents.

In the interior of the microvillus, a bundle of thin straight filaments runs longitudinally in an otherwise homogeneous, fine-textured cytoplasmic matrix. The filaments may extend downward from the microvilli into the terminal web, which is resolved with the electron microscope as a feltwork of exceedingly fine filaments oriented, for the most part, parallel to the free surface of the cell. At the sides of the cell the filaments of the terminal web converge upon the zonula adherens of the junctional complex of adjoining cells. This portion of the complex and the associated filaments of the web stain darkly with iron-hematoxylin and other cytological stains and appear to correspond to the *terminal bar* of the classical cytologists. Between the zonula adherens and the lumen, the membranes of adjacent epithelial cells are fused in a *zonula occludens*, which appears to deny access of material to the inter-

cellular space from the intestinal lumen. In the upper part of the epithelium the lateral boundaries of the cells are closely apposed and relatively straight but toward the base they may be irregularly interdigitated. In some phases of intestinal absorption the intercellular spaces near the base of the epithelium may be considerably widened.

Cell organelles are excluded from the terminal web, but in the subjacent apical cytoplasm there are numerous elongated mitochondria, with the usual internal structure, and a rather extensive network of tubular profiles of the agranular endoplasmic reticulum. A pair of centrioles may be encountered in this region. A well developed Golgi complex is situated at the apical pole of the elongated nucleus. The basal cytoplasm contains mitochondria and occasional profiles of granular reticulum. Free ribosomes are found in moderate numbers throughout the cell but are somewhat more plentiful toward the base.

The *goblet cells* are irregularly scattered

among the cylindrical absorptive cells. They are described in some detail in Chapter 4, as examples of unicellular glands. Their name derives from their fancied resemblance to a wine glass, because of the distention of their apical cytoplasm with accumulated mucigen droplets. The base or stalk of the cell is often considerably narrower than the distended *theca*, filled with secretion. The nucleus tends to be flattened and the surrounding cytoplasm strongly basophilic. The organelles are difficult to study with the light microscope in the mature goblet cell because of their close crowding.

In electron micrographs of the stalk, cisternae of granular endoplasmic reticulum are arranged more or less parallel to the base and the lateral surfaces of the cell. A few cisternae may continue upward into the thin layer of cytoplasm around the theca. A highly developed Golgi complex is situated between the nucleus and the mucinogen droplets in the theca. The individual droplets appear to originate in the Golgi complex and move up into the theca. Each is enveloped by a delicate membrane, which is often disrupted in preparation of the specimen. The basal and lateral

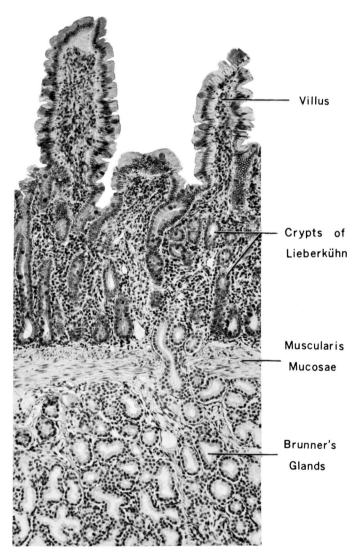

Villus

Crypts of Lieberkühn

Muscularis Mucosae

Brunner's Glands

Figure 26-3. Photomicrograph of a histological section of the duodenum of a macaque. The villi, crypts of Lieberkühn, and Brunner's glands are shown. A duct of Brunner's gland can be seen penetrating the muscularis mucosae to empty into one of the crypts. Hematoxylin and eosin. × 110.

plasma membranes are smoothly contoured except for a few lateral folds. The goblet cells are attached to the neighboring absorptive cells by typical juxtaluminal junctional complexes. Sparse microvilli may be present on the free surface, but their length and number is influenced by the degree of distention of the theca with mucigen. The tendency of mucigen droplets to swell in specimen preparation has made it difficult to study the mechanism of their release, but the membranes of the droplets appear to fuse with each other and with the plasmalemma, permitting the mucus to flow out while maintaining the integrity of the cell surface (Trier).

Occasional argentaffin cells are found at the base of the epithelium covering the villi, but they are more abundant in the crypts of Lieberkühn. Their fine structure is the same as has already been described for similar cells of the gastric mucosa (see p. 552). Everywhere in the small intestine lymphocytes can be seen migrating from the lamina propria into the epithelium of the villi.

CRYPTS OF LIEBERKÜHN. The epithelium covering the villi continues into the glands of Lieberkühn. The wall of the crypt is lined with a low columnar epithelium that contains numerous mitoses. Here regeneration takes place, and the new cells moving upward differentiate into goblet cells and into the columnar cells

with striated borders. All the stages in this process of differentiation are to be seen in the upper half of the crypt.

PANETH CELLS. In the small intestine, the large *cells of Paneth* occur regularly in the bottom of the glands of Lieberkühn (Fig. 26-10). They are narrow, pyramidal, or columnar with a round or oval nucleus near the cell base. They have intensely basophilic basal cytoplasm and large apical secretory granules or droplets. The granules stain with acid dyes, such as eosin or orange G, and histochemical tests indicate that they contain both carbohydrate and protein with a high arginine content.

In the mouse, the granules contain a sulfated mucosaccharide and a basic protein. The latter is believed to be *lysozyme,* an enzyme found in tears, leukocytes and mucous secretions which lyses bacteria. The presence of this enzyme suggests an antibacterial function of Paneth cell secretion (Spicer et al.).

In electron micrographs the basal cytoplasm is seen to be occupied by a small number of mitochondria and by lamellar arrays of cisternae of granular endoplasmic reticulum. A moderately dense content is often preserved in the lumen of the cisternae, and this sometimes takes the form of a highly concentrated protein secretory product that is precipitated in crystalline form (Behnke and Moe). A prominent Golgi complex is found in the su-

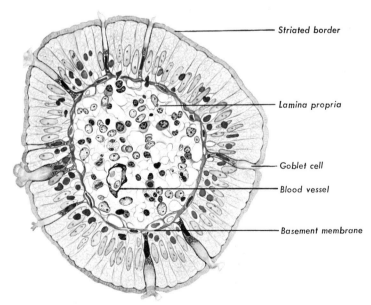

Striated border

Lamina propria

Goblet cell

Blood vessel

Basement membrane

Figure 26-4. Cross section of villus of human jejunum. Iron-hematoxylin-azan. × 350. (Redrawn and slightly modified from V. Patzelt.)

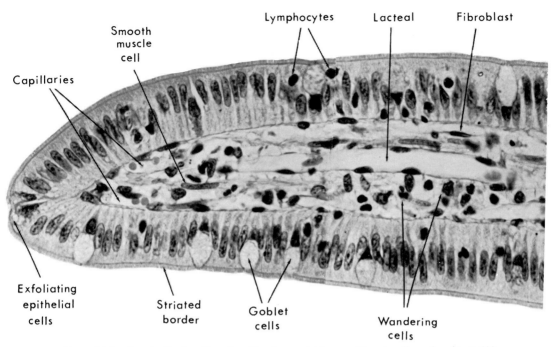

Smooth muscle cell   Lymphocytes   Lacteal   Fibroblast

Capillaries

Exfoliating epithelial cells   Striated border   Goblet cells   Wandering cells

Figure 26-5.   Longitudinal section of a villus from cat jejunum. Hematoxylin and eosin. × 600.

pranuclear region, and formative stages of secretory granules are associated with its stacks of parallel saccules. The upper region of the cell is occupied by large secretory granules, each enclosed by a membrane. In addition to the secretory granules, perinuclear cytoplasm of the Paneth cell contains numerous lysosomes 0.5 to 2 μ in diameter. Microtubules and bundles of tonofilaments are also present in the cytoplasm (Moe). Neither the mechanism responsible for discharge of the Paneth granules nor the functional significance of their secretion are known. On the basis of microchemical analysis of slices of intestinal mucosa including the bottoms of the crypts, it has been suggested that they may secrete peptidase (Linderstrøm-Lang). They concentrate radioactive zinc, a trace element that is an essential component of certain enzymes and a specific activator of peptidase. But no digestive enzyme has yet been specifically localized to the Paneth cells.

ARGENTAFFIN CELLS. Argentaffin cells are commonly found between the cells lining the glands of Lieberkühn. They differ from the rest of the epithelium in their form and by the presence of specific granules in their cytoplasm. They are scattered singly, and their number varies greatly. They are common in the duodenum, occur in moderate number in the stomach, and are relatively few in the jejunum and ileum, except for the appendix, where they occur in considerable numbers. Their basal location in the epithelium, and the fact that their granules tend to be concentrated between the nucleus and the basement lamina, early led to the suggestion that they might constitute a diffuse endocrine system (*enterochromaffin system*). Although direct proof is lacking, it is now widely accepted that they contain the substance 5-hydroxytryptamine (serotonin), which is a powerful stimulant of smooth muscle contraction. The content of 5-hydroxytryptamine in tissues is closely correlated with the number of argentaffin cells. Administration of reserpine, which causes release of serotonin, also results in a marked reduction in the numbers of argentaffin cells. Tumors arising from these cells, *argentaffinomas* or carcinoid tumors, are often accompanied by marked vasomotor, respiratory, and gastrointestinal symptoms caused by liberation of excessive amounts of serotonin into the blood.

There are no morphological observations establishing that the granules are discharged from these cells. It seems more likely that the active substance bound to the matrix of the granules is released and diffuses across the in-

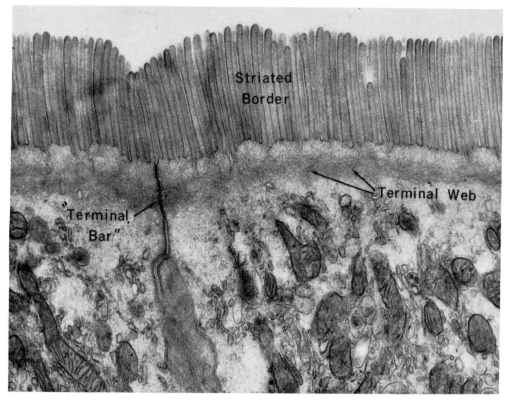

Figure 26-6. Electron micrograph of portions of two intestinal epithelial cells of the hamster, showing the striated border, the terminal web, and the junctional complex, which corresponds to the terminal bar seen with the light microscope. × 25,000. (Courtesy of E. Strauss.)

tact cell membrane. The normal function of the argentaffin cells is not well understood. It has been suggested, however, that 5-hydroxy-tryptamine may serve as a transmitter substance that can be released under certain circumstances from the epithelium into the wall of the alimentary tract and there stimulate the neuromuscular apparatus of these organs, increasing peristaltic action.

LAMINA PROPRIA. The lamina propria of the mucous membrane fills the spaces between the glands of Lieberkühn and forms the cores of the villi (Figs. 26-4 and 26-5). It is a peculiar type of connective tissue that resembles reticular connective tissue in containing a stroma of argyrophilic fibers similar to that of lymphatic tissue. Close to the fibers are fixed cells with oval, pale nuclei, comparable to the primitive reticular elements of the lymphatic tissue stroma. Some of them become macrophages, which may contain pigment. Sometimes they react positively to tests for iron. In vitally stained animals, however, they contain,

as a rule, few dye granules. The storage of dye is more pronounced in the macrophages of the lamina propria in the lower ileum and cecum.

The argyrophilic stroma of the lamina propria is condensed adjacent to the epithelium to support the basement lamina. Fine elastic networks extend from the muscularis mucosae along the blood vessels. They also surround the glands of Lieberkühn. The argyrophilic framework in many places contains strands of smooth muscle, which arise from the inner surface of the muscularis mucosae and run toward the surface. They are especially prominent in the core of the villi. Here they are arranged parallel to the axis of the villus, around the minute terminal branches of the lymphatic plexus called the *central lacteal* (Fig. 26-5). Large numbers of free cells are found in the meshes of the argyrophilic stroma of the lamina propria. The most numerous are small lymphocytes; medium-sized forms also occur, but large lymphocytes are rare. There are numerous plasma cells in all stages of development. The lamina propria always contains granular leukocytes, mainly eosinophils, most of which have migrated from the blood vessels. Mast cells are infrequent in the human intestine. Some of those that do occur are small, young cells with only a few granules.

Many lymphocytes and a few granular leukocytes penetrate the epithelium on the villi or in the glands of Lieberkühn, and pass between the epithelial cells into the lumen. This phenomenon increases in intensity along the tract and reaches its highest development in the large intestine.

Another peculiar type of wandering cell found in the epithelium of the crypts in many animals is a cell with a small, round, dark nucleus and a large, swollen body containing a number of large, round granules or droplets that stain bright red with eosin—the *globular leukocyte*. Sometimes they divide mitotically. They are also found in a degenerating condition with a pyknotic nucleus.

LYMPHATIC TISSUE. The lamina propria of the small intestine contains great numbers of isolated lymphatic nodules ("solitary follicles") varying from 0.6 to 3 mm. in diameter. They are scattered all along the intestine but are more numerous and larger in the distal part. In the ileum they may be found near the surface of the *plicae circulares* or between them. If they are small, they occupy only the deeper layer of the mucous membrane above the muscularis mucosae. The larger ones occupy the whole thickness of the mucosa, bulge on its surface, and may even extend through the muscularis mucosae into the submucous layer. They are visible to the naked eye, and their surface is free of villi and usually also of crypts.

Groups of many solitary nodules massed together are called *aggregated nodules* or *Peyer's patches*. They occur, as a rule, only in the ileum, but occasionally may be found elsewhere. Their normal number is estimated at 30 to 40. They always occur on the side of the intestinal wall opposite the line of attachment of the mesentery and are recognizable grossly as elongated, oval, slightly thickened areas. Their long diameter varies from 12 to 20 mm.; the short, from 8 to 12 mm. They consist of dense lymphatic tissue with large lymphocytopoietic or reaction centers in their interior. The periphery is marked by a thin layer of condensed reticular fibers. The lamina propria and the submucosa in the vicinity of the nodules are always infiltrated with lymphocytes. In old age the follicles and the patches of Peyer undergo involution.

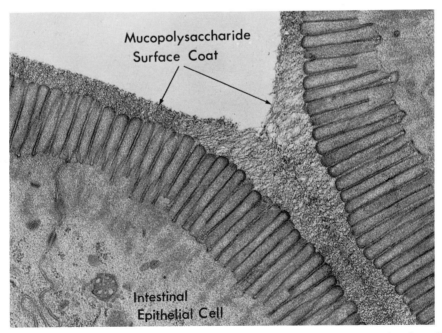

Figure 26-7. Brush borders of epithelial cells on two neighboring villi of cat intestine, illustrating the well developed mucopolysaccharide surface coat. × 30,000. (Courtesy of S. Ito.)

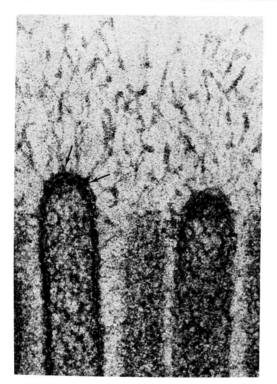

Figure 26-8. Electron micrograph of the tips of several microvilli from cat ileum, showing the branching protein-polysaccharide (mucopolysaccharide) filaments attached at one end to the outer leaflet of the unit membrane (at arrows). × 120,000. (Courtesy of S. Ito, after D. W. Fawcett, J. Histochem. & Cytochem., *13*:75, 1965.)

MUSCULARIS MUCOSAE. This layer averages 38 μ in thickness and consists of an inner circular and an outer longitudinal layer of smooth muscle and of elastic networks.

SUBMUCOSA. The submucous layer consists of rather dense connective tissue with an abundant elastic tissue component and occasional lobules of adipose tissue. In the duodenum it is occupied by a thick layer of *duodenal glands* or *Brunner's glands.*

DUODENAL GLANDS (GLANDS OF BRUNNER). These submucosal glands, present only in mammals, are usually encountered first in the region of the pyloric sphincter, but in man they may sometimes extend a few centimeters into the pyloric region of the stomach. In the distal two thirds of the duodenum the glands of Brunner gradually diminish in size and finally disappear. They show a tendency to occupy the cores of the circular folds and are separated by gland-free intervals (Fig. 26-2). In some cases they extend into the upper part of the jejunum.

The terminal secretory portions of the glands consist of richly branched and coiled tubules arranged in lobules 0.5 to 1.0 mm. in diameter situated in the submucosa (Fig. 26-3). The ducts penetrate the muscularis mucosae to open into a crypt of Lieberkühn.

Examined with the electron microscope, the secretory cells of the submucosal glands present a combination of the fine structural features of zymogenic and mucus-secreting cells. They have numerous mitochondria and abundant basal ergastoplasm or granular reticulum. Their dense secretory granules bear a superficial resemblance to pancreatic zymogen cells. The Golgi complex is unusually large. It is believed that this organelle may be concerned with synthesis of the carbohydrate moiety of the secretory product and with its combination with the protein moiety synthesized in the granular endoplasmic reticulum (Friend).

In the species in which it has been studied, the secretion is a clear, viscous, and distinctly alkaline fluid (pH 8.2 to 9.3). Its principal

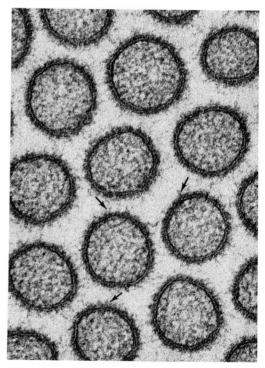

Figure 26-9. Electron micrograph of rat intestinal microvilli in transverse section. The protein-polysaccharide surface coat is present (at arrows), but the filaments are much shorter on the sides of the microvilli than on the tips. × 120,000. (Courtesy of S. L. Palay.)

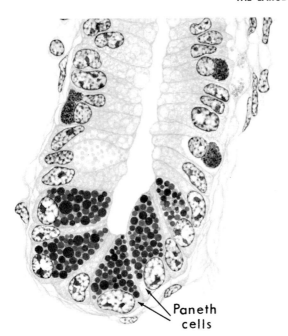

Paneth
cells

Figure 26-10. Drawing of a crypt of Lieberkühn, illustrating the Paneth cells at the base of the crypt. Higher up in the crypt are three argentaffin cells. Hematoxylin and eosin.

function is thought to be to protect the duodenal mucosa against the erosive effects of the acid gastric juice by reason of its mucoid nature, its alkalinity, and possibly by the buffering capacity of its bicarbonate content (Grossman).

MUSCULARIS. The external and internal layers of the muscular coat are well developed in the small intestine. They are usually described as longitudinal and circular layers. Between these layers is the sympathetic *myenteric nerve plexus*. Some strands of smooth muscle cells pass from one layer into the other. The external serosal coat consists of a layer of mesothelial cells resting on loose connective tissue. At the attachment of the mesentery, the serous layer of the intestines is continuous with the leaves of the mesentery.

THE APPENDIX

The appendix is a blindly ending evagination of the cecum in man and many animals. Its wall is thickened by an extensive development of lymphatic tissue, which forms an almost continuous layer with many large and small lymphatic nodules (Fig. 26-12). The small lumen in cross section has an angular form and often contains masses of dead cells

and detritus. In other cases it is obliterated. It is difficult to draw a distinct line between the normal and certain pathological conditions in this organ. Villi are absent. The glands of Lieberkühn radiating from the lumen have an irregular shape and variable length and are embedded in the lymphatic tissue. The epithelium of the surface of the glands contains only a few goblet cells and consists mostly of columnar cells with a striated border. The zone of mitotically active undifferentiated cells is shorter than in the small intestine. In addition to occasional Paneth cells, argentaffin cells are regularly present in the depths of the glands, and in smaller numbers in the upper parts of the glands. They are much more plentiful than in the small intestine, and may number 5 to 10 to a gland.

The lymphatic tissue of the appendix is similar to that of the tonsils and often shows chronic inflammatory changes. The muscularis mucosae of the appendix is poorly developed. The submucosa forms a thick layer with blood vessels and nerves and occasional fat lobules. The muscularis externa is reduced in thickness, but always shows the two usual layers. The serous coat is similar to that covering the rest of the intestines.

THE LARGE INTESTINE

The mucous membrane of the large intestine does not form folds except in its last portion, the rectum. Villi cease, as a rule, above the ileocecal valve. The mucosa of the large intestine therefore has a smooth surface, which is lined by simple columnar epithelium with a thin striated border.

The *glands of Lieberkühn* are straight tubules, and they attain a greater length in the large than in the small intestine—up to 0.5 mm., and up to 0.7 mm. in the rectum. They differ from the glands in the small intestine in their greater abundance of goblet cells (Figs. 26-14 and 26-15). At the bottom of the crypts are the usual proliferating, undifferentiated epithelial cells and occasionally argentaffin cells. As a rule there are no cells of Paneth.

The structure of the *lamina propria* is essentially the same as in the small intestine; eosinophilic leukocytes are abundant, often penetrating the epithelium of the crypts. Scattered lymphatic nodules are always present in varying numbers and are also found in the rectum.

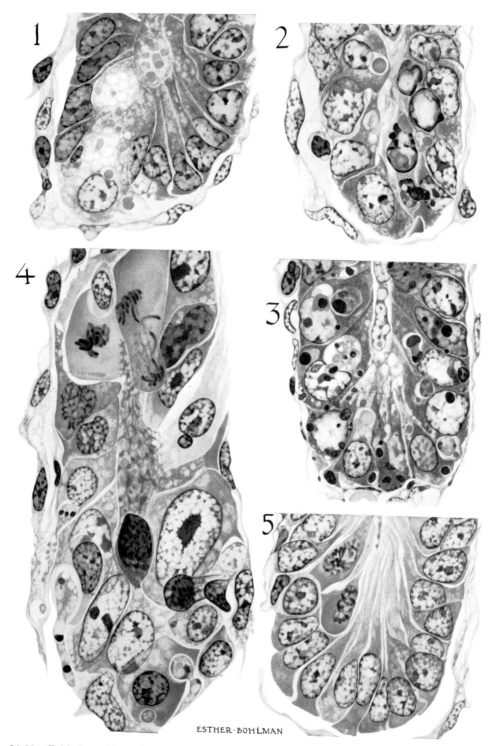

Figure 26-11. Epithelium of base of crypts of Lieberkühn from duodenum of rat, showing degenerative and regenerative changes after total body exposure to 600 roentgens of x-rays. *1,* Normal; *2,* one half hour; *3,* three hours; *4,* 28 hours; and *5,* five days after irradiation. (After M. Pierce, in Histopathology of Irradiation from External and Internal Sources. Courtesy of Atomic Energy Commission.)

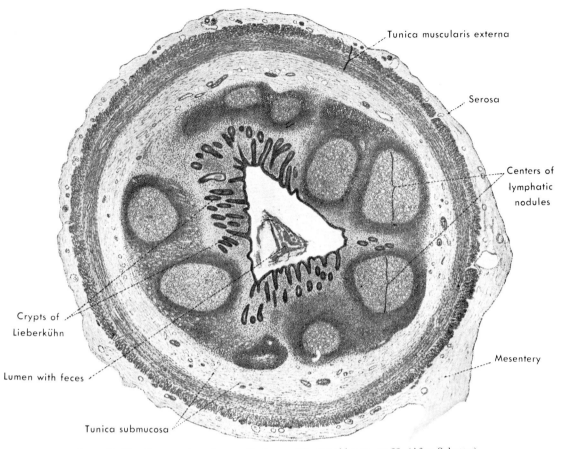

Figure 26-12. Cross section of appendix from a 23 year old man. × 22. (After Sobotta.)

They reach far into the submucous layer (Fig. 26-13).

The *muscularis mucosae* is well developed and consists of longitudinal and circular strands. It may send slender bundles of muscle cells toward the surface of the mucosa. The submucous layer does not present any peculiarities. The muscularis externa differs from the corresponding coat of the small intestine in the arrangement of its outer longitudinal layer, which is localized in three thick, longitudinal bands, the *taenia coli*. In the rectum it again becomes a continuous layer all around the periphery. The serous coat of the colon in its free portion forms the *appendices epiploicae*, pendulous protuberances consisting of adipose tissue and accumulations of cells similar to those in the omentum.

In the anal region the mucous membrane is thrown into longitudinal folds, the *rectal columns of Morgagni*. The crypts of Lieberkühn in this region suddenly become short and dis-appear, and along an irregular line, about 2 cm. above the anal opening, stratified squamous epithelium appears. This is the transition zone between the mucous membrane and skin. At the level of the external sphincter the surface layer assumes the structure of the skin; sebaceous and large, apocrine, circumanal glands appear. The lamina propria here contains a plexus of large veins, which, when varicose and abnormally dilated, present as hemorrhoids.

THE HISTOPHYSIOLOGY OF INTESTINAL ABSORPTION

An important function in the digestion of the chyme in the small intestine is attributed to the liver and pancreas, which empty their secretions into the duodenum. The bile, in conjunction with the mixing action of peristalsis, reduces the lipid of the diet to a fine emulsion of triglycerides, and the pancreatic juice contributes to the chyme, lipolytic, proteolytic, and carbohydrate splitting enzymes. The wall of the intestine itself contributes the important secretion *intestinal juice* or *succus entericus,* which is mainly a product of the glands of Lieberkühn. It has been reported to contain several enzymes (intestinal lipase, maltase, peptidase), but these vary with the degree of contamination of the juice by cells and are not present after centrifugation. It appears, therefore, that a number of the enzymes formerly believed to be secreted into the lumen actually reside in the striated border of the intestinal absorptive cells. Development of a method for isolation of a centrifugal fraction consisting of brush borders (Crane) has made it possible to localize several enzymes to this region of the absorptive cells: the invertase and maltase responsible for the terminal stages of carbohydrate digestion, alkaline phosphatase, leucine aminopeptidase, and an adenosine triphosphatase. At least two of these, alkaline phosphatase and maltase, have been localized to the membrane itself. Thus the microvillous border is not only a device for increasing the surface area for absorption, but is the site of the enzymes responsible for the terminal steps in the hydrolytic digestion of carbohydrates and proteins and for the active transport of the products into the epithelial cell.

The intraluminal digestion of most foodstuff reduces it to subunits of molecular size whose absorption cannot be followed morphologically. By means of labeling with fluorescent compounds, for fluorescence microscopy, or with isotopes for autoradiography, some information has been gained about the absorption of proteins. The suckling newborn of many mammalian species can absorb intact protein, including antibodies, in the jejunum and ileum but not in the duodenum. Protein and particulate matter is taken up by pinocytosis (Clarke). Within a few weeks after birth they lose this ability. Adult mammals, including man, can take up no more than trace amounts of intact protein but must hydrolyze it, by intraluminal digestion, to amino acids before it can be absorbed.

Of the various classes of nutritive substances, *fat* is the one that lends itself best to morphological study, because lipid can be fixed and intensely stained by osmium for visualization with light or electron microscopes. In jejunal biopsies of previously fasted humans, taken 20 minutes after ingestion of corn oil, the cytoplasm of the cells at the tips of the villi is

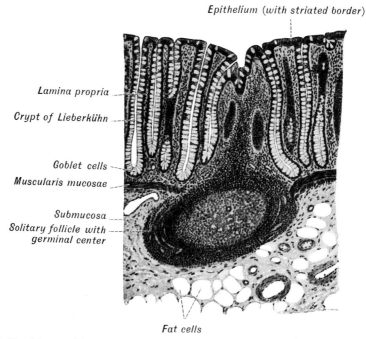

Epithelium (with striated border)

Lamina propria

Crypt of Lieberkühn

Goblet cells

Muscularis mucosae

Submucosa

Solitary follicle with germinal center

Fat cells

Figure 26-13.   Mucosa of human transverse colon, showing a solitary follicle. × 70. (After Braus.)

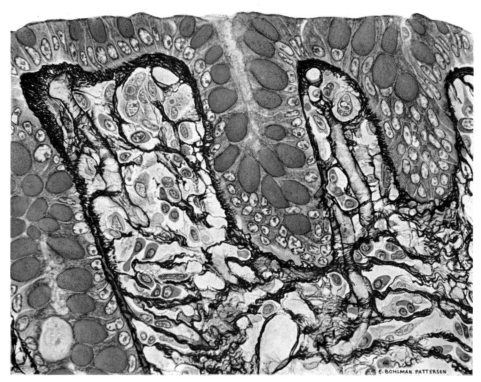

Figure 26-14. Slightly tangential section through mucous membrane of human colon. The reticular fibers are condensed beneath the epithelium and about the blood vessels. The mucigen of the goblet cells is stained blue. Bielschowsky-Foot and Mallory-azan stains. × 600.

crowded with lipid droplets. Efforts to follow the pathway of lipid absorption in experimental animals first led to the conclusion that minute droplets of lipid were taken into the cell by pinocytosis (Palay and Karlin). In electron micrographs, minute particles could be seen between the microvilli and in small invaginations of the cell membrane at the bottom of the clefts between microvilli (Fig. 26-16). Droplets accumulated in membrane limited vesicles in the apical cytoplasm and in the Golgi complex (Fig. 26-17). Vesicles containing lipid then appeared to move to the lateral cell membranes and to discharge their contents into the intercellular clefts. These extracellular lipid droplets or *chylomicrons* (Fig. 26-18) completed their passage across the intestinal epithelium by moving between the cells, traversing the basement lamina, and entering the lacteals of the villi.

There seems to be no doubt that ingested lipid can be taken into the absorptive cells in limited amounts by pinocytosis, but the quantitative importance of this mechanism is now questioned. Biochemical investigations indicate that pancreatic lipase, acting upon the emulsified fat in the chyme, hydrolyzes the bulk of it to fatty acids, mono-, and diglycerides. These combine with bile salts to form 30 to 100 Å lipid micelles that diffuse into the cell by virtue of their solubility in the lipid-rich plasma membrane. In vitro experiments have shown that entry of the products of lipid hydrolysis into the cell does not require energy and can occur at 0° C., a temperature level at which it may be assumed that pinocytosis does not occur. The formation of the lipid droplets observed within the cells, however, is temperature dependent (Strauss). It now appears that the bulk of the lipid absorbed enters the cell passively as micelles containing fatty acids and monoglycerides, and that in the agranular reticulum in the apical cytoplasm of the absorptive cells, these are re-esterified to triglyceride and combined with protein to form chylomicrons observed within and between the epithelial cells. Much has yet to be learned about the mechanisms by which the chylomicrons

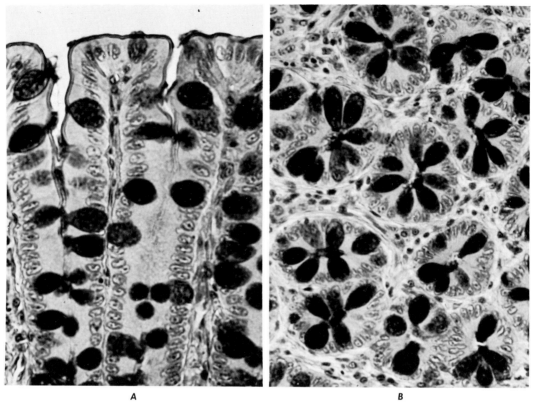

A   **B**

Figure 26-15. Sections of the crypts of the colon of a macaque. *A,* Vertical section of the mucosa, showing the columnar cells and goblet cells. × 550. *B,* Horizontal section of the crypts, showing the radial disposition of goblet cells around the lumen and the cellular lamina propria between crypts. Periodic acid–Schiff reaction and hematoxylin. Photomicrograph. × 425.

traverse the lamina propria and enter the lacteals.

An important mechanism for the transmission of substances absorbed into the blood and lymph is the movement of the villi. This can be observed in a living animal if a loop of the intestine is split open and the surface of the mucous membrane is watched with a binocular microscope. There seems to be no relation between the movements of the individual villi. Every villus contracts independently, approximately six times a minute. Here and there a villus suddenly becomes shorter by about one half its length, while its thickness remains unchanged; then it expands again. Thus, during the contraction, the volume of the villus is greatly reduced and the contents of its capillaries and especially of the central lacteal are forwarded into the submucous plexus. When the villus expands, the liquid that penetrates the epithelium is believed to enter the central lacteal and the blood capillaries. The expan-

sion calls forth another contraction, and so on. The contraction is obviously due to the shortening of the longitudinal muscular strands of the core of the villus. The movement is believed to be regulated by the submucous plexus of Meissner. Direct mechanical stimulation of the base of a villus with a bristle also calls forth a contraction; the stimulus radiates from the affected villus to the surrounding ones.

BLOOD VESSELS OF THE GASTROINTESTINAL TRACT

The arrangements of the blood and lymph vessels in the wall of the stomach and in the wall of the intestine are basically similar. Because the important differences depend mainly on the presence of villi, the small intestine shows significant peculiarities.

In the stomach the arteries arise from the two arterial arches along the lesser and greater curvatures and are distributed to the ventral and dorsal surfaces. In the intestine, the arteries reach one side with the mesentery. They run in the serous coat and break up into large branches that penetrate the muscularis externa and enter the submucous layer, where they form a large submucous plexus (Fig. 26-19). In the stomach and colon the submucous plexus gives off branches directed toward the surface. Some of these break up into capillaries supplying the muscularis mucosae; others form capillary networks throughout the mucosa and surrounding the glands. The capillary net is especially prominent around the foveolae of the gastric mucosa.

From the superficial, periglandular capillary networks, veins of considerable caliber arise. They form a venous plexus between the bottom of the glands and the muscularis mucosae. From this plexus, branches run into the submucosa and form a venous plexus. From this submucous plexus, the large veins follow the arteries and pass through the muscularis externa into the serous membrane. In the stomach the veins of the submucous plexus are provided with valves and a relatively thick muscular coat.

In the small intestine the submucous arterial plexus gives off two kinds of branches that run toward the mucosa. Some of these arteries ramify on the inner surface of the muscularis mucosae and break up into capillary networks that surround the crypts of Lieberkühn in the same way as they surround the glands of the stomach. Other arteries are especially destined for the villi, each villus receiving one or sometimes several such small arteries. These vessels enter the base of the villus and form a dense capillary network immediately under its epithelium (Fig. 26-20). Near the tip of the villus one or two small veins arise from the superficial capillary network and run downward, to anastomose with the glandular venous plexus, and pass on into the submucosa, where they join the veins of the submucous plexus. These veins in the intestine have no valves. However, their continuations, which pass through the muscularis externa with the arteries, are provided with valves. Valves disappear in the collecting veins of the mesentery.

LYMPH VESSELS OF THE GASTROINTESTINAL TRACT

In the stomach the lymphatics begin as an extensive system of large lymphatic capillaries in the superficial layer of the mucous membrane between the glands. They are always deeper than the blood capillaries. They anastomose everywhere throughout the mucous membrane. They surround the glandular tubules and take a downward course to the inner surface of the mucous membrane, where they form a plexus of fine lymphatic vessels. Branches of the plexus pierce the muscularis mucosae and form a plexus of lymphatics in the submucosa that is provided with valves. From the submucous plexus larger lymphatics run through the muscularis externa. Here they receive numerous tributaries from the lymphatic plexus in the muscular coat and then follow the blood vessels into the retroperitoneal tissues. In the wall of the colon the lymphatics show a similar arrangement.

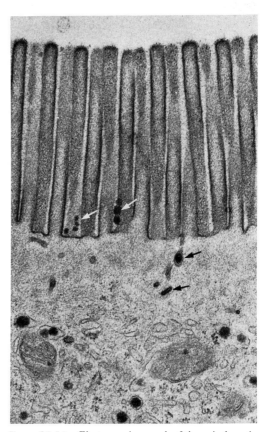

Figure 26-16. Electron micrograph of the apical portion of a cell from the rat jejunum, one hour after oral administration of linolenic acid and tristearin. Small droplets of lipid are found among the microvilli (white arrows), also in small vesicular invaginations of the cell surface, and in vesicles in the terminal web (black arrows). Similar droplets are found in the profiles of agranular reticulum deep to the terminal web. × 32,000. (Courtesy of S. L. Palay and J. P. Revel.)

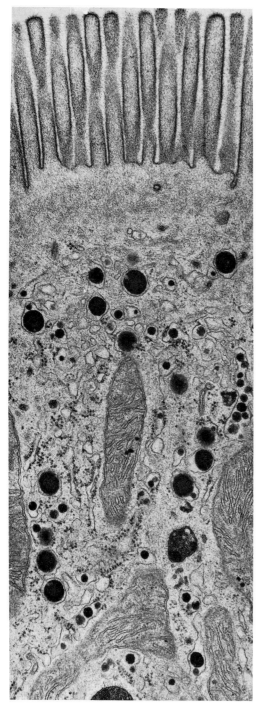

Figure 26-17. Electron micrograph of rat intestinal cell at a somewhat later stage of lipid absorption than is shown in Figure 26-16. Lipid continues to accumulate in sizable droplets within the smooth reticulum, but very little is seen in inpocketings of the cell surface or in vesicles traversing the terminal web. Though pinocytosis undoubtedly occurs, it is probably not the principal mechanism for absorption of lipid. × 32,000. (Courtesy of S. L. Palay and J. P. Revel.)

The lymphatic vessels of the intestine are important in the absorption of fat from the small intestine. During digestion, all their ramifications are filled with milky white lymph —a fine emulsion of neutral fats. This white lymph, drained from the intestine, is called *chyle,* and the lymphatics that carry it are called *lacteals.*

In the small intestine the most conspicuous parts of the lymphatic system are the *central lacteals* in the core of the villi. Each conical villus has one lacteal, which occupies an axial position and ends blindly near the tip. The broader villi of the duodenum may contain two or perhaps more lacteals that intercommunicate. The lumen of these lacteals, when distended, is considerably larger than that of the blood capillaries. The wall consists of thin endothelial cells and is everywhere connected with the argyrophilic reticulum and surrounded by thin, longitudinal strands of smooth muscle.

The central lacteals at the base of the villi anastomose with the lymphatic capillaries between the glands, which have an arrangement similar to that in the stomach. They also form a plexus on the inner surface of the muscularis mucosae. Branches of this plexus, provided with valves, pierce the muscularis mucosae and form, in the submucosa, a loose plexus of larger lymphatics. The latter also receives tributaries from the dense network of large, thin-walled lymphatic capillaries, which closely surround the surface of the solitary and aggregated follicles. The large lymphatics that run from the submucous plexus through the muscularis externa into the mesentery receive additional branches from a dense, tangential plexus located between the circular and longitudinal layers of the muscularis externa.

NERVES OF THE INTESTINAL TRACT

The nerve supply seems to be similar in its organization in all parts of the intestinal tube and consists of an intrinsic and an extrinsic part. The first of these is comprised of nerve cells and their fibers located in the wall of the intestine. The extrinsic nerves are represented by the preganglionic fibers of the vagus and the postganglionic fibers of the sympathetic. The latter run to the intestine from the celiac plexus. They enter the intestinal wall through the mesentery along the branches of the large vessels.

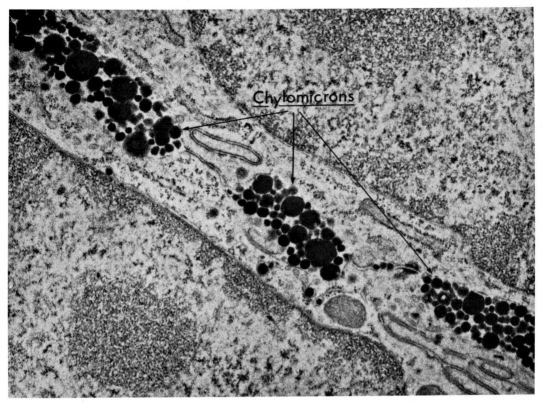

Figure 26-18. Electron micrograph of the boundary between two rat intestinal epithelial cells during lipid absorption. The absorbed lipid has been discharged through the lateral cell surfaces and is seen to have accumulated here as aggregations of chylomicrons in the intercellular spaces. × 30,000. (Courtesy of S. L. Palay and J. P. Revel.)

Numerous groups of nerve cells and bundles of nerve fibers are seen in the narrow space between the circular and the longitudinal layers of the muscularis externa. This is the *myenteric plexus of Auerbach* (Fig. 26-21). In the submucosa, similar elements form the *submucous plexus of Meissner*. These plexuses form the intrinsic nervous mechanism of the intestinal wall.

The nerve cells of the enteric ganglia are connected by strands of nonmyelinated nerve fibers of both extrinsic and intrinsic origin. These nerve cells appear in two principal forms, which may present differences in their secondary characteristics. The first type occurs exclusively in the myenteric plexus. It is a multipolar cell with short dendrites that terminate in brushlike arborizations on the bodies of cells of the second type in the same ganglion. The axon can be traced for a considerable distance through neighboring ganglia and is supposed to form connections with cells of the second type in other ganglia. These neurons are associative.

The cells of the second type are far more numerous and show great variations in their forms. Their dendrities vary in number and are often missing. They begin as diffuse receptive endings in relation with nerve cells of the first and of the same (second) type in the ganglia of origin or in other ganglia. The axon enters a fiber bundle and divides; its branches terminate in the circular or longitudinal layer of the muscularis externa in connection with smooth muscle cells. Thus the neurons of the second type are motor. Those in the myenteric plexus supply the muscularis externa; those of the submucous plexus supply the muscularis mucosae and the muscles of the villi.

Cells of a third cell type occur in the enteric plexuses and are also scattered in the submucosa and in the interior of the villi. This is the "interstitial cell," with a finely vacuolated protoplasm and short, branching processes

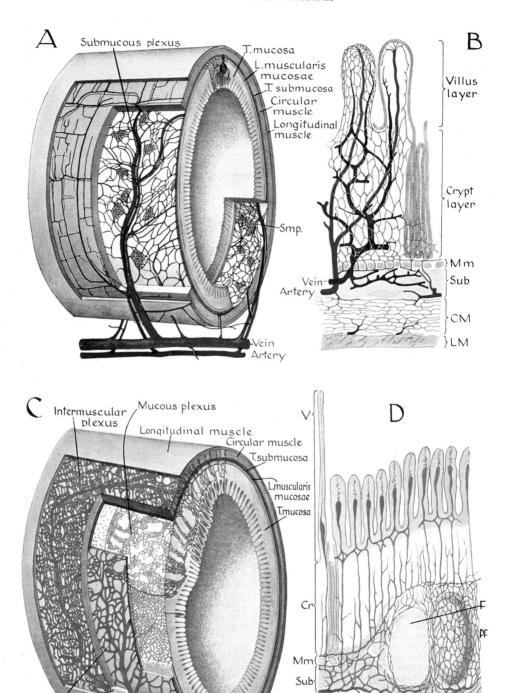

Figure 26-19. Diagrams of distribution of blood vessels, *A* and *B,* and of lymphatics, *C* and *D,* in the small intestine of the dog. *B* and *D* are drawn on a larger scale to show details. *CM,* Circular muscle; *Cr,* crypt; *F,* follicle; *LM,* longitudinal muscle; *Mm,* lamina muscularis mucosae; *PF,* perifollicular plexus; *Smp,* submucous plexus; *Sub,* tunica submucosa; *V,* villus. (Redrawn and slightly modified from Mall.)

that interlace with other processes to form an irregular feltwork. It does not contain obvious neurofibrils and may possibly be of microglial nature.

Most of the nonmyelinated fibers of the bundles that connect the ganglia, and the fibers in the ganglia, are processes of the enteric neurons. The rest are formed by extrinsic fibers, mainly of vagal and to some extent of sympathetic origin. The vagal fibers terminate as pericellular arborizations on cells of the second type in the enteric ganglia. The sympathetic fibers cannot be distinguished from the axons of the motor cells in the fiber bundles. They do not seem to enter into synaptic relationship with the nerve cells of the ganglia but take part, together with axons of intrinsic neurons, in the formation of the intramuscular plexuses and terminate in connection with the muscular cells. The sympathetic fibers supply the blood vessels, too. Some of them have also been described as forming a plexus in the subserous coat and ending freely in the connective tissue.

If the intestine is detached from the mesentery and placed in warm Tyrode solution, it will show normal peristaltic movements if the mucous membrane is stimulated by objects introduced into the lumen. This shows that the intestine is an autonomous organ whose movements are determined by the local neuromuscular mechanism and that these are only regulated through the extrinsic nerves. Numerous nerve endings of sensory nature have been found under and in the epithelial layers of the villi.

Some investigators believe that the enteric plexuses mediate complete reflex arcs, the sensory component being enteric, a cell of the plexus, with dendritic endings in contact with the epithelium of the villi or the glands of Lieberkühn, while the axons transmit the impulse to another enteric neuron whose axon ends in the smooth muscles. Most authors hold, however, that all neurons of the enteric plexuses are of efferent nature and that therefore the sensory nerve endings in the mucous membrane must be of extrinsic nature. The local reflexes in the intestine are explained as "axon reflexes." The axons of the enteric neurons are supposed to divide into two branches, one of which receives stimuli that are transmitted to the other branch without passing through the cell body.

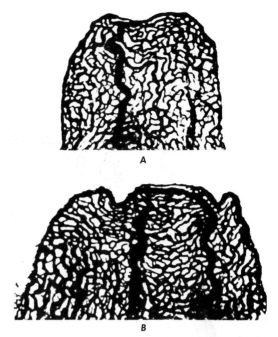

Figure 26-20. Two villi of rat intestine injected with India ink in gelatin. The villi in this species are thin, leaflike structures whose broad surface is presented in this figure. In the duodenum (*B*) they are larger and more richly vascularized than they are farther along in the jejunum (*A*). The large surface area presented by the villi and their rich network of capillaries favors absorption of nutrients. × 100.

REMARKS ON THE HISTOGENESIS OF INTESTINES

The histogenesis of the mucous membrane of the intestine resembles that of the stomach. At first the boundary between the epithelium and the connective tissue is even. The development of villi begins in embryos of 20 mm. in the duodenum and gradually extends downward. In the duodenum, jejunum, and the upper part of the ileum, the villi arise as isolated epithelial outgrowths. In the remaining parts of the intestine, longitudinal ridges develop, which later are subdivided by the transverse furrows into single villi. The number of the villi in a given stretch increases through the appearance of new outgrowths in the hollows between the older villi. In a fetus of 100 mm., villi are found all along the intestine, including the colon, although they disappear from the colon in the later stages. This is due either to a fusion of the villi from their bases upward or to their shortening through the stretching of the growing wall. In an embryo of 55 mm., the supranuclear protoplasm of the

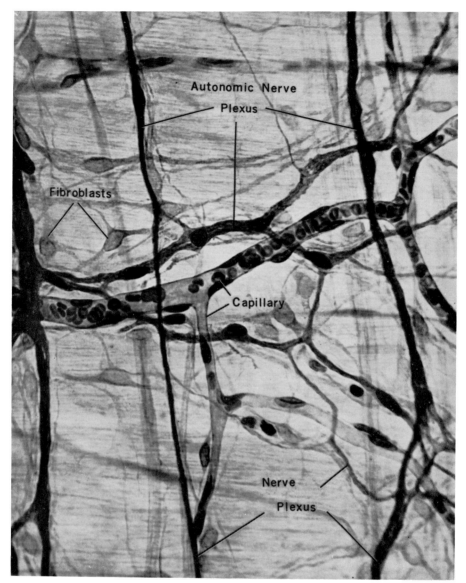

Figure 26-21. Photomicrograph of a whole mount of the longitudinal muscle coat of rabbit intestine impregnated with silver to show the nerve bundles of Auerbach's plexus. × 300. (After K. C. Richardson, J. Anat., *94:*451, 1960, labeling added.)

epithelial cells on the tips of the villi acquires a transparent aspect, while on the free surface a condensed cytoplasmic layer develops. Between these elements, scattered goblet cells appear.

In the fetus of four months, the epithelium of the villi has a manifold appearance. In the lower parts of the small intestine, the common epithelial cells with the clear supranuclear parts contain a multitude of coarse yellow granules. They are called *meconium corpuscles*

and are similar to those seen in the lumen of the intestine. Their yellowish color is due to adsorption of bile pigment.

Between the common epithelial cells are many typical goblet cells. Beginning with the fourth month, argentaffin cells make their appearance. During the seventh month the cells of Paneth appear. In the human fetus they seem to occur not only in the crypts, but also on the villi.

The development of the glands of Lieberkühn also starts in the duodenum and proceeds downward. In a fetus of the fourth month the excavations between the villi are lined with small, crowded cells with a cytoplasm darker than that of the epithelium of the villi. From these cells, evaginations arise that penetrate the subjacent connective tissue. In the seventh month, besides the formation of glands from new invaginations, dichotomous division of the blind ends of the glands contributes largely to the continuing increase in the number of glands. Bifurcation of the crypts proceeds in the newborn.

The glands of Brunner make their appearance during the sixth month as massive, epithelial ingrowths in the depth of the duodenal crypts. In a fetus of 290 mm., they are numerous in the upper part of the duodenum and consist of branching tubules. Further downward they are smaller and the intervals between them are larger.

REFERENCES

Behnke, O., and H. Moe: An electron microscopic study of mature and differentiating Paneth cells in the rat. J. Cell Biol., *22:* 633, 1964.

Benditt, E. P., and R. L. Wong: On the concentration of 5-hydroxytryptamine in mammalian entero-chromaffin cells and its release by reserpine. J. Exper. Med., *105:*509, 1957.

Bensley, R. R.: The structure of the glands of Brunner. The Decennial Publ., University of Chicago, *10:*279, 1903.

Brown, A. L.: Microvilli of the human jejunal epithelial cell. J. Cell Biol., *12:*623, 1962.

Bulbring, E., and R. C. Y. Lin: The effect of intraluminal application of 5-hydroxy-tryptophan on peristalsis, the local production of 5-HT and its release in relation to intraluminal pressure and propulsive activity. J. Physiol., *140:*381, 1958.

Clarke, S. L., Jr.: The ingestion of proteins and colloidal materials by columnar absorptive cells of the small intestine in suckling rats and mice. J. Biophys. & Biochem. Cytol., *5:*41, 1959.

Crane, R. K.: Intestinal absorption of sugars. Physiol. Rev., *40:*789, 1960.

Crane, R. K.: Hypothesis for mechanism of intestinal active transport of sugars. Federation Proc., *21:*891, 1962.

Deane, H. W.: Some electron microscopic observations on the lamina propria of the gut, with comments on the close association of macrophages, plasma cells and eosinophils. Anat. Rec., *149:*453, 1964.

Eicholtz, A., and R. K. Crane: Studies on the organization of the brush border in intestinal epithelial cells. J. Cell Biol., *26:*687, 1965.

Erspamer, V.: Occurrence and distribution of 5-hydroxytryptamine (enteramine) in the living organism. Zeitschr. f. Vit. Hormon Fermentforsch., *9:*74, 1957.

Florey, H. W.: The secretion and function of intestinal mucus. Gastroenterology, *43:*326, 1962.

Florey, H. W., R. D. Wright, and M. A. Jennings: The secretions of the intestine. Physiol. Rev., *21:*141, 1936.

Friend, D. S.: The fine structure of Brunner's glands in the mouse. J. Cell. Biol., *25:*563, 1965.

Garry, R. C.: The movements of the large intestine. Physiol. Rev., *14:*103, 1934.

Gershon, M. D., and L. L. Ross: Studies on the relationship of 5-hydroxytryptamine and the enterochromaffin cell to anaphylactic shock in mice. J. Exper. Med., *115:*367, 1962.

Grossman, M. I.: The glands of Brunner. Physiol. Rev., *38:*675, 1958.

Hanssen, O., and L. Herman: The presence of an axial structure in the microvillus of the mouse convoluted proximal tubule cell. Lab. Invest., *11:*610, 1962.

Ito, S.: The enteric surface coat on cat intestinal microvilli. J. Cell Biol., *27:*475, 1965.

Jennings, M. A., and H. W. Florey: Autoradiographic observations of the mucous cells of the stomach and intestine. Quart. J. Exper. Pathol., *41:*131, 1956.

Ladman, A. J., H. A. Padykula, and E. W. Strauss: A morphological study of fat transport in the normal human jejunum. Am. J. Anat., *112:*389, 1963.

Landboe-Christensen, E.: The Duodenal Glands of Brunner in Man, Their Distribution and Quantity. An Anatomical Study. Copenhagen, E. Munksgaard; London, Oxford University Press, 1944.

Leblond, C. P., H. Puchtler, and Y. Clermont: Structures corresponding to terminal bars and terminal web in many types of cells. Nature, *186:*784, 1960.

Miller, D., and R. K. Crane: The digestive function of the epithelium of the small intestine. II. Localization of disaccharidase hydrolysis in the isolated brush border portion of the intestinal epithelial cells. Biochem. Biophys. Acta, *52:*293, 1961.

Moe, H.: The ultrastructure of Brunner's glands of the cat. J. Ultrastruct. Res., *4:*58, 1960.

Monesi, V.: The appearance of enterochromaffin cells in the intestine of the chick embryo. Acta Anat., *41:*97, 1960.

Palay, S. L., and L. J. Karlin: An electron microscope study of the intestinal villus. I. The fasting animal. II. The pathway of fat absorption. J. Biophys. & Biochem. Cytol., *5:*363, 373, 1959.

Palay, S. L., and J. P. Revel: The morphology of fat absorption. *In* Meng, H. C., ed.: Lipid Transport. Springfield, Ill., Charles C Thomas, 1964, pp. 1–11.

Patzelt, V.: Der Darm. *In* von Möllendorff, W., and W. Bargmann, eds.: Handbuch der mikroskopischen Anatomie des Menschen. Berlin, Julius Springer, 1936, Vol. 5, part 3, p. 1.

Ratzenhofer, M., and D. Leb: Über die Feinstruktur der argentaffinen und der anderen Erscheinungsformen der "Hellen Zellen" Feyrter's im Kaninchen-Magen. Zeitschr. f. Zellforsch., *67:*113, 1965.

Richardson, K. C.: Electronmicroscopic observations on Auerbach's plexus in the rabbit with special reference to the problem of smooth muscle innervation. Am. J. Anat., *103:*99, 1958.

Richardson, K. C.: Studies on the structure of the autonomic nerves in the small intestine, correlating the silver-impregnated image in light microscopy with the permanganate-fixed ultrastructure in electronmicroscopy. J. Anat. (London), *94:*457, 1960.

Selzman, H. M., and R. A. Liebelt: Paneth cell granules of mouse intestine. J. Cell Biol., *15:*136, 1962.

Senior, J. R.: Intestinal absorption of fats. J. Lipid Res., *5:*495, 1964.

Singh, I.: The prenatal development of enterochromaffin cells in the human gastro-intestinal tract. J. Anat. (London), *97:*377, 1963.

Singh, I.: On argyrophile and argentaffin reactions in individual granules of enterochromaffin cells of the human gastro-intestinal tract. J. Anat. (London), *98:*497, 1964.

Spicer, S. S., M. W. Staley, M. G. Wetzel, and B. K. Wetzel: Acid mucosubstance and basic protein in mouse Paneth cells. J. Histochem. and Cytochem., *15:*225, 1967.

Strauss, E. W.: The absorption of fat by intestine of golden hamster *in vitro.* J. Cell Biol., *17:*597, 1963.

Strauss, E. W.: Electron microscopic study of intestinal fat absorption *in vitro* from mixed micelles containing linolenic acid, monoolein, and bile salt. J. Lipid Res., *7:*307, 1966.

Trier, J. S.: Studies on small intestinal crypt epithelium. I. The fine structure of the crypt epithelium of the proximal small intestine of fasting humans. J. Cell Biol., *18:*599, 1963.

Zetterqvist, H.: The Ultrastructural Organization of the Columnar Absorbing Cells of the Mouse Jejunum. Stockholm, Aktiebolaget Godvil, 1956.

CHAPTER TWENTY-SEVEN

The Liver, Bile Ducts, and Gallbladder

LIVER

The liver is the largest gland in the body, weighing about 1500 gm. in the adult. It functions both as an *exocrine gland,* secreting bile through a system of bile ducts into the duodenum, and as an *endocrine gland,* synthesizing a variety of substances that are released directly into the bloodstream. An appreciation of the importance of the liver and a correlation of its structure with its functions depend upon an understanding of its blood supply and its strategic location in the circulation. It receives a large volume of venous blood from the intestinal tract via the *portal vein* and a smaller volume of arterial blood via the *hepatic artery.* It is drained by the *hepatic veins* into the inferior vena cava near the heart. The liver is thus interposed between the intestinal tract and the general circulation. It therefore receives, in the portal blood, all of the material absorbed from the intestinal tract except the bulk of the lipid, which is transported in the *chyle* via the mesenteric lymphatics to the thoracic duct. The absorbed products of digestion are taken up and metabolized in the liver or are transformed there and returned to the blood for storage or utilization elsewhere. The liver may also receive toxic substances from the intestine or from the general circulation and is capable of degrading them by oxidation or hydroxylation or detoxifying them by conjugation. The products of their degradation or their harmless conjugates are then excreted in the bile. The bile is a complex fluid that can be regarded as a *secretion* in that it plays an important role in digestion, but it can also be regarded as a vehicle for *excretion* to the extent that it carries detoxified waste and potentially harmful materials to the intestine for ultimate elimination.

The liver also synthesizes several important protein components of the blood plasma and it exercises an important degree of control over the general metabolism by virtue of its capacity to store carbohydrates as glycogen and to release glucose to maintain the normal concentration of the latter in the blood.

Histological Organization of the Liver

The liver is composed of epithelial cells arranged in plates or laminae that are interconnected to form a continuous tridimensional lattice. The laminae are disposed radially with respect to terminal branches of the hepatic veins, which traditionally have been designated as *central veins* because of their location in the centers of prismatic units of liver parenchyma that constitute the liver *lobules* (Fig. 27-1). The radially disposed plates of liver cells are exposed on either side to the blood flowing in a parallel system of vascular channels, the *hepatic sinusoids* (Fig. 27-2). The radially oriented sinusoids closely conform to the broad surfaces of the cellular laminae and intercommunicate through fenestrations in them to form a labyrinthine system of thin-walled vessels intimately related to a very large surface area of liver parenchyma.

THE LIVER LOBULE. In the pig and a few other species a well defined layer of connective tissue clearly demarcates the lobules. In most mammals, however, there is no boundary between the lobules, the hepatic parenchyma appearing quite continuous. The radial pattern of the laminae and sinusoids is such that one can, nevertheless, recognize the units of structure and assign imaginary boundaries to the lobules by relying upon the regularly distributed central veins and portal canals as landmarks.

The lobules in sections are typically hex-agonal, with the corners of the polygon each occupied by a *portal canal* (Figs. 27-3 and 27-5). This structure consists of a small branch of the portal vein and one of the hepatic artery, as well as a bile ductule, enclosed in a common investment of connective tissue. Blood enters the hepatic sinusoids from small branches of the hepatic artery and portal vein, flows through the lobule centripetally, and leaves via the central vein (Fig. 27-5).

The traditional lobule as defined above is not comparable with the lobules of most glands, which are centered on the ducts that

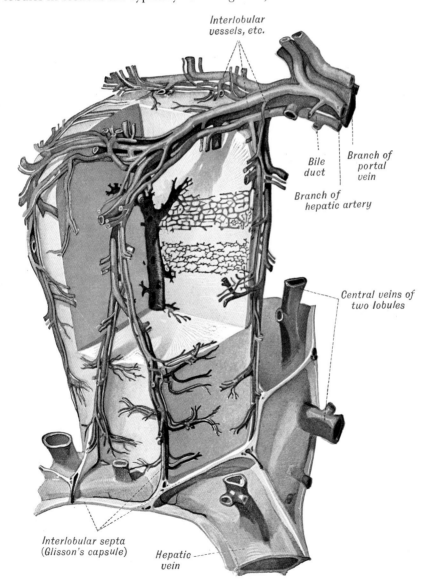

Interlobular vessels, etc.

Bile duct

Branch of portal vein

Branch of hepatic artery

Central veins of two lobules

Interlobular septa (Glisson's capsule)

Hepatic vein

Figure 27-1. Wax reconstruction (by A. Vierling) of a lobule of the liver of a pig. A portion of the lobule has been cut away to show the bile capillaries and sinusoids. × 400. (After Braus.)

drain them. The liver lobule as just presented is conceptually convenient, however, for as a result of differential deposition of glycogen or fat, the hepatic tissue of which it is composed frequently exhibits microscopically distinguishable zones, concentric about the central vein. Moreover, in pathological conditions, necrosis may selectively involve the central or the peripheral zone, depending upon the nature of the disease process.

The lobular pattern appears to develop as a consequence of the hydrodynamics of the blood flow through the liver. From this point of view the liver may be considered as a tough sac filled with fluid, in which is suspended a plastic spongework of liver tissue. In the flow of fluid through the liver, the terminal branches of the portal vein are sources and the radicles of the hepatic vein are sinks (Fig. 27-5). The flow from the one to the other is thought to determine the radial pattern of the sinusoids characteristic of the lobule. It follows also that the cells nearest the branches of the portal vein receive blood first and therefore have first call upon the nutrient and oxygen content of the portal blood. As the latter diminish in the passage of blood from the periphery toward the center of the lobule, a gradient of metabolic activity is established, which is expressed in the morphologically detectable zonation of the lobule.

Some histologists have objected to the classical definition of the liver lobule because it is inconsistent with the lobular organization typical of other exocrine glands. In an effort to make the liver conform to the same general plan, Mall proposed an alternative concept of liver lobulation according to which the portal canal was considered to be the center of the lobule, and the branches of the hepatic vein were said to be situated around its periphery. The lobule defined in this way is called a *portal lobule.* In such a lobule, the bile would drain toward a duct located with the vascular supply in the center of the lobule, as is the case in most other glands.

In some respects this is a more satisfactory way of interpreting the architecture of the liver than the *classical lobule,* but it has been argued that the portal lobule is not the smallest unit of functional organization of the liver. A variant of the portal lobule has been proposed by Rappaport and his colleagues, who consider the functional unit to be a mass of parenchymal tissue associated with the fine terminal branches of the portal vein, hepatic artery, and bile duct. These branches leave the portal canals at intervals, coursing perpendicular to the canals and to the central vein, and run along the side of the hexagon that forms the section of the classical lobule. The associated mass of hepatic tissue is smaller than either of the lobules proposed earlier and is composed of parts of two adjacent classical lobules (Fig. 27-7). It is called a *liver acinus* and is defined as the tissue supplied by a terminal branch of the portal vein and of the hepatic artery and drained by a terminal branch of the bile duct. The limits of the acinus are not defined by any recognizable anatomical landmarks but extend outward to the terminal branches of the hepatic veins and to the imaginary outer limits of acini associated with neighboring portal canals. The parenchyma is continuous from one acinus to the next, and indeed from one classical lobule to the next. Therefore if the supply and drainage of one unit should fail, it would still be supplied and drained by others. This concept of liver structure, although still not universally accepted, has proved useful in the understanding of some aspects of liver physiology and in accounting for some manifestations of liver pathology, especially that following bile duct occlusion and that found in cirrhosis of the liver.

The *classical lobule,* the *portal lobule,* and the *acinus* should not be considered as conflicting concepts of liver structure but as complementary ones. Because of the complexity of the function of the liver, it is sometimes useful to think in terms of one and at other times in terms of another. It is noteworthy that the traditional lobulation is not present in the lower vertebrates nor in the mammalian embryo.

THE BLOOD SUPPLY.   The principal afferent blood vessel of the liver is the portal vein, which receives blood from the digestive tract and from the spleen. It enters the liver at the porta, together with the hepatic artery and the bile duct. The hepatic artery, in all mammals, carries much less blood than the portal vein, though the relative amounts vary in different species. These two vessels and the bile duct branch together as they penetrate the liver mass, with fine branches eventually occupying the portal canals at the periphery of the lobules (Fig. 27-1). They are accompanied throughout by a network of lymphatics. It is to be emphasized, however, that none of the vessels of the larger portal canals are in direct communication with the liver parenchyma. The canal is bounded by a continuous plate of hepatic cells with only occasional fenestrations through which the tiny terminal branches of the artery, vein, and bile duct penetrate the liver parenchyma, running along the boundaries between the classical lobules and occupying the center of the functional units or acini.

These groups of terminal branches are accompanied by very sparse connective tissue and a fine network of lymphatics. The difference in structure and in function between them and typical portal canals needs to be emphasized. It is not via the larger portal canals but through these smaller terminal branches of the vessels that blood enters the sinusoids of the parenchyma. It is here, too, that the terminal ductules of the bile duct, sometimes called the *canals of Hering*, join the parenchyma to receive the bile from the system of minute cana-

liculi between the liver cells. Here, too, the lymphatics receive the abundant liver lymph comprised of the interstitial fluid and plasma that has drained into the perivascular spaces from the parenchyma and sinusoids. The virtue of the functional unit of Rappaport is that it emphasizes these important relationships.

In the larger portal canals, fine branches of both the portal vein and the hepatic artery supply an elaborate capillary network that is intimately associated with the branches of the bile duct. From this network, collecting venules re-enter the portal vein, so that there is, in a sense, a minute portal system, receiving blood from the hepatic artery, inserted into the greater portal system. From the extent of this capillary plexus it has been suggested that in the normal liver of some species at least, the most important function of the hepatic artery is to supply this plexus in the portal canals.

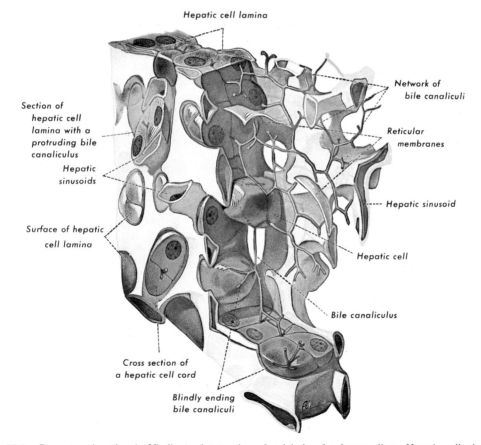

Hepatic cell lamina

Network of bile canaliculi

Section of hepatic cell lamina with a protruding bile canaliculus

Reticular membranes

Hepatic sinusoids

Hepatic sinusoid

Surface of hepatic cell lamina

Hepatic cell

Bile canaliculus

Cross section of a hepatic cell cord

Blindly ending bile canaliculi

Figure 27-2. Reconstruction (by A. Vierling) of a portion of a lobule of a human liver. Hepatic cell plates in brown with red nuclei; sinusoids blue; bile capillaries green. The depiction of the bile capillaries at the upper right is misleading for it suggests that they are independent structures with a wall of their own. Electron microscopy has shown that this is not the case. × 1000. (After Braus.)

Only a relatively small volume of arterial blood enters the sinusoids directly from the branches of the hepatic artery in the core of the functional unit.

The details of branching in the core of the functional unit are very difficult to analyze in sections, but they have been studied by injection and corrosion. Throughout its length, the branch of the portal vein gives off distributing venules that send a branch in either direction, and from these arise the final branches that enter the sinusoids. The artery sends off branches that form a more typical arborization and end in the sinusoids. The lymphatic network appears to end blindly in the connective tissue.

Shunt vessels carrying blood directly from the artery to the portal vein have been described, but there is no evidence that they are abundant or functionally important in the normal liver. Also described are fine terminal branches of the artery extending deep into the lobule and entering the sinusoids directly, but these are certainly not common, and it seems possible that their description is the result of a misinterpretation of the lobular pattern.

The blood leaves the lobule through a terminal radicle of the hepatic vein, the central vein of the classical lobule. Its wall is penetrated by innumerable pores opening directly into the sinusoidal labyrinth. There is no continuous limiting plate of liver cells around the central vein like that around the portal canal. The central veins are the intralobular branches of the hepatic vein. They join to form an intercalated vein (the sublobular vein of the older literature). Several of these unite to form a collecting vein, and these in turn join to form the hepatic veins, which pursue a course through the liver independent of the portal venous system. There may be two or more hepatic veins that enter the inferior vena cava. The intralobular veins are highly contractile and act as throttle veins to control the flow of blood

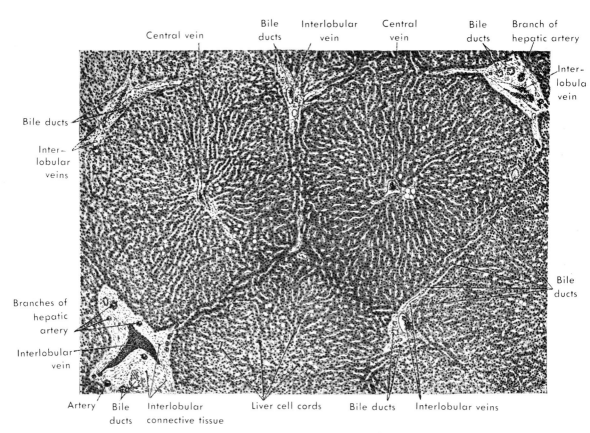

Figure 27-3. Portion of liver from a 22 year old man. Two complete lobules are surrounded by portions of other lobules. × 70. (After Sobotta.)

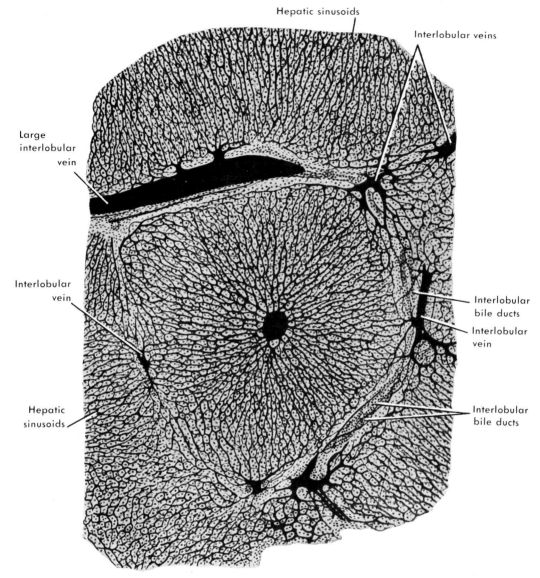

Figure 27-4. Portion of liver of a rabbit injected through the portal vein with Berlin blue and gelatin. A complete lobule surrounds the central vein. × 54. (After Sobotta.)

through the liver lobules and the entire portal vein bed, which serves as an important blood reservoir.

This simple vascular pattern has a complex history, both in phylogeny and in embryology. Much of the work that has been done on the frog liver by transillumination is not directly applicable to the mammalian liver because of differences in the pattern of circulation.

Experiments involving ligature of the various vessels entering or leaving the liver have often given confusing results because there are other vessels that contribute in a minor way to the circulation of the liver. The most important of these are the arteries and veins of the diaphragm, which sometimes anastomose with vessels in the liver. These anastomoses are variable. They may be rapidly enlarged or new ones may possibly be formed as occasion demands. They are of importance in the interpretation of experiments involving

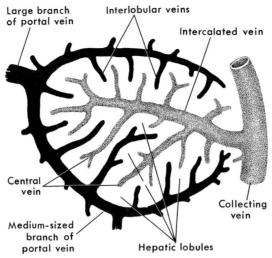

Large branch
of portal vein

Interlobular veins

Intercalated vein

Central
vein

Collecting
vein

Medium-sized
branch of
portal vein

Hepatic lobules

Figure 27-5. Diagram showing that the branches of the portal vein (black) are separated from the radicles of the hepatic veins (stippled) by a uniform layer of hepatic tissue (white). (Redrawn and modified from Pfuhl.)

alterations in blood flow after ligation of the main vessels and of changes in the circulation in cirrhosis.

HEPATIC SINUSOIDS. The hepatic sinusoids are larger than capillaries and more irregular in shape, and their lining cells are directly associated with the epithelial cells of the parenchyma with essentially no intervening connective tissue. The lining of the sinusoids consists of a thin layer of cells that differ from typical capillary endothelium in that they are markedly phagocytic and their boundaries do not blacken with silver nitrate. This latter property led some early investigators to suggest that the lining was a syncytium. Various cytological and experimental studies that were carried out in the era of light microscopy cast doubt upon this interpretation, and studies with the electron microscope have now established beyond question that the endothelium is made up of separate cells.

Whether the lining has one or two types of cells has long been a subject of controversy. Those who recognize two, identify one as a typical *endothelial cell* with a small compact nucleus staining so darkly that structural details cannot be made out in it. The other is considered to be a fixed macrophage, the *stellate cell of Kupffer*, described as a larger cell with a large oval nucleus and a small prominent nucleolus (Fig. 27-8). It is often figured with processes traversing the sinusoid, and it frequently contains granules of pigment, engulfed erythrocytes in various stages of disintegration, and

granules containing iron. These cells phagocytose particulate materials injected into the bloodstream. They are therefore stained intensely with such vital dyes as lithium carmine and trypan blue. They also take up carbon particles of India ink (Fig. 27-9) and of Thorotrast, a colloidal solution of thorium dioxide that has been much used in studying them. Some very fine materials are ingested by both types of cells, and cells intermediate between the two have been described (Fig. 27-8). Furthermore, with repeated injections of colloidal material the phagocytes become both larger and more numerous. Many investigators, therefore, believe that the indifferent endothelium-like cell may transform into a phagocytic cell when the necessity arises and that the different appearances of the lining cells represent different functional states of a single cell type.

The phagocytes may retain ingested material that is not metabolized for long periods of time. Under some conditions the macrophages may detach themselves from the sinusoid wall and enter the circulation through the hepatic vein in large numbers, and it is possible that their number may be augmented by cells recruited from other parts of the body through the bloodstream.

Two important questions concerning the lining of the sinusoids that have long been debated are: Is it continuous or does it have significant discontinuities, and how is it related to the underlying parenchymal cells? Physiological observations on the rates of clearance of substances from the blood, and on the large size of the molecules and colloidal particles which readily pass through the wall of the sinusoid, have made it seem probable that there are openings in it that permit the blood plasma, but not the blood cells, to pass freely through. The electron microscope has provided visual and experimental confirmation. In the common laboratory species the lining cells have typical overlapping junctions in some places, but in others the attenuated margins of neighboring cells may be separated by openings 0.1 to 0.5 μ across (Fig. 27-10). It has been shown that in as little as 30 seconds after the injection of Thorotrast into the portal vein, dense particles of thorium dioxide can be found in electron micrographs on both surfaces of the endothelium and on the surface of the underlying hepatic cells.

Openings in the walls of the blood vessels are rare in the circulatory system of vertebrates. Therefore, when the discontinuities in the hepatic sinusoids were first demonstrated

by electron microscopy, there was some concern that they represented artifacts of specimen preparation. The methacrylate embedding material, then in general use, was known to produce discontinuities in some structures during polymerization. As preparative methods have improved and embedding media have been introduced that are relatively free of such distortions, the lining of the hepatic sinusoids continues to appear interrupted, while the endothelia of capillaries in other organs prepared identically show no such openings. The absence of typical continuous cell to cell junctions evidently explains the failure of attempts to impregnate the outlines of the endothelial cells with silver. It is now the consensus that the wall of the sinusoids is discontinuous in most mammals including man. There is reason to believe, however, that there are significant species differences in the degree of endothelial discontinuity. In calves, for example, the lining of the sinusoids is reported to be continuous (Wood).

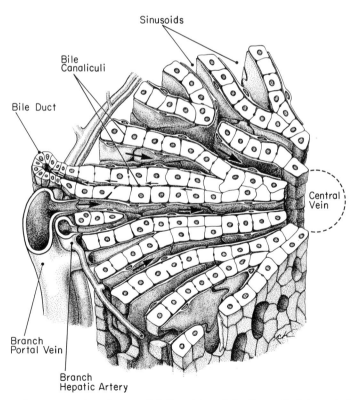

Figure 27-6. Diagrammatic representation of the radial disposition of the liver cell plates and sinusoids around the terminal hepatic venule or central vein, showing the centripetal flow of blood from branches of the hepatic artery and portal vein, and the centrifugal flow of bile (small arrows) to the small bile duct in the portal space. (Redrawn and modified from Ham, Textbook of Histology. Philadelphia, J. B. Lippincott Co.)

The question of the relationship of the sinusoid lining to the underlying liver cells also seems to have been settled by the electron microscope. The controversy stemmed from the fact that in histological sections of human postmortem material, an obvious space, called the *space of Disse,* could be seen between the sinusoid lining and the liver cells. It did not appear in biopsy material nor in the usual sections of livers of laboratory animals used in research. It was therefore regarded by many histologists as a consequence of agonal or postmortem change in the liver. In electron micrographs of well fixed material, the endothelium of the sinusoids is not closely applied to a smooth parenchymal cell surface, as was formerly thought to be the case, but instead rests lightly on the tips of a large number of irregularly oriented microvilli on the surface of the liver cell (Fig. 27-10). There is therefore a true perivascular space in the normal liver into which the microvilli project. The space of Disse

described by pathologists was evidently the result of an edematous expansion of this space. The term has now come to be applied freely to the narrow perivascular space revealed by the electron microscope in the normal liver.

The endothelium of the liver sinusoids does not have a continuous basal lamina or basement membrane. Thus there is no filtration barrier spanning the fenestrations in the sinusoid wall. Occasional bundles of collagen fibers are encountered in the space of Disse, forming the argyrophilic reticulum described by light microscopists (Fig. 27-20), but the space contains no true ground substance and plasma can apparently move freely through it. Although its content is plasma rather than interstitial fluid, it must be considered an interstitial space and not a lymphatic space, because it is not lined by endothelium as a lymphatic space should be. It may, nevertheless, play a major role in the formation of the abundant liver lymph.

It is evident that direct access of the plasma to the surface of the liver cell is a structural feature of great functional importance in the active exchange of metabolites between the liver and the bloodstream. The efficiency of this exchange is further promoted by the increase in surface achieved by the microvilli. From measurement of electron micrographs it is estimated that the length of the plasma membrane covering the microvilli and lining the clefts between them is six times greater than the linear extent of cell surface measured across the bases of the microvilli.

THE CYTOLOGY OF THE HEPATIC PARENCHYMAL CELLS. The liver cells are polyhedral, with six or more surfaces. The surfaces are of three sorts: those exposed to the perisinusoidal space; to the lumen of the bile canaliculus; and to the adjacent liver cell. The morphological differences between these surfaces are submicroscopic and are described above and on page 597. The nuclei are large and round with a smooth surface but may vary in size from cell to cell. The variation in size has been shown to be an expression of polyploidy. Most cells have a single nucleus, but binucleate cells are frequent, especially in certain species (Fig. 27-11). The nuclei in a binucleate cell are of the same size. The nucleus is typically vesicular with scattered chromatin clumps and one or more prominent nucleoli. Mitosis is extremely rare in the liver of a normal adult, but may be abundant in repair after an injury.

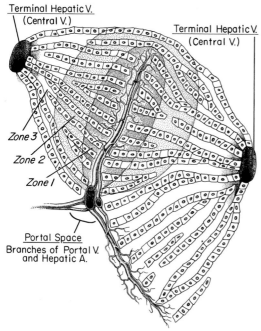

Terminal Hepatic V.
(Central V.)

Terminal Hepatic V.
(Central V.)

Zone 3
Zone 2
Zone 1

Portal Space
Branches of Portal V.
and Hepatic A.

Figure 27-7. Diagram illustrating the functional unit of liver parenchyma (the acinus) according to Rappaport et al. It consists of the parenchyma centered around the terminal branches of the hepatic artery and portal vein. It is to be noted that the cells in Zone 1 nearest these vessels have first call upon the incoming oxygen and nutrients, while the cells of Zone 2 are less favored and those of Zone 3 near the terminal hepatic venules are least favorably situated. (Redrawn after Rappaport, A. M., A. J. Borowy, W. M. Lougheed and W. N. Lolto, Anat. Rec., *119:*11, 1954.)

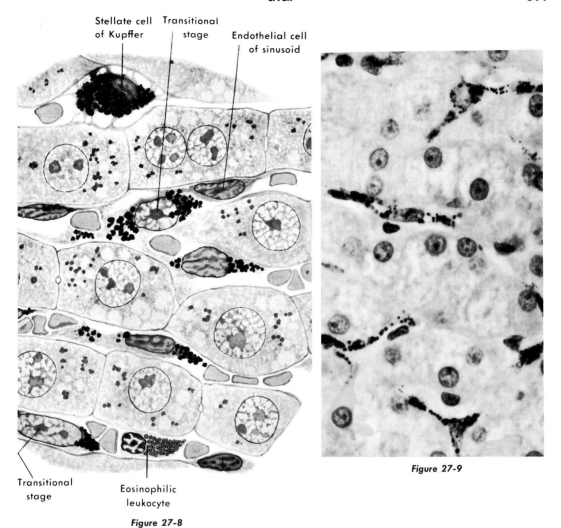

Stellate cell Transitional
of Kupffer stage

Endothelial cell
of sinusoid

Figure 27-9

Transitional
stage

Eosinophilic
leukocyte

Figure 27-8

Figure 27-8. Liver of rabbit injected intravenously with India ink, showing endothelial cells of wall of sinusoid in the resting condition and transitions to stellate cells of Kupffer. Note absence of carbon in liver cells. Hematoxylin-eosin-azure II stain. (After A. A. Maximow.)

Figure 27-9. Liver of dog injected with India ink, showing uptake of carbon by the lining cells. × 675. (Courtesy of A. J. Ladman.)

The cytoplasm of the liver cell presents an extremely variable appearance which reflects to some extent the functional state of the cell. The principal source of variation is in the content of the stored material—glycogen and fat. In the preparation of the usual histological sections both fat and glycogen have been removed, but the presence of glycogen is indicated by irregular empty spaces and that of fat by round vacuoles. By appropriate methods both fat and glycogen may be preserved and stained. The content of these materials in the liver may vary extensively with the diet or the stage of digestion. The content of individual cells varies accordingly. The cytoplasm of liver cells in well nourished animals contains conspicuous strands or irregular masses of material that are strongly basophilic and can be shown by histochemical methods to be rich in ribonucleoprotein (Fig. 27-12). After a prolonged fast these *basophilic bodies* are reduced in size and number and the cytoplasm is mainly eosinophilic. Owing to such variations in different nutritional conditions, it was formerly thought that the basophilic masses represented a storage form of protein. It is now known that

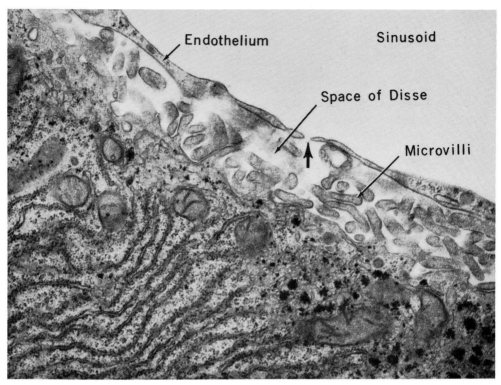

Figure 27-10. Electron micrograph of part of the surface of a rat liver cell bordering on a sinusoid. Numerous irregularly oriented microvilli project into a narrow space between the hepatic cell and the endothelium lining the sinusoid. The perivascular space is often called the space of Disse. Notice the small discontinuity in the lining of the sinusoid (at arrow). × 18,000. (Courtesy of K. R. Porter and G. Millonig; labeling added.)

these nucleic acid rich structures are the sites where protein synthesis takes place in the cell, but they are not sites of storage comparable to deposits of glycogen or lipid. In the normal animal, protein is not stored to any significant extent.

In histological specimens prepared for light microscopy, both mitochondria and the Golgi complex can be demonstrated. The cytocentrum is so small that it is not discernible among the crowded inclusions of the cytoplasm of the resting cell, and when the cell is in mitosis it is ordinarily not seen at the poles of the spindle even with the highest powers of the light microscope. The mitochondria are numerous and, for the most part, filamentous, but they vary somewhat in size and shape in different parts of the lobule and in different physiological conditions. The Golgi complex is typically demonstrated as a compact network usually located near the bile canaliculus. Inasmuch as bile canaliculi may occur on a number of sides of the polyhedral cell, it follows that there is not a single Golgi complex but several.

Their position near the bile canaliculi is in keeping with the presumed function of the Golgi apparatus in the secretory pathway that is followed by constituents of the bile from the cytoplasm to the bile canaliculi.

ZONATION WITHIN THE LIVER LOBULE. In organs with multiple functions, it is often possible to demonstrate cytological differences between cells performing different functions. In the liver, despite its manifold and quite diverse activities, the cells are all basically very similar in their appearance. All of the parenchymal cells are probably capable of carrying out all of the functions of the liver. However, cytologists have long believed that the degree of their activity under normal conditions depends primarily on their location within the lobule. The classical lobule can be divided into concentric zones on the basis of the cytological evidences of activity of the cells. A zone of varying width around the periphery of the lobule has been designated the "zone of permanent function." Next there is an intermediate "zone of varying activity" and finally a narrow zone around the central vein that is called the "zone of permanent repose" (Noel). These correspond respectively to the portions of the lobule where the liver cells are most favorably situated, intermediate, and least favorably situated with respect to the sequence in which oxygen and nutrients reach them in the blood entering the sinusoids from the terminal branches of the hepatic artery and portal vein at the periphery of the lobule (at the center of the functional unit of Rappaport). This zonation is quite striking in the mouse but less obvious in other species.

Typically, after the feeding of a large meal, glycogen is deposited first in the zone of permanent function at the periphery of the lobule. During active digestion glycogen fills cells progressively farther into the intermediate zone until, in extreme cases, all but the cells immediately adjacent to the central vein may be filled with it. With the conclusion of digestion, carbohydrate is returned to the blood, as needed, by removal of the glycogen, beginning at the most centrally located deposits. If the fast is prolonged, glycogen may ultimately disappear completely at the periphery. Thus in an animal such as the mouse, which normally feeds at night, there is a diurnal tide of glycogen within the lobule, which may be spectacularly accentuated by restricting the feeding time to one hour a day with the animal fasting the rest of the day.

Accompanying this tide is a corresponding change in the mitochondria. Those in the zone of permanent repose are thin, elongated, and sparse, staining so lightly that they are frequently seen only with difficulty in mitochondrial preparations. In the zone of permanent function, however, they are large, deeply staining spheres or short rods that may crowd the cytoplasm. In the intermediate zone, the rods become progressively elongated until, as one approaches the central zone, they are slender filaments. The width of the intermediate zone varies with the state of the diurnal tide of alimentation. In other species, including man, such changes are not demonstrable.

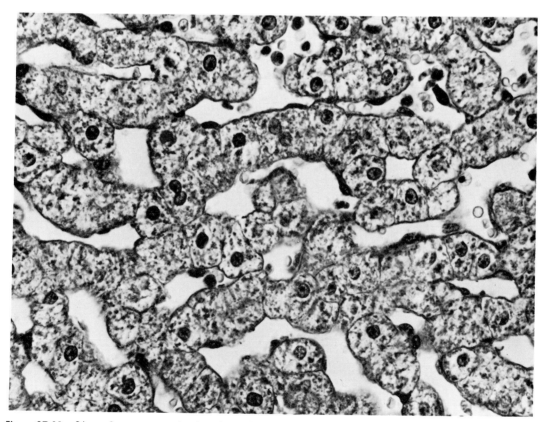

Figure 27-11. Liver of a macaque, showing the typical arrangement of the cells in interconnected and fenestrated plates or laminae. A few of the cells are binucleate. The sinusoids in this preparation are more open than usual. × 470.

Under certain conditions, both pathological and physiological, fat may accumulate in the liver. Usually this appears first in the cells of the central zone as small spherical droplets; these become progressively larger by coalescence as well as by further accumulation, until the cell may be distended by a single large drop. In certain conditions, notably some sustained dietary deficiencies, fat is deposited in the peripheral rather than in the central zone. In both cases, fat may disappear when the condition responsible is corrected.

Position in the lobule may not be the only determining factor in the relative activity of liver cells. Application of the fluorescent antibody technique to localize the sites of production of plasma albumin has shown marked differences among liver cells immediately adjacent to one another, and the distribution of active cells in this case appears to bear little relation to the familiar zonation within the lobule (see Fig. 1-24C).

Submicroscopic Structure of the Liver Cell

The fine structure of the liver cell nucleus has few features that distinguish it from the nuclei of other cells. The counterpart of the chromatin appears as ill defined masses of fine filaments or granules of moderate density. Somewhat larger granules 300 Å in diameter, called *perichromatin granules,* are located near the masses of chromatin. These are usually surrounded by a clear zone about 250 Å wide. These granules stain with uranyl acetate and indium and are therefore believed to contain nucleic acids. The nucleoli consist of fine fibrils (60 Å) and dense granules (150 Å), and both of these components are present in the anastomosing strands that constitute the nucleolonema. As in other cell types, the nuclear envelope consists of two parallel membranes bounding a perinuclear cisterna. The outer element of the nuclear envelope bears occasional ribosomes on its cytoplasmic surface and

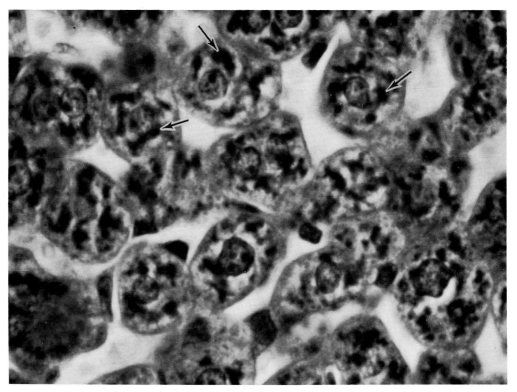

Figure 27-12. Photomicrograph of rat liver stained with eosin and methylene blue. The deeply stained basophilic bodies (at arrows) in the cytoplasm correspond to the aggregations of granular endoplasmic reticulum seen in electron micrographs. × 1250.

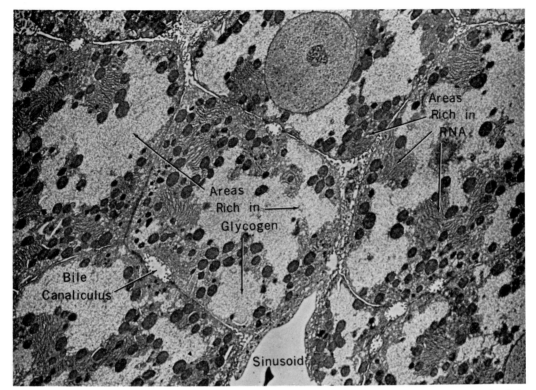

Figure 27-13. Electron micrograph of rat liver at relatively low magnification, showing the topographical relations of the hepatic cells, bile canaliculi, and sinusoids. The hepatic cells often show a segregation of cytoplasmic components into areas rich in glycogen and relatively free of organelles, and areas rich in ribonucleoprotein associated with aggregations of the endoplasmic reticulum. × 3500. (Courtesy of K. R. Porter and C. Bruni.)

is continuous at certain points with the membranes of the granular endoplasmic reticulum.

The liver cell contains both the granular or rough surfaced endoplasmic reticulum and the smooth surfaced form. The rough reticulum usually occurs in the form of parallel aggregations of from three to 20 cisternae (Fig. 27-15). These are spaced somewhat farther apart and are less precisely parallel than the cisternae in the pancreas and other protein secreting cell types. The cisternae are studded with numerous ribosomes, but the ends of their profiles are apt to be slightly expanded and free of granules. The parallel arrays of cisternae with their associated ribosomes correspond to the basophilic bodies seen with the light microscope in stained histological sections. In addition to the ribosomes associated with the cytoplasmic membranes, there are others that are clustered in spiral or rosette patterns free in the cytoplasmic matrix. Such groups of ribosomes,

called *polysomes* or *polyribosomes*, are believed to be the active units in the synthesis of protein. The ribosomes associated with the membranes of the reticulum are in similar patterned clusters, but their arrangement is only seen to advantage when the section passes parallel to a cisterna and permits a surface view of its membrane.

The smooth surfaced reticulum consists of a close-meshed plexus of branching and anastomosing tubules (Fig. 27-16). Owing to the thinness of the sections, however, the continuity of the system is not always evident, and it may appear as a congeries of separate profiles of irregular outline. Sites of continuity between the rough and smooth surfaced reticulum are frequently observed.

When adequately preserved, glycogen appears as dense particles 300 to 400 Å in diameter, occurring either singly or in aggregates 0.1 to 0.2 μ in diameter. Glycogen is not uni-

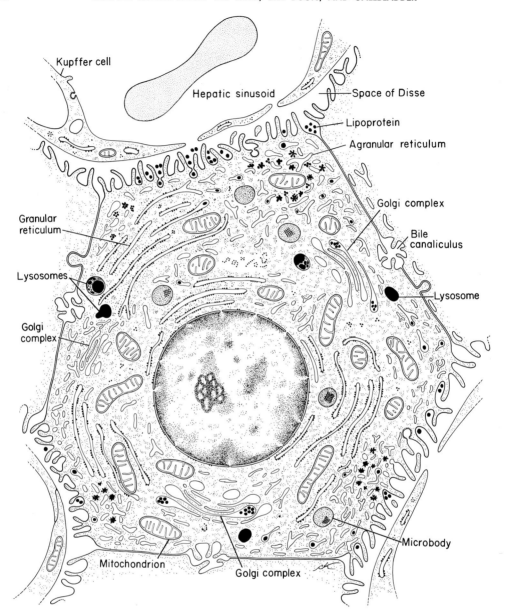

Figure 27-14. Drawing depicting the relationship of the liver cells to each other and to the sinusoids and showing the principal components of the hepatic cell as seen in electron micrographs. (Drawing by Sylvia Colard Keene.)

formly dispersed in the cytoplasm but tends to be closely associated with the areas of smooth endoplasmic reticulum (Fig. 27-17).

The Golgi system of the cell consists of several parts, each situated near a bile canaliculus. Each complex is made up of three to five flat saccules or cisternae in close parallel array. The ends of the cisternae are often dilated and contain numerous moderately dense granules 300 to 800 Å in diameter.

The mitochondria are in no way unusual in their fine structure. Lamellar or tubular cristae project into a matrix of relatively low density. A number of matrix granules are usually seen in each mitochondrial profile.

Several membrane limited bodies 0.2 to 0.5 μ in diameter and having a heterogeneous dense content are found near each bile canaliculus. These peribiliary dense bodies have been shown to contain hydrolytic enzymes and therefore correspond to the lysosomes isolated from homogenates of liver cells by de Duve. The lysosomes are believed to be involved in intracellular digestion, but from a consideration of the function of the liver it is not clear what substances would require digestion other than damaged organelles lost to the wear and tear of normal functional activity.

A related kind of cytoplasmic particle is the *microbody* or *peroxisome,* a spherical body enclosed by a membrane and containing a crystalline structure eccentrically placed in a moderately dense, finely granular matrix. Their crystalline inclusions have been isolated and found to contain *uricase.* It is presumed that microsomes function within the cytoplasm in a manner comparable to the lysosomes, but their actual significance in the economy of the cell remains to be elucidated.

THE BILE CANALICULI. These are minute canals that run between liver cells throughout the parenchyma. As a rule, a single canaliculus runs between each adjacent pair of cells. Thus, in a plate of liver cells that is one cell thick the bile canaliculi form a network having hexagonal meshes with a single cell in each mesh (Fig. 27-2). However, because the laminae of parenchymal cells branch and anastomose, the canaliculi form a three dimensional net with polyhedral meshes. In amphibians there are small branches that extend between cells from a core canaliculus and end blindly. It is now generally agreed that there are no such blind branches in the mammalian liver. The canaliculi form a continuous network without a break from lobule to lobule throughout the parenchyma. Intracellular branches have been reported to penetrate the cytoplasm, but these descriptions seem to be a misinterpretation of vacuoles that often occur in the cytoplasm adjacent to the canaliculus and in conjunction with the Golgi complex. These may appear more prominently under conditions of anoxia or during excretion of vital dyes and may, in fact, discharge into the canaliculus, but no permanent intracellular bile canals have been demonstrated. The membrane lining the canaliculi is a site of adenosine triphosphatase activity, and histochemical reactions for this enzyme provide a useful method for selectively staining this system of minute intercellular canals (Fig. 27-18).

From observations with the light microscope it seemed reasonable to assume that the bile canaliculi were distinct entities having walls of their own. Indeed, it was suggested that their hexagonal network around the hepatic cells contributed significantly to the structural stability of the liver. The electron microscope has now shown that the lumen of the bile canaliculus is merely an expansion of the intercellular space and that its wall is simply a local specialization of the surfaces of adjoining hepatic cells (Fig. 27-19). Over most of their length the apposed membranes of the two cells are relatively straight and separated by an intercellular space about 150 Å wide. At the site of the bile canaliculus they diverge to form a canalicular intercellular space 0.5 to 1 μ in diameter. The portion of the cell membrane bordering on this space bears short microvilli that project into its lumen. Along the margins of the canaliculus the membranes of the apposing cells are in close contact and are apparently fused to form a junction comparable to the zonula occludens of other epithelia. These two bands of tight junction evidently seal the commissures of the canaliculus and prevent its contents from escaping into the narrow intercellular cleft on either side. A narrow zone of cytoplasm immediately adjacent to the canaliculus is free of organelles and has the finely fibrillar structure characteristic of a firmly gelated ectoplasmic layer.

There is also some evidence that in life there is a matrix material between the microvilli that is not revealed in electron micrographs. That the canaliculi and their junctional complexes form a fairly rigid structure possessing some integrity is demonstrated by the fact that they persist as tubules when the cells are teased apart. Tubular fragments of them may also be found in homogenates of liver tissue.

The bile canaliculi vary in diameter, becoming somewhat distended with active secretion and more or less collapsed with decreasing activity. When distended, the microvilli are more widely scattered and appear to be shorter, and when collapsed, they may pack the lumen so completely that it is virtually occluded. This is possibly the reason why the canaliculi are hard to see in the light microscope.

The junction of the bile canaliculus with the bile duct system is not easily demonstrated. The fine terminal branches of the bile duct leave the portal canal with the terminal branch of the portal vein and penetrate the parenchyma between two lobules—that is, in the core of a functional unit of Rappaport. They are so small and have such thin walls that they are recognized only with difficulty. They appear so different from the smallest bile ducts that they are designated ductules or *cholangioles*. They have small diverticula that expand against the adjacent parenchyma and are applied tightly to it, cell to cell. The bile capillaries continue between the hepatic cells to empty into the lumen of the diverticulum. The whole arrangement is well demonstrated if the cholangioles and bile canaliculi are distended, as they are following occlusion of the bile duct. The diverticula then appear particularly distended and have consequently been designated *ampullae*. The ends of the canaliculi here are the only ends in the continuous polygonal network.

THE CONNECTIVE TISSUE. For an organ of its size the liver has remarkably little connective tissue. Underlying the surface capsule, extending into the portal canals, and following them to their finest branches, is a small amount of dense connective tissue. The connective tissue skeleton of the liver was discovered after the parenchyma was macerated away in water, leaving the fibrous skeleton floating free. It is called Glisson's capsule. On the surface it forms the thin connective tissue layer beneath the peritoneal mesothelium. Within the portal canals, it forms a common sheath around the branches of the portal veins, the hepatic artery, and the bile duct, and it contains the network of lymphatics that drains the lymph from the liver. In these sites it is typical connective tissue with dense collagenous fibers and occasional fibroblasts. Within the lobule the only skeletal structure is a network of reticular fibers between the sinusoid lining and the hepatic cell plates (Fig. 27-20). This is demonstrated by various techniques, but especially well by some of the silver techniques. At the periphery of the lobule, where the portal veins enter the sinusoids, the collagenous fibers of the portal canals become con-

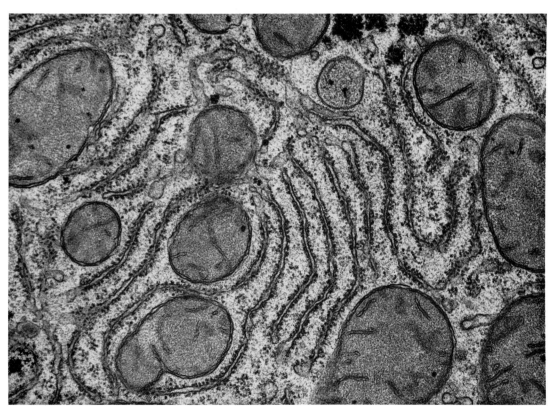

Figure 27-15. Electron micrograph showing an area of granular endoplasmic reticulum from hamster liver, corresponding to one of the basophilic bodies seen with the light microscope. The mitochondria and the granular reticulum are often in close topographical relation to one another. × 34,000. (After Jones, A. L., and D. W. Fawcett, J. Histochem. and Cytochem., *14:*215, 1966.)

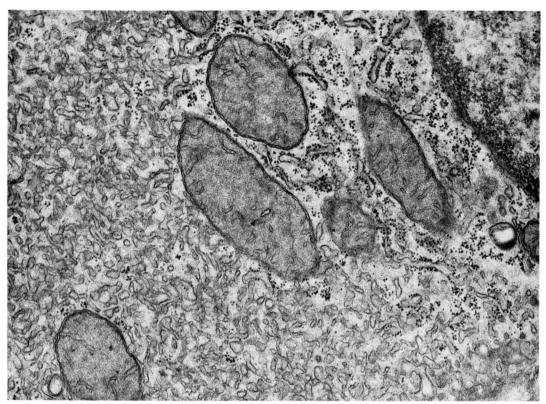

Figure 27-16. Electron micrograph of a hamster liver cell showing an area of granular reticulum and free ribosomes near the nucleus at the upper right. At the left is an area of agranular reticulum, which is unusually concentrated because this animal had been given phenobarbital, a drug that causes hypertrophy of cytomembranes of this type. × 30,000. (After Jones, A. L., and D. W. Fawcett, J. Histochem. and Cytochem., *14*:215, 1966.)

tinuous with the network of reticular fibers surrounding the sinusoids. This reticulum is the supporting tissue of the liver parenchyma. It contains no fibroblasts, the fibers apparently being formed by the sinusoid lining cells as they are in other regions of the reticuloendothelial system.

LYMPH SPACES. The liver produces a large amount of lymph. The major part of the thoracic duct lymph comes from the liver, less from the intestine via the mesenteric lymphatics, and still less from the other organs of the posterior part of the body. The hepatic lymph differs from the rest of the lymph in that it contains a large amount of plasma protein, with the ratio of albumin to globulin only a little higher than in the plasma. The origin of liver lymph is still a matter of active investigation. The network of lymphatics follows the portal vein to its finest terminal branches. Here it ends in the tenuous connective tissue sheath. No lymphatics have been demonstrated within the lobule. The most probable

assumption is that plasma traversing the discontinuities in the sinusoid lining and entering the space of Disse moves along toward the periphery of the lobule, bathing the microvilli and exchanging material with the hepatic cells as it goes. Then it apparently percolates into the tissue space around the interlobular twigs of the bile duct, the portal vein, and their accompanying lymphatics. It thus becomes the tissue fluid of this space, and the liver lymph is drained from it by the lymphatic vessels (Fig. 27-21).

Regeneration

The liver parenchyma, compared to that of many other organs, is fairly stable in that the cells rarely need to be replaced in a normal adult. It is, nevertheless, capable of spectacular regeneration. In the rat, two thirds of the liver may be removed and in a few days most of the tissue extirpated will be replaced. Similarly, after administration of some hepatotoxic

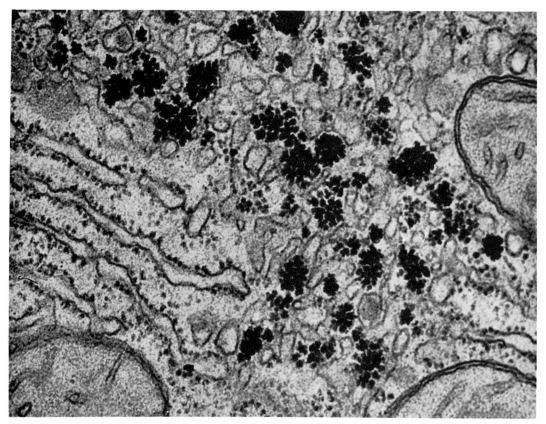

Figure 27-17. An electron micrograph of a small area of liver at higher magnification, showing the common close relation of the aggregates of glycogen to the profiles of the smooth surfaced endoplasmic reticulum. At the left are parts of three cisternae of granular reticulum with associated ribosomes. × 59,000. (After Jones, A. L., and D. W. Fawcett, J. Histochem. and Cytochem., *14:*215, 1966.)

agents, notably the chlorinated hydrocarbons, a substantial part of each lobule may be destroyed, and in this case too, the lost tissue is rapidly replaced.

Regeneration after partial hepatectomy consists of growth and cell division throughout the remaining liver mass. Hence the division into lobes is not restored. Most of the research on regeneration has been done on the rat and the mouse, in which the amount restored is usually as great as the amount removed, although in old rats it may be somewhat less. In other animals, the amount regenerated may be considerably less, in inverse ratio to the size of the animal.

Central necrosis after a toxic dose of carbon tetrachloride may involve as much as one third to one half of each lobule and is remarkably uniform throughout the liver in the rat or mouse. In an uncomplicated case only the parenchymal cells are killed, leaving the sinusoid linings intact, so that the circulation through the lobule is maintained. The necrotic cells are removed by autolysis, while the cells in the remaining part of the lobule divide rapidly by mitosis. The mass of normal liver tissue increases until in five or six days the original pattern of the liver is completely restored. If the dose of carbon tetrachloride is repeated at regular intervals when regeneration is still in progress, thus repeatedly producing new injury before the old has been repaired, fibrosis appears, and if it is continued long enough, cirrhosis of the liver ensues.

If the cellular injury is at the periphery of the lobule, as after bile duct occlusion or after treatment with certain hepatotoxic agents, there may be cell division throughout the remaining tissue but there is also considerable mitotic activity in the epithelium of the bile ductules and smaller bile ducts, with a corresponding increase in the number of ductules and small ducts. The ductules penetrate into the injured peripheral part of the lobule, apparently to re-establish a pathway for bile drainage that has been interrupted by the death of the peripheral cells and dissolution of their bile canaliculi. If the injury continues, the increase in ductules and ducts may develop into a spectacular proliferation of the bile ducts. If it does not continue, the normal architecture of the liver is rapidly restored, with the disappearance of the new ducts and ductules. It is not clear whether the duct cells atrophy and disappear or transform into parenchymal cells. In repair after severe injury, the occurrence of intermediate cells gives credence to the latter possibility.

The problem of the initiation of mitosis in a normally quiescent tissue and of its cessation when the lost tissue has been replaced has been extensively investigated, and partial hepatectomy with the ensuing regeneration is an important system in which to study a great variety of biological problems.

Histophysiology

Virtually all of the reactions of intermediary metabolism can take place in the liver. Because of the remarkable range of its biochemical potentialities and its strategic location in the circulation, it acts as a vital organ for processing nutrients absorbed from the gastrointestinal tract and for transforming them into materials needed by the other specialized tissues of the body.

One of its most important functions is the maintenance of the normal blood glucose concentration. Liver cells take up glucose from the blood and by means of a series of enzymatic reactions polymerize it to form *glycogen*, the storage form of carbohydrate. Simpler compounds, such as lactic acid, glycerol, and pyruvic acid, can be converted in the liver into glucose and thence to glycogen. As the need arises, glycogen is broken down to glucose again by a process of phosphorylation, catalyzed by the enzyme *phosphorylase*. This enzyme is usually in an inactive form but is specifically activated by the hormones *epinephrine* and *glucagon*, which act upon the liver and cause it to release glucose into the blood.

Many of the enzymes involved in glycogenesis and glycogenolysis are free in the cytoplasmic matrix. These functions, therefore, cannot be attributed to any particular cell

organelle. However, in electron micrographs, the glycogen is usually localized in areas of cytoplasm rich in the smooth surfaced endoplasmic reticulum. The exact significance of this close topographical relationship is not yet clear, but the enzyme glucose-6-phosphatase, which is known to reside in these membranes, may participate in some way in the release of glucose to the blood.

The liver also plays a decisive role in the transport of lipids and in the maintenance of constant lipid levels in the circulating blood. The lipids in the bloodstream are derived from ingested food, from mobilization of fat reserves in adipose tissue, or by synthesis from carbohydrate or protein in the liver. The main vehicle for the transport of lipids from all of these sources is the plasma *lipoprotein*, and it is in the liver that the transformation of lipids into lipoprotein takes place. Small spherical particles 300 to 1000 Å in diameter are seen in electron micrographs of the livers of fed animals in

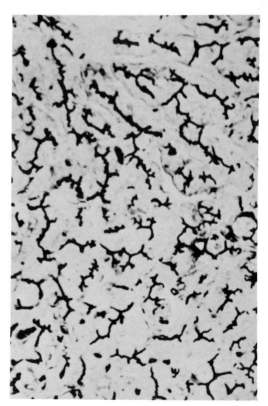

Figure 27-18. Photomicrograph of rat liver, showing the branching pattern of bile canaliculi, which are demonstrated here by their positive histochemical staining reaction for adenosine triphosphatase. × 200. (Courtesy of A. Novikoff.)

agranular terminal expansions of the granular reticulum, in tubular elements of the smooth reticulum, in inpocketings of the cell surface, and in the space of Disse (Fig. 27-22). In the isolated perfused liver, the number of these particles is strikingly increased when fatty acids are added to the perfusate. It is believed that they represent very low density *lipoproteins* being formed in the liver and released into the space of Disse. It is speculated that triglycerides are formed from fatty acids in the smooth reticulum and that these are combined there with protein synthesized in the granular reticulum to form lipoprotein particles. There is also good evidence that the reticulum, particularly the agranular form, plays an important part in the synthesis of cholesterol in the liver. An experimentally induced increase in the abundance of smooth reticulum is accompanied by an enhanced capacity to synthesize cholesterol from acetate (Jones).

The liver is the site of synthesis of plasma proteins, and the rate of their production is quite substantial. Studies on the isolated perfused organ indicate that the liver of an adult rat synthesizes 13 mg. or more of albumin per day. It is likely that the organelle principally involved is the granular endoplasmic reticulum. A fine flocculent or filamentous substance is sometimes observed in the lumen of the cisternae, and protein with the properties of albumin has been identified in liver microsomes, but the entire secretory pathway has not been worked out.

The liver is responsible for the metabolism of a large variety of lipid soluble drugs, including the barbiturates commonly used as sedatives. The enzymes responsible for the degradation of these compounds are localized mainly in the smooth surfaced microsome fraction of liver homogenates and hence reside in the agranular reticulum of the intact liver cell. Moreover, it has recently been found that administration of such drugs induces a marked increase in the smooth surfaced membranes of the cytoplasm and that this morphological change is accompanied by a concomitant increase in the drug metabolizing enzymes (Fig. 27-15). These changes evidently do not represent toxic effects of the drug but rather an

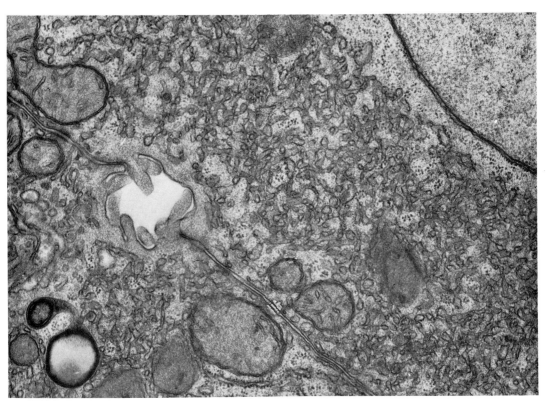

Figure 27-19. Electron micrograph of portions of two adjacent cells of hamster liver showing a typical bile canaliculus. The neighboring cytoplasm is unusually rich in agranular reticulum. × 30,000.

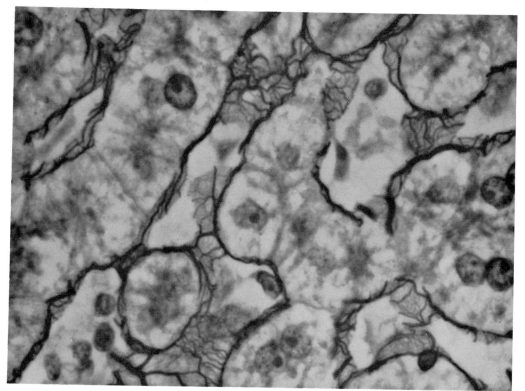

Figure 27-20. Photomicrograph of rat liver prepared by Pap's silver method for demonstrating reticulum. A fine meshwork of argyrophilic fibers is situated between the hepatic cells and the cells lining the sinusoids. × 1250.

adaptive response of the liver cell, one which enhances its efficiency in eliminating the inducing drug. These morphological and biochemical changes thus appear to be the basis of *drug tolerance,* the progressive loss of effectiveness of a drug with continued use. Certain of the steps in the metabolism of steroid hormones in the liver are also localized in the endoplasmic reticulum and probably depend upon some of the same hydroxylating enzymes that are involved in the metabolism of exogenous drugs.

The formation of salts of *bile acids* and of *bile pigments* and their addition to the bile constitute the most important excretory functions of the liver. Bile acids are derived from cholesterol, which is absorbed in the diet or synthesized in the liver cells. The bile salts have a detergent action in the intestine, emulsifying fats and promoting their absorption. Most of the bile salts are reabsorbed from the intestine and return to the liver in the portal blood, to be secreted again. Eighty per cent or more of the bile salts are recirculated in this way. The cycling is referred to as the *enterohepatic circulation.*

The mechanism of bile production is not completely understood but it is apparently more complex than the conventional concept —the secretion of bile into the bile capillaries, its collection in the bile ducts, and its concentration in the gallbladder. The presence of the extensive capillary network around the bile ducts has led to the suggestion that materials may be added to or taken from the bile in this region, perhaps both, as in the tubules of the kidney.

When the elimination of bile into the intestine is interrupted by occlusion of the bile ducts, the liver continues to produce components of bile, such as bile pigments and bile salts. Almost immediately these materials appear in the hepatic lymph. There is no evidence that they are regurgitated through or between the hepatic cells until some days later, when actual liver injury has developed. They appear to escape through the walls of cholangioles, which become distended to form

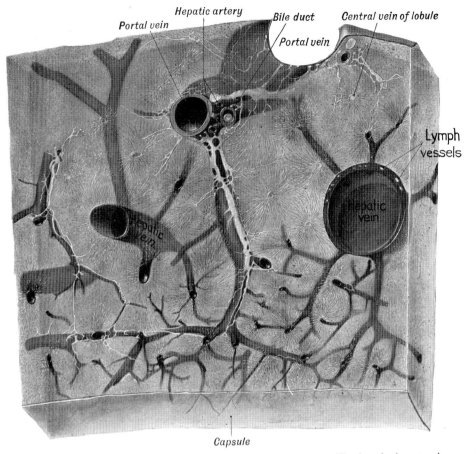

Portal vein   *Hepatic artery*   *Bile duct*   *Central vein of lobule*

Portal vein

Lymph vessels

Hepatic vein

Hepatic vein

Capsule

Figure 27-21. Thick section of liver of adult cat, cleared in oil of wintergreen. The lymphatic network appears pale and the blood vessels dark. The lymphatic vessels are confined to the interlobular connective tissue, where they surround the branches of the larger blood vessels and bile ducts. × 16. (After F. C. Lee.)

ampullae. The distention does not appear to involve disruption but merely a change in permeability, for it is immediately reversed when the obstruction of the bile duct is removed. The pigment that escapes into the lymph is returned to the blood. It becomes concentrated in the blood and in the tissues to produce *obstructive jaundice*.

BILE DUCTS

The constituents of the bile are emptied into the bile canaliculi, which communicate with the interlobular bile ducts by the canals of Hering. The finest radicles of the bile ducts are 15 to 20 μ in diameter and have a small lumen surrounded by cuboidal epithelial cells. They do not have a striated border, and their cytoplasm rarely contains fat droplets. The cells show an occasional mitosis. These small

ducts lie on a basement membrane immediately surrounded by dense collagenous bundles.

The interlobular bile ducts form a richly anastomosing network that closely surrounds the branches of the portal vein. Closer to the porta, the lumen of the ducts gradually becomes larger, while the epithelium becomes taller (the ducts of the second order) and has a layer of mitochondria at the base of the cell and another near the free border. These cells commonly contain fat droplets and, when these are numerous, cholesterol crystals. Although a faint thickening of the periphery of these cells may be seen in some animals, it is not found in man. Lymphocytes are frequently seen migrating through the epithelium into the lumen. As the ducts become larger, the surrounding layers of collagenous connective tissue become thicker and contain many elastic fibers. At the transverse fossa of the liver, the main ducts from the different lobes of the liver fuse to form the *hepatic duct*, which, after receiving the *cystic duct*, continues from the gallbladder to the duodenum as the *common bile duct (ductus choledochus)*.

The epithelium of the extrahepatic ducts is tall columnar. The mucosa is thrown into many folds and is said to yield an atypical variety of mucus. The scanty subepithelial connective tissue contains large numbers of elastic fibers, some lymphoid cells and occasional leukocytes; many of these penetrate the epithelium and pass into the lumen. Scattered bundles of smooth muscles first appear in the common bile duct; they run in the longitudinal and oblique directions, and form an incomplete layer around the wall of the duct. As it nears the duodenum, the smooth muscle layer of the ductus choledochus becomes more prominent, and its intramural portions function as a sort of sphincter in regulating the flow of bile.

THE GALLBLADDER

The gallbladder is a pear-shaped, hollow viscus closely attached to the posterior surface of the liver. It consists of a blindly ending fundus, a body, and a neck, which continues into the cystic duct. Normally it measures approximately 10 by 4 cm. in adult man, and in most animals it has a capacity of 1 to 2 ml. per kg. of body weight. It shows marked variations in shape and size and is frequently the seat of pathological processes that change its size and the thickness of its wall. The mucosa is easily destroyed, so that in most specimens removed even a short time after death, large areas of epithelium are found to be desquamated or disintegrating.

WALL. The wall consists of the following layers: a mucous layer consisting of a surface epithelium and a lamina propria, a layer of smooth muscles, a perimuscular connective tissue layer, and a serous layer, covering a part of the organ. The mucous layer is thrown into

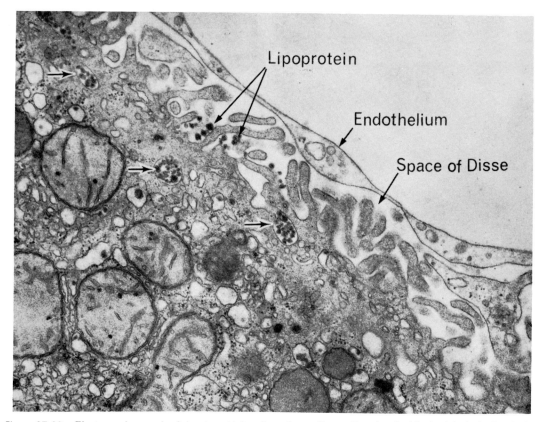

Figure 27-22. Electron micrograph of the sinusoidal surface of a rat liver cell perfused with physiological salt solution containing fatty acid. Particles of serum low density lipoprotein are seen within the smooth reticulum and in vacuoles (at arrows) discharging their contents into the space of Disse. × 28,000. (Courtesy of A. L. Jones.)

frequent folds or rugae. The major folds are subdivided into many smaller folds; they are easily seen in the contracted or even the partially distended organ. But when the viscus is greatly distended its wall becomes much thinner and most of the folds disappear, although some of them can always be seen.

The epithelium consists of a single layer of tall columnar cells, with oval nuclei located toward the base of the cells. The cytoplasm stains faintly with eosin. An inconspicuous striated border is present; occasionally, neutral fat and other lipids may be dem-

onstrated in the cell bodies. Mitochondria occur in two zones of these cells, as in the epithelium of the bile ducts. Goblet cells do not occur. Except in the neck of the viscus, there are no glands in its mucosa.

With the electron microscope the apical surface of the tall columnar cells is found to bear a large number of microvilli, but these are somewhat shorter and less regular in their orientation than are those of the striated border of the intestinal epithelium. At the tips of the microvilli the membrane bears minute filiform appendages that have been called *an-*

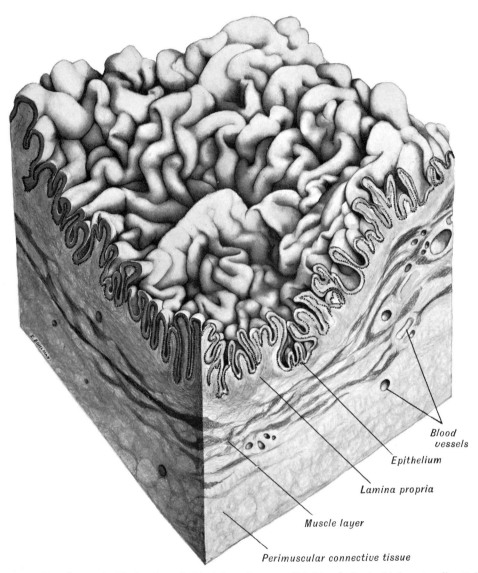

Blood vessels

Epithelium

Lamina propria

Muscle layer

Perimuscular connective tissue

Figure 27-23.   Camera lucida drawing of a block from human gallbladder. Stained with hematoxylin. × 32.

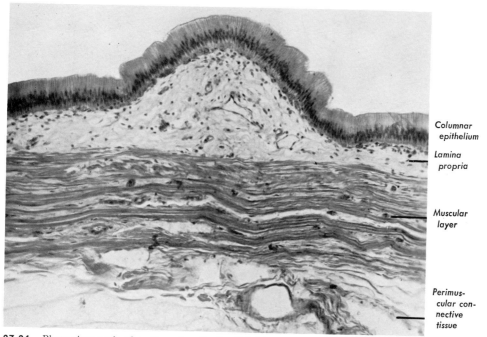

Columnar
epithelium

Lamina
propria

Muscular
layer

Perimus-
cular con-
nective
tissue

Figure 27-24. Photomicrograph of section of wall of gallbladder of *Macacus rhesus*. Fixation by vascular perfusion. × 142.

tennulae microvilares (Yamada). These are similar to the filamentous surface coat found on intestinal mucosa and on various other epithelia.

The lateral cell boundaries are relatively straight at the apical portion of the epithelium, but from the level of the nucleus to the basal lamina there is a complex plication and interdigitation of the cell surface. The intercellular space in the upper portion of the epithelium is 150 to 200 Å wide and is sealed near the lumen by a typical junctional complex. Toward the base the intercellular space may be narrow or greatly widened. The degree of distention of the intercellular clefts at the base appears to depend upon the functional state of the gallbladder epithelium.

In the lamina propria and in the perimuscular layer near the neck of the gallbladder are simple tubuloalveolar glands. Their epithelium is cuboidal and clear, and the dark nuclei are compressed at the base of the cell. They thus stand out sharply against the darker, tall columnar epithelium of the gallbladder. These glands are said to secrete mucus.

Outpouchings of the mucosa have sometimes been confused with glands. These outpouchings are lined with and are continuous with the surface epithelium and extend through the lamina propria and the muscular layer. These are the *Rokitansky-Aschoff sinuses* and probably are indicators of a pathological change in the wall of the organ that permits an evagination of the mucosa through the enlarged meshes of the muscular network. They are not found in embryonic gallbladders and should not be confused with the "true" ducts of Luschka, described later, for the latter never communicate with the lumen of the gallbladder.

The next layer of the wall is composed of an irregular network of longitudinal, transverse, and oblique smooth muscle fibers, accompanied by a network of elastic fibers. The spaces between the bundles of muscles are occupied by collagenous, reticular, and some elastic fibers, with a sprinkling of fibroblasts. The blood vessels and lymphatics contained in the perimuscular layer send branches into and through the muscular layer to the mucosa.

External to the muscular layer is a fairly dense connective tissue layer which completely surrounds the gallbladder and is in places continuous with the interlobular connective tissue of the liver (Fig. 27-25). It contains many collagenous and a few elastic fibers and scattered fibroblasts, with a few macrophages and lym-

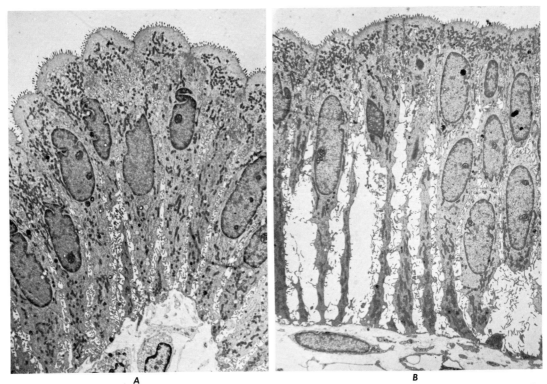

Figure 27-25. Photomicrograph of rabbit gallbladder epithelium. *A*, With a hyperosmotic solution in the lumen the net water flux is very low and the intercellular spaces at the base of the epithelium are relatively inconspicuous. *B*, In a gallbladder actively transporting fluid in vitro, the intercellular spaces are greatly distended. × 1400. (Courtesy of G. Kaye, J. Cell Biol., *30:*237, 1966.)

phoid wandering cells, small lobules of fat cells, and the blood vessels, nerves, and lymphatics supplying the organ.

Not infrequently, particularly in the hepatic surface and near the neck, peculiar ductlike structures may be seen. They can be traced for considerable distances in this connective tissue layer, and some of them connect with the bile ducts. They never connect with the lumen of the gallbladder and are probably aberrant bile ducts laid down during the embryonic development of the biliary system. They have been called "true" *Luschka ducts*, to distinguish them from epithelial outpouchings of the mucosa.

The portion of the gallbladder not attached to the liver is covered with the peritoneum. Through it the ramifying arteries, veins, and lymphatics can be seen with the unaided eye. This serosal layer is continuous with that covering the liver.

The gallbladder at its neck continues into the cystic duct. The wall of the latter is thrown into prominent folds which constitute the *spiral valve of Heister*. These are said to contain smooth muscle bundles and are thought to prevent distention or collapse of the cystic duct when the latter is subjected to sudden changes of pressure.

BLOOD VESSELS. The gallbladder is supplied with blood by the cystic artery. The venous blood is collected by veins that empty primarily into capillaries of the liver and only secondarily into the cystic branch of the portal vein. A prominent feature of the gallbladder is its rich supply of lymphatic vessels, of which there are two main plexuses, one in the lamina propria (but not within the rugae) and the other in the connective tissue layer. The latter plexus receives tributaries from the liver, thus affording an explanation for hepatogenous cholecystitis. These plexuses are collected into larger lymphatics, which pass through the lymph node or nodes at the neck of the bladder and then accompany the cystic and common bile ducts. They pass through several lymph nodes near the duodenum and finally communicate with the cisterna chyli.

NERVES. The nerves are branches of the splanchnic sympathetic and the vagus nerves. Study of the effects of stimulation of these nerves has given rise to contradictory reports in the hands of different investigators. It is probable that both excitatory and inhibitory fibers are contained in each of them. Of greater clinical importance are the sensory nerve endings, because overdistention or spasms of the extrahepatic biliary tract inhibit respiration and set up reflex disturbances in the gut tract.

HISTOPHYSIOLOGY. The gallbladder serves as a reservoir for bile, which is probably excreted by the liver continuously, if at different rates. Ingestion of fat or meat automatically discharges this reservoir. After a standard meal of egg yolks, three fourths of its contents are expelled within 40 minutes.

The prevalent view that bile is expelled by action of the gallbladder musculature is supported by much physiological evidence, including the fact that the musculature responds to intravenous injection of cholecystokinin, a

secretin-like substance extracted from the mucosa of the small intestine.

Of special clinical importance is the concentrating function of the gallbladder. Its mucous membrane withdraws water and inorganic ions from the bile. How it accomplishes this is not fully understood, but recent experimental studies suggest a possible mechanism. In gallbladders known to be transporting fluid in vivo, the intercellular spaces at the base of the epithelium are always distended and the subepithelial capillaries are dilated. In experiments carried out in vitro, if either sodium or calcium is omitted from the medium, there is no fluid transport and the intercellular spaces are narrow. If either ion is replaced, fluid transport is restored and the intercellular spaces again appear distended. It is believed that during concentration of bile, active transport of solute across the lateral cell membrane increases the concentration of solute in the intercellular space. Because of the resulting osmotic gradient, water moves into and through the cell to the intercellular space, causing its distention. Development of hydrostatic pres-

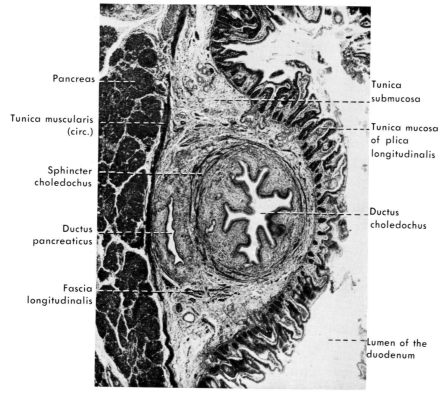

Figure 27-26. Transverse section of plica longitudinalis of a 43 cm. human fetus. × 34. (After E. A. Boyden, Surgery, *1*:25, 1937.)

sure in this space drives the solution across the basement lamina into the submucosa (Kaye).

The functional capacity of the gallbladder is assessed clinically by observing its capacity to concentrate halogen salts of phenolphthalein which are opaque to x-rays (Graham-Cole test). Failure to visualize the gallbladder after this test indicates that the organ is diseased or occluded. Whether under normal conditions it will absorb more than negligible amounts of other constituents of the bile has never been demonstrated. But if the mucosa is damaged, it may lose its concentrating power or become semipermeable. Undoubtedly, absorption of bile salts under such conditions is an important factor in the precipitation of gallstones. After obstruction of the cystic duct the bile may be resorbed in toto or replaced by "white bile," a colorless fluid consisting largely of exudate and mucus.

There is little evidence in favor of a secretory function of the gallbladder. In the pathological gallbladder two or three types of granular inclusions are found in the epithelial cells. Their chemical nature is not known. Nor is it clear whether they arise in the cells and are extruded into the lumen, or whether they represent abnormal deposits of material absorbed from the bile. A variety of mucus is added to the bile as it passes down the larger bile ducts, and mucus secreting glands are fairly numerous in the neck. In a few animals a gallbladder is never present. Its surgical removal in man is often followed by a marked dilatation of the biliary passages.

THE CHOLEDOCHODUODENAL JUNCTION

In man this zone comprises the portion of the duodenal wall that is traversed by the ductus choledochus and ductus pancreaticus, and the short ampulla into which they usually empty. For most of its length it consists of an oblique passage through the tela submucosa; it is guarded proximally by a contractile "window" in the muscle of the duodenum and distally by the valvules of the ampulla of Vater. From fenestra to ostium, the associated bile and pancreatic passages are invested by a common musculus proprius, the *sphincter of Oddi*.

In man this may consist of four parts: *the sphincter choledochus* (Fig. 27-26), a strong annular sheath which invests the common bile duct from just outside the fenestra to its junction with the pancreatic duct; *the fasciculi*

longitudinales, longitudinal bundles which span the interval between the two ducts and extend from the margins of the fenestra to the ampulla; *the sphincter ampullae*, a meshwork of fibers about the ampulla of Vater (if present), which is strongly developed in only one sixth of adults; and *the sphincter pancreaticus*, present in variable form, either alone or combined with the sphincter choledochus in a figure-of-eight configuration. The sphincter choledochus is so placed that its contraction stops the flow of bile. The longitudinal fasciculi tend to shorten the intramural portion of the ducts, thus facilitating the flow of bile into the duodenum. The sphincter ampullae, when strongly developed, can create abnormally a continuous channel between bile and pancreatic ducts. An undesirable consequence of this is to permit reflux of bile into the pancreatic duct.

HISTOPHYSIOLOGY. The most important part of the musculus proprius is the sphincter choledochus. During fasting this muscle retains the bile against the secretory pressure of the liver, causing it to back up into the gallbladder, the mucosa of which then concentrates it. Upon ingestion of food, the sphincter relaxes and the gallbladder contracts, with the result that the concentrated bile soon reaches the duodenum.

Experimentally the classic studies of Bergh and Layne have shown that the human sphincter can act independently of duodenal musculature and that spasms of the sphincter produce pain resembling biliary colic. Usually such pain is referred to anterior quadrants but later it may be referred to the scapular region.

It has not yet been proved that psychic stimuli or reflexes can induce physiological spasm of the sphincter (biliary dyskinesia). The sphincter is not relaxed by neuromimetic drugs but only by food, certain hydragogue cathartics, and antispasmotics. Jorpes and Mutt have developed the first therapeutically effective form of cholecystokinin. Its intravenous injection causes contraction of the gallbladder and relaxation of the sphincter. Cinéroentgenograms of cholecystectomized patients demonstrate that contraction begins in the middle segment of the choledochoduodenal junction and progresses in either direction (Torsoli et al.), thus verifying in the living patient the anatomical demonstration of three sphincters along the intramural course of the bile duct: namely, the sphincter choledochus superior, the sphincter choledochus inferior, and the sphincter ampullae (Boyden, 1957).

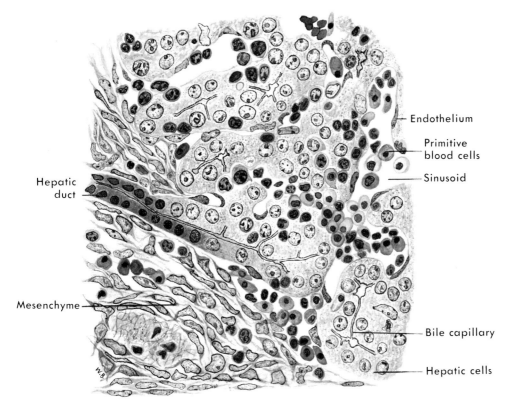

Figure 27-27. Head of hepatic duct of 16 mm. human embryo. Note continuity of hepatic duct and its lumen with hepatic cell cords and bile capillaries, respectively. Eppinger stain for bile capillaries. × 700.

HISTOGENESIS OF THE LIVER AND ITS DUCTS

The liver arises early in the embryo as a diverticulum of the midgut. It appears as a ventral outgrowth, which soon becomes hollow and lined by columnar epithelium; its cavity is continuous with that of the intestine. The hepatic diverticulum then extends into the mesenchyme of the septum transversum. In a 4 mm embryo the liver consists of a thin stalk capped by a proliferating mass of liver cell cords. In a 10 mm embryo the stalk has divided into two main branches, which go to the right and left lobes of the liver. There is also a caudal diverticulum of the stalk, which is the primordium of the future gallbladder and cystic duct. The liver cell cords continue to proliferate and even in embryos of 10 mm they contain bile capillaries. At these stages, the liver cords are distinctly tubular and may have five or six liver cells radiating around each lumen. In embryos of about 20 mm, with the ingrowth of connective tissue about the portal vein into the liver, interlobular bile ducts appear in this connective tissue and accompany the portal vein throughout its future ramifications.

As the connective tissue continues to extend into the liver substance along with the branches of the portal vein, the liver becomes divided into lobules. The exact mechanism by which the small liver of the newborn grows into the large organ of the adult is not known.

Blood formation begins early in the liver and becomes so developed here that for a time the liver is the main blood forming organ of the embryo. Blood formation stops in the liver at about the seventh month of fetal life, although this potency remains throughout the life of the individual and not infrequently is brought into play in the course of certain diseases.

Bile capillaries form a continuous system in the youngest human embryos. At first these canaliculi are continuous with the main hepatic ducts and, during the progressive embryonic development of the liver, with the finer branches of the interlobular ducts. There are two main theories as to the mode of origin of the ducts. The more probable of these is that the liver cells develop by branching from the head of the embryonic duct primordium and that, with the ingrowth of connective tissue into the liver substance, those liver cords nearest the connective tissue are transformed into ducts.

REFERENCES

LIVER

Arey, L. B.: On the presence of so-called portal lobules in the seal's liver. Anat. Rec., *51:*315, 1932.

Ashworth, C. T., and E. Sanders: Anatomic pathway of bile formation. Am. J. Path., *37:*343, 1960.

Ashworth, C. T., V. A. Stembridge, and E. Sanders: Lipid absorption, transport and hepatic assimilation studied with electron microscope. Am. J. Physiol., *198:*1326, 1960.

Biava, C. G.: Studies on cholestasis: A re-evaluation of the fine structure of normal human bile canaliculi. Lab. Invest., *13:*840, 1964.

Brauer, R. W.: Liver circulation and function. Physiol. Rev., *43:*115, 1963.

Bruni, C., and K. R. Porter: The fine structure of the parenchymal cell of the normal rat liver. I. General observations. Am. J. Path., *46:*691, 1965.

Bucher, N. L. R., J. F. Scott, and J. C. Aub: Regeneration of the liver in parabiotic rats. Cancer Res., *11:*457, 1951.

Caesar, R.: Elektronenmikroskopischer Nachweis von Fettpartikeln im disseschen Raum. Zeitschr. f. Zellforsch., *54:*793, 1961.

Daems, W. Th.: The micro-anatomy of the smallest biliary pathways in mouse liver tissue. Acta Anat., *46:*1, 1961.

Deane, H. W.: The basophilic bodies in hepatic cells. Am. J. Anat., *78:*227, 1946.

Elias, H.: A re-examination of the structure of the mammalian liver. I. Parenchymal architecture. II. The hepatic lobule and its relation to the vascular and biliary systems. Am. J. Anat., *84:*311 and *85:*379, 1949.

Fawcett, D. W.: Observations on the cytology and electron microscopy of hepatic cells. J. Nat. Cancer Inst., 15 (Suppl.):1475, 1955.

Fouts, J. R.: Factors influencing the metabolism of drugs in liver microsomes. Ann. N. Y. Acad. Sci., *104:*875, 1963.

Glinos, A. D.: The mechanism of liver growth and regeneration. *In* McElroy, W. D., and B. Glass, eds.: The Chemical Basis of Development. Baltimore, Johns Hopkins Press, 1958, p. 813.

Hamashima, Y., J. G. Harter, and A. H. Coons: The localization of albumin and fibrinogen in human liver cells. J. Cell Biol., *20:* 271, 1964.

Hampton, J. C.: An electron microscope study of the hepatic uptake and excretion of submicroscopic particles injected into the blood stream and into the bile duct. Acta Anat., *32:*262, 1958.

Hampton, J. C.: A re-evaluation of the submicroscopic structure of liver. Texas Rep. Biol. Med., *18:*602, 1960.

Hampton, J. C.: Liver. *In* Kurtz, S. M., ed.: Electron Microscopic Anatomy. New York, Academic Press, 1964, p. 41.

Hanzon, V.: Liver cell secretion under normal and pathologic conditions studied by fluorescence microscopy on living rats. Acta Physiol. Scandinav., Suppl. 101, *28:*1, 1952.

Harkness, R. D.: Regeneration of liver. Brit. M. Bull., *13:*87, 1957.

Helweg-Larsen, J. F.: Nuclear class series; studies on frequency distribution of nuclear sizes and quantitative significance of formation of nuclear class series for growth of organs in mice with special reference to influence of pituitary growth hormone. Acta Path. et Microbiol. Scandinav., Suppl. 92, p. 3, 1952.

Jefferson, N. C., M. I. Hassan, H. L. Popper, and H. Necheles: Formation of effective collateral circulation following excision of hepatic artery. Am. J. Physiol., *184:*589, 1956.

Jézéquel, A., K. Arakawa, and J. W. Steiner: The fine structure of the normal neonatal mouse liver. Lab. Invest., *14:*1894, 1965.

Johnson, F. P.: The isolation, shape, size, and number of the lobules of the pig's liver. Am. J. Anat., *23:*273, 1918.

Jones, A. L., and D. T. Armstrong: Increased cholesterol biosynthesis

following phenobarbital induced hypertrophy of agranular endoplasmic reticulum. Proc. Soc. Exper. Biol. & Med., *119:* 1136, 1965.

Jones, A. L., and D. W. Fawcett: Hypertrophy of the agranular endoplasmic reticulum in hamster liver induced by phenobarbital (with a review of the functions of this organelle in liver.) J. Histochem. & Cytochem., *14:*215, 1966.

Knisely, M. H.: The structure and mechanical functioning of the living liver lobules of frogs and Rhesus monkeys. Proc. Inst. Med. Chicago, *16:*286, 1947.

Kupffer, C. v. Über die sogenannten Sternzellen der Säugthierleber. Arch. f. Mikr. Anat., *54:*254, 1899.

Lee, F. C.: On the lymph-vessels of the liver. Carnegie Contributions to Embryol., *15:*63, 1923.

Luck, D. J. L.: Glycogen synthesis from uridine diphosphate glucose; the distribution of the enzyme in liver cell fractions. J. Biophys. & Biochem. Cytol., *10:*195, 1961.

Noel, R.: Recherches histo-physiologiques sur la cellule hépatique des mammifères. Arch. Anat. Micr., *19:*1, 1923.

Novikoff, A. B., and E. Essner: The liver cell; some new approaches to its study. Am. J. Med., *29:*102, 1960.

Orrenius, S., J. L. E. Ericksson, and L. Ernster: Phenobarbital induced synthesis of microsomal drug metabolizing enzyme system and its relationship to the proliferation of endoplasmic membranes. J. Cell Biol., *25:*627, 1965.

Palade, G. E., and P. Siekevitz: Liver microsomes; an integrated morphological and biochemical study. J. Biophys. & Biochem. Cytol., *2:*171, 1956.

Porter, K. R., and C. Bruni: An electron microscope study of the early effects of 3'-Me-DAB on rat liver cells. Cancer Res., *19:* 997, 1959.

Rappaport, A. M., Z. J. Borowy, W. M. Lougheed, and W. N. Lotto: Subdivision of hexagonal liver lobules into a structural and functional unit; role in hepatic physiology and pathology. Anat. Rec., *119:*11, 1954.

Remmer, H., and H. J. Merker: Effect of drugs on the formation of smooth endoplasmic reticulum and drug metabolizing enzymes. Ann. N. Y. Acad. Sci., *123:*79, 1965.

Rhodin, J. A. G.: Ultrastructure and function of liver sinusoids. Proc. 4th Internat. Symp. Reticuloendothelial System, Kyoto, Japan.

Rouiller, Ch.: Les canalicules biliaires. Étude au microscope electronique. Compt. ren. soc. biol., *148:*2008, 1954.

Rouiller, Ch.: Les canalicules biliaires. Étude au microscope electronique. Acta Anat., *26:*94, 1956.

Trotter, N.: Electron opaque, lipid-containing bodies in mouse liver at early intervals after partial hepatectomy and sham operation. J. Cell. Biol., *25:*41, 1965.

Wakim, K. G., and F. C. Mann: The intrahepatic circulation of blood. Anat. Rec., *82:*233, 1942.

Wilson, J. W.: Liver. Ann. Rev. Physiol., *13:*133, 1951.

Wilson, J. W.: Hepatic structure in relation to function. *In* Brauer, R. W., ed.: Liver Function: A Symposium on Approaches to the Quantitative Description of Liver Function. Washington, American Institute of Biological Sciences, Publ. No. 4, 1958, p. 175.

Wilson, J. W., and E. H. Leduc: Abnormal mitosis in mouse liver. Am. J. Anat., *86:*51, 1950.

Wilson, J. W., and E. H. Leduc: Role of cholangioles in restoration of the liver of the mouse after dietary injury. J. Path. & Bact., *76:*441, 1958.

GALLBLADDER AND BILE DUCTS

Bergh, G. S., and J. A. Layne: A demonstration of the independent contraction of the sphincter of the common bile duct in human subjects. Am. J. Physiol., *128:*690, 1940.

Boyden, E. A.: An analysis of the reaction of the human gall bladder to food. Anat. Rec., *40:*147, 1928.

Boyden, E. A.: The anatomy of the choledochoduodenal junction in man. Surg., Gynec. & Obstet., *104:*641, 1957.

Chapman, G. B., A. J. Chiardo, R. J. Coffey, and K. Weineke: The fine structure of the human gall bladder. Anat. Rec., *154:*579, 1966.

Diamond, J. M.: Transport of salt and water in rabbit and guinea pig gall bladder. J. Gen. Physiol., *48:*1, 1964.

Evett, R. D., J. A. Higgins, and A. L. Brown, Jr.: The fine structure of normal mucosa in the human gall bladder. Gastroenterology, *47:*49, 1964.

Halpert, B.: Morphological studies on the gall bladder. II. The "true Luschka ducts" and "Rokitansky-Aschoff sinuses" of the human gall bladder. Bull. Johns Hopkins Hosp., *41:*77, 1927.

Hayward, A. F.: Aspects of the fine structure of gall bladder epithelium of the mouse. J. Anat., *96:*227, 1962.

Hayward, A. F.: Electron microscopic observations on absorption in the epithelium of the guinea-pig gall bladder. Zeitschr. f. Zellforsch., *56:*197, 1962.

Jorpes, J. E., and V. Mutt: Secretin, pancreozymin and cholecystokinin; their preparation and properties. Gastroenterology, *36:* 377, 1959.

Kaye, G. I., H. O. Wheeler, R. T. Whitlock, and N. Lane: Fluid transport in rabbit gall bladder. A combined physiological and electron microscope study. J. Cell Biol., *30:*237, 1966.

Petrén, T.: Die Venen der Gallenblase und der extrahepatischen Gallenwege beim Menschen und bei den Wirbeltieren. Stockholm. Idun, 1933.

Pfuhl, W.: Die Leber und die Gallenblase und die extrahepatischen Gallengänge, *In* von Möllendorff, W., and W. Bargmann, eds.: Handbuch der mikroskopischen Anatomie des Menschen. Berlin, Julius Springer, 1932, Vol. 5, part 2, pp. 235 and 426.

Schwegler, R. A., Jr., and E. A. Boyden: The development of the pars intestinalis of the common bile duct in the human fetus, with special reference to the origin of the ampulla of Vater and the sphincter of Oddi. I. The involution of the ampulla. II. The early development of the musculus proprius. III. The composition of the musculus proprius. Anat. Rec., *67:*441, *68:*17, and *68:*193, 1937.

Torsoli, A., M. L. Ramorino, L. Palagi, C. Colagrande, I. Baschieri, S. Ribotta, and M. Marinosci: Observations roentgencinématographiques et electromanométriques sur la motilité des voies biliaries. Sem. Hôp. Paris, *37:* 790, 1961.

Whitlock, R. T., and H. O. Wheeler: Coupled transport of solute and water across rabbit gall bladder epithelium. J. Clin. Invest., *43:*2249, 1964.

Yamada, E.: The fine structure of the gall bladder epithelium of the mouse. J. Biophys. & Biochem. Cytol., *1:*445, 1955.

CHAPTER TWENTY-EIGHT

Pancreas

Next to the liver, the pancreas is the largest gland connected with the alimentary tract. It consists of an *exocrine portion,* which elaborates about 1200 ml. of digestive juice a day, and an *endocrine portion,* whose secretion plays an important part in the control of the carbohydrate metabolism of the body. Unlike the liver, in which the exocrine and endocrine functions are both carried on by the same cells, the pancreas has exocrine and endocrine functions that are carried on by different groups of cells.

The pancreas is a pinkish white organ lying retroperitoneally at about the level of the second and third lumbar vertebrae. On the right its head is adherent to the middle portion of the duodenum, and its body and tail extend transversely across the back wall of the abdomen to the spleen. In the adult it measures from 20 to 25 cm. in length and varies in weight from 65 to 160 gm. It is covered by a thin layer of connective tissue which does not, however, form a definite fibrous capsule. It is finely lobulated, and the outlines of the larger lobules can be seen with the naked eye.

EXOCRINE PORTION

The pancreas is a compound acinous gland whose lobules are bound together by loose connective tissue through which run blood vessels, nerves, lymphatics, and excretory ducts. The acini that form the external secretion vary from rounded structures to short tubules (Fig. 28-1). They consist of a single row of pyramidal epithelial cells converging toward a central lumen and resting upon a basal lamina supported by delicate reticular fibers. The size of the lumen varies with the functional condition of the organ, being small when the organ is at rest but becoming distended with secreted material during active secretion. Between the acinar cells are fine secretory capillaries connected with the central lumen.

The acinar cells show rather striking differences in the various stages of secretion. In general, the basal part of the cell, when seen in the living condition, is homogeneous or may show a faint striation, owing to the presence of filamentous mitochondria in it. The apical portion of the cell is filled with highly refractile spherical bodies. These are the secretion granules or droplets, which vary greatly in number, depending on the stage of secretion.

In sections stained with hematoxylin and eosin after Zenker-formol fixation, the basal parts of the acinar cells stain a dark purple, while the secretory granules are a bright orange-red. In sections stained with the basic dye methylene blue, the basal cytoplasm stains intensely, owing to the presence of high concentrations of ribonucleoprotein in this part of the cell. The basophilic material, commonly called *ergastoplasm,* may have a lamellar or filamentous appearance after some fixatives (Fig. 28-2).

The Golgi apparatus is located in the supranuclear region and varies in its size and location in different physiological conditions. The zymogen granules or droplets arise in the Golgi region; they are particularly numerous in fasting animals and relatively few after a large meal or after injection of pilocarpine, which causes a massive release of secretion (Fig. 28–4). After discharge of the zymogen droplets the Golgi apparatus enlarges as new secretory droplets are formed.

SUBMICROSCOPIC STRUCTURE OF THE PANCREATIC ACINAR CELLS. The fine structure of the pancreatic acinar cell has probably been studied more intensively than that of any other gland. The intracellular synthetic pathway and the mechanism of discharge of its granules were described in considerable detail in Chapter 4 (see pp. 98 to 100) and will only be reviewed here.

The basal half is occupied by tubular elements of granular endoplasmic reticulum and extensive parallel arrays of cisternae. Free ribosomes are abundant in the cytoplasmic matrix. The long mitochondria have well developed cristae and numerous matrix granules. The Golgi complex consists of stacks of parallel cisternae, very numerous small vesicles, and condensing vacuoles containing secretory material of relatively low density. Mature zymogen "granules" or droplets with very dense contents are also found in close topographical relation to the Golgi complex. Occasional lipid droplets and lysosomes are commonly found in this region.

The free surfaces of the acinar cells usually bear a few short, irregularly oriented microvilli (Fig. 28-8). The apical cytoplasm is crowded with zymogen droplets, and some are found in the process of discharging their content into the lumen of the acinus (Figs. 28-6 and 28-8). It is evident from such images that the zymogen is not in the form of a granule but is fluid and flows out through an opening created by fusion of its limiting membrane with the cell surface membrane. The lumen of the acinus is usually filled with moderately dense homogeneous material representing zymogen already secreted. Normally the zymogen droplets in the apex of the cell remain discrete even though closely crowded together. In cells that are very actively secreting, however, a zymogen droplet whose membrane has become continuous with the plasma membrane may be joined in similar fashion by a second and this one in turn by a third. In this way a series of interconnected zymogen droplets may come to

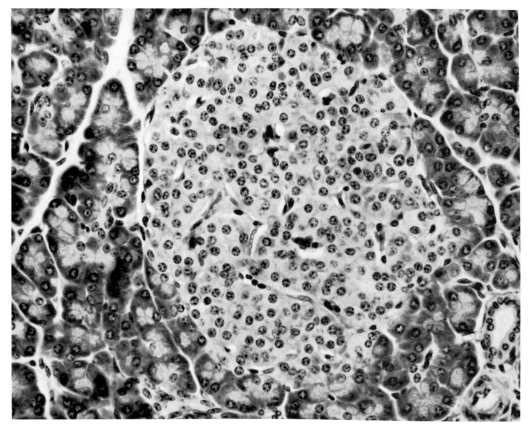

Figure 28-1. Photomicrograph of an islet of Langerhans and surrounding acinar tissue in guinea pig pancreas. Hematoxylin and eosin. × 500.

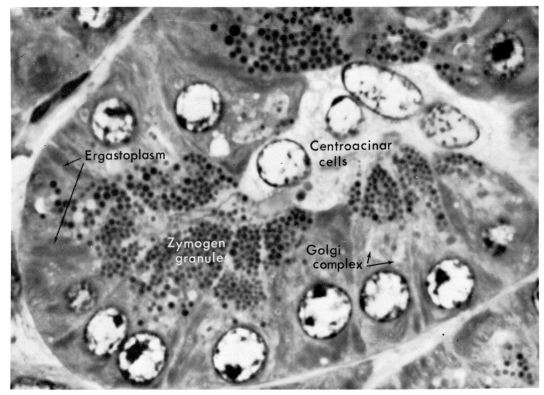

Figure 28-2. Photomicrograph of human pancreas, showing an acinus and its centroacinar cells. The ergastoplasm, Golgi complex, and zymogen granules of the acinar cells are clearly identifiable. The fixation of the nuclei is less than ideal, but adequate preservation of this organ from postmortem material is difficult. Formalin, osmium fixation, Epon section, stained with toluidine blue. × 3200. (Courtesy of S. Ito.)

extend for some distance downward into the apical cytoplasm (Fig. 28-9).

According to the current interpretation, the digestive enzymes of the pancreas are synthesized in the basal cytoplasm of the acinar cells, where they accumulate in the lumen of the endoplasmic reticulum. Through it, they are channeled into the Golgi region, where they are segregated in vesicular elements of the Golgi complex and concentrated into typical zymogen droplets. In most species it is only after the product has undergone this concentration that it is sufficiently insoluble to resist extraction during specimen preparation. Consequently, zymogen droplets are visible in the Golgi region and apex of the cell but their precursors in the endoplasmic reticulum are extracted, and its lumen usually appears empty. Nevertheless, the presence of the digestive enzymes within the reticulum has been established in biochemical studies of the microsome fraction. In the guinea pig, and occasionally in the bat and the dog, electron micrographs of

stimulated glands reveal, in the lumen of the reticulum, dense spherical bodies that resemble zymogen droplets. In these species, at least, segregation of the product evidently can occur in the reticulum as well as in the Golgi apparatus.

ISLETS OF LANGERHANS

Scattered throughout the exocrine portion of the pancreas are richly vascularized small masses of endocrine cells comprising the *islets of Langerhans*. These can be stained differentially by perfusion of the gland with a dilute solution of neutral red. When this is done, the islets can be identified with the naked eye and counted. In the adult human their number is estimated to range from 200,000 to 1,800,000. They are somewhat more numerous in the tail of the pancreas than in its body or head.

The islets are more or less completely demarcated from the surrounding acinar tissue by a thin layer of reticular fibers, but there is normally very little reticulum within the islet other than that associated with the capillaries. Occasionally isolated islet cells or groups of a few cells may be found among the acinar cells or closely associated with the small ducts. The islet cells are arranged in irregular cords and are paler staining than the surrounding acinar cells (Fig. 28-10). No secretory granules can be seen within them in routine hematoxylin and eosin preparations, but with special stains such as Mallory-azan at least three types of granular cells can be distinguished. One of these, called the *alpha cell* (A cell) contains granules that are insoluble in alcohol, while the granules of the other principal type, the *beta cell* (B cell), are soluble in alcohol. The alpha cells are less numerous and in man tend to be situated around the periphery of the islet with the beta cells in the interior.

The mitochondria of the islet cells resemble those of the ducts in being delicate filaments compared to the coarser filamentous mitochondria of the acinar cells. The Golgi apparatus of the beta cell is distinctly larger than that of the alpha cell but in neither cell type is it as conspicuous as in the acinar tissue.

In a number of animal species, if the pancreas is freshly fixed in Zenker-formol and stained with Mallory-azan or with the Masson method, three types of granular cells can be identified in the islets (Fig. 28-10). The granules of the alpha cells are relatively large and are colored a brilliant red, and those of the beta cells are smaller and stain brownish orange. A third type called the *delta cell* (Bloom; Thomas) is filled with small blue-staining granules. In the dog the alpha, beta, and delta cells are estimated to comprise 20, 75, and 5 per cent, respectively, of the total. In addition to the granular cell types, the islets of the guinea pig pancreas also contain a nongranular cell designated the *C cell*.

SUBMICROSCOPIC STRUCTURE OF THE ISLET CELLS. The presence of the four cell types just described has now been verified in electron microscopic studies. The alpha cells are the most striking, owing to their large numbers of very dense spherical granules (Fig. 28-12).

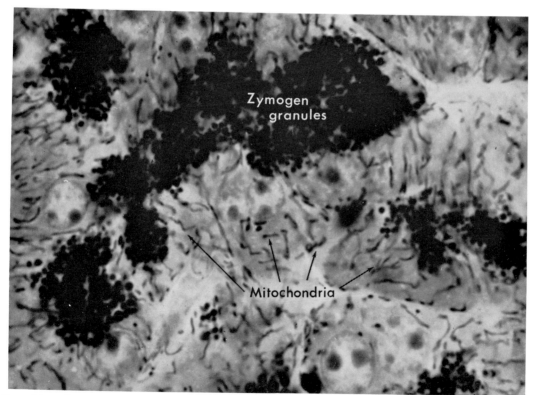

Figure 28-3. Photomicrograph of pancreatic acinar cells of a rat, showing their filamentous mitochondria and zymogen granules. Acrolein fixation, polyester wax embedding. Cason stain. × 3000. (Courtesy of N. Feder.)

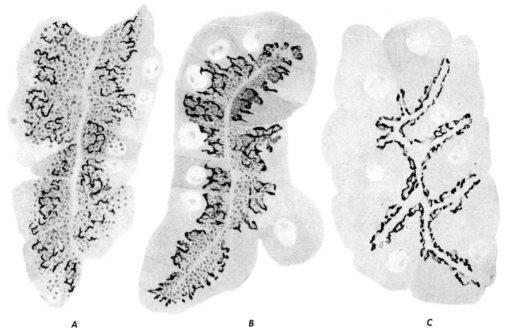

Figure 28-4. Sections through three pancreatic acini of mice, showing changes in the zymogen granules and Golgi apparatus. *A,* During starvation; *B,* normal pancreas; *C,* three hours after the injection of pilocarpine. Method of Kolatschew. × 950. (Redrawn after Nassonow.)

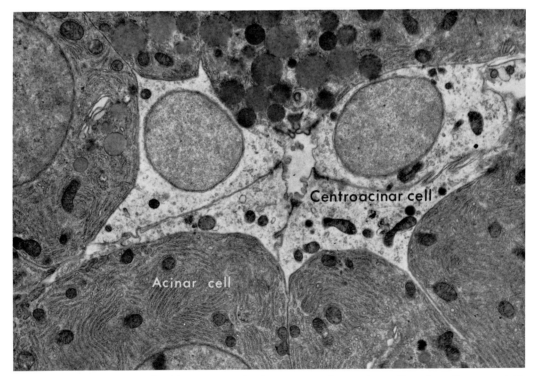

Figure 28-5. Electron micrograph of bat pancreas showing portions of two acinar cells and, at the upper right, a centroacinar cell. The abundance of granular endoplasmic reticulum in acinar cells that are active in protein synthesis stands in marked contrast to the virtual absence of reticulum in the relatively inert centroacinar cells. × 8000.

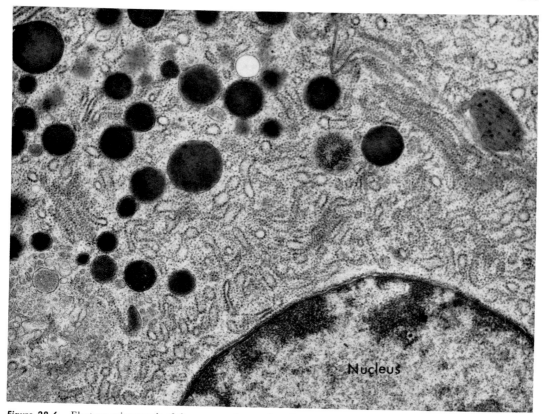

Figure 28-6. Electron micrograph of the supranuclear region of a pancreatic acinar cell from a bat, showing zymogen granules and tubular elements of granular endoplasmic reticulum. The periphery of the Golgi complex appears at the lower left. × 20,000.

These are enclosed in a membrane, which, in osmium fixed material, is separated from the granule by a narrow clear zone. In tissue preserved with aldehyde fixatives the very dense granule appears to have a less dense outer zone to which the membrane is closely applied. It is believed that this less dense outer component is extracted in the usual preparative procedure, leaving a clear space between the dense core of the granule and its limiting membrane.

In ultrathin sections, favorably oriented mitochondria are long slender rods with the usual internal membrane structure, but shorter profiles are more common. There are a few cisternal profiles of the granular endoplasmic reticulum and a moderately well developed, juxtanuclear Golgi complex.

The beta cells have somewhat larger mitochondria and a more prominent Golgi complex. The endoplasmic reticulum is usually less extensive than that of the alpha cell. The beta cells show marked species variations in the character of their granules. In some species the granules are homogeneous and moderately dense and are distinguishable from alpha cell granules only by their slightly different size and density. In man, bat, dog, and certain other species the beta granules have a very distinctive appearance because they contain one or more small dense crystals (Fig. 28-13). In the human these are rectangular or polygonal and at high magnification show periodic internal structure (Like). The crystals are surrounded by a matrix of low density, or one easily extracted in specimen preparation, for the dense crystals enclosed in a loose fitting membrane stand out against an almost clear background (Fig. 28-13).

The existence of the delta cell as a type morphologically distinguishable from alpha and beta cells was long a subject of controversy. The existence of such cells in many, if not all, mammalian species can no longer be questioned, but whether they are a physiologically

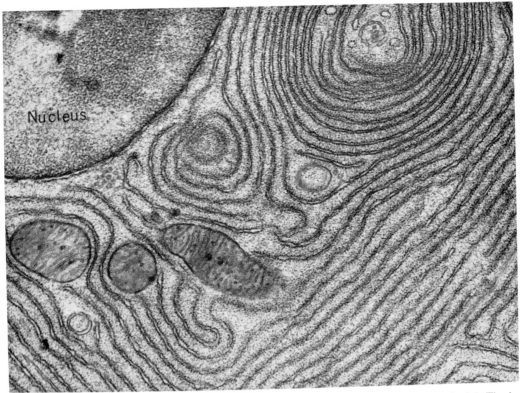

Figure 28-7. Electron micrograph of the basal region of a pancreatic acinar cell of a bat recently fed. The long parallel cisternal profiles of the granular reticulum sometimes become rearranged into concentric systems after the stimulus of feeding. × 24,000. (After D. W. Fawcett, Lab. Invest., *10:*1162, 1961.)

distinct cell type or merely a stage in the cycle of one of the other cell types remains an open question. Their granules tend to be slightly larger and considerably less dense than the alpha granules (Fig. 28-14), and some authors consider their separate identity established (Munger). However, the fact that in man, forms intermediate between typical alpha granules and delta granules can be found, and the fact that both types may be present in the same cell, has led others to consider the delta cells to be altered alpha cells (Like), a possibility considered by Bloom in the original description of these cells. In electron micrographs the transition from alpha to delta type granules is often accompanied by a gradual loss of the morphological integrity of the mitochondria, Golgi complex, and other membranous components of the cytoplasm. The nucleus, however, remains nearly normal in appearance and the cell is evidently viable. If the delta cells are the result of some regressive change in alpha cells, the physiological significance of

this change and its regular occurrence in a number of species remain to be explained.

The cells of the islets tend to be polarized toward the capillaries. Granules are seen in very close association with the cell membrane at the vascular pole of the cell, but they do not appear to be discharged intact and no adequate morphological explanation of the mode of release of the product has been forthcoming. The capillaries of the islets of Langerhans are of the type in which areas of endothelium of appreciable thickness alternate with extremely attenuated areas penetrated by numerous pores or fenestrations.

THE DUCT SYSTEM

The lumen of each acinus is continuous with the lumen of a small duct bounded by the *centroacinar cells,* so named because they are surrounded by and appear to extend into the center of the acinus. The centroacinar cells are easily distinguished by their pale staining in histological sections and by the very low density of their cytoplasm and the paucity of their organelles in electron micrographs (Fig. 28-5). The terminal portion of the duct system, which they surround, drains proximally into the *intralobular* or *intercalated ducts*. These are lined by cells similar to the centroacinar cells and forming a low columnar epithelium. These are tributaries of larger *interlobular ducts* lined by a columnar epithelium in which goblet cells and occasional argentaffin cells are interspersed. Small mucous glands may bulge slightly from the ductal epithelium. The interlobular ducts join the main pancreatic ducts, of which there are two. The larger or *duct of Wirsung* begins in the tail and runs through the substance of the gland, receiving throughout its course numerous branches, so that it gradually increases in size as it nears the duodenum. In the head of the pancreas, it runs parallel with the ductus choledochus, with which it may have a common opening, or it may open independently in the ampulla of Vater. The opening and closing

of these ducts are controlled by the sphincter of Oddi (p. 610). The accessory *duct of Santorini* is about 6 cm. long. It is practically always present and lies cranial to the duct of Wirsung. These larger ducts have a moderately thick wall of dense connective tissue containing some elastic fibers.

In addition to the system of ducts just described, the pancreas is said to contain a system of anastomosing small *tubules*, which arise from the large ducts and run in the connective tissue surrounding them. These tubes have a diameter of 12 to 27 μ; they are connected both with the islets of Langerhans and the small mucous glands, and only occasionally with the acini. These structures, although studied most extensively in the guinea pig, are also said to be present in man. Their epithelium is of a low, irregularly cuboidal type. They show occasional mitoses. The cytoplasm is homogeneous in most cases. Occasional goblet cells and a few cells with true mucous granules may be found within them.

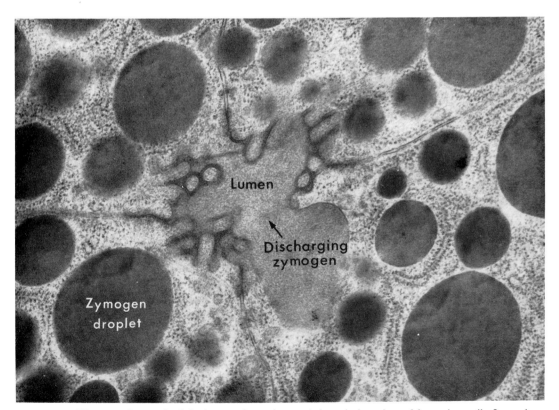

Lumen

Discharging
zymogen

Zymogen
droplet

Figure 28-8. Electron micrograph of the lumen of an acinus and the apical portions of four acinar cells. Large dense zymogen droplets or granules are found in the cell apex. The limiting membrane of one of these as fused with the cell membrane and its zymogen is being discharged into the lumen. The free surface of the acinar cells bears short microvilli. $\times$ 38,000.

Some of the projections from these tubules consist of islet cells, singly or in groups, but the most striking feature of the tubules is their connection, by one or more short stalks, with large islets of Langerhans. These ductules are composed of undifferentiated epithelium, and from them new islets, and probably also new acini, arise from time to time, particularly after injury to the pancreas. They do not carry any secretion.

BLOOD VESSELS, LYMPHATICS, AND NERVES

The arterial supply of the pancreas is from branches of the celiac and superior mesenteric arteries. From the celiac it receives branches through the pancreaticoduodenal and splenic arteries; it also receives small branches from the hepatic artery. The inferior pancreatico-duodenal artery is a branch of the superior mesenteric. The vessels run in the interlobular connective tissue and give off fine branches that enter the lobules. Veins accompany the arteries throughout and lead the blood either directly into the portal vein or indirectly through the splenic vein.

The exact lymphatic supply of the gland has not been worked out in detail. The lymphatic drainage is principally into the celiac nodes about the celiac artery.

The nerve supply is mainly by unmyelinated fibers arising from the celiac plexus. These fibers accompany the arteries into the gland and end about the acini. There are also many sympathetic ganglion cells in the interlobular connective tissue. The organ also receives myelinated fibers from the vagus nerves. In electron micrographs axons are seen penetrating the basement lamina to end in intimate contact with the base of the acinar cells (Fig. 28-16). These nerve terminals often contain numerous synaptic vesicles. The source of these nerves is not clear, but it is likely that they are the terminations of branches from the vagus and may be involved in regulation of secretion.

HISTOGENESIS

The pancreas arises from two diverticula of the duodenum close to the hepatic diverticulum. The two primordia of the pancreas are known as the ventral and the dorsal pancreas; these fuse, and the duct of the ventral pancreas becomes part of the main pancreatic duct. The great mass of the organ is formed by the dorsal pancreas, which gives rise to the body and tail and part of the head. The duct of this primordium becomes the future accessory duct. Most of the main pancreatic duct of the adult is formed from the remainder of the duct of the dorsal primordium, which fuses with the duct of the ventral primordium.

At first each primordium consists of a network of anastomosing tubules lined by a single layer of cells. These differentiate into acini in which the characteristic secretion granules appear, and also into islets of endocrine cells. It is probable that the acini do not develop into islets but that the latter come directly from the embryonic tubules of the duct system.

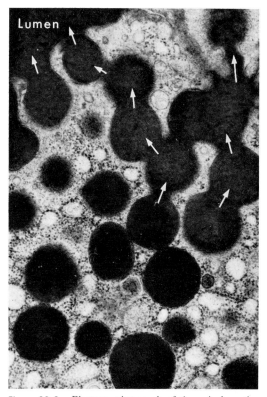

Figure 28-9. Electron micrograph of the apical portion of an acinar cell from a dog pancreas. A zymogen granule or droplet opening onto the lumen may be joined to a second and this to a third, so that zymogen may be discharged through several intercommunicating membrane limited vacuoles. × 24,500. (After A. Ichikawa, J. Cell Biol., *24:*369, 1965.)

REGENERATION

If the bulk of the pancreas is removed experimentally, the organ regenerates only

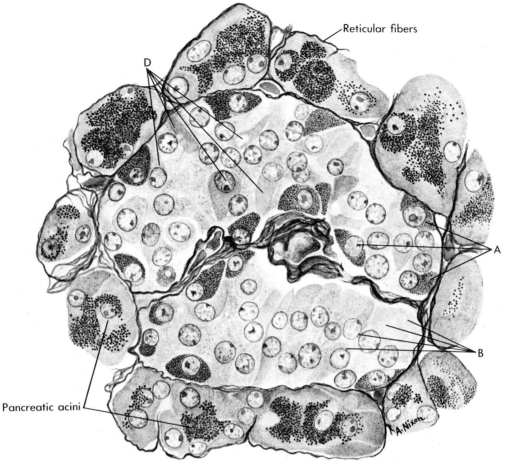

Figure 28-10. Section of human pancreas. The central part of the figure is an islet of Langerhans with granular cells of types alpha, beta, and delta. Mallory-azan stain. × 960. (After Bloom, 1931.)

slightly. If a portion of the tissue is injured by a wound, mitotic figures appear in the ductal epithelium and many new *islets* are formed, but few, if any, new *acini* develop as a result of the injury. If the main pancreatic ducts are ligated, there is at first a rapid disintegration of the pancreatic acini, followed by a much slower disintegration of the original islets; at the same time ducts begin to proliferate and give rise to many new islets and to some new acini. This process extends over a period of months and even years. One week after the ligation, in the guinea pig and rabbit, most of the acini have degenerated; after one month, there is considerable generation of new islets and some acini from the ducts; then, most of the acini degenerate (at a year and a half). After nearly three years, it is said that only the main duct is present as a blindly ending structure, that there are no acini left, and that a few new islets have arisen by sprouting from the ducts. It seems fairly well assured that the pancreas, even in the adult, is provided with undifferentiated cells which can give rise to new acini and to a great extent to new islets of Langerhans.

HISTOPHYSIOLOGY OF THE EXOCRINE PANCREAS

The external secretory function of the pancreas follows a rhythmical cycle, with a low level of continuous secretion accentuated periodically by nervous and hormonal stimulation associated with eating. The relative importance of hormonal and nervous control of pancreatic function is still a subject of debate. The presence of food in the antrum of the stomach and passage of the acid products of gastric digestion into the duodenum result in release into the blood of two different hormones, *secretin* and *pancreozymin*. Secretin causes

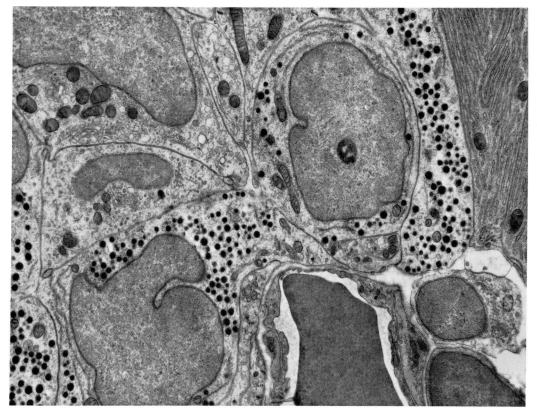

Figure 28-11. An electron micrograph of a peripheral area of an islet of Langerhans from bat pancreas. The cells with numerous granules are alpha cells and at the upper left are portions of several beta cells largely devoid of granules. An acinar cell is seen at the upper right and a capillary below. × 8200.

the pancreas to secrete a large volume of fluid containing a high concentration of sodium bicarbonate but very little enzymatic activity. This alkaline juice serves to neutralize the acid chyme entering the intestine from the stomach and provides the neutral or alkaline pH required for optimal activity of the pancreatic enzymes. Pancreozymin, carried by the blood to the pancreas, causes secretion of large amounts of digestive enzymes. Acting alone it does not significantly increase the volume of outflow from the pancreatic duct, but the coordinated action of secretin and pancreozymin results in a copious secretion of enzyme rich pancreatic juice. Stimulation of the vagus nerve has an effect similar to that of pancreozymin, increasing enzyme secretion but not greatly influencing the volume of pancreatic juice.

Because food in the intestine can stimulate pancreatic flow and enzyme secretion when all nervous connections between the in-

testine and the pancreas have been severed, some physiologists have been inclined to discount the importance of the nervous system in pancreatic secretion. However, atropine, which blocks the action of the parasympathetic nervous system, causes a marked inhibition of enzyme secretion from the intact pancreas. This fact suggests that cholinergic nervous stimulation is important. The electron microscopic observation of numerous nerve axons in close contact with acinar cells (Fig. 28-16) and the presence in them of the small vesicles characteristic of functioning nerve terminals is strongly indicative of direct involvement of the nervous system in the control of pancreatic function.

The pancreas secretes proteases, nucleases, amylases, and lipases—enzymes for digestion of the three major classes of nutrients, proteins, carbohydrates, and fats. Proteolytic enzymes account for 70 per cent of the enzymes of the pancreatic juice and include *trypsin* and *chymotrypsin,* which act upon whole protein or products of its partial degradation, and *carboxypeptidase,* which is specific for cleavage of a particular linkage in small peptides. *Ribonuclease* and *deoxyribonuclease* degrade ribonucleoprotein and deoxyribonucleoprotein. *Pancreatic amylase* hydrolyzes starch and glycogen to yield disaccharides, and *pancreatic lipase* splits triglycerides into fatty acids and glycerol. When these enzymes are within the acinar cells, they are enclosed in membranes and are present as inactive precursors. Thus, they do not injure the pancreas, but in the pathological condition *acute pancreatitis,* the proenzymes may be converted into active enzymes that destroy the pancreas itself.

HISTOPHYSIOLOGY OF THE ENDOCRINE PANCREAS

Extirpation of the pancreas in animals results in severe *diabetes,* a disturbance in carbohydrate metabolism in which the concentration of glucose in the blood rises and the excess is excreted in the urine. Such a condition quickly results in the death of the animal, but this is delayed if the pituitary gland is also removed.

If the pancreatic ducts are ligated, the animals do not suffer diabetes. Although the acinar tissue degenerates, the islets of Langerhans persist and may even increase in number. One of the great achievements in modern therapeutics, the treatment of diabetes with *insulin,* rests upon the demonstration that extracts of pancreatic tissue, in which degeneration of the acinar tissue had been induced by ligation of the ducts, relieved the symptoms of diabetes. Insulin was subsequently obtained from the whole or intact pancreas by preventing the destructive effect of the acinar secretion upon the hormones of the islets of Langerhans. Insulin has been isolated in crystalline form and is the first naturally occurring protein of biological importance for which the precise ar-

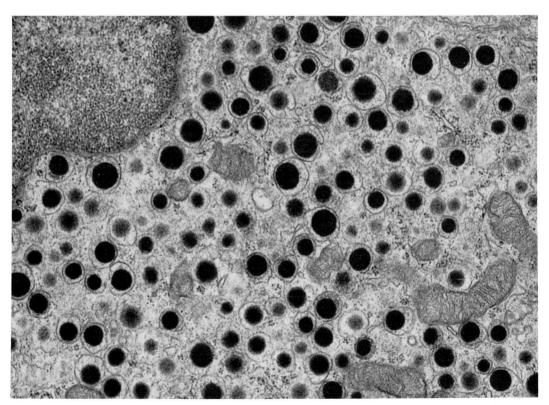

Figure 28-12. Electron micrograph of a juxtanuclear area of an alpha cell in a human islet of Langerhans. The alpha granules have a very dense spherical core and a less dense outer region bounded by a membrane. × 24,000. (Courtesy of A. Like.)

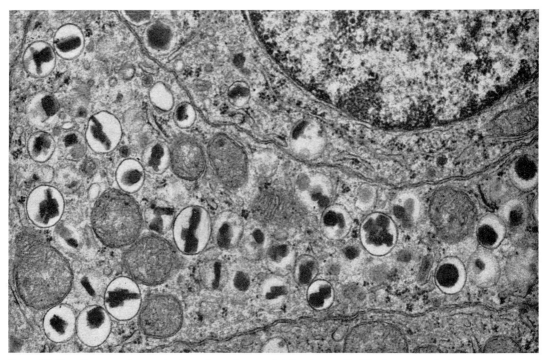

Figure 28-13. Electron micrograph of portions of two adjoining beta cells. The beta granules in man and several other species are membrane bounded spherical vesicles containing dense crystals of varying configuration. × 26,000. (Courtesy of A. Like.)

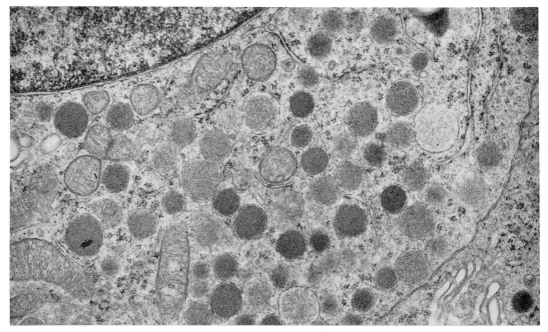

Figure 28-14. Electron micrograph of a portion of a delta cell. The granules are homogeneous and tend to fill their limiting membrane, but they vary considerably in density. It is not clear whether these cells represent a distinct type or are altered alpha cells. × 21,000. (Courtesy of A. Like.)

rangement of amino acids has been determined. It has a calculated molecular weight of 5734, but molecules of this weight tend to polymerize to give determined molecular weights of 12,000 and multiples thereof. By combining insulin with protamine a preparation is obtained that is effective over a longer period of time after injection.

Insulin increases the uptake of glucose by cells and favors the conversion of glucose to glycogen. In the absence of insulin the blood sugar rises and glycogen stores in the liver and other tissues are depleted. In the presence of an excess of insulin the blood sugar is rapidly lowered, and convulsions and death may ensue if the effect is not counteracted by administration of sugar.

Insulin is a product of the beta cells of the islets of Langerhans. In patients with diabetes these cells are damaged or lacking. Diabetes can be produced in animals by administration of *alloxan*, which causes more or less selective damage to the beta cells. In patients with tumors of the pancreas composed mainly of beta cells, the blood sugar may be very low. The symptoms of hypoglycemia may be relieved by surgical removal of the tumor.

Although nerves are involved in the secretory activity of the exocrine pancreas, the secretion of insulin appears to depend upon humoral factors. Denervated or grafted pancreas releases insulin normally in response to variations in the level of blood glucose.

Curiously enough, the islets of Langer-

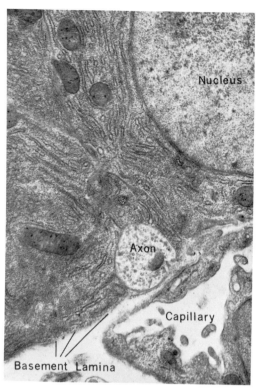

Figure 28-16. Electron micrograph of a nerve axon between the bases of two neighboring pancreatic acinar cells from bat. The axon contains "synaptic vesicles" and lies within the basal lamina of the acini. × 10,000.

hans also secrete a hormone, *glucagon*, which has an effect opposite to that of insulin. Administration of glucagon results in breakdown of liver glycogen and an elevation in the concentration of glucose in the blood. The hormone is believed to be a product of the alpha cells. Administration of cobalt chloride causes varying degrees of destruction of the alpha cells, and the amount of extractable glucagon is then diminished. In comparative studies on different species the amount of glucagon extractable from the pancreas is correlated with the relative abundance of alpha cells.

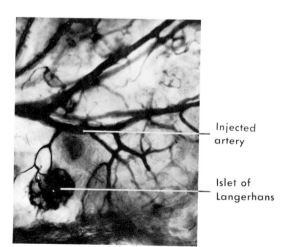

Figure 28-15. Photomicrograph of a vascular injection of pancreas of guinea pig showing blood supply to an islet of Langerhans. From a preparation of R. R. Bensley. × 95.

REFERENCES

Banting, F. G., and C. H. Best: The internal secretion of the pancreas. J. Lab. & Clin. Med., 7:251, 1922.

Baum, J., B. E. Simmons, R. H. Unger, and L. L. Madison: Localization of glucagon in the alpha cells in the pancreatic islet by immunofluorescent techniques. Diabetes, 11:371, 1962.

Beams, H. W.: Golgi apparatus, canalicular apparatus, vacuome, and mitochondria in the islets of Langerhans of the albino rat. Anat. Rec., 46:305, 1930.

Benscome, S. A., R. A. Allen, and H. Latta: Functioning pancreatic islet cell tumors studied electron microscopically. Am. J. Path., *42:*1, 1963.

Benscome, S. A., and D. C. Pease: Electron microscopy of the pancreatic islets. Endocrinol., *63:*1, 1958.

Bensley, R. R.: Studies on the pancreas of the guinea pig. Am. J. Anat., *12:*297, 1911.

Bensley, S. H., and C. A. Woerner: The effects of continuous intravenous injection of an extract of the alpha cells of the guinea pig pancreas on the intact guinea pig. Anat. Rec., *72:*413, 1938.

Björkman, N., C. Hellerström, B. Hellman, and B. Petersson: The cell types in the endocrine pancreas of the human fetus. Zeitschr. f. Zellforsch., *72:*425, 1966.

Bloom, W.: A new type of granular cell in the islets of Langerhans of man. Anat. Rec., *49:*363, 1931.

Caramia, G., B. L. Munger, and P. E. Lacy: The ultrastructural basis for the identification of cell types in the pancreatic islets. I. Guinea pig. Zeitschr. f. Zellforsch., *67:*533, 1965.

Caro, L. G., and G. E. Palade: Protein synthesis, storage and discharge in the pancreatic exocrine cell: An autoradiographic study. J. Cell Biol., *20:*4, 1964.

de Duve, C.: Glucagon; the hyperglycaemic glycogenolytic factor of the pancreas. Lancet, *2:*99, 1953.

Dunn, S. J., H. L. Sheehan, and N. G. B. McLetchie: Necrosis of islets of Langerhans produced experimentally. Lancet, *1:*484, 1943.

Ekholm, R., T. Zelander, and Y. Edlung: The ultrastructural organization of the rat exocrine pancreas. J. Ultrastruct. Res., *7:* 61, 1962.

Gomori, G.: Observations with differential stains on human islets of Langerhans. Am. J. Path., *17:*395, 1941.

Gomori, G.: Pathology of the pancreatic islets. Arch. Path., *36:*217, 1943.

Grossman, M. I.: Nervous and hormonal regulation of pancreatic secretion. *In* de Reuck, A. V. S., and M. P. Cameron, eds.: The Exocrine Pancreas. Ciba Foundation Symposium. Boston, Little, Brown & Co., 1961, p. 220.

Ichikawa, A.: Fine structural changes in response to hormonal stimulation of the perfused canine pancreas. J. Cell Biol., *24:*369, 1965.

Lacy, P. E.: Electron microscopy of the islets of Langerhans. Diabetes, *11:*509, 1962.

Laguesse, E.: Le pancréas: La glande ancienne ou exocrine. Rev. Gén. d'Histol., *1:* fasc. 5, 1906.

Laguesse, E.: Le pancréas: La glande nouvelle ou endocrine. Rev. Gén. d'Histol., *2:* fasc. 5, 1906.

Lane, M. A.: The cytological characters of the areas of Langerhans. Am. J. Anat., *7:*409, 1907.

Latta, J. S., and H. T. Harvey: Changes in the islets of Langerhans of the albino rat induced by insulin administration. Anat. Rec., *82:*281, 1942.

Lazarow, A.: Protection against alloxan diabetes. Anat. Rec., *97:*37, 1947.

Lazarow, A.: Cell types of the islets of Langerhans and the hormones they produce. Diabetes, *6:*22, 1957.

Like, A. A.: The ultrastructure of the islets of Langerhans in man. Lab. Invest., *16:* 937, 1967.

Munger, B. L., F. Caramia, and P. E. Lacy: The ultrastructural basis for the identification of cell types in the pancreatic islets. II. Rabbit, dog, and opossum. Zeitschr. f. Zellforsch., *67:*776, 1965.

Palade, G. E., P. Siekewitz, and L. G. Caro: Structure, chemistry and function of the pancreatic exocrine cell. *In* de Reuck, A. V. S., and M. P. Cameron, eds.: The Exocrine Pancreas. Ciba Foundation Symposium. Boston, Little, Brown & Co., 1961.

Robb, P.: The development of the islets of Langerhans in the human fetus. Quart. J. Exper. Physiol., *46:*335, 1961.

Sanger, F., and E. O. P. Thompson: Amino-acid sequence in the glycyl chain of insulin. Biochem. J., *53:*353, 1953.

Sanger, F., and H. Tuppy: Amino-acid sequence in the phenylalanyl chain of insulin. Biochem. J., *49:*481, 1951.

Sjöstrand, F. S.: The fine structure of the exocrine pancreas cells. *In* de Reuck, A. V. S., and M. P. Cameron, eds.: The Exocrine Pancreas. Ciba Foundation Symposium. Boston, Little, Brown & Co., 1961, p. 1.

Sjöstrand, F. S., and V. Hanzon: Ultrastructure of Golgi apparatus of exocrine cells of mouse pancreas. Exper. Cell Res., *7:*415, 1954.

Soskin, S., and R. Levine: Carbohydrate Metabolism. 2nd ed. Chicago, University of Chicago Press, 1952.

Staub, A., L. Sinn, and O. K. Behrens: Purification and crystallization of glucagon. J. Biol. Chem., *214:*619, 1955.

Thomas, T. B.: Cellular components of the mammalian islets of Langerhans. Am. J. Anat., *62:*31, 1937.

Thompson, E. O. P.: The insulin molecule. Scientific American, *192:*36, 1955.

Warren, S., and P. M. LeCompte: The Pathology of Diabetes Mellitus. 3rd ed. Philadelphia, Lea & Febiger, 1952.

Zimmermann, K. W.: Die Speicheldrüsen der Mundhöhle und die Bauchspeicheldrüse. *In* von Möllendorff, W., and W. Bargmann, eds.: Handbuch der mikroskopischen Anatomie des Menschen. Berlin, Julius Springer, 1927, Vol. 5, part 1, p. 61.

CHAPTER TWENTY-NINE

Respiratory System

To maintain their metabolic processes, higher animals require molecular oxygen. The respiratory system provides for the intake of oxygen and the elimination of carbon dioxide, which are transported to and from the tissues of the body by the circulatory system. The respiratory tract may be divided into the *conducting* and the *respiratory portions*. The former comprises the air conducting tubes that connect the exterior of the body with that portion of the lungs where the exchange of gases between blood and the air takes place. These tubes are the passages of the *nose*, the *pharynx*, the *larynx*, and the *trachea*, and the *bronchi* of various sizes. At the ends of the smallest branches of the air conducting passages is the respiratory portion of the lungs, formed by many small air filled vesicles called *alveolar sacs* and *alveoli*. In addition to its function in respiration, the pharynx serves as part of the alimentary tract connecting the mouth with the esophagus. The larynx also contains the organ of phonation.

THE NOSE

The nose is a hollow organ composed of bone, cartilage, muscles, and connective tissue. Its skin is provided with unusually large sebaceous glands and small hairs. The integument continues through the anterior nares into the vestibule of the nose. The epithelium here is stratified squamous, and there are stiff hairs that are believed to help in excluding particles of dust from the inspired air. The remainder of the nasal cavity is lined with mucus-secreting, pseudostratified ciliated epithelium and with a highly specialized form of ciliated epithelium in the olfactory sensory area.

The ciliated columnar epithelium is like that of the larynx and trachea in having goblet cells richly interspersed among the ciliated cells. A basement lamina separates the epithelium from the underlying connective tissue layer with its mixed mucous glands. The mucus from these glands keeps the lining of the nasal cavity moist. Beneath the epithelium of the lower nasal conchae are rich venous plexuses, which serve to warm the air passing through the nose. The tissue containing these plexuses is capable of considerable engorgement but differs from erectile tissue by the absence of septa containing smooth muscle.

Lymphocytes and other leukocytes migrating through the epithelium, and collections of lymphatic tissue beneath it, are characteristic features of the respiratory epithelium of the nose, especially near the nasopharynx.

The inspired air passes from the nasal cavity by way of the nasopharynx and pharynx to the larynx. The nasal part of the pharynx is lined by ciliated columnar epithelium. In its oral part it is lined by stratified squamous epithelium, which is continuous with that of the mouth above and the esophagus below. The structure of the pharynx is described on page 526.

THE ORGAN OF OLFACTION. The receptors for the sense of smell are located in the *olfactory epithelium*. In fresh condition it is yellowish brown in contrast to the surrounding pink mucous membrane. The olfactory area extends from the middle of the roof of the nasal cavity some 8 to 10 mm. downward on

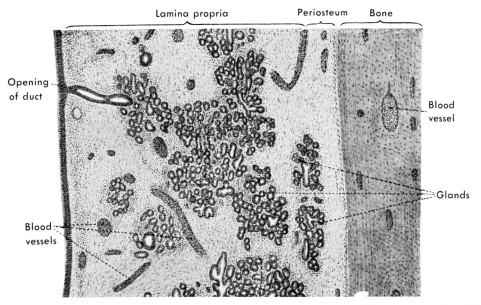

Figure 29-1.   Section of respiratory mucosa of osseous portion of nose of a 22 year old man. × 45. (After Sobotta.)

each side of the septum and on the surface of the upper nasal conchae. The total surface of these areas on both sides is about 500 sq. mm. The outlines of the olfactory area are irregular.

The olfactory epithelium is a tall pseudo-stratified columnar epithelium about 60 μ thick. It consists of three kinds of cells: supporting cells, basal cells, and olfactory cells.

The *supporting cells* were traditionally described as tall, slender elements with an axial bundle of tonofibrils and a prominent "cuticular plate" immediately beneath the free surface, inserting at either side into a prominent "terminal bar." In electron micrographs these specializations are found to be a typical terminal web continuous with the zonula adherens of a well developed junctional complex that attaches the supporting cells to the adjacent sensory cells. The free surface of the cell bears numerous long slender microvilli that project into the overlying blanket of mucus. There is a small Golgi complex in the apical cytoplasm, and pigment granules that are responsible for the brown color of the olfactory area. In some species the supporting cells are secretory and contain numerous mucigen granules in the apical cytoplasm.

Between the bases of the supporting cells, the *basal cells* form a single layer of small conical elements with dark nuclei and branching processes.

The *olfactory cells,* evenly distributed between the supporting cells, are bipolar nerve cells. Their round nuclei occupy a zone between the nuclei of the supporting cells and the connective tissue. The apical portion of the cell, a modified dendrite, extends as a cylindrical process from the nucleus to the surface of the epithelium. The proximal end tapers into a thin, smooth filament about 1 μ thick. This is an axon—a fiber of the olfactory nerve. It passes into the connective tissue and, with similar fibers, forms small nerve bundles. These are collected into about 20 macroscopically visible *fila olfactoria.*

The cytoplasm of the olfactory cell contains a network of neurofibrils, which are especially distinct around the nucleus. The olfactory cell may be slightly constricted at the level of its junctional complexes with the neighboring supporting cells. Distal to this the bulbous head of the olfactory cell dendrite projects above the general surface of the epithelium (Fig. 29-6). This portion is sometimes called the *olfactory vesicle.* Radiating from its surface are six to eight olfactory cilia originating from basal bodies set in an ectoplasmic superficial layer of cytoplasm having the character of a terminal web. These olfactory cilia are for the most part nonmotile and extremely long. In the frog, where they have been studied in some detail with the electron microscope, they attain lengths of 150 to 200 μ. They have an atypical structure. The proximal segment of the ciliary shaft is about 250 mμ in diameter and contains the usual 9 + 2 arrangement of longitudinal fibrils. A few microns from their base there is an abrupt narrowing of the shaft to about 150 mμ. This slender portion of the shaft continues to the tip of the cilium, comprising some 80 per cent of its overall length. In this segment the axial filaments are 11 singlets instead of the usual two singlets and nine doublets. These slender distal segments of the olfactory cilia course parallel to the surface of the epithelium embedded within a thick layer of mucus but with their tips near its surface. On the basis of the anatomical and physiological evidence now available, these specialized cilia appear to be the component of the sense organ that is excited by contact with odorous substances.

The unmyelinated fibers of the olfactory nerve are kept together by a delicate connective tissue rich in macrophages. The fila olfactoria pass through openings of the cribriform plate of the ethmoid bone and enter the olfactory bulb of the brain, where the primary olfactory center is located. The olfactory mucous membrane is also provided with myelinated nerve fibers originating from the trigeminal nerve. After losing their myelin

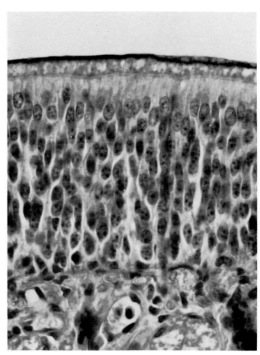

Figure 29-3. Photomicrograph of a celloidin embedded section of mammalian olfactory epithelium. Masson stain. × 475.

they enter the epithelium and end with fine arborizations under its free surface between the supporting cells. These endings are receptors for stimuli other than odors.

The lamina propria of the olfactory mucous membrane is fused with the periosteum. Among its cells are numerous pigment cells and some lymphoid cells that migrate into the epithelium.

Beneath the epithelium the lamina propria contains a rich plexus of blood capillaries. In its deeper layers it contains a plexus of large veins and dense networks of lymph capillaries. The latter continue into large lymphatics, which course toward the lymph nodes on either side of the head. A colored mass injected into the subarachnoid spaces of the brain can penetrate into the lymph capillaries of the olfactory region as well as into the sheaths of the fila olfactoria. This indicates a possible pathway for infections to spread from the nasal mucous membrane to the meninges.

The lamina propria in the olfactory area contains the branched, tubuloalveolar *olfactory glands* of Bowman. The secretory portions are mainly parallel to the surface, whereas the

Olfactory
fibers   Vein   Opening of gland to surface

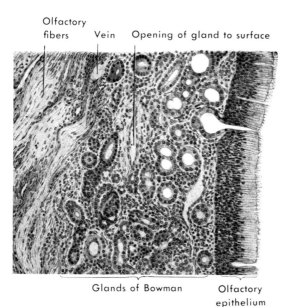

Glands of Bowman   Olfactory
epithelium

Figure 29-2. Cross section of olfactory mucous membrane on the medial surface of the middle concha, from a man. × 70. (After Schaffer.)

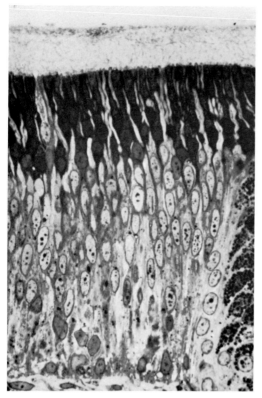

Figure 29-4. Photomicrograph of an araldite embedded section of olfactory epithelium from a frog. The slender, lighter-staining cells that extend to the surface of the epithelium are the olfactory rods of the bipolar receptor cells. The darker cells making up the bulk of the upper third of the pseudostratified epithelium are sustentacular cells. At the lower right is a portion of a gland of Bowman. Toluidine blue stain. × 600. (After T. Reese, J. Cell Biol., *25:*209, 1965.)

narrow duct assumes a perpendicular course and opens on the surface. Immediately under the epithelium the duct is often considerably enlarged. The low pyramidal cells of the secretory portions are serous, containing secretory granules.

Histophysiology. The olfactory stimuli are probably of chemical nature. The secretion of the glands of Bowman keeps the surface of the olfactory epithelium moist and furnishes the necessary solvent. As most odoriferous substances are much more soluble in lipids than in water, and as the olfactory cells and their cilia contain a considerable amount of lipids, odoriferous substances, even if present in extreme dilution, may presumably become concentrated in the membranes of these structures. The continuous stream of the secretion of the olfactory glands, by removing the remains of the stimulating substances, keeps the receptors ready for new stimuli. In this respect the olfactory glands doubtless have a function similar to that of the glands connected with the taste buds.

The olfactory epithelium in man is easily affected by inflammation of the mucous membrane of the nose and is often more or less altered and replaced by atypical epithelium.

Histogenesis. The olfactory region appears in the embryo a little later than the primordia of the eye and ear. In embryos of 4.9 mm. it is a paired, thickened, ectodermal area at the anterior edge of the medullary plate. The plate is later gradually invaginated and recedes from the surface. Some of the

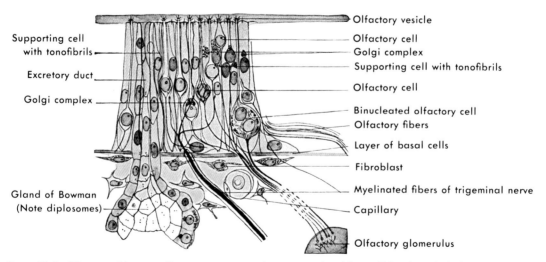

Figure 29-5. Diagram of human olfactory mucous membrane as analyzed by traditional cytological methods. (After Kolmer.)

epithelial cells are transformed into olfactory elements, which send out axons growing toward the anterior part of the brain vesicle.

PARANASAL SINUSES. Connected with the nasal cavity, and forming cavities in the respective bones, are the frontal, ethmoidal, sphenoidal, and maxillary sinuses—the *accessory sinuses of the nose*. They are lined with ciliated epithelium similar to that of the nasal cavity but containing fewer and smaller glands. The cilia beat so as to move the blanket of mucus toward the nasal cavity. The mucosa of all the sinuses is delicate and cannot be differentiated as a separate layer from the periosteum of the bones, to which it is usually tightly adherent.

THE LARYNX

The larynx is an elongated, irregularly tubelike structure, whose walls contain hyaline and elastic cartilages, connective tissue, striated muscles, and a mucous membrane with associated glands. It serves to connect the pharynx with the trachea. As a result of changes in its shape resulting from the contraction of its muscles, it produces variations in the opening between the vocal cords. The size of this opening and the degree of muscular tension determine the pitch of the sounds made by the passage of air through the larynx.

The framework of the larynx is made of several cartilages. Of these the thyroid and cricoid cartilages and the epiglottis are unpaired, whereas the arytenoid, corniculate, and cuneiform are paired. The thyroid and cricoid and the lower parts of the arytenoids are hyaline cartilages. The *extrinsic muscles* of the larynx connect it with surrounding muscles and ligaments and facilitate deglutition. The *intrinsic muscles* connect the cartilages of the larynx; by their contraction they give different shapes to the laryngeal cavity and thus play a role in phonation.

The anterior surface of the *epiglottis* and the upper half of its posterior surface, the *aryepiglottic folds,* and the *vocal cords* are covered with stratified squamous epithelium. In the adult, ciliated epithelium usually begins at the base of the epiglottis and extends down the larynx, trachea, and bronchi.

The cilia are 3.5 to 5 μ long and beat toward the mouth; thus they move foreign particles, bacteria, and mucus from the lungs

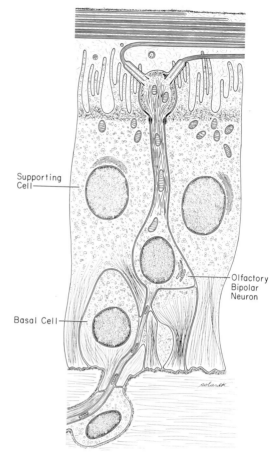

Figure 29-6. Diagrammatic representation of the essential features of the olfactory epithelium based upon electron microscopic studies. The height of the epithelium has been foreshortened. The vertical lines in the rod or dendrite of the olfactory bipolar neuron represent neurotubules (microtubules).

toward the exterior of the body. Cilia have been seen to beat after death for 50 to 70 hours.

Goblet cells in varying numbers are scattered between the cylindrical cells. The glands of the larynx are of the tubuloacinous, mixed mucous variety. Some of the ducts also secrete mucus. The alveoli secrete mucus and may have serous crescents. A few taste buds are scattered on the undersurface of the epiglottis.

The *true vocal cords* contain the vocal or inferior thyroarytenoid ligaments. Each of these (one on each side) consists of a band of elastic tissue bordered on its lateral side by the thyroarytenoid muscle and covered medially by a thin mucous membrane consisting of stratified squamous epithelium. The antero-

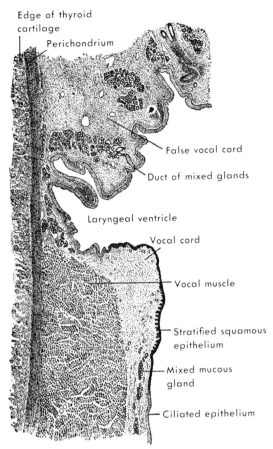

Figure 29-7. Frontal section through the middle of the glottis of a 9 year old boy. × 15. (After von Ebner.)

geal nerve sends sensory nerves, and the inferior laryngeal nerve sends motor nerves, to the larynx.

THE TRACHEA

The trachea is a thin walled, flexible tube about 11 cm. long and 2 to 2.5 cm. in diameter. It is continuous with the larynx above and ends below by dividing into the two main bronchi.

The lining of the trachea is ciliated pseudostratified columnar epithelium and rests on a rather thick basement lamina. Numerous goblet cells are scattered throughout the epithelium. The lamina propria contains an abundance of elastic fibers and numerous small glands like those of the larynx. These glands, most of which are external to the elastic fibers, open by short ducts on the free surface of the epithelium. In the posterior portion of the trachea, the glands extend through the muscular layer. Stimulation of the recurrent laryngeal nerve activates secretion in these glands. The lamina propria also contains accumulations of lymphatic tissue.

The most characteristic feature of the trachea is its supporting framework of 16 to 20 C-shaped hyaline cartilages that encircle it on its ventral and lateral aspects. Because the

posterior dimension of the space between the vocal cords is usually said to be about 23 mm. in men and 18 mm. in women. The shape of this opening between the vocal cords undergoes great variations in the different phases of respiration and in the production of various sounds in talking and singing. Contraction of the thyroarytenoid muscle approximates the arytenoid and thyroid cartilages, and this relaxes the vocal cords.

BLOOD VESSELS, LYMPHATICS, AND NERVES. The larynx is supplied by the upper, middle, and lower laryngeal arteries, which, in turn, arise from the superior and inferior thyroid arteries. The veins from the larynx empty into the thyroid veins. The larynx contains several rich plexuses of lymphatics, which lead into the upper cervical lymph nodes and to those about the trachea. The superior laryn-

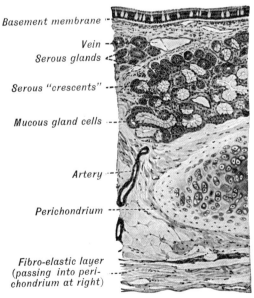

Figure 29-8. Cross section through part of the wall of a human trachea. × 60. (After Braus.)

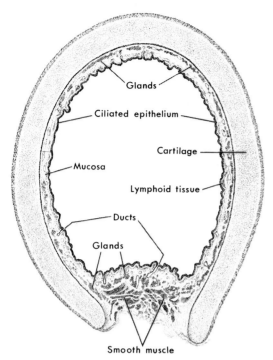

Glands

Ciliated epithelium

Cartilage

Mucosa

Lymphoid tissue

Ducts

Glands

Smooth muscle

Figure 29-9. Cross section through the trachea of a 9 year old boy. × 6. (Redrawn and modified from Kölliker-von Ebner.)

successive incomplete cartilaginous rings are separated by interspaces bridged by fibro-elastic tissue, the tube has much more pliability and extensibility than if they formed a continuous sheet. Some of the cartilages branch obliquely around the trachea. With advancing age they become fibrous, but they do not ossify, as the thyroid cartilage of the larynx often does. They are surrounded by dense connective tissue that contains many elastic and reticular fibers.

The posterior wall of the trachea, adjacent to the esophagus, is devoid of cartilages. Their place is taken by a thick layer of smooth muscle bundles, which, in the main, run transversely. They are inserted into the dense elastic fiber bundles surrounding the tracheal cartilages and are joined to the mucous membrane by a layer of loose connective tissue.

BLOOD VESSELS, LYMPHATICS AND NERVES. A delicate network of lymphatics is found in the mucosa, and a much coarser plexus occurs in the submucosa. These lead into the lymph nodes, which accompany the trachea along its entire length. The arteries for the trachea are mainly from the inferior thyroid. The nerves

supplying the trachea arise from the recurrent branch of the vagus nerve and from the sympathetic. The sympathetic nerves of the trachea contain small ganglia, from which fibers lead to the smooth muscle in its posterior wall. Myelinated sensory nerves are also found.

THE LUNGS

The lungs are paired organs occupying a great part of the thoracic cavity and constantly changing in form with the different phases of respiration. The right lung consists of three lobes and the left lung of two, with each lobe receiving a branch of the primary bronchus of the same side. The outer surface of the lungs is closely invested by a serous membrane, the *visceral pleura.*

In children the lungs, because of their great blood supply, are a pale pink. With advancing age they become gray, owing to accumulation of inhaled carbon particles in phagocytic cells in the connective tissue septa of the lung. This darkening of the lung is especially marked in city dwellers.

Each of the five lobes of the lungs is divided by thin connective tissue septa into great numbers of roughly pyramidal portions of pulmonary tissue, the *lobules.* These are so arranged that the apex of each points toward the hilus, and the base is oriented toward the surface of the lung. These gross lobules are not seen as easily in the adult lung as in the embryonic, except at the surface. The progressive deposition of carbon under the pleura from the inspired air marks the outlines of these lobules distinctly. Each lobule is supplied by a small bronchiole.

BRONCHIAL TUBES. The trachea divides into two main branches called the primary bronchi. These enter the substance of the lungs at the hilus, one on each side, and, coursing downward and outward, divide into two smaller bronchi on the left side and three on the right. These give rise to smaller bronchi from which several orders of *bronchioles* originate. With the development of lung surgery, knowledge of the segmental distribution of the secondary bronchi in the lobes has become important. According to Boyden, the right lung is made up of 10 principal bronchopulmonary segments, while the left lung can be divided into eight segments. The basic pattern of the secondary bronchi appears, however, to be subject to considerable variation. It has been

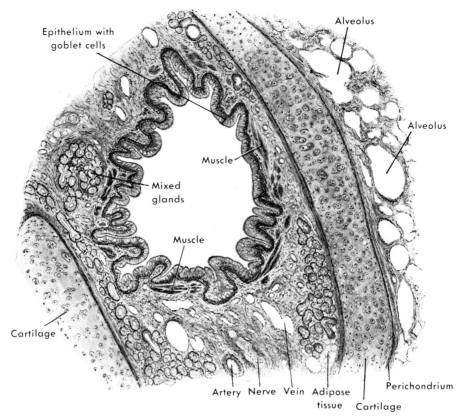

Figure 29-10. Cross section through a small bronchus of a man. × 30. (After Schaffer.)

estimated that there are from 50 to 80 terminal bronchioles in each lobule. Each *terminal bronchiole* continues into one, two, or more *respiratory bronchioles.* These break up into 2 to 11 *alveolar ducts,* from which arise the *alveolar sacs* and *alveoli.* Thus the main successive divisions of the bronchial tree are primary bronchi, secondary bronchi, bronchioles, terminal bronchioles, respiratory bronchioles, alveolar ducts, alveolar sacs, and alveoli. An *atrium* has been described as connecting the alveolar sacs and the alveolar (see p. 638).

Before the bronchi enter the lungs their structure is practically identical with that of the trachea. But as soon as they enter the lungs, the *cartilage rings* disappear and are replaced by irregularly shaped *cartilage plates,* which completely surround the bronchi. As a result, the intrapulmonary bronchi and their branches are cylindrical and not flattened on one side, as are the trachea and the extrapulmonary portions of the bronchi. As the cartilage plates become irregularly distributed around the tube, the muscular layer com-

pletely surrounds the bronchus. The cartilage disappears from the wall when the diameter of the bronchiole reaches about 1 mm.

The innermost layer of the bronchus is a mucous membrane continuous with that of the trachea and lined by the same type of epithelium. The lamina propria consists of a small amount of reticular and collagenous connective tissue and many elastic fibers. It contains a few lymphoid cells and is set off from the epithelium by a prominent basement lamina. The mucosa of the bronchus, in histologic sections, shows a marked longitudinal folding due to the contraction of the smooth muscle in the wall. It is claimed that these folds disappear when the lung is distended.

Next to the mucosa is a layer of smooth muscle fiber bundles, which run around the tube but never form a closed ring as in the blood vessels and intestines. Instead, the muscles form an interlacing feltwork, the meshes of which become larger in the smaller bronchioles. Numerous elastic fibers are intimately associated with the smooth muscle cells. As will be discussed later, the elastic fibers and smooth muscles throughout the lung play an important part in the changes in its volume that occur during respiration. A dense network of blood vessels accompanies and penetrates this myoelastic layer.

The outermost layer of the bronchial wall consists of dense connective tissue, which contains many elastic fibers. It surrounds the plates of cartilage and is continuous with the connective tissue of the surrounding pulmonary tissue and with that accompanying the large vessels.

Mucous and mucoserous glands are found, as in the trachea, as far out in the bronchial tree as the cartilage extends. The glands are usually deep to the muscular layer, through which their ducts penetrate to open on the free surface.

Diffuse lymphatic tissue, often with nodules, occurs regularly in the mucosa and in the fibrous tissue around the cartilage, especially where the bronchi branch.

With the progressive decrease in the size of the bronchi and bronchioles as they proceed from the trachea, the layers of their walls become thinner, and in some of them the elements fuse into a single layer. The smooth muscle, however, is distinct up to the end of the respiratory bronchioles, and even continues in the walls of the alveolar ducts.

Respiratory Structures of the Lungs

The functional *unit* of the lung or *primary lobule* is composed of all the structures beginning with a respiratory bronchiole, including alveolar duct, atria, alveolar sac, and alveoli, with all the associated blood vessels, lymphatics, nerves, and connective tissue. In the newborn, the pulmonary lobule (unit) is small. The respiratory bronchiole has not yet developed, and the alveoli are represented as shallow pouches on the walls of the alveolar ducts (Fig. 29-17A).

In a section of lung the respiratory portion of the organ appears as a lacework of large spaces separated by thin walled septa (Fig. 29-17B). Here and there this lacework is traversed by the thick walled bronchi and arteries and veins of various sizes. But a different picture is seen if a thick section is examined with the binocular microscope. Here the lung appears as an irregular honeycomb in which the polyhedral alveoli and alveolar sacs form

the "cells" (Figs. 29-12 and 29-16). This honeycomb is traversed by the system of bronchioles and the alveolar ducts, into which the atria, alveoli, and alveolar sacs open.

The lungs should be fixed, for histological purposes, either by way of the trachea or by injection through the pulmonary artery, with the lungs still in the body to prevent overdistention. The usual method of dropping a bit of lung into fixing fluid gives a highly distorted picture, for the lung shrinks greatly when the reduced pressure of the pleural cavity is raised and the air in the organ prevents the penetration of the fixative. Some aspects of the structure of this organ may be seen best in sections of 60 to 120 μ thickness. Hematoxylin and eosin staining gives but a poor idea of the architecture of the lung. Special staining and injection methods are necessary for a more complete picture. Furthermore, the lung changes its form continuously with every inspiration and expiration (Fig. 29-26).

RESPIRATORY BRONCHIOLES. In the adult the respiratory bronchioles begin with a diameter of about 0.5 mm. They are short tubes, lined in their first part with a ciliated columnar epithelium devoid of goblet cells. A short distance down the bronchiole, the ciliated columnar epithelium loses its cilia and becomes low cuboidal. These bronchioles have walls composed of collagenous connective tis-

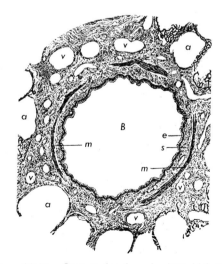

Figure 29-11. Cross section through a bronchiole (*B*) 0.7 mm. in diameter. *a*, Alveoli; *e*, epithelium; *m*, circular muscle; *s*, lamina propria with cross sections of elastic fibers; *v*, veins. Lung fixed by filling it with alcohol. × 55. (After von Ebner.)

sue containing bundles of interlacing smooth muscles and elastic fibers. They lack cartilage. A few alveoli bud off from the side of the respiratory bronchiole opposite that along which the branch of the pulmonary artery runs. A thin continuation of the cuboidal epithelium of the bronchiole extends onto the alveolar wall, according to the observations of Low and Sampaio with the electron microscope. These alveoli are the first of the respiratory structures of the lung and are responsible for the term "respiratory bronchiole." These bronchioles soon branch and radiate into 2 to 11 *alveolar ducts.* They are surrounded by alveoli that have risen from adjacent ducts.

ALVEOLAR DUCTS. The structure of the alveolar ducts is hard to visualize in ordinary histological sections of the distended lung. In thick sections, particularly when studied with the binocular microscope, the alveolar ducts are seen as thin walled tubes. They usually follow a long, tortuous course and give off several branches, which in turn may branch again. They are closely beset with thin walled outpouchings, the alveolar sacs (and single alveoli). These blind polyhedral sacs open only on the surface that faces the alveolar duct. Be-

cause the alveolar sacs are closely packed against one another, their openings occupy the greater part of the wall of the alveolar duct. The wall of the alveolar duct between the mouths of the alveolar sacs is supported by strands of elastic and collagenous fibers and smooth muscle cells. In thin sections of the lung, only small portions of these fibers and muscle are seen. They appear as slight enlargements or knobs parallel to the long axis of the alveolar duct. In thicker sections it becomes evident that these are merely transversely or tangentially cut small portions of the long connective tissue fibers and muscle bundles, which are interwoven in three planes around the mouths of the alveolar sacs.

ALVEOLAR SACS AND ALVEOLI. From the alveolar ducts arise single alveoli and alveolar sacs containing two to four or more alveoli.

It has been suggested that the space between the ends of the alveolar duct and the alveolar sacs be termed the *atrium.* The structures described under this term have not been generally accepted as forming a distinct entity, some authors considering them simply parts of the alveolar ducts.

The alveoli are thin walled polyhedral

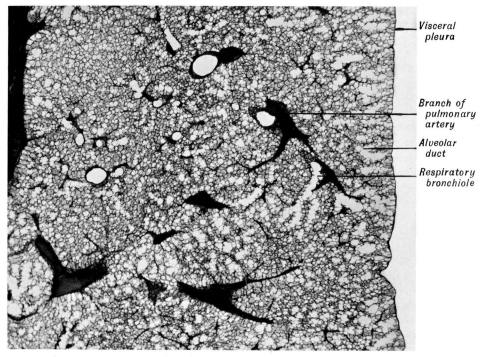

Visceral pleura

Branch of pulmonary artery

Alveolar duct

Respiratory bronchiole

Figure 29-12. Photomicrograph of a thick (120 μ) section of lung of *Macacus rhesus.* × 10.

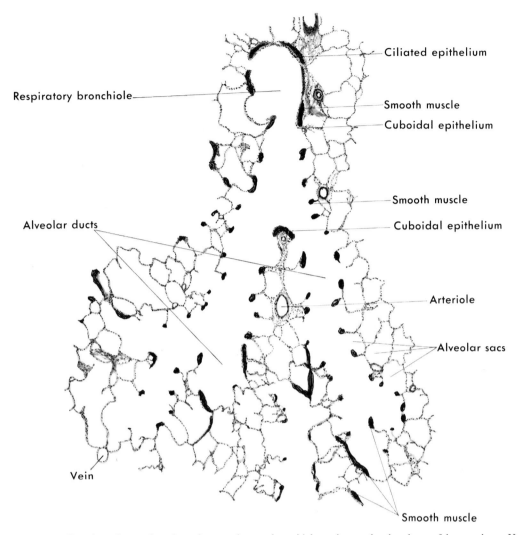

Ciliated epithelium

Respiratory bronchiole

Smooth muscle

Cuboidal epithelium

Smooth muscle

Cuboidal epithelium

Alveolar ducts

Arteriole

Alveolar sacs

Vein

Smooth muscle

Figure 29-13. Drawing of a section through a respiratory bronchiole and two alveolar ducts of human lung. Note the smooth muscle in the walls of the alveolar ducts. (Slightly modified from Baltisberger.)

sacs, one side of which is always lacking. Air may thus diffuse freely from the alveolar ducts into the alveolar sacs and into the cavities of the alveoli. The most conspicuous feature of the alveolar walls is a dense network of capillaries, which anastomose so freely that many of the spaces between them are smaller than the diameters of the vessel lumina (Fig. 29-18). The alveolar walls contain a closely woven network of branching reticular fibers. These, along with the less numerous elastic fibers, form the tenuous supporting framework for the thin-walled air sacs and their numerous capillaries. The capillaries are so situated that they bulge into the alveoli, and the greater portion of their surface is presented to the alveolar air.

The larger reticular and elastic fibers occupy a central position in the interalveolar septa, with the anastomosing capillaries weaving back and forth through the meshes of the fibers to jut first into one and then into the other of the adjacent alveolar spaces. This relationship of supporting fibers to capillaries is best seen in the lung of the newborn, in which the interalveolar septa have a thick, cellular central stroma that becomes more attenuated with advancing age, owing to the thinning and stretching of the alveolar walls.

Small openings called *alveolar pores* are found in the thin wall separating adjacent alveoli. Their presence was detected in sections of lung from a patient with fibrinous

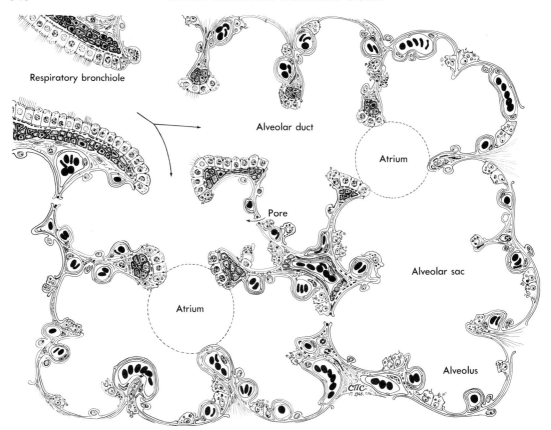

Figure 29-14. Schematic representation of the respiratory unit of the lung: respiratory bronchiole, alveolar ducts, alveolar sacs, and alveoli. The atria indicated by the circles are spaces bounded on one side by the termination of the alveolar duct and on the other by the openings of the alveolar sacs. (Slightly modified after S. Sorokin, *in* R. O. Greep, ed.: Histology. 2nd ed. New York, McGraw-Hill Book Co., 1966.)

pneumonia, in which strands of fibrin could be seen passing through from one alveolus to the other. These minute apertures measure only about 7 to 9 μ in diameter and are found in the openings between capillaries (Fig. 29-18). From one to six may be found in an alveolar septum, and larger numbers have been reported. There is no longer any doubt of their occurrence, but their significance is problematical. They may conceivably provide a collateral air circulation that tends to prevent atelectasis when secondary bronchi become obstructed. They may also be pathways that permit the spread of bacteria from one alveolus to its neighbors in pneumonia.

The mouths of the alveolar sacs are completely surrounded by a wavy wreath of collagenous fibers. These continue from one sac to the next and help to give some substance to the wall of the alveolar duct. These wreaths probably straighten out with deep inspiration. The collagenous fibers are accompanied by elastic fibers. The dense networks of reticular fibers within the walls of the alveoli and alveolar sacs are continuations of these collagenous fibers, which, in turn, merge with the collagenous fibers in the walls of the arteries, veins, and bronchioles. The elastic fibers are likewise continuations of those of the bronchioles.

LINING OF THE ALVEOLI. Throughout several decades of study of the lungs with the light microscope, one of the most controversial problems in histology was that of the structure

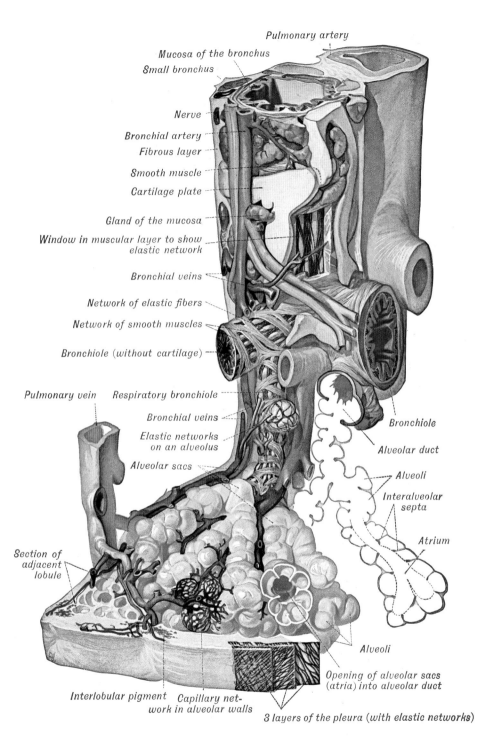

Figure 29-15. Portion of a pulmonary lobule from the lung of a young man. Free reconstruction by Vierling, somewhat foreshortened. Mucosa and glands, green; cartilage, light blue; muscles and bronchial artery, orange; elastic fibers, blue-black; pulmonary artery, red; pulmonary and bronchial veins, dark blue. × 32. (After Braus.)

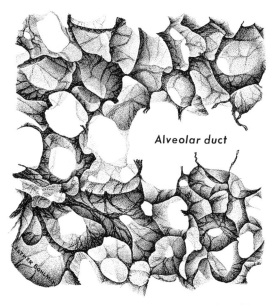

Figure 29-16. Portion of a thick (120 μ) section of lung of *Macacus rhesus* stained with orcein for elastic fibers and light green. Note the honeycomb of alveoli connected with the alveolar duct. × 120.

of the lining of the alveolar wall. All agreed that the respiratory tree in the embryo was lined by continuous epithelium of endodermal origin. According to some histologists, the epithelial lining persisted, but the growth of alveoli in late fetal life and their expansion after birth resulted in an extreme attenuation of those portions of the epithelial cells overlying the capillaries, while the thicker portions of the cells containing the nuclei remained grouped in the meshes of the capillary net. However, the thin film of epithelium presumed to extend over the capillaries was usually not visible with the light microscope, and other histologists insisted that the alveolar lining was discontinuous, with only isolated groups of epithelial cells present between the capillaries, whose walls were believed to be exposed directly to the alveolar air. Still others regarded the alveolar ducts and alveoli as connective tissue spaces entirely devoid of a lining of endodermal origin.

This uncertainty was finally resolved by electron microscopic studies by Low and later by Karrer, which clearly demonstrated that there is a thin continuous cellular covering of the alveoli that is at or just below the limit of visibility with the light microscope (Fig. 29-21). In many places it is as thin as the most attenuated areas of the capillary endothelium.

The alveolar epithelium is separated from the endothelium by a continuous basement lamina. In addition to the squamous *pulmonary epithelial cells* (small alveolar cells), there are numerous rounded or cuboidal cells in the lining that are called *septal cells* or *alveolar cells* (great alveolar cells).

Pulmonary Epithelial Cells. These extremely thin squamous cells form a more or less continuous outer layer of the alveolar wall, interrupted only by occasional alveolar cells that protrude between them into the air space. The nuclei are flattened and resemble those of endothelial or mesothelial cells. The shapes of the cells are, of course, related to the degree of inflation of the lung and the tension on the interalveolar septa at the time of fixation.

Alveolar or Septal Cells. These cuboidal or rounded elements of the alveolar epithelium are readily visualized with the light microscope. They may occupy niches in the alveolar wall and be mainly deep to the squamous epithelial cells, or they may be so situated in the epithelium that they bulge into the alveolar lumen. They occur singly or in groups of two or three. In electron micrographs they are found to rest on the basal lamina of the epithelium; they possess short microvilli on their free surface and form junctional complexes with neighboring squamous alveolar epithelial cells (Fig. 29-22). They are therefore considered to be part of the epithelium and not merely cells of mesenchymal origin wandering through the epithelium (Sorokin). The Golgi complex is extensive; vesicular and cisternal profiles of granular endoplasmic reticulum are common, and there are abundant free ribosomes in the cytoplasmic matrix. The cell thus has some of the fine structural characteristics of a secretory cell.

The most distinctive cytological feature of the alveolar cell is the presence of numerous dense, osmiophilic bodies 0.2 to 1.0 μ in diameter that have an internal structure consisting of thin parallel or concentric lamellae (Fig. 29-23). These *multilamellar bodies* or *cytosomes* seen in electron micrographs correspond in number and location to the vacuoles observed in these cells in histological sections of paraffin embedded lung tissue. They are limited by a membrane, and their histochemical reactions and solubilities suggest that they are rich in lipid, particularly phospholipid. These bodies are occasionally seen at the free surface of the cell, where they appear to discharge their contents in much the same manner as described for the release of secretory products by various glandular cells. These bodies have recently been the subject of intensive investigation because of the suggestion that they may represent intracellular stores of a surface active material which, upon release, spreads upon the surface of the epithelium, lowering surface tension and tending to stabilize alveolar diameter. Although the circumstantial evidence for this relationship is strong, the material in the multilamellar bodies has not yet been proved to be identical with the surfactant.

ALVEOLAR PHAGOCYTES (DUST CELLS). In practically every section of lung, free phagocytic cells are encountered in the alveoli. When they contain particles of inhaled dust they are sometimes called "dust cells." In certain cardiac diseases attended by pulmonary vascular congestion, they become filled with granules of *hemosiderin* resulting from phagocytosis and degradation of blood pigment. There is no general agreement as to the origin of the alveolar phagocytes. Some investigators claim that they

arise by exfoliation of the alveolar or septal cells; others consider them indistinguishable from macrophages in other parts of the body and trace their origin to hematogenous lymphocytes and monocytes that emigrate from the capillaries.

Low and Sampaio instilled thorium into the trachea of rats and found that the epithelial lining of the alveoli was not phagocytic, but that the alveolar phagocytes took up the label avidly. More recently Ladman and Finley reported uptake of Thorotrast by alveolar cells dislodged from the lungs of dogs. While it may be that the fixed alveolar cells possess a limited capacity for phagocytosis, there is a marked difference between their activity and that of the free alveolar phagocytes. There are also marked differences in cytochemical reactions of the septal cells and free macrophages that suggest that they may be functionally distinct (Sorokin).

In tissue cultures of the lungs and in certain in vivo experiments, inconspicuous cells in the septa mobilize in a few hours and assume

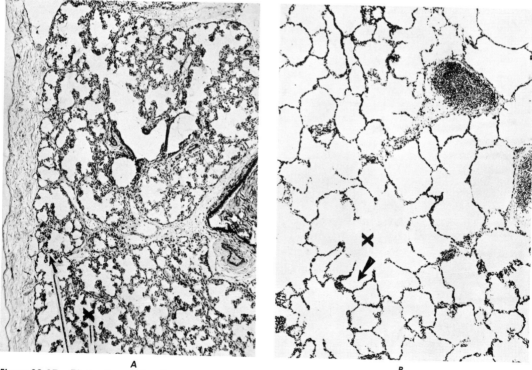

A   B

Figure 29-17. Photomicrographs of section of lung. *A,* Human newborn, and *B,* 12 year old girl. Both specimens fixed immediately after death by the intratracheal injection of Zenker-formol solution. Note increase in size of alveolar ducts (*x*) and alveoli (arrow). Mallory-azan stain. × 82. (Courtesy of C. G. Loosli.)

Alveolar pore   Alveolar capillary

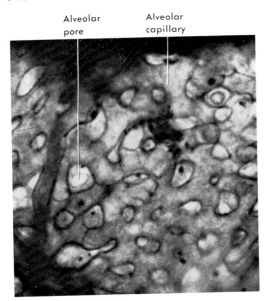

Figure 29-18. Photomicrograph of lung, showing a surface view of an alveolar septum with its close meshed capillary plexus. An alveolar pore is shown in one of the meshes of the capillary net. (After E. R. Weibel, Zeitschr. f. Zellforsch., *57*:648, 1962.)

from the capillaries of the alveolar septa and portions of the alveolar ducts. They run in the intersegmental connective tissue, independently of the arteries, and join to form the pulmonary veins. In passing through the lung, the pulmonary artery is usually above and behind its accompanying bronchial tube, whereas the vein is below and in front of it.

The bronchial arteries and veins are much smaller than the pulmonary vessels. These arteries arise from the aorta or the intercostal arteries and follow the bronchi. They are distributed to the walls of the bronchi, their glands, and the interlobular connective tissue beneath the pleura. Most of the blood carried by the bronchial arteries is brought back by the pulmonary veins. In the alveoli that arise from the respiratory bronchioles, there are

the appearance and function of typical macrophages. Whether these are the alveolar cells in the epithelium is not clear. In acute pneumococcal infections of the lungs of dogs and monkeys, the principal reaction of the "septal cells" appeared to be one of enlargement without detachment from the alveolar walls. No phagocytic properties are observed in them. Under these conditions the chief source of macrophages appears to be hematogenous lymphocytes and monocytes that transform into macrophages after they enter the alveoli early in the disease. Whatever the origin of the alveolar phagocyte, it acts as a typical macrophage in defense of the lung, including the continual removal of dust particles.

BLOOD VESSELS. The lungs receive most of their blood from the pulmonary arteries. These are of large caliber and of elastic type. The branches of these arteries in general accompany the bronchi and their branches as far as the respiratory bronchioles. The arterial paths in the lung, however, are subject to considerable variation. From the respiratory bronchioles they divide, and a branch passes to each alveolar duct and is distributed in a capillary network over all the alveoli that communicate with this duct. The venules arise from the capillaries of the pleura and

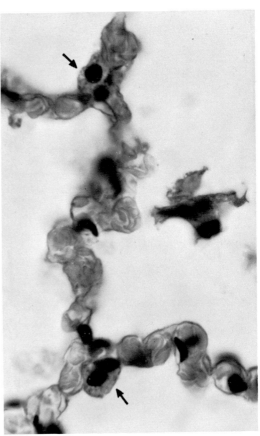

Figure 29-19. Photomicrograph of alveolar wall of lung of 18 year old man. Note the thin membrane between the lumina of the capillaries and the air spaces. Arrows point to "septal cells" or "alveolar cells" in their characteristic location on the alveolar walls. Hematoxylin-eosin-azure II stain. × 1000. (Courtesy of C. G. Loosli.)

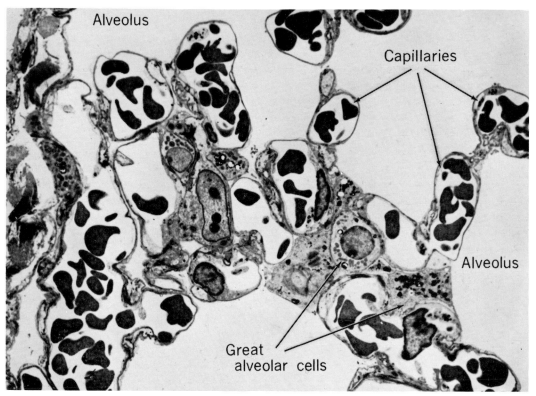

Figure 29-20. Electron micrograph of mouse lung. × 1800. (Courtesy of J. Rhodin.)

capillary anastomoses between the terminations of the pulmonary and the bronchial arteries.

LYMPHATICS. There are two main divisions of the lymphatics of the lungs. One set is in the pleura and the other in the pulmonary tissue. They communicate infrequently. Both drain into the lymph nodes at the hilus of the lung. The lymphatics of the pleura form a dense network with large and small polygonal meshes. The large meshes are formed by large vessels and demarcate the lobules; the small meshwork is formed of smaller vessels that mark out the anatomical units. There are many valves in these lymphatics that control the flow of lymph so that it passes to the hilus and not into the pulmonary tissue. These pleural lymphatics join to form several main trunks, which drain into the lymph nodes at the hilus.

The pulmonary lymphatics may be divided into several groups, which include those of the bronchi, of the pulmonary artery, and of the pulmonary vein. The lymphatics in the bronchi terminate in the alveolar ducts, and their end branches join the lymphatic radicles of the plexuses about the pulmonary artery and vein. There are no lymphatic vessels beyond the alveolar ducts. The pulmonary artery is accompanied and drained by two or three main lymphatic trunks. The lymphatics associated with the pulmonary vein begin with its radicles in the alveolar ducts and in the pleura. All the lymphatics of the pulmonary tissue drain toward the hilar nodes. Efferent trunks from the hilar nodes anastomose to form the right lymphatic duct, which is the principal channel of lymph drainage from both the right and left lungs. There are no valves in the intrapulmonic lymphatics except in a few vessels, in the interlobular connective tissue near the pleura, which accompany the branches of the pulmonary veins. These lymphatic vessels connect the pulmonary and pleural lymphatic plexuses. As their valves point only toward the pleura, they provide a mechanism whereby lymph can flow from the pulmonary tissue into the pleural lymphatics if the normal flow of lymph from the pulmonary tissue toward the hilus is interrupted.

As has been mentioned, the mucous membrane of the bronchi is infiltrated with lymphocytes and often contains lymphatic follicles. There are other accumulations of lymphatic tissue in the adventitia of the pulmonary arteries and veins, but these, as a rule, do not form nodules in the normal lung.

NERVES. The pulmonary plexuses at the root of the lung are formed by branches of the vagus and from the thoracic sympathetic ganglia. The bronchoconstrictor fibers are from the vagus nerve, while the bronchodilator fibers are from the sympathetic and arise mainly from the inferior cervical and first thoracic ganglia. The pulmonary vessels are supplied with both sympathetic and parasympathetic nerve fibers. The effect of these fibers on the vessels is not understood, as the experimental evidence is contradictory. The sympathetic fibers act as vasoconstrictors for the bronchial arteries.

THE PLEURA. The cavities containing the lungs are lined by a serous membrane, the *pleura,* which consists of a thin layer of collagenous tissue containing some fibroblasts and macrophages and several prominent layers of elastic fibers running at various angles to the outer surface. It is covered by a layer of mesothelial cells like those of the peritoneum. The layer lining the wall of the thoracic cavity is called the *parietal pleura;* that reflected over the surface of the lungs is known as the *visceral pleura.* A prominent feature of the pleura is the great number of blood capillaries and lymphatic vessels distributed in it. The few nerves of the parietal pleura are connected with the phrenic and intercostal nerves. The nerves to the visceral pleura are believed to be branches of the vagus and of the sympathetic nerves supplying the bronchi.

HISTOGENESIS. The lung arises in the embryo as a median diverticulum of the foregut caudal to the bronchial clefts. Its prenatal growth can be divided into three periods: glandular, canalicular, and alveolar (Loosli

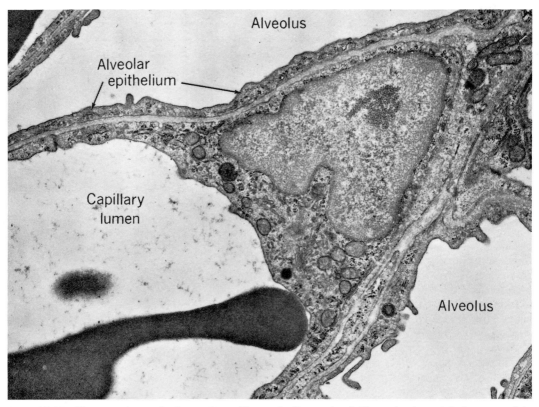

Figure 29-21. Electron micrograph of part of a capillary and adjacent alveoli, illustrating (*upper left*) the nature of the alveolocapillary membrane or blood-air barrier, which consists of three layers: the alveolar epithelium, an interstitial space occupied by a basement lamina, and the capillary endothelium. × 20,500. (Courtesy of E. R. Weibel.)

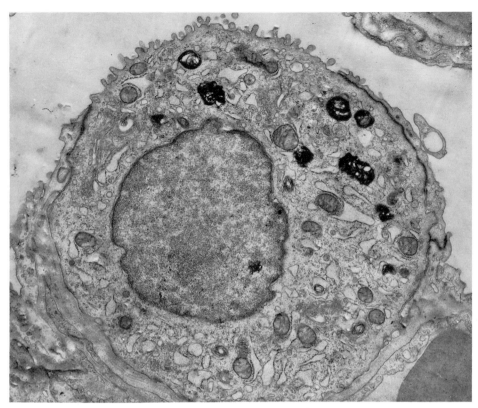

Figure 29-22. An alveolar cell from opossum lung. Notice the short microvilli on its free surface and its junctional complexes with the thin alveolar epithelial cells that partially cover its sides. A Golgi complex and numerous dilated cisternae of granular endoplasmic reticulum can be seen in its cytoplasm. (After S. Sorokin, J. Histochem. & Cytochem., *14*:834, 1966.)

and Potter). The diverticulum growing caudally is this primordium of the trachea, and it divides into right and left branches representing the primary bronchi. These rapidly elongate and branch dichotomously during the second to sixth week of gestation to produce several successive generations of hollow tubules lined with columnar epithelial cells. These tubules grow into a highly cellular mesenchyme in such a way as to resemble a glandular organ. From 16 to 23 generations of bronchial branches are formed during fetal life, and no new terminal bronchioles are formed after birth. Thus the air conducting portion of the respiratory tract completes its branching phase of growth quite early in intrauterine life. The branching of the pulmonary arteries that accompany the bronchial tree also appears to occur in this same period.

During the canalicular period of development, from the fourth to the seventh month, there is a more rapid growth of the mesen-

chymal tissue associated with the peripheral portions of the bronchial tree. Connective tissue cells and fibrils become prominent and an extensive system of capillaries develops. The capillaries are closely associated with air channels in a manner not unlike their relation to the respiratory membrane in the adult. No alveoli are present at this stage.

The alveolar stage of development occupies the period from 6½ months to full term. The lung loses its glandular character and becomes increasingly vascular. The bulbous expansions at the ends of the bronchial tree branch further, and alveoli arise as shallow evaginations from the sides of the channel walls. The connective tissue fibers become distributed around the alveolar openings. The epithelium becomes attenuated, and the capillaries establish a close relation to walls of the future respiratory surface.

The majority of investigators consider the initial respiratory air spaces to be alveoli

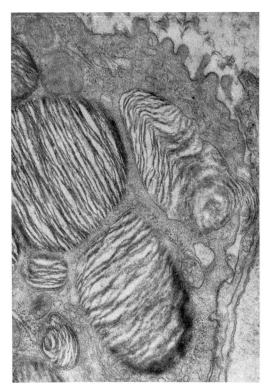

Figure 29-23. Several dense lamellar bodies in an alveolar cell of mouse lung. One at the right is apparently releasing some of its content into the lumen. × 37,500. (After K. Hatasa and T. Nakamura, Zeitschr. f. Zellforsch., *68:*266, 1965.)

similar in size to those seen in the adult lung. In man it would seem that these saccular spaces correspond more correctly to alveolar ducts and that definitive alveoli are absent. At term, the alveoli are shallow indentations on the respiratory channels. According to Dubreuil and coworkers, the adult type of respiratory unit does not become apparent until several years after birth. One has only to compare (in Fig. 29-17) the inflated lung of the newborn with the expanded lung of a 12 year old to note the marked increase in size of the alveolar ducts and the alveoli. Whether growth of the lung takes place only by an increase in size and distention of existing ducts and alveoli, or also by some other process, needs further study.

　　Results on postnatal growth of the human lung are conflicting; some workers report that no new pulmonary acini develop after birth, while others conclude that there is a rapid and steady increase in the number of alveoli in early childhood. It seems likely that the respiratory portion of the lung grows mainly by enlargement in length and width of respiratory bronchioles, alveolar ducts, alveolar sacs, and alveoli, rather than by increased numbers of these structures (Loosli and Potter).

　　REPAIR OF THE LUNG. The lung is frequently the seat of inflammatory conditions that leave it unimpaired on healing. In certain infections, however, notably tuberculosis, large masses of pulmonary tissues are destroyed. In this case healing is always attended by connective tissue scar formation. There is no evidence to show that the pulmonary tissue can regenerate after destruction.

　　HISTOPHYSIOLOGY. The primary function of the lungs is to serve as a means for the assimilation of oxygen from the air and for the removal of carbon dioxide from the body. The network of blood capillaries in the wall of the air sacs is separated from the air by a thin, moist membrane, which permits the

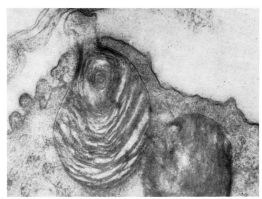

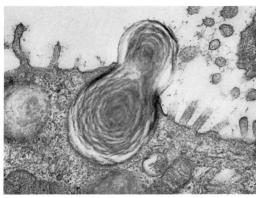

Figure 29-24. Lamellar bodies in mouse alveolar cells apparently in the process of being secreted in much the same manner as that described for merocrine secretions in the pancreas and other glands. × 37,500. (After K. Hatasa and T. Nakamura, Zeitschr. f. Zellforsch., *68:*266, 1965.)

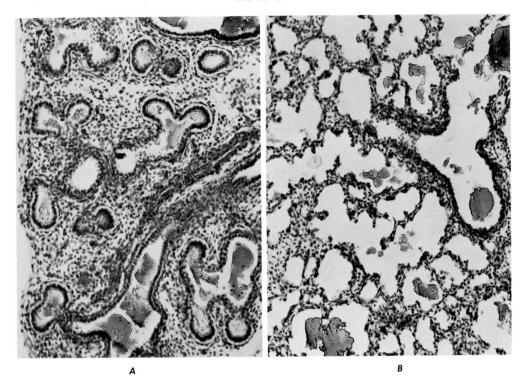

A   B

Figure 29-25. Photomicrographs of section of lung. *A,* Of 147 gm. (4 month) fetus, and *B,* of a 440 gm. (6½ month) fetus. Both specimens show Thorotrast aspirated by intrauterine respirations. Although fetal respiration is considered by some to be normal, the majority now believe it occurs only in fetal distress. The lung of the 6½ month fetus was expanded by extrauterine respiration. Note change in character of lung structure from glandular type (previable) to respiratory type (viable). Respiratory portion of lung of older fetus consists essentially of alveolar ducts; alveoli are absent or are represented only by shallow indentations on duct walls. Hematoxylin and eosin. × 45 (After Davis and Potter.)

ready diffusion of oxygen into the blood and carbon dioxide out of it. The exchange of gases between blood and inspired air takes place across a barrier consisting of three layers: the thin epithelium, the basement lamina, and the capillary endothelium. The movement of the gases is considered to be by a process of passive diffusion, except that the liberation of carbon dioxide from carbonic acid is now known to be greatly accelerated by *carbonic anhydrase.*

The capillaries in the respiratory portions of the human lung are estimated to have a surface area of 140 square meters. The lung also eliminates approximately 800 ml. of water a day in the expired air. Under abnormal conditions it may also remove certain other substances from the blood, such as alcohol.

The lung has a large margin of reserve; that is, the body at rest uses but a small portion —about one twentieth—of the pulmonary aerating surface.

The alveoli probably change but little during inspiration, and the flow of blood is actually faster then. It appears more and more likely that the great increase in the volume of the lungs in inspiration takes place mainly through a great distention of the alveolar ducts, but the smaller bronchi and bronchioles also distend with inspiration.

The pressure within the lung is that of the atmosphere. The lungs are maintained in a partially distended condition by the reduced pressure of the potential space between the two layers of the pleura. An increase in the size of the thorax, such as occurs with every inspiration, still further decreases pressure in the pleural cavity; consequently the lung sucks in more air and becomes larger, and its elastic and reticular fibers are put under still greater tension. This is a purely passive activity on the part of the lung. In expiration, as the thoracic cavity becomes smaller, the pressure in the pleural cavity rises slightly (although it is still below atmospheric pressure). This decreases the tension on the elastic and reticular fibers, and they recoil, pulling the lung into a more

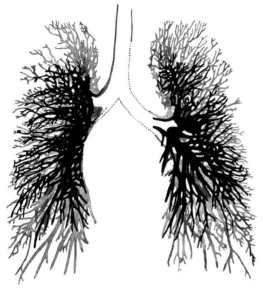

Figure 29-26. Tracings from x-ray shadows of human lungs in deep inspiration (gray) and forced expiration (black). (Redrawn and slightly modified from Macklin.)

contracted state and thus forcing some of the air out of it. It is probable that the smooth muscles of the alveolar ducts and the bronchioles also help force the air out of the lung by their contraction.

When the pleural cavity on one side is connected with the outside air, either by accident or by surgical intervention, the pressure in the lungs and in the pleural cavity become equalized at that of the atmosphere. The lung then collapses immediately, because the force that normally opposes the contraction of its elastic elements has been removed. This condition is known as *pneumothorax*. Such a lung remains collapsed until pressure in the pleural cavity is reduced by absorption of the air contained in it.

With each inspiration the descent of the diaphragm enables the bronchi in the lower lobes of the lungs to extend. Because the main bronchi are not fixed in the thorax but descend on inspiration, a mechanism is provided whereby the bronchi of the upper lobes of the lungs extend at the same time.

REFERENCES

Adams, F. H.: Fetal and neonatal cardiovascular and pulmonary function. Annual Rev. Physiol., 27:257, 1965.

Adams, F. H.: Functional development of the fetal lung. J. Pediat., 68:794, 1966.

Avery, M. E.: The alveolar lining layer. A review of studies on its role in pulmonary mechanics and in pathogenesis of atelectasis. Pediatrics, 30:324, 1962.

Avery, M. E., and J. Mead: Surface properties in relation to atelectasis and hyaline membrane disease. Am. J. Dis. Child., 97:517, 1959.

Bargmann, W.: Die Lungenalveole. In von Möllendorff, W., and W. Bargmann, eds.: Handbuch der mikroskopischen Anatomie des Menschen. Berlin, Julius Springer, 1936, Vol. 5, part 3, p. 799.

Bertalanffy, F. D.: Respiratory tissue: Structure, histophysiology and cytodynamics. Int. Rev. Cytol., 16:233, 1964.

Beusch, L., K. Schaefer, and M. E. Avery: Granular pneumonocytes: Electron microscopic evidence of their exocrine function. Science, 145:1318, 1964.

Bloom, G.: Studies on the olfactory epithelium of the frog and the toad with the aid of light and electron microscopy. Zeitschr. f. Zellforsch., 41:89, 1954.

Boyden, E. A.: Segmental Anatomy of the Lungs; A Study of the Patterns of the Segmental Bronchi and Related Pulmonary Vessels. New York, Blakiston Division, McGraw-Hill Book Co., 1955.

Boyden, E. A.: The terminal air sacs and their blood supply in a 37-day infant lung. Am. J. Anat., 116:413, 1965.

Boyden, E. A., and D. H. Tompsett: The changing patterns in the developing lungs of infants. Acta Anat., 61:164, 1965.

Bremer, J. L.: Postnatal development of alveoli in the mammalian lung in relation to the problem of the alveolar phagocyte. Carnegie Contributions to Embryol., 25:83, 1935.

Buckingham, S.: Studies on the identification of an antiatelectasis factor in normal sheep lung. Am. J. Dis. Child., 105:521, 1961.

Buckingham, S., and M. E. Avery: Time of appearance of lung surfactant in the foetal mouse. Nature, 193:688, 1962.

Campiche, M.: Les inclusions lamellaires des cellules alvéolaires dans le poumon du raton. Relations entre l'ultrastructure et la fixation. J. Ultrastruct. Res., 3:302, 1960.

Campiche, M., A. Gautier, E. I. Hernandez, and A. Raymond: An electron microscopic study of the fetal development of the human lung. Pediatrics, 32:976, 1963.

Clements, L. P.: Embryonic development of the respiratory portion of the pig's lung. Anat. Rec., 70:575, 1938.

de Lorenzo, A. J.: Electron microscopic observations of the olfactory mucosa and olfactory nerve. J. Biophys. & Biochem. Cytol., 3:839, 1957.

Dubreuil, G., A. Lacoste, and R. Raymond: Observations sur le développement du poumon humain. Bul. d'Histol. Appliq. à la Physiol., 13:235, 1936.

Hatasa, K., and T. Nakamura: Electron microscopic observations of lung alveolar epithelial cells of normal young mice with special reference to formation and secretion of osmiophilic lamellar bodies. Zeitschr. f. Zellforsch., 68:266, 1965.

Karrer, H. E.: The ultrastructure of mouse lung; general architecture of capillary and alveolar walls. J. Biophys. & Biochem. Cytol., 2:241, 1956.

Karrer, H. E.: The ultrastructure of mouse lung: The alveolar macrophage. J. Biophys. & Biochem. Cytol., 4:693, 1958.

Krahl, V. E.: Anatomy of the mammalian lung. In American Physiological Society: Handbook of Physiology. Baltimore, Williams & Wilkins Co., 1964, Section 3, Vol. I, p. 213.

Ladman, A. J., and T. N. Finley: Electron microscopic observations of pulmonary surfactant and the cells which produce it. Anat. Rec., 154:372, 1966.

Le Gros Clark, W.: Inquiries into the anatomical basis of olfactory discrimination. Proc. Roy. Soc. B, 146:299, 1957.

Loosli, C. G.: Interalveolar communications in normal and in pathologic mammalian lungs. Arch. Path., 24:743, 1937.

Loosli, C. G.: The pathogenesis and pathology of experimental type I pneumococcic pneumonia in the monkey. J. Exper. Med., 76:79, 1942.

Loosli, C. G., and R. F. Baker: The human lung: microscopic structure and diffusion. Ciba Foundation Symposium on Pulmonary Structure and Function, 1962, p. 194.

Loosli, C. G., and E. L. Potter: Pre- and postnatal development of the respiratory portion of the human lung, with special reference to the elastic fibers. Am. Rev. Resp. Dis., 80:5, 1959.

Low, F. N.: The pulmonary alveolar epithelium of laboratory mammals and man. Anat. Rec., *117*:241, 1953.

Low, F. N., and M. M. Sampaio: The pulmonary alveolar epithelium as an entodermal derivative. Anat. Rec., *127*:51, 1957.

Macklin, C. C.: The musculature of the bronchi and lungs. Physiol. Rev., *9*:1, 1929.

Macklin, C. C.: Residual epithelial cells on the pulmonary alveolar walls of mammals. Tr. Roy. Soc. Canada, 3rd ser., Sec. V, *40*:93, 1946.

Miller, W. S.: The Lung. 2nd ed. Springfield, Ill., Charles C Thomas, 1947.

Pattle, R. E.: Properties, function, and origin of the alveolar lining layer. Proc. Roy. Soc. B, *148*:217, 1958.

Pump, K. K.: The circulation of the primary lobule of the lung. Dis. Chest, *39*:614, 1961.

Pump, K. K.: The bronchial arteries and their anastomoses in the human lung. Dis. Chest, *43*:245, 1963.

Pump, K. K.: The morphology of the finer branches of the bronchial tree of the human lung. Dis. Chest, *46*:379, 1964.

Reese, T. S.: Olfactory cilia in the frog. J. Cell Biol., *25*:209, 1965.

Robertson, O. H.: Phagocytosis of foreign material in the lung. Physiol. Rev., *21*:112, 1941.

Sorokin, S. P.: A morphologic and cytochemical study on the great alveolar cell. J. Histochem. & Cytochem., *14*:884, 1967.

Spencer, H., and D. Leof: The innervation of the human lung. J. Anat. (London), *98*:599, 1964.

Tobin, C. E.: Human pulmonic lymphatics. Anat. Rec., *127*:611, 1957.

Weibel, E. R.: Morphometrische Analyse von Zahl, Volumen und Oberfläche der Alveolen und Kapillaren der menschlichen Lunge. Zeitschr. f. Zellforsch., *57*:648, 1962.

Weibel, E. R.: Morphometrics of the lung. *In* American Physiological Society: Handbook of Physiology. Baltimore, Williams & Wilkins Co., 1964, Section 3, Vol. I, p. 285.

CHAPTER THIRTY

The Urinary System

The urinary system consists of the kidneys, ureters, urinary bladder, and urethra. The system functions to clear the blood of the waste products of metabolism and to regulate the concentrations of many constituents of the body fluids. In the male the urethra not only conveys the urine to the outside but also serves the reproductive system as the pathway for the discharge of semen.

KIDNEYS

The human kidneys are paired organs situated retroperitoneally on the posterior wall of the abdominal cavity on either side of the vertebral column. They are roughly bean-shaped, 10 to 12 cm. in length, 5 to 6 cm. in width, and 3 to 4 cm. in thickness. A deep concavity, the *hilus,* is found on the medial border. A large excretory duct, the *ureter,* emerges from the hilus and courses downward to the urinary bladder, which is situated in the pelvis directly behind the pubis. The kidney is closely invested by a thin but strong capsule of dense collagenous fibers. The glandular part of the kidney surrounds a large cavity, the *renal sinus,* that extends inward from the hilus and contains the *renal pelvis.* The remainder of the sinus around the renal pelvis is occupied by loose connective tissue and adipose tissue, through which the blood vessels and nerves pass into the renal tissue.

The pelvis is a funnel-shaped expansion of the upper end of the ureter, which sends into the substance of the kidney two or three sizable outpocketings called *major calyces.* These in turn have a number of smaller outpocketings called *minor calyces* (Fig. 30-1).

When the cut surface of the hemisected kidney is viewed with the naked eye, a darker reddish brown *cortex* is readily distinguishable from a lighter *medulla.* The medulla is made up of 8 to 18 conical structures called *renal pyramids,* having their base toward the cortex and their apex or *papilla* projecting into the lumen of a minor calyx. The lateral boundaries of each pyramid are defined by inward extensions of the darker cortical tissue forming the *renal columns* (of Bertin). A renal pyramid together with the cortical tissue overlying its base and covering its sides constitutes a renal lobe. Each of these corresponds to the unipyramidal kidney of common laboratory rodents. In fetal life the separate lobes are recognizable as distinct convexities on the surface or the organ, but later in development they fuse into a continuous smooth-contoured cortex.

The gray substance of each pyramid is radially striated by brownish lines, which converge toward the apex of the papilla. These striations result from the straight parts of the uriniferous tubules and the blood vessels that parallel them. The tip of each papilla, the *area cribrosa,* is perforated by 10 to 25 small openings, where the terminal segments of the uriniferous tubules open into a minor calyx.

Regional specializations along the lengths of the tubules are reflected in grossly distinguishable zones in the medulla, which differ slightly in color or pattern. There is an *inner* and *outer zone* of the medulla and the outer zone is sometimes further subdivided into a darker and thicker *inner layer* or *band* and a lighter and thinner *outer band.*

From the bases of the medullary pyramids thin, radially directed striations extend into the cortical substance. These bear some resemblance to the striations in the pyramid but do not extend through the entire thickness of the cortex. These markings are called the *medullary rays* (of Ferrein) and represent continuations of bundles of tubules from the pyramid into the cortex (Fig. 30-2). Each medullary ray and its associated cortical tissue can be considered a *renal lobule,* although they are not separated from one another by connective tissue septa as is often the case in lobules of other glands.

Uriniferous Tubules

The tubules comprising the kidney have two principal portions. The first portion, the *nephron,* corresponding to the secretory elements of other glands, is concerned with the formation of urine, and the second portion, the *collecting tubule,* serves as the excretory duct conveying the urine to the renal pelvis. These two components arise from separate primordia that become connected secondarily. This is in contrast to the development of other glands, in which the ducts and secretory portions arise from a single primordium that branches dichotomously and becomes secretory in the distal part of its arborescent pattern. The nephron is the functional unit of this organ, and there are estimated to be one to three million in each kidney. At the proximal end of each of these long tortuous tubules is a thin-walled expansion called *Bowman's capsule,* which is deeply indented by a tuft of capillaries, the *glomerulus.* This globular mass of capillaries surrounded by its chalice-shaped capsule together comprise the nearly spherical *renal corpuscle.* It has a vascular pole where the afferent and efferent vessels enter and leave the glomerulus, and a urinary pole where the slit-like cavity within the capsule of Bowman is continuous with the lumen of the proximal convoluted portion of the nephron (Fig. 30-4). The tortuous tubules of neighboring nephrons in the cortex intermingle so extensively that the identity and shape of the individual units cannot be ascertained from sections. What is known of their three dimensional configuration has been established by their reconstruction from serial sections (Grafflin) or by macerating the tissue and teasing out the individual nephrons by time consuming micromanipulation (Oliver).

THE NEPHRON.   The secretory portion of the uriniferous tubule, beginning with the renal corpuscle and ending at the proximal end of the system of collecting ducts, is the nephron. Along its length are several morphologically distinct segments, each having a characteristic configuration and occupying a definite position in the cortex or medulla. Each

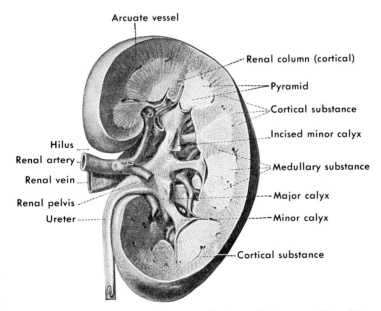

Arcuate vessel

Renal column (cortical)

Pyramid

Cortical substance

Incised minor calyx

Hilus

Renal artery

Renal vein

Renal pelvis

Ureter

Medullary substance

Major calyx

Minor calyx

Cortical substance

Figure 30-1.   Human kidney, seen from behind, after removal of part of the organ. Three fifths natural size. (After Braus.)

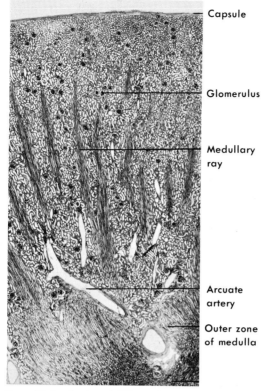

Capsule

Glomerulus

Medullary ray

Arcuate artery

Outer zone of medulla

Figure 30-2. Section of kidney of *Macacus rhesus*. Fixation by vascular perfusion—hence the empty blood vessels. Photomicrograph (slightly retouched). × 13.

segment is lined by a specific type of epithelium specialized for particular functions in the formation of urine.

The nephron consists of six successive parts: the renal corpuscle, the convoluted and straight portions of the proximal tubule, a thin segment, and the straight and convoluted portions of the distal tubule. The convoluted portion of the proximal tubule (*proximal convoluted tubule*) and the convoluted portion of the distal tubule (*distal convoluted tubule*) are both in the cortex close to the renal corpuscle. The portion of the nephron between the two convoluted segments takes the form of a loop, the *loop of Henle*, extending from the cortex for a variable distance into the medulla. It consists of two radially oriented limbs running parallel to each other and connected by a sharp bend. The loop of Henle includes the straight portion of the proximal tubule (the descending thick limb), the descending and ascending thin limbs, and the straight portion of the distal tubule (ascending thick limb). The distal

convoluted tubule is joined to the collecting tubule by a short connecting tube.

A fluid called the *glomerular filtrate* is formed in the renal corpuscle as an ultrafiltrate of the blood plasma that circulates through the glomerular capillaries. As this fluid passes through the various segments of the nephron, its composition is modified by secretion of certain substances into it and reabsorption of water and other constituents from it. The final product, *urine*, is drained through the collecting ducts into the renal pelvis.

Renal Corpuscle. The capsule of Bowman develops around the tuft of glomerular capillaries as a double walled cup composed of squamous epithelium (Fig. 30-4). The wall closely applied to the glomerulus is the *visceral layer* (glomerular epithelium), the outer wall is the *parietal layer* (capsular epithelium), and the thin, slit-like cavity between them is the *capsular space* (Bowman's space). At the vascular pole of the renal corpuscle, the visceral layer is reflected off the glomerular vessels to become continuous with the squamous epithelium of the parietal layer. At the urinary pole, the capsular epithelium is continuous with the cuboidal epithelium in the neck of the proximal convoluted tubule (Fig. 30-4).

In the development of the renal corpuscle, the parietal layer remains a typical squamous epithelium of flat polygonal cells, but the visceral layer becomes so extensively modified that, in the adult, it is debatable whether it can still be considered an epithelium in the strict sense. Its cells, called *podocytes,* have a small perikaryal region and a number of radiating processes, which in turn give rise to large numbers of small secondary processes called *end feet* or *pedicels*. In sections examined with the electron microscope, the cell body of the podocyte is rarely found in extensive contact with the basal lamina but instead stands off from it one or two microns and is attached to it here and there by short cell processes. Between these points of contact are rows of small cross sectional profiles of the foot processes of neighboring cells that extend under the podocyte cell body and interdigitate with its own secondary processes. These complex relationships are depicted diagrammatically, in greatly simplified form, in Figures 30-4 and 30-5, and the typical appearance of these elements in thin sections is illustrated in Figure 30-8.

The foot processes or pedicels are aligned

upon the outside of a continuous basal lamina (basement membrane), which they share with the glomerular endothelium on the inside. Adjacent foot processes are not in intimate contact with one another but are separated by narrow gaps or slits about 250 Å wide, now often referred to as *filtration slits* or *slit pores*. In electron micrographs of good resolution these gaps are seen to be bridged by a thin dense line 60 Å or less in thickness. This is interpreted as the cross sectional profile of an exceedingly thin *slit membrane* extending between the outer leaflets of the plasma membranes of adjacent foot processes at the level of the basal lamina. This structure is considered to be similar to the tenuous diaphragm that closes the pores of fenestrated capillaries. The podocytes have nuclei of complex form, often deeply infolded.

Their cytoplasm contains a well developed Golgi complex, cisternal profiles of granular endoplasmic reticulum and abundant free ribosomes. Cytoplasmic filaments and microtubules are plentiful, both in the cell body and extending out into the primary and secondary cell processes.

The endothelium lining the outer or peripheral aspect of the glomerular capillaries is extremely attenuated and is perforated by circular pores or fenestrae 500 to 1000 Å in diameter. Although not all investigators are in agreement, a majority believe that these pores differ from those of fenestrated capillaries elsewhere in the body in that the pore is not traversed by a thin diaphragm but appears to be open. They also tend to be somewhat larger and more numerous (Fig. 30-7*A*).

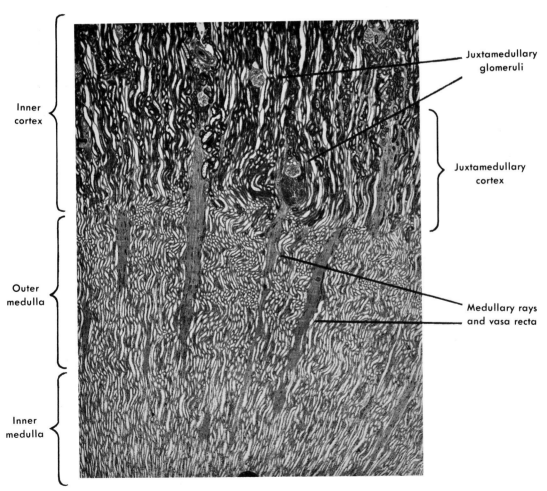

Figure 30-3.   Section of dog kidney, showing medullary rays and vasa recta extending from juxtamedullary glomeruli to the border of the inner medulla. Mallory stain. × 30. (After Thorburn et al., Circulation Res., *13*:290, 1963.)

On the outer aspect of the glomerular capillaries the basal lamina (basement membrane) of the endothelium is fused with that of the overlying visceral epithelium, so that in the adult these two cellular layers are separated by a continuous basal lamina 0.1 to 0.15 μ in thickness. It is a feltwork of very fine filaments of two or more sizes, embedded in a matrix that appears homogeneous at the level of resolution presently attained.

The thicker portions of the endothelial cells, containing the nucleus, are usually on the inner side of the capillaries. In this region are also found cells of another type, variously called *deep cells* or *mesangial cells*. They are stellate in form and extend their processes between the endothelium and the basal lamina or occupy lenticular clefts within the substance of the basal lamina. These cells have a number of characteristics in common with the pericytes of capillaries elsewhere.

Figure 30-4. Highly schematic representation of the renal corpuscle. The parietal layer of Bowman's capsule is depicted considerably thicker than it actually is, and the visceral layer overlying the capillaries of the glomerulus is greatly simplified with only the major processes of the podocytes depicted. Although earlier described as a cluster of simple loops, the capillaries are now believed to branch and anastomose to form a network. (Redrawn and modified after Bargmann.)

The basement lamina is the only continuous layer in the glomerular capillary wall and has been regarded by some as the principal filter tending to hold back large molecules. The evidence for this is derived from the use of particulate tracers such as ferritin. When such substances are administered intravenously, it can be shown that they freely penetrate the endothelial pores but tend to accumulate against the inner aspect of the basement lamina. The marker particles do gradually infiltrate this layer and may ultimately pass through it. Inasmuch as no such piling up of marker occurs at the endothelial pores or the slits, it is believed by some investigators that the basement lamina is the principal filter of the renal corpuscle. However, ferritin is an extremely large molecule, and its impedance by the basement lamina cannot be taken as evidence that this is the site of the filtration barrier to smaller protein molecules. Experiments have recently been done using horseradish peroxidase (mol. wt. 40,000) and myeloperoxidase (mol. wt. 160,000) as protein tracers, which are detectable by ultrastructural cytochemistry. The smaller peroxidase is found to pass rapidly through the endothelial fenestrae, across the basement lamina, and through the epithelial slits into Bowman's space (Fig. 30-10). The larger peroxidase readily passes the basement lamina but is held up at the level of the epithelial slits. These findings are interpreted to mean that the epithelial "slit pores" are the filtration barrier responsible for differential glomerular permeability to proteins of varying molecular size (Graham and Karnovsky).

It has been shown that the basement lamina is not a static structural component but is constantly being turned over. The fact that the visceral epithelial cells exhibit some of the cytological characteristics of synthetically active cells has led to the suggestion that they may play a role in the formation and continual renewal of the basement lamina. Experimental substantiation of this belief has been provided by adding silver nitrate to the drinking water of rats for a period of time sufficient to mark the glomerular basement lamina with a black line of deposited silver. In the weeks following cessation of silver nitrate ingestion, it can be shown that new, unlabeled basement lamina has been deposited on the epithelial side (Kurtz and Feldman). It is also speculated that the mesangial cells may play some role in

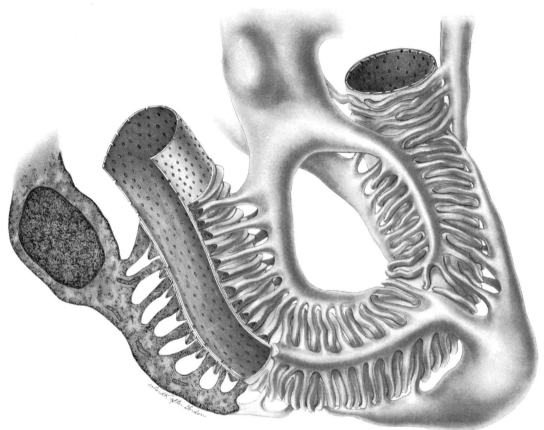

Figure 30-5. Highly schematic representation of the interdigitating pattern of secondary processes (foot processes or pedicles) of the podocytes on the outer surface of a glomerular capillary loop. This arrangement provides a very large area of slender filtration slits or slit pores between adjacent processes. (Redrawn and modified after Gordon, *in* A. W. Ham: Histology. 5th ed. Philadelphia, J. B. Lippincott Co., 1965.)

the maintenance and reconditioning of the basement lamina by removal of residues of filtration and indeed that they participate in the turnover of this layer by removal of the older deep portions of the filter as it is renewed at the epithelial surface (Farquhar).

The Proximal Tubule. The short transitional region from Bowman's capsule to the tubule is sometimes referred to as the "neck," although a marked constriction here is by no means typical. The *proximal convoluted tubule* averages 14 mm. in length and 60 μ in diameter and is extremely tortuous. This segment of the nephrons makes up the bulk of the kidney cortex. In addition to many small loops, the proximal convoluted tubule rather consistently forms a large loop directed toward the periphery. From there it returns to the vicinity of its renal corpuscle and then courses toward

the nearest medullary ray and, straightening out, runs inward toward the medulla. In the outer zone of the medulla it tapers down in its terminal portion and continues into the *loop of Henle.* The epithelium of the proximal convolution consists of a single layer of cells, bearing a conspicuous brush border of closely packed microvilli. Each cell contains a single spherical nucleus in an eosinophilic cytoplasm. In cytological preparations the Golgi apparatus forms a crown around the upper pole of the nucleus, and long rodlike mitochondria in the basal half of the cell are oriented parallel to the cell axis. In well preserved tissues this orientation of the mitochondria may result in a faint vertical striation of the cell base, even without special staining for mitochondria. The lateral limits of the cells are rarely seen because the sides of the cells are

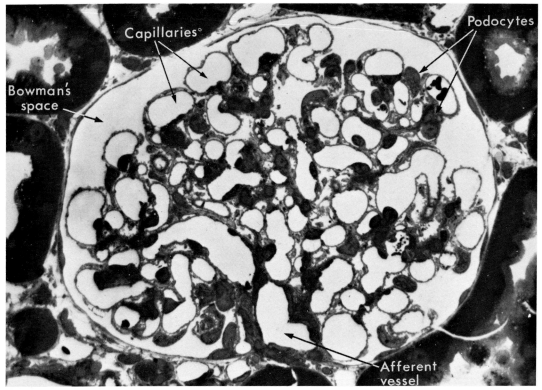

Figure 30-6. A thin plastic section of a renal corpuscle from a rat kidney fixed by perfusion and showing the open lumens of the capillary. The irregularity of their outer surface is due to the sections of podocyte processes on their exterior. × 700. (Courtesy of A. Aoki.)

elaborately fluted and interdigitate with corresponding ridges and grooves on the neighboring cells. In favorable preparations, affording surface views of the epithelium, some of the major interdigitations of the cell surfaces can be seen with the light microscope, but the true complexity of the shape of these cells can only be appreciated by careful study of electron micrographs. There are large columnar ridges that extend the full height of the cell, but an even greater number of slender lateral processes at the cell base extend under adjacent cells and occupy deep recesses in their base (Fig. 30-14). The resulting compartmentation of the base of the epithelium in micrographs of thin sections was originally attributed to a simple infolding of the basal plasma membrane. It is evident, however, that most of the basal compartments are not open at any point to the cytoplasm of the overlying cell. It is clear therefore that many of them are, in fact, sections of basal processes of neighboring cells. In addition to the basal processes, there are less extensive lateral processes that are confined

to the juxtaluminal region of the epithelium (Bulger).

In kidney tissue fixed either for light or electron microscopy the lumen of the proximal tubule is often occluded by the apposition of the brush borders of the surrounding cells. The possibility was formerly entertained that this was the normal condition and that the glomerular filtrate might percolate through the interstices among the microvilli of the brush borders. This constriction of the tubules and obliteration of the lumen is now known to be an artifact. If the fixative is dripped onto the surface of the living kidney or if it is perfused under conditions that involve no agonal fall of blood pressure, then all of the proximal tubules have a large open lumen (Fig. 30-12).

The microvilli on the free surface of the proximal tubule are long, regularly oriented, and closely packed. Arising from the clefts between the microvilli and extending downward into the apical cytoplasm are numerous tubular invaginations sometimes called *apical canaliculi* (Fig. 30-13). The membrane lining them has a filamentous outer surface coat and short projections from the cytoplasmic face of the membrane. In this respect the tubules closely resemble the so-called coated vesicles seen in many other cell types. Also found in the apical cytoplasm are clear vacuoles of varying size and others with a content of appreciable density. The apical canaliculi and the associated vacuoles appear to be involved in the cellular mechanism for absorption and concentration of protein from the glomerular filtrate. Evidence for this was obtained at the light microscope level by intravenous injection of peroxidase and subsequent demonstration of a peroxidase reaction in the apical vacuoles of the proximal convoluted tubule (Straus). In a recent application of the sensitive new peroxidase method for ultrastructural cytochemistry, it has been reported that the protein enzyme can be demonstrated in the brush border and apical canaliculi as early as 90 seconds after intravenous injection (Graham and Karnovsky). Later it is found in the vacuoles, where it undergoes progressive concentration. Whether the apical tubules open directly into the vacuoles or whether vesicles bud off from their ends and transport quanta of the absorbed material to the vacuoles has not been settled. Many of the protein absorption vacuoles give histochemical reactions for acid hydrolases and are evidently sites of concentration and intracellular digestion of the absorbed protein.

Although the whole length of the proximal convolution seems to have essentially the same structure in ordinary histological preparations, certain experiments (vital staining; poisoning with uranium, chromium, or bichloride of mercury; and others) allow a subdivision of this tubule into three or four successive segments, which show specific reactions to the different noxious factors. Simi-

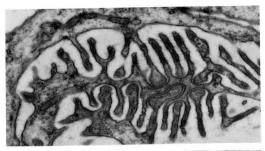

A

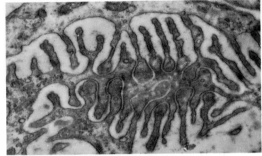

B

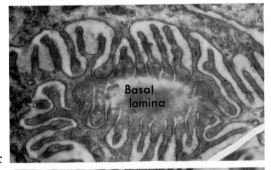

Basal lamina

C

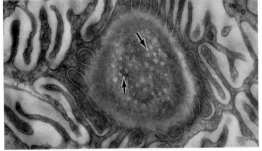

D

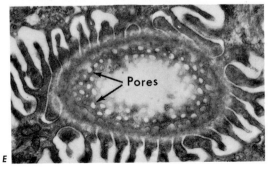

Pores

E

Figure 30-7. An electron micrograph of a series of sections tangential to the wall of a glomerular capillary loop cut at successively deeper levels. A and B are through the interdigitating foot processes of podocytes on the external surface of the capillary. C is a section just grazing the basal lamina. D shows oblique sections of basal lamina and an en face view of the fenestrations of the endothelium. E breaks through into the lumen in the center, but this clear area is surrounded by a rim of endothelium clearly showing its abundant pores. (Courtesy of A. Aoki.)

lar conclusions on functional differentiation within these segments of the nephron have been drawn from histochemical studies in a variety of vertebrates (Fig. 30-27).

Loop of Henle. The loop of Henle consists of the straight portion of the proximal tubule, the descending and ascending thin limbs, and the ascending thick limb, which is simply the straight portion of the distal tubule. In rats and certain other species whose kidneys have a single pyramid, the corresponding segments of the loops tend to be in register, and this regularity of arrangement is reflected in a zonation within the medulla that is detectable on naked eye inspection of the cut surface. An *outer* and *inner zone of the medulla* can be recognized, and an *inner* and *outer band* are distinguishable within the outer zone of the medulla. The boundary between the outer and inner band of the outer medulla is at the junctions of the straight portion of the proximal tubules with the thin descending limbs of Henle's loops. The transition between the inner and

outer medulla is at the junctions of the ascending thin limbs with the ascending thick limbs. The inner medulla contains collecting tubules, thin limbs of the loop of Henle, and blood vessels (Osvaldo and Latta).

In the human, similar zonation of the medulla is detectable but with some difficulty, for the loops of Henle are of different lengths depending upon the position of their renal corpuscle in the cortex and the length of their thin segment (Fig. 30-11). The short ones are associated with those renal corpuscles that are located nearer the surface of the kidney, and they are about seven times as numerous as the long ones. Their bend is always formed by the thick ascending limb and is in the outer part of the medulla. The thin descending limb may be very short or even absent. In the latter event, the proximal convolution continues directly into the thick ascending limb. In the longer loops, which belong to the deeper lying renal corpuscles, the bend is formed by the thin limb. These loops sometimes extend nearly

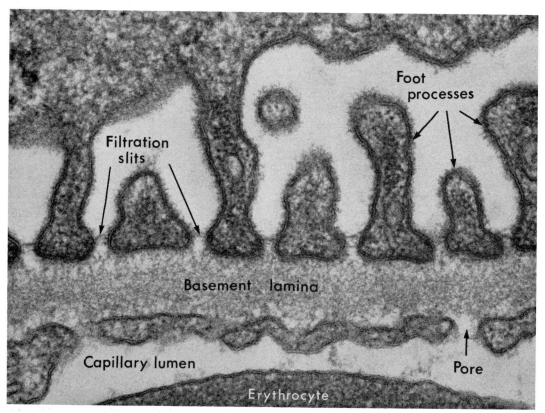

Figure 30-8. Electron micrograph of a portion of the wall of a glomerular capillary, showing pores in the extremely attenuated endothelium. On the outer surface of the basement lamina are the foot processes of the podocytes with the narrow filtration slits between them. × 70,000. (Courtesy of D. Friend.)

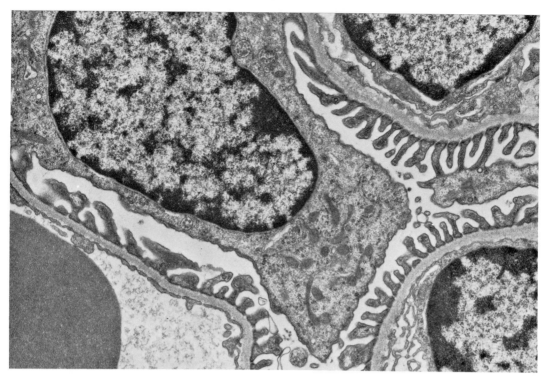

Figure 30-9. Electron micrograph of a podocyte and portions of three capillaries surrounded by a moderately thick basement lamina with numerous foot processes on its external surface. The two capillaries at upper and lower right are collapsed. × 20,000. (Courtesy of D. Friend.)

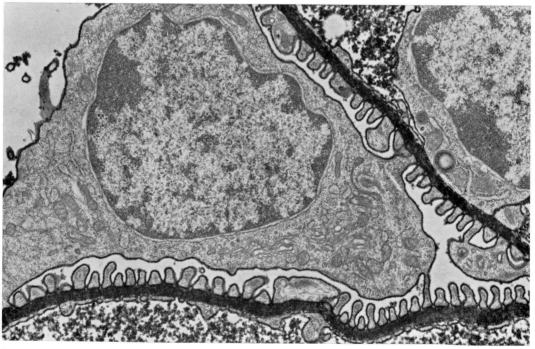

Figure 30-10. A somewhat similar area from the renal corpuscle of an animal that had received an intravascular injection of the enzyme peroxidase (mol. wt. 40,000). The histochemical reaction for this enzyme shows it as dense material in the blood plasma of the capillaries (*below* and *upper right*). Its presence in the basement lamina makes this structure appear black. It also appears to coat the surface of the podocyte and the foot processes. × 20,000. (Courtesy of D. Friend.)

to the apex of the papilla. In this event the length of the thin limb may vary from 4.5 to 10 mm. or even more.

The junction of the outer and inner zones of the medulla is marked by the transition of the thin limb to the ascending thick limb of the long loops of Henle. The boundary between the outer and inner bands of the outer medulla in the human kidney is somewhat obscured by the prevalence of short loops in this region having the junctions between their successive segments at different levels.

The transition from the straight portion of the proximal tubule to the descending thin limb is abrupt (Fig. 30-15). The type of epithelium changes from cuboidal to squamous with a thickness of 0.5 to 2 μ, and there is a sudden termination of the brush border, with the long, closely packed microvilli giving way to very sparse, irregularly oriented microvilli, usually less than 0.4 μ in length, on the luminal surface of the thin limb. The somewhat flattened nuclei cause the central portions of the cells to bulge into the lumen. Because of their small caliber and thin wall and the bulging of the nuclei into the lumen, descending thin limbs in cross section bear a superficial resemblance to capillaries (Fig. 30-16).

In electron micrographs, typical cellular units containing a nucleus make up only a small portion of the wall. Most of the thin epithelium is composed of small units 1 to 3 μ across, separated from one another by pairs of membranes extending from basement lamina to lumen. These short segments of the epithelium are too small to contain a nucleus and often enclose only one or two mitochondria. They are attached to one another by juxtaluminal junctional complexes. This unusual appearance of the epithelium is attributed to the fact that its cells, like those of the visceral layer of Bowman's capsule or of the proximal convolution, have extraordinarily complex shapes with elaborately interdigitated outlines. The short segments of epithelium in the thin limb seen in micrographs thus represent sections through the deeply intercrescent peripheral processes of the cells. These do not so commonly extend under the adjacent cells to form basal compartments, as do those seen in sections of the thicker epithelium in the proximal and distal tubules. Instead, the processes take up the full thickness of the epithelium, and cell processes interdigitate like the teeth of flat gears. The

epithelium rests upon a moderately thick basement lamina and the cytoplasm contains relatively few organelles. The cells of the thin segment of the nephron show a gradual simplification of their structure as they descend deeper into the pyramid. The interdigitating processes become fewer and the microvilli shorter and less abundant.

In the human kidney the shape of the cells in the thin limb is less complex than in the rat and mouse. The interdigitating lateral cell processes are relatively few or entirely lacking. The epithelium is appreciably higher than in other species. The basal cell membrane is, for the most part, smooth-contoured and rests upon a basement lamina that is distinctly thicker than that in the laboratory rodents. The luminal surface has a few short microvilli coated with radiating fine filaments, and each cell bears a single flagellum (Bulger et al.).

The transition from the ascending limb of the thin segment to the ascending thick limb or straight portion of the distal tubule is usually fairly sudden. The height of the epithelium increases and it stains darker. Rod-shaped mitochondria cause a distinct vertical striation of its basal region. The lateral borders of the cells are somewhat more easily distinguished than in the proximal tubule, and the cells lack a brush border. A pair of centrioles is found in the apical cytoplasm and from one of these a single flagellum may project into the lumen.

In electron micrographs the base of the epithelium is elaborately compartmentalized with basal infoldings of the membrane of each cell mingling with undermining basal processes of neighboring cells. The mitochondria are long, with complex internal membrane structure and numerous dense granules in their matrix. There are cisternal profiles of granular endoplasmic reticulum and many free ribosomes.

The thick ascending limb of Henle's loop or straight portion of the distal tubule has on the average a length of 9 mm. It enters the cortical tissue, returns to the renal corpuscle of its nephron and attaches to its vascular pole, particularly to the afferent arteriole in the region of its juxtaglomerular cells. That side of the tubule in contact with the afferent arteriole forms an elliptical disk of taller cells measuring 40 by 70 μ in man. This area, called the *macula densa,* has been reported to have some significance in the hemodynamics of the kidney, but its precise role has not been defined. From here the straight portion passes into the distal convoluted portion of the tubule.

Distal Convolution. This portion of the tubule has many short loops and irregular contortions. It usually forms a loop directed toward the surface above the corresponding renal corpuscle. Its length is estimated at 4.6 to 5.2 mm., its diameter at 20 to 50 μ.

The epithelium of the distal convolution is lower and the lumen is larger than in the proximal convolution. There is no brush border, but in electron micrographs the free surface of the cells may show a few short microvilli. In the basal parts of the cells, a distinct striation can be seen with the light microscope. The limits of the cells are fairly distinct.

In electron micrographs, the apical cytoplasm of the epithelium is free of canalicular invaginations, hyaline droplets, and lysosomes. The base is more elaborately compartmentalized and more deeply invaded by membranes than in the proximal convolution (Fig. 30-19). Here too, the narrow basal compartments bounded by pairs of membranes appear for the most part to represent interdigitating lateral processes of adjacent cells. The nuclei are nearer the lumen, and the basal half of the epithelium contains large numbers of long, vertically oriented mitochondria. In a cross section of the distal tubule, the cells are more numerous than in the proximal tubule. Instead of three or four, five to eight nuclei can usually be counted.

COLLECTING TUBULES. The connections of the nephrons with the collecting tubules are located in the cortex of the kidney along medullary rays. The distal tubules are continuous with *arched collecting tubules* (connecting tubules), which are tributaries of straight collecting tubules located in the medullary rays. In the medullary ray the collecting tubules pass inward through the outer zone of the medulla without further fusions. When they reach the inner zone, they join at acute angles with other similar tubules, and this is repeated about seven times. These convergences of collecting tubules in the medulla near the pelvis lead to the formation of large, straight collecting tubules called *papillary ducts* (of Bellini). These have a lumen measuring 100 to 200 μ in diameter and open on the area cribrosa at the apex of each papilla.

The system of the intrarenal excretory ducts

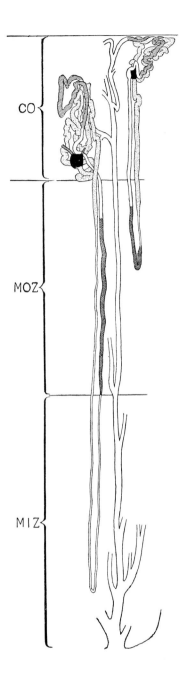

Figure 30-11. Diagram of two nephrons and their connection with collecting tubules. *CO*, Cortex; *MOZ*, outer zone of medulla; *MIZ*, inner zone of medulla. Malpighian corpuscles, black; proximal convolution, stippled; thin limb of Henle, white; thick limb of Henle, cross-hatched and then white (to indicate the opacity and clearness seen in macerated preparations, but not in sections); distal convolution, obliquely striated; collecting tubules, white. (Redrawn and slightly modified from Peter.)

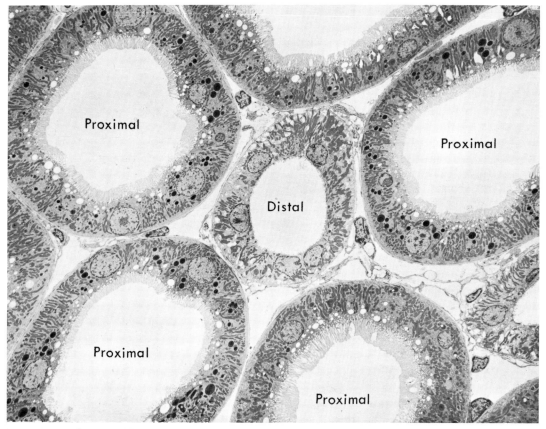

Figure 30-12. Low magnification electron micrograph from the cortex of rat kidney fixed by vascular perfusion. The field includes five proximal convoluted tubules in transverse section, showing their open lumen and prominent brush border. Two distinct segments of the proximal convolution can be recognized. The first portion has a deeper brush border (section at *lower right*). The second portion has a thinner brush border and prominent dense bodies in the cytoplasm (other three labeled sections). × 2000. (After A. Maunsbach, J. Ultrastruct. Res., *15*:242, 1966.)

has an epithelium typically quite different from that of the various parts of the nephron. In the smallest collecting tubules the cells are cuboidal and sharply outlined; they contain a darkly staining round nucleus and have a clear cytoplasm (Fig. 30-22). The latter contains a few fine mitochondria and, at the surface, a pair of centrioles with a central flagellum.

As the collecting tubules grow larger, the cells become higher, and finally, in the ducts of Bellini, they acquire a tall columnar form. They are always arranged in a regular single layer, with all the nuclei at one level and with the free surfaces bulging slightly into the lumen of the tubule. The cytoplasm keeps its pale appearance. The centrioles remain at the bulging free surface. In the area cribrosa, the simple columnar epithelium of the ducts of

Bellini continues onto the surface of the papilla.

The length of the collecting tubules is estimated at 20 to 22 mm. and the length of the nephron at 30 to 38 mm.

The Juxtaglomerular Cells

Among the smooth muscle cells in the wall of the afferent arteriole just before its entrance into the glomerulus are cells that contain conspicuous cytoplasmic granules (Ruyter; Oberling). These cells are in contact with the intima of the artery on the one side and on the other side they are intimately related to the base of the cells of the *macula densa,* a specialized region of the wall of the distal tubule that marks the beginning of the distal convolution. These *juxtaglomerular cells* have a slightly basophilic cytoplasm and their specific granules are most clearly demonstrated by the Bowie stain. In electron micrographs they have a moderately abundant granular endoplasmic reticulum and a well developed Golgi complex. The granules appear to arise in the cisternae of the Golgi complex, as in glandular cells. When first formed the granules are 90 to 400 μ long, of variable shape, and have a crystalline internal structure with a periodicity of 50 to 100 Å. Coalescence of these elements gives rise to mature granules, which are irregularly shaped conglomerates that may retain evidences of crystalline order but more often appear dense and homogeneous.

The secretory nature of these granules was established in experimental studies that demonstrated changes in granule content of the juxtaglomerular cells in renal ischemia (Goormaghtigh), variations in salt intake and in adrenalectomy (Hartroft; Dunihue). These studies led to the hypothesis that these cells are the site of production of the vasopressor substance *renin*. Support for this thesis has come from the finding that the solubility characteristics of renin and of the granules of the juxtaglomerular cells are similar and that there is a direct correlation between the level of renin determined by bioassay and the degree of granulation of the juxtaglomerular cells. Microdissection methods have localized the renin to the immediate vicinity of the renal corpuscle, and recently, by application of the fluorescent antibody technique, renin has been shown to reside in the granules of the juxtaglomerular cells (Edelman and Hartroft).

The Macula Densa

Where it comes into contact with the afferent arteriole, the epithelium lining the straight portion of the distal tubule is locally thickened to form the *macula densa* (Figs. 30-20 and 30-21). The bases of the cells are in very close relation to the juxtaglomerular cells, and the basement membrane between them is exceedingly thin. This close topographical relationship has been interpreted as suggesting some interchange of substances between the macula densa and the juxtaglomerular cells. Consistent with such a relationship is the report

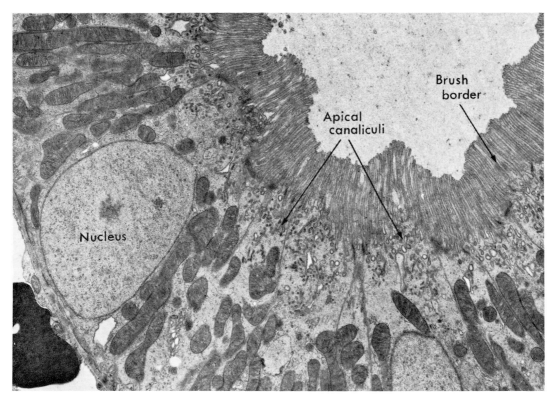

Figure 30-13. Electron micrograph of a sector of the wall of a proximal tubule of rat kidney. × 6000. (Courtesy of R. Bulger.)

that the polarity of the Golgi complex in the cells of the macula densa is toward the juxtaglomerular cells, whereas in the remainder of the circumference of the distal tubule, it is toward the lumen (McManus).

The finding that the cells of the macula densa show changes in their histochemically demonstrable enzymatic activities when the rate of secretion of the juxtaglomerular cells is altered provides further indication that the two structures are functionally related. It is common practice therefore to refer to the two together as the *juxtaglomerular apparatus.*

Blood Supply

Because the kidneys serve to clear the blood of accumulated waste products of metabolism, they have a very large blood flow, averaging about 1200 ml./min. through both kidneys of a 70 kg. man. A knowledge of the blood supply of the kidney is essential to an understanding of its function.

The *renal artery* enters the hilus of the kidney and divides into two main sets of branches directed toward the dorsal and ventral aspects of the organ. In the adipose tissue surrounding the pelvis these branches in turn divide into smaller *interlobar arteries* that enter the substance of the kidney and course peripherally in the renal columns between the pyramids or lobes of the kidney. At the level of the base of the pyramids the interlobar arteries arch over to run parallel to the surface of the organ as the *arcuate arteries* at the corticomedullary junction. Small *interlobular arteries,* given off from the arcuate arteries at regular intervals, course radially toward the kidney surface (Fig. 30-24).

The interlobular arteries give off numerous *afferent arterioles* to the glomeruli. The blood is carried from the glomeruli via *efferent arterioles.* The efferent vessels of glomeruli situated in the outer part of the cortex are of small diameter and break up to form the cortical intertubular capillary network. The efferent vessels of the more deeply situated glomeruli (juxtamedullary glomeruli) are of larger caliber and pass into the medulla, breaking up into bundles of thin-walled vessels larger than ordinary capillaries, called *vasa recta* (Fig. 30-23). The efferent vessels of the juxtamedullary glomeruli and the vasa recta both

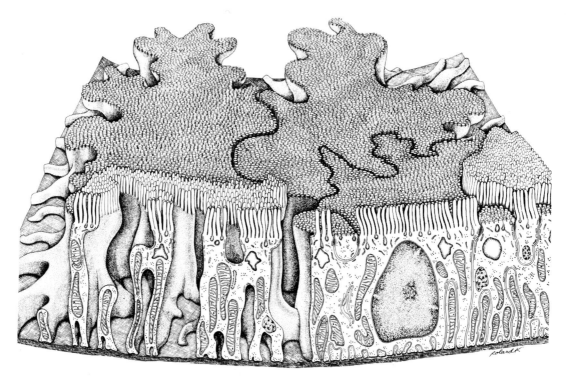

Figure 30-14. Drawing of the shapes and interrelations of the cells of the proximal convoluted tubule. As in fluted columns, some of the interdigitated lateral processes extend the full height of the cell; others are confined to the base and extend beneath adjacent cells. (After R. Bulger, Am. J. Anat., *116:*237, 1965.)

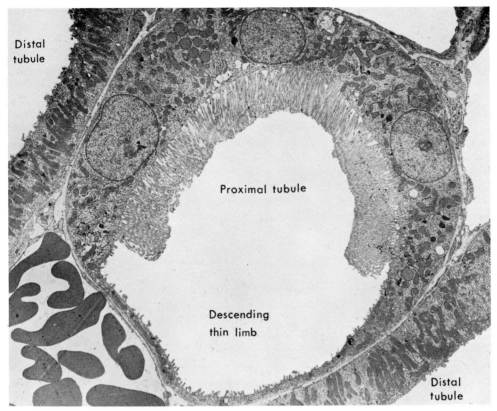

Figure 30-15. Electron micrograph of the abrupt junction of the straight portion of the proximal tubule with the thin limb of the loop of Henle. Slightly oblique section through the junction. The brush border stops suddenly and the epithelium becomes very thin. × 4200. (After Osvaldo and Latta, J. Ultrastruct. Res., *15:*144, 1966.)

contribute branches to an intertubular capillary network in the medulla.

The vasa recta form hairpin loops at various levels, turning back toward the cortex and running close to and parallel with the vessels from which they recur. The descending vessels penetrate the outer medulla to different depths before turning back. As more vessels turn back, the vascular bundles taper down as they approach the inner medulla. The descending vessels forming the arterial limbs of the *vascular bundle* or *rete* are slightly smaller than the recurrent vessels that constitute the venous limbs (Fig. 30-17). The fine structure of the vessel walls also differs, the arterial component having a continuous endothelium while the venous component has a thin fenestrated endothelium (Fig. 30-16). The proximity of the vessels in the vascular bundles and the large surface they present to one another facilitates rapid movement of diffusible substances between the ascending and descending limbs of the loops. The vasa recta thus serve as efficient countercurrent exchangers for diffusible substances.

The capillaries of the outermost layers of the cortex are drained toward the surface by radially arranged branches, the *superficial cortical veins,* which join veins of characteristic configuration on the surface of the kidney, called *stellate veins.* This outer mantle of venous channels is drained by a relatively small number of *interlobular veins* into the *arcuate veins* that accompany the arteries of the same name (Fig. 30-26). The capillaries in the deeper part of the cortex empty into radially oriented *deep cortical veins,* of which there are some 400 per square centimeter running parallel to a corresponding number of interlobular arteries. The blood in these flows inward to the arcuate veins and thence to the *interlobar* veins, which finally become confluent in the hilus to form the *renal vein.*

The hemodynamics of the renal circulation are such that the flows to various zones of the kidney are very different. Measurements of

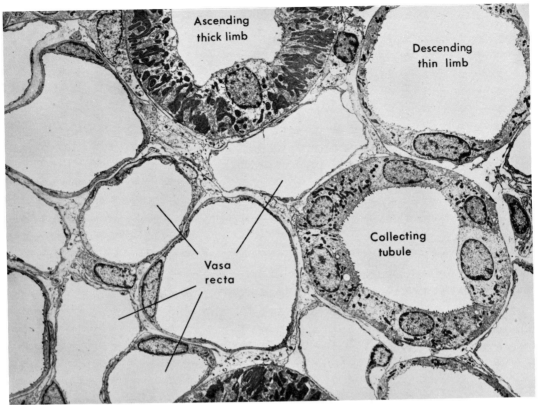

Figure 30-16. Electron micrograph of the inner band of the outer zone of rat kidney medulla, showing ascending thick limb, descending thin limb, collecting tubule, and the vasa recta. × 3000. (After A. Maunsbach, J. Ultrastruct. Res., *15:*242, 1966.)

blood flow distribution in the unanaesthetized dog give values of 472 ml./100 gm./min. in the cortex; 132 ml./100 gm./min. in the outer medulla, and 17 ml./100 gm./min. in the inner medulla (Thorburn et al.). Although the cortical flow is normally very rapid, strong stimulation of sympathetic nerves may diminish it almost to zero. Under various stressful circumstances, the cortex of the kidney becomes pale, and red blood may appear in the renal vein. Evidently under these conditions the renal cortex is relatively ischemic and the bulk of the blood that would normally pass through the cortical glomeruli for filtration is bypassed through the juxtamedullary glomeruli and the vasa recta into the interlobular veins and thence to the renal vein.

Lymphatics

Networks of lymphatic capillaries are found both in the capsule of the kidney and in the glandular tissue. Both groups are connected by occasional anastomoses. The lym-

phatics of the capsule join the lymph vessels of the neighboring organs. The lymph capillaries in the glandular tissue form dense networks between the uriniferous tubules, especially in the cortex. They pass into lymphatics that accompany the larger blood vessels and leave the kidney at the hilus. They are not present in the glomeruli or medullary rays.

Nerves

Macroscopic dissection shows that the sympathetic celiac plexus sends many nerve fibers into the kidney. Their distribution inside the organ has not been worked out satisfactorily. It is relatively easy to follow nonmyelinated and myelinated fibers along the course of the larger blood vessels. They provide the adventitia with sensory nerve endings and the muscular coat with motor endings. Along with the afferent arterioles, nerve fibers may reach the renal corpuscles, and some of them seem to form end branches on their surface. The nerve supply of the uriniferous tubules, however, has not been clearly demonstrated. Some investigators describe plexuses of fine nerve fibers that surround and seem to penetrate the basement lamina. On its inner surface they are supposed to form another plexus, from which terminal branches arise to end with minute end-knobs between the epithelial cells. There is the possibility that the silver stains on which these descriptions are based were impregnating reticulum. The finer innervation of the kidneys needs to be studied at the electron microscope level where fine nerve fibers can be identified with greater certainty.

Histophysiology of the Kidneys

In producing urine, the kidneys do not produce new material in significant amounts but eliminate water and some of the waste products of metabolism that are carried in solution in the blood. In addition to their *excretory function,* in which they dispose of waste and foreign substances, the kidneys have equally important *conservative functions,* by which they retain the amounts of water electrolytes, and other substances needed by the body, while eliminating excesses of these substances. They therefore play an important role in the maintenance of the constancy of the internal environment of the organism. The kidney carries out its function by an ingenious combination of filtration, passive diffusion, active secretion, and selective absorption. The form, topographical relations, and microscopic organization of its components represent structural adaptations favoring these processes.

THE GLOMERULUS. The blood circulates through the glomerular capillaries with a *hydrostatic pressure* of about 70 mm./Hg. This tends to press the fluid constituents of the blood through the pores and intercellular spaces of the endothelium, across the basement lamina, through the filtration slits between foot processes of the podocytes, and into Bowman's capsule. The hydrostatic pressure in the capillaries is opposed by an average *colloid osmotic pressure* of about 32 mm. Hg and a *capsular pressure* of about 20 mm. Hg. The net *filtration pressure* is thus about 18 mm. Hg. With some 1300 ml. of blood flowing through the glomeruli of both kidneys each minute, approximately 125 ml. of glomerular filtrate is produced. Analysis of fluid aspirated from Bowman's capsule by micropuncture has established that it is an ultrafiltrate of blood plasma with almost the same composition as the interstitial fluid. It contains small molecules such as phosphates, creatinine, uric acid and urea, and small amounts of albumin, but is free of larger protein molecules and substances combined with them. As stated earlier, the site of the barrier to large molecules is still debated, but the most recent evidence indicates that molecules of molecular weight 100,000 and larger are arrested at the slit pores rather than in the basement lamina.

Of the 125 ml. of filtrate formed per minute in the glomeruli, 124 ml. are reabsorbed as the fluid passes through the various segments of the nephrons and the collecting ducts, leaving a volume of only 1 ml. to be excreted as urine. This small remainder is not simply derived by absorption of water; its contents are modified in its passage along the tubules by

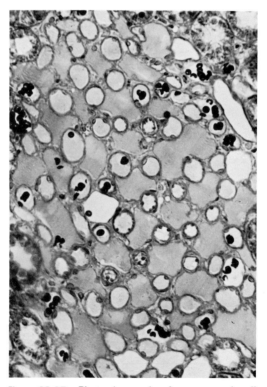

Figure 30-17. Photomicrograph of a rete or bundle of vasa recta from a dog kidney. Notice that the vessels are of two morphological types: the descending arterial limbs are capillaries with a round cross section and walls of appreciable thickness; the ascending venous limbs are larger, more irregular in outline, and have exceedingly thin walls. The latter are filled here with gray precipitate of plasma, while the former appear empty or contain a few erythrocytes. × 250.

(1) diffusion of some substances back into the blood, (2) absorption by osmotic work, and (3) excretion of other substances into the lumen.

The transport of certain substances into and out of the nephron can be rather precisely measured in healthy humans and is the basis of a variety of clinical measurements of their kidney function. *Inulin* is a nonmetabolized carbohydrate which, when injected intravenously, rapidly appears in the glomerular filtrate but is not secreted or absorbed by the tubules. It can be used, therefore, as a means of measuring the amount of plasma filtered by all of the glomeruli of both kidneys. This calculation is based upon the concentrations of inulin in the urine and in the plasma during the experiment. The volume of plasma containing the same amount of inulin as that found in the urine is the amount of plasma which has been "cleared" of this substance by filtration during the period of the test. The *inulin clearance* furnishes a standard from which it is possible to estimate what proportions of other substances are reabsorbed or excreted by cells in various parts of the tubule.

PROXIMAL CONVOLUTION. Much of our knowledge of the functions of renal tubules has been derived from studies on amphibian species, in which it is possible to puncture the glomerular capsule and the tubules at different levels in living animals and carry out microchemical analyses on the fluid aspirated. The change in the composition of the filtrate as it passes along the nephron can thus be studied directly. Similarly, fluid of known composition can be perfused through a segment of tubule between two pipettes and the substances added to or subtracted from it can be determined. By these and other methods, it has been shown that 85 per cent or more of the sodium chloride and water of the glomerular filtrate is reabsorbed in the proximal tubule. In this process the cells actively transport sodium from the lumen, and the water and chloride passively follow it to maintain osmotic equilibrium.

Normally all of the glucose in the filtrate

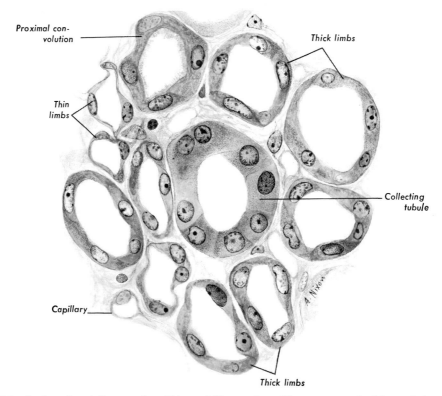

Figure 30-18.   Section of medullary ray from kidney of *Macacus rhesus.* The organ was fixed by perfusion—hence the slightly dilated condition of the tubules. Iron-hematoxylin stain. About 600 ×.

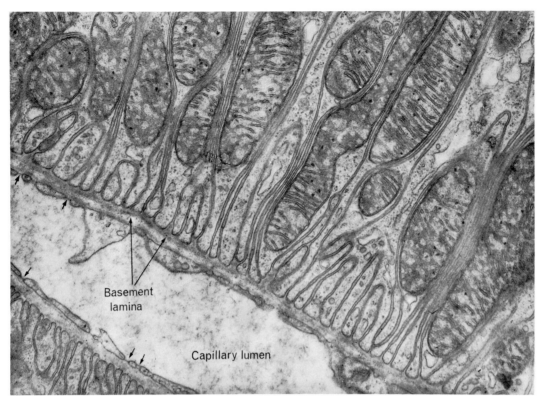

Basement lamina

Capillary lumen

Figure 30-19. Electron micrograph of a portion of the base of a distal convoluted tubule of guinea pig kidney, illustrating the small and large basal compartments. The latter contain long mitochondria oriented perpendicular to the cell base. Notice that the peritubular capillary is of the fenestrated type with several of its pores indicated by arrows. × 20,000. (Courtesy of A. Ichikawa.)

is also reabsorbed in the proximal convoluted tubule, and it is calculated that nearly ½ pound of glucose and more than three pounds of sodium chloride are recovered per day from the glomerular filtrate of man. If the level of glucose in the blood is raised experimentally above a certain level, the glucose is not completely absorbed and appears in the urine. This *tubular maximum for reabsorption of glucose* (glucose Tm) is a useful index of the reabsorptive capacity of the kidney tubules.

Other metabolically important substances that are reabsorbed in the proximal tubule are amino acids, protein, acetoacetic acid, and ascorbic acid. On leaving the proximal tubules, the fluid contains essentially none of these substances. The absorption of proteins in the proximal tubule has been followed morphologically by intravenous administration of peroxidase and its subsequent detection by a histochemical method (Graham and Karnovsky). Similar studies have been carried out by administration of ferritin and ^{125}I labeled albumin by micropuncture, followed by direct or autoradiographic visualization of the tracer

substance (Maunsbach). The results of these studies are in close agreement, all showing uptake in the apical invaginations and apical vacuoles within a very few minutes. In 30 to 60 minutes the label is localized in acid phosphatase–containing dense granules interpreted as lysosomes. It is assumed that absorbed albumin is degraded by the lysosomes and not returned to the bloodstream.

Thus, some useful substances are conserved by reabsorption. On the other hand, the end products of metabolism, *urea, uric acid,* and *creatinine,* which are of little or no use to the body, are not avidly reabsorbed but are allowed to remain in the urine and are eliminated from the body. While some 99 per cent of the water of the glomerular filtrate is conserved, only 40 per cent of the urea and none of the creatinine is reabsorbed.

In addition to its capacity for active reabsorption, the proximal tubule has the capacity to secrete creatinine, para-aminohippuric acid, the organic iodine compound, Diodrast, and sulfonic dyes such as phenol red. The secretory capacity of the proximal tubule

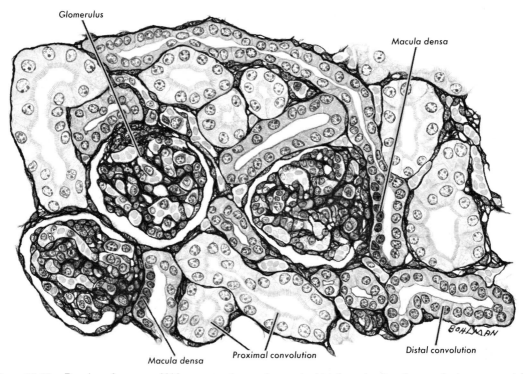

Glomerulus

Macula densa

Macula densa

Proximal convolution

Distal convolution

Figure 30-20. Drawing of an area of kidney cortex from a six month old infant, showing the macula densa, a specialized area of the distal tubule adjacent to the renal corpuscle and its afferent arteriole. Mallory-azan stain. × 200.

does not have the physiological importance in man that it does in some lower animals, particularly those fish that have aglomerular kidneys. However, the substances that are secreted are useful in the clinical evaluation of kidney function and renal blood flow. When introduced into the blood in moderate concentrations, Diodrast and para-aminohippuric acid are entirely removed during a single passage of blood through the kidneys. Since it is impossible to remove by filtration all the substances dissolved in the blood and have any fluid plasma left, the complete removal of a substance in one passage of blood through the kidney must occur in part by filtration and in part by excretory work. Knowing the concentration of such a substance in the blood and the amount found in the urine produced in a given period of time, one can calculate the blood flow through the kidney. The blood flow is equal to the plasma flow plus the cell volume found by hematocrit. From the values for Diodrast clearance and for inulin clearance, one can determine the fraction of renal plasma flow which is filtered by the glomeruli. Thus,

$$\text{Filtration fraction} = \frac{\text{Inulin clearance}}{\text{Diodrast clearance}}$$

If now one raises the concentration of Diodrast in the blood, a point is reached at which the kidney fails to remove all the material from the blood. The maximum concentration which is completely cleared is taken as a measure of the *excretory capacity of the tubule* (*Tm–tubular maximum*). If the values are known for renal plasma flow and inulin clearance, the measurement of other substances (such as urea, uric acid, and phosphate and bicarbonate buffers) in the blood and urine can be related to the activities of the total number of nephrons with regard to these substances. In this way it has been determined which substances are secreted, which are reabsorbed, and which diffuse passively from the glomerular filtrate. The localizations of these specific events in various portions of the tubule are less well known.

Loop of Henle and Distal Tubule. The loop of Henle is an essential element in the production of hypertonic urine. Only the birds and mammals which have a thin segment in the loop produce a urine that is hypertonic to the blood plasma. The fluids in the renal cortex are isosmotic with plasma, but there is a continuous increase in osmotic pressure from the corticomedullary junction to the tip of the papilla. This is attributed to the arrangement of the loop of Henle and the properties of the different segments of its wall. In the descending limb, the wall is freely permeable to sodium and to water, whereas the ascending limb is believed to be impermeable to water; its cells are the site of a "sodium pump" that moves sodium from the urine into the interstitial spaces of the medulla, increasing the osmotic concentration there. Water therefore leaves the descending limb of the loop by passive diffusion and the urine becomes increasingly concentrated as it passes deeper into the medulla toward the turn of the loop. A constantly increasing proximodistal osmotic gradient is therefore maintained. Owing to the arrangement of the descending and ascending limbs of the vessels in the bundles of vasa recta, which are very close to one another (Figs. 30-16 and 30-17), they constitute a countercurrent exchange system permitting equilibration of concentration of the blood in the descending and ascending limbs. This arrangement is thought to keep these vessels from disturbing the osmotic gradient in the medulla, which is necessary for concentration of the urine.

The active pumping of sodium out of the ascending limb of the loop of Henle renders the urine hypotonic by the time it reaches the distal convoluted tubule. The pumping of sodium continues in the distal convolution, but some of the sodium is replaced by other cations, such as potassium and hydrogen, or by ammonia derived from glutamine by oxidative deamination. The distal tubule is therefore the principal site of acidification of the urine.

In the *absence* of the antidiuretic hormone of the posterior lobe of the hypophysis, the distal tubule and collecting ducts are impermeable to water. Under these conditions the urine passing through the medulla would remain dilute in spite of the concentration gradient in the surrounding interstitium. In the *presence* of antidiuretic hormone, the collecting ducts become highly permeable to water, and thus exposure to the high osmolarity of the medulla results in removal of water and secretion of concentrated urine. By hormonal regulation of the permeability of the distal tubule and collecting ducts, the concentration of the urine can be varied over a wide range.

The efficiency of reabsorption of sodium is under hormonal control. Aldosterone secreted by the zona glomerulosa of the adrenal cortex acts specifically on the renal tubules to increase their rate of sodium absorption. In the absence of aldosterone there is a serious loss of sodium in the urine; when it is present in normal amounts some 1200 gm. of sodium are reabsorbed each day and only a few hundred milligrams escape in the urine.

PASSAGES FOR THE EXCRETION OF URINE

The excretory passages convey the urine from the parenchyma of the kidney to the outside. Their walls are provided with a well developed coat of smooth muscle. Its contractions move the urine forward.

The calyces, the pelvis, the ureter, and the bladder all have a similar structure, although the thickness of the wall gradually increases in the sequence indicated. The inner surface is lined with a mucous membrane. There is no distinct submucosa, and the lamina propria of the mucosa is attached to the smooth muscle coat, which is covered by an adventitial layer of connective tissue.

Although it is of mesodermal origin in the

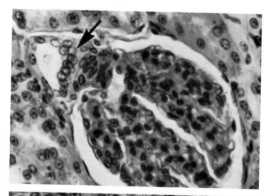

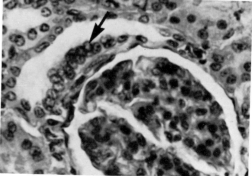

Figure 30-21. Photomicrograph of two renal corpuscles from macaque kidney, showing (at arrows) two typical examples of the macula densa, an area of the wall of the distal tubule where the cells are thicker and the nuclei are crowded together and superimposed. × 175.

ureter and of endodermal origin in the bladder, the lining of the mucous membrane in all the parts of the urinary tract just mentioned is the same, *transitional epithelium.* In the calyces it is two or three cells thick and in the ureter four or five. In the empty bladder six to eight cell layers are seen. In the contracted condition of the wall of the viscus, the epithelium is thick and its cells are rounded or even columnar or club-shaped. In the distended condition, the epithelium is thin and the cells are greatly flattened and stretched parallel to the surface.

Electron micrographs of transitional epithelium reveal certain fine structural features peculiar to this tissue. The free surface of the epithelial cells has a characteristic scalloped appearance, and there is a superficial ectoplasmic layer consisting of a feltwork of fine filaments. In the cytoplasm of the superficial cells are flattened vesicles which present fusiform profiles in section. The limiting membrane of these structures is thicker than other cytoplasmic membranes and has the dimensions and trilaminar structure typical of the cell surface membrane. These components are peculiar to the cells of transitional epithelium, and it has been speculated that they may be structures in which surface membrane is stored and from which it may be mobilized rapidly to provide the membrane necessary for expansion of the surface in distention of the bladder (Porter). In addition, these cells contain numerous small dense bodies interpreted as lysosomes.

The epithelium lining the excretory passages seems to be impermeable to the normal, soluble substances of the urine. If the viscus is damaged, this property may, of course, be greatly altered. *Intraepithelial cysts*—round or oval cavities filled with a peculiar colloidal substance—often develop in the epithelium of the ureter and bladder. No true glands are present in the calyces, the pelvis, or the ureter, but glands may be simulated here by small, solid nests of epithelial cells within the thick-

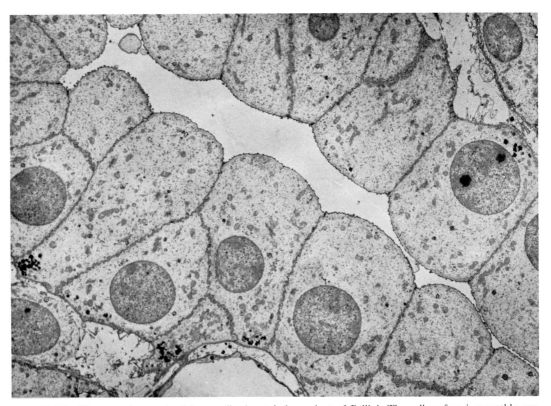

Figure 30-22. Electron micrograph of large collecting tubule or duct of Bellini. The cell surface is smoothly contoured and convex; the cytoplasm contains relatively few organelles and does not give the appearance of being metabolically active. × 2000. (Courtesy of J. Rhodin.)

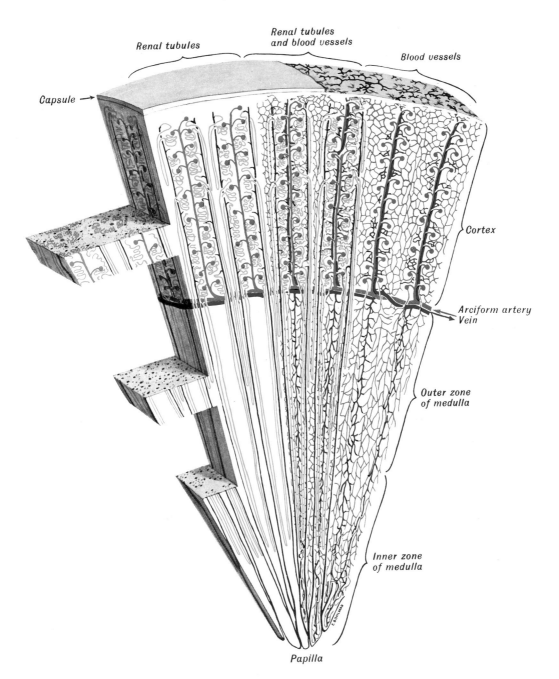

Figure 30-23. Diagram of relations of blood vessels, nephrons, and collecting ducts in kidney. The actual structures are much more complicated than those indicated here. Arteries, red; veins, blue; glomeruli, red dots; nephrons, green; collecting ducts, black. Six interlobular arteries and attached glomeruli are shown. The right-hand pair shows their relation to the veins, the left-hand pair their relation to nephrons, and the central pair their relations to both nephrons and veins. The intertubular capillaries of the cortex and medulla are shown, but the descending bundles of vasa recta running downward from the juxtamedullary glomeruli are not clearly illustrated. (Extensively modified from the diagrams of Peter, Braus, and von Möllendorff.)

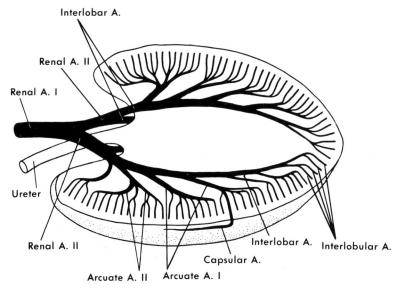

Figure 30-24. Schematic transverse section of a dog kidney to show the branching and distribution of the renal artery. (After A. Kügelgen and K. J. Otto, *in* Zwanglose Abhandlungen aus dem Gebiet der normalen und pathologischen Anatomie. Vol. 5. Stuttgart, Georg Thieme, 1959.)

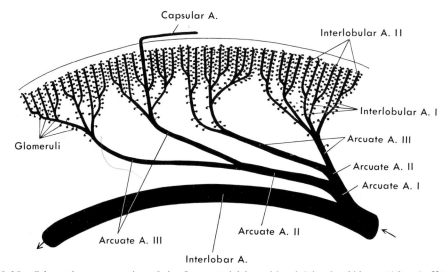

Figure 30-25. Schematic representation of the finer arterial branching in the dog kidney. (After A. Kügelgen and K. J. Otto, *in* Zwanglose Abhandlungen aus dem Gebiet der normalen und pathologischen Anatomie. Vol. 5. Stuttgart, Georg Thieme, 1959.)

ness of the epithelial sheet. In the urinary bladder, however, and in the vicinity of the internal urethral orifice, small invaginations of the epithelium into the subjacent connective tissue can be found. They contain numerous, clear, mucus-secreting cells and are similar to the glands of Littré in the urethra.

No distinct "basement membrane" can be discerned with the light microscope between the epithelium and the lamina propria, but a thin basal lamina is revealed in electron micrographs. The connective tissue, especially in the ureter, forms thin folds that may penetrate deep into the epithelium.

The dense connective tissue of the mucous membrane generally does not form any papillae. It contains elastic networks and sometimes small lymphatic nodules. Its deeper layers have a looser arrangement. The mucous membrane in the empty ureter, therefore, is thrown into several longitudinal folds, which in cross sections cause a festooned appearance of the edge of the lumen (Fig. 30-28). In the bladder the deep, looser layer of connective tissue is especially abundant, so that in the contracted condition of the organ, the mucous membrane forms numerous thick folds. In some places a thin layer of smooth muscle fibers seems to divide the connective tissue into a superficial lamina propria and a deeper submucous layer.

The muscular coat of the urinary passages generally consists of an *inner* longitudinal and an *outer* circular layer. Beginning with the lower third of the ureter, a third external longitudinal layer is added, which is especially prominent in the bladder. In contrast to those of the intestine, the smooth muscles in the urinary passages do not form regular layers but appear as loose, anastomosing strands, separated by abundant connective tissue and elastic networks, which continue into the lamina propria mucosae.

In the small calyces, which are hollow cones capping the papillae of the pyramids, the strands of the inner longitudinal muscle layer end at the attachment of the calyx to the papilla. The outer circular strands reach higher up and form a muscular ring around the base of the papilla.

The calyces show periodic contractions moving from their base to their apex. This muscular activity helps to move the urine out of the papillary ducts into the calyces. The muscular coat of the ureter also performs slow

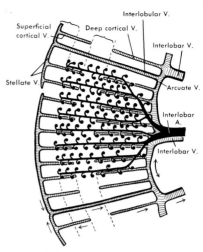

Figure 30-26. Schematic representation of the vascular architecture and vascular zones of the cortex. (After A. Kügelgen, *in* Zwanglose Abhandlungen aus dem Gebiet der normalen und pathologischen Anatomie. Vol. 5. Stuttgart, Georg Thieme, 1959.)

peristaltic movements. The waves of contraction proceed from the pelvis toward the bladder.

Because the *ureters* pierce the wall of the bladder obliquely, their openings are usually closed by the pressure of the contents of the bladder and are open only when the urine is forced through them. A fold of the mucous membrane of the bladder acts as a valve and usually prevents the backflow of the urine. In the "intramural" part of the ureters, the circular muscular strands of their wall disappear, and the connective tissue of the mucous membrane is occupied by longitudinal muscular strands whose contraction opens the lumen of the ureter.

The muscular coat of the *bladder* is very strong. Its thick strands of smooth muscle cells form three layers, which, however, cannot be clearly distinguished from each other. The outer longitudinal layer is developed best on the dorsal and ventral surfaces of the viscus, while in other places its strands may be wide apart. The middle circular or spiral layer is the thickest of all. The inner layer in the body of the bladder consists of relatively sparse, separate longitudinal or oblique strands. In the region of the trigone, thin, dense bundles of smooth muscle form a circular mass around the internal opening of the urethra—the internal sphincter of the bladder.

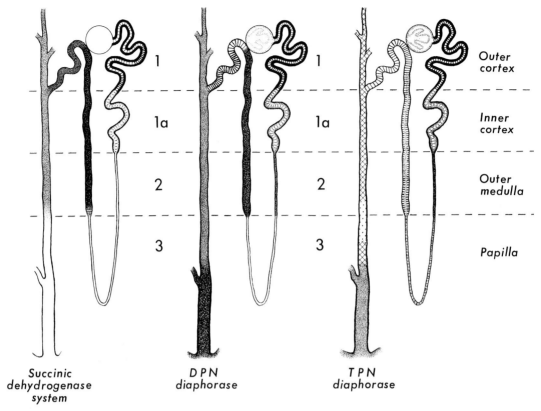

Figure 30-27. Diagram of the segmental localization of three oxidative enzymes in the rat nephron in relation to the zones of the kidney. The stippling and the types of cross hatching represent different color reactions; the intensity of the stippling and of the cross hatchings reflect intensities of the stains. Such preparations offer further evidence that the conventional segments of the nephron may be subdivided into smaller functional segments. The functional significance of this distribution of enzymes in the nephron is not known. (Redrawn and modified from the colored diagram of W. H. Sternberg, E. Farber, and C. Dunlap.)

BLOOD VESSELS, LYMPHATICS, AND NERVES. The blood vessels of the excretory passages penetrate first through the muscular coat and provide it with capillaries. Then they form a plexus in the deeper layers of the mucous membrane. From here small arteries pass toward the surface and form a rich capillary plexus immediately under the epithelium.

The deeper layers of the mucosa and the muscularis in the pelvis and the ureters contain a well-developed network of lymph capillaries. In the bladder they are said to be present only in the muscularis.

Nerve plexuses, small ganglia, and scattered nerve cells can be found in the adventitial and muscular coats of the ureter. Most of the fibers supply the muscles, but some fibers of apparently efferent nature have been traced into the mucosa and the epithelium.

A sympathetic nerve plexus in the ad-ventitial coat of the bladder, the *plexus vesicalis*, is formed in part by the pelvic nerves, which originate from the sacral nerves, and in part by the branches of the hypogastric plexus. The vesical plexus sends numerous nerves into the muscular coat. A continuation of the nerve plexus, but seemingly without nerve cells, is found in the connective tissue of the mucous membrane. Here the sensory nerve endings are located. Many fibers penetrate into the epithelium between the cells, forming varicose free endings.

Urethra

MALE URETHRA. The male urethra has a length of 18 to 20 cm. Three parts can be distinguished. The short proximal segment surrounded by the prostate is the *pars prostatica*. Here the posterior wall of the urethra forms an

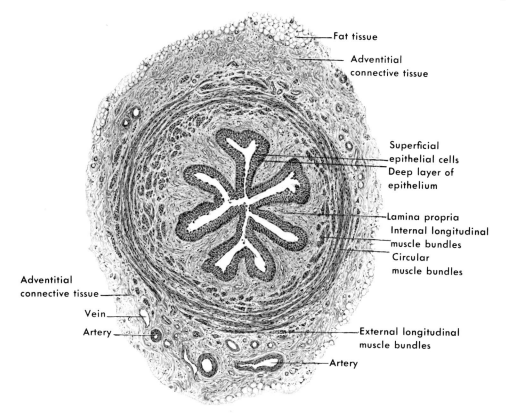

Figure 30-28. Cross section of markedly contracted human ureter. × 30. (After Schaffer.)

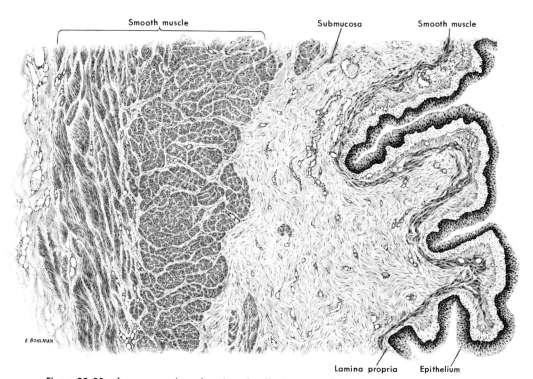

Figure 30-29. Low power view of section of wall of contracted urinary bladder of *Macacus rhesus*.

elevation, the *colliculus seminalis*. On its surface, in the midline, the *utriculus prostaticus* opens. Located to the right and to the left of this are the two slitlike openings of the ejaculatory ducts and the numerous openings of the prostatic gland. The second very short segment (18 mm. long), the *pars membranacea*, extends from the lower end of the prostate to the bulb of the corpus spongiosum penis. The third portion, the *pars spongiosa* (*pars cavernosa*), about 15 cm. long, passes lengthwise through the corpus spongiosum of the penis.

The prostatic part is lined by the same transitional type of epithelium as the bladder. The pars membranacea and the pars cavernosa are lined by a stratified or pseudostratified columnar epithelium. Patches of stratified squamous epithelium are common in the pars spongiosa. In the terminal enlarged part of the canal, the fossa navicularis, stratified squamous epithelium occurs as a rule. In the surface epithelium, occasional mucous goblet cells may be found. Intraepithelial cysts containing a colloid-like substance are common. Lymphocytes migrating through the epithelium are rare.

The lamina propria of the mucosa is a loose connective tissue with abundant elastic networks. No separate submucous layer can be distinguished. This connective tissue contains numerous scattered bundles of smooth muscle, mainly longitudinally directed. In the outer layers, however, circular bundles are also present. The lamina propria has no distinct papillae; the latter appear only in the fossa navicularis. The membranous portion of the urethra is surrounded by a mass of striated muscle, a part of the urogenital diaphragm.

The surface of the mucous membrane of the urethra shows many recesses, the *lacunae of Morgagni*. These outpocketings continue into deeper, branching tubules, the *glands of Littré*. The larger ones among them are found especially on the dorsal surface of the pars spongiosa of the urethra. They run obliquely in the lamina propria and are directed with their

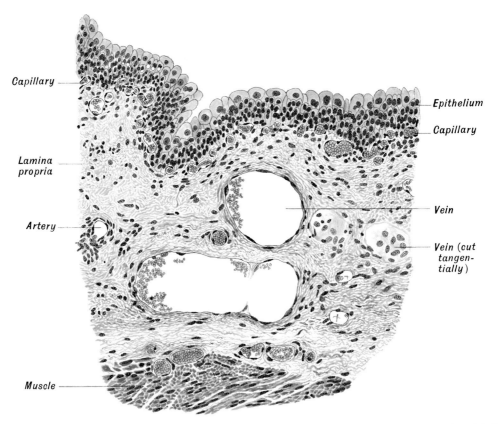

Figure 30-30. Section of wall of human urinary bladder in contracted condition; capillaries penetrate the epithelium. × 150. (After A. A. Maximow.)

Encapsulated sensory nerve ending

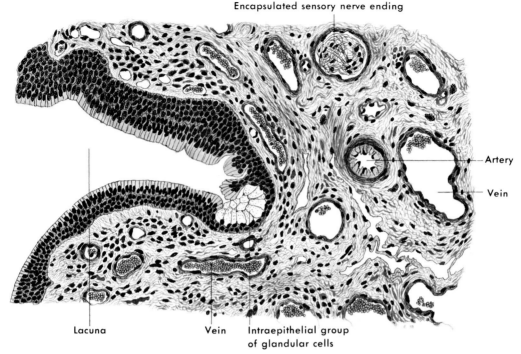

Artery

Vein

Lacuna   Vein   Intraepithelial group
of glandular cells

Figure 30-31. Section of cavernous part of male human urethra. × 165. (After A. A. Maximow.)

blind end toward the root of the penis. They sometimes penetrate far into the corpus spongiosum. The glands of Littré are lined with the same epithelium as the surface of the mucous membrane, but in many places this epithelium is transformed into compact intraepithelial nests of clear cells, which have the staining reactions of mucus. In old age some of the recesses of the urethral mucosa may contain concretions similar to those of the prostate.

FEMALE URETHRA. The female urethra is 25 to 30 mm. long. Its mucous membrane forms longitudinal folds and is lined with stratified squamous epithelium. In many cases, however, pseudostratified columnar epithelium can be found. Numerous invaginations are formed by the epithelium. The outpocketings in their wall are lined in many places with clear mucous cells, as in the glands of Littré of the male urethra. The glands may accumulate colloid material in their cavities or may even contain concretions.

The lamina propria, devoid of papillae, is a loose connective tissue with abundant elastic fibers. It is provided with a highly developed system of venous plexuses and has, therefore, a character resembling the corpus spongiosum of the male.

The mucous membrane with its veins is surrounded by a thick mass of smooth muscles; the inner layers of the latter have a longitudinal, the outer layers a circular, arrangement. Distally, the smooth muscles are strengthened by a sphincter of striated muscle.

HISTOGENESIS OF THE KIDNEY

The independent origin of the nephrons and the collecting tubules in the embryo has been mentioned. The nephrons develop through differentiation of a compact, mesenchyme-like tissue, the *metanephric blastema,* which arises from the mesoderm. The system of excretory ducts arises as a hollow outgrowth of the wolffian duct, in much the same manner as other epithelial' glands develop. This outgrowth grows forward in the mesenchyme as the primordium of the ureter and of the renal pelvis. It forms four branches—the primordia of the calyces, which end blindly in club-shaped dilatations, each of which forms secondary, tertiary, and progressively smaller branches corresponding to the collecting tubules of various orders.

In human embryos of 7 mm. the metanephric blastema adheres to the wall of the dilated primordium of the pelvis and appears in sections as a semilunar *cap*. As the branches of the pelvis form, the metanephric cap separates into a piece for each branch (human embryos of 9.5 mm.), so that the ampullar dilatation of each branch carries its own metanephric cap.

In human embryos 13 to 19 mm. in length, the edges of the cap covering each blind end of the collecting tubules swell and glide down its sides. As the ampulla divides dichotomously, the metanephrogenic cap is divided equally between the two new ampulae.

The roundish, compact metanephric body soon acquires an eccentric lumen around which its cells become radially arranged; it is now called the metanephric vesicle. Next it stretches and is transformed into an S-shaped tubule, which grows rapidly in length and becomes tortuous; this is the future nephron. One end of it coalesces with, and opens into, the neighboring collecting tubule. The other

end enlarges and flattens slightly, and a tuft of capillaries develops within its concavity and establishes connections with a terminal of the renal artery. In this way the malpighian or renal corpuscle is formed, with its capsule and glomerulus. In the meantime the collecting tubules continue to grow toward the periphery and to branch dichotomously, still keeping their metanephrogenic caps.

Succeeding generations of nephrons with their renal corpuscles are added to the branching tree of the collecting tubules, until the whole metanephric blastema is exhausted. This continues in the human fetus throughout the latter period of intrauterine life and comes to its end six or eight days after birth.

When the glomerulus first develops in the concavity of the wall of the capsule of Bowman, the visceral epithelium is much thicker than the parietal. Later, both layers become simple squamous epithelia. Soon after the S-shaped tubule of the nephron becomes con-

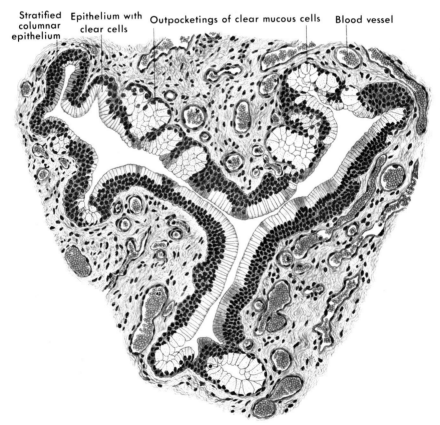

Figure 30-32.   Section of urethral gland (gland of Littré) from cavernous part of male human urethra. × 165. (After A. A. Maximow.)

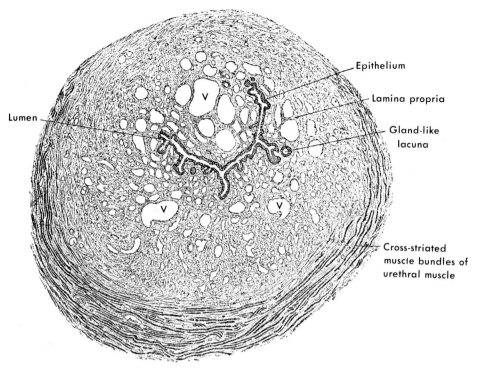

Lumen

Epithelium

Lamina propria

Gland-like lacuna

Cross-striated muscle bundles of urethral muscle

Figure 30-33. Cross section through urethra of a woman. The darker portions of the lamina propria are smooth muscle bundles. × 10. (After von Ebner.)

nected with the collecting tubule, the histological differentiation of the different parts of the nephron begins. The proximal part, adjacent to the capsule, becomes tortuous, and its epithelium develops a glandular character, increases in height, and its cytoplasm stains with acid dyes. The following stretch of the tubule forms a loop, which slips out of the coils formed by the convoluted tubule and extends toward the renal pelvis. The epithelium of the collecting tubules soon acquires its typical clear appearance; this differentiation begins in the deeper parts, which are nearer to the pelvis, and gradually extends peripherally.

The terminal branches of the collecting tubules and the nephrons may sometimes miss each other and remain disconnected. In such cases the convoluted tubules with their renal corpuscles continue for some time to elaborate urine and, having no outlet, are gradually transformed into cysts. The cystic kidney is a not uncommon abnormality of development.

REFERENCES

Barajas, L.: The development and ultrastructure of the juxtaglomerular cell granule. J. Ultrastruct. Res., *15:*400, 1966.

Bulger, R. E.: The shape of rat kidney tubular cells. Am. J. Anat., *116:*237, 1965.

Bulger, R. E., C. C. Tisher, C. H. Myers, and B. F. Trump: Human renal ultrastructure. II. The thin limb of Henle's loop and the interstitium in healthy individuals. Lab. Invest., *16:*124, 1967.

Chambers, R., and R. T. Kempton: Indications of function of the chick mesonephros in tissue culture with phenol red. J. Cell & Comp. Physiol., *3:*131, 1933.

Chandra, S., J. C. Hubbard, F. R. Skelton, L. L. Bernardis, and S. Kamura: Genesis of juxtaglomerular cell granules. A physiologic, light and electron microscopic study concerning experimental renal hypertension. Lab. Invest., *14:*1834, 1965.

Dunihue, F. W., and W. G. Boldosser: Observations on the similarity of mesangial to juxtaglomerular cells. Lab. Invest., *12:*1228, 1963.

Edelman, R., and P. M. Hartroft: Localization of renin in the juxtaglomerular cells of the rabbit and dog through the use of the fluorescent antibody technique. Circulation Res., *9:*1069, 1961.

Edwards, J. G.: Studies on aglomerular and glomerular kidneys. Am. J. Anat., *42:*75, 1928.

Ericsson, J. L.: Transport and digestion of hemoglobin in the proximal tubule. II. Electron microscope. Lab. Invest., *14:*16, 1965.

Farber, E., W. H. Sternberg, and C. E. Dunlap: Histochemical localization of specific oxidative enzymes. I. Tetrazolium stains for diphosphopyridine nucleotide diaphorase and triphosphopyridine nucleotide diaphorase. III. Evaluation studies of tetrazolium staining methods for diphosphopyridine nucleotide diaphorase, triphosphopyridine nucleotide diaphorase and the succindehydrogenase system. J. Histochem., *4:*254, 284, 1956.

Farquhar, M. G.: Glomerular permeability investigated by electron microscopy. *In* Small Blood Vessel Involvement. *In* Diabetes, p. 31, A.I.B.S., 1964.

Farquhar, M. G., and G. E. Palade: Functional evidence for the existence of a third cell type in the renal glomerulus. Phagocytosis of filtration residues by a distinctive "third" cell. J. Cell Biol., *13:*55, 1962.

Farquhar, M. G., S. L. Wissig, and G. E. Palade: Glomerular permeability. I. Ferritin transfer across the normal glomerular capillary wall. J. Exper. Med., *113*:47, 1961.

Forster, R. P.: Kidney cells. *In* Brachet, J., and A. E. Mirsky, eds.: The Cell; Biochemistry, Physiology, Morphology. New York, Academic Press. 1961, Vol. 5, p. 89.

Gersh, I.: Histochemical studies on the mammalian kidney. II. The glomerular elimination of uric acid in the rabbit. Anat. Rec., *58*:369, 1934.

Gersh, I.: The correlation of structure and function in the developing mesonephros and metanephros. Carnegie Contributions to Embryol., *26*:33, 1937.

Goormaghtigh, N.: Existence of an endocrine gland in the media of the renal arterioles. Proc. Soc. Exper. Biol. & Med., *42*:688, 1939.

Gottschalk, C. W.: Micropuncture studies of tubular function in the mammalian kidney. Fifth Bowditch Lecture. Physiologist, *4*:35, 1961.

Grafflin, A. L.: The normal, acromegalic and the hyperplastic human nephron. Arch. Path., *27*:691, 1939.

Graham, R. C., and M. J. Karnovsky: The early stages of absorption of injected horseradish peroxidase in the proximal tubules of mouse kidney: Ultrastructural cytochemistry by a new technique. J. Histochem. & Cytochem., *14*:291, 1966.

Graham, R. C.: Glomerular permeability. Ultrastructural cytochemical studies using peroxidases as protein tracers. J. Exper. Med., *124*:1123, 1966.

Hartroft, P. M.: Juxtaglomerular cells. Circulation Res., *12*:525, 1963.

von Kügelgen, A., B. Kuhlo, M. Kuhlo, and K. J. Otto: Die Gefässarchitectur der Niere. Stuttgart, Georg Thieme Verlag, 1959.

Kurtz, S. M., and J. D. Feldman: Experimental studies on the formation of the glomerular basement membrane. J. Ultrastruct. Res., *6*:19, 1962.

Lassen, N. A., and J. B. Longley: Countercurrent exchange in vessels in the renal medulla. Proc. Soc. Exper. Biol. & Med., *106*:743, 1961.

Longley, J. B., and E. R. Fisher: Alkaline phosphatase and the periodic acid–Schiff reaction in the proximal tubule of the vertebrate kidney; a study in segmental differentiation. Anat. Rec., *120*:1, 1954.

Maunsbach, A. B.: The influence of different fixatives and fixation methods on the ultrastructure of rat kidney proximal tubule cells. I. Comparison of different perfusion fixation methods and of glutaraldehyde, formaldehyde and osmium tetroxide fixatives. J. Ultrastruct. Res., *15*:242, 1966.

Maunsbach, A. B.: Absorption of I¹²⁵ labeled homologous albumin by rat kidney proximal tubule cells. J. Ultrastruct. Res., *15*:197, 1966.

Maunsbach, A. B.: Isolation and purification of acid phosphatase containing autofluorescent granules from homogenates of rat kidney cortex. J. Ultrastruct. Res., *16*:13, 1966.

Miller, F.: Hemoglobin absorption by the cells of the proximal convoluted tubule in mouse kidney. J. Biophys. & Biochem. Cytol., *8*:689, 1960.

Miller, F., and G. Palade: Lytic activities in renal protein absorption droplets. An electron microscopical cytochemical study. J. Cell Biol., *23*:519, 1964.

von Möllendorff, W.: Der Exkretionsapparat. In von Möllendorff, W., and W. Bargmann, eds.: Handbuch der mikroskopischen Anatomie des Menschen, Berlin, Julius Springer, 1930, Vol. 7, part 1, p. 1.

Oliver, J.: New directions in renal morphology; A method, its results and its future. The Harvey Lectures, *40*:102, 1944–45.

Osvaldo, L., and H. Latta: The thin limb of the loop of Henle. J. Ultrastruct. Res., *15*:144, 1966.

Pease, D. C.: Electron microscopy of the tubular cells of the kidney cortex. Anat. Rec., *121*:723, 1955.

Peter, K.: Untersuchungen über Bau und Entwicklung der Niere. Jena, G. Fischer, 1927.

Pierce, E. C.: Renal lymphatics. Anat. Rec., *90*:315, 1944.

Policard, A.: Le tube urinaire des mammifères. Rev. Gén. d'histol., *3*:fasc. 10, 1905.

Rhodin, J.: Correlation of ultrastructural organization and function in normal and experimentally changed proximal convoluted tubule cells of the mouse kidney. Stockholm, Aktiebolaget Godvil, 1954.

Rhodin, J.: Anatomy of kidney tubules. Int. Rev. Cytol., *7*:485, 1958.

Rhodin, J.: Electron microscopy of the kidney. Am. J. Med., *24*:661, 1958.

Richards, A. N., and A. M. Walker: Methods of collecting fluid from known regions of the renal tubules of amphibia and of perfusing the lumen of a single tubule. Am. J. Physiol., *118*:111, 1937, and following papers.

Richards, A. N.: Processes of urine formation. Proc. Roy. Soc. B., *126*:398, 1938.

Schloss, G.: The juxtaglomerular E-cells of rat kidneys in diuresis and antidiuresis, after adrenalectomy and hypophysectomy, and in avitaminosis A, D and E. Acta Anat., *6*:80, 1948.

Schmidt-Nielsen, B.: Urea excretion in mammals. Physiol. Rev., *38*:139, 1958.

Sjöstrand, F. S., and J. Rhodin: The ultrastructure of the proximal convoluted tubules of the mouse kidney as revealed by high resolution electron microscopy. Exper. Cell Res., *4*:426, 1953.

Smith, H. W.: The Kidney. New York, Oxford University Press, 1951.

Smith, H. W.: Principles of Renal Physiology. New York, Oxford University Press, 1956.

Spargo, B.: Kidney changes in hypokalemic alkalosis in the rat. J. Lab. & Clin. Med., *43*:802, 1954.

Spargo, B., F. Straus, and F. Fitch: Zonal renal papillary droplet change with potassium depletion. Arch. Path., *70*:599, 1960.

Sternberg, W. H., E. Farber, and C. E. Dunlap: Histochemical localization of specific oxidative enzymes. II. Localization of diphosphopyridine nucleotide diaphorase and triphosphopyridine nucleotide diaphorase and the succindehydrogenase system in the kidney. J. Histochem., *4*:266, 1956.

Straus, W.: Localization of intravenously injected horseradish peroxidase in the cells of the convoluted tubules of rat kidney. Exper. Cell Res., *20*:600, 1960.

Thorburn, G. D., H. H. Kopald, J. A. Herd, M. Hollenberg, C. C. C. O'Morchoe, and A. C. Barger: Intrarenal distribution of nutrient blood flow determined with krypton⁸⁵ in the unanaesthetized dog. Circulation Res., *13*:290, 1963.

Tobian, L.: Relationship of juxtaglomerular apparatus to renin and angiotensin. Circulation, *25*:189, 1962.

Trueta, J., A. E. Barclay, P. M. Daniel, K. J. Franklin, and M. M. L. Prichard: Studies of the Renal Circulation. Springfield, Ill., Charles C Thomas, 1947.

Ullrich, K. J., K. Kramer, and J. W. Boylan: Present knowledge of the countercurrent system in the mammalian kidney. Progress in Cardiovascular Diseases, *3*:395, 1961.

Walker, A. M., P. A. Bott, J. Oliver, and M. C. MacDowell: The collection and analysis of fluid from single nephrons of the mammalian kidney. Am. J. Physiol., *134*:580, 1941.

Wirz, H., B. Hargitay, and W. Kuhn: Lokalisation des Konzentrierungsprozesses in der Niere durch direkte Kryoskopie. Helvet. physiol. et pharmacol. Acta, *9*:196, 1951.

Yamada, E.: The fine structure of the renal glomerulus of the mouse. J. Biophys. & Biochem. Cytol., *1*:551, 1955.

Zimmermann, K. W.: Über den Bau des Glomerulus der Säugetiere, Weitere Mitteilungen. Zeitschr. f. mikr.-anat. Forsch., *32*:176, 1933.

CHAPTER THIRTY-ONE

Male Reproductive System

TESTIS

The testis is a compound tubular gland enclosed in a thick fibrous capsule, the *tunica albuginea*. On the posterior aspect of the organ, a thickening of the capsule projects into the gland as the *mediastinum testis*. Thin fibrous septa, called the *septula testis*, extend radially from the mediastinum to the tunica albuginea, dividing the organ into about 250 pyramidal compartments, the *lobuli testis*. The septula may be incomplete toward the periphery, so that the lobules intercommunicate, but where their apices converge upon the mediastinum they are more completely separated.

Each lobule is made of one to four highly convoluted *seminiferous tubules*. These are 150 to 250 μ in diameter, 30 to 70 cm. long and extremely tortuous (Figs. 31-2 and 31-37). The combined length of the seminiferous tubules in all the lobules of the human testis is estimated to be 250 m. They constitute the *exocrine* portion of the testis, which is in essence a cytogenous gland whose secretory product is whole cells, the *spermatozoa*. The tubules are usually highly convoluted loops, but they may branch or end blindly. At the apex of each lobule its seminiferous tubules pass abruptly into the *tubuli recti*, the first segment of the system of excretory ducts. They in turn are confluent with the *rete testis*, a plexiform system of epithelium lined spaces in the connective tissue of the mediastinum.

On the inner aspect of the tunica albuginea, dense connective tissue gives way to a looser layer provided with numerous blood vessels, the *tunica vasculosa testis*. A loose connective tissue of similar character extends inward from this layer to fill all of the interstices among the seminiferous tubules. It contains fibroblasts, macrophages, mast cells, and perivascular mesenchymal cells. In addition there are nests of epithelioid cells, called the *interstitial cells* or *Leydig cells*. These constitute the *endocrine tissue* of the testis.

The testes are suspended in the scrotum at the end of the spermatic cords, each of which consists of the excretory duct of the testis, the *ductus deferens*, and the blood vessels and nerves supplying the testis on that side. The *epididymis*, an elongated organ closely applied to the posterior surface of the testis, is made up of the convoluted proximal part of the excretory duct system. Each testis and epididymis is surrounded on its anterior and lateral surfaces by a cleftlike serous cavity that arises late in embryonic development as a detached portion of the peritoneal cavity.

The testes develop in the dorsal wall of the peritoneal cavity and later descend into the scrotum, each carrying with it an outpocketing of the peritoneum, the *tunica vaginalis propria testis*, which forms the serous cavity around the testis. It consists of an outer parietal and an inner visceral layer closely applied to the tunica albuginea of the testis on its anterior and lateral surfaces. On the posterior aspect of the testis, where the blood vessels and nerves enter the organ, the visceral layer is reflected

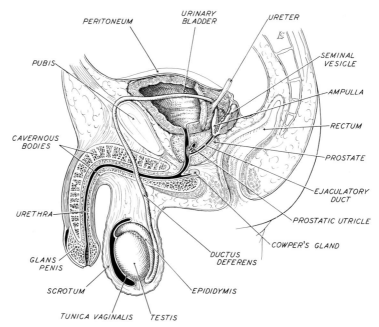

Figure 31-1. Diagrammatic representation of the male genital system. The midline structures are shown in sagittal section; bilateral structures, such as testis, epididymis, vas deferens, and seminal vesicle, are depicted in the round. (After C. D. Turner.)

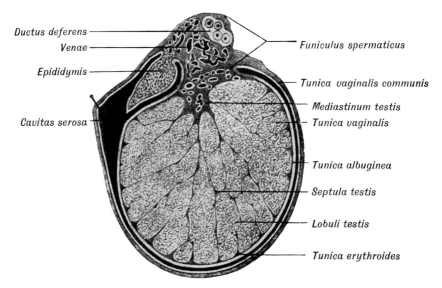

Figure 31-2. Cross section of human testis with its envelopes. × 2. (After Eberth.)

from its surface and is continuous with the parietal layer (Fig. 31-2). After removal of the parietal layer, the visceral coat covering the testis appears as a free, smooth surface covered with mesothelium, which is the remnant of the coelomic or germinal epithelium that covers the primordium of the gonad in the embryo and gives rise to the glandular tissue of the testis. The *tunica vaginalis propria* enables the testis, which is sensitive to pressure, to glide freely in its envelopes.

SEMINIFEROUS EPITHELIUM

In the adult, the seminiferous tubules are lined by a complex stratified epithelium composed of two major categories of cells: *supporting cells* and *spermatogenic cells.* The supporting elements are of a single kind, the *Sertoli cell,* while the spermatogenic cells include several morphologically distinguishable types: *spermatogonia, primary spermatocytes, secondary spermatocytes, spermatids,* and *spermatozoa* (Fig. 31-4). These are not ontogenetically distinct cell types but are clearly distinguishable successive stages in the continuous process of differentiation of the male germ cells.

Each Sertoli cell is fixed to the basal lamina (basement membrane) of the seminiferous epithelium and has its nucleus and cell center situated near it. The remainder of the cell forms an extraordinarily elaborate system of thin processes that extend upward to the free surface, surrounding the spermatogenic cells and filling all the interstices among them. The earliest of the germ cells, the spermatogonia, also rest upon the basal lamina, while the later stages are found at successively higher levels in the epithelium (Figs. 31-6 and 31-7). The continual proliferative activity of the seminiferous epithelium is confined to the spermatogonia and spermatocytes near the base, and the neogenesis of succeeding generations of cells in this region displaces the more mature forms to higher levels as they differentiate, so that, as mature spermatozoa, they come to border directly upon the lumen.

SERTOLI CELLS OR SUSTENTACULAR CELLS.

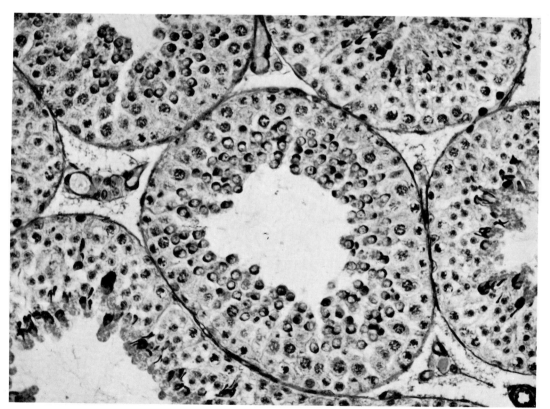

Figure 31-3. Photomicrograph of guinea pig testis, showing several seminiferous tubules in cross section. Blood vessels and a few interstitial cells are seen in the angular interstices between the tubules. Notice that different stages of the cycle of the seminiferous epithelium are found in adjacent tubules. × 220.

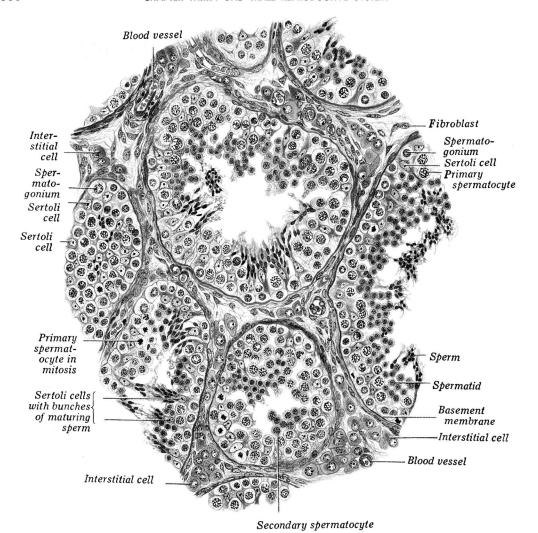

Blood vessel

*Inter-
stitial
cell*

*Sper-
mato-
gonium*

*Sertoli
cell*

*Sertoli
cell*

*Primary
spermat-
ocyte in
mitosis*

*Sertoli cells
with bunches
of maturing
sperm*

Interstitial cell

Fibroblast

*Spermato-
gonium*

Sertoli cell

*Primary
spermatocyte*

Sperm

Spermatid

*Basement
membrane*

Interstitial cell

Blood vessel

Secondary spermatocyte

Figure 31-4.   Section of human testis (obtained at operation). The transected tubules show various stages of spermatogenesis. × 170. (After A. A. Maximow.)

Owing to the elaborate shape of the Sertoli cells and the limitations of resolution of the light microscope, their outlines cannot be seen distinctly. Earlier this gave rise to the widespread belief that they constituted a syncytium, but this interpretation is now known to be erroneous. In sections parallel to the basement lamina of the epithelium, the bases of the Sertoli cells can sometimes be seen with the light microscope as distinctly outlined polygonal areas. Electron micrographs clearly show pairs of apposed membranes at the boundary between adjacent Sertoli cells and between the latter and the germ cells. Therefore, the spermatogenic cells are not embedded in a "Sertolian syncytium" as was formerly thought but instead occupy deep recesses of conforming shape in the lateral and apical surfaces of the sustentacular cells. The shapes of the Sertoli cells are remarkably elaborate because of their close coaptation to the highly irregular and changing contours of the differentiating germ cells that they surround.

The nucleus of the Sertoli cell is generally ovoid in outline but may have one or more deep infoldings of its surface. It is about 9 by 12 μ in average size, with a relatively homogeneous nucleoplasm except for a large and highly characteristic nucleolus consisting of an oval acidophilic portion flanked by two rounded basophilic masses. The tripartite structure of this unusual nucleolus is confirmed in electron micrographs, which show a typical nucleolonema organized around a homogeneous central area of relatively low density and two adjacent darker masses of finely granular material.

In histological preparations the cytoplasm contains slender elongated mitochondria often oriented parallel to the long axis of the cell, wavy bundles of fibrils, numerous lipid droplets, and occasional lipofuscin pigment granules. In electron micrographs there is nothing unusual in the fine structure of these organelles and inclusions. Slender spindle-shaped crystals 10 to 25 μ long, called the crystalloids of Charcot-Böttcher, are also commonly found in Sertoli cells of human testis but not in other species (Figs. 31-6 and 31-8). These consist of dense straight filaments about 150 Å in diameter. The filamentous subunits are poorly ordered and there may be irregular defects in the crystals. Their chemical nature and physiological significance are unknown. Fine filaments are present in the cytoplasmic matrix, and microtubules are abundant and usually oriented parallel to the long axis of the cell. It is not clear whether the fibrillar texture of the cytoplasm seen by light microscopy is attributable to a clumping of the filaments by the fixative into coarser bundles or whether the microtubules also contribute to this appearance.

Granular endoplasmic reticulum is sparse in the Sertoli cells, but the agranular form of this organelle is better developed. For the most part, it is in the form of a network of tubules. These are occasionally continuous with concentric systems of fenestrated cisternae that resemble annulate lamellae. The presence of a moderately extensive smooth surfaced reticulum in the Sertoli cells has been interpreted by some as evidence for their possible secretion of estrogenic steroid hormones.

The Sertoli cells provide mechanical support and protection for the developing germ cells, and it is not unlikely that they participate importantly in their nutrition, although this has not been clearly established. They may also play an active role in the release of the mature spermatozoa. The Sertoli cells are never observed in division in the mature testis, but they are highly resistant to heat, ionizing radiation, and various toxic agents that easily destroy the more sensitive spermatogenic cells.

It will facilitate the student's understanding of the complex cytological changes that take place in the germ cells of the seminiferous epithelium if the structure of the end product—the spermatozoon—is described first.

The Spermatozoon

The mature spermatozoon consists of a *head* and a *tail*. The tail is further divisible into a *neck, middle piece, principal piece,* and *end piece*

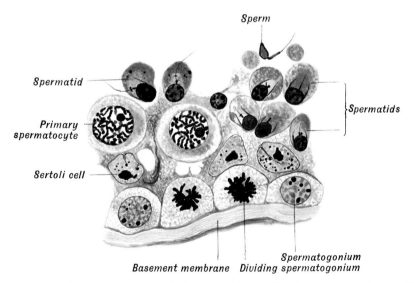

Figure 31-5. Human testis from young adult; seminiferous epithelium with mitoses of spermatogonia. The spermatids show a caudal sheath. Iron-hematoxylin stain. × 750. (After A. A. Maximow.)

on the basis of slight differences in thickness along its length (Fig. 31-9 and 31-10). There are significant differences in the internal structure of these segments, but in fresh preparations or sections these details cannot be resolved. Special cytological methods or electron microscopy are required to bring out these features. The *middle piece* is cylindrical in form and has a length of 5 to 7 μ and a thickness of somewhat more than 1 μ. It extends from a slender connecting piece immediately behind the posterior pole of the head to a ringlike structure called the *annulus*. The *principal piece*

is about 45 μ long and about half a micron thick at the base, gradually tapering toward the *end piece*. The latter is about 5 μ long.

The shape of the mammalian sperm head varies greatly from species to species, whereas the structural organization of the tail is quite constant. In the human, the head is a flattened, almond-shaped body measuring 4 to 5 μ in length and 2.5 to 3.5 μ in width. It consists of the condensed nucleus, covered on its anterior two thirds by the *acrosomal cap* or *head cap* (Figs. 31-11 and 31-12). The tail consists of a core of longitudinal filaments surrounded in the

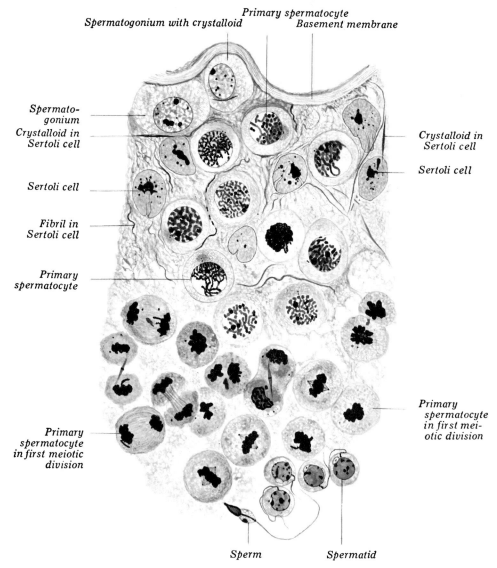

Figure 31-6. Section of same testis as in Figure 31-4; seminiferous epithelium with primary spermatocytes in first meiotic division. Iron-hematoxylin stain. × 750. (After A. A. Maximow.)

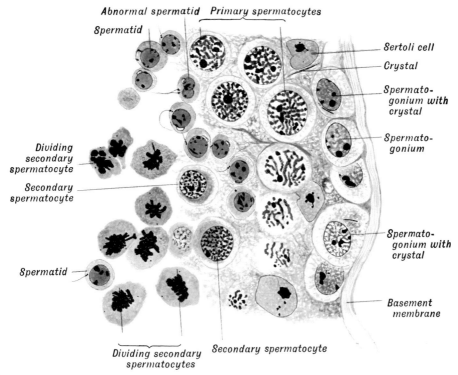

Figure 31-7. Section of same testis as in Figure 31-4; seminiferous epithelium with mitoses of secondary spermatocytes—second meiotic division. The loosening of the spermatocytes and spermatids from their normal attachment to the Sertoli cells is an artifact of specimen preparation. × 750. (After A. A. Maximow.)

middle piece by a helical *mitochondrial sheath* and in the principal piece by a *fibrous sheath* of circumferentially oriented dense fibers (Fig. 31-13). The junction of the middle piece and principal piece is marked by the *annulus,* a dense ring adherent to the flagellar membrane. The junction of the principal piece and the end piece is marked by the abrupt termination of the fibrous sheath. The end piece has no special sheath, being enclosed only by the plasma membrane that invests the entire sperm. The tail is attached to an *articular fossa* in the base of the nucleus by a short conical *connecting piece* that occupies the narrow neck region of the spermatozoon.

The internal organization of the tail and the changes that occur along its length are best understood from a study of transverse sections at successive levels from anterior to posterior (Fig. 31-15). The core or *axoneme* of the tail consists of the complex of hollow fibrils characteristic of all flagella, two single fibrils in the center and nine doublets around them. This axial filament complex runs through the tail for its entire length with no significant

change in size or arrangement of its fibers until it reaches the terminal half micron of the end piece, where the doublets are reduced to singlets; these end at slightly different levels in the abrupt taper at the tip of the tail. In the middle piece, the axial filament complex is surrounded by a row of nine coarse *outer fibers* that arise in the neck as caudal continuations of nine segmented columns that form the wall of the connective piece. These fibers vary in their cross sectional shape and size, with numbers 1, 5, and 6 being larger than the others. The outer coarse fibers are in turn surrounded by the *mitochondrial sheath.* In the principal piece, the variations in size of the outer fibers are more marked (Fig. 31-15*B*), and they are surrounded by the fibrous sheath. This consists of dense semicircular ribs, which are fused at their ends to two longitudinal columns that run along the dorsal and ventral aspects of the fibrous sheath. In the human sperm tail, the outer coarse fibers taper rapidly and extend only a short distance into the principal piece. In the rodents, fibers 3 and 8 terminate abruptly within a few microns of the end of

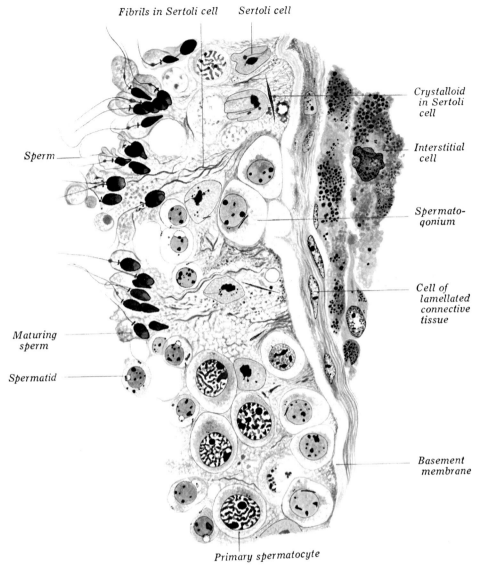

Fibrils in Sertoli cell   *Sertoli cell*

Crystalloid in Sertoli cell

Interstitial cell

Sperm

Spermatogonium

Cell of lamellated connective tissue

Maturing sperm

Spermatid

Basement membrane

Primary spermatocyte

Figure 31-8.   Section of same testis as in Figure 31-4; seminiferous epithelium with bunches of maturing sperm, connected with Sertoli cells. Iron-hematoxylin stain. × 750. (After A. A. Maximow.)

the middle piece, while the remaining fibers extend far into this segment, tapering very gradually and finally terminating in its distal third (Fig. 31-15C to F). A cross section through the end piece of the sperm tail is essentially identical to that of a cilium.

If one examines a transverse section through the principal piece, it is observed that the axis through the dorsal and ventral columns of the fibrous sheath divides the cross section of the tail asymmetrically (Fig. 31-14). A *minor compartment* containing three coarse

fibers is found on one side and a *major compartment* containing four on the other side. These fibers are presumed to be accessory contractile elements. The asymmetry in their distribution is believed to be reflected in the movements of the sperm tail. The principal plane of bending appears to be perpendicular to the dorsoventral axis, and the more rapid "power stroke" is assumed to be toward the side having four fibers, two of which are especially large. The details of the mechanism of sperm tail movements have yet to be worked out.

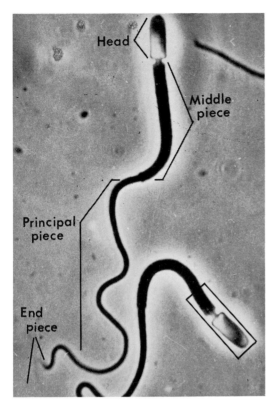

Figure 31-9. A phase contrast photomicrograph of a bat spermatozoon, with the principal regions of the sperm indicated. A segment such as that enclosed in the rectangle of the lower sperm is shown in longitudinal section in the electron micrograph (Figure 31-11). × 4500. (After D. W. Fawcett and S. Ito, Am. J. Anat., *116*:567, 1965.)

Spermatogenesis

Spermatogenesis comprises the sequence of events by which spermatogonia are transformed into spermatozoa. For convenience of description it may be divided into three principal phases. In the first, called *spermatocytogenesis,* the spermatogonia proliferate by mitotic division to replace themselves and to give rise to spermatocytes. In the second, *meiosis,* the spermatocytes undergo two maturation divisions, which reduce the chromosome number by half and produce a cluster of spermatids. In the third phase, called *spermiogenesis,* the spermatids undergo a remarkable series of cytological transformations leading to the formation of spermatozoa.

SPERMATOCYTOGENESIS. For spermatogenesis to continue without exhausting the supply of germinal cells, the spermatogonia must perpetuate themselves and also produce generation after generation of spermatocytes.

In testicular tissue preserved in Zenker-formol fixative at least two types of spermatogonia can be distinguished.

The *type A spermatogonium* has a spherical or ellipsoid nucleus with very fine chromatin granules and one or two irregularly shaped nucleoli attached to the inner aspect of the nuclear envelope. The cytoplasm is homogeneous and pale-staining. In some spermatogonia of this type the nucleoplasm is dark, and a large pale-staining nuclear vacuole is present. These cells are designated as dark type A spermatogonia to distinguish them from the others with paler nucleoplasm and no nuclear vacuole. The *type B spermatogonium* has a spherical nucleus containing chromatin granules of varying size, many of which are distributed along the nuclear envelope. The single nucleolus is centrally located and often has granules of chromatin associated with it. The cytoplasm is not significantly different from that of the type A spermatogonium.

The type A spermatogonium may remain

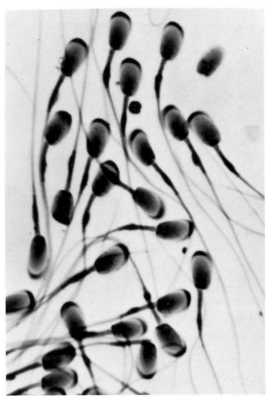

Figure 31-10. Photomicrograph of chinchilla sperm stained by the Feulgen reaction and counterstained with light green. The crescentic acrosome can be seen at the leading edge of the sperm head. × 3000.

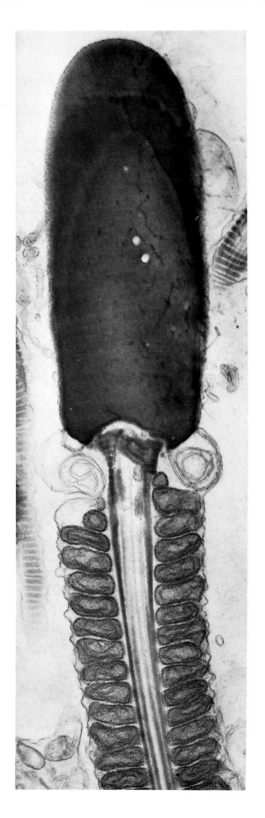

dormant for a considerable period and then undergo a series of divisions that give rise to other type A spermatogonia. Of these progeny, certain ones remain dormant to serve as stem cells for future cycles of spermatogonial renewal and spermatocytogenesis. Others proceed to transform through recognizable intermediates into type B spermatogonia. The division of type B spermatogonia then gives rise to primary spermatocytes.

MEIOSIS. Somatic cells contain a double (diploid) set of chromosomes. If the sperm and ovum were also diploid, their fusion in fertilization would produce a doubling of the chromosome number. This is prevented because, during gametogenesis in both sexes, the developing germ cells undergo a special type of division called meiosis, in which they pass through two nuclear divisions in succession while the chromosomes divide only once. The nuclei of the sperm and ovum therefore have a single (haploid) set of chromosomes.

The primary spermatocytes at first resemble the spermatogonia from which they arise, but as they move away from the basal lamina, they accumulate more cytoplasm and become distinctly larger. Soon after their formation they enter prophase of the first maturation division, their chromatin becoming reorganized into the diploid number of thin threadlike chromosomes characteristic of the *leptotene* stage of meiosis. The homologous chromosomes of the two sets then pair and fuse in the *zygotene* stage to form half the original number of chromosomal strands. Because of their greater thickness and deeper staining they show up more clearly than those of the leptotene stage. When the pairing of the chromosomes to form doublets or bivalents is complete, they contract longitudinally to form the much coarser and more obvious strands typical of the *pachytene* stage. In this stage there is a longitudinal splitting of each homologous

---

Figure 31-11. Electron micrograph of a frontal longitudinal section of the head and anterior portion of the middle piece of a bat spermatozoon (see Fig. 31-9). The acrosome is barely distinguishable as a dark gray crescentic structure at the apex of the head. The nucleus is extremely dense and homogeneous. The cross-banded structure connecting the head and the longitudinal filaments of the tail is believed to be a modified centriole. Mitochondria arranged in a flat helix around the base of the flagellum form the mitochondrial sheath. Osmic acid fixation. × 28,000.

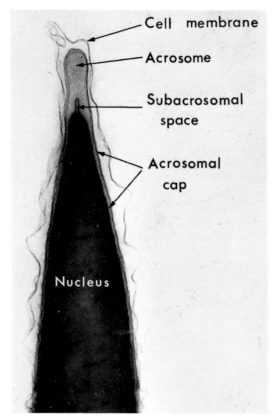

Figure 31-12. Electron micrograph of a bat sperm head in sagittal section, showing the relations of the lighter staining acrosomal cap to the very dense nucleus. The thickened region of the cap at the anterior edge of the head is commonly called the acrosome. × 40,000.

plished, resulting in the formation of smaller secondary spermatocytes with only half the number of chromosomes originally present. The secondary spermatocytes remain in interphase only very briefly and therefore are seldom encountered in sections of seminiferous tubules. They very soon go into the second maturation division, which has a brief prophase followed by a metaphase, anaphase, and telophase that are essentially the same as those of mitosis except that they involve the haploid number of chromosomes.

In the human spermatogonium there are 46 chromosomes, consisting of 22 pairs of *autosomes* and one pair of sex chromosomes (XY). The different pairs of autosomes vary in size and in the location of the kinetochore, but the two members of any given pair of autosomes are identical. The sex chromosomes in the female (XX) are also identical, but those of the male (XY) differ markedly in size (Fig. 31-16). At the end of the first maturation division in spermatogenesis, each bivalent chromosome including the XY separates into

chromosome into two *sister chromatids*, so that each pachytene element consists of four chromatids. It is also at this period that *crossing over* occurs, in which corresponding regions of the chromatids of the two chromosomes are exchanged. These stages of meiotic prophase are extremely prolonged, extending over several days. For this reason a great many spermatocytes in different stages of prophase can be seen in cross sections of seminiferous tubules.

At the end of prophase the nuclear membrane disappears. The bivalents arrange themselves on the equatorial plate in *metaphase*. In *anaphase* of the first meiotic division whole chromosomes move to the poles, in contrast to the half chromosomes that separate in mitosis. The chromosomes that separate may differ, however, from those of both maternal and paternal sets because of the exchanges that may have taken place during crossing over. *Anaphase* and *telophase* are quickly accom-

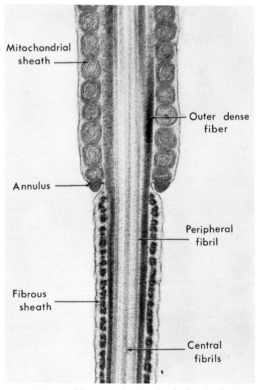

Figure 31-13. Electron micrograph of a longitudinal section through the caudal end of the middle piece and beginning of the principal piece of chinchilla sperm. × 26,000.

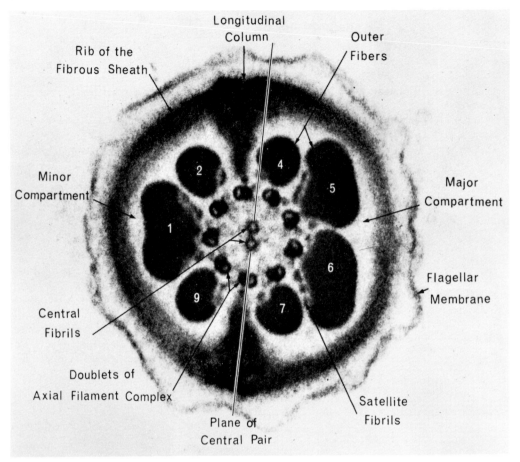

Figure 31-14. Electron micrograph of a transverse section of the principal piece of the guinea pig spermatozoon correctly oriented with the longitudinal columns of the fibrous sheath running along the dorsal and ventral aspects of the tail. Notice the asymmetry, with four coarse fibers on one side and three on the other side of the dorsoventral axis.

its two constituent chromosomes along the line of their previous conjugation. Therefore of the two secondary spermatocytes resulting from the first maturation division, one will contain 22 autosomes and an X chromosome, while the other will contain 22 autosomes and a Y chromosome. Since all of the eggs produced by the female are the same, containing 22 autosomes plus X, those sperm developing from spermatocytes containing X will be *female determining,* in that fertilization will result in a zygote containing 44 + XX (female), while sperm developing from secondary spermatocytes containing a Y chromosome will be *male determining,* for the zygote will contain 44 + XY (male).

Electron microscopic studies have shown that the divisions of the type B spermatogonia and the spermatocytes differ from ordinary cell

divisions in another important respect. Division of the cell body, *cytokinesis,* is incomplete, and the daughter cells remain connected by protoplasmic bridges at the site where the constricting cleavage furrow encounters the spindle remnant. Such spindle bridges occur as transient structures in mitosis of somatic cells, but in the seminiferous epithelium they remain, after resorption of the spindle, as sizable communications between the daughter cells (Fig. 31-17). They persist to a late stage in the differentiation of the spermatids into spermatozoa. It has been the traditional view that each spermatogonium developed into a primary spermatocyte that ultimately divided into two secondaries, and these in turn divided to form four individual spermatids. It now appears that cytokinesis of the last spermatogonial division is incomplete, resulting in pairs of conjoined primary spermatocytes. These produce groups of four interconnected secondary spermatocytes, which divide to form clusters of eight conjoined spermatids (Fig. 31-18). The exact stage and mechanism of the ultimate separation of the spermatids into individual spermatozoa is not known. Partial failures of this process may account for the frequency of abnormal double spermatozoa in the ejaculate.

SPERMIOGENESIS. The term *spermiogenesis* describes the sequence of developmental events by which spermatids are transformed into mature sperm. Each of the relatively small spherical or polygonal spermatids resulting from division of the secondary spermatocytes has a nucleus 5 to 6 μ in diameter with pale-staining finely granular chromatin and several darker chromatin masses. A small Golgi apparatus can be seen in the juxtanuclear cytoplasm. The first sign of differentiation of a specific component of the spermatozoon is the appearance of several small granules within the Golgi apparatus. In some species these are first observed in the spermatocytes; in others they are not seen until the spermatid stage. These *proacrosomal granules* are rich in carbohydrate and are most clearly demonstrated in specimens stained by the periodic acid–Schiff reaction. In electron micrographs each is found to be enclosed within a membrane limited vesicle of the Golgi apparatus (Fig. 31-21). Although the general features of spermiogenesis can be followed with the light microscope, the finer details described below are based upon examination of electron micrographs. As development progresses the several separate granules coalesce into a single large globule, the *acrosomal granule*, contained within a membrane bounded *acrosomal vesicle* or vacuole (Fig. 31-22). This becomes adherent to the outer aspect of the nuclear envelope. The point of its adherence marks the future anterior tip of the sperm nucleus. The Golgi apparatus remains closely associated with the surface of the acrosomal vesicle, and it continues to form small vesicles that coalesce with

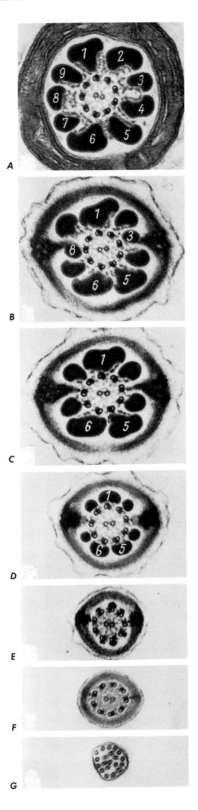

Figure 31-15. Electron micrograph of transverse sections of the guinea pig sperm tail at successive levels from anterior to posterior. *A,* Middle piece; *B,* first portion of the principal piece; *C, D,* and *E,* three different levels spaced along the principal piece; *F,* near the end of the principal piece; *G,* near the tip of the end piece. (After D. W. Fawcett, Zeitschr. f. Zellforsch., 67:279, 1965.)

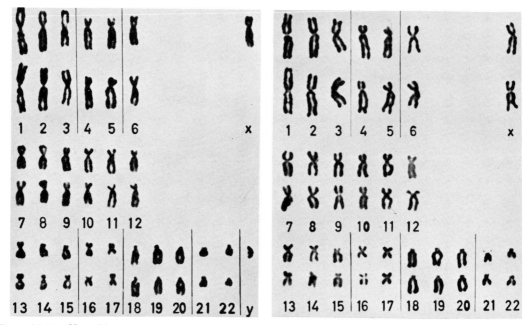

Figure 31-16. Normal human karyotypes, with the pairs of chromosomes identified by number and arranged in groups according to their length and shape and the position of the centromere. *Left,* male karyotype (22 + XY). *Right,* female karyotype (22 + XX). (Courtesy of J. H. Tjio and T. T. Puck.)

the membrane, contributing their contents to the enlargement of the acrosomal vesicle.

It is convenient to divide spermiogenesis into four phases, and that period from the appearance of the proacrosomal granules to the development of a hemispherical acrosomal granule fixed to the nucleus is referred to as the *Golgi phase.*

In the second or *cap phase,* the limiting membrane of the acrosomal vesicle increases its area of adherence to the nuclear envelope, forming a thin fold that spreads outward from the pole of the nucleus, ultimately to cover its entire anterior half or two thirds as a membranous *head cap.* The acrosome meanwhile remains localized at the pole of the nucleus (Fig. 31-24).

In the third or *acrosomal phase* of spermiogenesis, there is redistribution of the acrosomal substance, a condensation of the nucleoplasm, and an elongation of the spermatid. The bulk of the acrosome remains localized at the anterior pole of the nucleus, but in this phase of spermiogenesis its substance gradually spreads in a thin layer into the fold of membrane comprising the head cap until the acrosome and head cap are coextensive and constitute the *acrosomal cap* (often simply called the *acrosome*). In its definitive form it is a caplike

structure, limited by a membrane and containing a substance rich in carbohydrate. It varies in its size and shape in different species but is present on the sperm of all mammals and in many other forms. The spermatid nucleus becomes elongated and slightly flattened during this period. Its uniformly dispersed fine granular nucleoplasm becomes transformed into thin strands or filaments that subsequently shorten and thicken into coarse dense granules.

During the fourth or *maturation phase* of spermiogenesis, there is little further change in the relatively simple acrosome of the human sperm, but in other species it continues to undergo further alterations and take on the shape characteristic of the species (Figs. 31-25 and 31-26). The dense granules in the condensing nucleus become coarser, increasing in size at the expense of the intervening spaces until they finally coalesce and the nucleus is transformed into a homogeneous dense mass devoid of visible substructure. By the time this condition has been reached, the nucleus has attained the flattened pyriform shape characteristic of the human sperm head. Defects in the condensation of the nucleoplasm often leave one or more clear areas of variable shape and size, recognized with the light microscope as nuclear vacuoles. These are large and of frequent occurrence in the human sperm but small and relatively uncommon in the sperm of other species.

While the early stages of acrosome formation are in progress at the anterior pole of the nucleus, the centrioles migrate to the opposite end of the spermatid. There the distal centriole becomes oriented perpendicular to the cell surface and gives rise to a slender flagellum that grows out into the narrow extracellular cleft between the spermatid and the surrounding Sertoli cell (Fig. 31-27A). As the nucleus begins to elongate and condense, the pair of centrioles and the base of the flagellum recede from the surface and take up a position at the caudal pole of the nucleus. At about the same time, cytoplasmic microtubules arise and become laterally associated to form a roughly cylindrical structure, called the *caudal sheath* or *manchette*, which extends caudally from a ringlike specialization of the cell membrane at the posterior margin of the acrosomal cap. Concurrently with the appearance of the man-

chette, there is a marked elongation of the spermatid, so that the bulk of the cytoplasm is displaced well behind the caudal pole of the nucleus, where it surrounds the proximal part of the flagellum.

The flagellum at this time consists only of the *axial filament complex* (axoneme), with two central fibrils and nine peripheral doublets that are continuous with the wall of the distal centriole. The centriole is encircled by a ring of moderately dense filamentous or granular material. This annular structure was called the "ring centriole" by classical cytologists in the belief that it arose by unequal division of one of the centrioles; however, electron microscopic studies provide no evidence in support of this interpretation. Instead, it appears to be a derivative of the *chromatoid body* (Fig. 31-27B and C). This loose ring is intimately associated with another small dense ring that arises as a local specialization on the inner aspect of the plasma membrane, where it is reflected from the cell body onto the flagellum.

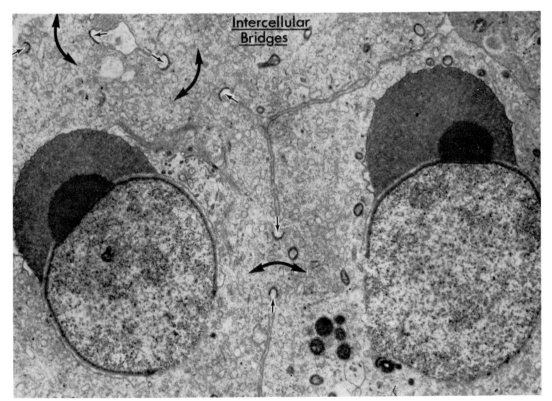

Figure 31-17. Electron micrograph showing two guinea pig spermatids and the intercellular bridges by which they are joined to each other and to two other spermatids of the same cluster. The small arrows indicate the local thickening of the cell membrane encircling the bridges. The large arrows passing through the bridges indicate the sites of continuity of the cytoplasm from cell to cell. × 9000.

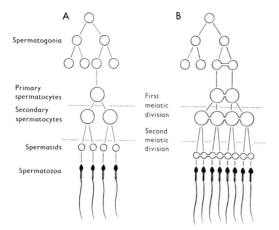

Figure 31-18. Diagram of mammalian spermatogenesis. *A,* As traditionally depicted; *B,* as revised on the basis of electron microscopic observations of intercellular bridges connecting the developing germ cells. In most species primary and secondary spermatocytes and spermatids all seem to be joined by bridges. Late in their differentiation, the spermatids separate to give rise to individual spermatozoa. (After D. W. Fawcett, Exper. Cell Res., *8* (Suppl.):174, 1961.)

In the further differentiation of the tail, nine longitudinally oriented segmented columns arise around the centrioles and are joined to each other proximally and to the base of the nucleus to constitute the *connecting piece.* Distally the nine structural elements forming the connecting piece are joined to nine thick longitudinal fibers that develop concurrently just peripheral to the doublets of the axial filament complex. The distal centriole and the large ring that earlier encircled it gradually disappear as the connecting piece and outer fibers of the tail develop. The smaller, dense ring fixed to the flagellar membrane persists, and in the further elongation of the tail, it is carried distally several microns. As it moves back, the manchette disappears and mitochondria gather around the segment of flagellum between the annulus and the nucleus and wrap helically around it to complete the differentiation of the middle piece.

While these events are in progress, a succession of circumferentially oriented ribs or

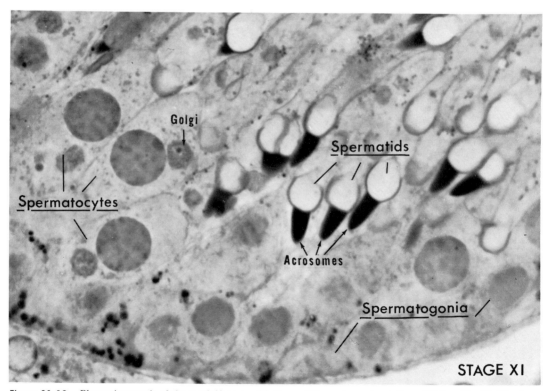

Figure 31-19. Photomicrograph of the seminiferous epithelium of the guinea pig at Stage XI (see Fig. 31-28), showing spermatogonia, spermatocytes in diplotene phase of meiosis, and one generation of spermatids in an advanced stage of acrosome formation, but showing as yet no condensation of the nucleus. Epon section, PAS-toluidine blue. × 1500.

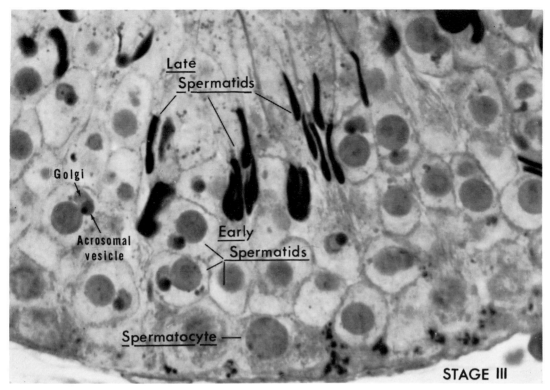

Figure 31-20. Photomicrograph of guinea pig seminiferous epithelium at Stage III, showing one or two spermatocytes and two generations of spermatids, one in an advanced state of differentiation with condensed flattened nuclei and the other in the Golgi phase of acrosome formation. In the latter, one can identify the acrosomal vesicle with the Golgi complex closely applied to it. Epon section, PAS-toluidine blue. × 1500.

hoops are deposited around the tail fibers distal to the annulus to form the *fibrous sheath* of the principal piece. The origin and nature of the outer fibers and the fibrous sheath, and the factors controlling their precise organization during development, are intriguing unsolved problems in cell differentiation.

With the completion of this regional differentiation of the tail, the excess cytoplasm is cast off as a membrane limited anucleate mass called the *residual body of Regaud* consisting of fine granules, lipid droplets, and degenerating organelles. The final separation of clusters of conjoined spermatids into individual sperm appears to coincide with the casting off of the residual cytoplasm. Soon thereafter the sperm heads are released from the Sertoli cells and the spermatozoa are set free in the lumen of the seminiferous tubule.

The Cycle of the Seminiferous Epithelium

Spermatogenesis has been most thoroughly studied in the common laboratory rodents, where it displays a degree of order and regularity that facilitates a systematic analysis of the process. As stated earlier, several stages of development are found at different levels in the germinal epithelium, with the most primitive germ cells found at the base and the more differentiated cells located at successively higher levels. The development of any one generation of germ cells goes on concurrently with the development of more advanced generations that have been displaced toward the lumen by the proliferation of new cells at deeper levels. The cells of different stages are not randomly distributed but occur in a number of well defined and easily recognized combinations. In the guinea pig, for example, 12 such cellular associations are identified. These are illustrated in the 12 vertical columns of Figure 31-28 and are designated by the Roman numerals at the bottom of each column. In any histological section of guinea pig testis, the cross sections of neighboring seminiferous tubules will vary in their appearance because of the different combinations of de-

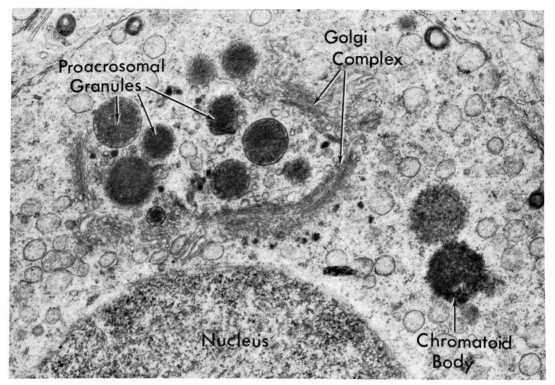

Figure 31-21. Electron micrograph of a sector of the nucleus and adjacent Golgi region of an early guinea pig spermatid, illustrating the accumulation of proacrosomal granules in the Golgi complex. The chromatoid body is seen nearby. × 16,000.

velopmental stages they contain. If enough tubules are examined, 12 different cell associations will be found, corresponding to the vertical columns in Figure 31-28. In studying this figure, it should be realized that any spermatogonium, in the course of its differentiation into a spermatozoon, passes through all of the stages encountered by starting at the bottom of column I and reading from left to right along the horizontal rows of the figure from the bottom to the top row.

Because all of the generations of cells are developing, the cell population at any point along the length of a seminiferous tubule changes with time, passing successively through all 12 stages and then repeating the sequence. The *cycle of the seminiferous epithelium* is defined as the series of changes occurring in a given area of the epithelium between two successive appearances of the same cellular association. The duration of the cycle has not been determined for the guinea pig, but it is about 12 days in the rat, and any given spermatogonium takes about four cycles or 48 days to complete its differentiation and be released

as a mature spermatozoon (Clermont and Leblond).

The various cell associations also occur in an orderly sequence along the length of the seminiferous tubule. Thus, instead of considering the changes at a given point in the tubule, one can look at it from a different point of view, namely, the series of successive cell associations found along the length of the same tubule. The *wave of the seminiferous epithelium* is then the distance between two successive identical cell associations.

The sequence of pictures along a wave is similar to the sequence of events taking place in one given area during a cycle of the seminiferous epithelium. In the rat there are said to be about 12 waves along the length of each tubule. The length of each segment in the wave corresponds roughly to the relative duration of that particular cell association or stage of the cycle.

THE CYCLE OF THE SEMINIFEROUS EPITHE-LIUM IN MAN.   In contrast to the very regular ordering of germinal elements in rodents, the appearance of the seminiferous epithelium in histological sections of the human testis at first suggests a haphazard arrangement of its cell types. Because of this apparent disorder, it was believed until recently that no synchronicity of germ cell development existed in man that was comparable to that found in rodents and that no "cycle of the seminiferous epithelium" could be defined.

This has now been found to be erroneous. Six well defined stages can be recognized, but instead of taking up the entire cross section of the seminiferous tubule as in rodents, the recognizable stages or cell associations in man occupy small areas in the tubular epithelium (Fig. 31-29).

The germinal epithelium is therefore a mosaic of irregularly shaped areas made up of the six different cell associations, and three or more stages of the cycle may be seen in a single cross section of a tubule. The situation is further complicated by the fact that the cells at the borders of these areas may intermingle to give atypical or heterogeneous associations of cells. The six typical associations are depicted in Figure 31-30.

The duration of the cycle of the seminiferous epithelium has recently been determined by autoradiographic analyses of testicular biopsies of human volunteers. Within one hour of local injection of tritiated thymidine the label was found in nuclei of preleptotene spermatocytes in stage III, but not in the pachytene spermatocytes of that stage or in any other cells more advanced in their development. With the passage of time these labeled cells would be expected to pass through leptotene, zygotene, and early pachytene stages of meiotic prophase and reappear at the end of the cycle in a stage III cell association as midpachytene spermatocytes. Serial biopsies revealed that the midpachytene spermatocytes of stage III first showed the label at 16 days after the initial injection of thymidine. It was thus established that the duration of one cycle is 16 days. As expected, labeled spermatids in stage III were found at 32 days (two cycles). Assuming one cycle to develop from spermatogonia to preleptotene spermatocytes, and one to advance from spermatids to release of spermatozoa, the total duration of spermatogenesis in man is

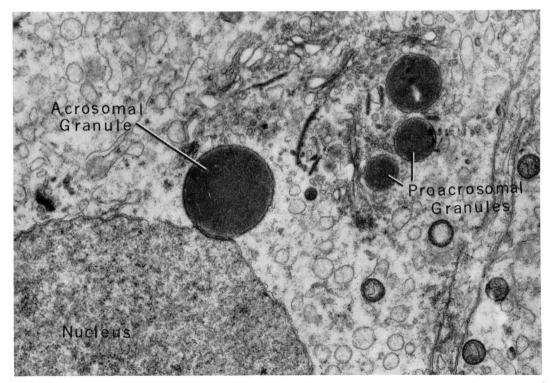

Figure 31-22.   Electron micrograph of the Golgi region of a guinea pig spermatid at a stage when the proacrosomal granules have begun to coalesce and one has become adherent to the nuclear envelope at a point that will be the future tip of the sperm nucleus. × 16,000. (After D. W. Fawcett and R. Hollenberg, Zeitsch. f. Zellforsch., 60:276, 1963.)

estimated to be four consecutive cycles or 64 days (Clermont).

Degenerative and Regenerative Phenomena

In seasonally breeding mammals, active spermatogenesis, having begun at puberty, is repeated and discontinued periodically for the rest of the life of the animal. Each time, it continues only during the period of rut, at the end of which the spermatogenic cells degenerate and are cast off. Concomitantly, the seminiferous tubules shrink and contain only Sertoli cells and some few spermatogonia. In this condition they resemble in structure the tubules of a prepubertal testis. At the beginning of a new period of sexual activity, spermatogonia multiply and rapidly produce the various generations of spermatogenic cells, while the Sertoli cells are compressed and become inconspicuous. In the lower vertebrates, these cyclic changes of the testis related to the seasons are still more prominent.

In man and other mammals that are not seasonal breeders spermatogenesis is continuous. Nevertheless, in an active human testis the tubules often contain, in the germinal epithelium and in their lumen, degenerating spermatogenic cells, which finally disintegrate into granular and fatty detritus. This is not pathologic unless it exceeds certain limits. The degenerating cells are seen in segments of the tubule in which the seminiferous epithelium is active and normal spermatogenesis is in full progress.

Abnormal spermatogenic cells can often be found. In the spermatogonia, abnormality usually manifests itself by hypertrophy. Among the spermatocytes giant forms are also common, as well as cells with two or more nuclei, sometimes of unequal size. Multinucleated giant spermatids are not uncommon. These abnormalities appear to be a consequence of the peculiar mode of cytokinesis in the dividing germinal cells, which normally leaves them connected by intercellular bridges. Failure of initial constriction between the daughter cells or a subsequent opening up of the bridges between two or more cells may lead to the formation of multinucleated spermatocytes or spermatids. Spermatids with two or even more nuclei may continue to develop; thus, monster

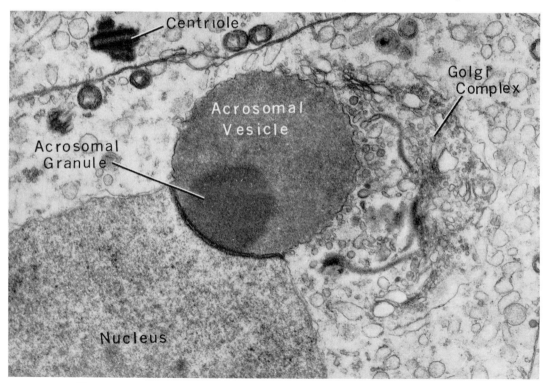

Figure 31-23. Electron micrograph of a spermatid in which all of the proacrosomal granules have fused into a single acrosomal granule enclosed within the acrosomal vesicle, to which the Golgi complex is closely applied. × 16,000. (After D. W. Fawcett and R. Hollenberg, Zeitsch. f. Zellforsch., *60*:276, 1963.)

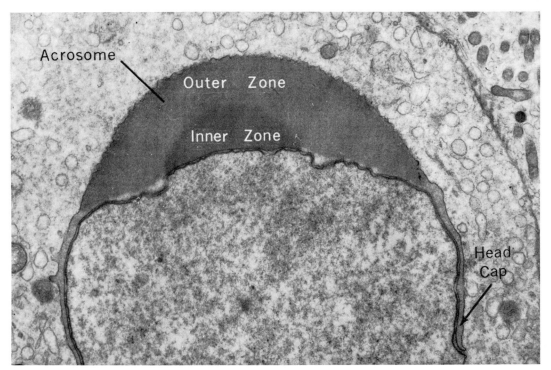

Acrosome

Outer Zone

Inner Zone

Head Cap

Figure 31-24. The enlargement of the acrosome has ceased and the Golgi complex has migrated into the caudal cytoplasm. The acrosomal vesicle is extending down over the equator of the nucleus to form the future head cap. Outer and inner zones of different density are distinguishable in the acrosome. × 16,000. (After D. W. Fawcett and R. Hollenberg, Zeitsch. f. Zellforsch., *60:*276, 1963.)

sperm with two or more tails, or with one tail and two heads, may arise. The degenerating and monstrous spermatogenic cells are carried with the mature sperm into the epididymis, where some of the degenerate cells may be reabsorbed by the epithelium of the excretory ducts.

The sex cells of the seminiferous epithelium are sensitive to noxious factors of various kinds. In pathological conditions of general (infectious diseases, alcoholism, dietary deficiencies) or local (injury, inflammation) character, the degenerative changes, especially the formation of multinucleated giant cells by the coalescing spermatids, may become prominent. Exposure of the testis to a sufficient dose of x-rays causes an extensive degeneration of spermatogenic cells and may produce sterilization. These cells are also sensitive to high temperature. Even the normal internal temperature of the body is incompatible with their normal development. In the majority of adult mammals the testes are lodged in the scrotum, which has a lower temperature than the body.

Testes that fail to descend into the scrotum during development and remain in the abdomen never produce mature sperm and show atrophic tubules containing only Sertoli cells and scattered spermatogonia. Failure of descent of the testis is called *cryptorchidism.* In experimentally produced cryptorchidism the testis soon shrinks and contains only Sertoli cells and remnants of sex cells; after a long time the tubules may disappear. The seminiferous tubules atrophy in rats fed on a diet lacking vitamin E; they degenerate to a lesser extent in vitamin A deficiency.

In all such cases the Sertoli cells are more resistant than spermatogenic cells. Some of the spermatogonia, however, seem in many cases to remain intact at the base of the epithelium between the Sertoli elements. Under favorable conditions when the noxious factor is removed (for instance, on replacing the artificially ectopic testis in the scrotum), a more or less complete regeneration of the seminiferous epithelium from these residual cells may take place. In mammals with a short life, spermato-

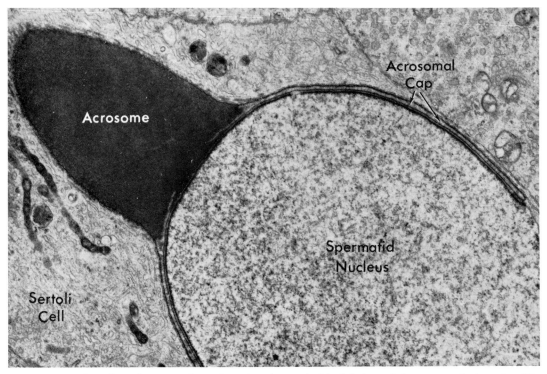

Figure 31-25.   The guinea pig acrosomal cap shown here has reached its full size and the acrosome is elongating. The spermatid nucleoplasm which here is homogeneous and of low density will soon begin to condense into coarse threads. × 12,000.

genesis continues until death without change. In man, although spermatogenesis continues far into the senile period, the seminiferous tubules undergo gradual involution with advancing age. A testis of a man older than 35 will always show an increasing number of scattered atrophic tubules; in the remaining parts of the gland, spermatogenesis may continue without visible alterations. Sometimes in very old persons all the tubules are depleted of spermatogenic cells and contain only atrophic Sertoli cells.

INTERSTITIAL TISSUE

The interstitial cells of Leydig are irregularly polyhedral, 14 to 21 μ in diameter, and occur in isolated clusters or in rows along the small blood vessels. Their large spherical nuclei contain a small amount of peripherally disposed chromatin and one or two prominent nucleoli. Binucleate cells are common. Adjacent to the nucleus is a large clear centrosome with a pair of centrioles and a well developed Golgi apparatus. The cytoplasm is strongly acidophilic. Mitochondria are present in small numbers and vary in size and shape. There are a few lipid droplets, and golden brown deposits of lipochrome pigment occur in men of all ages but are more abundant in the aged. In addition to these inclusions the human interstitial cells may contain conspicuous crystals 2 to 3 μ thick and up to 20 μ in length. These are the *crystals of Reinke*. Highly variable in size and shape, they may be rounded or pointed at the ends. They are isotropic in polarized light and have the solubility and staining properties of protein. Having little affinity for the common histological stains, they appear nearly colorless in routine preparations but can be clearly displayed by staining with azocarmine. Such crystals occur in the testes of most men from puberty to senility, but their number is subject to considerable individual variation. They are not found in other species.

The majority of investigators describe a small fusiform interstitial cell that is relatively free of granular inclusions, pigment, and crystals but contains a few lipid droplets. These are generally interpreted as immature forms, and it is believed that new Leydig cells can arise during adult life by differentiation from primitive spindle cells in the adventitia of the small blood vessels.

The interstitial tissue exhibits striking species differences in its amount and in its lipid content. In the common laboratory rodents the cells contain many large lipid droplets (Fig. 31-33). On the other hand, in opossum, where the interstitial tissue is very plentiful, droplets of lipid are rarely found. The significance of these variations is not known.

At the electron microscope level, the most striking cytological feature of the interstitial cell is the extent of the development of its smooth surfaced endoplasmic reticulum. Cisternal profiles of granular reticulum are occasionally found, but the bulk of the cytoplasm is filled with a branching and anastomosing system of smooth surfaced tubules. The membranes of this agranular reticulum are believed to contain the enzymes necessary for several of the steps in the biosynthesis of androgenic steroid hormones from cholesterol. The mitochondria, in common with those of other steroid secreting endocrine glands, have tubular cristae instead of the usual platelike projections from the inner membrane. Although the Golgi apparatus appears large and active, there is no evidence of its accumulation of a cell product. Indeed electron micrographs reveal no inclusions that appear to be secretory droplets and provide no clues to the mechanism of release of steroid hormone by these cells.

The crystals of Reinke in electron micrographs present varied patterns of internal structure depending upon the plane of section. Although they were originally interpreted as a lattice of 150 Å particles arranged in straight rows 190 Å apart, micrographs of better resolution reveal a highly regular hexagonal pattern bearing a close resemblance to knit fabric (Fig. 31-36). The crystal therefore does not seem to be made up of globular macromolecules but to be composed of closely compacted microtubules, giving in cross section the appearance of myriad small openings bounded by a regular hexagonal pattern of dense septa 120 Å thick.

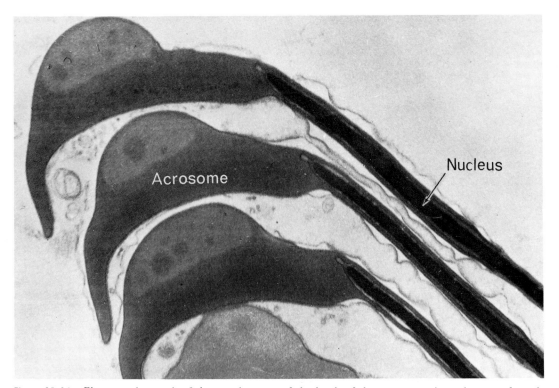

Figure 31-26. Electron micrograph of the anterior parts of the heads of three mature guinea pig sperm from the epididymis. The nucleus has condensed into a flat dense disk, seen here in sagittal section, and the large acrosome has taken on the characteristic curved shape. The final shaping of the acrosome in this species takes place in the epididymis. × 24,000.

A

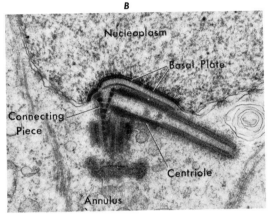

B

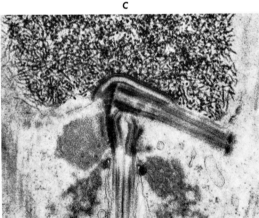

C

Figure 31-27. *A,* Electron micrograph of an early spermatid, showing the chromatoid body and the pair of centrioles and base of the flagellum moving inward to become fixed to the caudal pole of the nucleus. *B,* Spermatid in the early stages of nuclear condensation. The proximal centriole has now become fixed in a shallow recess in the base of the nucleus lined by a thickening of the nuclear envelope called the basal plate. *C,* Slightly later stage. The condensation of the nucleus is farther advanced. The chromatoid body has become disposed around the base of the flagellum and differentiation of the segmented connecting piece has begun.

The discovery of this unusual internal structure makes the chemical nature and functional significance of these crystals even more obscure.

ENDOCRINE FUNCTION OF THE TESTIS

In addition to producing sperm, the testis elaborates the male sex hormone testosterone. An adequate production of this hormone is necessary for the attainment of normal size and secretory activity of the accessory glands of reproduction—the seminal vesicles, prostate, and bulbourethral glands. Upon castration these glands undergo a striking diminution in size. These regressive changes can be prevented by administration of testosterone.

The dependence of the prostate upon the testosterone secreted by the testis is the rationale for castration in the treatment of individuals with cancer of the prostate gland. The tumor often undergoes marked regression after removal of the testes, and the life of the patient can be substantially prolonged.

Testosterone is also responsible for the development and maintenance of secondary sex characteristics, such as the male distribution of head, beard, and pubic hair, the distribution of subcutaneous fat, the low voice, and muscularity. Castration of boys in the prepubertal period results in failure of these characteristics to develop to the degree typical of the adult. Testosterone is produced by the interstitial cells. Unlike the germinal elements of the seminiferous tubules, these cells are not temperature sensitive. Thus persons with undescended testes (cryptorchidism) may have normal sexual behavior and display normal secondary sex characteristics but, as a rule, they are sterile. The seminiferous tubules are atrophic because of their exposure to the higher temperature in the abdominal cavity.

The reciprocal effects of the hormones of the hypophysis and testes are discussed in Chapter 17. Here it need only be recalled that both the endocrine and exocrine functions of the testis are dependent upon the hypophyseal gonadotropic hormones. The luteinizing hormone (LH), also known as interstitial cell stimulating hormone (ICSH), activates the interstitial cells, and this effect appears to be increased if follicle stimulating hormone (FSH) is administered at the same time. Maintenance of the structure of the seminiferous tubules seems to depend upon the action of FSH and

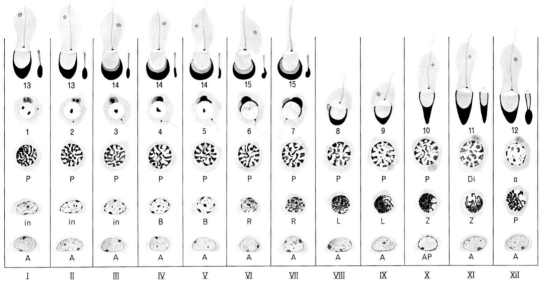

Figure 31-28. Schematic representation of spermatogenesis in the guinea pig. From the lower left, left to right along the horizontal rows, from the bottom to the top, all of the changes in differentiation from a type A spermatogonium to release of a spermatozoon can be followed. The vertical columns represent the 12 different cell associations or stages of spermatogenesis to be found in cross sections of seminiferous tubules. From the time of appearance of one of these associations at a given point in a tubule until the reappearance of the same association is defined as the cycle of the seminiferous epithelium. For photomicrographs of Stages III and XI, see Figures 31-19 and 31-20. (From Y. Clermont, Fertil. & Steril., 6:563, 1960.)

testosterone. Hypophysectomy leads to testicular atrophy, which can be reversed by the injection of gonadotropins. Administration of androgen decreases the gonadotropin secretion by the hypophysis. After castration, gonadotropin accumulates in the pars distalis of the hypophysis, where the basophilic cells show characteristic changes that permit their identification as "castration cells." The influence of the adrenal cortex on the gonads is discussed in Chapter 20.

BLOOD VESSELS, LYMPHATICS, AND NERVES OF THE TESTIS

The blood supply of the testis is derived mainly from the internal spermatic artery. Some branches penetrate the interior of the gland in the region of the mediastinum, while others run to the anterior side, in or under the albuginea, in the tunica vasculosa. From the mediastinum and from the septula testis, the smaller branches penetrate into the interior of the lobules and break up into capillaries, forming loose networks around the seminiferous tubules. The course of the veins corresponds to that of the arteries. Everywhere in the interstitial tissue between the seminiferous tubules,

networks of lymph capillaries can be demonstrated. The nerves, from the internal spermatic plexus, surround the blood vessels with fine plexuses.

EXCRETORY DUCTS

DUCTULI OR CANALICULI EFFERENTES. At the upper part of the posterior aspect of the testis, 12 or more efferent ductules arise from the rete and emerge on the surface of the testis. They measure about 0.6 mm. in diameter and 4 to 6 mm. in length. Through numerous spiral windings and convolutions they form 5 to 13 conical bodies about 10 mm. in length—the *vascular cones* (coni vasculosi). They have their bases toward the free surface of the head of the epididymis and their apices toward the mediastinum testis. They are held together by connective tissue and constitute part of the head of the epididymis (Fig. 31-37).

The ductuli efferentes have a characteristic epithelium. The lumen has a festooned outline because it is lined by alternating groups of tall and low cells. The latter form "intraepithelial glands," small, cuplike excavations in the thickness of the epithelium. The clear cells of these excavations contain pale secre-

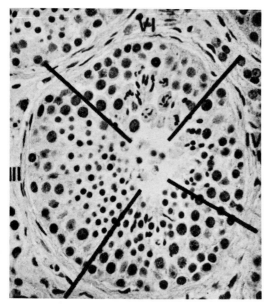

Figure 31-29. In the human the stages of spermatogenesis do not occupy the whole circumference of a tubule as in other species. In this photomicrograph, for example, four different associations of cells are found in the same cross section. (From Y. Clermont, Am. J. Anat., *112*:50, 1963.)

tion and pigment granules. A brush border and a central flagellum are found on the free surface. The formation of bleblike projections into the lumen has been interpreted as a sign of secretory activity, but the possibility that this is a fixation artifact has not been excluded. In animals intravitally stained, the cells contain dye inclusions, presumably by absorption from the lumen. The tall cells usually have a conical form with the broad end toward the lumen. On the free surface are cilia, which beat toward the epididymis and move the sperm in this direction. Their cytoplasm stains intensely and contains numerous fat droplets and pigment granules. Often both cell types are distributed irregularly.

Outside the thin basement membrane is a thin layer of circularly arranged smooth muscle cells. In the ducts forming the coni vasculosi, the muscular layer becomes more prominent.

DUCTUS EPIDIDYMIDIS. The convoluted tubules of the vascular cones gradually fuse into the single ductus epididymidis (Fig. 31-40). This highly tortuous, long canal (4 to 6 m.) forms, with the surrounding connective tissue, the *body* and *tail* of the epididymis. The duct

gradually straightens out and merges into the ductus deferens, which has a length of 40 to 45 cm.

In the proximal, convoluted part of the ductus epididymidis, the lumen is lined by a tall, pseudostratified columnar epithelium (Fig. 31-40). The cross sections of the duct have a regular, circular outline. On the inner surface of the basal lamina, small angular basal cells containing lipid droplets form a discontinuous layer. On their free surfaces the columnar cells carry a tuft of long (30 μ), nonmotile *stereocilia* (Fig. 31-41). In the cytoplasm immediately above the nucleus is an unusually large Golgi apparatus. Near to the free surface are occasional fat droplets, lipochrome pigment inclusions, and granules that have been interpreted as secretion granules. The nature of the secretory product, if any, has not been defined, and some now consider these granules to be lysosomes. In the distal part of the duct the epithelium gradually becomes lower.

The basement lamina is surrounded by a highly developed capillary network and by a circular layer of smooth muscle fibers, which probably help to move the sperm along the ducts.

In electron micrographs, the stereocilia are found to have neither basal bodies nor internal filaments and are simply very long microvilli. The nuclei of the epithelial cells in man, dog, and certain other species may contain dense spherical inclusions of unknown nature. The cytoplasm is characterized by the presence of an extraordinarily large Golgi apparatus and an extensive development of agranular endoplasmic reticulum. Small coated vesicles and multivesicular bodies are numerous in the apical cytoplasm and in the Golgi region. Dense spherical bodies resembling secretory granules are abundant in the epithelium of some segments of the long convoluted duct, but their precursors are not evident in the endoplasmic reticulum or the Golgi, and they have not been observed to discharge into the lumen. Many of these give a strong histochemical reaction for acid phosphatase and therefore are probably lysosomes related to an absorptive rather than a secretory function of the epididymis.

Nerves form a plexus of fine fibers connected with the muscles of the vessels and of the wall of the duct. Small sympathetic ganglia have also been described.

A number of rudimentary structures are

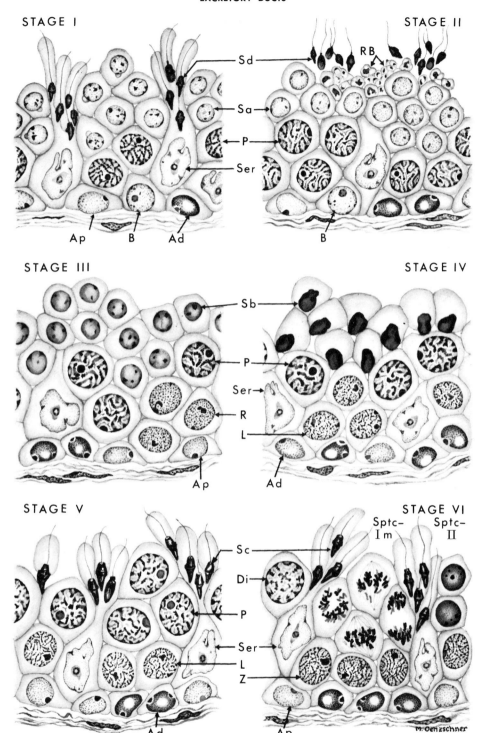

Figure 31-30. Diagram of the six recognizable cell associations or stages of the cycle of the human seminiferous epithelium. *Ser,* Sertoli cell; *Ad* and *Ap,* dark and pale type A spermatogonia; *B,* type B spermatogonia; *R,* resting primary spermatocyte; *L,* leptotene spermatocyte; *Z,* zygotene spermatocyte; *P,* packytene spermatocyte; *Di,* diplotene spermatocyte; *Sptc-Im,* primary spermatocyte in division; *Sptc-II,* secondary spermatocyte in interphase; *Sa, Sb, Sc, Sd,* spermatids in various stages of differentiation; *Rb,* residual bodies of Regaud. (From Y. Clermont, Am. J. Anat., *112:*35, 1963.)

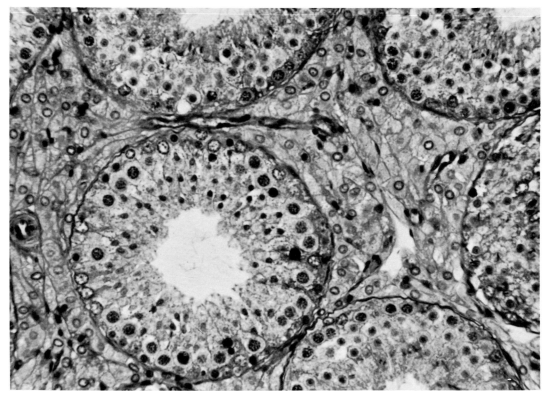

Figure 31-31. The amount of interstitial tissue varies greatly with the species. In the opossum testis shown in this photomicrograph it is exceptionally abundant. Compare with that of the guinea pig in Figure 31-3, where the interstitial cells are quite sparse. In the human they are intermediate. × 450.

found attached to the testis and epididymis and to the further sections of the excretory duct. The *appendix testis (hydatid Morgagni)* is the remainder of the abdominal end of the duct of Müller. It is located at the upper pole of the testis, near the head of the epididymis, and is a small nodule consisting of vascular connective tissue and lined with columnar, sometimes ciliated, epithelium. The *appendix epididymidis* is believed to be the rudiment of a portion of the mesonephros body. It is a nodule, 3 by 2 mm., containing a cyst lined with columnar epithelium and connected with the head of the epididymis by a stalk of variable length. The *ductuli aberrantes* are blindly ending epithelial tubules, one in connection with the rete testis and the other with the lower part of the ductus epididymidis. They are rudiments of the tubules of the mesonephros. The *paradidymis,* also a rudiment of the mesonephros, is a group of coiled epithelial tubules in the connective tissue of the spermatic cord at the level of the head of the epididymis. In some cases, especially in newborn infants, small

nodules with the structure of the cortex of the adrenal may be found in the connective tissue of the tail of the epididymis. In the neighborhood of the paradidymis small accumulations of chromaffin tissue have been described.

DUCTUS DEFERENS. On passing into the ductus deferens, the excretory passage develops a larger lumen and a thicker wall. Under the basal lamina of the epithelium the lamina propria mucosae rises in longitudinal folds, which cause the highly irregular outline of the lumen seen in cross section. The pseudostratified columnar epithelium is lower than in the epididymis, and the cells usually have stereocilia. The connective tissue of the mucous membrane contains extensive elastic networks. The 1 mm. thick layer of smooth muscle is highly developed. It consists of inner and outer longitudinal layers, and a powerful intermediate layer of circular muscle. On the periphery there is an adventitial coat of connective tissue. The firm duct is easily palpable through the thin skin of the scrotum.

The *spermatid cord* consists of the ductus

deferens and its accompanying spermatic artery, pampiniform plexus of veins, and nerves of the plexus spermaticus. The cord is enclosed by a discontinuous layer of loose longitudinal strands of striated muscle, the *cremaster muscle,* which similarly encloses the testes and serves to raise them in response to cold, fear, and other stimuli.

The ductus deferens, after crossing the ureter in the abdominal cavity, dilates into a spindle-shaped enlargement, the *ampulla.* At the distal end of the latter it forms a large, glandular evagination, the *seminal vesicle.* Then, as the short (19 mm.) and straight *ejaculatory duct* (0.3 mm. in diameter), it pierces the body of another gland, the *prostate,* at the base of the urinary bladder, and opens by a small slit into the prostatic part of the urethra, on a small thickening of its posterior wall, the *colliculus seminalis* or *verumontanum* (Fig. 31-43). The openings of the ejaculatory ducts are located to the right and to the left of a blind invagination

on the summit of the colliculus, the *utriculus masculinus,* which represents in the male the homologue of the uterus.

In the ampulla of the ductus deferens, the mucous membrane and its epithelium are thrown into numerous thin, irregularly branching folds, which in many places fuse to produce in section a netlike system of partitions with angular meshes. The epithelium shows evidence of secretion. From the excavations between the folds, numerous tortuous branched outpocketings reach far into the surrounding muscular layer and are lined with a single layer of columnar, clear cells of glandular nature containing secretion granules. The musculature is much less regularly arranged here than in the other parts of the ductus deferens.

EJACULATORY DUCTS. The epithelium lining the ejaculatory ducts is a simple or pseudostratified columnar epithelium, probably endowed with glandular functions. Its

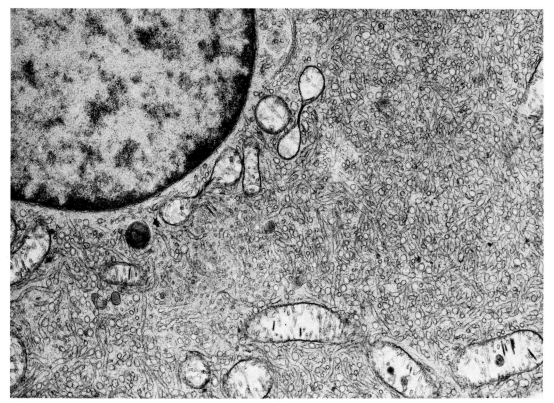

Figure 31-32. Interstitial cells in some species contain abundant droplets of lipid, while others are virtually devoid of lipid. The electron micrograph of opossum interstitial cell shown here is free of lipid. The cytoplasm is occupied by a very extensive agranular endoplasmic reticulum. × 10,000. (After A. Christensen and D. W. Fawcett, J. Biophys. & Biochem. Cytol., 9:653, 1961.)

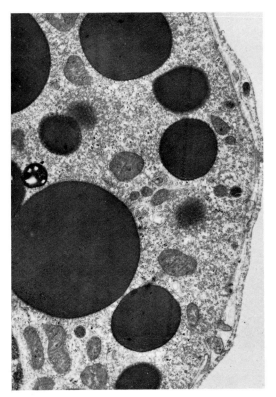

Figure 31-33. Electron micrograph of a portion of an interstitial cell from chinchilla testis. This is typical of those species with lipid-rich interstitial tissue. Between the lipid droplets are numerous mitochondria and an extensive agranular endoplasmic reticulum. × 7500.

cells contain a large quantity of yellow pigment granules. Near the openings of the ducts the epithelium often assumes the structure of "transitional" epithelium. The mucous membrane of the ducts forms many thin folds reaching far into the lumen; its connective tissue is provided with abundant elastic networks. The dorsomedial walls of the ducts contain a series of outpocketings of glandular nature, which may be accessory seminal vesicles. The ducts proper are surrounded only by connective tissue.

AUXILIARY GLANDS OF THE MALE REPRODUCTIVE TRACT

The glands associated with the excretory duct of the testis are the seminal vesicles and the prostate and bulbourethral glands.

SEMINAL VESICLES. The seminal vesicles are elongated saccular organs with numerous lateral outpocketings from an irregular branching lumen. They are evaginations of the ductus deferens and are basically similar to it in structure. The wall consists of an external connective tissue sheet with elastic networks, a middle layer of smooth muscle thinner than in the duct, and a mucous membrane resting upon a thin submucous layer of loose connective tissue. The mucous membrane forms an intricate system of thin, primary folds, which branch into secondary and tertiary folds. These project far into the lumen and anastomose frequently. In this way numerous cavities of different sizes are formed, separated by thin, branching partitions. All open into the larger central cavity, but in sections many of them seem to be isolated. Some are provided with glandlike invaginations similar to those in the ampulla.

The epithelium shows great individual variations, which probably depend on age and

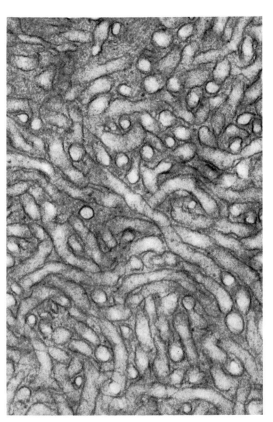

Figure 31-34. Electron micrograph of human interstitial cell cytoplasm at high magnification, illustrating the tubular character of the smooth surfaced endoplasmic reticulum and its extraordinary abundance. This organelle is presumed to be mainly concerned with biosynthesis of androgenic steroid hormones. × 75,000. (Courtesy of E. Yamada.)

Figure 31-35. Electron micrograph of a portion of a crystal of Reinke from a human interstitial cell.

physiological conditions. As a rule, it is pseudo-stratified and consists of a layer of round basal cells and a layer of larger, superficial, cuboidal or low columnar cells. All basal cells have a supranuclear pair of centrioles, while in the superficial cells the centrioles are located just beneath the surface and give rise to a central flagellum. The cells contain numerous granules and clumps of yellow pigment that colors with lipid stains, reacts negatively to tests for iron, and first appears at the time of puberty. A similar pigment is also found in the smooth muscles and in the connective tissue of the seminal vesicles. In many places the epithelial cells, especially in the deeper crypts between the folds and in the glandlike structures, contain secretion granules. The secretion of the seminal vesicles is a yellowish, viscid liquid containing globulin. In sections it appears as coagulated, netlike, deeply staining masses in the lumen. After castration, the epithelium atrophies, but can be restored by injections of testosterone (Fig. 31-44).

The muscular wall of the seminal vesicles

is provided with a plexus of nerve fibers and contains small sympathetic ganglia.

PROSTATE GLAND. The prostate is about the size of a horse chestnut and surrounds the urethra at its origin from the urinary bladder. It is a conglomerate of 30 to 50 small, compound tubuloalveolar or saccular glands, from which 16 to 32 excretory ducts originate and open independently into the urethra on the right and left sides of the colliculus seminalis (Fig. 31-45). The form of the glands is irregular. Large cavities, sometimes cystic, alternate with narrow, branching tubules. The blind ends of the secreting portions are sometimes narrower than the excretory ducts. In many places branching papillae and folds with a thin core of connective tissue project far into the lumen. In sections they may appear as isolated, epithelium lined islands in the cavities. The basement lamina is indistinct, and the glandu-

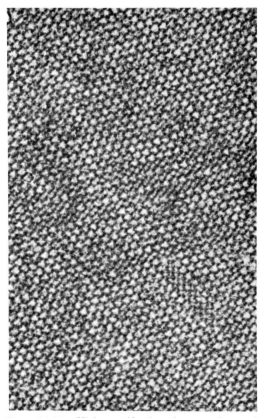

Figure 31-36. High-magnification electron micrograph of the lattice of a crystal of Reinke. Instead of being composed of regularly spaced globular molecules, the crystal has a honeycomb appearance in section as though made up of closely compacted tubular subunits. (Courtesy of H. Fahrenbach.)

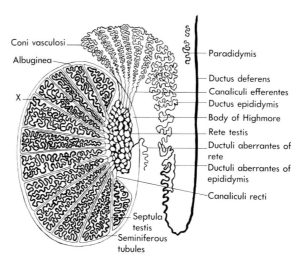

Coni vasculosi

Albuginea

X

Paradidymis

Ductus deferens
Canaliculi efferentes
Ductus epididymis
Body of Highmore
Rete testis
Ductuli aberrantes of rete
Ductuli aberrantes of epididymis
Canaliculi recti

Septula testis
Seminiferous tubules

Figure 31-37. Diagram of arrangement of seminiferous tubules and excretory ducts in the human testis and epididymis. *x*, Communication between seminiferous tubules of different lobules.

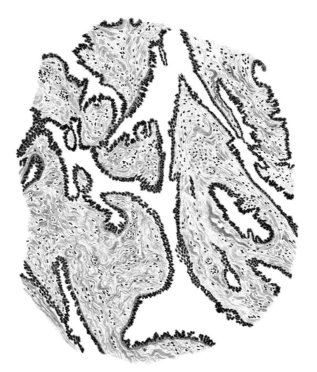

Figure 31-38. Section of human rete testis. × 140. (After A. A. Maximow.)

lar epithelium rests upon a layer of connective tissue with dense elastic networks and numerous blood capillaries. In the larger alveolar cavities it may be low cuboidal or even squamous, but in most places it is simple or pseudostratified columnar. The cytoplasm of the cells contains numerous secretory granules. Some of them stain black with iron hematoxylin, but the majority are colored with lipid stains. Sometimes, on the free surfaces of the cells, drops of cytoplasm seem to be in the process of detachment from the cell body. It is not clear to what extent this appearance is artifactitious. The epithelial cells become small and lose their secretion granules after castration. Injections of testosterone restore the cells quickly to their normal appearance and activity (Fig. 31-48).

The abundant interstitial tissue of the prostate consists of dense connective tissue with collagenous fibers, and elastic networks and many smooth muscle fibers arranged in strands of varying thickness. The connective tissue forms a capsule at the periphery of the organ. Together with the smooth muscle fibers it is arranged in thick, broad septa, widely separat-

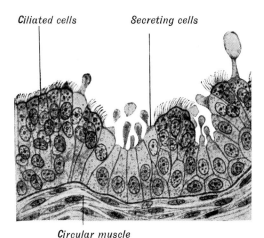

Ciliated cells   Secreting cells

Circular muscle

Figure 31-39. Part of cross section of human ductus efferens. Groups of ciliated cells alternate with groups of secreting cells. × 450. (After Eberth.)

ing the glands and radiating from the region of the colliculus seminalis to the periphery. Around the urethra, the smooth muscles form a thick ring—the internal sphincter of the bladder.

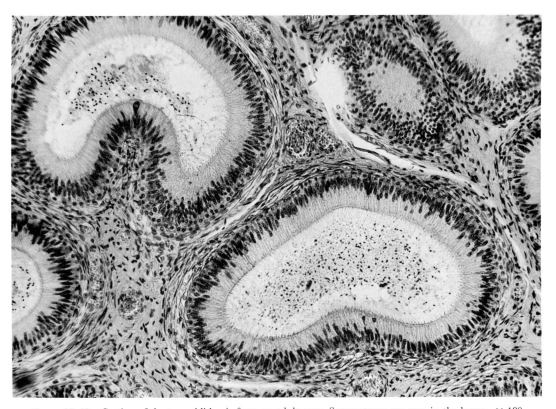

Figure 31-40. Section of ductus epididymis from an adult man. Spermatozoa are seen in the lumen. × 180.

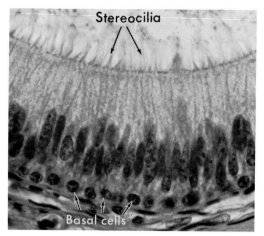

Figure 31-41. Photomicrograph of human epididymal epithelium, showing the characteristic row of basal cells and the stereocilia on the free surface.

The *secretion of the prostate* is a thin, opalescent liquid with a slightly acid (pH 6.5) reaction. It has a rather low protein content but contains diastase, beta glucuronidase, several proteolytic enzymes, and a potent fibrin-olysin. It is the main source of the citric acid and acid phosphatase of the semen. In sections the secretion in the glandular cavities appears granular. It contains occasional desquamated cells and spherical or ellipsoid, often concentrically lamellated bodies—the *prostatic concretions* (Figs. 31-46 and 31-47*B*). These are believed to originate through condensation of the secretions, may become calcified, and may exceed 1 mm. in diameter. The concretions are added to the semen and can be found in the ejaculate; the larger ones sometimes remain in the gland and are lodged in cysts. Their number increases with age.

The prostate is abundantly provided with plexuses of mostly nonmyelinated nerve fibers connected with small sympathetic ganglia. Sensory nerve endings of various kinds (end bulbs, genital corpuscles, and so on) are scattered in the interstitial connective tissue. Free nerve endings have been described in the epithelium.

The *utriculus prostaticus*, lodged in the mass of the prostate gland and opening on the colliculus seminalis, according to some recent ob-

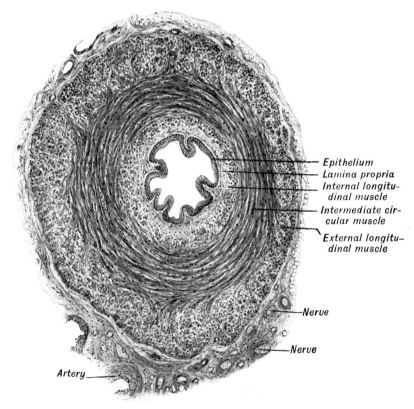

- Epithelium
- Lamina propria
- Internal longitudinal muscle
- Intermediate circular muscle
- External longitudinal muscle
- Nerve
- Nerve
- Artery

Figure 31-42. Cross section of human ductus deferens. × 30. (After Schaffer.)

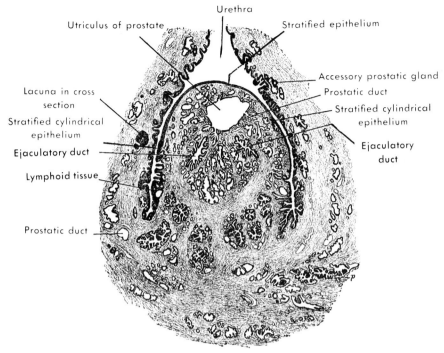

Figure 31-43. Cross section through colliculus seminalis of a young man. The urethra has been incised above. The utriculus of the prostate has prostatic ducts emptying into it. × 10. (After von Ebner, from Schaffer.)

servations, is not a vestigial organ without any function but is an accessory gland of the male sexual apparatus. It is a blind vesicle of considerable size lined by a mucous membrane with many folds and with glandlike invaginations. The epithelium is similar to that of the prostate. Sometimes patches of ciliated columnar epithelium can be found.

BULBOURETHRAL GLANDS. The bulbourethral glands (of Cowper), each the size of a pea, are of the compound tubuloalveolar variety. In some respects they resemble mucous glands. Their ducts enter the posterior section of the cavernous part of the urethra. The ducts as well as the secreting portions are of irregular size and form, and in many places they show cystlike enlargements. The terminal portions end blindly or are connected by anastomoses. The connective partitions between the glandular lobules measure 1 to 3 mm. in diameter and contain elastic nets and thick strands of striated and smooth muscles. The latter may penetrate with the connective tissue into the interior of the lobules.

The structure of the epithelium in the secreting portions and in the ducts is subject to great functional variations. In the enlarged alveoli the cells are usually flattened; in the other glandular spaces they are cuboidal or columnar with the nuclei at the base. The cytoplasm contains small mucoid droplets and

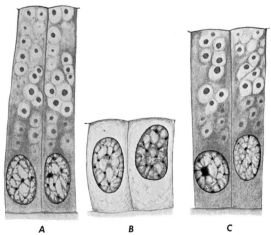

A   B   C

Figure 31-44. Sections of seminal vesicle of rat. *A,* From normal animal; *B,* from 20 day castrate; *C,* from 20 day castrate receiving 29 injections of testis hormone in 20 days. Note absence of secretion granules in *B.* Bouin; hematoxylin. High magnification. (After Moore, Hughes, and Gallagher.)

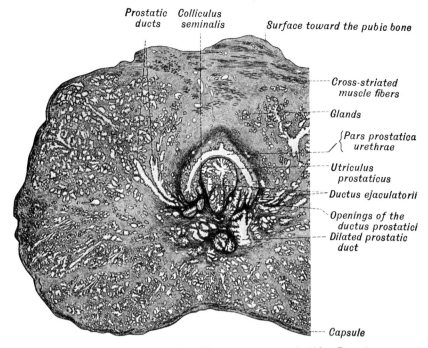

Prostatic   *Colliculus*
ducts   *seminalis*   *Surface toward the pubic bone*

--- *Cross-striated*
    muscle fibers

--- *Glands*

{*Pars prostatica*
/{ *urethrae*

--- *Utriculus*
    prostaticus

--- *Ductus ejaculatorii*

Openings of the
  ductus prostatici
--- *Dilated prostatic*
    duct

--- *Capsule*

Figure 31-45.   Cross section of human prostate. × 4. (After Braus.)

spindle-shaped inclusions staining with acid dyes. It has been suggested that they leave the cell body as such and then dissolve and mix with the mucin. The cells also contain colloidal droplets of various sizes. The excretory ducts are lined with a pseudostratified epithelium resembling that of the urethra and may contain large patches of secreting cells. They are also provided with small accessory glandular outpocketings having the structure of the glands of Littré of the urethra.

After fixation, the secretion appears in the lumen of the glandular spaces and ducts as angular precipitates that stain brightly with eosin. In life it is a clear, viscid, mucuslike lubricant, which can be drawn out into long, thin threads. Unlike true mucus, it does not form a precipitate with acetic acid. In the boar, the secretion is extremely viscous and rubbery and plays an important role in the gelation of the seminal plasma that takes place soon after ejaculation in this species. The secretion is rich in sialoprotein.

THE PENIS

The penis is formed of three cylindrical bodies of cavernous or erectile tissue, the two *corpora cavernosa penis* and the unpaired *corpus*

cavernosum urethrae. Arising from the ascending rami of the pubis on either side, the corpora cavernosa converge and join at the pubic angle. From there they run distally side by side to their conical distal ends, forming the dorsal two thirds of the shaft of the penis. On the upper surface of the penis, along the line of their junction, is a shallow longitudinal groove occupied by the dorsal artery and vein. On their lower surface the corpora cavernosa form a deep groove occupied by the corpus cavernosum urethrae (corpus spongiosum) (Fig. 31-51). The latter, beginning with the bulbus urethrae between the crura of the corpora cavernosa penis, is traversed throughout its length by the *urethra* and ends with an acorn-shaped or mushroom-shaped enlargement, the *glans penis,* bearing on its posterior aspect a pair of concavities which cap the conical ends of both corpora cavernosa penis.

The erectile tissue of the corpora cavernosa is a vast spongelike system of irregular vascular spaces fed by the afferent arteries and drained by the efferent veins. In the flaccid condition of the organ the cavernous spaces contain but little blood and appear as collapsed irregular clefts. In erection they become large cavities engorged with blood under high pressure. This increased inflow of blood and relatively restricted outflow causes the enlargement and the rigidity of the penis.

Each of the *cavernous bodies* is surrounded by a thick (1 mm.), resistant fibrous membrane, the *tunica albuginea*. Its collagenous fibers are arranged in an outer, mainly longitudinal, and an inner, circular layer, and are accompanied by elastic networks. Between the two cavernous bodies the tunica albuginea forms a fibrous partition, which is pierced by numerous clefts through which the cavernous spaces of both sides communicate. On the inner surface of the albuginea, especially in the posterior part of the corpora, there is a layer of dense connective tissue containing a multitude of small veins draining the cavernous spaces.

The cavernous spaces are largest in the central zone of the cavernous bodies. In the collapsed condition, they may have a diameter of 1 mm. Toward the periphery they gradually diminish in size. The partitions between them, the *trabeculae*, consist of dense fibrous tissue and contain thick collagenous bundles, elastic fibers, fibroblasts, and strands of smooth mus-

cle fibers. Their surface is lined with endothelium, which is continuous with that of the incurrent arteries and of the excurrent veins.

The tunica albuginea of the corpus cavernosum urethrae is much thinner than that of the corpora cavernosa penis and contains circularly arranged smooth muscle fibers in its inner layer. It also is provided with abundant elastic networks. The blood lacunae here, unlike those of the corpora cavernosa penis, are everywhere the same in size. The trabeculae between them contain more numerous elastic fibers, whereas smooth muscle fibers are relatively scarce. The cavernous spaces occupying the axis of the corpus cavernosum urethrae gradually pass into the venous plexus of the urethral mucosa.

The *glans penis* consists of dense connective tissue containing a plexus of large anastomosing veins, with circular and longitudinal smooth muscles in their thick walls. The longitudinal muscle strands often bulge into the lumen of the veins.

The skin covering the penis is thin and is

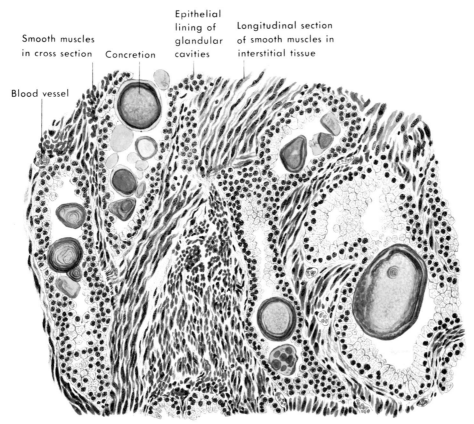

Smooth muscles in cross section **Concretion** **Epithelial lining of glandular cavities** **Longitudinal section of smooth muscles in interstitial tissue**

Blood vessel

Figure 31-46. Human prostate. × 190. (After A. A. Maximow.)

provided with an abundant subcutaneous layer containing smooth muscles, but is devoid of adipose tissue. The skin on the distal part of the penis is devoid of hair and has only sweat glands in limited numbers. The glans is covered by an encircling fold of skin, the *prepuce*. Its inner surface, adjacent to the glans, is moist and has the character of a mucous membrane. On the surface of the glans penis the dermis is fused with the deeper connective tissue of the glans. In this region peculiar sebaceous glands are described (*glands of Tyson*), which are not associated with hairs. They show great individual variations in number and distribution.

Blood Vessels. The erectile tissue of the penis is supplied with blood from the arteria penis. It breaks up into several large branches (arteria profunda penis and dorsalis penis, among them), which run to different parts of the organ, but all anastomose. In all these branches, even before they enter the erectile tissue, the intima forms long ridgelike thickenings which project into the lumen. They consist of loosely arranged collagenous and elastic fibers and contain strands of smooth muscle fibers, mostly arranged longitudinally.

Wherever the arterial branches enter into the corpora cavernosa through the tunica albuginea, they assume a longitudinal, forward course and give off many new branches. In the flaccid condition of the penis they have a convoluted or curled course—*helicine arteries.* They have a thick media. When they reach 65 to 80 μ in diameter (precavernous arteries), they run in the longitudinal trabeculae of the corpora cavernosa and open directly into the cavernous spaces.

The intima of the helicine arteries is also provided with longitudinal ridges of connective tissue and smooth muscle fibers, as in the branches of the arteria penis before they enter the erectile tissue. The ridges are more frequent at the places of division of the vessels. The arterial supply of the corpus cavernosum urethrae is similar to that of the corpora cavernosa penis.

The major part of the blood leaves the corpora cavernosa penis through the vena profunda penis. Its radicles have a thick muscular wall. They arise under the albuginea, especially in the posterior regions of the erectile bodies, through confluence of a multitude of

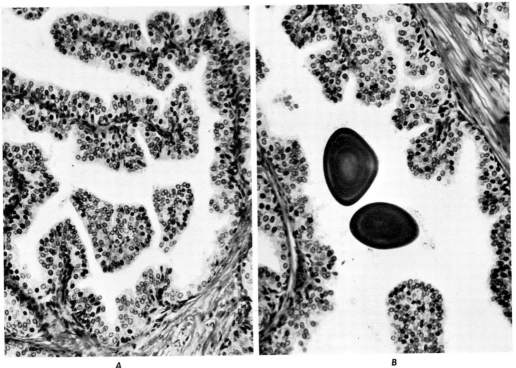

A   **B**

Figure 31-47. Photomicrographs of human prostate. *A,* The character of the epithelium. *B,* Typical concretions. Hematoxylin and eosin. × 150.

branched "postcavernous" venules. The latter run parallel to the surface under the tunica albuginea, have a length of 300 to 400 μ or more, and do not have any muscles in their thin walls. They originate from the peripheral cavernous spaces, which are in direct or indirect communication with the largest axial blood spaces. The blood from the corpus spongiosum is drained mainly through the vena dorsalis penis. Unlike those of the corpora cavernosa penis, the first radicles of this vein start from the lacunae with large openings and leave the corpus by the shortest way, by piercing the albuginea.

The arrangement and structure of the afferent and efferent blood vessels in the corpora cavernosa penis explains the *mechanism of erection*. The arteries play the active, the veins the passive role. The erection begins with the relaxation of the tonus of all smooth muscles in the arteries and in the erectile bodies. The blood pressure overpowers the elastic resistance of the tissue and stretches the media in the arteries. The presence of longitudinal ridges in the intima is believed to enable the lumen in such places to enlarge greatly and quickly. The lacunae of the cavernous bodies are filled with arterial blood. As the helicine arteries open, especially into the large axial spaces, these spaces compress the peripheral, smaller spaces and the thin-walled veins under the tunica albuginea that drain them. In this way the outflow of the blood is throttled down. The blood accumulates in the corpora cavernosa under increasing pressure, and the erectile tissue therefore becomes rigid. The helicine arteries during erection are passively stretched, and their convolutions are straightened out. Since in the corpus spongiosum there is no difference between axial and peripheral lacunae and the draining veins are not compressed, there is relatively little retention of blood, and the circulation continues freely. Consequently the corpus spongiosum never attains great rigidity during erection.

After ejaculation the arterial musculature regains its tonus. The afflux of the arterial blood is reduced to the usual amount. The excess blood that has accumulated in the corpora cavernosa penis is slowly pressed out into the veins through the contraction of the smooth muscles of the trabeculae and the recoil of the elastic networks. Owing to the compression of the peripheral small veins and to the presence of the valves, the return of the penis to the

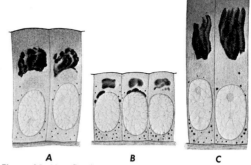

Figure 31-48. Sections of cells of posterior lobe of prostate gland of rat. *A,* From normal animal; *B,* from 20-day castrate; *C,* from 20-day castrate receiving 29 injections of testis hormone in 20 days. The changes in the Golgi net are quite striking. Mann-Kopsch technique. High magnification. (After Moore, Price, and Gallagher.)

flaccid condition is accomplished only gradually.

LYMPHATICS. Dense, superficial networks of lymphatic capillaries are found in the skin of the penis, of the prepuce, and of the shaft. They form a dorsal superficial lymph vessel, which runs toward the medial inguinal lymph nodes. Deep nets of lymphatic capillaries collect the lymph from the glans; they form a plexus on each side of the frenulum and continue into a dorsal subfascial lymph vessel.

NERVES. The nerves of the penis belong to the cerebrospinal (nervi pudendi) and to the sympathetic (plexus cavernosus) systems. They first supply the striated muscles of the penis (such as the bulbocavernosus) and also furnish the sensory nerve endings in the skin and the mucous membrane of the urethra. Among these sensory endings, free-branching nerve endings in the epithelium of the glans, the prepuce, and the urethra can be distinguished. Besides, there are free nerve endings in the subepithelial connective tissue of the skin and the urethra. Thirdly, numerous encapsulated corpuscles of various types are present: *corpuscles of Meissner* in the papillae of the skin of the prepuce and the glans, *genital corpuscles* in the deeper layers of the stratum papillare of the dermis of the glans and in the mucous membrane of the urethra, and *corpuscles of Vater-Pacini* along the dorsal vein in the subcutaneous fascia, in the deeper connective tissue of the glans, and under the albuginea in the corpora cavernosa. The sympathetic nervous plexuses are connected with the smooth muscles of the vessels and form ex-

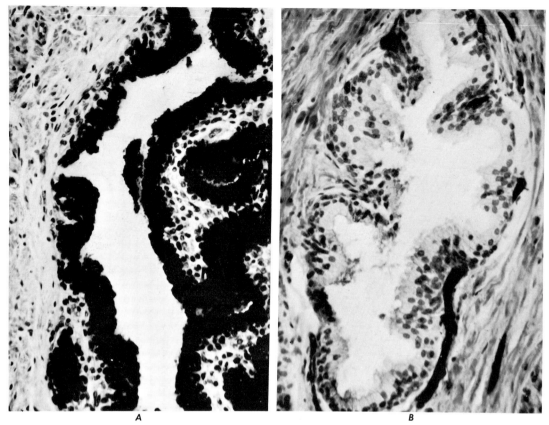

Figure 31-49. Photomicrographs of human prostate. *A,* Stained for the enzyme acid phosphatase and *B,* stained for alkaline phosphatase. The intense blackening of the epithelium in the acid phosphatase reaction is characteristic of the prostate. Alkaline phosphatase is not present in the epithelium but only in the small blood vessels. × 180. (Courtesy of G. Gomori.)

tensive, nonmyelinated networks among the smooth muscles of the trabeculae in the corpora cavernosa.

SEMEN

As the sperm pass along the excretory ducts, the secretions of the ducts and accessory glands are added to them; the final product is the *semen.* The sperm in the seminiferous tubules seem to be nonmotile. They are slowly forwarded into the tubuli recti and the rete testis, perhaps by passive pressure of liquid accumulating in the tubules, which cannot expand because they are surrounded by the firm albuginea. The seminiferous tubules may actively move the quiescent sperm by executing peristaltic movements. The flattened cells investing the seminiferous tubules have been shown to have many of the fine structural characteristics of smooth muscle cells (Cler-

mont; Ross). In some species slow contractile movements of the seminiferous tubules have been observed.

In the ductuli efferentes, the epithelium with cilia beating toward the epididymis takes care of the further transport of the sperm. The glandular cells devoid of cilia undoubtedly add their secretion to the moving mass of sperm.

The long, winding duct of the epididymis is slowly traversed by the sperm. They are kept here, especially in the tail, for a long time, sometimes for months. Here the majority of them lose the last remnant of cytoplasm attached to the middle piece. In some species the acrosome undergoes continuing morphological differentiation during the passage of the sperm through the epididymis, and the fertilizing capacity is known to increase progressively. What moves the sperm forward in the ductus epididymidis is not entirely clear, but the duct has an outer layer of smooth muscle that is probably responsible. During sexual excitement the circular smooth muscle surrounding the tubules shows rhythmic contractions, and during ejaculation it is of primary importance in expulsion of stored sperm.

The secretion of the epithelium of the ductus epididymidis is believed to add nutritive material to the sperm, but the nutritional requirements of the sperm in this environment are not known. As a rule, sperm taken from the epididymis are more resistant to environmental changes than are those from the testis.

The epididymis is the site of storage of spermatozoa. The sperm do not accumulate in the ductus deferens. This part of the excretory system, with its heavy muscular coat, is adapted only to their speedy transportation during sexual activity.

The function of the seminal vesicles is primarily glandular. Their thick secretion contributes substantially to the volume of the ejaculate. It is rich in *fructose,* which is the principal sugar of the semen and provides the carbohydrate substrate utilized as an energy source by motile spermatozoa of the ejaculate. The secretion contains small amounts of yellowish pigment, mainly *flavins,* which give the semen a strong fluorescence in ultraviolet light —a property of some medicolegal importance in the detection of semen stains.

In the process of *ejaculation* the muscular tissue of the prostate also contracts and discharges its abundant liquid secretion; it dilutes the thick part of the semen and helps stimulate the movements of the sperm. The semen, entering the urethra and mixing with the secretion of the glands of Cowper and Littré, is expelled by the contraction of the bulbocavernosus muscle compressing the bulbus urethrae.

The average volume of the ejaculate in man is about 3.5 ml., and of this the sperm account for less than 10 per cent, the rest being *seminal plasma.* The sperm density varies from 50,000 to 150,000 per ml. Each ejaculate therefore contains 200 to 300 million sperm. The tail performs whipping, undulatory movements; the sperm advances with the head forward and simultaneously rotates on its long axis. Its speed is 14 to 23 μ a second.

Under suitable conditions the sperm may remain alive outside the body for several days. They also survive for some time in the excretory ducts after death. In the uterus and the fallopian tube, living sperm have been found some days after coitus. They can now be stored in the frozen state for months or years and retain their fertilizing capacity upon thawing.

Besides the sperm, the semen contains degenerated cells, probably cast off from the epithelium of the excretory ducts and the urethra. Occasionally, columnar epithelial cells and wandering cells of connective tissue origin may also occur. There are, furthermore, round, hyaline bodies of unknown origin, lipid granules, at times concretions from the prostate, and a multitude of fat, protein, and pigment granules. When the semen cools and begins to dry, peculiar crystals of various forms develop—the *crystals of Böttcher.* They are believed to consist of phosphate of *spermine,* a polyamine compound present in considerable amounts in human semen and contributed mainly by the prostate.

It has been claimed that the different components of the semen are discharged from the urethra in a certain sequence. With the development of the erection the slimy secretion of the glands of Cowper and Littré lubri-

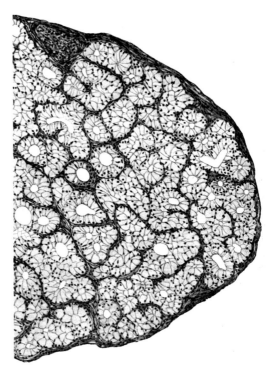

Figure 31-50. Part of a lobule of the bulbourethral gland of a 23 year old man. Zenker. × 120. (Slightly modified from Stieve.)

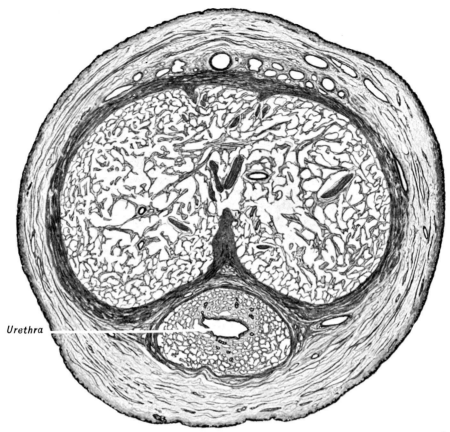

Urethra

Figure 31-51. Cross section of penis of a 21 year old man. The septum in the corpus cavernosum penis is incomplete, because the section is from the distal part of the organ. The penis was fixed by injection of formalin into the corpus cavernosum. × 3½. (Slightly modified from Stieve.)

cates the urethra. At the beginning of the ejaculation the prostatic secretion is discharged first. Then the masses of sperm accumulated in the vas deferens and the ductus epididymidis are expelled. The final portion of the ejaculate is probably the thick secretion of the seminal vesicles. In some animals (mouse) the abundant secretion of the seminal vesicles is coagulated in the vagina by an enzyme contained in the prostatic juice, and thus a solid plug is formed in the vagina which temporarily occludes its lumen and prevents the escape of the semen.

REFERENCES

Anberg, A.: The ultrastructure of the human spermatozoon. Acta Obstet. Gynec. Scandinav., *36*(Suppl. 2):1, 1957.

Bawa, S. R.: The fine structure of the Sertoli cell of the human testis. J. Ultrastruct. Res., *9*:459, 1963.

Bishop, M. W. H., and A. Walton: Spermatogenesis and the structure of mammalian spermatozoa. *In* Marshall's Physiology of Reproduction. 3rd ed. London, Longmans, Green & Co., 1960, Vol. 1, part 2, p. 1.

Bishop, D.: Sperm motility. Physiol. Rev., *42*:1, 1962.

Bröckelman, J.: Fine structure of germ cells and Sertoli cells during the cycle of the seminiferous epithelium in the rat. Zeitschr. f. Zellforsch., *59*:820, 1963.

Christensen, A. K.: The fine structure of testicular interstitial cells in guinea pig. J. Cell. Biol., *26*:911, 1965.

Christensen, A. K., and D. W. Fawcett: The normal fine structure of opossum testicular interstitial cells. J. Biophys. & Biochem. Cytol., *9*:653, 1961.

Christensen, A. K., and D. W. Fawcett: The fine structure of the interstitial cells of the mouse testis. Am. J. Anat., *118*:551, 1966.

Clermont, Y.: Contractile elements in the limiting membrane of the seminiferous tubules of the rat. Exper. Cell. Res., *15*:438, 1958.

Clermont, Y.: The cycle of the seminiferous epithelium of man. Am. J. Anat., *112*:35, 1963.

Crabo, B.: Fine structure of the interstitial cells of the rabbit testes. Zeitschr. f. Zellforsch., *61*:587, 1963.

Fawcett, D. W.: Intercellular bridges. Exper. Cell Res., Suppl. *8*:174, 1961.

Fawcett, D. W.: Sperm tail structure in relation to the mechanism of movement. *In* Bishop, D. W., ed.: Spermatozoan Motility. Washington, American Association for the Advancement of Science, Publication No. 72, 1962, p. 147.

Fawcett, D. W.: The anatomy of the mammalian spermatozoon with particular reference to the guinea pig. Zeitschr. f. Zellforsch., *67*:279, 1965.

Fawcett, D. W., and M. H. Burgos: The fine structure of Sertoli cells in human testis. Anat. Rec., *124*:401, 1956.

Horstmann, E.: Die Kerneinschlüsse im Nebenhodenepithel des Hundes. Zeitschr. f. Zellforsch., *65*:770, 1965.

Horstmann, E., R. Richter, and E. Roosen-Runge: Zur elektronen-

mikroskopie der Kerneinschlüsse im menschlichen Nebenhodenepithel. Zeitschr. f. Zellforsch., *69:*69, 1966.

Huggins, C.: The physiology of the prostate gland. Physiol. Rev.,
*25:*281, 1945.

Ladman, A. J., and W. C. Young: An electron microscopic study of
the ductuli efferentes and rete testis of the guinea pig. J. Biophys.
& Biochem. Cytol., *4:*219, 1958.

Leblond, C. P., and Y. Clermont: Definition of the stages of the
cycle of the seminiferous epithelium of the rat. Ann. N. Y. Acad.
Sci., *55:*548, 1952.

Macklin, C. C., and M. T. Macklin: The seminal vesicles, prostate
and bulbo-urethral glands. *In* Cowdry, E. V., ed.: Special Cytology. 2nd ed. New York, Paul B. Hoeber, Inc., 1932, Vol. III,
p. 1771.

Mann, T.: Biochemistry of Semen and of the Male Reproductive
Tract. London, Methuen & Co., 1964

Nicander, L.: Fine structure and cytochemistry of nuclear inclusions
in the dog epididymis. Exper. Cell Res., *34:*533, 1964.

Price, D.: Normal development of the prostate and seminal vesicles
of the rat, with a study of experimental post-natal modifications.
Am. J. Anat., *60:*79, 1936.

Rasmussen, A. T.: Interstitial cells of the testis. *In* Cowdry, E. V., ed.:
Special Cytology. 2nd ed. New York, Paul B. Hoeber, Inc.,
1932, Vol. III, p. 1673.

Roosen-Runge, E. C.: The process of spermatogenesis in mammals.
Biol. Rev., *37:*343, 1962.

Roosen-Runge, E. C., and L. O. Giesel, Jr.: Quantitative studies on
spermatogenesis in the albino rat. Am. J. Anat., *87:*1, 1950.

Schmidt, F. C.: Licht- und elektronenmikroskopische Untersuchungen am menschlichen Hoden und Nebenhoden. Zeitschr.
f. Zellforsch., *63:*707, 1964.

Stieve, H.: Männliche Genitalorgane. *In* von Möllendorff, W., and
W. Bargmann, eds.: Handbuch der mikroskopischen Anatomie
des Menschen. Berlin, Julius Springer, 1930, Vol. 7, part 2, p. 1.

Tjio, J. H., and T. T. Puck: The somatic chromosomes of man. Proc.
Nat. Acad. Sci., *44:*1229, 1958.

Yamada, E.: Some observations on the fine structure of the interstitial cell in the human testis. *In* Breese, S. S., Jr., ed.: 5th International Conference on Electron Microscopy. Vol. 2, p. LL-1.
New York, Academic Press, 1962.

Yamada, E.: Some observations on the fine structure of the interstitial cell in the human testis as revealed by electron microscopy. Gunma Symp. on Endocr., Vol. 2, p. 1. Maebashi, Japan,
Gunma University Institute of Endocrinology, 1965.

Young, W. C.: Die Resorption in den Ductuli efferentes der Maus
und ihre Bedeutung für das Problem der Unterbindung im
Hoden-Nebenhodensystem. Zeitschr. f. Zellforsch, *17:*729, 1933.

CHAPTER THIRTY-TWO

Female Reproductive System

The female genital system consists of the ovaries, oviducts, uterus, vagina, and external genitalia (Fig. 32-1). In the sexually mature female the ovary, tube, and uterus undergo marked changes in their structure and functional activity in relation to the menstrual cycle and pregnancy. These changes are regulated by complex neural and hormonal mechanisms.

OVARY

The human ovaries are slightly flattened paired organs, each measuring 2.5 to 5 cm. in length, 1.5 to 3 cm. in width, and 0.6 to 1.5 cm. in thickness. One of the edges, the *hilus,* is attached by the *mesovarium* to the broad ligament, which extends from the uterus laterally to the wall of the pelvic cavity.

The ovary has a thick peripheral zone or *cortex,* which surrounds the *medulla* or *zona vasculosa.* Embedded in the connective tissue of the cortex are *follicles* containing the female sex cells, *ova.* The follicles are present in a wide range of sizes representing various stages of their development. When a follicle reaches maturity it ruptures at the surface of the ovary to release the ovum, which then gains access to the open end of the neighboring oviduct. The boundary between the ovarian cortex and medulla is poorly defined. The medulla consists mainly of loose connective tissue and a mass of contorted blood vessels that are large in proportion to the size of the ovary.

The ovary is covered by a continuous sheet of squamous or cuboidal epithelium, which was named the *germinal epithelium* in the belief that the primordial oocytes originated from it. The term persists although the evidence now strongly favors the extragonadal origin of the primordial germ cells. Beneath the germinal epithelium is a layer of dense connective tissue, the *tunica albuginea* (Fig. 32-4).

OVARIAN FOLLICLES. Embedded in the stroma of the cortex deep to the tunica albuginea. are the follicles. The younger the person, the more numerous they are. In a normal young adult over 400,000 have been counted in serial sections of both ovaries. Their number decreases progressively throughout life and at menopause they are hard to find, although a few may persist into old age. The vast majority are *primordial* or *unilaminar follicles.* They are found mainly in the periphery of the cortex, where they form a thick layer immediately beneath the tunica albuginea (Figs. 32-4 and 32-5). Each consists of a large round oocyte surrounded by a single layer of flattened *follicular cells.* Owing to the large size of the oocyte, there may be several follicular cells around its circumference in sections. Primordial follicles may rarely contain more than one oocyte, but such polyovular follicles are quite uncommon.

Primordial Follicles (Unilaminar Follicles). The oocyte has a large, eccentrically placed, vesicular nucleus with pale, finely dispersed chromatin and a large nucleolus. Associated with the juxtanuclear cell center is a well developed Golgi apparatus surrounded by numerous small mitochondria. The primordial oocyte is enveloped by a single layer of flattened *follicular* or *granulosa cells*. The surfaces of the oocyte and the enveloping follicular cells at this stage are smooth and in close apposition.

In electron micrographs the prominent juxtanuclear Golgi complex exhibits short parallel arrays of cisternal profiles and large numbers of small vesicles. Similar vesicular profiles are distributed in smaller numbers throughout the ooplasm, and it is believed that these may originate in the Golgi apparatus. Annulate lamellae are often found adjacent to the nucleus or free in the neighboring ooplasm. The spherical or short plump mitochondria tend to congregate in the vicinity of the cell center. Later, when the oocyte begins to grow, they become dispersed throughout the ooplasm. The endoplasmic reticulum in the early stages of oocyte development takes the form of vesicles or slightly elongated profiles bearing a few ribosomes. Longer cisternal profiles subsequently arise in limited numbers and finally become associated in parallel arrays (Fig. 32-11). Multivesicular bodies are a common component of the ooplasm but are more numerous in later stages of development.

Primary Follicles. The transition from an inactive primordial follicle to a developing primary follicle involves cytological changes in the oocyte, the follicular cells, and the adjacent connective tissue. As the oocyte enlarges, the single layer of flattened follicular cells first become cuboidal or low columnar (Figs. 32-5*B* and 32-6), and then through mitotic division give rise to granulosa cells that form a stratified epithelium. In multilaminar follicles the oocyte is surrounded by the *zona pellucida*, a refractile, deeply staining layer of uniform thickness interposed between the oocyte and the granulosa cells (Figs. 32-9 and 32-10). As the growing follicles increase in size, they gradually move deeper into the cortex (Figs. 32-2 and 32-3). Concurrently with the proliferation of the granulosa cell layer, a sheath of stroma cells, the *theca folliculi*, develops around the follicle. This layer subsequently differentiates into a highly vascular, inner layer of secretory cells, the *theca interna*, and an outer layer, the *theca externa*, composed mainly of connective tissue. Numerous small vessels penetrate the theca externa to supply a rich capillary plexus in the theca interna, but the granulosa cell layer remains avascular throughout the growth of the follicle.

As the oocyte grows there is a noticeable change in the distribution of its organelles. The Golgi complex, which initially was a sin-

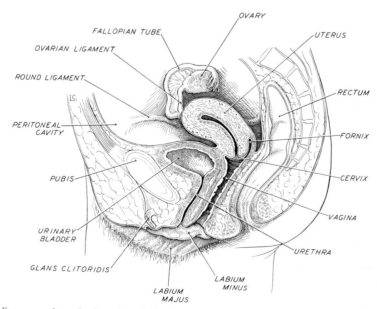

Figure 32-1. A diagrammatic sagittal section of the female pelvis, showing the genital organs and their relations to the bladder, urethra and rectum. (After C. D. Turner.)

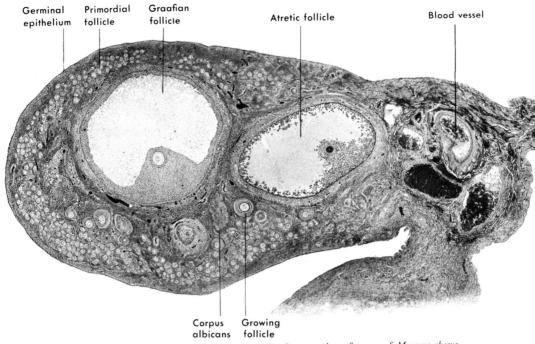

Figure 32-2. Retouched photomicrograph of transection of ovary of *Macacus rhesus*.

gle mass in the juxtanuclear region of the early oocyte layer, gives rise to multiple Golgi complexes widely dispersed in the ooplasm. In the full grown oocyte these are located mainly in the cortex near the plasma membrane or *oolemma*. Although the granular endoplasmic reticulum is not a prominent organelle in the oocyte, it gradually becomes more extensive and the number of free ribosomes in the ooplasm increases. The number of small vesicles and multivesicular bodies also increases markedly. There are a few lipid droplets and occasional heterogeneous masses identified as lipochrome pigment. Dense granules rich in lipid, and corresponding to the yolk platelets of lower animals, are found in mammalian oocytes but are smaller and less numerous in primates than in other species.

In electron micrographs of advanced unilaminar follicles, irregular microvilli on the surface of the oocyte project into discontinuous spaces that develop between the oocyte and the surrounding granulosa cells. Amorphous material deposited around the microvilli in these clefts represents the onset of formation of the zona pellucida, which becomes visible with the light microscope, around oocytes 50 to 80 μ in diameter, in multilaminar primary follicles. The zona pellucida is a gel-like neutral pro-

tein-polysaccharide. The cellular origin of its substance is not entirely clear. Its secretion is usually attributed to the follicular cells, but there is some evidence that the oocyte may also participate in its formation.

In the granulosa cells of the growing primary follicle, the mitochondria, the granular reticulum, and free ribosomes gradually increase in abundance and the Golgi apparatus becomes more prominent. In some species lipid droplets are common in the cytoplasm. Slender processes from these cells penetrate the zona pellucida, where they mingle with microvillous projections from the oocyte (Fig. 32-11). Some of these make contact with the oolemma, but protoplasmic continuity between the granulosa cells and the oocyte has not been demonstrated.

Secondary Follicles.   In the course of the continuing proliferation of the granulosa cells, the enlarging follicle becomes oval in shape and the oocyte eccentric in position. When the follicle reaches a diameter of about 0.2 mm., several irregular spaces filled with clear *liquor folliculi* appear among the granulosa cells. The increase in the amount of this fluid is associated with further increase in size of the follicle and a confluence of the irregular spaces among the granulosa cells to form a single crescentic cavity, the *antrum*. Thenceforth the follicle is described as a *secondary* or *vesicular follicle* (Fig. 32-4). By the time the formation of the antrum begins, the oocyte has usually attained its full size. The ovum grows no more thereafter, but the follicle as a whole continues to enlarge until it reaches a diameter of 10 mm. or more.

The typical small vesicular follicle is lined by a stratified epithelium (granulosa cells), which displays a local thickening on one side called the *cumulus oophorus*. This thicker region protruding into the liquid filled cavity has the oocyte in its center (Figs. 32-2 and 32-4). Although the lining of the follicle is described as a stratified epithelium, its granulosa cells are less compact in their organization than the cells of most epithelia. They may be columnar or polyhedral immediately surrounding the

zona pellucida, but elsewhere liquor folliculi accumulates between them and they become angular or stellate in form and are connected with one another by short processes. In growing follicles small accumulations of densely staining material may appear among the granulosa cells. These are the *Call-Exner bodies*. Whether they are intra- or extracellular has been a subject of dispute, but the prevailing view is that they are droplets within the cytoplasm of certain granulosa cells. They stain positively with the PAS reaction and may represent intracellular precursors of follicular fluid.

Mature Follicle. In the human, follicles require 10 to 14 days from the beginning of the cycle to reach maturity. As they approach their maximum size they are large vesicles that occupy the full thickness of the ovarian cortex

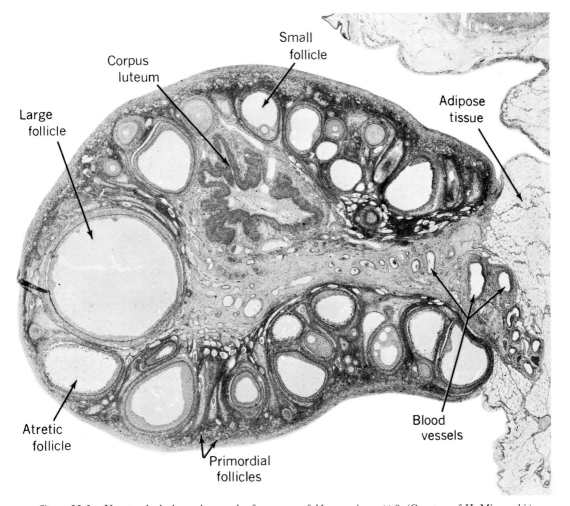

Figure 32-3. Unretouched photomicrograph of an ovary of *Macacus rhesus*. × 8. (Courtesy of H. Mizoguchi.)

and bulge from the free surface of the organ. The follicles are tense and the liquid in the follicular cavity is presumably under considerable pressure, and the outer part of the wall is quite thin. The protein and polysaccharide of the follicular liquid is precipitated by fixatives and appears finely granular in sections. The epithelium lining the cavity, called the *membrana granulosa,* is limited on the outside by a prominent basal lamina that separates it from the theca. In late stages of follicular growth, mitotic figures gradually decrease in number among the granulosa cells. Intercellular spaces among the cells of the inner layers of the membrana granulosa become more prominent. The connection of the ovum with the membrana granulosa is gradually loosened by the development of new liquid filled intercellular spaces in the cumulus oophorus. In the loosening up of the cumulus, one or more layers of radially disposed, columnar granulosa cells remain attached to the ovum, forming the *corona radiata,* a loose cellular investment which persists even after ovulation. The peripheral cytoplasm of the human ovum contains relatively few yolk

granules and is rather clear. The eccentric nucleus (*germinal vesicle*) is about 25 μ in diameter and contains a large nucleolus.

The theca folliculi reaches its highest development in the mature follicle. The theca interna is composed of large spindle-shaped or polyhedral cells with oval nuclei and fine lipid droplets in their cytoplasm (Fig. 32-8). They are enmeshed in a network of thin reticular fibers that are continuous with those of the theca externa and the rest of the ovarian stroma. Although they are modified connective tissue cells, the cells of the theca interna have cytological characteristics similar to those of cells in other steroid secreting endocrine glands. They are therefore believed to elaborate the female sex hormones, *estrogens.* Consistent with the presumed endocrine function of the theca interna is its rich capillary plexus.

The theca externa consists of concentrically arranged fibers and fusiform cells that do not appear to have any secretory function. The larger blood vessels of the theca externa supply the capillaries of the theca interna.

The number of follicles that begin to de-

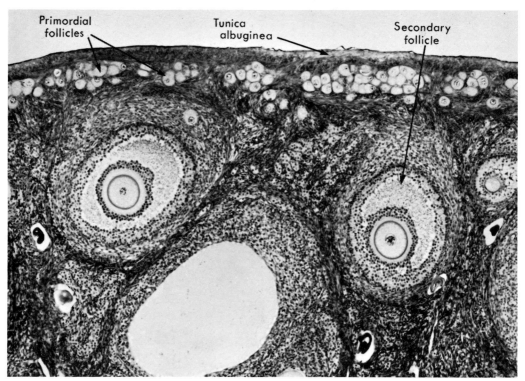

Figure 32-4. Photomicrograph of cat ovary, showing numerous primordial follicles and two secondary follicles with a well developed antrum. × 100.

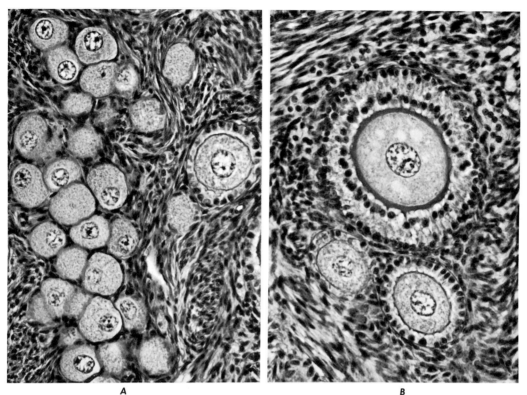

A   **B**

Figure 32-5. Photomicrographs of areas from the cortex of the cat ovary. *A,* Primordial follicles and an early primary follicle. *B,* Two unilaminar primary follicles and one more advanced. × 350.

velop in each cycle is considerably greater than the number that reach maturity. They may degenerate at any stage of development from primordial follicles onward (see page 728). Of the few that reach maturity, some involute but, as a rule, one ruptures and releases an ovum.

OVULATION. The process in which the follicle ruptures and sets free the ovum, enabling it to meet the spermatozoa and become fertilized, is called *ovulation.* Usually only one ovum is released from the human ovary at a time, but occasionally two, and rarely more, may be discharged. A follicle ripens at intervals of about 28 days in the human female, although variations of a week or more are not uncommon. Normally ovulation occurs on or about the fourteenth day of an ideal 28 day cycle. Cycles of typical duration may occur without associated ovulation. These are called *anovulatory cycles.* The stages preparatory to rupture of the follicle have been extensively studied in histological sections of ovaries, and the actual process of ovulation has been directly observed in living rats (Blandau) and in humans (Decker; Doyle).

The ovum and the granulosa cells immediately surrounding it are loosened from the remainder of the cumulus oophorus in the last stages of follicular maturation and float free in the liquor folliculi. During this period, the follicular fluid seems to accumulate faster than the follicle grows, and the part of the follicular wall that bulges on the surface of the ovary becomes progressively thinner. The follicular fluid that forms just before ovulation is more watery than the rest and appears to be secreted at a rapid rate. The first indication of impending ovulation is the appearance on the outer surface of the follicle of a small oval area, the *macula pellucida* or *stigma,* in which the flow of blood slows and then ceases, resulting in a local change in color and translucency of the follicular wall. The germinal epithelium overlying this area becomes discontinuous and the intervening stroma greatly thinned out. Pressure of the accumulating follicular fluid causes this thin area to bulge outward as a clear vesicle or cone. In the rat, where these events have been observed in greatest detail, the formation of the stigma takes place in 5 minutes or less.

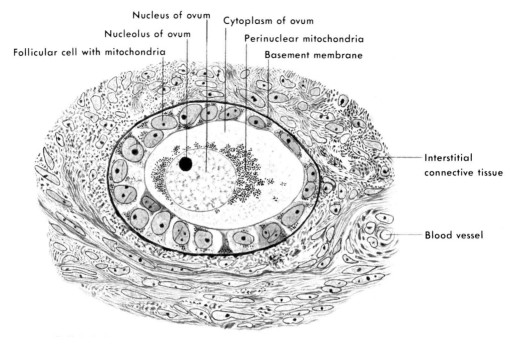

Figure 32-6. Follicle in first stages of growth from ovary of adult woman. Aniline-acid fuchsin stain. × 780. From a preparation of C. M. Bensley. (After A. A. Maximow.)

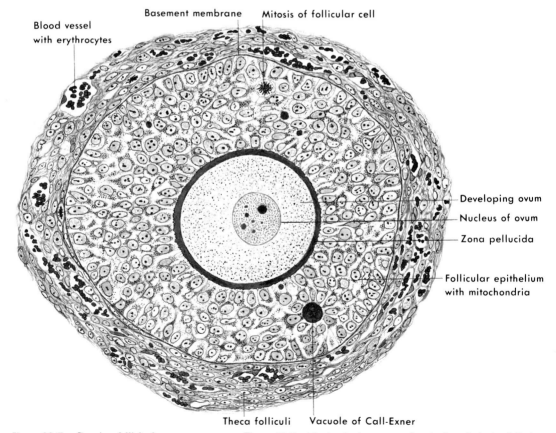

Figure 32-7. Growing follicle from same ovary as Figure 32-6 with developing ovum already five sixths its full size. × 375. (After A. A. Maximow.)

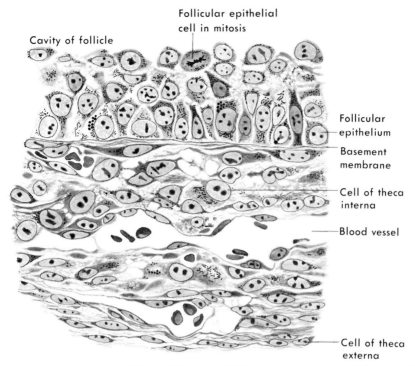

Figure 32-8. Section of part of wall of large follicle under high magnification. × 780. (After A. A. Maximow.)

The cone then ruptures and in a minute or two the ovum and its adherent mass of cumulus cells are pushed through the orifice, followed by a gush of follicular fluid (Fig. 32-12). The fluid immediately associated with the ovum appears viscous, while that which follows is quite thin.

The turgid fronds or fimbriae of the fallopian tube are closely applied to the surface of the ovary at the time of ovulation. Their active movements, and the currents created in the surface film by the cilia on their epithelial cells, are responsible for drawing the ovum into the open ostium of the oviduct.

MATURATION OF THE OVUM. In early embryos the primitive germ cells are located in the endoderm of the yolk sac and in subsequent development they migrate to the genital ridges and into the developing ovary. After birth they undergo no further proliferation but remain quiescent within primordial follicles for many years. During this period they are *primary oocytes,* homologous to the primary spermatocytes in the male. In both, the prophase of meiotic division is quite prolonged. It occurs in the oocyte late in the phase of growth of the follicle. The first meiotic or maturation division takes place shortly before ovulation.

The chromatin is equally divided between the daughter cells, but one of them, the *secondary oocyte,* receives practically all of the cytoplasm. The other becomes the *first polar body,* a minute cell containing a nucleus and a minimal amount of cytoplasm. The first maturation division is completed within the ovarian follicle a few hours before ovulation (Fig. 32-13).

Immediately after the expulsion of the first polar body, the nucleus of the secondary oocyte enters the second meiotic division, but it progresses only to metaphase, where it is arrested until fertilization. The chromatin mass is then divided equally, but again the bulk of the cytoplasm is retained by one daughter cell —the mature *ovum.* The other daughter cell is the small *second polar body.* In the human, observations on the formation of the polar bodies are incomplete. The first polar body undergoes rapid fragmentation and disappears. The second, which is formed after fertilization of the ovum, persists only through the first few cleavages (Fig. 32-28A) and then disappears. As in spermatogenesis, the consequence of the meiotic divisions is the production of a mature gamete with the haploid number of chromosomes.

FERTILIZATION. The newly ovulated

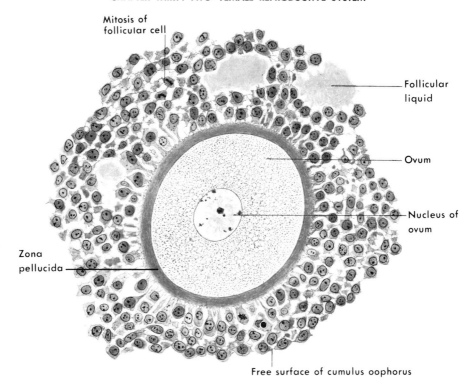

Mitosis of
follicular cell

Follicular
liquid

Ovum

Nucleus of
ovum

Zona
pellucida

Free surface of cumulus oophorus

Figure 32-9. Ovum of a mature follicle with surrounding follicular cells, under higher magnification. × 375. (After A. A. Maximow.)

tubal ovum in most mammalian species, including man, is surrounded by a *corona radiata* of adhering granulosa cells. Concurrently with the invasion of this mass of cells by spermatozoa, their attachments to one another are loosened. The gradual dispersion of the cells of the corona radiata is attributed to a depolymerization of the protein-polysaccharide intercellular substance and to increased surface activity of the cells themselves.

Upon reaching the zona pellucida, the sperm head gradually penetrates this layer. The details of this process are still poorly understood. The spermatozoon remains actively motile during its penetration, but whether this movement contributes to the process; and to what extent local lysis of the zona by enzymes in the sperm acrosome may be involved, are questions that have yet to be satisfactorily answered. Once within the vitelline space, the movements of the sperm cease and it is apparently drawn into the ooplasm by activity of the egg surface. *Fertilization* proper consists of the entry of the spermatozoon into the ovum. This event somehow stimulates the ovum to complete the second meiotic division and cast off

the second polar body. This is followed by fusion of the egg and sperm nuclei to restore the diploid chromosome number, and cleavage of the egg ensues.

If the ovum is not fertilized it gradually fragments and is absorbed or phagocytized. The length of the period during which the human ovum remains fertilizable is not precisely known, but it is probably less than 24 hours.

FORMATION OF THE CORPUS LUTEUM. Following ovulation and discharge of the liquor folliculi, the wall of the follicle collapses and its granulosa cell lining is thrown into folds (Fig. 32-15). There may be some associated bleeding from the capillaries of the theca interna, resulting in the formation of a central clot. The cells of the plicated granulosa layer and those of the theca interna then undergo striking cytological alterations. They enlarge, accumulate lipid, and are transformed into plump, pale-staining polygonal cells—the *lutein cells*. After these postovulatory changes have taken place, the follicle is called the *corpus luteum*. Two kinds of lutein cells are distinguishable within it. Those derived from the granulosa cells make up the bulk of the lutein tissue and are called *granulosa lutein cells*. Those at the periphery, originating from the cells of the theca interna, are smaller and more deeply staining and are called the *theca lutein cells* (Fig. 32-16). The lipid in the lutein cells is dissolved in routine histological preparations, leaving numerous vacuoles. Their vacuolated cytoplasm gives them an appearance reminiscent of the cells of the adrenal cortex. In electron micrographs they have mitochondria with tubular cristae and the abundant agranular endoplasmic reticulum characteristic of steroid secreting cells. The corpus luteum secretes the hormone *progesterone*.

While the cells of the collapsed follicular wall are undergoing luteinization, the capillaries of the theca interna sprout and invade the lutein tissue (Fig. 32-14). Connective tissue elements also penetrate the developing corpus luteum from its periphery, forming a delicate reticulum around the lutein cells and gradually converting the resolving blood clot in the central cavity into a fibrous core.

If the ovum is not fertilized, the ruptured follicle gives rise to a *corpus luteum of menstruation (corpus luteum spurium)*, which lasts for only

about 14 days. Its rate of secretion of progesterone then drops as it undergoes histological involution. The lutein cells become loaded with lipid and ultimately degenerate. In the succeeding months the connective tissue cells become pyknotic, hyaline intercellular material accumulates, and the former corpus luteum is reduced to a white scar, the *corpus albicans* (Fig. 32-18). This slowly sinks deeper into the interior of the ovary and gradually disappears over a period of many months or years.

If ovulation is followed by fertilization, the corpus luteum enlarges further and becomes a *corpus luteum of pregnancy*, which persists for about 6 months and then gradually declines up to full term. After delivery its involution is accelerated and it undergoes changes leading to the formation of a scar similar to that left behind by the corpus luteum of menstruation.

ATRESIA OF FOLLICLES. The period of sexual activity in the human female extends over about 30 years. Ordinarily only one ovum is discharged each month. It follows that the number of ova that reach maturity and are

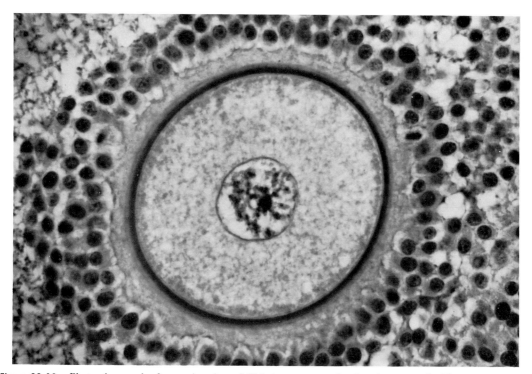

Figure 32-10. Photomicrograph of ovum in a large follicle in cat ovary, showing the zona pellucida and surrounding granulosa cells. Compare with Figure 32-9. × 475.

ovulated probably does not exceed 400. Of the 400,000 or more oocytes in the ovaries at birth, 99 per cent are destined to degenerate and disappear in the process called *follicular atresia*. This depletion of the stock of oocytes begins in intrauterine life, becomes prominent at birth and before puberty, and continues on a smaller scale throughout reproductive life. Every normal ovary, therefore, contains degenerating follicles. Why only a few follicles reach maturity and rupture, while the majority degenerate at various stages of development, is not known. Nor do we have any clear idea of the biological significance of this wastage of oocytes.

Atresia may begin at any stage of development of the follicle, even in ones that are apparently mature. In a primary follicle doomed to destruction, the ovum shrinks and degenerates, a process followed by the dissolution of the granulosa cells. The resulting small cavity in the stroma is rapidly closed without leaving a trace. In primary and small secondary follicles the earliest sign of abnormality is often the eccentric location of the egg nucleus, which goes on to develop a coarse granularity and finally becomes pyknotic. In follicles of larger size the histological changes in atresia become somewhat more complex and variable. In the cyclic atresia of follicles in the adult human ovary the process appears to be initiated in the follicle wall with secondary effects upon the oocyte. One of the earliest indications of this atretic process is the invasion of the granulosa layer and cumulus oophorus by strands of vascularized connective tissue. This is followed by a loosening and shedding of the granulosa cells into the follicular cavity and a hypertrophy of the theca interna. In follicles exhibiting these changes, the oocyte may still appear normal in routine histological preparations. As the degeneration of the granulosa cells advances, the follicle collapses, its outlines become wavy, and the cavity is filled by a large number of fibroblasts, wandering cells, and blood capillaries. The remnants of the degenerated follicular epithelium are rapidly resorbed. The folded and

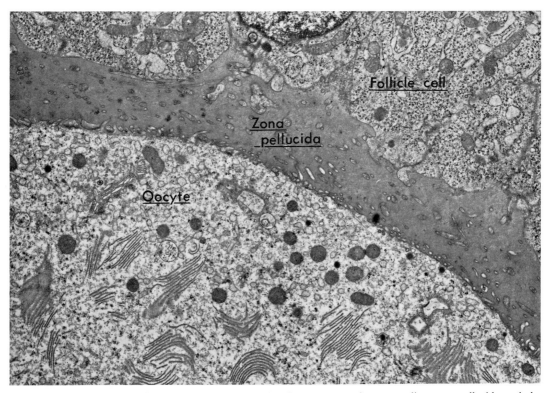

Figure 32-11. Electron micrograph of a peripheral sector of a rat oocyte, its surrounding zona pellucida and the associated follicle cells. Notice that irregular microvilli from the oocyte and larger processes from the follicle cells are both embedded in the substance of the zona pellucida. × 7500. (Courtesy of D. J. Szollosi and R. J. Blandau.)

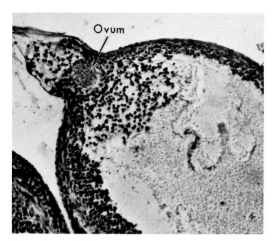

Figure 32-12. Photomicrograph of an ovulating ovarian follicle from the rat. The cumulus with the enclosed egg (at arrow) can be seen passing through the stigma. (Courtesy of R. J. Blandau.)

collapsed zona pellucida may remain alone amid the connective tissue elements.

The theca interna also undergoes important changes. The basement lamina that separates it from the epithelium often increases in thickness, and is transformed into a thick layer of hyaline substance, the "glassy membrane," which is characteristic of follicles in advanced atresia. The large cells of the theca interna increase further in size and are usually arranged in radial groups or strands, separated from one another by partitions of smaller fusiform cells and by fibers (Fig. 32-19). The cells acquire a typical epithelioid character and are filled with lipid and fat droplets. They are identical with the theca lutein cells but reach a higher degree of development in the atretic follicle. The cavity of the atretic follicle, containing the collapsed zona pellucida and connective tissue, is now surrounded by a broad, festooned layer of epithelioid, lipid-containing theca interna cells, arranged in radial cords and provided with a rich capillary network. The microscopic appearance of such an atretic follicle is rather similar to that of an old corpus luteum. Such structures have therefore been called *corpora lutea atretica*. The main differences are, of course, the presence of the glassy membrane, degenerated granulosa cells, and a zona pellucida in the center of the atretic follicle.

Strands of fibrous connective tissue and blood vessels ultimately penetrate the glassy membrane and the remains of the degenerated

elements in the interior are destroyed. The resulting scar with its hyaline streaks sometimes resembles a corpus albicans but is usually much smaller, and it sooner or later disappears in the stroma of the ovary. The layer of hypertrophic theca interna cells surrounding the cavity of the atretic follicle is broken up by the invading strands of fibrous tissue into separate cell islands of various shapes and sizes. These islands are irregularly scattered in the stroma and may persist for a time. They contribute to the so-called "interstitial gland" of the ovary.

THE INTERSTITIAL TISSUE OF THE OVARY. The stroma of the human ovarian cortex con-

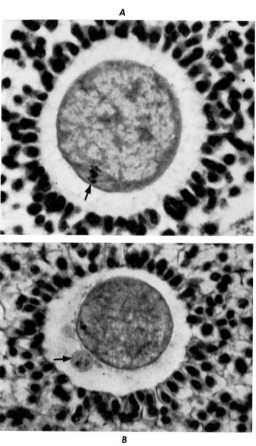

Figure 32-13. Photomicrographs of two stages in the maturation of the rat ovum. *A*, Section of a rat egg shortly before ovulation, showing the first polar spindle with diploid chromosomes on the metaphase plate (at the arrow). (Courtesy of R. J. Blandau.) *B*, Ovulated egg recovered from the ampulla of the oviduct but before sperm penetration. The first polar body lies in the perivitelline space (at arrow). The second maturation spindle can be seen just above it. (Courtesy of R. J. Blandau.)

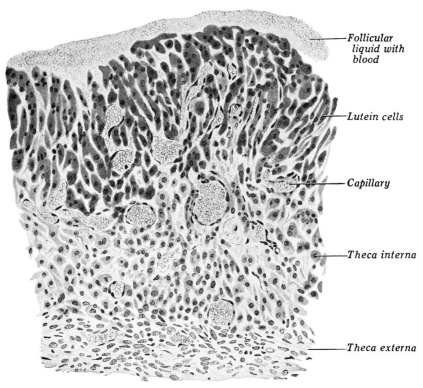

Follicular liquid with blood

Lutein cells

Capillary

Theca interna

Theca externa

Figure 32-14. Early stage of formation of human corpus luteum. Capillaries invade the granulosa, which is transformed into a layer of lutein cells. (Redrawn from R. Meyer.)

sists of spindle-shaped cells and networks of reticular fibers. Elastic fibers occur only in the walls of blood vessels. The cells bear a superficial resemblance to smooth muscle but do not have myofilaments in their cytoplasm. The stromal cells can differentiate into ovarian *interstitial cells* and, in ovarian pregnancy, they are capable of transformation to *decidual cells.*

The endocrine function and developmental potentialities of the layer of specialized interstitial tissue comprising the theca folliculi have already been described. Thus the interstitial tissue of the ovarian cortex is composed of reticular fibers and spindle-shaped cells with potentialities distinct from those of fibroblasts. The medulla, on the other hand, is made up of more typical loose connective tissue with fibroblasts, many elastic fibers, and strands of smooth muscle cells accompanying the blood vessels.

In many mammals the ovarian stroma contains conspicuous clusters and cords of large polygonal epithelioid cells called the *interstitial cells of the ovary.* They are rich in lipid and resemble lutein cells. In some species

they have been shown to secrete ovarian hormones. Because of their epithelioid appearance and presumed secretory function these cells, dispersed in the stroma, are referred to collectively as the *interstitial gland.* In animal species that have large litters, particularly among the rodents, the development of the interstitial gland may be very extensive. Cell foci originating from the breaking up of the hypertrophied theca interna of atretic follicles persist, enlarge, and fuse. Through the continuous addition of new cells, a large part of the organ is ultimately transformed into a diffuse mass of large, closely packed, lipid-containing interstitial cells that are almost identical in appearance to granulosa lutein cells. The follicles and the corpora lutea are embedded in this cell mass, and only a thin tunica albuginea separates it from the germinal epithelium on the surface.

The interstitial gland is poorly developed in the human ovary. Interstitial cells are found in the greatest numbers during the first year of life, when atretic follicles are most numerous, and they are believed to arise from the hypertrophied theca interna of regressing follicles. The interstitial gland involutes at puberty with the onset of menstruation and the cyclic development of corpora lutea. In the adult human ovary, cells of this kind either are absent or are present only in small numbers widely scattered in the stroma.

In the hilus of the ovary and in the adjacent mesovarium, groups of large epithelioid cells may be found closely associated with vascular spaces and unmyelinated nerve fibers. These cell clusters, now simply called *hilus cells*, were originally named the *sympathicotropic hilus gland* and were considered to be chromaffin cells. This view is now less widely accepted, since they do not always stain with chromates. Moreover, convincing evidence has been presented that they are similar to the Leydig cells of the testis. They are rich in lipid, contain cholesterol esters and lipochrome pigment, and may even have cytoplasmic crystals apparently identical to the crystals of Reinke (see Chapter 31). They have the histochemical and cytologic characteristics of actively secreting endocrine cells. They are prominent during pregnancy and at the menopause. Tumors or hyperplasia of the ovarian hilus cells are accompanied by masculinization. This clinical observation and their cytological and cytochemical resemblances to Leydig cells have led to the belief that they secrete androgens.

In the broad ligament and in the mesovarium, the occurrence of small accumulations of "interrenal" tissue corresponding to adrenal cortical tissue has also been described.

VESTIGIAL ORGANS ASSOCIATED WITH THE OVARY. Certain vestigial organs are found in connection with the ovary. The most important of these is the *epoöphoron*. It consists of several parallel or divergent tubules, running in the mesovarium from the hilus of the ovary toward the oviduct and fusing with a

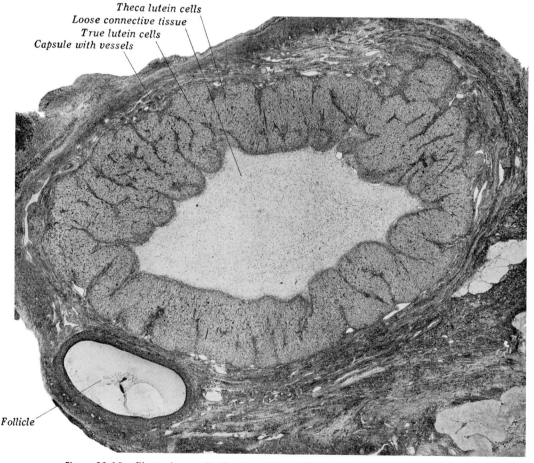

Theca lutein cells
Loose connective tissue
True lutein cells
Capsule with vessels

Follicle

Figure 32-15. Photomicrograph of section of corpus luteum from human ovary. × 11.

longitudinal canal parallel to the oviduct. All of these tubules end blindly. They are lined by low cuboidal or columnar epithelium, which is sometimes ciliated, and are surrounded by a condensed connective tissue layer containing smooth muscle. The upper end of the longitudinal duct sometimes ends in a cyst-like enlargement, the *hydatid of Morgagni,* while its other end may extend far toward the uterus as the so-called *duct of Gartner.* The transverse tubules and the longitudinal duct of Gartner together comprise the *epoöphoron.* Between the epoöphoron and the uterus in the tissue of the broad ligament is another group of irregular fragments of epithelial tubules, the *paroöphoron.* The epoöphoron is the rudiment of the genital part of the embryonic mesonephros and is the homologue of the epididymis of the male. The paroöphoron is the remnant of the caudal part of the mesonephros and corresponds to the paradidymis of the male.

Vessels and Nerves. The principal arterial supply to the ovary is from the ovarian artery, which arises from the aorta below the level of the renal vessels and reaches the ovary through the infundibulopelvic ligament. Along the mesovarial border of the ovary this vessel anastomoses with the uterine artery, which courses upward along the lateral aspect of the uterus from the region of the cervix. Relatively large vessels from the region of anastomosis of the uterine and ovarian arteries enter the hilus of the ovary and branch profusely as they course through the medulla. Because of their tortuous course, they are called *arteriae helicinae,* or helicine arteries. These vessels, like those in the corpora cavernosa penis, may show longitudinal ridges on their intima. In the periphery of the medulla they form a plexus, from which smaller twigs penetrate radially, passing between the follicles to enter the cortex, where they break up into loose networks of capillaries. These are continuous with dense networks in the theca of the larger follicles. The veins accompany

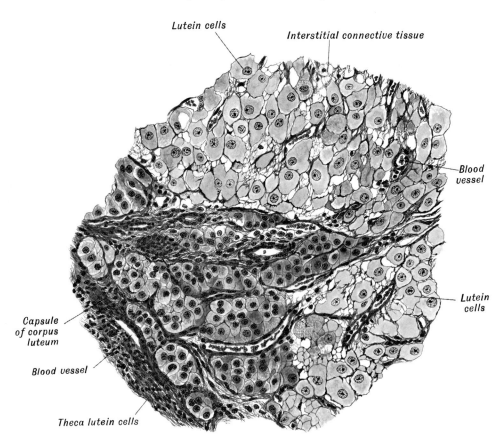

Figure 32-16. Cross section of peripheral layer of human corpus luteum of pregnancy, stained for reticular fibers by the Bielschowsky method. × 235. (After A. A. Maximow.)

the arteries. In the medulla they are large and tortuous and form a plexus in the hilus.

Networks of lymph capillaries arise in the cortex, especially in the theca externa of the large follicles. Lymph vessels with valves are found only outside the hilus.

The nerves of the ovary are derived from the ovarian plexus and from the uterine nerves. They enter the organ through the hilus, together with the blood vessels. They consist, for the most part, of nonmyelinated fibers, but thin myelinated fibers are also present. The presence of sympathetic nerve cells in the ovary has not been confirmed. The majority of the nerves supply the muscular coat of blood vessels. Many fibers penetrate into the cortex and form plexuses around the follicles and under the germinal epithelium. It seems doubtful that they penetrate through the basement lamina into the epithelium of the follicles. Sensory fibers ending in corpuscles of Pacini have been described in the ovarian stroma.

THE OVIDUCT OR FALLOPIAN TUBE

The *oviduct or uterine tube* (fallopian tube) is the part of the female reproductive tract that receives the ovum, provides the appropriate environment for its fertilization, and transports it to the uterus. It is a muscular tube about 12 cm. long situated in the edge of the mesosalpinx, which is the upper free margin of the broad ligament of the uterus. Its lumen communicates with the uterine cavity at one end and is open to the peritoneal cavity at the other. Several segments along its length are identified by different descriptive terms. The part of the tube traversing the wall of the uterus is called the *pars interstitialis*. The narrow medial third near the uterine wall is the *isthmus*. The expanded intermediate segment is the *ampulla*, and the funnel-shaped abdominal opening is the *infundibulum*. The margins of the latter are drawn out into numerous tapering, fringe-like processes, the *fimbriae*.

Histological Organization. The wall of the oviduct consists of a mucous membrane, a muscular layer, and an external serous coat. The mucous membrane in the ampulla is thick and forms numerous elaborately branched folds. The lumen in cross section, therefore, is a labyrinthine system of narrow spaces between profusely branching folia cov-

Figure 32-17. Photomicrograph of a small area of a human corpus luteum showing lutein cells and numerous engorged capillaries. Azan stain. × 500.

ered by epithelium (Fig. 32-20C). In the isthmus, the longitudinal folds are much shorter and less highly branched (Fig. 32-20B), and in the interstitial part, they are reduced to low ridges (Fig. 32-20A).

The epithelium is of the simple columnar variety (Fig. 32-21) but may sometimes appear pseudostratified when cut obliquely. It is highest in the ampulla and diminishes in height toward the uterus. It consists of two kinds of cells. One of these, especially numerous on the fimbriae and in the ampulla, is provided with cilia that beat toward the uterus. The other cell type is devoid of cilia and appears to be secretory. The secretion may provide the ovum with nutritive material, and in some species, notably the rabbit, it adds to the ovum an outer albuminous envelope. In the monotremes and some marsupials, a shell, as well as an albuminous coat, is formed about the ova. The two types of epithelial cells are probably different functional states of a single cell type. In women the epithelium of the oviduct undergoes cyclic changes along

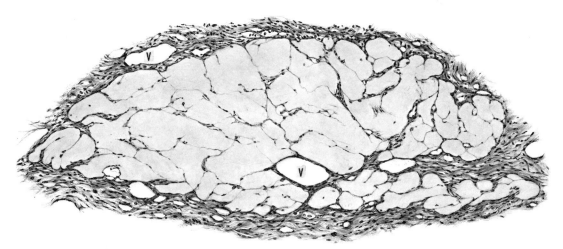

Figure 32-18. Corpus albicans of human ovary. Fixation by perfusion—hence the empty vessels (*V*). Dense hyaline material separates the residual cells of the corpus luteum. The whole structure is surrounded by the stroma of the ovary. × 135.

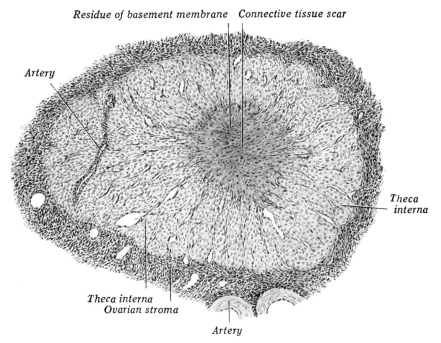

Figure 32-19. Atretic follicle with a well developed theca interna, from the ovary of a 39 year old woman. × 85. (After Schaffer.)

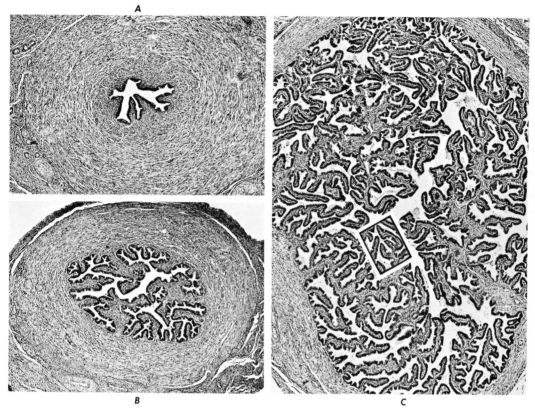

Figure 32-20. Photomicrographs of the fallopian tube of a 23 year old woman. × 30. *A*, The pars interstitialis; *B*, the isthmus; *C*, the outer portion of the ampulla. The area enclosed in the rectangle is shown at higher magnification in Figure 32-21.

with those of the uterine mucous membrane (Fig. 32-22). True glands are absent in the oviduct.

The lamina propria of the mucous membrane in the oviduct consists of a network of reticular fibers and of numerous fusiform cells. Wandering cells and mast cells also occur in limited numbers. The fixed cells here seem to have the same potencies as those in the uterus. In cases of tubal pregnancy, some of them are transformed into typical decidual cells.

No true muscularis mucosae, and therefore no submucous layer, can be distinguished. The mucous membrane is surrounded by the muscular coat, which consists of two layers of smooth muscle bundles. The inner layer is circular or spiral; the outer is principally longitudinal, but there is no distinct limit between the two. Toward the periphery, longitudinal bundles gradually appear in increasing numbers between the circular bundles. The smooth muscle bundles are em-

bedded in an abundant, loose connective tissue and extend into the broad ligament. Toward the uterus the muscularis increases in thickness. The peritoneal coat of the fallopian tube has the usual serosal structure.

At the time of ovulation the oviduct exhibits active movements. The abdominal opening of the oviduct contains large blood vessels in its mucosa, especially veins, and these extend into the fimbriae. Between the vessels, muscle fibers form a network. This results, in effect, in a sort of erectile tissue. At the time of ovulation the vessels are engorged with blood, and the resulting enlargement and turgescence of the fimbriae, together with the contraction of their intrinsic muscle, brings the opening of the tubal infundibulum into contact with the surface of the ovary.

The rhythmic contractions of the oviduct are probably of primary importance in the transport of the ovum. Contraction waves pass from the infundibulum to the uterus, and the

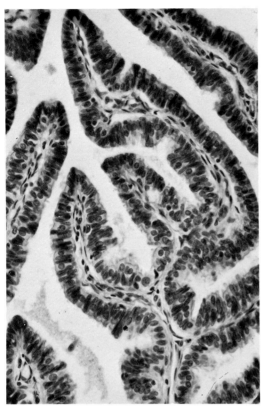

Figure 32-21. Photomicrograph of the branching folds of the mucous membrane of the human fallopian tube. × 280. For orientation see rectangle in Figure 32-20.

beat of the cilia on the mucosa is in the same direction.

BLOOD VESSELS, LYMPHATICS, AND NERVES. The mucous membrane and its folds, as well as the serous coat, contain abundant blood and lymph vessels. The lymph channels within the folds of the mucous membrane are extensive and appear in sections as long clefts that are often mistaken for artifactitious splits in the tissue, but careful inspection reveals their smooth endothelial lining. In periods of vascular engorgement, when these lymphatics are also distended with lymph, they no doubt contribute to the increased turgor of the tissue and stiffen the mucosal folds.

Larger nerve bundles are found accompanying the vessels in the serous layer and in the peripheral parts of the longitudinal muscle. The circular muscle layer contains a dense plexus of thin nerve bundles supplying the muscle fibers and penetrating into the mucous membrane.

UTERUS

The uterus is the portion of the reproductive tract that receives the fertilized ovum from the oviduct, provides its attachment, and establishes the vascular relations necessary for sustenance of the embryo throughout its development. In the human it is a single pear-shaped organ with a thick muscular wall (Figs. 32-1 and 32-23). It is slightly flattened dorsoventrally and contains a correspondingly flattened uterine cavity. In the nonpregnant condition, the uterus is about 6.5 cm. long, 3.5 cm. wide, and 2.5 cm. thick. Several regions are distinguished. The expanded upper portion, comprising the bulk of the organ, is the *body* or *corpus uteri*. The rounded upper end of the body, where the uterine tubes join the uterus, is often referred to as the *fundus*. The slightly constricted middle portion is the *isthmus,* and the cylindrical lower part is the *cervix.* The portion of the cervix that protrudes into the vagina is the *portio vaginalis.* The slender cervical canal that passes from the uterine cavity down through the cervix opens into the vagina at the *external os.*

The wall of the uterus consists of three layers. (1) A serous membrane, the *peritoneum,* covers the fundus and much of the posterior aspect of the organ. The peritoneum is reflected onto the bladder anteriorly and onto the rectum posteriorly, so that this layer is found only on part of the surface of the uterus. (2) The greater part of the thickness of the uterine wall is a mass of smooth muscle, the *myometrium.* (3) The organ is lined with a glandular mucous membrane called the *endometrium.*

MYOMETRIUM. The smooth muscle fibers of the muscular layer are arranged in cylindrical or flat bundles separated by thin septa of connective tissue containing isolated smooth muscle cells. Several layers can be distinguished in the myometrium according to the direction and disposition of the bundles. The layers are not sharply demarcated, however, because fiber bundles frequently cross over from one layer into another.

Immediately beneath the mucous membrane is a thin layer called the *stratum submucosum.* Its fibers are predominantly longitudinal, but some oblique and circular bundles may be found. This layer forms distinct muscular rings around the intramural portions of the oviducts. The next layer is the thickest and is called the *stratum vasculare* because it contains many large blood vessels that give it a spongy appearance. Circular and oblique muscle bundles are predominant. In the succeeding *stratum supravasculare,* the fibers are mainly circular and longitudinal. Finally, the outermost *stratum subserosum* is a thin longitudinal muscle layer. The two most superficial layers send muscular bundles out into the wall of the oviduct, the broad ligament, and the round ligament.

The smooth muscle cells of the myometrium ordinarily have a length of about 50 μ. In pregnancy, when the mass of the uterus increases about 24 times, they hypertrophy to a length of more than 500 μ. Although smooth muscle hypertrophy accounts for much of the enlargement of the gravid uterus, there also appears to be an increase in the number of the muscle fibers through division (Fischer-Wasels) and through transformation of the embryonic connective tissue cells into new muscular elements, especially in the innermost layers of the myometrium (Stieve). During return of the uterus to normal size after delivery, the muscle cells

show fatty infiltration and rapidly diminish in size. It is possible that some of them degenerate.

The connective tissue between the muscular bundles consists of collagenous fibers, fibroblasts, embryonic connective tissue cells, macrophages, and mast cells. A typical argyrophilic reticulum is continuous with the intermuscular collagenous tissue. Elastic networks are especially prominent in the peripheral layers of the uterine wall. From there they extend inward between the muscle bundles. The innermost layers of the myometrium do not contain elastic fibers except those in the walls of the blood vessels.

The cervix is composed mainly of dense collagenous and elastic fibers, among which fibroblasts and a variable number of smooth muscle cells are distributed. The dense fibrous nature of the cervix accounts for the firmer consistency of this part of the uterus.

ENDOMETRIUM. Beginning with puberty at 12 to 15 years of age and continuing until *menopause* at age 45 to 50, the uterine mucous membrane undergoes monthly cyclic changes

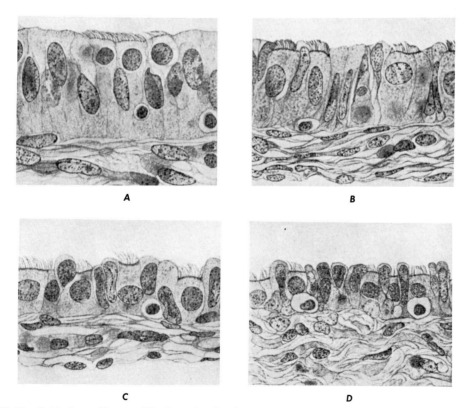

A B

C D

Figure 32-22. Epithelium of human fallopian tube, showing variations in the epithelium during the cycle. *A,* Follicular phase; *B,* early luteal phase; *C,* premenstrual; *D,* pregnancy. × 700. (After Snyder.)

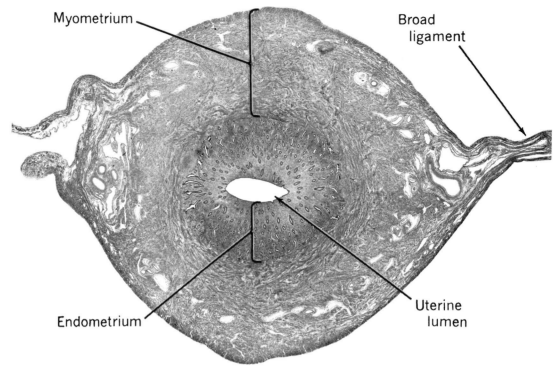

Myometrium

Broad ligament

Endometrium

Uterine lumen

Figure 32-23. Photomicrograph of the uterus of a macaque in transverse section, illustrating the relative thickness of the myometrium and the late proliferative endometrium. × 9. (Courtesy of H. Mizoguchi.)

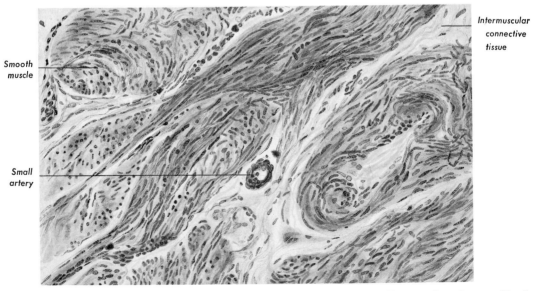

Intermuscular connective tissue

Smooth muscle

Small artery

Figure 32-24. Section of myometrium of a 36 year old woman. Low magnification. Hematoxylin-eosin-azure II stain. (Drawn by Miss A. Nixon.)

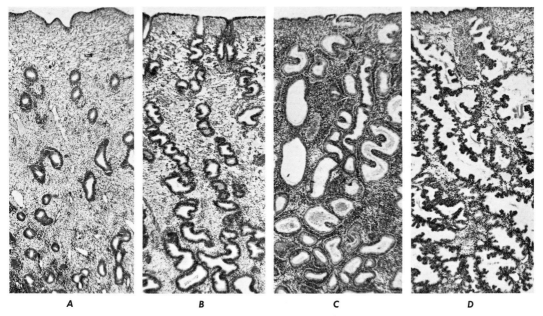

Figure 32-25. Photomicrographs of human endometrium in different days of the cycle. *A,* Proliferative endometrium of the ninth day. *B,* Early secretory endometrium, fifteenth day. *C,* Secretory endometrium, nineteenth day. *D,* Gestational hyperplasia, twelfth day of pregnancy. (Courtesy of A. T. Hertig.)

in structure in response to rhythmical variations in the secretion of ovarian hormones. At the end of each cycle there is a partial destruction of the endometrium accompanied by a more or less abundant extravasation of blood. The products of these destructive changes appear as a bloody vaginal discharge, the *menstrual flow,* which continues for 3 to 5 days.

The endometrium is approximately 5 mm. in thickness at the height of its development in an ordinary menstrual cycle. It consists of a surface epithelium invaginated to form numerous tubular *uterine glands* that extend down into a very thick lamina propria that is usually referred to as the *endometrial stroma.*

The surface epithelium is simple columnar and is composed of a mixture of ciliated and secretory cells. The epithelium of the uterine glands is similar, but the ciliated cells are fewer. The direction of ciliary beat is said to be upward in the glands and toward the vagina on the endometrial surface. The glands are, for the most part, simple tubules but may show some bifurcation in the zone adjacent to the myometrium. They occasionally penetrate a short distance among the muscle bundles. Under pathological conditions the myometrium may be extensively

invaded in this manner, a change described by the term *adenomyosis.* In old age, the endometrium atrophies and becomes thin. The openings of the glands may become partly obliterated and they then become distended to form small cysts.

The endometrial stroma strongly resembles mesenchyme. Its irregularly stellate cells have large ovoid nuclei. The cell processes appear to be in contact throughout the tissue and adhere to the delicate framework of reticular fibers. Elastic fibers are absent except in the walls of the arterioles. There is a ground substance, which at times is rich in metachromatic protein-polysaccharide. In the interstices of this reticulum of stellate cells are lymphoid wandering cells and granular leukocytes. Macrophages are not uncommon but, for some unknown reason, they are not mobilized to phagocytize the blood extravasated in menstruation.

A knowledge of the blood supply of the endometrium is of special importance for an understanding of the mechanisms of menstruation and of placentation. From the uterine arteries that course in the broad ligaments along the sides of the uterus, branches penetrate to the stratum vasculare of the myometrium. In this layer circumferentially oriented *arcuate arteries* run toward the midline,

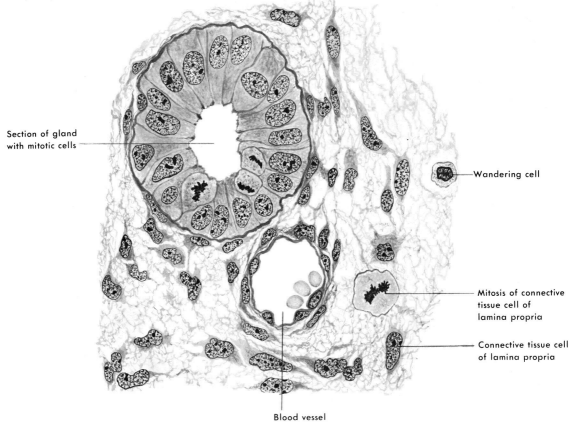

Section of gland
with mitotic cells

Wandering cell

Mitosis of connective
tissue cell of
lamina propria

Connective tissue cell
of lamina propria

Blood vessel

Figure 32-26.   Section of mucous membrane of human uterus on day 11 of menstrual cycle. × 415. (After A. A. Maximow.)

where they anastomose with corresponding vessels from the other side. Branches from the arcuate arteries pass through the deeper layers of the myometrium to reach the endometrium. Where they cross the myometrial-endometrial junction, they give off small *basal arteries* supplying the deepest portion of the endometrium, the *basalis* or *stratum basale* (the portion which is not sloughed off during menstruation). Continuing upward into the thicker layer commonly called the *functionalis,* the arteries are unbranched but highly contorted. These "coiled arteries" ramify into arterioles that supply a rich capillary bed in the superficial portion of the endometrium. The thin walled veins form an irregular anastomosing net with sinusoidal enlargements at all levels of the endometrium. During most of the cycle the coiled arteries constrict and dilate rhythmically, so that the surface is alternately blanched and suffused with blood

(Markee). These vessels play an important role in menstruation.

ISTHMUS AND CERVIX. The mucous membrane of the corpus uteri passes, sometimes gradually but more often abruptly, into that of the isthmus, which remains thin and shows few signs of cyclic changes. It lacks coiled arteries and usually does not bleed during menstruation. The stroma is dense and the glands are sparse and oblique to the surface.

The mucosa of the cervix has a thickness of 2 to 3 mm. and a different structure, having branching folds, the *plicae palmatae,* on its surface. The surface of the cervical canal is lined by a tall columnar epithelium, in which the oval nuclei are at the base of the cells and the greater part of their cytoplasm is filled with mucus. The mucosa contains numerous large glands, which differ from those of the corpus and isthmus in that they are extensively branched and are lined with tall, mucus-se-creting columnar cells similar to those of the surface epithelium (Fig. 32-39). Some of the cells are ciliated. The cervical canal is usually filled with mucus. Often the ducts of some of the glands are occluded and the glands are transformed into cysts, which may reach the size of a pea. These are the so-called *nabothian cysts*.

The mucosa of the cervix does not take part in the menstrual changes. An increase in vaginal mucus, which comes largely from the cervix, occurs at about the middle of the cycle (Papanicolaou). In pregnancy the cervical glands enlarge, proliferate, and accumulate large quantities of mucus. The connective tissue between them is reduced to thin partitions.

The outer surface of the portio vaginalis is smooth and covered with a mucous membrane similar to that of the vagina. It consists of a stratified squamous epithelium containing abundant glycogen and a lamina propria with small papillae well separated from one another. The transition between the columnar, mucus-secreting epithelium of the cervical canal and the stratified squamous epithelium of the portio vaginalis is abrupt. As a rule the borderline is just inside the *external os* of the cervix. In some individuals, patches of colum-nar epithelium may extend for short distances onto the surface of the portio vaginalis, forming so-called "erosions." In others stratified epithelium extends into the vaginal end of the cervical canal.

CYCLIC CHANGES IN THE ENDOMETRIUM. In the course of a normal menstrual cycle, the endometrium passes through a continuous sequence of morphological and functional changes, but for convenience of description the cycle is divided into three recognizable stages that are correlated with the functional activities of the ovary. These are the *proliferative*, the *secretory*, and the *menstrual* phases. The proliferative phase coincides with the growth of the ovarian follicles and their secretion of estrogenic hormone. The secretory phase is the period when the corpus luteum is functionally active and secreting progesterone, and the menstrual phase ensues when the hormonal stimulation of the endometrium by the ovary declines (Fig. 32-27).

The Proliferative or Follicular Phase. During this phase, which begins at the end of the menstrual flow, there is a two- to three-fold increase in thickness of the endometrium. Mitoses are numerous in the epithelium and in the stroma. The straight tubular glands increase in number and in length (Fig. 32-25*A*). Their epithelium is columnar and the lumen

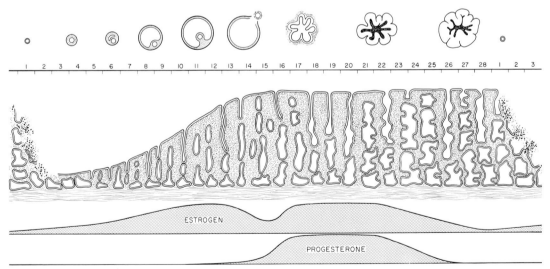

Figure 32-27. Diagram correlating the events in the ovary and the endometrium during a 28 day cycle with the levels of circulating ovarian hormones. One complete cycle and the beginning of another are indicated. The ovarian changes involve the growth of a follicle, its rupture at ovulation, corpus luteum formation and regression. The endometrial development involves increase in thickness and in the complexity of the glands. The rise of estrogenic hormone is correlated with development of the follicle and progesterone with the development of the corpus luteum.

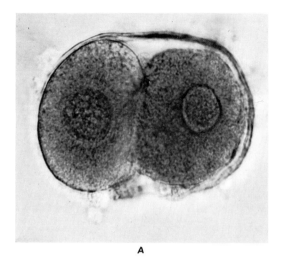

A

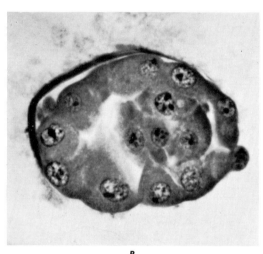

B

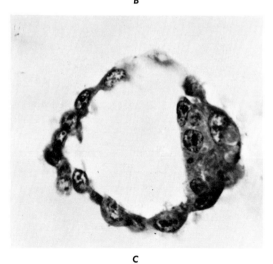

C

narrow. The ground substance of the stroma is abundant and metachromatic. The coiled arteries are elongating but are only moderately convoluted and do not extend into the superficial third of the endometrium. Toward the end of this phase, the glands become somewhat sinuous and their cells begin to accumulate glycogen (Fig. 32-25*B*).

The proliferative growth of the endometrium may continue for a day after ovulation on about day 14 of an ideal 28 day cycle. There may be some diapedesis of erythrocytes into the stroma beneath the surface epithelium, and rarely a little blood may enter the uterine lumen and reach the vagina. Such *intermenstrual bleeding* is rare in the human, but estrous bleeding is common in the dog.

The Secretory or Luteal Phase. Some further thickening of the endometrium occurs in this phase, but this is largely attributable to edema of the stroma and to the accumulation of secretion in the uterine glands. The glandular epithelium early in the secretory phase of the endometrium shows a characteristic displacement of the nuclei toward the free surface, owing to the accumulation of a large amount of glycogen in the basal cytoplasm. This appearance is transient and is no longer seen after active secretion is established. The glands continue to grow, becoming quite tortuous and ultimately developing a marked sacculation, resulting in a relatively wide lumen of irregular outline containing a carbohydrate-rich secretion (Fig. 32-25*C*).

The elongation and convolution of the coiled arteries continues in this phase. They extend into the superficial portion of the endometrium and become more prominent in sections because of the enlargement of the periarterial stromal cells.

Figure 32-28. Photomicrographs of early human ova. *A,* Segmenting human ovum. Two cell stage recovered from the fallopian tube. Ovulation age 1½ to 2½ days. Notice polar body between the two blastomeres. × 500. *B,* Free human blastocyst. Section of a 58 cell intrauterine blastocyst. Segmentation cavity is just beginning to form. Zona pellucida is disappearing. Ovulation age 4 days. × 600. *C,* Free human blastocyst. Section of a 107 cell blastocyst recovered from the uterine cavity. The inner cell mass is at the right. Ovulation age 4½ days. × 600. (All three micrographs after A. Hertig, J. Rock, and E. Adams, Am. J. Anat., *98:*435, 1956.)

A

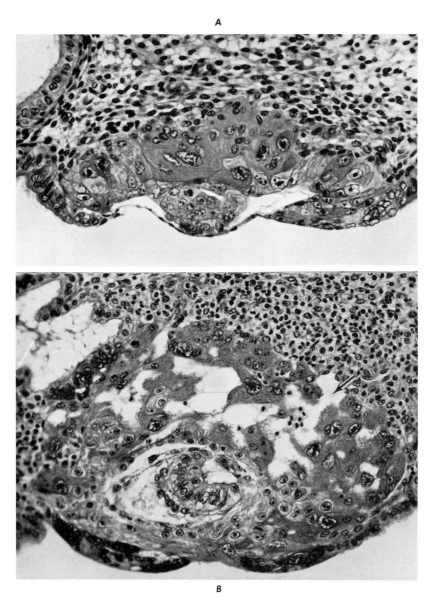

B

Figure 32-29. Photomicrographs of early human implantation sites. *A,* Human 7 day implantation. The embryo is a simple bilaminar disk. Development of an amniotic cavity is beginning. There is a solid plaque of syncytio- and cytotrophoblast. × 300. (After Hertig and Rock, 1941. Courtesy of the Carnegie Institution of Washington.) *B,* Human 9-day implantation. The embryo is a bilaminar disk. The syncytiotrophoblast now shows prominent lacunae. Notice at arrow maternal blood space communicating with lacuna. × 25. (After Hertig and Rock. Courtesy of the Carnegie Institution of Washington.)

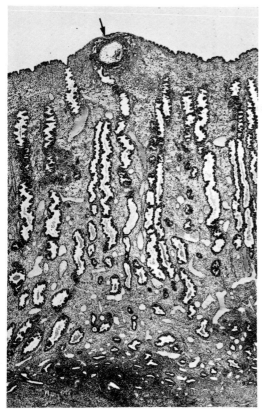

Figure 32-30. Human gestational endometrium with an 11 day implantation site (at the arrow). The entire thickness of the endometrium is shown. The glands are secretory, the stroma edematous, and the superficial veins are dilated. × 18. (After Hertig and Rock, 1941. Courtesy of Carnegie Institution of Washington.)

The Menstrual Phase. About two weeks after ovulation, in a cycle in which fertilization fails to occur, the stimulation of the endometrium by ovarian hormones declines and marked vascular changes take place. The coiled arteries constrict, so that the superficial zone of the endometrium is blanched for hours at a time. The glands cease secreting and there is a loss of interstitial fluid, so that the height of the endometrium shrinks somewhat while the stroma appears more cellular and stains more deeply. Many leukocytes are found in the stroma. After about two days of intermittent ischemia the coiled arteries close down, making the superficial zone ischemic, while blood continues to circulate in the basal zone. After a variable number of hours, the constricted arteries open up for a short time; the walls of the damaged vessels near the surface burst, and blood pours into the stroma

and soon breaks out into the uterine lumen. Such blood does not clot. Subsequently, patches of blood-soaked tissue separate off, leaving the torn ends of glands, arteries, and veins open to the surface. Blood may ooze from such veins, refluxing from the intact basal circulation. The menstrual discharge thus contains (1) altered arterial and venous blood, with normal, hemolyzed, and sometimes agglutinated erythrocytes; (2) partially disintegrated or autolyzed epithelial and stroma cells; and (3) the secretions of the uterine, cervical, and vulval glands. Sometimes there are tissue fragments in the menstrual discharge, but blood clots are considered abnormal. The average loss of blood is 35 ml. By the third or fourth day of the flow, the entire lining of the uterus presents a raw wound surface.

The endometrium deep to the zone of extravasation remains intact during menstruation, although it does shrink down. Glands typical of the secretory phase may be recognizable, as such, until the end of menstruation. Before the vaginal discharge has ceased, epithelial cells glide out from the torn ends of the glands, and the surface epithelium is quickly restored. The superficial circulation is then resumed, the stroma again becomes rich in ground substance, and the follicular phase of the new cycle begins.

The typical condition illustrated in Figure 32-27 is not always realized. In some cycles, the ovary may not produce a ripe follicle. In such *anovulatory cycles* the endometrial changes are minimal. The proliferative endometrium develops as usual, but since there is no ovulation and no corpus luteum is formed, the endometrium does not progress to the secretory phase but continues to be of the proliferative type until menstruation begins.

The various events of the normal menstrual cycle are so characteristic and reproducible that an experienced pathologist can establish the date of the cycle with surprising accuracy from examination of endometrial curettings or biopsies. It is also possible from examination of biopsies in the second half of the cycle to determine whether a woman is having an ovulatory or an anovulatory cycle. Such examinations are essential in the clinical investigation of the causes of infertile marriage or the nature of disease of the ovaries or disorders of menstruation. It is therefore of practical value to be able to recognize the principal phases of the endometrial cycle. The criteria, in brief, are as follows. (1) *Proliferative or follicular phase:* endometrium 1 to 5 mm. thick; straight, narrow glands becoming wavy; the epithelium tall, becoming vacuolated; many mitoses in all tissues; and no coiled arteries in the superficial third. (2) *Secretory or luteal phase:* endometrium 3 to 6 mm. thick; glands wavy or sacculated with wide lumina; epithelial cells tall with surface blebs; stroma edematous superficially; mitoses confined to coiled arteries which are present near the surface. (3) *Premenstrual phase:* endometrium 3 to 4 mm. thick, greatly contorted glands and arteries; dense stroma with leukocytosis. (4) *Menstrual phase:* endometrium 0.5 to 3 mm. thick; superficially extravasated blood; the glands and arteries appear collapsed; the stroma is dense; and the surface is denuded.

Endocrine Regulation of the Female Reproductive System

The histology of the female reproductive system cannot be fully understood without some overview of the interactions of the brain, the hypophysis, the ovaries, and the uterus in the regulation of the cyclic changes involved in reproduction. Although some of these relations have already been presented in Chapter 17, a brief recapitulation may promote understanding of the cyclic changes described in this chapter.

The cyclic activities of the ovary are under the control of the anterior lobe of the hypophysis. The secretion of follicle stimulating hormone (FHS) is responsible for the growth of the follicle up to the point of ovulation. Luteinizing hormone (LH), together with

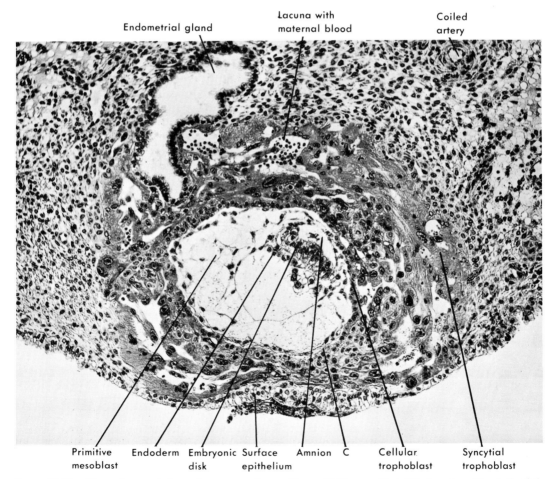

Figure 32-31. Photomicrograph from the same section as Figure 32-30, magnified 160 diameters. The bulk of the ovum consists of masses of trophoblast (syncytium) invading the endometrium. Within the syncytial trophoblast is the cellular trophoblast with obvious cell boundaries. The cells are arranged as a simple epithelium except for the clump at *C.* The cellular trophoblast immediately surrounds the primitive chorionic mesoblast in which the embryo is suspended. (After Hertig and Rock, 1941. Courtesy of the Carnegie Institution of Washington.)

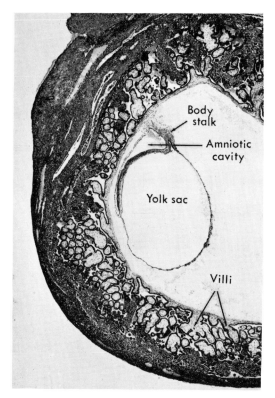

Figure 32-32. Human embryo of ovulation age 18 to 19 days. The curved embryonic disc lies between a large yolk sac and a smaller crescentic amniotic cavity. The body stalk bends back and blends with the chorionic mesoblast. Many secondary villi project into an extensive intervillous space. × 15. (Courtesy of A. T. Hertig.)

FSH, is required for ovulation and for the early development of the corpus luteum. The endometrium of the uterus exhibits two phases of functional activity that are correlated with the events in the ovary—a *follicular* (or *proliferative*) *phase* of endometrial growth, coinciding with maturation of the follicles and their ovulation, and a *luteal* (or *secretory*) *phase,* correlated with the development of a corpus luteum and during which the endometrium is prepared for reception of a fertilized egg.

At the end of the follicular phase in most mammals, morphological and neural changes occur that make the female receptive to the male at or near the time of ovulation. This is the period of heat or *estrus.* Although the menstrual cycle in the human female is basically similar to the estrus cycle of other species, receptivity to the male is not limited to the end of the follicular phase and there is no outward indication that ovulation has occurred.

During the ensuing luteal phase of the cycle the preparation of the endometrium for reception of a fertilized ovum is more extensive in the primates than in many other animals. If no egg reaches the uterus the bulk of the endometrium breaks down after about two weeks. Its discharge is attended by uterine bleeding—*menstruation.*

In a cycle in which the ovum is fertilized, the secretion of gonadotropins by the trophoblast helps maintain the corpus luteum beyond its usual lifespan, and it becomes the corpus luteum of pregnancy. The continuing function of the corpus luteum prevents the regressive and ischemic changes that lead to menstruation in an infertile cycle. Instead the secretory endometrium persists and undergoes further hyperplasia, and menstruation is suppressed for the duration of pregnancy.

The temporal correlation of the events in the endometrium with those of the ovary is mediated by ovarian hormones. The developing follicle, particularly its theca interna, secretes the steroid hormones *estradiol* and *estrone,* collectively described as *estrogens.* These stimulate growth of the uterine endometrium. In species exhibiting estrus, the estrogens also act upon the central nervous system to bring about sexual receptivity and its associated behavioral manifestations. After ovulation, the collapsed follicle is reorganized and transformed into a corpus luteum that secretes *progesterone* and possibly other *progestogens.* These are responsible for the secretory changes in the endometrium that are characteristic of the luteal phase of the cycle.

The secretion of gonadotropins by the hypophysis is influenced by various factors. The rhythm of hypothalamic stimuli carried by the neurohumoral pathway to the anterior hypophysis appears to be determined by some internal clock, but it can also be influenced by psychic factors and various external stimuli. Production of excess ovarian hormones also acts upon the hypothalamus to diminish gonadotropin secretion. This feedback mechanism is not only operative in the regulation of the normal cycle but is the basis for the recent successes in conception control, wherein orally administered analogues of ovarian progestogens act through the hypothalamus and hypophysis to suppress ovulation.

Implantation

After fertilization takes place in the upper part of the oviduct, segmentation of the ovum proceeds as it passes down the tube (Fig. 32-28*A* and *B*). When it reaches the uterus on about the fourth day, it consists of many cells arranged in a hollow sphere called the *blastocyst* (Fig. 32-28*C*). The blastocyst remains free in the lumen of the uterus for a day or so and then attaches to the surface of the secretory endometrium. The blastocyst by this time has differentiated into (1) an assemblage of cells at one pole called the *inner cell mass*, which is destined to form the embryo proper, and (2) a layer of primitive trophoblast cells making up the rest of the wall of the blastocyst. The trophoblast cells are concerned with the attachment and implantation of the ovum and with the subsequent establishment of the *placenta*, the organ in which the physiological exchange of nutrients and waste products takes place between the embryonic and the maternal circulation. When the trophoblast makes contact with the surface of the endometrium, its cells proliferate rapidly, forming, at the interface between the ovum and the maternal tissue, a multinucleate mass of protoplasm in which no cell boundaries are discernible—the *syncytial trophoblast*. This actively erosive syncytium destroys the surface epithelium and permits the blastocyst to sink into the underlying stroma (Fig. 32-29*A*). By the eleventh day the blastocyst is entirely within the endometrium; the trophoblast has formed a broad layer completely surrounding the inner cell mass, and the uterine epithelium has repaired the breach made in it by the implanting ovum (Figs. 32-30 and 32-31). This form of implantation, in which the embryo and its associated membranes become embedded in and completely encapsulated by the endometrium, is called *interstitial implantation* and is characteristic of the human.

From the ninth to the eleventh day the expanding trophoblastic shell becomes permeated by a labyrinthine system of intercommunicating lacunae containing blood liberated by erosion of maternal blood vessels (Fig. 32-31). This extravasated blood evidently

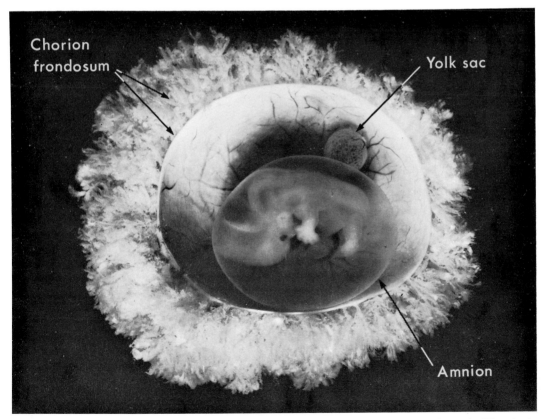

Figure 32-33. Photograph of a 40 day old human embryo (Carnegie No. 8537), showing placental villi projecting from the entire surface of the chorion. (After D. G. McKay, C. C. Roby, A. T. Hertig and M. V. Richardson. Am. J. Obst. & Gynec., *69*:735, 1955. Courtesy of the Carnegie Institution of Washington.)

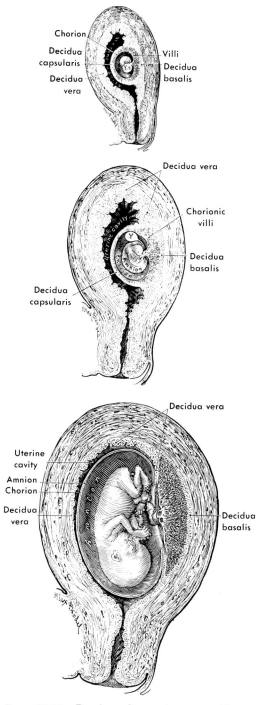

Figure 32-34. Drawings of successive stages of human pregnancy showing the gradual obliteration of the uterine lumen, the disappearance of the decidua capsularis, and the establishment of the definitive discoid placenta. (Drawings by M. Brödel, from J. Williams, Am. J. Obst. & Gynec., *13:*1, 1927.)

serves as a source of nourishment for the embryo and represents the first step toward the establishment of the uteroplacental circulation upon which the growth of the embryo will later depend. Two forms of trophoblast are recognizable, an inner layer of *cytotrophoblast* composed of individual cells and a thicker outer layer of *syncytiotrophoblast.* The cytotrophoblast is mitotically active and contributes to the increasing mass of the syncytiotrophoblast by forming new cells that fuse with and become part of the syncytium.

At the 11-day stage, the embryo proper consists of a bilaminar disk of epithelial cells—a thick plate of ectoderm and a thinner layer of primitive endoderm. The ectodermal plate is continuous at its margins with a thin layer of squamous cells of cytotrophoblastic origin that enclose a small *amniotic cavity.* The endoderm is similarly continuous with a thin sheet of cells forming the *yolk sac.* Surrounding these structures are large spaces traversed by tenuous strands of extraembryonic mesenchyme (mesoblast). These spaces constitute the *exocoelom.* The surrounding broad zone of trophoblast is called the *chorion.* Communications between the lacunae in the syncytial trophoblast and the maternal vessels are now more frequent.

PLACENTA

FORMATION AND STRUCTURE.   From the eleventh to the sixteenth day of pregnancy the trophoblast continues to proliferate rapidly and the implantation cavity is progressively enlarged at the expense of the surrounding maternal tissue. Invasion of the maternal blood vascular system by syncytiotrophoblast becomes increasingly extensive. The large lacunae in the syncytial labyrinth communicate at many places with venous sinuses in the endometrium. From the fifteenth day onward, solid cords of trophoblast grow outward from the surface of the chorion to form the *primary chorionic villi.* These are soon invaded at their base by chorionic mesenchyme, which advances toward their growing tips, converting the primary villi into *secondary villi* (Fig. 32-32). The secondary villi then consist of an outer layer of syncytial trophoblast, an inner layer of cytotrophoblast, and a mesenchymal core. They are bathed in maternal blood that flows sluggishly through a labyrinthine system of intercommunicating channels collectively comprising the *intervillous space*.

From the ends of the secondary chorionic villi, solid cords of trophoblast, the *cytotrophoblastic cell columns*, extend across the intervillous space and, upon reaching the opposite wall, spread along it, coalescing with similar outgrowths from neighboring villi to form a more or less continuous *trophoblastic shell* interrupted only at sites of communication of maternal vessels with the intervillous space. It consists mainly of cytotrophoblast, but some areas of syncytiotrophoblast can be found. Through its interstitial growth the trophoblastic shell provides a mechanism for rapid circumferential expansion of the entire implantation site and for enlargement of the intervillous space. From the time of its formation throughout the remainder of pregnancy, the intervillous space is lined by trophoblast and traversed by anchoring villi that are attached to the maternal tissue via the trophoblastic shell. The villi absorb nutriments from the maternal blood in the intervillous space and excrete wastes into it. The efficiency of this process is greatly enhanced by the development of a functioning vascular system in the embryo.

Fetal blood vessels differentiate in the mesenchymal cores of the secondary villi as discontinuous endothelial-lined spaces, which later fuse to form continuous vascular channels. These become connected with the embryonic heart via vessels that differentiate in the mesenchyme of the inner surface of the chorion and in the body stalk of the umbilical cord. By the twenty-first to the twenty-third day, fetal blood begins to circulate through the capillaries of the villi. With their vascularization, the secondary villi become *tertiary* or *definitive placental villi* (Fig. 32-37). These radiate from the entire periphery of the chorion (Fig. 32-33). In the subsequent growth of the placenta, the anchoring or stem villi, which extend across to the trophoblastic shell, develop numerous lateral branches whose unattached tips float free in the blood of the intervillous space.

The products of conception occupy only a portion of the entire endometrium of pregnancy (*decidua*). Different regions are identified by separate terms descriptive of their topographical relation to the implantation site. The portion that underlies the implantation site and forms the maternal component of the

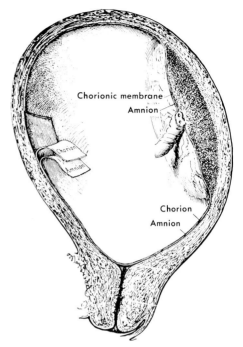

Figure 32-35. Drawing of the disposition of the fetal membranes in the later months of pregnancy. The amnion and chorion have come into contact and have become adherent to each other and to the decidua vera. (Drawings by M. Brödel, from J. Williams, Am. J. Obst. & Gynec., *13:*1, 1927.)

placenta is the *decidua basalis*. The thin superficial portion between the implantation site and the lumen is the *decidua capsularis*, and that lining the remainder of the uterus down to the internal os is the *decidua vera*. (Figs. 32-34, 32-35, and 32-36).

Up to about the eighth week, the villi are equally numerous around the entire surface of the chorion (Fig. 32-33), but as pregnancy advances the villi adjacent to the decidua basalis enlarge and rapidly increase in number, while those facing the decidua capsularis degenerate, leaving this surface of the chorion smooth and relatively avascular after the third month. This region is thenceforth called the *chorion laeve*, while the villous portion toward the base is called the *chorion frondosum*. This latter becomes confined to a circular area that goes on to form the definitive discoid placenta.

As the volume of the conceptus increases and it bulges further into the lumen, the decidua capsularis becomes greatly attenuated. Its vascularity is jeopardized and it degenerates. By four and a half months, the decidua capsularis has disappeared and the chorion

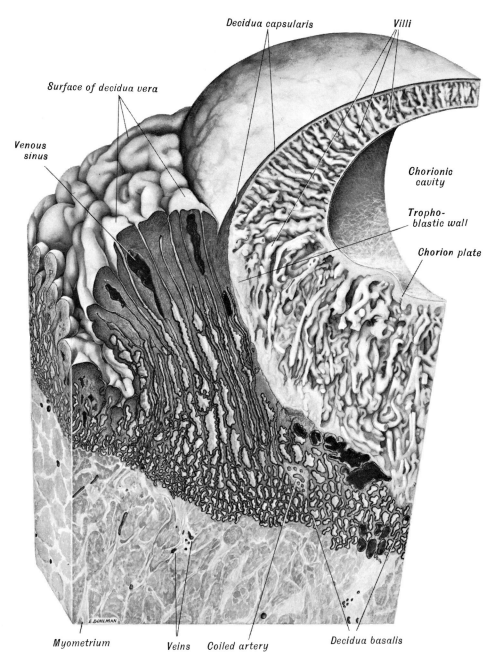

Figure 32-36. Margin of implantation site from a 4 week pregnancy. The ovum is enclosed in the maternal decidua. The villi adjacent to the decidua basalis are long, have many secondary and a few tertiary branches, and are anchored to the decidua by a wall of cytotrophoblast. The decidua vera exhibits three zones: (1) a superficial compact zone with decidual cells; (2) a spongy zone of dilated and sacculated glands; (3) a basal zone of narrow glands, which may be entirely absent. In the implantation site the compact zone has been obliterated by the development ovum except for the attenuated decidua capsularis. The embryo and the amnion surrounding it are not shown. × 17. (Courtesy of G. W. Bartelmez.)

laeve has fused with the decidua vera of the opposite wall, largely obliterating the uterine lumen (Fig. 32-35). The later development of the placenta involves a steady growth in size and length of the villi of the chorion frondosum and a concomitant expansion of the inter-villous space. During the fourth and fifth months the placental disk is partitioned into 15 to 20 *cotyledons* by the formation of incomplete septa that project from the decidual plate into the intervillous space. There are also changes during this period in the histological organization of the villi.

Early in gestation the syncytiotrophoblast of the villi is underlain by a more or less continuous layer of cytotrophoblast. Autoradiographic studies have established that the cytotrophoblast constitutes a rapidly dividing germinal layer that provides cells which coalesce with the syncytium. In the placenta from the fourth month onward, the proliferation of cytotrophoblast cells in the villi declines, and they continue to fuse with the syncytium until they have virtually all disappeared. Cytotrophoblast persists, however, in the basal plate, the placental septa, and in isolated islands on the stem villi. Until recently, histochemical evidence tended to implicate cytotrophoblast of these sites in the elaboration of placental hormones. Immuno-histochemical studies have now localized human chorionic gonadotropin in the syn-cytiotrophoblast. The cytotrophoblast is therefore regarded by many as a rapidly proliferating, relatively undifferentiated tissue, while the syncytiotrophoblast is considered to be the synthetically active, differentiated form of trophoblast.

PLACENTAL CIRCULATION. Blood poor in oxygen is carried from the fetus to the placenta in the *umbilical arteries* of the umbilical cord. At the junction of the cord with the placenta, the umbilical arteries divide into a number of radially disposed placental arteries that branch freely in the chorionic plate. Numerous branches from these pass downward into the stem villi and ramify in the arborescent pattern of subsidiary villi down to the capillary networks of the terminal villi. The oxygen-rich venous blood is collected into thin walled veins, which return the blood through vessels of increasing caliber that follow the course of the arteries to the chorionic plate. There they join veins that converge upon the single um-

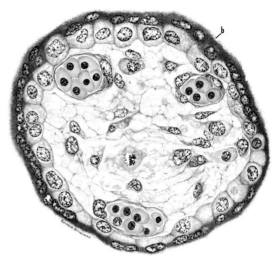

Figure 32-37. Section through placental villus from a 2 cm. human embryo. The brush border (*b*) on the syn-cytial trophoblast is barely visible. Beneath it is the continuous layer of cellular trophoblast. The vessels in the mesenchyme are filled with primitive erythrocytes. One mesenchymal cell in mitosis. × 450.

bilical vein, which carries the blood through the umbilical cord to the ductus venosus, from whence it enters the inferior vena cava near its point of confluence with the right atrium.

On the maternal side, blood from the arcuate branches of the uterine arteries is carried by the coiled arteries through openings in the basal plate of the placenta into the intervillous space. The flow from the maternal arterioles is pulsatile and is delivered at a pressure considerably higher than that prevailing in the intervillous space. It therefore spurts from the basal plate deep into the intervillous space in jets (Fig. 32-38). As its pressure is dissipated, it flows back around and over the surface of the placental villi, permitting exchange of metabolites with the fetal blood (Ramsey). Since the human has a *hemochorial placenta*, the trophoblast of the villi is exposed directly to maternal blood, and the diffusion barrier in the mature placenta consists only of the thin layer of syncytiotrophoblast, its basal lamina, and the wall of the subjacent fetal capillaries.

The pressure of the incoming blood and its fountain-like distribution tends to force the blood back toward the basal plate, where it is drained away through numerous communications between the intervillous space and dilated veins in the decidua basalis.

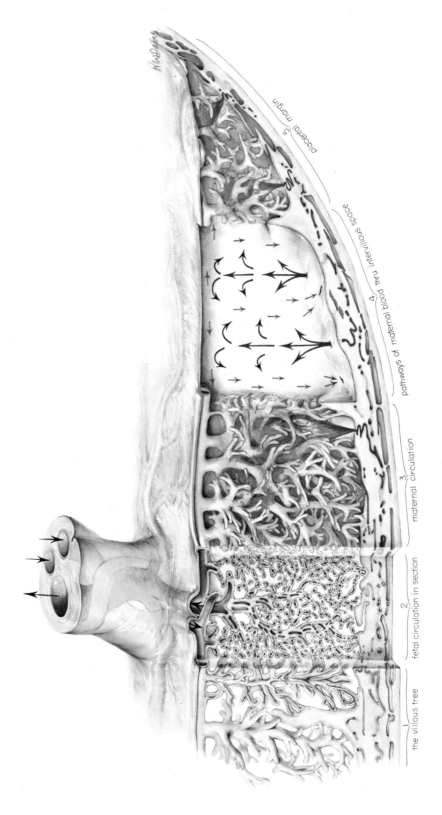

Figure 32-38. Placenta, showing structure and circulation. The head of maternal blood pressure drives entering blood toward the chorionic plate in fountain-like spurts. As the head of pressure is dissipated, lateral dispersion of blood occurs. Inflowing arterial blood pushes venous blood out into the endometrial veins. (After E. M. Ramsey and J. W. Harris. Contributions to Embryology, No. 261, Vol. 38, 1966. Courtesy of the Carnegie Institution of Washington. Drawing by Ranice Davis Crosby.)

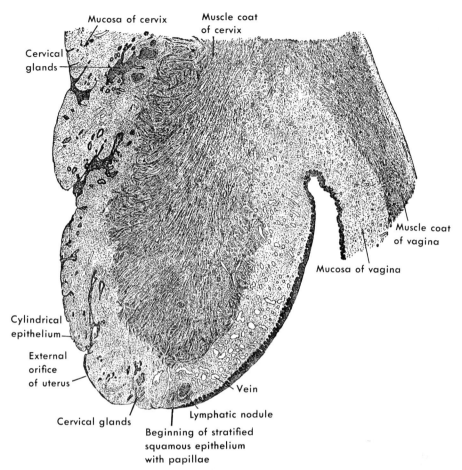

Cervical glands

Cervical glands

Mucosa of cervix

Muscle coat of cervix

Muscle coat of vagina

Mucosa of vagina

Cylindrical epithelium

External orifice of uterus

Vein

Lymphatic nodule

Beginning of stratified squamous epithelium with papillae

Figure 32-39. Sagittal section through posterior half of the portio vaginalis uteri and the fornix vaginae of a young woman. × 10. (After von Ebner.)

VAGINA

The vagina is a distensible muscular tube extending from the vestibule of the female external genitalia to the cervix of the uterus. The lower end of the vagina is marked by a transverse semicircular fold or fenestrated membrane, the *hymen.* The wall of the vagina consists of three layers: the mucous membrane, the muscular coat, and the adventitial connective tissue.

The adventitial coat is a thin layer of dense connective tissue, which merges into the loose connective tissue joining the vagina to the surrounding structures. In this connective tissue there is an extensive venous plexus, nerve bundles, and small groups of nerve cells.

The interlacing smooth muscle bundles of the muscular layer are arranged circularly and longitudinally. The longitudinal bundles are far more numerous, especially in the outer half of the layer. Striated fibers of the bulbocavernosus muscles form a sphincter around the ostium of the vagina.

The mucous membrane consists of a surface epithelium and an underlying lamina propria. The epithelium is of the stratified squamous variety and has a thickness of 150 to 200 μ. Under normal conditions the superficial cell layers in primates do not show cornification, although they contain granules of keratohyalin. The nuclei usually remain stainable and the cells become loaded with glycogen. In a prolapsed vagina, when the mucous membrane is exposed to air, the superficial cells do keratinize like those in the epidermis.

The lamina propria is a dense connective tissue. Toward the muscular layer it becomes looser, and this layer may be considered a submucosa. In the anterior wall of the vagina, papillae associated with the deep surface of the epithelium are scarce and small, but in the posterior wall the lamina propria sends numerous papillae far into the covering epithelium. Immediately under the epithelium there is a dense network of fine elastic fibers. From there fine fibers run downward to the muscular layer. Accumulations of lymphocytes are numerous, and sometimes lymph nodules are present. Lymphocytes are always found migrating into the epithelium. The deeper layers of the lamina propria contain a dense plexus of small veins.

There are no glands in the vagina. The mucus lubricating it originates from the glands of the cervix and is made acid by the fermentative action of bacteria on the glycogen from the vaginal epithelium.

The *hymen*, present in the virgin, is a fold of the mucous membrane with a thin connective tissue core and stratified squamous epithelium on both surfaces.

EXTERNAL GENITALIA

The external genital organs of the female comprise the *clitoris*, the *labia majora* and *minora*, and certain glands that open into the *vestibule*, the space flanked by the labia minora.

The *clitoris* corresponds embryologically to the dorsal part of the penis. It consists of two small, erectile, cavernous bodies, ending in a rudimentary *glans clitoridis*, which is covered by the mucous membrane of the vestibule. The vagina and the urethra open into this space, which is lined with stratified squamous epithelium. Around the opening of the urethra and

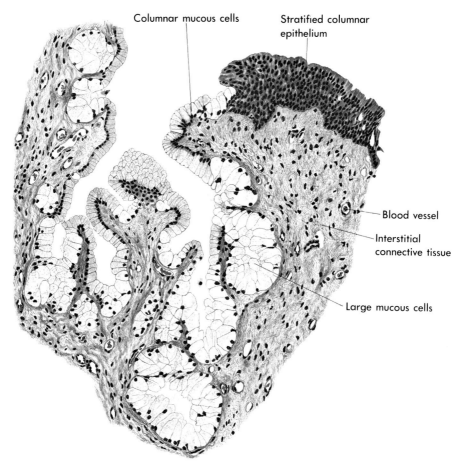

Figure 32-40. Section of gland of Bartholin. A large duct with patches of stratified columnar epithelium gives off smaller branches lined with columnar mucous cells and continuing into tubuloalveolar terminal portions which are lined with large mucous cells. × 185. (After A. A. Maximow.)

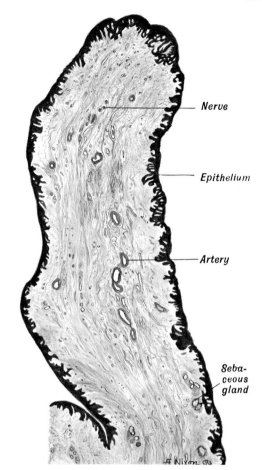

Nerve

Epithelium

Artery

Sebaceous gland

Figure 32-41. Cross section of labium minus of a 34 year old woman.

on the clitoris are several small *vestibular glands* (*glandulae vestibulares minores*). They resemble the glands of Littré in the male urethra and contain mucous cells.

Two larger glands, the *glands of Bartholin* (*glandulae vestibulares majores*), each about a centimeter in diameter, are located in the lateral walls of the vestibule and open on the inner surface of the labia minora. They are of the tubuloalveolar type, closely corresponding structurally to the bulbourethral glands of the male and secreting a similar lubricating mucus (Fig. 32-40). After the thirtieth year they begin to undergo gradual involution.

The *labia minora* are covered with stratified squamous epithelium and have a core of spongy connective tissue permeated by fine elastic networks. Blood vessels are very numerous. The epithelium contains pigment in its deeper layer and has a thin keratinized

layer on the surface. Numerous large sebaceous glands are found on both surfaces. There are no associated hairs (Fig. 32-41).

The *labia majora* are folds of skin containing a large amount of subcutaneous adipose tissue and a thin layer of smooth muscle, corresponding to the tunica dartos of the scrotum. The outer surface is covered with hair; the inner is smooth and hairless. Sebaceous and sweat glands are numerous on both surfaces.

The outer genital organs are richly supplied with sensory nerve endings. Meissner corpuscles are scattered in the papillae and genital corpuscles are present in the subpapillary layer. Pacinian corpuscles have been found in the deeper parts of the connective tissue of the labia majora and in the cavernous bodies of the clitoris.

REFERENCES

Adams, E. C., and A. T. Hertig: Studies on guinea pig oocytes. I. Electron microscopic observations on the development of cytoplasmic organelles in oocytes of primordial and primary follicles. J. Cell Biol., *21:*397, 1964.

Adams, E. C., A. T. Hertig, and S. Foster: Studies on guinea pig oocytes. II. Histochemical observations on some phosphatases and lipid in developing and atretic oocytes and follicles. Am. J. Anat., *119:*303, 1966.

Amoroso, E. C.: Placentation. *In* Parkes, A. S., ed.: Marshall's Physiology of Reproduction. 3rd ed. London, Longmans, Green & Co., Ltd., 1952, Vol. 2, p. 127.

Amoroso, E. C.: Histology of the placenta. Brit. M. Bull., *17:*81, 1961.

Anderson, E., and H. W. Beams: Cytological observations on the fine structure of the guinea pig ovary with special reference to the oogonium, primary oocyte and associated follicle cells. J. Ultrastruct. Res., *3:*432, 1960.

Austin, C. R.: The Mammalian Egg. Oxford, Blackwell Scientific Publications, 1961.

Baker, T. G.: A quantitative and cytological study of oogenesis in the rhesus monkey. J. Anat., *100:*761, 1966.

Baker, T. G.: A quantitative and cytological study of germ cells in human ovaries. Proc. Roy. Soc. B, *158:*417, 1963.

Bartelmez, G. W.: Some effects of fixation and other insults on uterine epithelial cells in primates. Anat. Rec., *77:*509, 1940.

Bartelmez, G. W., and C. M. Bensley: Human uterine gland cells. *In* Cowdry, E. V., ed.: Special Cytology. 2nd ed. New York, Paul B. Hoeber, Inc., 1932, Vol. III, p. 1523.

Björkman, N.: A study of the ultrastructure of the granulosa cells of the rat ovary. Acta Anat., *51:*125, 1962.

Blanchette, E. J.: A study of the fine structure of the rabbit primary oocyte. J. Ultrastruct. Res., *5:*349, 1961.

Blanchette, E. J.: Ovarian steroid cells. II. The lutein cell. J. Cell Biol., *31:*517, 1966.

Blandau, R. J.: Ovulation in the living albino rat. Fertility and Sterility, *6:*391, 1955.

Blandau, R. J.: Biology of eggs and implantation. *In* Young, W. C., ed.: Sex and Internal Secretions. 3rd ed. Baltimore, Williams & Wilkins, 1961, Vol. 2, p. 797.

Bloom, W.: The ovary. *In* Histopathology of Irradiation from External and Internal Sources. National Nuclear Energy Series, Vol. 22–I, Chapter 13. New York, McGraw-Hill Book Co., 1948.

Chiquoine, A. D.: The identification, origin and migration of the primordial germ cells in the mouse embryo. Anat. Rec., *118:*135, 1954.

Corner, G. W.: Cytology of the ovum, ovary and fallopian tube. *In* Cowdry, E. V., ed.: Special Cytology. 2nd ed. New York, Paul B. Hoeber, Inc., 1932, Vol. III, p. 1565.

Corner, G. W.: Influence of the ovarian hormones, oestrin and progestin, upon the menstrual cycle of the monkey. Am. J. Physiol., *113:*238, 1935.

Corner, G. W.: Ourselves Unborn. New Haven, Yale University Press, 1945.

Danforth, D. N.: The fibrous nature of the human cervix, and its relations to the isthmic segment in gravid and non-gravid uteri. Am. J. Obstet. Gynec., *53:*541, 1947.

Daron, G. H.: The arterial pattern of the tunica mucosa of the uterus in *Macacus rhesus.* Am. J. Anat., *58:*349, 1936.

Deane, H. W.: Histochemical observations on the ovary and oviduct of the albino rat. Am. J. Anat., *91:*363, 1952.

Decker, A.: Culdoscopic observations on the tubo-ovarian mechanism of ovum reception. Fertility and Sterility, *2:*253, 1951.

Dempsey, E. W., and G. B. Wislocki: Histochemical reactions associated with basophilia and acidophilia in the placenta and pituitary gland. Am. J. Anat., *76:*277, 1945.

Doyle, J. B.: Exploratory culdotomy for observation of tubo-ovarian physiology at ovulation time. Fertility and Sterility, *2:*474, 1951.

Enders, A. C.: Observations on the fine structures of lutein cells. J. Cell Biol., *12:*101, 1962.

Enders, A. C.: A comparative study of the fine structure of trophoblast in several hemochorial placentas. Am. J. Anat., *116:*29, 1965.

Enders, A. C., and W. R. Lyon: Observations on the fine structure of lutein cells. II. The effects of hypophysectomy and mammotrophic hormones in the rat. J. Cell Biol., *22:*127, 1964.

Everett, J. W.: Pituitary-ovarian relationships. *In* Soskin, S., ed.: Progress in Clinical Endocrinology. New York, Grune & Stratton, 1950, p. 319.

Everett, J. W.: The mammalian female reproductive cycle and its controlling mechanisms. *In* Young, W. C., ed.: Sex and Internal Secretions. 3rd ed. Baltimore, Williams & Wilkins, 1961, Vol. 1, p. 497.

Greep, R. O.: Histology, histochemistry and ultrastructure of adult ovary. *In* Smith, D. E., ed.: The Ovary. Baltimore, Williams & Wilkins, 1962.

Gruenwald, P.: The development of the sex cords in the gonads of man and mammals. Am. J. Anat., *70:*359, 1942.

Hertig, A. T.: Gestational hyperplasia of the endometrium. Lab. Invest., *13:*1153, 1964.

Hertig, A. T., and J. Rock: Two human ova of the previllous stage, having an ovulation age of about eleven and twelve days respectively. Carnegie Contributions to Embryol., *29:*127, 1941.

Hertig, A. T., and J. Rock: Two human ova of the previllous stage, having a developmental age of about seven and nine days respectively. Carnegie Contributions to Embryol., *31:*67, 1945.

Hertig, A. T., J. Rock, E. C. Adams, and W. J. Mulligan: On the preimplantation stages of the human ovum; a description of four normal and four abnormal specimens ranging from the second to the fifth day of development. Carnegie Contributions to Embryol., *35:*199, 1954.

Jost, A.: The role of fetal hormones in prenatal development. The Harvey Lectures, Series 55, 1959–60, p. 201. New York, Academic Press, 1961.

Latta, J. S., and E. S. Pederson: The origin of ova and follicle cells from the germinal epithelium of the ovary of the albino rat as demonstrated by selective intravital staining with India ink. Anat. Rec., *90:*23, 1944.

Long, H. A., and H. M. Evans: The oestrus cycle in the rat and its associated phenomena. Memoirs of the University of California, Vol. 6. Berkeley, University of California, 1922.

Markee, J. E.: Menstruation in intraocular endometrial transplants in the Rhesus monkey. Carnegie Contributions to Embryol., *28:*219, 1940.

Odor, D. L.: Electron microscopic studies on ovarian oocytes and unfertilized tubal ova in the rat. J. Biophys. & Biochem. Cytol., *7:*567, 1960.

Odor, D. L.: The ultrastructure of unilaminar follicles of the hamster ovary. Am. J. Anat., *116:*493, 1965.

Pinkerton, J. H. M., D. G. McKay, E. C. Adams, and A. T. Hertig: Development of the human ovary—a study using histochemical techniques. Obstet. Gynec. N. Y. *18:*152, 1961.

Price, D.: An analysis of the factors influencing growth and development of the mammalian reproductive tract. Physiol. Zool., *20:* 213, 1947.

Ramsey, E. M.: Circulation in the intervillous space of the primate placenta. Am. J. Obstet. Gynec., *84:*1649, 1962.

Ramsey, E. M., and J. W. S. Harris: Comparison of uteroplacental vasculature and circulation in Rhesus monkey and man. Carnegie Contributions to Embryol., *38:*61, 1966.

Reid, D. E.: Textbook of Obstetrics. Philadelphia, W. B. Saunders Co., 1962.

Reynolds, S. R. M.: Formation of fetal cotyledons in the hemochorial placenta. Am. J. Obstet. Gynec., *94:*425, 1966.

Rock, J., and A. T. Hertig: Information regarding the time of human ovulation derived from a study of three unfertilized and eleven fertilized ova. Am. J. Obstet. Gynec., *47:*343, 1944.

Sawyer, C. H., J. W. Everett, and J. E. Markee: A neural factor in the mechanism by which estrogen induces the release of luteinizing hormone in the rat. Endocrinol., *44:*218, 1949.

Simkins, C. S.: Development of the human ovary from birth to sexual maturity. Am. J. Anat., *51:*465, 1932.

Snyder, F. F.: Changes in the human oviduct during the menstrual cycle and pregnancy. Bull. Johns Hopkins Hosp., *35:*141, 1924.

Tersakis, J.: The ultrastructure of normal human first trimester placenta. J. Ultrastruct. Res., *9:*268, 1963.

Wislocki, G. B., and H. S. Bennett: The histology and cytology of the human and monkey placenta, with special reference to the trophoblast. Am. J. Anat., *73:*335, 1943.

Wislocki, G. B., and G. L. Streeter: On the placentation of the macaque (Macaca mulatta) from the time of implantation until the formation of the definitive placenta. Carnegie Contributions to Embryol., *27:*1, 1938.

Witschi, E.: Migration of the germ cells of human embryos from the yolk sac to the primitive gonadal folds. Carnegie Contributions to Embryol., *32:*67, 1948.

Young, W. C., ed.: Sex and Internal Secretions. 2 vols. 3rd ed. Baltimore, Williams & Wilkins Co., 1961.

CHAPTER THIRTY-THREE

Mammary Gland

The mammary glands are specialized accessory glands of the skin that have evolved in mammals to provide for the nourishment of offspring, which are born in a relatively immature and dependent state in this class of animals. They are paired glands that are laid down in the embryo along two lines called the *mammary lines,* extending from the axilla to the groin on either side of the midline on the ventral aspect of the thorax and abdomen. Mammary glands may arise anywhere along these lines. The number formed and their location varies with the species. In man only two normally develop, but additional accessory nipples or glandular masses are not uncommon.

In their structure and mode of development, mammary glands somewhat resemble sweat glands. Their differentiation during embryonic life is similar in the two sexes. In the male, however, little additional development occurs in postnatal life, while in the female the glands undergo extensive structural changes correlated with age and with the functional condition of the reproductive system. The greatest development of the female breast is reached in about the twentieth year, with atrophic changes setting in by the age of 40 and becoming marked after the menopause. In addition to these gradual changes there are variations in the size of the breasts correlated with the menstrual cycle and striking changes in the amount and functional activity of the glandular tissue during pregnancy and lactation.

RESTING MAMMARY GLAND. The mammary gland is a compound tubuloalveolar gland consisting of 15 to 25 irregular lobes radiating from the mammary papilla or *nipple.* The lobes are separated by layers of dense connective tissue and surrounded by abundant adipose tissue. Each lobe is provided with a *lactiferous duct* 2 to 4.5 mm. in diameter and lined by stratified squamous epithelium. The duct opens on the nipple and has an irregular angular outline in cross section. Beneath the *areola,* the circular pigmented area around the nipple, each of the ducts has a local dilatation, the *sinus lactiferus.* Distal to this the duct becomes constricted again and emerges at the end of the nipple as a separate opening 0.4 to 0.7 mm. in diameter.

Each lobe is subdivided into lobules of various orders, of which the smallest consist of elongated tubules, the *alveolar ducts,* covered by small saccular evaginations, the *alveoli.* The interlobular connective tissue is dense; the intralobular connective tissue is more cellular and contains fewer collagenous fibers and almost no fat. This intralobular loose connective tissue surrounding the system of ducts is believed to permit greater distensibility when the epithelial portions of the organ hypertrophy during pregnancy and lactation. The secretory portions of the gland, the alveolar ducts and alveoli, consist of cuboidal or low columnar secretory cells resting on a basement lamina and a discontinuous layer of processes of *myoepithelial cells.* The highly branched myoepithelial cells enclose the glandular alveoli in a loosely meshed, basket-like network. They usually lie between the secretory cells and the basement lamina. The presence of myoepi-

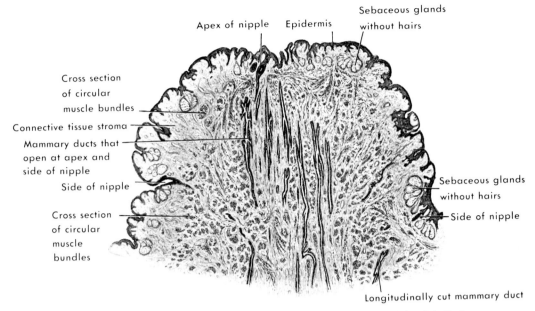

Figure 33-1. Nipple of female breast in perpendicular section. × 6. (After Schaffer.)

thelial cells is interpreted as further evidence that mammary glands are morphogenetically related to sweat glands.

There has been much discussion about the presence of alveoli in the nonlactating breast. According to most descriptions of the resting phase, the epithelial structures consist only of ducts and their branches. Some authors, however, believe that the resting breast always has a few alveoli budded off from the ends of the duct system and that these are arranged into small lobules. Part of the difficulty in resolving this question naturally arises from the rarity of the opportunity to obtain normal human breast tissue at known phases of the menstrual cycle. It is clear, however, that early in the cycle the cytoplasmic mass of the epithelial elements is greatly reduced and there is little or no lumen. In this condition, in which the cells seem to form more or less solid strands, it is not easy to distinguish alveoli from primary ducts. Late in the cycle, the epithelial cells are cuboidal or low columnar, the lumen is evident and contains some secretion, and the surrounding connective tissue stroma is highly vascular. To determine whether these elements are alveolar ducts or alveoli, or both, would require study of serial sections. Because both are potentially secretory, the distinction does not seem an important one. There are microscopically detectable cyclic changes in the terminal duct-

ular and possibly in the alveolar portions of the mammary glands, but these are relatively slight. The gross changes of size, and the sense of engorgement experienced by the woman at certain times in the cycle are attributable mainly to hyperemia and some edema of the connective tissue of the breast.

It is to be noted that the mammary gland does not have a single duct. Each lobe is an independent compound alveolar gland whose primary ducts join into larger and larger ducts. These drain into a lactiferous duct, and each of these opens separately at the tip of the nipple. The mammary gland is therefore a conglomeration of a variable number of such independent glands.

NIPPLE AND AREOLA. The epidermis of the nipple and areola is invaded by unusually long dermal papillae, whose capillaries bring blood close to the surface, imparting a pinkish color to this region in immature and blonde individuals. The skin becomes pigmented at puberty, and the degree of pigmentation increases during pregnancy. An elaborate pattern of bundles of smooth muscle disposed longitudinally along the lactiferous ducts and circumferentially both within the nipple and around its base make it possible for the nipple to become erect in response to certain stimuli and flat at other times. In the areola are the accessory *areolar glands of Montgomery*, which are intermediate in their structure between sweat glands and true mammary glands. Along the margin of the areola are large sweat and sebaceous glands, which usually lack associated hairs or rudimentary hairs.

The skin of the nipple and areola is richly innervated with free nerve endings and Meissner's corpuscles in the dermal papillae. The skin beyond the areola has rich neural plexuses around hair follicles, as well as nerve endings resembling Merkel's disks and Krause's end-bulbs. Pacinian corpuscles may also be found deep in the dermis and in the glandular tissue. The presence of a rich innervation of the nipple area is of functional importance, because response to the stimulus of suckling is required for maintenance of normal lactation.

THE ACTIVE MAMMARY GLANDS. Pregnancy brings about changes in the levels of circulating hormones that result in profound changes in the mammary glands. During the first half of gestation there is a rapid growth and branching from the terminal portion of the duct system of the gland. The growth of the epithelial structures takes place, at least in part, at the expense of the interstitial adipose tissue of the breast, which regresses concurrently with the growth of the glandular tissue. There is also, in this period of growth, an increasing infiltration of the interstitial tissue with lymphocytes, plasma cells, and eosinophils. In the later months of pregnancy the actual hyperplasia of the glandular tissue slows down, and the subsequent enlargement of the breasts is largely a consequence of enlargement of the parenchymal cells and distention of the alveoli with a hyaline eosinophilic secretion rich in lactoproteins but relatively poor in lipid. This constitutes the *colostrum*, the first milk that comes from the breasts after

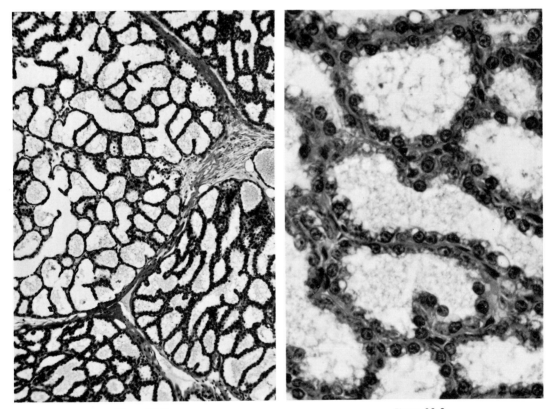

Figure 33-2.   **Figure 33-3.**

Figure 33-2. Photomicrograph of mammary gland from a lactating cat. Notice the variation from lobule to lobule in the degree of distention of the alveolar ducts and alveoli. × 110.
Figure 33-3. Photomicrograph of lactating cat mammary gland at higher magnification. Large vacuoles can be seen in some of the cells. These represent lipid droplets extracted in specimen preparation. The precipitate in the gland lumen is principally lactoproteins. × 560.

birth. It has special laxative properties and is believed to contain antibodies that provide the newborn with some measure of passive immunity. During the first few days after delivery the degree of infiltration of the stroma of the gland by lymphoid elements becomes less intense, and the colostrum gives way to a copious secretion of milk rich in lipid.

The histological appearance of different parts of the active mammary gland varies considerably. Apparently different areas are not all in the same functional state at the same time. In some places the secretory portions are filled with milk: their lumen is wide and the

walls are dilated and thin. In other areas, the lumen is narrow and the epithelium relatively thick.

The shape of the epithelial cells varies from flat to low columnar. The boundary between them is usually indistinct. If the cells are tall, their distal ends, as in sweat glands, are often definitely separated and project into the lumen of the alveoli as rounded or dome-shaped protrusions. The nucleus may be round or oval and is at about the middle of the cell. If the cells are short, their free surface is usually more or less smooth.

In the cytoplasm are short, rod-shaped

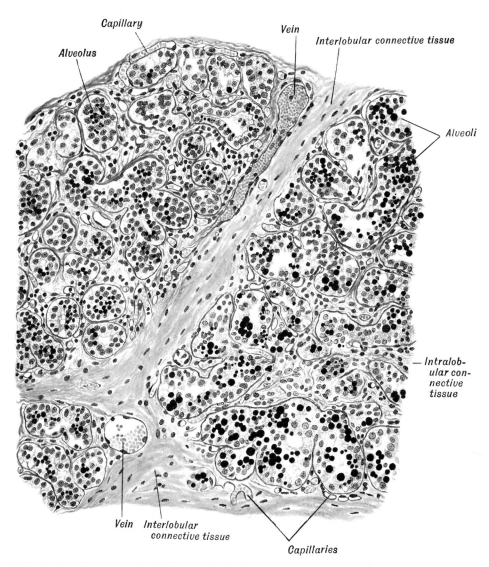

Figure 33-4. Section of mammary gland of woman in the sixth month of pregnancy, showing the beginning of secretory activity with osmic acid-stained droplets of fat (black) in the hypertrophic epithelium. × 187. (After A. A. Maximow.)

mitochondria, few in number in the flattened cells but more plentiful in the taller ones. Some basophilic substance is usually found at the base of the cells. Droplets of fat, often of large size, accumulate near the free surface and often project into the lumen. After the extraction of fat in preparing histological sections, large clear vacuoles remain in place of the lipid droplets. In addition to the accumulations of lipid, small proteinaceous secretory granules can also be seen in the apical region of the cell. Cyclic changes in the Golgi apparatus during the different phases of secretion have been described. The lumen of the alveoli is crowded with fine granular material and lipid droplets similar to those that protrude from the cells.

The mammary gland was formerly believed to have a mode of release of its product that was intermediate between *merocrine* secretion, in which the secretory materials pass out through the cell apex without appreciable loss of cytoplasm, and *holocrine* secretion, in which the entire cell is given up in contributing its contents to the secretion. The cells of the mammary gland were believed to undergo a partial disintegration in which the fat-filled apical portion of the cell, projecting into the lumen, was described as constricting off from the base of the cell, which remained in place. It was believed that the remainder of the cell rapidly replaced the lost protoplasm and reaccumulated secretion. This mode of release was called *apocrine secretion*. Studies with the electron microscope have now radically changed our views as to the various mechanisms of release of cell products, and it is now doubtful whether the traditional concept of apocrine secretion is still applicable to the mammary gland.

In electron micrographs the main cytological features of the glandular cells are in accord with descriptions resulting from use of the light microscope. The chromophilic areas of the basal cytoplasm contain cisternal profiles of the granular endoplasmic reticulum. There are a moderate number of mitochondria, a supranuclear Golgi complex, and a number of dense lysosomes. It is evident that the cell has two distinct secretory products, formed and released by different mechanisms. The protein constituents of the milk, like other protein secretions, are elaborated on the ribosome-studded membranes of the endoplasmic reticulum; they first become visible in the form of moderately dense spherical granules about 400 mμ in diameter in vesicles associated with the

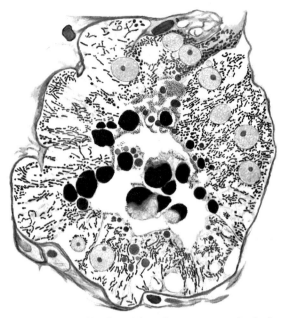

Figure 33-5. Alveolus of lactating mammary gland of a rabbit. The cells contain mitochondria and droplets of fat (stained black with osmic acid). The latter, with the adjacent protoplasm, are extruded into the lumen. × 1000. (After A. A. Maximow.)

Golgi complex. They are transported to the cell surface in these membranous vesicles, which fuse with the plasmalemma and discharge their contained granules into the lumen of the acinus. The mode of formation and release of this particulate component of the milk is therefore identical to that of protein secreting glands generally classified as *merocrine*. The fatty components of the milk do not appear to develop in association with the Golgi apparatus but arise as lipid droplets free in the cytoplasmic matrix. These increase in size and move into the apical region, where they come to project into the lumen covered by a thin layer of cytoplasm. These droplets are ultimately cast off, enveloped by a detached portion of the cell membrane and a thin rim of the subjacent cytoplasm. This mode of release could be considered *apocrine* in the sense that it involves loss of some cytoplasm, but the amount lost is certainly far less than envisioned by the classical cytologists responsible for the term.

The myoepithelial cells lie on the epithelial side of the basement lamina. Their processes are filled with parallel arrays of myofilaments 50 Å in diameter. There are spindle-shaped densities among the myofilaments like those found in smooth muscle cells. The cell organelles are concentrated in the perinuclear

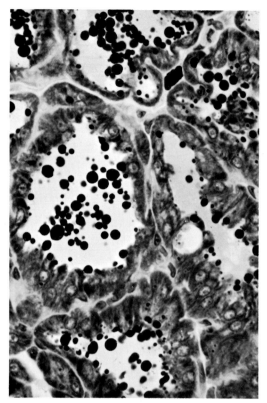

Figure 33-6. Photomicrograph of lactating mammary gland from a mouse, fixed in osmium tetroxide. The large droplets of lipid are preserved both in the apex of the cells and in the lumen of the acini. The smaller protein granules are not visible. × 560. (Preparation by N. Feder.)

region of the cell body, but occasional mitochondria and profiles of the endoplasmic reticulum extend into the cell processes. Considering that myoepithelial cells are derived from the embryonic ectoderm, while smooth muscle cells have a mesodermal origin, the cytological characteristics of the two are remarkably similar.

ENDOCRINE CONTROL OF MAMMARY GLAND FUNCTION. The functioning of the mammary glands is dependent upon the interplay of multiple and complex nervous and endocrine factors. Some are involved in development of the mammary glands to a functional state (mammogenesis), others in the establishment of milk secretion (lactogenesis), and still other factors are responsible for maintenance of lactation (galactopoiesis).

The primary and secondary ducts that develop during embryonic and fetal life continue to grow in both sexes only in proportion to the growth of the body as a whole, until shortly before puberty, when, in the female, a more rapid extension of the duct system begins. This does not take place in the absence of the ovaries. The growth of the duct system appears to depend primarily upon estrogen, but for complete development of the alveoli both estrogen and progesterone are required. The production of these ovarian hormones during pregnancy depends in turn upon the gonadotropic hormones (FSH and LH), so that the hypophysis must be at least indirectly involved in growth of the mammary gland. However, estrogen and progesterone fail to produce full mammary growth in hypophysectomized animals, and there is now ample evidence that the hypophysis also has a direct effect upon mammary growth by reason of its secretion of *prolactin* and *somatotropin* (STH). Minor effects upon mammary growth have also been traced to indirect effects of *adrenocorticotropic hormone* (ACTH) and *thyrotropic hormone* (TSH), acting upon the adrenal cortex and thyroid. It is now believed that to obtain full morphological development of the gland comparable to that normally attained in late pregnancy, prolactin, progesterone, estrogen, somatotropin, and adrenal corticoids are all needed (Turner; Cowie and Folley). It should be recalled that the placenta also secretes estrogen, progesterone, and a potent prolactin-like hormone, and no doubt it contributes importantly to the growth stimulus for the mammary glands.

Even in the presence of fully developed prolactational mammary glands, the initiation of milk secretion will not take place in hypophysectomized animals, and in a number of animal species adrenal cortical hormone has also been shown to be essential. Therefore, it is now thought that when the inhibiting levels of circulating estrogen and progesterone fall abruptly at the end of pregnancy, the increased output of prolactin by the hypophysis and the secretion of adrenal cortical steroids bring about milk secretion from the fully developed mammary gland.

The continued secretion of prolactin by the hypophysis appears to be necessary for maintenance of lactation, for hypophysectomy results in abrupt cessation of milk production. The secretion of normal levels of prolactin by intact animals is dependent upon a neurohormonal reflex, in which the periodic sensory stimulus of suckling acts upon supraoptic and paraventricular nuclei in the hypothalamus of the brain to promote the release of prolactin. Interruption of this reflex by denervation of nipples results in failure of lactation.

The discussion until now has been concerned with endocrine stimulated growth of the gland and the initiation and maintenance of secretion. We turn now to the mechanisms for removal of milk from the glands. The milk secreted in the intervals between suckling remains for the most part within the alveoli and alveolar ducts. Only a small proportion passes into the larger ducts and lactiferous sinuses. This small amount can be expressed or withdrawn *passively* by cannulation of the ducts, but the great bulk of the milk can only be obtained by *active participation* of the mother and depends upon the stimulus of suckling, which acts via the hypothalamus to cause release of the hormone *oxytocin* from the neurohypophysis. This in turn stimulates the myoepithelial cells of the gland to contract, ejecting the accumulated milk from the alveoli and fine ducts into the larger ducts and sinuses of the gland.

REGRESSION OF THE MAMMARY GLAND. If regular suckling is permitted, lactation can be maintained for many months or even for several years. However, if milk is not removed, the glands become greatly distended and milk production quickly ceases. This is in part due to interruption of the neurohormonal reflex mechanism for maintenance of prolactin secretion, but the engorgement of the breasts may also compress the blood vessels, resulting in diminished access of oxytocin to the myoepithelial cells. After a few days the secretion remaining in the alveolar spaces and ducts is absorbed and the glandular elements gradually return to the resting state. The gland, however, does not return completely to its original state, because many of the alveoli that had formed during the period of pregnancy do not disappear entirely, and the remains of the secretion may sometimes be retained in the mammary ducts for a considerable time. The gland remains in such a resting condition until the following pregnancy, when the same cycle of changes is repeated.

INVOLUTION OF THE MAMMARY GLAND. In old age, the mammary gland gradually undergoes involution. The epithelium of the secretory portions, and partly also of the excretory duct, atrophies, and the gland tends, in a general way, to return to the prepubertal condition, in which there are only a few scattered ducts. On the other hand, the epithelium is not infrequently the seat of a pathological growth.

Equally striking changes occur in the interstitial connective tissue. This becomes decidedly less cellular; the number of collagenous fibrils decreases, and the whole mass becomes more homogeneous and stains much less intensely with eosin.

BLOOD AND LYMPHATIC VESSELS. The blood supply of a functioning mammary gland is much greater than that of a resting gland. The arteries arise from the internal mammary artery, the thoracic branches of the axillary artery, and the intercostal arteries. They pass mainly along the larger ducts and break up

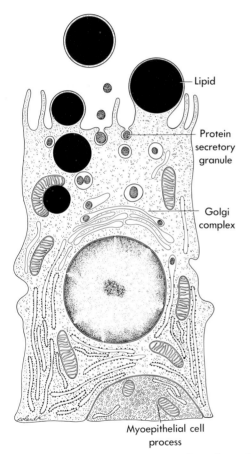

Lipid

Protein secretory granule

Golgi complex

Myoepithelial cell process

Figure 33-7. Diagrammatic representation of a cell from a lactating mammary gland, showing large lipid droplets being cast off enclosed in a layer of cytoplasm, and small granules of protein secretion being concentrated in the Golgi apparatus and released by coalescence of their small vesicles with the plasma membrane. A myoepithelial cell process is depicted in cross section between the epithelial cell and the basal lamina. (Drawing based upon observations of W. Bargmann and A. Knoop, Zeitschr. f. Zellforsch., *49*:344, 1959.)

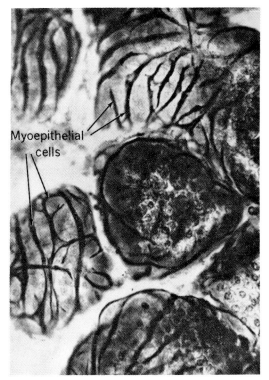

Figure 33-8. Surface view of contracted alveoli from the goat mammary gland, showing silver stained, basket-like processes of the myoepithelial cells. (After K. C. Richardson, Proc. Roy. Soc. B., *136:*30, 1949.)

into dense capillary networks on the external surface of the basement lamina of the secretory portions. The veins drain into the axillary and internal mammary veins.

The lymphatic vessels begin with capillary networks located in the connective tissue layers surrounding separate alveoli. They collect along the course of the mammary ducts into a subpapillary lymphatic network. From here several large vessels lead the lymph mainly into the lymph nodes in the axilla, but they also have connections with the lymphatics leading beneath the sternum, and even those crossing the midline to the other breast.

HISTOGENESIS OF THE MAMMARY GLAND. The primordium of the mammary gland appears in a human embryo of 8 mm. as a paired thickening of the epidermis, the "milk line," which begins at the root of the upper extremity and proceeds to the inguinal fold. It continues to thicken and becomes the mammary fold. This is retained in man in only a limited region of its cranial portion as a pair of flat, lens-shaped thickenings. These become hemispherical or club-shaped epithelial thickenings directed toward the underlying connective tissue. This, in turn, thickens and lifts the developing gland slightly above the rest of the surface of the organism (in human embryos 19 to 30 mm. long). In most mammals several pairs of such thickenings are formed.

The cells of this epithelial bud are cylindrical and are arranged radially, while the deeper layers are polyhedral. By continuing to multiply they form, on the ventral convex surface of the body, in human embryos of 50 to 60 mm., the primordia of 16 to 25 projections, with swellings at their ends. These projections gradually elongate in the direction of the connective tissue layer and become the mammary ducts. Their number varies with the age of the embryo, for they do not all originate at once. For this reason their lengths, at any given moment, are not equal. The peripheral cells at first maintain their cylindrical shape, while the others are multiangular and have round nuclei. Externally they are gradually covered by a condensing connective tissue. In the course of time each of these cylindrical, epithelial projections or shafts gives rise by elongation to larger and larger numbers of branches. These are also expanded at their ends and are the primordia of the future ducts. A lumen appears in them, except in the terminal swellings, owing to the moving aside and the partial degeneration of the constituent cells. Some of the cells in contact with the connective tissue develop into myoepithelial cells.

In newborns of both sexes the glands have a diameter of 3.5 to 9 mm., and at this time they contain a number of distinct alveolar portions, some of which, however, are rudimentary. At the same time, in the lumen of the developing and branching ducts, a substance is formed that suggests colostrum. This secretion is called witch's milk and contains little but degenerating, fatty epithelial cells; it can be squeezed out of the papilla in newborn infants, but soon disappears.

In males the mammary gland undergoes a regression after birth and only the nipple remains with the surrounding areola. In females, however, the development, although rather slow, continues, and the slow elongation and branching of the epithelial shaft go on throughout childhood. With the onset of sexual maturity, the development does not change qualitatively but increases in intensity and quantity.

Each original epithelial shaft forms numerous branches through the muliplication of its constituent cells. Having reached a certain degree of development, the organ undergoes only the slight changes already described, associated with the reproductive cycle.

REFERENCES

Azimov, G. J.: Some processes accompanying the secretion of milk. *In* Proc. XV Internat. Dairy Congr., *1:*15, London, 1959.

Bargmann, W., and A. Knoop: Über die Morphologie der Milchsekretion. Licht- und elektronenmikroskopische Studien an der Milchdrüse der Ratte. Zeitschr. f. Zellforsch., *49:*344, 1959.

Cowie, A. T., and S. J. Folley: The mammary gland and lactation. *In* Young, W. C., ed.: Sex and Internal Secretions. 3rd ed. Baltimore, Williams & Wilkins Co., 1961, p. 590.

Dabelow, A.: Die Milchdrüse. *In* von Möllendorff, W., and W. Bargmann, eds.: Handbuch der mikroskopischen Anatomie des Menschen, Berlin, Springer-Verlag, 1957, Vol. 3, part 3, p. 277.

Dempsey, E. W., H. Bunting, and G. B. Wislocki: Observations on the chemical cytology of the mammary gland. Am. J. Anat., *81:*309, 1947.

Foote, F. W., and F. W. Stewart: Comparative studies of cancerous versus non-cancerous breasts. I. Basic morphological characteristics. Ann. Surg., *121:*6, 1945.

Gardner, W. U., and G. van Wagenen: Experimental development of the mammary gland in the monkey. Endocrinol., *22:*164, 1938.

Hollmann, K. H.: L'ultrastructure de la glande mammaire normale de la souris en lactation. Étude au microscope électronique. J. Ultrastruct. Res., *2:*423, 1959.

Hollmann, K. H.: Sur des aspects particuliers des protéines élaboriés dans la glande mammaire. Étude au microscope électronique chez la lapine en lactation. Zeitschr. f. Zellforsch., *69:*395, 1966

Jeffers, K. R.: Cytology of the mammary gland of albino rat. I. Pregnancy, lactation and involution. II. Experimentally induced conditions. Am. J. Anat., *56:*257, 279, 1935.

Kon, S. K., and A. T. Cowie: Milk; The Mammary Gland and Its Secretion. New York, Academic Press, 1961.

Lasfargues, E. Y., and M. R. Murray: Hormonal influences on the differentiation of embryonic mouse mammary glands in organ culture. Develop. Bio., *1:*413, 1959.

Loeb, L.: The cytology of the mammary gland. *In* Cowdry, E. V., ed.: Special Cytology. 2nd ed. New York. Paul B. Hoeber, Inc., 1932, Vol. 3, p. 1632.

Miller, M. R., and M. Kasahara: Cutaneous innervation of the human female breast. Anat. Rec., *135:*153, 1959.

Richardson, K. C.: Contractile tissues in the mammary gland, with special reference to myoepithelium in the goat. Proc. Roy. Soc. Lond., Series B, *136:*30, 1949.

Turner, C. D.: General Endocrinology. 4th ed. Philadelphia, W. B. Saunders Co., 1966.

Verley, J. M., and K. H. Hollmann: Synthese et réabsorption des protéines, dans las glande mammaire en stase: Étude autoradiographique au microscope électronique. Zeitschr. f. Zellforsch. *75:*605, 1966.

Weatherford, H. L.: A cytological study of the mammary gland: Golgi apparatus, trophospongium, and other cytoplasmic canaliculi, mitochondria. Am. J. Anat., *44:*199, 1929.

Wellings, S. R., K. B. DeOme, and D. R. Pitelka: Electron microscopy of milk secretion in the mammary gland of the C3H/Crgl mouse. I. Cytomorphology of the prelactating and the lactating gland. J. Nat. Cancer Inst., *25:*393, 1960.

Wellings, S. R., B. W. Grunbaum, and K. B. DeOme: Electron microscopy of milk secretion in the mammary gland of the C3H/Crgl mouse. II. Identification of fat and protein particles in milk and in tissue. J. Nat. Cancer Inst., *25:*423, 1960.

Wellings, S. R., and J. R. Phelp: The function of the Golgi apparatus in lactating cells of the BALB/cCrgl mouse: An electron microscopic and autoradiographic study. Zeitschr. f. Zellforsch., *61:* 871, 1964.

CHAPTER THIRTY-FOUR

The Eye

The ability to react to light is a wide-spread property of living matter, but in complex animals certain cells are specifically adapted to respond to light. Scattered photoreceptive cells in lower animals probably distinguish only varying intensities of light and only crudely perceive the direction of the light stimuli. In the vertebrates, more efficient organs have evolved. The eyes not only react to various intensities and qualities of light but are capable of distinguishing the form and size of external objects and minute changes in their position.

STRUCTURE OF THE EYE IN GENERAL

The anterior segment of the eye, the *cornea*, is transparent, permitting the rays of light to enter. The rest of the wall of the eye is opaque and possesses a darkly pigmented inner surface, which absorbs light rays. The posterior segment of the eye is to a great extent lined with photosensitive nervous tissue, the *retina*, which develops as an outgrowth from the brain. The cavity of the eyeball is filled with transparent media arranged in separate bodies, which, together with the cornea, act as a system of convex lenses. These produce an inverted, reduced image of the objects in the outside world on the photoreceptive layer of the retina.

The wall of the eyeball is composed of three layers: the tough, fibrous, *corneoscleral coat;* the middle, vascular coat, or *uvea;* and the innermost layer, the photosensitive *retina.* The thick fibrous layer protects the delicate inner structures of the eye and, together with the intraocular fluid pressure, serves to maintain the shape and turgor of the eyeball. It is divided into a large opaque posterior segment, the *sclera,* and a smaller transparent anterior segment, the *cornea.* The uvea is concerned with the nutrition of the ocular tissues and also provides mechanisms for visual accommodation and reduction or exclusion of light. Its three regional differentiations are the *choroid,* the *ciliary body,* and the *iris.* The *choroid* is the highly vascular portion of the uvea that underlies the photosensitive retina. Extending forward from the *ora serrata* (the scalloped anterior margin of the photosensitive retina), to the corneoscleral junction, is the *ciliary body.* It forms a belt 5 to 6 mm. wide around the interior of the eyeball and contains the smooth muscle that makes this the instrument of accommodation, acting upon the lens to bring light rays from different distances to focus upon the retina. The *iris* is a thin continuation of the ciliary body projecting over the anterior surface of the lens with its free edge outlining the pupil. The diameter of the iris is approximately 12 mm. Its opening, the *pupil,* can be reduced or expanded through the contraction or relaxation of the *constrictor* and *dilator muscles* of the pupil. In this way the iris functions as an adjustable *optic diaphragm* regulating the amount of light entering the eye (Figs. 34-1 and 34-2).

The innermost tunic, the *retina,* contains in its sensory part the receptors for light and the first links in the chain of nervous pathways conveying impulses through the optic nerve to the brain. The spot where the nerve enters the eyeball, the *papilla of the optic nerve,* is a pink disk approximately 1.4 mm. in diameter and about 3 mm. medial to the posterior pole of the eye. The portion of the retina anterior to the ora serrata and lining the inner surface of the ciliary muscle (*ciliary portion of the retina*) and that lining the posterior surface of the iris (*iridial portion of the retina*) are not photosensitive.

The transparent *dioptric media* include the cornea and the contents of the cavity enclosed by the tunics of the eye. Because of the considerable difference between the index of refraction of the cornea (1.376) and of the surrounding air (1.0), the cornea is the chief refractive element of the eye. Of the enclosed transparent media the most anterior is the *aqueous humor*. It is contained in the *anterior chamber*, a small cavity bounded in front by the cornea and behind by the ciliary body, the iris, and the central portion of the anterior surface of the lens. The *posterior chamber*, also filled with aqueous humor, is a narrow, annular space enclosed by the lens, the iris, and the ciliary and vitreous bodies (Figs. 34-1 and 34-2).

The next of the transparent media is the *crystalline lens*. This is an elastic biconvex body

suspended from the inner surface of the ciliary body by a circular ligament, the *ciliary zonule*. It is placed directly behind the pupil, between the aqueous humor of the anterior chamber anteriorly and the vitreous body posteriorly. The lens is second in importance to the cornea as a refractive element of the eye, and is the dioptric organ of accommodation.

The greater portion of the cavity of the eye, between the posterior surface of the lens, and ciliary body, and the posterior wall of the eyeball, is the *vitreal cavity,* filled with a viscous transparent substance, the *vitreous humor* or *vitreous body*. It adjoins the retina and permits light to pass freely from the lens to the photoreceptors.

The retina is transparent during life. Only its outermost layer, the pigment epithelium, is opaque and forms the first barrier to the rays of light.

DIMENSIONS, AXES, PLANES OF REFERENCE

The adult human eyeball is a roughly spherical body about 24 mm. in diameter and weighing 6 to 8 gm. The center of the cornea

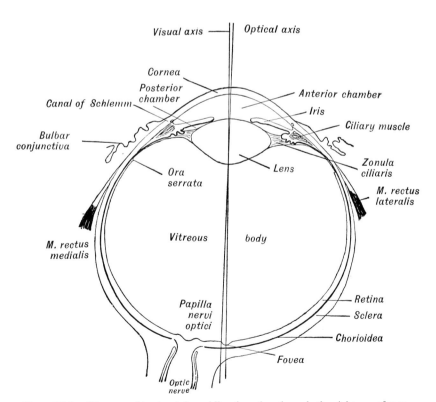

Figure 34-1. Diagram of horizontal meridional section through the right eye of man.

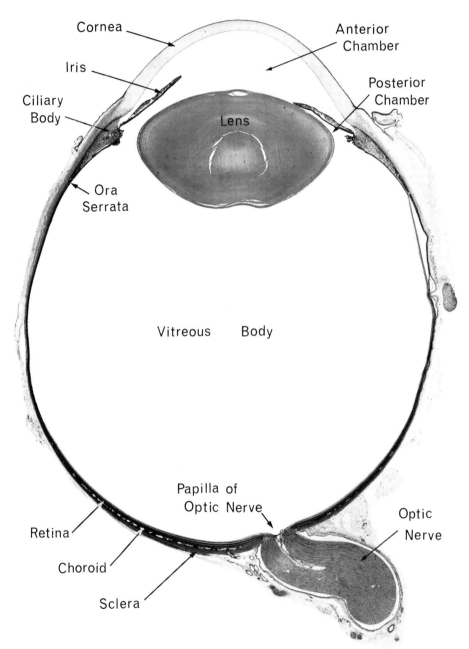

Figure 34-2. Photomicrograph of a meriodional section of the eye of a Rhesus monkey. × 10. (Courtesy of H. Mizoguchi.)

is the *anterior pole;* the *posterior pole* is located between the *fovea* (the spot of most distinct vision) and the optic papilla. The line connecting the two poles is the *anatomical axis.* The *visual axis* is the line drawn from the center of the fovea to the apparent center of the pupil (Fig. 34-1). The *equatorial plane* is vertical and perpendicular to the visual axis, passing through the greatest expansion of the eyeball, the *equator.* Other planes passing through the axis determine the *meridians* of the eye. The two most important are the vertical and the horizontal meridians. The first passes through the fovea and divides the eyeball, including the retina, into nasal and temporal halves. The plane of the horizontal meridian divides the eyeball and retina into an upper and a lower half. These two planes divide the eyeball and the retina into four quadrants, an upper nasal and an upper temporal, a lower nasal and a lower temporal.

The *anteroposterior diameter* along the axis of the eye is 24 mm., or a little more. The *inner axis,* the distance between the inner surface

of the cornea and the inner surface of the retina at the posterior pole, measures a little less than 22 mm. The *optical axis* passes through the optical centers of the refractive media, and is almost identical with the anatomical axis. The visual axis, where it touches the retina, is from 4 to 7 degrees lateral and 3.5 degrees below the optical axis.

The *radius of the curvature* of the large posterior segment around the fundus measures somewhat less than 13 mm., and gradually decreases toward the corneoscleral junction. The cornea has the smallest radius of curvature, approximately 7.8 mm. (outer corneal surface).

The eyeball is lodged in a soft tissue cushion filling the bony orbit of the skull and made up of loose connective and fatty tissue, muscles, fasciae, blood and lymphatic vessels, glands, and nerves. This permits the eye to move freely around its *center of rotation.* The eye is connected with the general integument by the conjunctiva. The lids are a mechanical protection against external noxious agents.

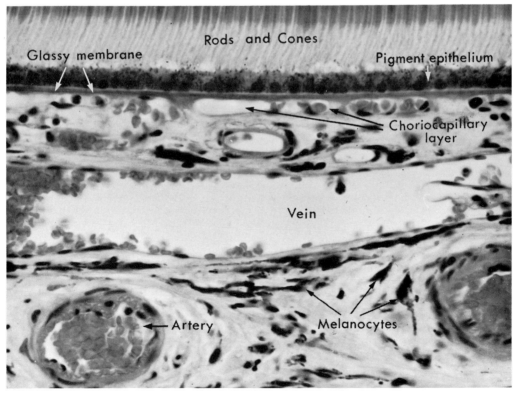

Figure 34-3. Photomicrograph of choroid and outermost layer of the retina. (After T. Kuwabara, *in* R. O. Greep, ed.: Histology. 2nd ed. New York, McGraw-Hill Book Co., 1966.)

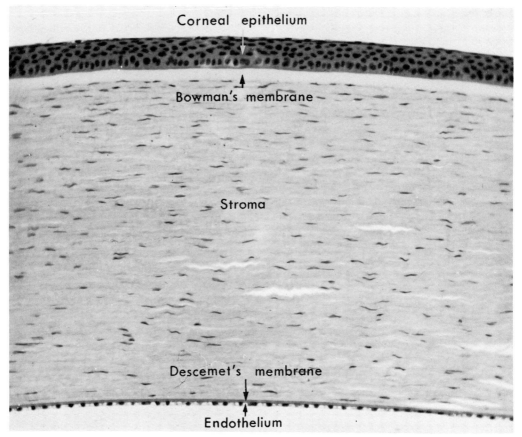

Figure 34-4. Photomicrograph of a section of human cornea. × 160. (After T. Kuwabara, *in* R. O. Greep, ed.: Histology. 2nd ed. New York, McGraw-Hill Book Co., 1966.)

FIBROUS TUNIC

SCLERA. The sclera is 1 mm. thick at the posterior pole, 0.4 to 0.3 mm. at the equator, and 0.6 mm. toward the edge of the cornea. It consists of flat collagenous bundles that run in various directions parallel to the surface. Between these bundles are networks of elastic fibers. The cells of the sclera are flat, elongated fibroblasts. Melanocytes also can be found in the deeper layers, especially in the vicinity of the entrance of the optic nerve (Fig. 34-3).

The tendons of the eye muscles are attached to the outer surface of the sclera, which, in turn, is connected with a dense layer of connective tissue—the *capsule of Tenon*—by an exceedingly loose system of thin collagenous membranes separated by clefts—the *space of Tenon*. This arrangement makes possible rotational movements of the eyeball in all directions.

Between the sclera and the choroid is a layer of loose connective tissue with elastic networks and numerous melanocytes and fibroblasts. When these two tunics are separated, part of this loose tissue adheres to the choroid and part to the sclera as its *suprachoroid lamina*.

CORNEA. The cornea is slightly thicker than the sclera, measuring 0.8 to 0.9 mm. in the center and 1.1 mm. at the periphery. In man the refractive power of the cornea, which is a function of the index of refraction of its tissue (1.376) and of the radius of curvature of its surface (7.8 mm.), is twice as high as that of the lens. The *transparency of the cornea* is high, though less than that of the aqueous humor. Its transparency is due partly to the great regularity of its structural composition, and partly to other factors of chemical nature still incompletely understood.

In a vertical section through the cornea, the following layers can be seen: (1) the epithelium, (2) the membrane of Bowman, (3) the stroma, or substantia propria, (4) the membrane of Descemet, and (5) the endothelium or mesenchymal epithelium (Fig. 34-4).

Epithelium. The epithelium is stratified squamous with an average thickness of 50 μ. It consists, as a rule, of five layers of cells. The outer surface is quite smooth and is composed of large squamous cells. As in other types of stratified squamous epithelium, the cells are connected with one another by many short interdigitating processes that adhere at desmosomes. The cytoplasm contains numerous mitochondria and scattered profiles of granular endoplasmic reticulum in a cytoplasmic matrix filled with randomly oriented fine filaments.

The epithelium of the cornea is extremely sensitive and contains numerous free nerve endings. It is endowed with a remarkable capacity for regeneration. Minor injuries heal rapidly by a gliding movement of the adjacent epithelial cells to fill the defect. Mitoses in the basal epithelial cells appear later and may be found at considerable distances from the wound. A few mitoses can be found in the basal cell layer under normal conditions.

Bowman's Membrane. The corneal epithelium rests upon a faintly fibrillar membrane of Bowman, 6 to 9 μ thick. This structure is not actually a membrane but the outer layer of the substantia propria, from which it cannot be separated, but it is nevertheless distinguishable with the optical microscope because its fibers are not so well ordered. With the electron microscope it is seen to consist of a feltwork of randomly arranged collagen fibrils, about 180 Å in diameter, which may show a periodic banding. The membrane does not contain elastin and ends abruptly at the margin of the cornea.

Stroma or Substantia Propria. This layer forms about 90 per cent of the cornea (Fig. 34-4). It is a transparent, regular connective tissue whose bundles form thin lamellae arranged in many layers. In each layer the direction of the bundles changes and those in successive layers cross at various angles (Figs. 6-28 and 34-5). The lamellae everywhere

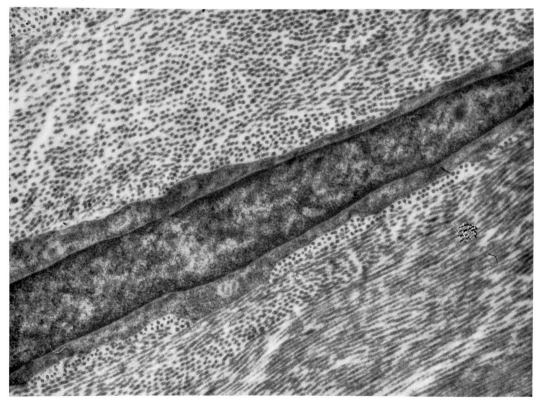

Figure 34-5. Electron micrograph of part of a fibroblast or keratocyte from the cornea and the surrounding layers of collagen fibers oriented at right angles to one another. (Courtesy of M. Jakus.)

interchange fibers and thus are kept tightly together. The collagen fibrils are somewhat thicker than those in Bowman's membrane, measuring about 230 Å thick on the average. Between the fibrils, the bundles, and the lamellae, there is a metachromatic protein-polysaccharide ground substance. The substances responsible for its metachromasia are chondroitin sulfate and keratosulfate. The cells of the stroma are long slender fibroblasts (keratocytes) lodged in narrow clefts among the parallel bundles of collagen fibrils. In addition the stroma always contains a number of lymphoid wandering cells, which migrate from the blood vessels of the corneal limbus. In inflammation enormous numbers of heterophilic leukocytes and lymphoid cells penetrate between the lamellae. The corneal stroma contains fine elastic networks especially abundant in the layers adjacent to the membrane of Descemet.

Membrane of Descemet. This homogeneous appearing lamella, 5 to 10 μ thick, can be isolated from the posterior surface of the substantia propria. At the periphery of the cornea, Descemet's membrane continues as a thin layer on the surface of the trabeculae of the iridial angle. In its structure it is essentially a very thick basement lamina (basement membrane), and it is probably elaborated by the corneal endothelium, which rests upon it (Figs. 34-4 and 34-6). Although it may appear homogeneous under the light microscope, Descemet's membrane of older individuals examined with the electron microscope may show an apparent cross striation with bands about 1070 Å apart, connected by filaments less than 100 Å in width and about 270 Å apart (Fig. 34-7*A*). Tangential sections of such corneas reveal a two dimensional array of nodes, about 1070 Å apart and connected by filaments to form hexagonal figures (Fig. 34-7*B*). The diagram in Figure 34-8 shows the relationship between the images seen in the two planes. Histochemical data, chemical analyses, and x-ray diffraction studies support the conclusion that the filaments forming this hexagonal array are an atypical form of collagen (Jakus). In young individuals Descemet's membrane is more homogeneous in appearance. It is suggested that the hexagonal pattern of fibers forms with advancing age by aggregation of collagen normally dispersed in

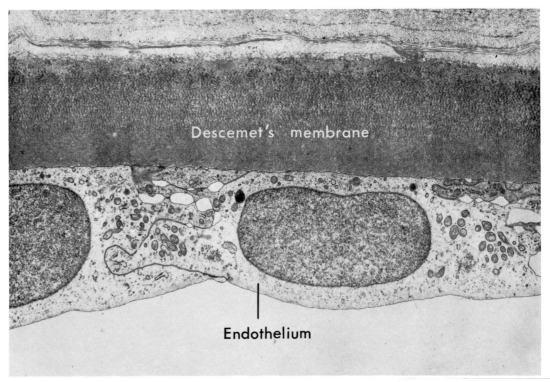

Figure 34-6. Electron micrograph of the endothelium and underlying Descemet's membrane from a human eye. (Courtesy of T. Kuwabara.)

the amorphous ground substance as tropocollagen. This and other atypical forms of collagen occur in the membrane at the periphery of the cornea, where randomly oriented fibrous bands with a 1000 Å periodicity are frequently encountered. These are particularly common in *Hassal-Henle bodies* or warts, the dome-shaped protrusions from the periphery of Descemet's membrane into the anterior chamber, which occur with increasing frequency in human eyes after the age of 20.

Corneal Endothelium or Mesenchymal Epithelium. The inner surface of the membrane of Descemet is covered by a layer of large, squamous cells (Fig. 34-6).

CORNEOSCLERAL JUNCTION. In a meridional section the boundary between the opaque sclera and the transparent cornea is an oblique line connecting the peripheral terminations of Bowman's and Descemet's membranes. The outer edge of the sclera overlaps slightly the border of the cornea. The collagenous bundles of the sclera continue directly into those of the cornea, where they become more precisely ordered, their striation loses its distinctness, and the tissue becomes more homogeneous and transparent.

At the marginal zone or *limbus* of the cornea, there is a gradual transition of its epithelium to that of the conjunctiva of the bulb. Where the membrane of Bowman ends, a subepithelial layer of loose connective tissue begins; it contains the loops of the blood vessels that furnish the nutritive materials to the cornea. These vessels are also the source of the wandering cells of the stroma mentioned earlier. The blood vessels that invade the corneal stroma in chronic inflammation arise from these loops.

On its inner surface, the corneoscleral junction is marked by a shallow furrow, the *internal scleral furrow,* or *sulcus.* Its posterior lip forms a small, centrally projecting ridge, the *scleral roll,* to which the ciliary body is fastened. Just peripheral to the termination of Descemet's membrane is the *trabecular meshwork.* This is a labyrinthine system of spaces lined by an attenuated epithelium that is continuous with the endothelium of the cornea. These *spaces of Fontana* within the trabecular meshwork communicate with the anterior chamber. The trabeculae separating the maze of minute intercommunicating passages are strands or septa of collagen fibrils completely covered by thin endothelial cells. It is through the spaces of Fontana that the aqueous humor drains from

A

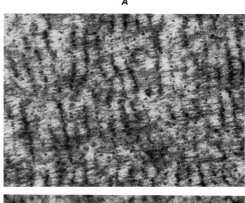

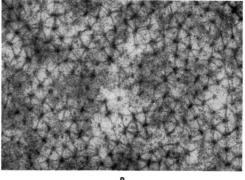

B

Figure 34-7. Electron micrographs of Descemet's membrane, showing the unusual configuration of collagen, characteristic of this layer. *A,* Cross section with its striated appearance; *B,* Tangential section, illustrating hexagonal arrangement of nodes connected by filaments. (Courtesy of M. Jakus.)

the anterior chamber into the *canal of Schlemm* (Fig. 34-10). This appears in sections as one to several small, epithelial lined cavities anterior and lateral to the trabecular meshwork near the bottom of the internal scleral furrow. These cavities are the cross sections of a circular canal, which parallels the border of the cornea and in many places breaks up into several irregular branches that then fuse again. The canal of Schlemm communicates with the venous system and is usually filled with clear aqueous humor but may rarely contain blood when there is stasis in the venous system. Obstruction to the filtration of aqueous humor through the spaces of Fontana or to its drainage via the canal of Schlemm results in the rise in intraocular pressure characteristic of the serious eye disease *glaucoma.*

THE UVEA (THE VASCULAR TUNIC)

CHOROID MEMBRANE. The choroid is a thin, soft, brown membrane adjacent to the inner surface of the sclera. Between the sclera

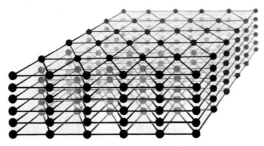

Figure 34-8. Diagram of structure of Descemet's membrane based on electron micrographs. See text for explanation. (Courtesy of M. Jakus.)

and the choroid is a potential cleft, the perichoroidal space; it is traversed by thin lamellae which run obliquely from the choroid to the sclera and form a loose, pigmented tissue layer—the *suprachoroid layer.* This is composed of fine, transparent membranes with fibroblasts on their surface and with a rich network of elastic fibers. Everywhere between and in the connective tissue lamellae large, flat melanocytes are scattered. In the suprachoroid, as in the rest of the uvea, there are also scattered macrophages. The lamellae of the suprachoroid pass without a distinct boundary into the substance of the choroid proper. This tunic can be subdivided into four main layers. From outside inward they are: (1) the vessel layer, (2) the capillary layer, (3) the glassy membrane or Bruch's membrane, and (4) a pigment epithelial layer (Fig. 34-3).

Vessel Layer. This layer consists of a multitude of large and medium-sized arteries and veins. The spaces between the vessels are filled with loose connective tissue rich in melanocytes. The lamellar arrangement here is much less distinct than in the suprachoroid. According to some, the vessel layer contains strands of smooth muscle independent of the arteries.

Choriocapillary Layer. This is formed by a capillary network arranged in one plane (Fig. 34-3). In places this layer is connected with the vascular layer. The individual capillaries have a large and somewhat irregular caliber. The net is especially dense and the capillary layer much thicker in the region underlying the fovea. Anteriorly it ends near the ora serrata.

Bruch's Membrane (Glassy Membrane). This is a refractile hyaline layer 1 to 4 μ thick between the choroid and the pigment

epithelium. It can be divided into two lamellae. The outer layer adjacent to the choriocapillaris consists of fine collagen fibers and a dense plexus of finest elastic fibers. The inner, thicker layer is homogeneous and is the basement lamina (basement membrane) of the pigment epithelium.

Pigment Epithelium. This sheet of heavily pigmented epithelial cells is derived from the posterior layer of the cuplike outgrowth of the embryonic nervous system that gives rise to the retina, and it has traditionally been included as one of the layers of the retina. Bruch's membrane, on the other hand, has been considered part of the choroid. The demonstration that this latter structure is, in part, the basement lamina of the pigment epithelium makes it illogical to assign the pigment epithelium to the retina and its basement lamina to the choroid. Some authors therefore prefer to consider the pigment epithelium as a component of the choroid. Although the cells of this layer extend processes that interdigitate with the retinal rods and cones, there is no actual anatomical connection between the photosensitive and pigment layers except at the head of the optic nerve and at the ora serrata. An artifactitious separation is found between the two layers in most histological preparations, and in the "separation of the retina" that is a common cause of partial blindness, the separation occurs along this plane of cleavage between the photosensitive elements of the retina and the pigment epithelium.

As seen in electron micrographs the cells have on their apical ends numerous irregular processes larger than ordinary microvilli. Numerous mitochondria are located toward the base of the cells, while the apical cytoplasm is occupied by very large round or oval melanin granules. Some of these extend a short distance into the cell processes.

CILIARY BODY. If the eyeball is cut across along its equator, and its anterior half, after removal of the vitreous, is inspected from within, a sharply outlined, dentate border is seen running around the inner surface of the wall in front of the equator (Fig. 34-11). This is the *ora serrata* of the retina. The zone between the ora and the edge of the lens is the *ciliary body,* a thickening of the vascular tunic. Its surface is covered by the darkly pigmented ciliary portion of the retina, which is not photosensitive. In a meridional section through the eye bulb, the ciliary body appears as a thin triangle with its small base facing the anterior chamber of the eye and attached there by its outer angle to the scleral roll. The long narrow angle of its triangular section extends backward and merges with the choroid (Fig. 34-9). The inner surface of the ciliary body is divided into a narrow anterior zone, the *ciliary crown,* and a broader posterior zone, the *ciliary ring.* The inner surface of the ring seen in surface view has shallow grooves, *ciliary striae,* which run forward from the teeth of the ora serrata. On its inner surface the ciliary crown has 70 radially arranged ridges, the *ciliary processes* (Figs. 34-10 and 34-11).

The main mass of the ciliary body, exclusive of the ciliary processes, consists of the *ciliary muscle.* It is smooth muscle and is composed of three portions. Closest to the sclera is the *muscle of Brücke,* whose bundles are deployed chiefly in the meridional direction. This outer part of the ciliary muscle stretches the choroid and is also called the *tensor muscle of the choroid.* Its role in accommodation is discussed in the section dealing with the lens. In the next inward portion of the ciliary muscle, the bundles of muscle cells radiate fanlike from the region of the scleral roll toward the cavity

of the eyeball. This is the *radial* or *reticular portion of the ciliary muscle.* The third or *circular portion of the ciliary muscle* (Müller's muscle) is usually absent in the newborn, appearing in the course of the second or third year. The contraction of this portion relaxes the tension on the lens and thus is important in accommodation for near vision. The interstices between the muscular bundles are filled with a small amount of connective tissue containing abundant elastic fibers and melanocytes (Fig. 34-10). The latter become especially numerous toward the sclera and where the connective tissue gradually passes into the lamellae of the suprachoroid.

The inner, *vascular layer of the ciliary body* consists of connective tissue with numerous blood vessels. In the ciliary ring it is the direct continuation of the same layer of the choroid. In the region of the ciliary crown it covers the inner surface of the ciliary muscle and forms the core of the ciliary processes. The vessels are almost exclusively capillaries and veins of varying caliber. The corresponding arteries ramify in the peripheral layers of the ciliary body. The connective tissue is dense, especially near the root of the iris, and contains abundant elastic fibers. In old age it often shows hyaline

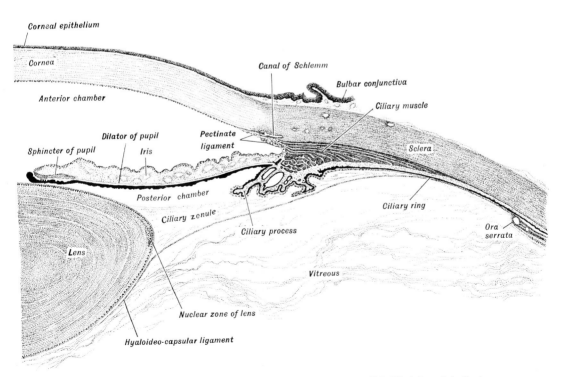

Figure 34-9.   Part of meridional section of human eye. × 14. (Modified from Schaffer.)

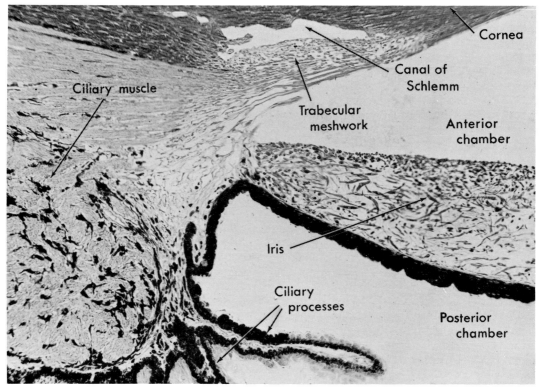

Figure 34-10. Photomicrograph of the angle of a normal human eye. (Courtesy of T. Kuwabara.)

degeneration. Melanocytes are usually found only near the surface of the muscle. The inner surface of the vascular layer of the ciliary body is lined by the continuation of the *glassy membrane* of the choroid. In the region of the ciliary body this membrane splits into three distinct lamellae.

The *ciliary portion of the retina* continues forward beyond the ora serrata and covers the inner surface of the ciliary body. It consists of an outer pigmented layer and a nonpigmented inner layer, and it does not receive light stimuli. The deeply pigmented epithelium consists of one layer of columnar cells and continues upon the posterior surface of the iris. The inner, colorless layer is a simple columnar epithelium. The height of its cells decreases from behind forward. Its inner surface is lined with a distinct extracellular layer—*the ciliary inner limiting membrane*—considered to be a continuation of the inner limiting membrane of the optical portion of the retina. In electron micrographs, these have the appearance of typical epithelial basement laminae.

Toward the root of the iris, on the anterior surface of the ciliary processes, the cells of the inner epithelial layer gradually accumulate pigment granules. On the posterior surface of the iris they are as heavily pigmented as the outer layer. This is the *iridial portion of the retina*.

IRIS. The posterior surface of the iris near the pupil rests upon the anterior surface of the lens; in this way the iris separates the anterior chamber from the posterior chamber. The margin of the iris connected with the ciliary body is called the *ciliary margin*, or the root of the iris. The pupil is surrounded by the *pupillary margin of the iris*. The iris diminishes in thickness toward both margins. Besides its individually varying color the anterior surface of the iris presents certain distinct markings. About 1.5 mm. from the pupillary margin a jagged line concentric with the pupillary margin separates the anterior surface into a *pupillary zone* and a wider *ciliary zone*. Near the pupillary and the ciliary margins the anterior surface has many irregular excavations, the *crypts,* which may extend deep into the tissue. In addition, there are oblique, irregularly arranged contraction furrows which are especially marked when the pupil is dilated.

The main mass of the iris consists of a loose, pigmented, highly vascular connective tissue. The anterior surface of the stroma is said to be lined with epithelium, which is a continuation of that on the posterior surface of the cornea. A thin layer of stroma immediately beneath the epithelium, the *anterior stromal sheet* or lamella, is devoid of blood vessels. Deep to this is a layer containing numerous vessels with walls unusually thick for their diameter. The posterior surface of the iris is covered with a double layer of heavily pigmented epithelium, the *iridial portion of the retina* (Figs. 34-10 and 34-14).

The anterior stromal sheet or lamella contains a few collagenous fibers and many fibroblasts and melanocytes in a homogeneous ground substance. The color of the iris depends on the quantity and the arrangement of the pigment and on the thickness of the lamella. If this layer is thin and its cells contain little or no pigment, the black pigment epithelium on the posterior surface, as seen through the colorless tissue, gives the iris a blue color (Fig. 34-15). An increasing amount of pigment brings about the different shades of gray and greenish hues. Large amounts of dark pigment cause the brown color of the iris. In albinos the pigment is absent or scanty, and the iris is pink because of its rich vascularity.

The epithelial pigment layer on the posterior surface of the iris is a direct continuation of the ciliary portion of the retina and, like it, originally consists of two layers of epithelium. The inner, nonpigmented layer of the ciliary portion of the retina becomes heavily pigmented in the iridial region with dark brown melanin granules that obscure the cell outlines. The posterior or inner surface is covered by the *limiting membrane of the iris*, which is a typical epithelial basement lamina (Fig. 34-13). The outer or anterior pigmented layer becomes less pigmented. These outer epithelial cells derived from the outer wall of the embryonic optic cup undergo a remarkable transformation into contractile elements—the myoepithelium of the dilator pupillae.

Being an adjustable diaphragm, the iris contains two muscles that keep the membrane stretched and hold it against the surface of the lens. The contraction of the circular *sphincter of the pupil* reduces the diameter of the pupil. It is a thin, flat ring surrounding the margin of the pupil. Its breadth changes, according to the contraction of the iris, from 0.6 to 1.2 mm. Its smooth muscle fibers are arranged in thin, circumferentially oriented bundles. The *dilator of the pupil* opens the pupil and consists of radially arranged myoepithelial elements, which form a thin membrane between the vessel layer and the pigment epithelium.

The innervation of the two muscles is quite different. The dilator is innervated by sympathetic postganglionic neurons located in the superior cervical ganglion. Their axons

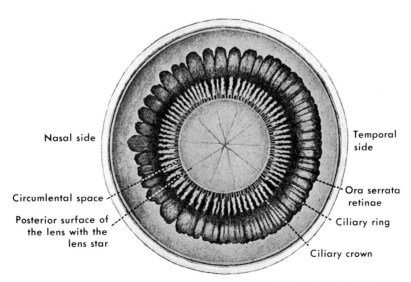

Figure 34-11. Anterior half of the right eye, seen from within. × 3. (After Salzmann.)

Nasal side

Temporal side

Circumlental space

Ora serrata retinae

Posterior surface of the lens with the lens star

Ciliary ring

Ciliary crown

pass to the gasserian ganglion, thence into the ophthalmic branch of the latter, and finally reach the dilator muscle through the long ciliary nerves. The sphincter muscle is innervated by parasympathetic fibers from postganglionic neurons located in the ciliary ganglion, and their axons reach the sphincter with the short ciliary nerves. The sympathetic and parasympathetic divisions of the autonomic nervous system thus have opposite effects upon the pupil. On the other hand, the sphincter and the ciliary muscles, which are both innervated by the short ciliary nerves, work in concert. When the eye accommodates for near vision by contraction of the ciliary muscle, there is always a simultaneous contraction of the pupillary sphincter.

In electron micrographs the axons among the contractile elements of the sphincter pupillae are seen to be packed with agranular "synaptic" vesicles typical of cholinergic axons. Axons associated with the dilator muscle contain a mixture of granular and

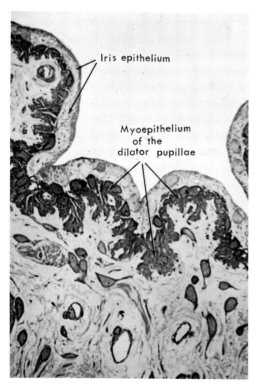

Figure 34-12. Photomicrograph of transverse section through the posterior surface of albino rabbit iris, showing the pale cuboidal iris epithelium and the underlying dark-staining myoepithelium of the dilator pupillae muscle. × 480. (After K. C. Richardson, Am. J. Anat., *114*:173, 1964.)

agranular vesicles typical of the endings of adrenergic sympathetic nerve fibers (Richardson).

REFRACTIVE MEDIA OF THE EYE

The cornea and the anterior and posterior chambers of the eye have been described. The other components of the refractive apparatus of the eye are the crystalline lens and vitreous body.

LENS. The lens is a transparent, biconvex body situated immediately behind the pupil. Its shape changes during the process of accommodation. Its outer form varies somewhat in different persons and also with age. Its diameter ranges from 7 mm. in a newborn to 10 mm. in an adult. Its thickness is approximately 3.7 to 4 mm., increasing during accommodation to 4.5 mm. and more. The posterior surface or pole is more convex than the anterior, the respective radii of curvature being 6.9 and 10 mm. The index of refraction is 1.36 in the peripheral layers and 1.4 in the inner zone. The lens weighs 0.2 gm. and is slightly yellow.

The lens is covered with a homogeneous, highly refractive *capsule,* an 11 to 18 μ carbohydrate-rich coating on the outer surface of the layer of flattened or cuboidal cells comprising the epithelium of the lens (Fig. 34-16). Toward the equator of the lens these cells approach a columnar form and become arranged in meridional rows. Becoming progressively elongated, the cells at the equator are transformed into *lens fibers* that constitute the bulk of the substance of the lens. In this transition or *nuclear zone* the cells have a characteristic arrangement. The epithelial cells are of prime importance for the normal metabolism of the lens. The capsule covering the posterior pole has no underlying epithelium.

In the human lens each fiber is a six-sided prism, 7 to 10 mm. long, 8 to 12 μ wide, and only 2 μ thick (Fig. 34-18). In the region of the nucleus the thickness may reach 5 μ. The prismatic fibers of the cortical zone of the lens are hexagonal in cross section with the closely apposed cell surfaces quite straight. It was formerly thought that a cementing substance between the lens fibers acted as a lubricant, permitting movement of the fibers with respect to one another during accommodation. No appreciable intercellular space is found, however, in electron micrographs. The cell surfaces

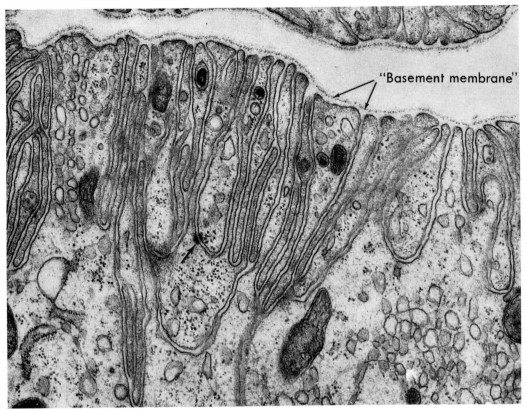

Figure 34-13. Electron micrograph of a small area of the posterior epithelium of the albino rabbit iris, showing that its free surface is covered by well defined basal lamina (basement membrane) and that processes of neighboring cells interdigitate in a complex manner, giving a spurious appearance of infolding of the cell surface. Notice the desmosome at the arrow. × 33,000. (After K. C. Richardson, Am. J. Anat., *114*:173, 1964.)

are about 150 Å apart and attached by occasional desmosomes. The cells of the lens epithelium and the fibers of the equatorial region both exhibit complex interdigitations of their surfaces. This is particularly marked at the "sutures," where cortical fibers from opposite sectors of the lens converge (Fig. 34-18). Since these interdigitations occur principally in the anterior curvature, periaxial zone, and equator—those regions that undergo the greatest dimensional changes—it has been suggested that their presence may be associated with changes of fiber shape in the mechanism of intracapsular accommodation (Wanko).

The lens fibers have a finely granular cytoplasm with a few small vesicles scattered through the ectoplasmic region of the cell and occasional mitochondria in the vicinity of the sutures, but in general the organelles and inclusions are exceedingly sparse (Fig. 34-19).

The lens is held in position by a system of fibers comprising the *ciliary zonule*. The zonule fibers (Figs. 34-9 and 34-17) are straight, homogeneous filaments varying in thickness up to 22 μ and having many branches. They seem to arise from the epithelium of the ciliary portion of the retina. Near the ciliary crown they fuse into thicker fibers and finally form about 140 bundles. At the anterior margin of the ciliary processes they leave the surface of the ciliary body and radiate toward the equator of the lens. The larger ones are straight and reach the capsule in front of the equator of the lens (*anterior sheet of the zonule*). The thinner fibers assume a slightly curved course and are attached to the posterior surface of the lens (*posterior zonular sheet*). All zonular fibers break up into a multitude of fine fibers, which fuse with the substance of the outermost layer of the capsule (Fig. 34-17). Where the vitreous body touches the lens capsule it forms the *hyaloideocapsular ligament*.

The radii of curvature of the surfaces of

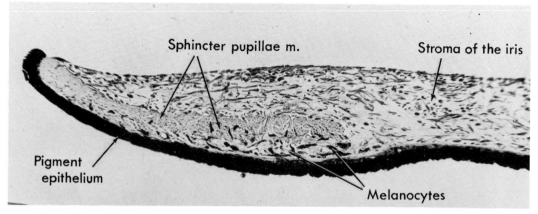

Figure 34-14. Photomicrograph of a transverse section of human iris. (Preparation by T. Kuwabara.)

the several dioptric media of the *normal* eye, especially of the lens, and their indices of refraction are such that light rays coming from a remote point form an inverted and real image of the object in the layer of the photoreceptive cones and rods in the retina. If the object is approaching, the light rays diverge more and more, and the image moves backward. A change of position of an object from infinite distance to about 5 meters causes the image to shift about 60 μ backward in the retina. Since this image is still within the outer segments of the rods and cones, accommodation is not needed. For nearer distances, accommodation is necessary.

In a camera the focusing of objects that move nearer to the lens is effected by moving the ground glass plate away from the lens. In the higher vertebrates and in man, the curvature of the lens is changed. When the eye is at rest, the lens is kept stretched by the ciliary zonule in the plane vertical to the optic axis. When the eye has to focus on a near object, the ciliary muscle, especially its meridional fibers, contracts and pulls the choroid and the ciliary body forward. This relieves the tension exerted by the zonule; the lens gets thicker, and its surface, especially at the anterior pole, becomes more convex. This increases the refractive power of the lens and keeps the focus within the photoreceptor layer.

VITREOUS BODY. The vitreous body fills the vitreal cavity between the lens and the retina. It adheres everywhere to the optical portion of the retina, and the connection is especially firm at the serrated margin. Farther forward it gradually recedes from the surface of the ciliary portion of the retina.

The fresh vitreous body is a colorless, structureless, gelatinous mass with a glasslike transparency. Its index of refraction is 1.334. When fixed, it undergoes considerable shrinkage and shows a network of extremely fine fibrils. Almost 99 per cent of the vitreous body consists of water, the remainder being hydrophilic polysaccharide, especially hyaluronic acid.

Extending through the vitreous body from the papilla of the optic nerve to the posterior surface of the lens is the *hyaloid canal* (canal of Cloquet). It is a residue remaining after the resorption of the embryonic hyaloid artery. It has a diameter of 1 mm. and is filled with aqueous liquid. In the living, especially in young persons, it is visible with the help of the slit lamp microscope. In the peripheral layers of the vitreous body, free cells float in the liquid. They are probably hematogenous lymphoid cells.

THE RETINA

The retina is the innermost of the three coats of the eyeball and is the photoreceptor organ. It arises in early embryonic development from a bilateral evagination of the prosencephalon, the *primary optic vesicle*. Later it is transformed by local invagination into the *secondary optic vesicle* (Fig. 34-36). Each optic cup remains connected with the brain by a stalk, the *future optic nerve*. In the adult the derivatives of the bilaminar secondary optic vesicle consist of an outer, pigmented epithelial layer and an inner sheet, the *retina proper*. The latter contains elements similar to those of the brain, and it may be considered to be a specially differentiated part of the brain.

The *optical* or *functioning portion of the retina* lines the inner surface of the choroid and extends from the papilla of the optic nerve to the serrated margin anteriorly. At the papilla, where the retina continues into the tissue of the nerve, and at the serrated margin, the retina is firmly connected with the choroid. About 2.5 mm. lateral to the border of the optic papilla, the inner surface of the retina shows a shallow, round depression, the *central fovea* (Fig. 34-24).

When detached from the pigment epithelium, the fresh retina is almost perfectly transparent. It has a distinctly red color because of the presence in its rod cells of *visual purple*, or *rhodopsin*. Light rapidly bleaches the visual purple; in darkness the color gradually reappears. The fovea and its immediate vicinity contain yellow pigment and are called the *macula lutea*. Large blood vessels circle above and below the central fovea, whereas only fine arteries and veins and capillaries are present in it. In the very center of the fovea, in an area measuring 0.5 mm. across, even the capillaries are absent, greatly increasing its transparency.

Only the portion of the image of an external object that falls upon the fovea is seen sharply. Accordingly, the eyes are moved so as to bring the object of special attention into this central part of the visual field. Photoreceptors are absent from the optic papilla. This is the "blind spot" of the visual field.

LAYERS OF RETINA. In the retina, exclusive of the fovea, the papilla, and the serrated margin, 10 parallel layers can be distinguished from outside inward (Fig. 34-21): (1) the pigment epithelium; (2) the layer of rods and cones (bacillary layer); (3) the outer limiting membrane; (4) the outer nuclear layer; (5) the outer plexiform layer; (6) the inner nuclear layer; (7) the inner plexiform layer; (8) the layer of ganglion cells; (9) the layer of optic nerve fibers; and (10) the inner limiting membrane. The numbers *1* to *10* in Figures 34-23, 34-25, 34-31, and 34-32 indicate the layers as listed here and shown in Figure 34-21.

REGIONS OF RETINA. The distribution of the cellular and fibrous elements varies considerably in detail from the fovea, in the center of the retina, to its anterior limit at the serrated margin. Thus seven concentric circular *regions* can be distinguished (Fig. 34-19). The inner three (I to III) comprise the *central area*, distinguished by the great number of ganglion cells in the eighth layer and by the general refinement and even distribution of the structural elements, especially of the rods and cones. The smallest and most precisely ordered sensory elements are in the fovea (region I), where they are accumulated in greatest numbers. The regions outside the central area (IV to VI), and the ora serrata (VII), constitute the *extra-areal periphery*. Here the elements are fewer, larger, less differentiated and less evenly

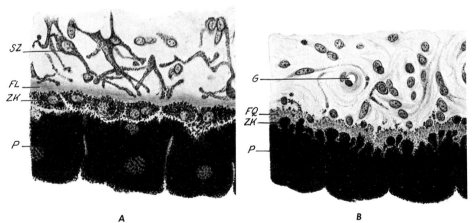

A   B

Figure 34-15. Sections of human iris. *A*, Posterior part of a radial (meridional) transection of a dark human iris, from an enucleated eyeball. *FL*, Fibrillae of the dilator muscle in longitudinal section; *P*, pigment epithelium of the inner (posterior) layer of the iridial portion of the retina; *SZ*, pigment-containing connective tissue cells (melanophores) of the vascular layer; *ZK*, pigment-containing cell bodies of the dilator muscle (outer or anterior layer of the iridial portion of the retina). *B*, Tangential section of a light human iris. *FQ*, Fibers of the dilator muscle in cross section; *G*, blood vessel in the stroma; other symbols as in *A*. × 380. (After Schaffer.)

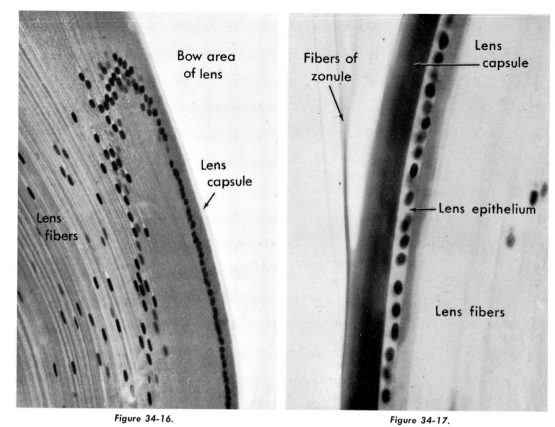

Figure 34-16.   *Figure 34-17.*

Figure 34-16.   Photomicrograph of the bow area of the human lens, where the epithelial cells become greatly elongated to form lens fibers. (Courtesy of T. Kuwabara.)

Figure 34-17.   Photomicrograph at higher magnification of human lens stained with the periodic acid–Schiff reaction. The lens capsule overlying the epithelium stains strongly. Zonule fibers merge with the capsule. (Preparation by T. Kuwabara.)

distributed. (Note that Roman numerals in text and legends refer to regions of the retina, whereas the Arabic numerals refer to the layers.)

VISUAL CELLS. These elements are the photoreceptors (*2* in Figs. 34-21 and 34-23). There are two kinds of visual cells, the *rod cells* and the *cone cells*. Their outer segments are the parts sensitive to light, and the light rays, before reaching them, must first penetrate most of the retina.

Rod Cells.   The rod cell is a long, slender, highly specialized cell with its outer portion vertical to the surface of the retina (Fig. 34-25*a*). The parallel arrangement of these elements is responsible for the regular striation of layer *2*. The scleral part of the rod cell, the *rod proper*, is situated between the outer limiting membrane and the pigment epithelium, its outward third being embedded among the pig-

ment-containing processes of the pigment epithelial cells. The vitreal end of the rod proper extends through the so-called outer limiting membrane into layer *4*. Each rod proper consists of an outer and an inner segment. The *outer segment* is a slender cylinder of uniform thickness, which appears homogeneous in the fresh condition. It possesses a peculiarly brilliant refractility and is positively birefringent in polarized light. This segment contains *rhodopsin* or visual purple, the photoreceptive substance that is responsible for absorption of light and initiation of the visual stimulus. The *inner segment* contains a remarkable aggregation of mitochondria localized in a circumscribed area described by light microscopists as the ellipsoid. The finer structure of the rod cells has been greatly clarified by electron microscopy. The outer segment in longitudinal section is seen to be composed of a very large number of parallel lamellae oriented transverse to the axis of the rod (Fig. 34-26*A*). Each lamella is in fact a closed, membrane limited sac flattened into a disk approximately 2 μ in diameter and about 140 Å thick. In section, therefore, the profile of each lamella or disk appears as a pair of parallel membranes continuous with one another at the ends and enclosing an exceedingly narrow cavity about 80 Å across. The outer segment is joined to the inner segment by a slender stalk, which contains nine longitudinally oriented fibrils terminating in a centriole or basal body in the distal end of the inner segment. In transverse sections the stalk has the appearance of a defective cilium, having the nine peripheral doublets but lacking the central pair of fibrils. Studies of the development of the photoreceptors have shown that the outer segments of the rods do in fact develop by modification of cilia. The inner segment contains many elongated mitochondria, generally oriented parallel to the long axis of the rod (Fig. 34-27). Cross striated fibrous rootlets may extend downward from the basal body of the rod outer segment among the mitochondria (Fig. 34-26).

The rods are fairly uniform in appearance, although their dimensions vary somewhat from region to region. Their thickness in the central area (regions I to III) is 1 to 1.5 μ, gradually increasing to 2.5 or 3 μ near the ora (region VII). Their length decreases from approximately 60 μ in the fovea to 40 μ in the far periphery.

The rest of the rod cell is made up of the *rod fiber* and the *rod body*. The *rod fiber* is a slender protoplasmic process, 1 μ or less in thickness, that extends from the base of the inner segment of the rod proper deep into layer *4*, the outer nuclear layer, where it joins a small spherical *rod body* containing the rod nucleus, which is smaller and stains more intensively than the cone nucleus. In the central area the course of the rod fibers assumes a slanting to horizontal position, while in the more peripheral regions it is vertical.

The rod proper with the outer fiber is the homologue of the receptive dendritic expansions of a neuron; the inner rod fiber corresponds to the emissive axon. In the central area the inner rod and cone fibers, and the portions of Müller's fibers which envelop them, form a thick fiber layer, the *outer fiber layer of Henle* (zone *5-a*).

The rod nuclei represent the majority of the nuclei of the fourth layer (*4*) in all regions

except in the fovea, where rods are few, and in its center, where they are absent.

All rod cells contain visual purple, except those in a zone 3 to 4 mm. wide at the serrated margin of the retina. The red color of the retina during life is attributable to this substance. As there are only a few rods in the periphery of the fovea and none in its center, this area appears devoid of rhodopsin. When the retina is exposed to light, rhodopsin breaks down, but it is constantly produced anew. This regeneration occurs only as long as the close relation of the rods with the pigment epithelium is preserved.

Cone Cells. These neurons (Fig. 34-25*b*) are made up of essentially the same parts as the rod cells, but they differ in certain details. There is no visual purple in the cones. Instead of a slender cylinder, the cone outer segment is a long conical structure, considerably wider than a rod at its base and tapering down to a blunt rounded tip. As in the rod, the outer segment is made up of a large number of lamellae, stacked one above the other. Each of these

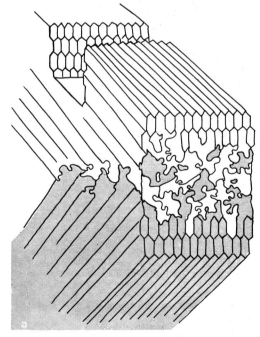

Figure 34-18. Schematic drawing of the arrangement of lens fibers in rows and their prevailing hexagonal cross sectional form, except in the suture area, where there may be considerable irregularities and interdigitation of fibers converging from opposite sectors of the lens. (After T. Wanko and M. Gavin: The Structure of the Eye. New York, Academic Press, 1961.)

consists of a pair of membranes. In many of the lamellae the two membranes are continuous at their margins and enclose a narrow closed space. In other lamellae the two membranes are continuous with the plasma membrane, and the narrow cleft between them is open to the extracellular space (Fig. 34-26B). This appears to be a consistent and possibly a significant difference between rods and cones.

The cone outer segment is also connected to the inner segment by an eccentrically placed modified cilium terminating in a basal body set in the distal end of the inner segment. The other member of the diplosome is usually oriented at a right angle to the basal body, and striated rootlets extend from it downward among the longitudinally oriented mitochondria that crowd the inner segment (Figs. 34-27 and 34-28).

The cones vary considerably in different regions of the retina. In the central fovea they measure 75 μ or more in length and from 1 to 1.5 μ in thickness. Their length gradually decreases to 45 μ in the periphery. The relative length of the outer and the inner segments is usually 3:4. In the fovea the two segments are approximately the same length. The proximal end of the inner cone segment occupies an opening in the "outer limiting membrane" (3), and protrudes slightly into the fourth layer.

The dense staining line traditionally called the *outer limiting membrane* is not a membrane at all. Instead it is found in electron micrographs to be a row of dense junctional complexes where the photoreceptor cells are attached to the Müller cells, which surround and support all of the neural elements between the *inner limiting membrane of the retina*, which represents the basal lamina of the Müller cells, and the *outer limiting membrane* just beneath their free surface. Distal to this row of junctional complexes, tufts of microvilli project from the free surface of the Müller cells into interstices between the rod and cone inner segments.

In teleostean fishes and amphibians the inner cone segment is contractile. It shortens in bright light and stretches in dim light or

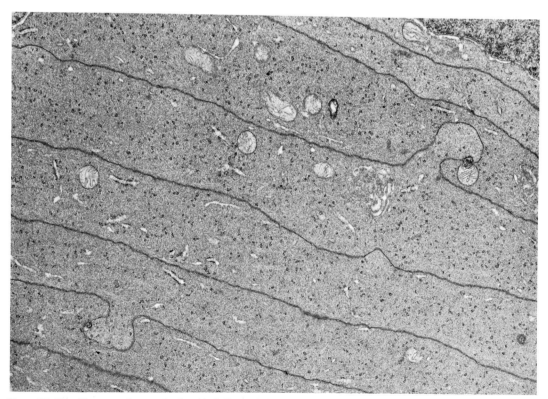

Figure 34-19. Electron micrograph of cortical fibers of the human lens. A few profiles of granular endoplasmic reticulum, occasional mitochondria, and numerous polyribosomes are distributed in an otherwise homogeneous and concentrated cytoplasmic matrix. (Courtesy of T. Kuwabara.)

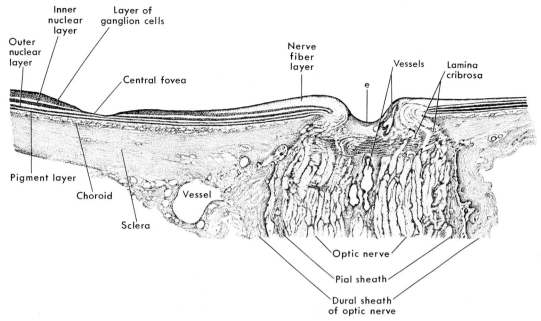

Figure 34-20. Central fovea and place of entrance of the optic nerve as seen in a horizontal meridional section of an enucleated human eye. *e,* Excavation. × 18. (Redrawn and slightly modified from Schaffer.)

darkness. The displacement of these cones is, accordingly, opposite in direction to that of the rods. It is not definitely established whether human cones are contractile.

Proximal to the outer limiting membrane, the inner cone segment merges with its *body,* containing a nucleus, which is larger and paler staining than the rod nucleus. The bodies and nuclei of the cones, in contrast to those of the rods, are arranged in a single row (*4-a*) immediately beneath the outer limiting membrane. Exceptional in this regard are the cones in the outer fovea, whose nuclei are accumulated in several rows (Fig. 34-23*I*). Only in this region do the cones have an *outer fiber.* But from the body of all cones a stout, smooth *inner fiber* descends to the middle zone of the outer plexiform layer (*5-b*), where it terminates with a thick triangular or clubshaped swelling, the *cone pedicle.* Up to a dozen short, barblike processes emanate from the base of each pedicle, except in the fovea, where there are usually none. These outgrowths are deployed horizontally in zone *5-c.* The length and course of the inner cone fibers may vary considerably, depending on the region, the longest (600 μ) and almost horizontally placed being those in the outer fiber layer of Henle (*5-a*) in the central area. The inner cone fibers have all the

characteristics of an axon, while the cone pedicle has those of the telodendra of a neuron.

The number of cones in the human retina is estimated at six to seven million (Østerberg). The ratio of the number of nerve fibers of the optic nerve (438,000) to the number of cones of one eye is 1:6 or 1:7.

The relative number and distribution of the rods and cones in different vertebrates present great variations, depending on the mode of life. In diurnal birds the cones are more numerous than the rods. In most diurnal reptiles there are only cones and no rods. In many nocturnal vertebrates only rods are present, although in others a few rudimentary cones can be found among numerous rods. On similar comparative data M. Schultze (1866) based his assumption that there is a difference in the function of the two kinds of photoreceptors (duplicity theory).

The cones in the adult primate retina, including those of the fovea, are quite distinct from the rods. The opinion that there is more than one variety of cone cell in mammals (including primates), and that this is related to certain theories of color perception, has not been verified. The evidence indicates that the cone cells throughout the primate retina are of one variety, although they vary in detail from

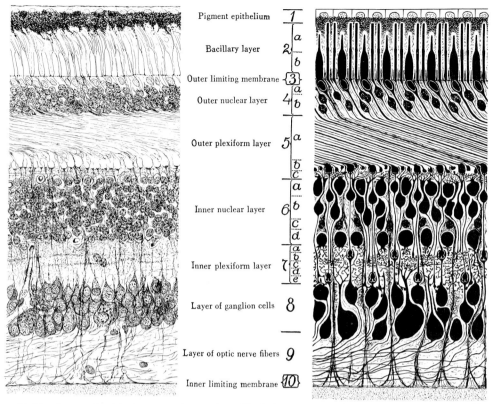

Pigment epithelium	1
Bacillary layer	2 {a / b}
Outer limiting membrane	3
Outer nuclear layer	4 {a / b}
Outer plexiform layer	5 {a / b c}
Inner nuclear layer	6 {a / b / c / d}
Inner plexiform layer	7 {a / b / c / d / e}
Layer of ganglion cells	8
Layer of optic nerve fibers	9
Inner limiting membrane	10

Figure 34-21. Layers of adult human retina (region III). Left figure stained routinely, about 400 ×. The right figure is a schematic reconstruction from sections stained with Golgi's method. (Slightly modified from Polyak.)

place to place. This is also true of the rods, although to a lesser degree.

HORIZONTAL CELLS. These cells are typical neurons whose bodies form the uppermost one or two rows of the inner nuclear layer (zone 6-a in Figs. 34-21 and 34-31). From the upper end of the body arise short dendritic twigs, producing several tufts spreading in the lower zone of the outer plexiform layer (5-c), where each tuft comes in contact with the vitreal face of one cone pedicle. The axon takes a horizontal course chiefly in zone 5-c, and its terminal twigs come into contact with both rod spherules and cone pedicles. The horizontal cells, accordingly, receive impulses from a group of cone cells of one locality and transmit them to a group of rod and cone cells of another locality (Fig. 34-31c).

BIPOLAR CELLS. These neurons connect the rods and cones with the ganglion cells of the retina, and through these with the visual centers of the brain. The bipolar cells stand approximately upright with respect to the retinal layers, except in the central fovea, where their position is oblique. Their nuclei are in the sixth layer, with a few in the fifth.

Each bipolar has one or several outward expansions that spread into the outer plexiform layer (5), where they synapse with the photoreceptors. With the aid of the electron microscope Sjöstrand has demonstrated the intricate manner in which the dendritic expansions of the bipolar cells penetrate into deep recesses in the terminal swellings of the rod cells. Similar studies of the synapses in the retina have been made by De Robertis and Franchi and others.

A single inward expansion of the bipolar cell spreads into the seventh layer, where it is synaptically related to the ganglion cells and other adjoining cells. Two groups of bipolars can be distinguished: centripetal bipolars, which transmit impulses from rods and cones to ganglion cells (Fig. 34-31d, e, f, and h), and centrifugal bipolars, which transmit in the opposite direction (i). The bipolar cells apparently play an essential role in distributing and rearranging the impulses received from the rods and cones before transmitting them to the third category of retinal neurons, the ganglion cells.

GANGLION CELLS. These cells (m, n, o, p,

and *s* in Fig. 34-31, and layer *8* in Fig. 34-21) represent the third link, the last in the retina, of the chain of neurons of the brain. The bodies are in the ganglion layer, with a few displaced into the lowermost zone of the inner nuclear layer. Their dendrites spread in the inner plexiform layer. Chromophilic substance is present in all. From the body or the chief dendritic trunk of each ganglion cell arises one axon that leaves the retina and becomes an optic nerve fiber terminating in the subcortical visual centers of the brain.

OPTIC NERVE FIBERS IN THE PRIMATE RETINA. Because of the presence of the central fovea, the optic nerve fibers have a special course. In general they converge radially toward the optic papilla. However, those originating in the upper temporal quadrant of the retina circle above the central area, while those originating in the lower temporal quadrant circle below it on their way to the papilla. They follow the larger retinal vessels fairly closely. A line connecting the fovea with the temporal circumference of the retina separates the optic nerve fibers of the upper from those of the lower temporal quadrant. This separation is preserved along the central visual pathway as far as the cortical visual center.

In primates each retina is divided into two halves along the vertical meridian passing through the center of the fovea. The fibers from the nasal half cross in the optic chiasma and pass to the optic tract of the opposite side; those from the temporal half enter the tract of the same side. Each optic tract is, therefore, composed of fibers from the temporal half of the retina of the same side and the nasal half of the retina of the opposite eye. This arrangement remains in the visual radiation in the occipital lobes of the brain. It accounts for the blindness in the opposite halves of the two fields of view (homonymous hemianopia) when the optic tract or the visual radiation of one side is interrupted.

SUPPORTING, OR NEUROGLIAL, ELEMENTS OF THE RETINA. The retina, being a modified part of the brain, contains supporting elements of neurolgial character. The most important are the radial cells of Müller (*u* in Fig. 34-31). These are present throughout the central area, including the fovea, as well as in the periphery.

Their oval nuclei lie in the middle zone of the inner nuclear layer (*6-c*, Fig. 34-21). The

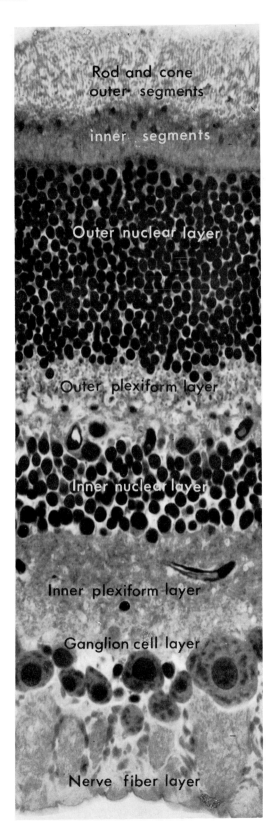

Figure 34-22. Photomicrograph of cat retina. (Courtesy of A. J. Ladman.)

cell body is a slender fiber or pillar which extends radially from the outer (*3*) to the inner limiting membrane (*10*). Their inner ends expand conically and form the *inner limiting membrane*. In the two plexiform layers the radial fibers give off many branches, which form a dense neuroglial network in whose meshes are lodged the ramifications of the neurons described earlier.

The cell bodies of Müller cells are beset with excavations, which envelop bodies of the ganglion cells, bipolars, horizontal cells, and the cone and rod cells. The bodies of the nervous elements appear to be completely enveloped in thin husks of supporting structures, which perhaps serve as insulators. The rod and cone fibers are also encased in thin sheaths formed by Müller's cells.

At the limit between the outer nuclear layer and the layer of the rods and cones, Müller cells, as described, have prominent junctional complexes that produce the linear density formerly interpreted as an *outer limiting membrane*.

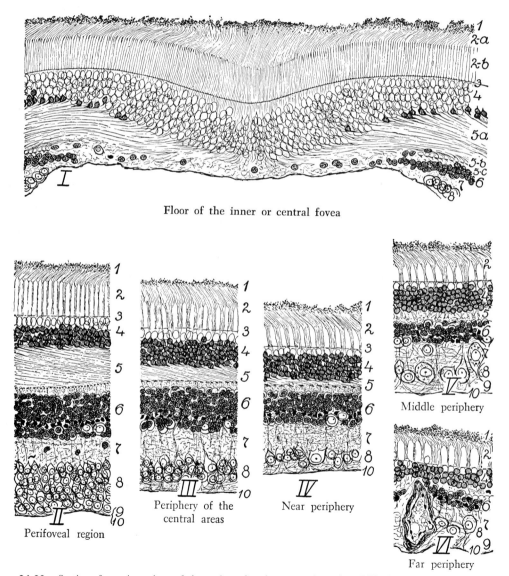

Floor of the inner or central fovea

Perifoveal region

Periphery of the central areas

Near periphery

Middle periphery

Far periphery

Figure 34-23. Sections from six regions of the retina of a rhesus monkey. Area VII, the ora serrata, is not shown here. (Slightly modified from Polyak.)

Figure 34-24. Photomicrograph of the fovea of a macaque retina, showing the marked reduction in thickness in this area of maximum visual acuity. (Courtesy of H. Mizoguchi.)

CENTRAL AREA AND FOVEA ("MACULA"). Slightly lateral to the papilla is the place of most distinct vision. This region, the *central area,* is characterized by the presence of cones and other nervous elements in numbers greater than elsewhere and by their structural specialization and synaptic perfection. In the center of this area, the layers inward to zone *5-a* are displaced laterally, producing a shallow depression on the vitreal surface of the retina called the *central fovea.* This permits an almost free passage of rays of light to the layer of photoreceptors, and it is here that the visual axis touches the retina.

The central fovea is a shallow bowl with its concavity toward the vitreous (Fig. 34-33). It is in the center of the central area, 2 to 2.5 mm. on the temporal side of the papilla. In its center a *floor* or *fundus* can be distinguished, with the *slopes* and a *margin of the fovea.* The width of the entire foveal depression measures 1.5 mm.

In the fundus of the central fovea, the cones are most numerous and are thinner and longer than elsewhere in the retina. This area, the *outer fovea,* contains 20,000 to 25,000 cones. This region, measuring about 400 μ across, probably corresponds to the portion of the field of view where vision is most discriminating. The *rod-free* area, where only cones are present, measures 500 to 550 μ in diameter and contains up to 30,000 cones.

Capillaries are present in the foveal slopes to the very edge of the foveal floor, or 275 μ from the very center. The *avascular central territory* is almost as large as the rodless area (500 to 550 μ).

FUNCTIONS OF THE EYE

Although the phenomenon of vision should be considered as arising from the activity of the visual system as a whole, it is convenient to subdivide it into at least four different processes: (I) refraction of the incoming rays and image formation on the retina; (II) conversion or transduction of quanta of incident light into nerve impulses by the rod and cone cells; (III) transmission and modification of the afferent barrage by the various neurons of the optic tract; (IV) perceptual interpretation of the complex pattern of electrical activity set up in the cortex by the afferent impulses. This last topic will not be considered here.

I. The eye is essentially a camera obscura provided with dioptric media: the cornea with the aqueous humor and the adjustable crystalline lens are optically active. The inner surface of this dark chamber is lined by the photosensitive retina. The rays of light emanating from each point of an illuminated object impinging on the cornea are refracted by it and converge on the lens. In the lens the rays are further refracted and focused in the photosensitive layer of the retina (*2* in the figures). The sum of the foci that correspond with the points on the surface of the object seen constitutes the retinal image of the object. In relation to the object the retinal image is inverted (because of the crossing of the rays in the pupil's aperture); it is a real image (since the foci are actually on the retina and not behind or in front of it), and it is very much reduced in size.

II. The *transduction* process is initiated photochemically and can be conveniently

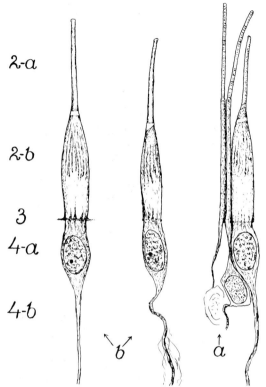

Figure 34-25. Rods (*a*) and cones (*b*) from an osmic acid-fixed, unstained, teased preparation of retina of a rhesus monkey (preparation of G. W. Bartelmez). Designation of layers as in Figure 34-21. Outer rod and cone segments in zone *2-a*, inner segments in *2-b*, rod bodies with their nuclei in zone *4-b*, cone bodies with nuclei in *4-a; 3*, outer limiting membrane; fiber apparatus visible in the upper portion of the inner cone segments. Some of the outer segments slightly bent. (Courtesy of S. Polyak.)

divided into primary and secondary steps. The primary step consists in the absorption of a light quantum by one of the visual pigments and a subsequent configuration change in the absorbing molecule. The secondary steps presumably consist of a series of reactions that ultimately lead to a depolarization of the receptor cell membrane and formation of the action potential that is propagated along the optic tract. The molecular basis of the primary photochemical absorption is now well understood, but almost nothing is known of the secondary reactions that generate the action potential. The status of this problem was reviewed by Wald (1960).

There are two general types of visual pigments: *rhodopsin*, located in the outer segments of the rod cells, and *iodopsin*, located in the

outer segments of the cones. The membranes forming the transverse laminae of the outer segments of these cells probably contain most of the pigment molecules. There is fairly direct physiological evidence for the central importance of rhodopsin in dark-adapted or scotopic vision: the spectral sensitivity curve of the human eye in dim light almost exactly parallels the absorption spectrum of rhodopsin measured in vitro in the visible region between 4000 and 6000 Å with a maximum at 5100 Å. Similarly, for cone vision, Rushton has made in vivo measurements of the absorption spectra of at least two, and possibly three, distinct foveal pigments in man. It is possible that they could provide a chemical basis for the classical trichromatic theory of color vision.

Rhodopsin and iodopsin consist of vitamin A_1 aldehyde (retinene$_1$) conjugated to a specific protein (rod opsin and cone opsin, respectively) through a Schiff base linkage between the terminal aldehyde group of retinene and an amino group of the opsin (Fig. 34-34).

Retinene can exist in any of five isomeric forms: all *trans*, 9-*cis*, 13-*cis*, 9,13-*dicis*, and 11-*cis*. All of these are planar molecules except for the 11-*cis* form, which is sterically hindered, so that the aromatic ring and side chain of conjugated double bonds are noncoplanar. It is the hindered 11-*cis* isomer that occurs naturally in unbleached rhodopsin. The significance of this requirement of the 11-*cis* isomer is probably that, in conjugation with opsin, the retinene must fit snugly against some specific surface contour of the protein molecule.

Upon exposure to visible light (bleaching), rhodopsin is converted through at least two intermediate stages to a mixture of all *trans* retinene and opsin. A molecule of rhodopsin absorbs one quantum of light and isomerizes to the short-lived *lumirhodopsin*, which is a complex of all *trans* retinene and opsin. There follows a rearrangement of opsin which leads to another relatively short-lived species called *metarhodopsin*, and this is hydrolyzed to the final bleached mixture of *trans* retinene and opsin. Hubbard and Kropf have shown that the primary triggering step in the transduction process, that is, the only thing actually done by light in any visual system, consists simply in the *cis-trans* isomerization of retinene. Thus, the unknown secondary processes that give rise to the action potential probably depend only on the formation of lumirhodopsin (or at most metarhodopsin), because the hydrolysis of metarhodopsin to retinene and opsin is much too slow to account for visual excitation.

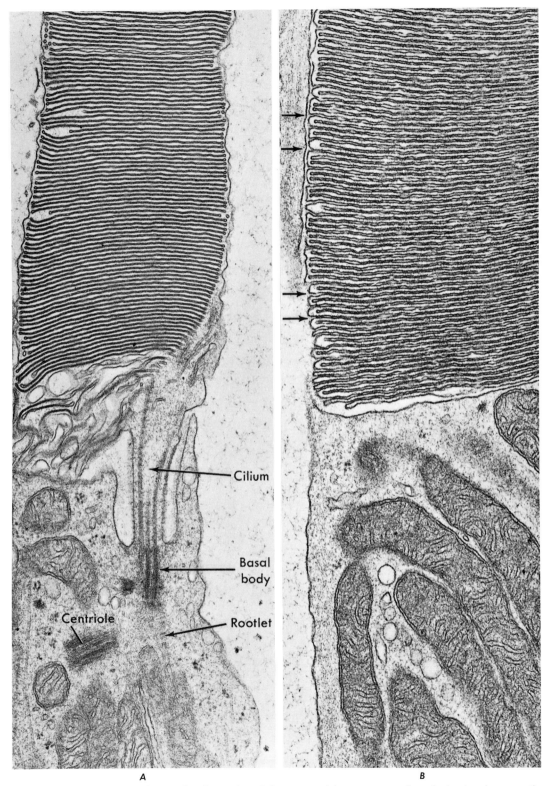

A

B

Figure 34-26. *A,* Electron micrographs of a portion of the outer and inner segment of a rod, showing the connection of the two by a modified cilium. *B,* Corresponding region of a cone. Notice at the arrows that some of the lamellae are open to the extracellular space. (Courtesy of T. Kuwabara.)

Figure 34-27.

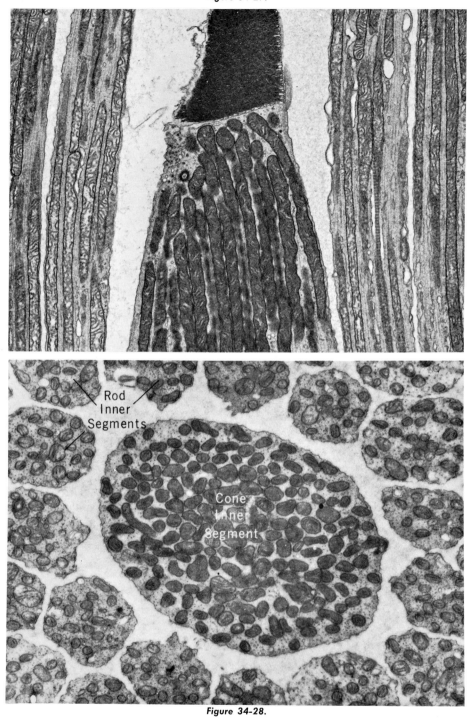

Figure 34-28.

Figure 34-27. Vertical section of the inner segments of a cone and several neighboring rods in the human retina, illustrating the larger size of the cone and the high concentration of longitudinally oriented mitochondria. (Courtesy of T. Kuwabara.)

Figure 34-28. Horizontal section through the inner segments of the photoreceptor elements in rat retina. Notice the larger size of the cone and the great number of mitochondria. (After Marchesi, Sears, and Barrnett, Invest. Ophthalmol., *3*:1, 1964.)

The *cis-trans* isomerization of retinene triggers a mechanism with extraordinary sensitivity by which a response can be produced in man by the absorption of as few as 5 quanta of the wavelength of maximum sensitivity, 5100 Å (Hecht and collaborators). Each of these quanta must be absorbed by separate rod cells in a small circumscribed area of the retina. It would thus appear that a slight, but crucial, shape change in as few as five molecules, each in a different receptor cell, is sufficient to generate a perceived visual sensation.

III. Stripped of many important details, the complex story of the interneuronic relationships in the retina is as follows. In the photosensitive rods and cones, light initiates a nervous process which in turn produces nervous impulses to be forwarded along the nervous pathways to the brain. Subjectively, this is interpreted as light, colors, shapes, sizes, position, and movement of the objects seen. The *synaptic mechanism* of the retina is composed of the following systems of neurons (Fig. 34-31): the rod cells (*a*) transmit impulses to two or three varieties of bipolars (*d, e-f*) and through these to all varieties of the ganglion cells (*m, n, o, p,* and *s*). The cones (*b*), on the other hand, discharge impulses to three or four bipolar varieties (*d, e-f,* and *h*), and through these to all varieties of ganglion cells (*m, n, o, p,* and *s*); the cones also stimulate the horizontal cells (*c*) and thus may influence distant rods (*a*) and cones (*b*).

The rods, it is believed, are responsive to weak light stimuli, thus being adapted for seeing in dim light. They do not respond selectively to lights of different wavelengths associated with the sensation of colors. Conversely, color sensations are initiated through the stimulation of cones, which are less responsive to weak "colorless" light. This makes the cones especially suitable for vision in bright light. At the third neuronal level, in the ganglion cells (*m, n, o, p,* and *s*), since all three bipolar varieties (*d, e-f,* and *h*) are synaptically connected with each of the several ganglion varieties, the rod and cone impulses apparently merge with one another. The fate of the impulses in the brain is unknown.

The synaptic relations suggest that the cones react in a more territorially restricted way than do the rods. In and near the central fovea, each cone is linked to one h-bipolar, which in turn is related to a single s-ganglion cell. This implies that the visual system here is made up of a great number of anatomical and

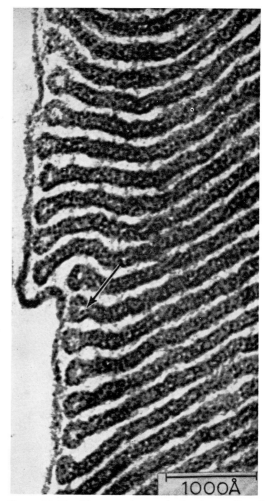

Figure 34-29. Electron micrograph showing profiles of the double membrane unit disks of the outer segment of a rod cell from frog retina. They exhibit a compact granular fine structure (see at arrow) when prepared with very low temperature and osmium fixation (osmium-cryofixation), low-temperature dehydration and embedding. (Courtesy of H. Fernández-Morán.)

functional units, each of which responds independently to a minute photic stimulus. This may be the structural basis for visual space perception or visual acuity.

The rods, being connected in groups to bipolars, always respond in groups, no matter how restricted the photic stimulus may be. Thus the smallest receptive rod territory is larger than the cone territory of the same region. Such grouplike connections might well result in reinforcement of the intensity of excitation generated in the rods.

In the central area the size of the recep-

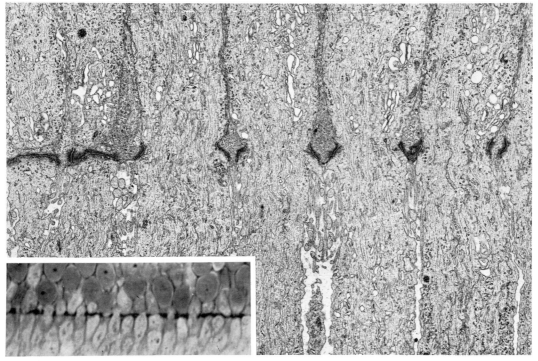

Figure 34-30. Electron micrograph of the region of the "outer limiting membrane" of the retina, showing that it is not a membrane as it appears to be with the light microscope (see inset) but is a row of junctional complexes between the rods and cones and the surrounding Müller cells. (Courtesy of T. Kuwabara.)

tor-conductor units corresponds roughly with that of the individual cones. This agrees with the difference in visual acuity in different localities of the retina, the acuity being at its peak in the very center of the field of view (corresponding with the foveal center) and at first rapidly, then more slowly, decreasing toward the periphery of the field of view.

In the primate retina at least 15 distinct varieties of neurons are present; these form at least 38 kinds of synapses with one another. In the retina, in addition to photoreception, many other processes usually associated with the central nervous system, such as selection, facilitation, inhibition, and summation of excitations, take place. The retina is thus essentially a *receptor-integrator* organ. (For further details see Polyak, *The Retina* and *The Vertebrate Visual System,* and the symposium on *Visual Mechanisms* edited by Klüver.)

BLOOD VESSELS OF THE EYE

These arise from the ophthalmic artery and can be subdivided into two groups, which are almost completely independent and anastomose with each other only in the region of the entrance of the optic nerve. The first group, the *retinal system,* represented by the central artery and vein, supplies a part of the optic nerve and the retina. The second, the *ciliary system,* is destined mainly for the uveal tunic.

LYMPH SPACES OF THE EYE

True lymph capillaries and lymph vessels are present only in the scleral conjunctiva. In the eyeball they are absent.

A mass injected into the space between the choroid and sclera penetrates along the walls of the vortex veins into the *space of Tenon.* The latter continues as the *supravaginal space* along the outer surface of the dural sheath of the optic nerve to the optic foramen. Again, it is possible to inject Tenon's space from the subarachnoid space of the brain. From the *anterior chamber* the injected liquid passes into the *posterior chamber* and also into Schlemm's canal. All these spaces cannot, however, be regarded as belonging to the lymphatic system.

The space of Tenon is more like a joint cavity and facilitates the movements of the eyeball.

The *aqueous humor* is believed to originate through secretion or transudation from the ciliary processes. It is a clear, watery fluid of slightly alkaline reaction, with an index of refraction of 1.33. It contains 0.77 per cent sodium chloride, traces of urea and glucose, practically no proteins, and few or no wandering cells. It is much like the cerebrospinal fluid. From the posterior chamber it permeates the vitreous. It also penetrates between the lens and the iris and through the pupil into the anterior chamber. The drainage of the aqueous humor from the anterior chamber is effected through the canal of Schlemm. The normal intraocular pressure (28 mm. of mercury), which maintains the spherical form of the eyeball, is the resultant of the rates of transudation and of drainage of the aqueous humor. In glaucoma the intraocular pressure may increase considerably.

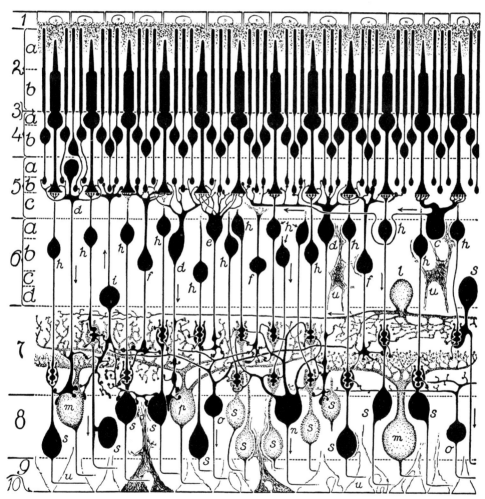

Figure 34-31.   Diagram representing the structures of the primate retina, based on numerous Golgi-stained preparations of man, chimpanzee, and macaque. Designations of layers and zones on the left side are as in Figure 34-21. In the upper part, the slender structures are the rod cells (*a*), the thicker ones the cone cells (*b*); *c*, horizontal cell; *d, e, f* and *h*, centripetal bipolar cells; *i*, centripetal bipolar cells; *l*, inner horizontal or association cell; *m, n, o, p* and *s*, ganglion cells; *u*, parts of the radial fibers of Müller, with their nuclei in 6, and their lower or inner ends forming the inner limiting membrane (10). Note the various synaptic relations between different neurons, reciprocal overlapping of expansions or its absence, the probable direction of the nervous impulses indicated by arrows, and other details. The indicated termination of the *l* axon is not completely proved. The rods and the cones are not designated by letters *a* and *b* as in Figure 34-25. (After Polyak.)

NERVES OF THE EYE

These are the optic nerve, supplying the retina, and the ciliary nerves, supplying the eyeball with motor, sensory, and sympathetic fibers.

The *optic nerve,* an evagination of the prosencephalon, the optic vesicle, is not a peripheral nerve like the other cranial nerves, but is a tract of the central nervous system. It consists of about 1200 bundles of myelinated fibers without neurolemma. The nerve fibers are kept together by the same kind of neuroglia as in the white substance of the central nervous system. On the surface of each bundle the glia form a thin membrane between the nervous elements and the connective tissue. A similar layer is also found at the periphery of the optic nerve.

The meninges and the intermeningeal spaces of the brain continue into the optic nerve. The outer sheath of the nerve is formed by the dura, which continues toward the eyeball and fuses with the sclera. The pia mater forms a connective tissue layer which is closely adherent to the surface of the nerve and fuses with the sclera at the entrance of the optic nerve. This pial layer sends connective tissue partitions and blood vessels into the nerve. Inflammatory processes can extend from the eyeball toward the meningeal spaces of the brain through the spaces between the sheaths.

The optic nerve leaves the posterior pole of the eyeball in a slightly oblique direction and continues into the entrance canal of the optic nerve. Just after leaving the eye through the openings in the lamina cribrosa, the fibers acquire their myelin sheaths. The central artery and the central vein reach the eyeball through the optic nerve; they penetrate the nerve on the lower side at a distance from the eyeball varying from 5 to 20 mm., usually 6 to 8 mm.

ACCESSORY ORGANS OF THE EYE

In an early stage of embryonic development the anterior segment of the eyeball projects freely on the surface. Later a circular fold of integument encircles the cornea. From its upper and lower parts the upper and lower lids grow toward each other over the surface of the cornea. In this way the conjunctival sac is formed, which protects and moistens the free surface of the eye and especially the cornea. The part lining the inner surface of the lids is the *palpebral conjunctiva,* and that covering the eyeball is the *bulbar conjunctiva.* The reflection of the palpebral onto the bulbar conjunctiva

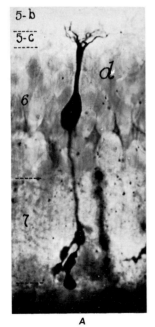 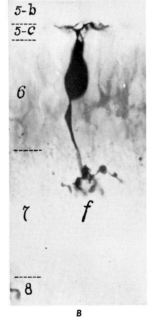 

Figure 34-32. Photomicrographs of centripetal bipolar cells of retina of rhesus monkey; *A,* Variety *d; B,* variety *f; C,* variety *h.* Method of Golgi. Designation of layers as in Figure 34-21. (Courtesy of S. Polyak.)

Figure 34-33. Diagram of the fovea. The layers are represented alternately in black and white in the right and left halves. The line dividing them is in the foveal center. Asterisks indicate the margins of the central or inner fovea (region I of the retina). The outer fovea is indicated by arrows. *Ch,* Choroid membrane. Designation of layers as in Figure 34-21. (Slightly modified from Polyak.)

forms deep recesses between the lids and the eyeball, the *superior* and the *inferior fornices.*

EYELIDS. The outermost layer is the skin. It is thin and provided with a few papillae and many small hairs with sebaceous and small sweat glands. The dermis contains a varying number of pigment cells with yellow or brown granules. The loose subcutaneous layer is rich in fine elastic fibers, and in Caucasians is almost completely devoid of fat. Toward the edge of the lid the dermis becomes denser and has higher papillae.

The *eyelashes* are large hairs obliquely inserted in three or four rows along the edge of the lid. With their follicles they penetrate deeply into the tissue. The sebaceous glands connected with the eyelashes are small and arrector muscles are missing. The eyelashes are replaced every 100 to 150 days.

Between and behind the follicles of the eyelashes are peculiar sweat glands, the *glands of Moll* (Fig. 34-35). Unlike ordinary sweat glands, the terminal portion here is generally straight or only slightly coiled. The ducts open, as a rule, into the follicles of the eyelashes. The epithelium of the terminal portions consists of an indistinct, outer myoepithelial layer and an inner layer of pyramidal, apocrine glandular elements. The lumen is often considerably dilated, and the glandular cells are flattened. In the ducts the epithelium consists of two distinct cell layers. The nature of the secretion of these glands is not known.

The next layer inward consists of the thin, pale, striated fibers of the palpebral portion of the *ring muscle of the eye* (orbicularis oculi). The part behind the follicles of the eyelashes or behind the ducts of the meibomian glands is the *ciliary muscle of Riolan.*

Deep to the orbicular muscle is a layer of connective tissue, the palpebral fascia, a continuation of the tendon of the palpebral levator (levator palpebri) muscle. In the upper part of the upper lid, strands of smooth muscle, the *superior tarsal muscle of Müller,* are attached to the edge of the *tarsus,* a plate of dense connective tissue that forms the skeleton of the lid. In the upper lid its breadth is about 10 mm., in the lower only 5 mm. The *glands of Meibom* are embedded in its substance (Fig. 34-35). They are elongated and arranged in one layer, parallel to one another and perpendicular to the length of the tarsal plate. Their openings form a single row immediately in front of the inner free edge of the lid, at the line of transition from the skin into the conjunctiva.

The meibomian glands are sebaceous but have lobated alveolar terminal portions. They are connected by short lateral ducts with a long central excretory duct lined with stratified squamous epithelium.

The innermost layer of the lid is the *conjunctiva.* At the inner edge of the margin of the lid the epidermis continues into the inner surface of the lid. Here the superficial cells become thicker, the number of layers decreases, mucous cells appear, and the epithelium as-

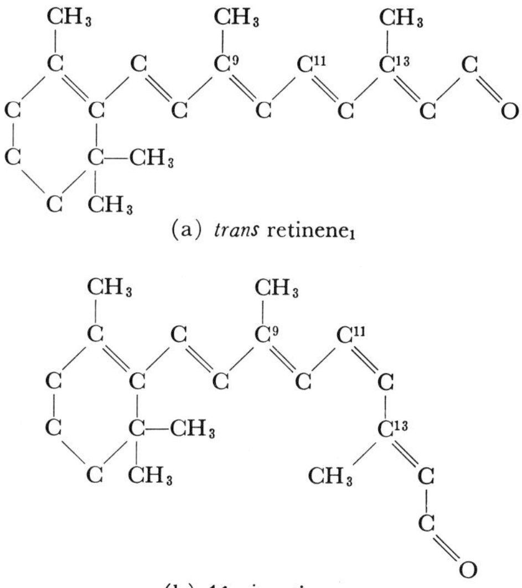

(a) *trans* retinene$_1$

(b) 11-*cis* retinene$_1$

Figure 34-34. Rhodopsin consists of 11-*cis* retinene, conjugated to a specific protein (rod opsin) through a Schiff-base linkage between the terminal aldehyde group of retinene and an amino group of the opsin. The primary photochemical step following the absorption of a light quantum by a rhodopsin molecule is the isomeric transition of the 11-*cis* retinene to the all *trans* form.

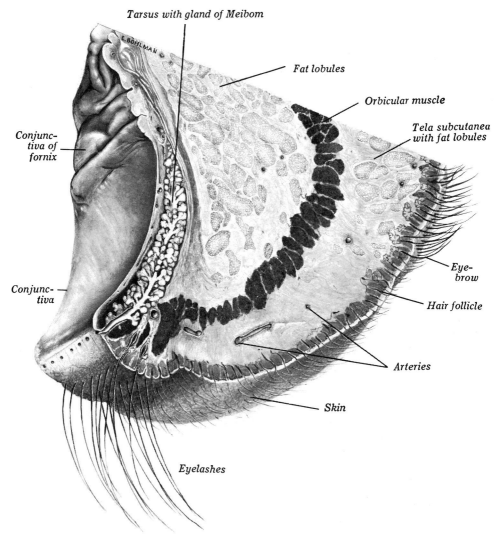

Tarsus with gland of Meibom

Fat lobules

Orbicular muscle

Tela subcutanea with fat lobules

Conjunctiva of fornix

Eyebrow

Conjunctiva

Hair follicle

Arteries

Skin

Eyelashes

Figure 34-35. Camera lucida drawing of a slice of the upper eyelid of a newborn infant. Stained with hematoxylin. × 12.

sumes a stratified columnar character, which is typical of the whole conjunctiva and varies only in thickness in different places. The superficial cells have a short prismatic form. Goblet cells are scattered between them.

At the upper edge of the tarsus the epithelium is sometimes reduced to two cell layers, and its surface presents many irregular invaginations. Some of them are lined with mucous cells and described as glands. In the conjunctiva of the fornix the epithelium is thicker.

The lamina propria of the conjunctiva is dense connective tissue. In the region of the fornix it is very loosely attached to the intra-

orbital fat tissue, permitting the free motion of the eyeball in the conjunctival sac.

In the region of the corneal limbus the epithelium of the conjunctiva assumes a stratified squamous character and continues as such onto the surface of the cornea. It may still contain a few scattered mucous cells.

The rudimentary *third eyelid,* or *semilunar fold* (the homologue of the nictitating membrane of the lower vertebrates), is formed by the scleral conjunctiva at the inner palpebral commissure, lateral to the lacrimal caruncle. It consists of connective tissue that contains smooth muscle fibers and is covered with conjunctival epithelium, which, on the outer surface, contains many mucous cells.

LACRIMAL GLAND. In connection with the conjunctival space there is a system of glands whose secretion moistens, lubricates, and flushes the surface of the eyeball and of the lids. Of these glands, only the lacrimal gland reaches a high degree of development. It has the size and shape of an almond and is lodged beneath the conjunctiva at the lateral upper side of the eyeball. It consists of a group of separate glandular bodies and sends out 6 to 12 excretory ducts, which open along the upper and lateral surfaces of the superior conjunctival fornix.

The lacrimal gland is of the tubuloalveolar type. Its terminal portions are provided with a relatively large lumen and with irregular, saccular outpocketings. The basement lamina is lined with glandular cells resembling those of the serous salivary type. They have, however, a narrower columnar shape and contain, besides small fat droplets, large, pale secretion granules whose number changes according to the functional conditions.

These cells are provided with secretory capillaries. Between their bases and the basement lamina are well developed basket (myoepithelial) cells. The smallest intralobular ducts are lined with a layer of low columnar or cuboidal cells and have a few myoepithelial cells. The larger intralobular ducts have a two layered epithelium.

On the inner surface of the lids, especially the upper one, near the upper edge of the tarsus, there are a varying number of small accessory lacrimal glands—the *tarsal lacrimal glands*.

After having washed the conjunctival cavity, the secretion of the lacrimal gland (the tears, a sterile liquid) reaches the region of the inner palpebral commissure (internal canthus). Here the two eyelids are separated by a triangular space, the *lacrimal lake*, in which the secretion accumulates temporarily. From here it passes through two tiny orifices called *lacrimal points*, one on the margin of each eyelid, into the *lacrimal ducts*. The latter converge medially into the lacrimal sac, whence the *nasolacrimal duct* leads into the inferior meatus of the nose.

The wall of the excretory lacrimal passages is formed by connective tissue lined with epithelium. The epithelium of the lacrimal ducts is stratified squamous. The lacrimal sac and the nasolacrimal duct are lined with a pseudostratified, tall columnar epithelium.

From the bottom of the lacrimal lake, between the two lacrimal ducts, there bulges a small, soft mass of tissue, the *lacrimal caruncle*. The top is covered with a thick, squamous epithelium in which only the uppermost layers are flattened, although not cornified. It con-

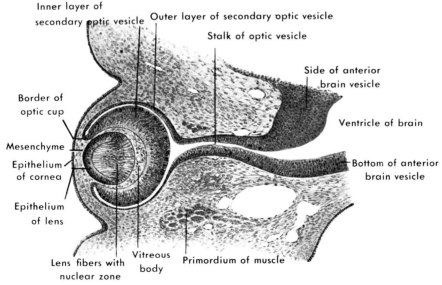

Figure 34-36. Primordium of eye of an 8 mm. mouse embryo. The cavity of the primary optic vesicle is reduced to a thin cleft. × 70. (After Schaffer.)

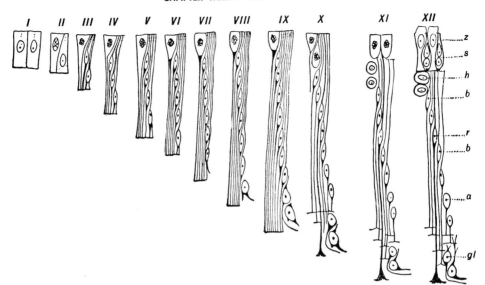

Figure 34-37. Diagram of the histogenesis of the retina. *I,* Simple regular columnar epithelium; *II,* pseudostratified epithelium with two and, *III,* with three rows of nuclei; the number of nuclear rows increases in *IV* to *VII; VII,* the lowermost cell has developed an axon; *VIII,* the first (lower) ganglion cell has separated from the inner surface, the ganglion cells and the amacrines having also severed their connections with the outer surface; *XI,* all cells except the indifferent stem cells, the visual cells, and the radial fibers are separated from the outer surface, the horizontal cells also being free. In *XII,* the rod cells (*s*) form a double layer between the cone cells (*z*); the cones have protoplasmic outgrowths; *a,* amacrines; *b,* bipolars, *gl,* ganglion cells; *h,* horizontal cells; *r,* radial fibers. (After Fürst, from Franz.)

tains mucous cells, and gradually merges into the conjunctival epithelium. The lamina propria contains bundles of striated muscles, sweat glands, abortive lacrimal glands, and tiny hairs with sebaceous glands. These are the source of the whitish secretion that often collects in the region of the inner palpebral commissure.

BLOOD AND LYMPH VESSELS OF THE EYE-LIDS. The arteries in each lid form two arch-like anastomoses, which run in front of the tarsus, one near the free margin of the lid, the other near the other margin of the tarsus. The palpebral conjunctiva is provided with dense, subepithelial capillary networks which can be easily studied in living condition with the aid of the slit-lamp microscope. Branches of the blood vessels in the scleral conjunctiva anastomose with the marginal blood vessels of the cornea and with the branches of the anterior ciliary arteries.

The lymphatics form a dense plexus in the conjunctiva behind the tarsus. In front of the latter there is another, thinner, pretarsal net. A third net can be distinguished in the skin and the subcutis. All these networks communicate with one another. The lymphatic capillaries of the scleral conjunctiva end blindly near the corneal margin.

The abundant supply of the conjunctiva with blood and lymph capillaries accounts for the rapid absorption of solutions introduced into the conjunctival sac.

HISTOGENESIS OF THE EYE

The stalk of the optic vesicle growing out of the brain is transformed into the optic nerve. The double walled vesicle formed gives rise to the retina (Fig. 34-36). Where the optic vesicle touches the ectoderm, the latter forms an invagination with a greatly thickened bottom, the *primordium of the lens.* It apparently develops as the result of inductive stimulation of the ectoderm by the optic vesicle. In amphibian larvae, after excision of the optic vesicle, the lens is not formed. The lens primordium comes to lie in the invagination of the optic vesicle. Simultaneously, mesenchyme and blood vessels grow into the choroidal fissure, in the lower part of the optic vesicle. These vessels give rise to the hyaloid and retinal vascular systems. The opposite margins of the fissure, which received the vessels, soon grow together, and the secondary optic vesicle assumes the form of a double walled cup, while the stalk is transformed into a solid strand, the optic nerve.

The lens primordium soon becomes detached from the ectoderm, and the space between the two is filled by a layer of mesenchyme—the primordium of the substantia propria of the cornea and of the connective tissue of the iris. The lens, surrounded by vascular mesenchyme, acquires a solid, spherical form, while the original cavity disappears. The inner, thicker sheet of the double wall of the optic cup differentiates into the *retina proper*. It remains permanently in direct continuation with the optic nerve. The outer sheet of the cup is transformed into the pigment epithelium. The surrounding mesenchyme comes into close relation with the optic cup and gives rise to the two outer tunics of the eyeball, the *uveal* and *fibrous* tunics. The structural differentiation of the retina proceeds in a way similar to that of the wall of the neural tube. It is characterized by proliferation, by shifting of the cells, and by the establishment of complex synaptic relationships. The eyeball attains full size toward the end of the first decade. The structure of the retina, including the central fovea, matures toward the end of the first year.

REFERENCES

Arey, L. B.: Retina, choroid and sclera. *In* Cowdry, E. V., ed.: Special Cytology. New York, Paul B. Hoeber, Inc., 1932, Vol. III, p. 1213.

Berliner, M. L.: Biomicroscopy of the Eye. New York, Paul B. Hoeber, Inc., 1949.

De Robertis, E.: Electron microscope observations on the submicroscopic organization of the retinal rods. J. Biophys. & Biochem. Cytol., *2*:319, 1956.

De Robertis, E., and C. M. Franchi: Electron microscope observations on synaptic vesicles in synapses of the retinal rods and cones. J. Biophys. & Biochem. Cytol., *2*:307, 1956.

Dowling, J. E.: Foveal receptors of the monkey retina: Fine structure. Science, *147*:57, 1965.

Duke-Elder, W. S.: The development, form, and function of the visual apparatus. *In* Textbook of Ophthalmology. London, H. Kimpton, 1932, Vol. I.

Fernández-Morán, H.: The fine structure of vertebrate and invertebrate photoreceptors as revealed by low-temperature electron microscopy. *In* Smelzer, H., ed.: The Structure of the Eye. New York, Academic Press, 1961, p. 521.

Fernández-Morán, H.: Lamellar systems in myelin and photoreceptors as revealed by high-resolution electron microscopy. *In* Edds, M. V., Jr., ed.: Macromolecular Complexes. New York, Ronald Press, 1961, p. 113.

Friedenwald, J. S.: The formation of the intraocular fluid. Am. J. Ophth., *32*:9, 1949.

Granit, R.: Receptors and Sensory Perception; A Discussion of Aims, Means, and Results of Electrophysiological Research into the Process of Reception. New Haven, Yale University Press, 1955.

Hartline, H. K.: Receptor mechanisms and the integration of sensory information in the eye. *In* Oncley, J. L., et al., eds.: Biophysical Science—A Study Program. New York, John Wiley & Sons, 1959, p. 515.

Hecht, S.: Rods, cones, and the chemical basis of vision. Physiol. Rev., *17*:239, 1937.

Hecht, S., S. Shlaer, and M. H. Pirenne: Energy, quanta, and vision. J. Gen. Physiol., *25*:819, 1942.

Hubbard, R., and A. Kropf: The action of light on rhodopsin. Proc. Nat. Acad. Sci., *44*:130, 1958.

Hubbard, R., and A. Kropf: Molecular aspects of visual excitation. Ann. N. Y. Acad. Sci., *81*:388, 1959.

Ishikawa, T.: Fine structure of the human ciliary muscle. Inves. Ophth., *1*:587, 1962.

Jakus, M. A.: Studies on the cornea. II. The fine structure of Descemet's membrane. J. Biophys. & Biochem. Cytol. (Suppl.), *2*:243, 1956.

Klüver, H., ed.: Visual Mechanisms. Biological Symposia, Vol. 7. Lancaster, Pa., Jaques Cattell Press, 1942.

Kolmer, W., and H. Lauber: Auge. *In* von Möllendorff, W., and W. Bargmann, eds.: Handbuch der mikroskopischen Anatomie des Menschen. Berlin, Julius Springer, 1936, Vol. 3, part 2.

Krause, A. C., and J. A. Sibley: Metabolism of the retina. Arch. Ophth., *36*:328, 1946.

Mann, I. C.: The Development of the Human Eye. New York, Macmillan Co., 1937.

Miller, W. H.: Visual photoreceptor structures. *In* Brachet, J., and A. E. Mirsky, eds.: The Cell; Biochemistry, Physiology, Morphology. New York, Academic Press, 1960, Vol. 4, p. 325.

Polyak, S.: The Retina. Chicago, University of Chicago Press, 1941.

Polyak, S.: The Vertebrate Visual System. Chicago, University of Chicago Press, 1957.

Richardson, K. C.: The fine structure of the albino rabbit iris with special reference to the identification of adrenergic and cholinergic nerves and nerve endings in its intrinsic muscles. Am. J. Anat., *114*:173, 1964.

Rushton, W. A. H.: Visual pigments in man and animals and their relation to seeing. *In* Butler, J. A. V., and B. Katz, eds.: Progress in Biophysics and Biophysical Chemistry. London, Pergamon Press, 1959, Vol. 9, p. 239.

Salzmann, M.: The Anatomy and Histology of the Human Eyeball in the Normal State (translated by E. V. L. Brown). Chicago, University of Chicago Press, 1912.

Sheldon, H., and H. Zetterqvist: An electron microscope study of the corneal epithelium in the vitamin A deficient mouse. Bull. Johns Hopkins Hosp., *98*:372, 1956.

Sidman, R. L. and G. B. Wislocki: Histochemical observations on rods and cones in retinas of vertebrates. J. Histochem., *2*:413, 1954.

Sjöstrand, F. S.: An electron microscope study of the retinal rods of the guinea pig eye. J. Cell. & Comp. Physiol., *33*:383, 1949.

Sjöstrand, F. S.: The ultrastructure of the outer segments of rods and cones of the eye as revealed by the electron microscope. J. Cell. & Comp. Physiol., *43*:15, 1953.

Smelzer, G. K., ed.: The Structure of the Eye (A Symposium). New York, Academic Press, 1961.

Tokuyasu, K., and E. Yamada: The fine structure of the retina studied with the electron microscope. J. Biophys. & Biochem. Cytol., *6*:225, 1959.

Tormey, J. McD.: Fine structure of the ciliary epithelium of the rabbit with particular reference to "infolded membranes," "vesicles" and the effects of Diamox. J. Cell. Biol., *17*:641, 1963.

Wald, G.: The photoreceptor process in vision. Am. J. Ophth., *40*:18, 1955.

Wald, G.: The molecular organization of visual systems. *In* McElroy, W. D., and B. Glass, eds.: Light and Life. Baltimore, The Johns Hopkins Press, 1960, p. 724.

Walls, G. L.: The Vertebrate Eye and Its Adaptive Radiation. Bloomfield Hills, Mich., Cranbrook Press, 1943.

Wanko, T., and M. A. Gavin: Electron microscopic study of lens fibers. J. Biophys. & Biochem. Cytol., *6*:97, 1959.

Wislocki, G. B., and A. J. Ladman: The demonstration of a blood-ocular barrier in the albino rat by means of the intravitam deposition of silver. J. Biophys. & Biochem. Cytol., *1*:501, 1955.

Wolken, J. J., J. Capenos, and A. Turano: Photoreceptor structures; *Drosophila melanogaster*. J. Biophys. & Biochem. Cytol., *3*:441, 1957.

CHAPTER THIRTY-FIVE

The Ear

The organ of hearing is divisible into three parts, each of which differs from the others not only in its gross anatomy but also in its histology and in the functions that it subserves in the translation of sound waves into meaningful information that can be processed in the central nervous system. The first part, the *external ear,* receives the sound waves. In the second part, the *middle ear,* the waves are transformed into the mechanical vibrations of bony *auditory ossicles.* These, in turn, by impinging upon the fluid-filled spaces of the third part, the *internal ear* (or labyrinth), generate specific nerve impulses that are conveyed by the acoustic nerve to the central nervous system. In addition to organs for analysis of sound, the internal ear contains vestibular organs, which are concerned chiefly with the function of maintaining equilibrium.

EXTERNAL EAR

The external ear includes the auricle and the external auditory meatus (Fig. 35-1).

AURICLE. The auricle consists of a single, highly irregular plate of elastic cartilage, 0.5 to 1 mm. thick, overlain by a flexible perichondrium containing abundant elastic fibers. The covering skin has a distinct subcutaneous layer only on the posterior surface of the auricle and is provided with a few small hairs and associated sebaceous glands, the latter sometimes being of considerable size. In old age, especially in men, large stiff hairs develop on the dorsal edge of the auricle and on the ear lobe. Sweat glands are scarce, and, when present, are small.

EXTERNAL AUDITORY MEATUS. The outer portion of the external auditory meatus is a medial continuation of the auricular cartilage, and the inner portion is a canal in the temporal bone (Fig. 35-1). It forms an S-shaped curve coursing medially and inferiorly and is bounded at its medial end by the tympanic membrane. The skin lining the meatus is thin and devoid of papillae, and is firmly attached to the underlying perichondrium and periosteum. Numerous hairs in the lining of the cartilaginous portion of the meatus tend to prevent entrance of foreign bodies. In old age these hairs enlarge considerably, as do those on the auricle. Sebaceous glands connected with the hair follicles are exceptionally large. In the bony portion of the meatus, small hairs and sebaceous glands are found only along the upper wall. No eccrine sweat glands are present in the meatus.

The external meatus contains *cerumen,* a brown, waxy secretion that protects the skin from desiccation and presumably from invasion by insects. It is a mixture of the secretion of the sebaceous and *ceruminous glands* of the skin of the meatus. Ceruminous glands are a special variety of coiled tubular apocrine sweat gland. In cross section, they appear to be aggregated into discrete lobules invested by connective tissue. Each glandular tubule is surrounded by a thin network of myoepithelial cells. In the resting state the gland lumen is large and the epithelial cells lining it are cuboidal. In the active state, however, the cells are columnar and the lumen is constricted. Ducts of ceruminous glands open either onto the free surface of the skin or, with the sebaceous glands, into the necks of hair follicles.

MIDDLE EAR

The middle ear comprises the *tympanic cavity* and its contents (the *auditory ossicles*), the *auditory* or *eustachian tube,* and the *tympanic membrane,* which closes the tympanic cavity externally.

Tympanic Cavity

The tympanic cavity is an irregular, air-filled space in the temporal bone. Its lateral wall is formed largely by the tympanic membrane and its medial wall by the lateral aspect of the bony wall of the internal ear (Fig. 35-2). Anteriorly it continues into the *auditory tube* and posteriorly it is connected, through the tympanic antrum, with air-filled cavities, or "cells," in the mastoid process of the temporal bone. The cavity contains the *auditory ossicles,* the tendons of two small muscles (the *tensor tympani* and the *stapedius*), connected with the ossicles, the *chorda tympani nerve,* and connective tissue (Fig. 35-2).

The epithelium lining the tympanic cavity is generally of the simple squamous type, but near the opening of the auditory tube and near the edge of the tympanic membrane it is cuboidal or columnar and provided with cilia. The presence of glands is generally denied, although detailed study of the mucous membrane here has not been undertaken.

AUDITORY OSSICLES. Three small bones —the *malleus,* the *incus,* and the *stapes*—extend from the attachment of the malleus to the tympanic membrane on the one hand to the medial wall of the tympanic cavity on the other, where the footplate of the stapes fits into the *fenestra vestibuli* or oval window, a hiatus in the wall of the osseous labyrinth (Figs. 35-1 and 35-2). The footplate is maintained in the fenestra by means of an annular fibrous liga-

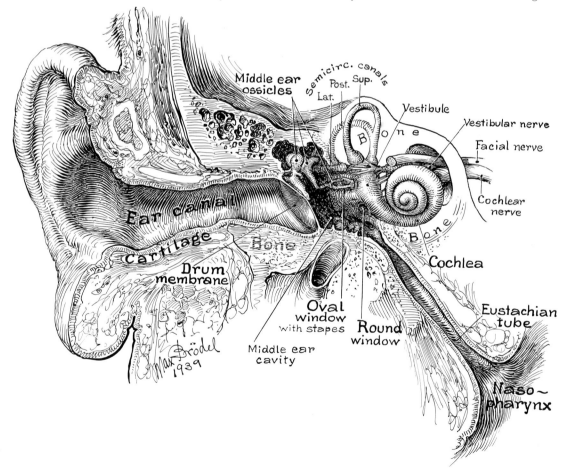

Figure 35-1. Schematic representation of the anatomic relations of the various parts of the human ear. (After M. Brödel, from Three Unpublished Drawings of the Anatomy of the Human Ear. W. B. Saunders Co.)

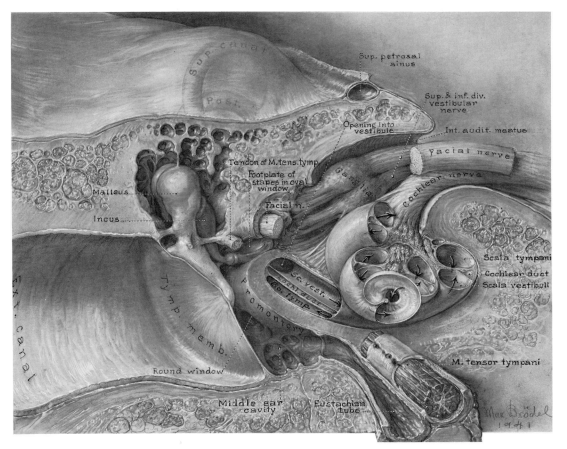

Figure 35-2. Drawing of some of the anatomical features of the external, middle, and inner ear. (After M. Brödel, from Three Unpublished Drawings of the Anatomy of the Human Ear. W. B. Saunders Co.)

ment. The three bones are connected to one another by means of typical diarthrodial joints and are supported in the cavity by minute connective tissue ligaments. Small patches of hyaline cartilage are usually found on the manubrium of the malleus and the footplate of the stapes. The mucous membrane lining the tympanic cavity is reflected over the ossicles and is firmly attached to their periosteum.

Tympanic Membrane

This oval, semitransparent membrane is shaped like a very flat cone with its apex directed medially (Figs. 35-1 to 35-3). Its conical form is maintained by the insertion, onto its inner surface, of the manubrium of the malleus, which tends to pull the center of the membrane medially. The tympanic membrane is formed of two layers of collagenous

fibers and fibroblasts similar to those of a flat tendon (Fig. 35-3). However, there is a flaccid portion in its anterosuperior quadrant (Shrapnell's membrane) that is devoid of collagenous fibers. In the outer layer of the membrane the collagen fibers have a radial arrangement, while those in the inner layer are disposed circularly. There are also thin networks of elastic fibers, located mainly in the central and peripheral parts of the membrane. Externally the membrane is covered by a thin (50 to 60 μ) layer of skin devoid of hairs and other appendages. Its inner surface is lined by the mucous membrane of the tympanic cavity, here only 20 to 40 μ thick and consisting of simple squamous epithelium overlying a lamina propria of sparse collagenous fibers and capillaries. Over the manubrium of the malleus is a layer of connective tissue through which vessels and nerves reach the center of the membrane.

Auditory Tube

From its origin in the anterior wall of the tympanic cavity the auditory tube extends posteromedially for about 4 cm. to an opening on the posterolateral wall of the nasopharynx. The rostral two thirds of the tube is supported medially by cartilage, and the portion toward the tympanic cavity is supported by bone.

The cartilage supporting the auditory tube is mainly medial to the lumen, but a ridge of cartilage running longitudinally for most of the length of the tube curves superolaterally, so that in cross section the cartilage has the appearance of a shepherd's crook (Fig. 35-4). The cartilage is elastic throughout most of its length, but at the isthmus it loses its elastic fibers and becomes hyaline. The lumen of the tube, flattened in the vertical plane, is largest at its pharyngeal end, decreases to a mere slit at the junction of the cartilaginous and bony portions (isthmus), and then expands again in its course through the temporal bone. The tube is lined by a mucous membrane, of variable thickness, thrown into folds (rugae) at both the pharyngeal and tympanic ends. In the bony portion of the auditory tube, the mucous membrane is relatively thin and is composed of low columnar ciliated epithelium resting upon a thin lamina propria firmly bound to the periosteum. The epithelium in the cartilaginous portion of the tube is pseudostratified and composed of tall columnar cells, many of which are ciliated. The underlying lamina propria is much more complex here than in the bony portion. Toward the pharyngeal orifice, it contains many compound tubuloalveolar glands that secrete mucus via ducts opening into the tubal lumen. In this vicinity, also, goblet cells are interspersed among the columnar epithelial cells.

There is considerable individual variation in number and distribution of ciliated cells and goblet cells, and in the degree of development of the glandular elements. Throughout the lamina propria, in both portions of the tube, a great many lymphocytes can be found, the number varying with age and from one individual to another. Often near the pharyngeal opening there are discrete collections of lymphoid tissue forming the tubal tonsils (of Gerlach). Opinions vary as to whether the lumen of the auditory tube is open at all times. It is known that during the act of swallowing

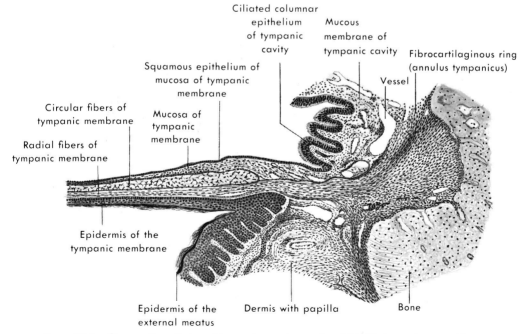

Figure 35-3. Cross section of edge of tympanic membrane of a child. (Redrawn from von Ebner.)

the lumen is opened for a short interval, allowing the pressure in the tympanic cavity to equalize with that outside.

INTERNAL EAR

The internal ear, called the labyrinth because of its complex structure, is composed of a series of fluid-filled sacs and tubules suspended in cavities of corresponding form in the petrous portion of the temporal bone (Fig. 35-5).

The canals and cavities in the bone comprise the bony or *osseous labyrinth*. Suspended within this system of cavities are the thin-walled, fluid-filled tubules and saccules of the *membranous labyrinth*, which constitute the *endolymphatic system*. This is surrounded by the cells and fluid of the *perilymphatic system*.

The Bony Labyrinth

There are two major cavities in the bony labyrinth: the *vestibule*, which houses the *saccule* and *utricle*, and anteromedial to it, the spirally coiled *cochlea*, which contains the *organ of Corti* (Figs. 35-1 and 35-2).

THE VESTIBULE. The vestibule is an irregularly ovoid cavity located medial to the tympanic cavity. Its wall facing the tympanic cavity is penetrated by the fenestra vestibuli, and certain recesses in its wall produce characteristic bony protrusions on the medial wall of the tympanic cavity in relationship to the fenestra. For a more detailed description, the student is referred to a textbook of gross anatomy. Three *semicircular canals* arise from recesses in the wall of the vestibule and return to it. According to their position they are named the superior, posterior, and lateral semicircular canals. Two of the recesses located anterosuperiorly accommodate the dilated *ampullae* of the superior and lateral *semicircular ducts* of the membranous labyrinth, and posteriorly a third recess houses the *posterior ampulla*. Given off from these recesses are the superior (or anterior), the lateral, and the posterior *semicircular canals*. The lateral canal curves laterally around the vestibule and rejoins it behind the posterior ampullary recess. The superior and posterior canals join each other superior to the vestibule in the recess for the *crus commune*, which opens into the medial part of the vestibule. From the medial wall of the vestibule a thin canal, the *vestibular*

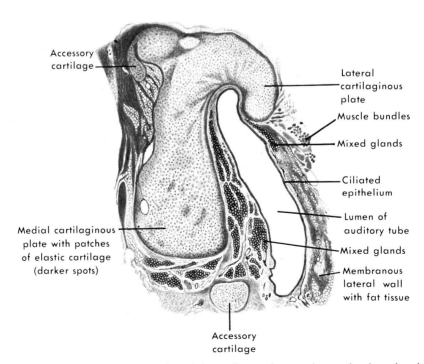

Accessory cartilage

Lateral cartilaginous plate

Muscle bundles

Mixed glands

Ciliated epithelium

Lumen of auditory tube

Mixed glands

Membranous lateral wall with fat tissue

Medial cartilaginous plate with patches of elastic cartilage (darker spots)

Accessory cartilage

Figure 35-4. Transection of cartilaginous portion of the auditory tube near its opening into the pharynx. × 11. (Redrawn from von Ebner.)

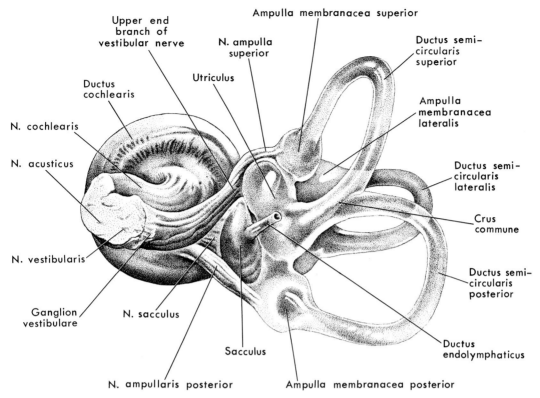

Upper end
branch of
vestibular nerve

Ampulla membranacea superior

N. ampulla
superior

Ductus semi-
circularis
superior

Utriculus

Ductus
cochlearis

Ampulla
membranacea
lateralis

N. cochlearis

N. acusticus

Ductus semi-
circularis
lateralis

Crus
commune

N. vestibularis

Ductus semi-
circularis
posterior

Ganglion
vestibulare

N. sacculus

Sacculus

Ductus
endolymphaticus

N. ampullaris posterior

Ampulla membranacea posterior

Figure 35-5. Right membranous labyrinth of an adult; medial and posterior aspects. About × 5. (Redrawn and modified from Spalteholz.)

aqueduct, extends to the posterior surface of the petrous portion of the temporal bone.

THE COCHLEA. The bony cochlea is anteromedial to the vestibule (Figs. 35-1, 35-2, and 35-5). It consists of a complex bony canal that makes two and three quarter spiral turns around an axis formed by the conical pillar of spongy bone called the *modiolus.* The base of the modiolus forms the deep end of the *internal acoustic meatus.* Blood vessels and nerve bundles of the cochlear division of the eighth cranial nerve pass through numerous openings into the bony substance of the modiolus. The nerve fibers reach the spiral ganglion, which courses within the modiolus along the inner wall of the cochlear canal. The cell bodies located in the *spiral ganglion* are bipolar afferent neurons (Fig. 35-11).

The lumen of the canal of the osseous cochlea (about 3 mm. in diameter) is divided along its whole course (about 35 mm. in man) into an upper and a lower section by the *spiral lamina.* The lamina is divided into two zones: an inner zone containing bone (the *osseous*

spiral lamina) and a fibrous outer zone (the *membranous spiral lamina*). The latter is also called the *basilar membrane* (Figs. 35-12, 35-14, and 35-15). At the attachment of the basilar membrane to the outer wall of the cochlea, the periosteum is thickened and forms a distinct structure that has been called the *spiral ligament,* although histologically it does not have the characteristics of a ligament (see Chapter 6). The cochlear canal is further subdivided by a thin membrane, the *vestibular membrane (Reissner's membrane),* which extends obliquely from the spiral lamina to the outer wall of the bony cochlea (Fig. 35-12). Thus, a cross section of the bony cochlea will show three compartments: an upper cavity, the *scala vestibuli;* a lower cavity, the *scala tympani;* and an intermediate cavity, the *scala media* (Fig. 35-12). The latter is the *cochlear duct,* a portion of the endolymphatic system that connects with the vestibular part of the membranous labyrinth by way of the small *ductus reuniens.*

The scala tympani and scala vestibuli are perilymphatic spaces. The scala vestibuli ex-

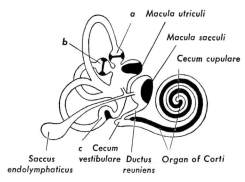

Figure 35-6. Diagram of membranous labyrinth with neuroepithelial areas in black. *a, b,* and *c,* respectively, designate the ampullae of the superior, lateral, and posterior semicircular canals. (Modified from von Ebner.)

tends into and through the perilymphatic cistern of the vestibule and reaches the inner surface of the *fenestra ovalis.* The scala tympani ends at the *fenestra rotundum.* At the apex of the cochlea the two scalae communicate through a small opening, the *helicotrema.*

The Membranous (or Endolymphatic) Labyrinth

The fluid-filled sacs of the membranous labyrinth arise embryologically from a single otic vesicle of ectodermal origin, and, although the semicircular ducts are derived from the utricle and the cochlear duct and the endolymphatic sac are derived from the saccule, all of these parts of the labyrinth are in communication and all are filled with *endolymph.*

UTRICLE, SACCULE, AND AMPULLAE. In the vestibule, the oblong utricle lies superior and then posterior to the roughly spherical saccule and communicates via five orifices with the three semicircular ducts and their ampullae (Fig. 35-5). The semicircular ducts are eccentrically placed in the bony canals and are lined by a simple squamous epithelium (Fig. 35-9). Each ampulla has a flattened floor and a hemispherical roof bulging on the concave side of the duct. Both the saccule and utricle give off ducts medially, which join and form the slender *endolymphatic duct* (Fig. 35-5), which in turn courses under the utricle and

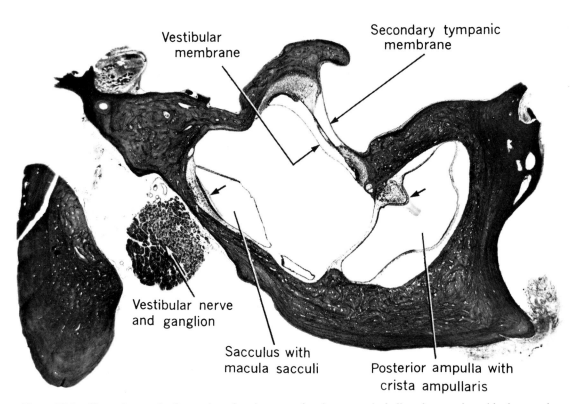

Figure 35-7. Photomicrograph of a section of a rhesus monkey inner ear, including the sacculus with the macula sacculi (at arrow) and the posterior ampulla with the crista ampullaris (at arrow). (Courtesy of H. Mizoguchi.)

then medially through the vestibular aqueduct to end on the posterior surface of the petrous portion of the temporal bone as a small dilation, the *endolymphatic sac*. The sac is located between layers of the meninges and is richly surrounded by blood vessels and connective tissue.

The epithelium lining the membranous structures in the vestibule is of simple squamous type similar to that found in the semicircular ducts except in the immediate vicinity of sensory areas. The sensory areas and cells just peripheral to them, however, are specialized and, in many respects, highly complex.

Crista Ampullaris and Maculae. The epithelium in the floor of the three ampullae is thrown into a transverse ridge, the *crista*, which is covered with the sensory epithelium and is bounded at either end by cells of the *planum semilunatum* (Figs. 35-7 and 35-8). The latter are perpendicular to the long axis of the crista.

Sensory epithelium on the cristae is histologically the same as that comprising the *maculae* of the utricle and saccule, with variation apparently only in the relative number of the different cell types. Classically, sensory epithelia in the vestibular portion of the internal ear are described as possessing two cell types, *hair cells* and *supporting cells*. Recent investigations have shown, however, that among the hair cells two morphological types can be distinguished.

Hair cells. Hair cells of type I are flask-shaped cells with a rounded base and constricted neck region (Fig. 35-10). The round nucleus is located basally and surrounded by a more or less dense population of mitochondria. Mitochondria also are found congregated at the apex of the cell immediately beneath the free surface, which bears specialized microvilli, or hairs, of considerable length, and a single cilium. From its constricted neck inferiorly the hair cell is enclosed in a chalice-like nerve terminal.

Hair cells of type II are simple columnar cells innervated by numerous small synaptic endings that are difficult to see with the light microscope (Fig. 35-10). Nuclei of type II hair cells can be found at various levels in the cell but usually form a row at a higher level in the epithelium than those of the type I hair cells and the supporting cells.

With the electron microscope the luminal border of both type I and type II hair cells is characterized by the presence of 40 to 80

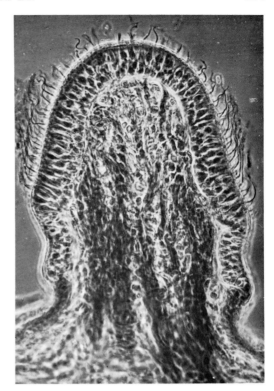

Figure 35-8. Phase contrast photomicrograph of an unstained section in plastic of guinea pig crista ampullaris, showing the hairs projecting from the hair cells of the neuroepithelium. (Courtesy of H. Engström.)

straight *hairs* (actually microvilli of unusual type) and a single modified *cilium*. The hairs have been described as *stereocilia* in the belief that they are nonmotile, whereas the cilium is considered to be a kinocilium, although the central pair of fibrils present in typical motile cilia are reported to be lacking. The hairs are arranged upon the cell surface in regular hexagonal array and in successive rows show a progressive increase of length from less than 1 μ on one side of the cell to 100 μ on the other side (Fig. 35-19). The longest hairs are on the side of the cell bearing the cilium. The hairs all have the same basic structure regardless of their length. They are noticeably constricted at the base and possess a core of longitudinally oriented fine filaments. These continue downward from the narrow base of the hair into a terminal web, which extends across the cell immediately below its specialized free border.

In both types of hair cells there are scattered profiles of granular endoplasmic reticulum, but smooth surfaced tubules and

Stapes

Semicircular
duct

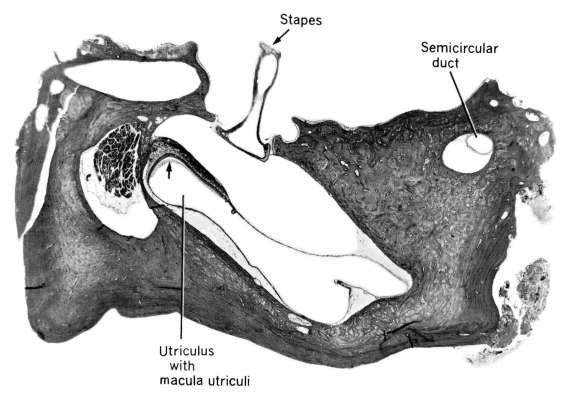

Utriculus
with
macula utriculi

Figure 35-9. Photomicrograph of inner ear of a rhesus monkey. The section includes the stapes in the fenestra ovalis, one of the semicircular ducts, and the utriculus with the macula utriculi (at arrow). (Courtesy of H. Mizoguchi.)

vesicles are more abundant. Vesicles about 200 Å in diameter are present in greatest profusion in the type II hair cells. The supranuclear Golgi complex is also more extensively developed in this type. Characteristic of the type I cell is the occurrence of a great many microtubules, mostly concentrated in the apical cytoplasm just beneath the terminal web.

The nature of the synaptic contact between the two types of hair cells and the terminations of the vestibular nerve fibers is quite different (Fig. 35-10). In the case of type I, the nerve envelopes the hair cell in a cuplike ending. At the base of the cell the intercellular space between the plasmalemma and the axolemma is about 300 Å wide, except in certain discrete areas where the intercellular substance is lacking and the membranes are only about 50 Å apart. Nearer the rim of the cuplike ending around the upper part of the hair cell, there are no obvious junctional specializations of the kind usually found at synapses, but there are in the axoplasm large

numbers of vesicles 500 to 2000 Å in diameter, some with dense cores.

The type II hair cell is not enveloped by a chalice-like ending, but a large number of separate terminal *boutons* impinge upon its surface. Among these, some investigators have distinguished endings containing "granulated" vesicles (efferent) and others containing "nongranulated" vesicles (afferent). In addition to these features both types of hair cells may have, in their peripheral cytoplasm, dense linear structures with associated small vesicles resembling the so-called *synaptic ribbons* found at the junction of the rod axon and bipolar cell dendrite in the retina. The membrane relationships between the calyciform ending of the nerve and the type I hair cell exhibit some of the morphological characteristics of the low resistance contacts found at electrical synapses. On the other hand the structure of the boutons terminating upon the type II hair cells suggests chemical mediation of the nerve impulses. It is clear that the synaptic relationships are far more complicated than was imagined from light microscope studies, and their exact nature remains unsettled.

The effective stimulus for vestibular hair cells is movement of the head in one or another plane. This, in turn, presumably sets up movement of the endolymph, which acts in some manner to trigger an impulse in the afferent vestibular nerve. The transducers of the original mechanical stimulus into electrical signals are presumably the hair-bearing surfaces of the hair cells. Exactly how a receptor potential

is set up in the hair cell and how it, in turn, influences the afferent nerve are problems that are only now being investigated. Recent evidence seems to indicate that bending of the hairs initiates the process, but so little is known of their physiological properties that no more can be said at present.

Supporting cells. The supporting cells have their nuclei near the base of the sensory epithelium and extend to its free surface, but their cell bodies are so irregularly contorted

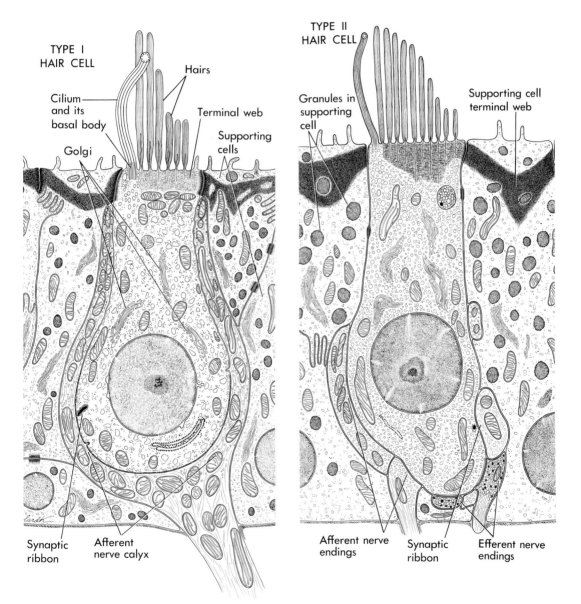

Figure 35-10. Schematic representation of the principal ultrastructural features of the vestibular type I and type II hair cells and their supporting cells. (Drawn by Sylvia Colard Keene.)

that the full extent of any given cell can never be seen in a single section (Fig. 35-10). One usually sees a mosaic of sections of many cells cut at different levels. With the light microscope little can be resolved in their cytoplasm, but in electron micrographs they are found to possess a cytoskeleton of bundles of microtubules running from the basal cytoplasm to the terminal web, which is far more elaborately developed in these cells than in the hair cells. They have a prominent Golgi complex and the cytoplasm is crowded with membrane limited granules resembling secretory granules. Little is known about the function of the supporting cells. They may contribute to the nutrition of the hair cells or may be involved in some way in the metabolism of the endolymph. Toward the periphery of the sensory region there is a gradual transition to the cells comprising the *planum semilunatum.*

The planum semilunatum is generally composed of columnar cells with infolded basal and lateral membranes. These cells have not been thoroughly studied, but it is thought that they have some function in elaboration of endolymph.

On the sloping sides of the crista ampullaris are very complex cells with highly infolded basal membranes and a dense cytoplasmic matrix with large vacuoles containing a flocculent material. These "dark" cells are reminiscent of other cells known to be involved in ion movement, and it has been speculated that they maintain the high K^+ level in endolymph. They have also been implicated in elaboration of sulfated mucopolysaccharides.

Cupulae and otoliths. Overlying the hairs in maculae are a multitude of minute (3 to 5 μ) crystalline bodies, *otoliths*. These are a mixture of calcium carbonate and a protein. In life, they are suspended within the jelly-like mucopolysaccharides that make up much of the endolymph.

The *cupulae* are gelatinous bodies located above the cristae. In life, these too are composed of protein-polysaccharide that is evidently much more viscous than the rest of the endolymph. When fixed, the structure is often

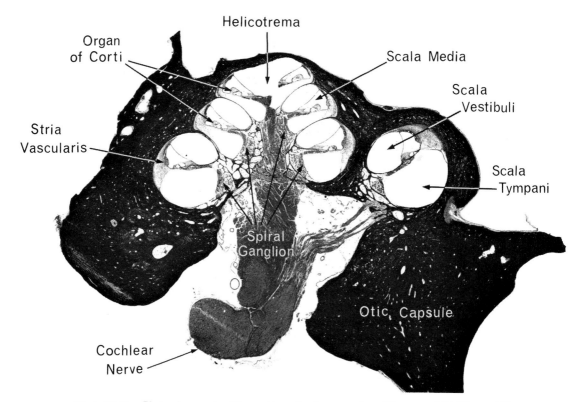

Figure 35-11. Photomicrograph of the cochlea of a rhesus monkey. (Courtesy of H. Mizoguchi.)

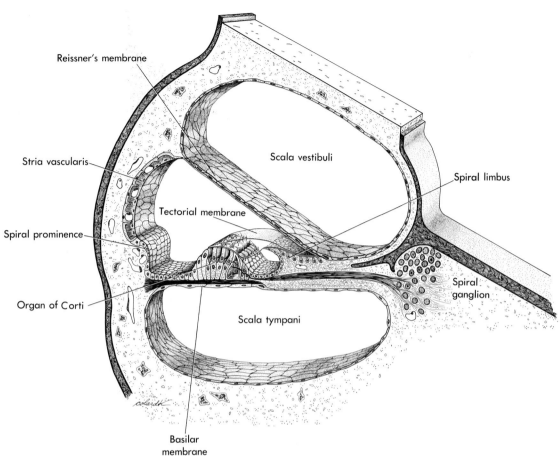

Reissner's membrane

Scala vestibuli

Stria vascularis

Spiral limbus

Tectorial membrane

Spiral prominence

Spiral ganglion

Organ of Corti

Scala tympani

Basilar
membrane

Figure 35-12. Schematic representation of a section through one of the turns of the cochlea. (Drawn by Sylvia Colard Keene.)

lost or deformed, and indeed this fact has, in the past, led some otologists to question its reality. That a cupula does exist is no longer doubted, but there is very little substantial information about its origin or composition.

ENDOLYMPHATIC SAC. The cell types encountered in different parts of the vestibular system are basically similar from one region to the other. In the endolymphatic sac, however, one finds cells that appear to be specialized for an absorptive function and these are structurally different from other cells in the vestibular membranous labyrinth. Unlike the other membranous sacs the endolymphatic sac usually contains cellular debris of one sort or another. The electrolyte concentration in its endolymph also differs from that elsewhere in the inner ear.

Histologically, there is a transition from the squamocuboidal cells of the endolymphatic duct to tall columnar cells in the sac. The latter have been variously described as covering protruding papillae or occupying crypts. Whichever is the case, there are two distinct columnar cell types present. One is a dense cell with a large irregularly shaped nucleus, a relatively unspecialized free surface, and a cell base with slightly infolded membranes. The other is a less dense cell characterized by long microvilli on its surface and many pinocytotic vesicles and vacuoles. Basally the cell membrane is smooth, but laterally it interdigitates extensively with other cells. There is good evidence that the endolymphatic sac acts as a site for absorption of endolymph and that it digests cellular debris and foreign material that may gain access to the endolymph.

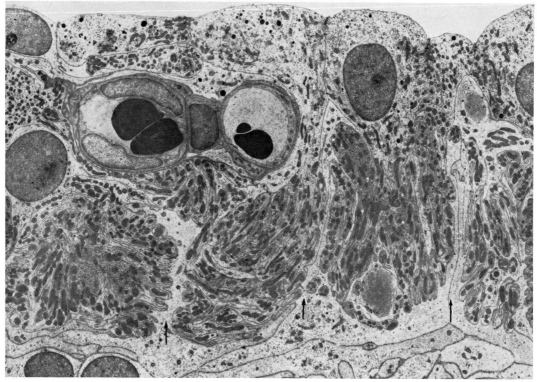

Figure 35-13. Electron micrograph of the stria vascularis of the cat inner ear, illustrating the intraepithelial capillaries, the ascending process of the basal cells (at arrows), and the elaborately infolded bases of the marginal cells. (After R. Hinojosa and E. Rodriguez-Echandia, Am. J. Anat., *118:*631, 1966.)

THE COCHLEAR DUCT. The cochlear duct is a highly specialized diverticulum of the saccule. It contains the *organ of Corti*—the effective organ of hearing—and a number of other specialized areas subserving different functions and having their own special histological characteristics. This is a very complex area, and in order to facilitate understanding, the different regions will be described individually in the following order: *vestibular membrane, stria vascularis, spiral prominence, organ of Corti,* and *tectorial membrane.* It can be seen in Figure 35-12 that this order of descriptions proceeds in a counterclockwise direction around the circumference of the cochlear duct.

Vestibular Membrane. The vestibular membrane is a delicate bilaminar structure extending across the cochlea from medial to lateral. Its inner surface is lined by cells that are differentiated in a manner suggesting that they may be involved in water and electrolyte transport. The bulging perinuclear region of the cell is readily apparent in the light microscope, but peripherally, the cell body is highly attenuated. The surface of these cells (toward the scala media) bears many short, clavate microvilli similar to those found on cells in the choroid plexus (see Chapter 12). At the basal surface, the membranes are highly infolded and interdigitate extensively with those of neighboring cells. A distinct basal lamina is found along this basal surface. Directly apposed to these cells with little or no intervening collagen is a layer of squamous perilymphatic cells of the scala vestibuli (see p. 830), so attenuated that they can scarcely be seen in well-fixed material.

Stria Vascularis. The epithelial covering of the vestibular membrane becomes continuous, at the outer wall of the cochlea, with the basal layer of cells in the specialized band of stratified epithelium called the *stria vascularis* (Figs. 35-11 to 35-13). With the light microscope it is possible to distinguish two cell types in this epithelium—a layer of light-staining *basal cells* and a darker-staining superficial layer of marginal cells possessing numerous mitochondria. In electron micrographs some workers have identified a third cell type, the *intermediate cells.* Although these latter are intermediate between marginal and basal cells in their location, they are difficult to distinguish cytologically from basal cells. The marginal cells have a smooth convex free surface, but the basal portion of these cells is divided by deep infoldings of the plasmalemma into a labyrinthine system of narrow compartments occupied by numerous mitochondria. The intermediate and basal cells have relatively few mitochondria and numerous processes. Ascending processes of the basal cells form cuplike structures surrounding and partially isolating each marginal cell from neighboring areas of the epithelium (Fig. 35-13). Capillaries penetrate into the stria vascularis and course longitudinally within the epithelium, surrounded by processes of the intermediate and marginal cells. The stria vascularis is presumed to be involved in the secretion of the endolymph, and the resemblance of the elaborate basal compartmentation of the marginal cells to similar basal specializations of other cells involved in ion transport has led to the suggestion that these cells may help maintain the unusual ionic composition of the endolymph.

Spiral Prominence. The stria vascularis ends inferiorly and its basal cell layer is continuous with the cells overlying the *spiral prominence* (Fig. 35-14). This prominence extends the whole length of the cochlear duct and rests upon a very richly vascularized thickening of the underlying periosteum. The epithelium of the spiral prominence continues downward and is reflected from the outer wall of the cochlea onto the basilar membrane, forming at its line of reflection the *external spiral sulcus.* The cells here take on a cuboidal shape, and those continuing onto the pars pectinata of the basilar membrane (see p. 830) are known as the *cells of Claudius.* In parts of the basal coil of the cochlea small groups of polyhedral cells (*cells of Boettcher*) are interposed between the basilar membrane and the cells of Claudius (Fig. 35-15).

ORGAN OF CORTI. Over the pars pectinata and pars arcuata the cells become columnar and bulge into the cochlear duct, forming the epithelial ridge called the *organ of Corti* (Figs. 35-11, 35-12, and 35-14). This highly

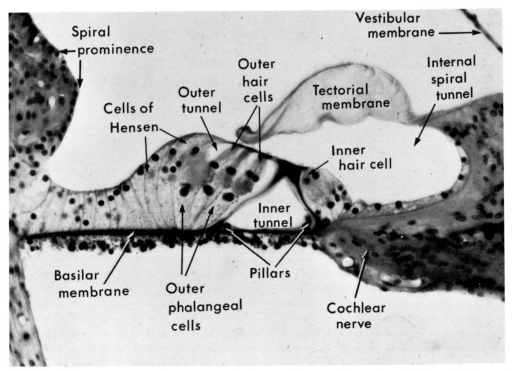

Figure 35-14. Photomicrograph of the organ of Corti of a cat. The tectorial membrane has been lifted away from the inner hair cells in specimen preparation. (Courtesy of H. Engström.)

specialized complex of epithelial cells extends throughout the length of the cochlea and is composed of *hair cells*, the receptors of stimuli produced by sound, and various *supporting cells*.

Supporting Cells. The several types of supporting cells have certain characteristics in common. They are tall, slender cells extending from the basilar membrane to the free surface of the organ of Corti, and they contain conspicuous tonofibrils. Although the cells are separated by large intercellular spaces, their upper surfaces are in contact with each other and with the hair cells to form a continuous free surface for the organ. This surface is called the *reticular membrane*. The supporting cells include inner and outer pillars, inner and outer phalangeal cells, border cells, and cells of Hensen.

Within the organ of Corti is the *inner tunnel*, a canal extending the length of the cochlea and bounded below by the basilar membrane and above by the inner and outer pillar cells. The bodies of the pillars are separated by clefts through which the tunnel communicates with the other intercellular cavities in the organ of Corti, including the outer tunnel or *space of Nuel*.

Inner pillars. The inner pillars have a broad base that rests on the basilar membrane

and a conical cell body with its apex extending upward (Figs. 35-15 and 35-16). The cytoplasm of the pillar cell contains the nucleus at the inner angle of the roughly triangular tunnel. The most distinctive feature of these cells is the darkly staining tonofibrils that course from the cell base through the cylindrical body of the pillar to end in the junctional complexes at the apex, where the cell expands into a flat flange to contact neighboring pillar cells and the inner hair cells. The contact between inner and outer pillar cells is of particularly large area and forms a structurally sound supporting mechanism. What appear to be tonofibrils with the light microscope are found in electron micrographs to be microtubules.

Outer pillars. The outer pillars are longer than the inner ones (Figs. 35-15 and 35-16). Their base is situated on the basilar membrane at the junction of the pars pectinata and pars arcuata, adjoining the base of the inner pillar. The cell body is similar to that of the inner pillar, but the free surface of the cell has a somewhat different shape. The head of the outer pillar abuts the head of the inner pillar and sends out a phalangeal process that forms a junction with the outer hair cells. The outer pillars, in fact, form the first row of phalanges.

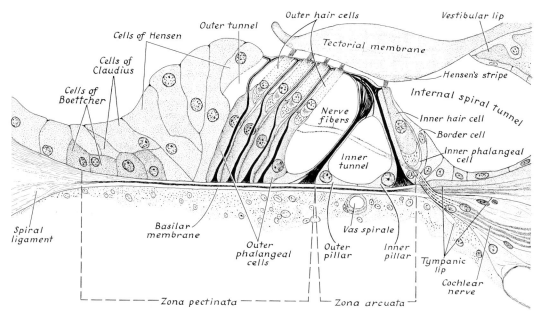

Figure 35-15. Radial transection of the organ of Corti, from the upper part of the first coil of human cochlea. (Slightly modified from Held.)

The inner pillars number approximately 5600, the outer ones 3800. On an average, three inner pillars are connected with two outer pillars.

Inner phalangeal cells. These cells are arranged in a row on the inner surface of the inner pillars and completely surround the inner hair cells. In contradistinction to the outer phalangeal cells there is no enlarged extracellular space between the supporting cells and the hair cells. Afferent and efferent nerve fibers travel through and are supported by the inner phalangeal cells. The relationship between supporting cells and inner hair cells is completely analogous to that of the supporting and hair cells of the vestibular system.

Outer phalangeal cells (of Deiters). The outer phalangeal cells act as supporting elements for the three to four rows of outer hair cells (Figs. 35-17 and 35-18). These phalangeal cells are columnar with their bases resting on the basilar membrane. Apically they surround the inferior third of the outer hair cell and also enclose the afferent and efferent nerve bundles traveling to the hair cell base. This portion of the cell does not reach the free surface of the organ of Corti, but on the side of the cell away from the outer pillar cells, it gives off a slender finger-like process internally reinforced by a bundle of microtubules. This phalanx expands at the surface of the organ of Corti to form a flat apical plate joined at its edges to the hair cell that it is supporting and to the hair cell in the row next to it. The plate-like expansion at the surface also contains abundant supporting microtubules.

The upper two thirds of the outer hair cells are not surrounded by other cells but are exposed within a fluid-filled space (the space of Nuel) that is in communication with the inner tunnel through the clefts between the pillars. The fluid that bathes the hair cells and occupies the space of Nuel and inner tunnel is apparently separated from the endolymphatic or perilymphatic spaces and thus may be of different composition than either perilymph or endolymph.

Border cells. The inner phalangeal cells continue into a row of slender cells, termed *border cells,* that delimit the inner boundary of the organ of Corti (Fig. 35-15). There is a gradual transition in height from these to the squamous cells lining the inner spiral sulcus.

Cells of Hensen. Adjacent to the last row of outer phalangeal cells are the tall cells of

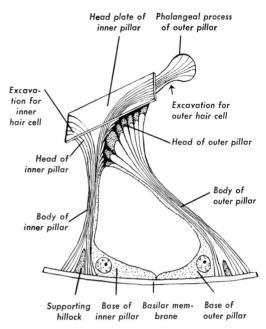

Figure 35-16. Diagram of inner and outer pillars of organ of Corti. (Modified from Kolmer.)

Hensen that constitute the outer border of the organ of Corti. They are arranged in several rows decreasing rapidly in height and laterally abutting the cells of Claudius.

COCHLEAR HAIR CELLS. In the cochlea, as in the vestibule, two types of hair cells are present (Figs. 35-12, 35-14, and 35-18). The *inner hair cells* are arranged in a single row along the whole length of the cochlea. The *outer hair cells* form three rows and are lodged between the outer pillars and the outer phalangeal cells. In the second coil of the cochlea, a fourth, and in the upper coil, a fifth row of outer hair cells is added.

Inner hair cells resemble type I cells in the vestibular labyrinth in many respects. They are relatively short, goblet-shaped cells with a slightly constricted neck region. The surface of the cell bears hairs, similar in structure to those on vestibular hair cells, but in the adult there is no associated cilium. However, a basal body and an associated typical centriole persist as the only remnants of the ciliary apparatus. The hairs are arranged on the cell surface in the form of a letter W or U with the base of the letter directed toward the centrioles. The rootlets of the hairs extend down into, and at times through, the terminal web. The cell body contains scattered ribosomes and 200 Å vesicles interspersed among larger vesic-

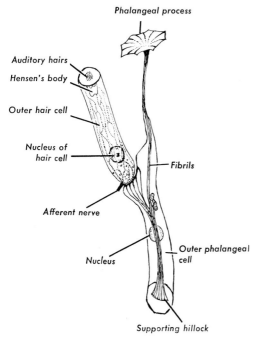

Phalangeal process

Auditory hairs

Hensen's body

Outer hair cell

Nucleus of hair cell

Fibrils

Afferent nerve

Nucleus

Outer phalangeal cell

Supporting hillock

Figure 35-17. Diagram of supporting cells of Deiters and the associated outer hair cell. (Modified from Kolmer.)

similar to that of the inner hair cells, but here there are more rows of hairs, and the length of the hairs varies from long at the periphery to short centrally (Figs. 35-19 and 35-22). Again, no cilium is present, although a basal body can be found at the base of the **W**. Immediately deep to the terminal web are dense lipid-like inclusions interspersed with elongated, highly convoluted elements of the granular endoplasmic reticulum. Mitochondria are generally aggregated in the basal cytoplasm and line up along the sides of the cell in relation to rows of smooth surfaced vesicles that are aligned parallel to the plasmalemma. These are characteristic of the outer hair cells. In some species more than one row may be present. Their function is unknown, but they bear some resemblance to the subsynaptic cisterns found at the base of the cell.

ular profiles, presumably representing the smooth endoplasmic reticulum. Mitochondria are aggregated under the terminal web and at the cell base but are scattered in smaller numbers throughout the cytoplasm. Numerous small nerves are in synaptic relation to the cell base. Two types of endings are described. There are endings containing many synaptic vesicles, of which many contain dense granules; these are usually associated with a subsynaptic cistern in the receptor cell and are considered to be *efferent* in nature. There are also smaller endings with vesicles generally devoid of granules. These presumably are *afferent* in nature, and generally have a synaptic ribbon associated with them.

Outer hair cells are much more specialized in their structure than inner hair cells. This has led to the speculation that the two cell types have different functions, and indeed that inner hair cells are possibly not involved in hearing. Outer hair cells, as previously stated, are supported on the apices of outer phalangeal cells and here receive innervation from the cochlear nerve. The synaptic relationships are essentially similar to those found in inner hair cells (Figs. 35-15 and 35-24). The hairs on the apex of these cells form a distinctive **W**

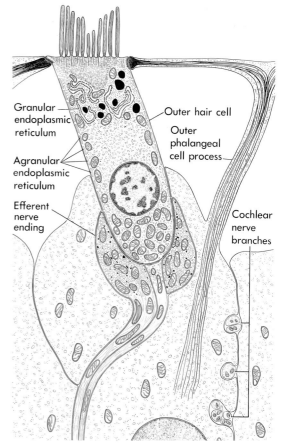

Granular endoplasmic reticulum

Agranular endoplasmic reticulum

Efferent nerve ending

Outer hair cell

Outer phalangeal cell process

Cochlear nerve branches

Figure 35-18. Schematic representation of the relationship of the outer hair cells to the outer phalangeal cells, as revealed in electron micrographs. (Drawn by Sylvia Colard Keene.)

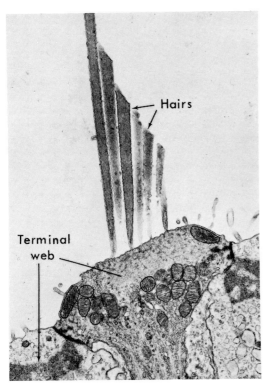

Figure 35-19. Electron micrograph showing the hairs on a hair cell. Notice their narrow base and the continuation of their fibrous core into the terminal web. (Courtesy of D. Hamilton.)

Spiral Limbus. In the inner angle of the scala media, the periosteal connective tissue of the upper surface of the osseous spiral lamina bulges into the scala media as the *spiral limbus* (Figs. 35-12, 35-14, and 35-15). Its edge overhangs the internal spiral sulcus (or tunnel). The two margins of the sulcus are the *vestibular lip* and *tympanic lip.* The collagenous fibers of the limbus continue laterally, via the tympanic lip, into the pars arcuata of the basilar membrane. Within the body of the limbus the fibers are arranged vertically to produce the distinctive *auditory teeth* (of Huschke). Between these collagenous fibers are stellate fibroblasts. Uniformly spaced along the upper margin of the limbus, between the auditory teeth, are the so-called *interdental cells,* which secrete the tectorial membrane. The bases of interdental cells are firmly embedded in the connective tissue of the limbus, but their apices spread out over the upper surface of the limbus, interdigitating and joined by junctional complexes. These form a continuous sheet over the upper surface of the limbus and complete the cellular investment of the cochlear duct.

The tectorial membrane. The tectorial membrane is secreted from the luminal surfaces of the interdental cells and overlies these cells as a cuticle. It extends laterally beyond the vestibular lip of the limbus to overlie the hairs on the hair cells of the organ of Corti (Figs. 35-12 and 35-14). Recent evidence indicates that the tips of the hairs are embedded within or are firmly bound to the membrane. If this is so, then micrographs showing a space between the hairs and the cuticle must be artifacticious. The tectorial membrane is composed primarily of a protein having a number of similarities to epidermal keratin. In fixed preparations numerous fibrils are observed within it, forming patterns suggesting a highly ordered structure.

The Perilymphatic Labyrinth

The perilymphatic system surrounds the whole of the membranous labyrinth and provides support for its epithelium lining. The distinct scalae vestibuli and tympani in the cochlea have been mentioned, but it must be remembered that similar, though less specialized, perilymphatic spaces surround the structures in the vestibule.

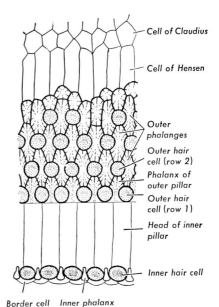

Figure 35-20. Diagram of the organ of Corti viewed from above, showing the relationship of the phalanges of the supporting cells to the hair cells. (Modified from Retzius, Kolmer, Schaffer.)

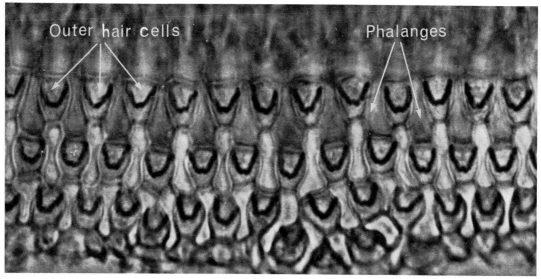

Figure 35-21. Surface view of the organ of Corti of a guinea pig. Notice the **U** or **W**-shaped row of hairs on the hair cells. See also Fig. 35-22. (Courtesy of H. Engström.)

Histologically the perilymphatic tissue is described as a reticulum, and close examination with the electron microscope shows that this reticulum is primarily composed of highly attenuated processes of many stellate cells. Except close to the periosteum of the bony labyrinth and to the membranous labyrinth, there are few extracellular fibers associated with these reticular cells. Immediately surrounding the membranous labyrinth, however, extracellular fibers are elaborated and, in some species, form a relatively dense, stable sheath 1 or 2 μ thick, composed of multitudes of short fibers. In the vicinity of the fibrocytes of the perilymphatic system, both in the cochlea and in the vestibule, are fiber bundles that have a characteristic form different from that of any other known extracellular fiber. The fiber bundles are composed of a variable number of dense 100 Å fibers, which can be shown to be composed of four 50 Å subunits that appear to be helically wound around one another. The dense fibers that form the bundles are embedded in an amorphous filamentous matrix.

Numerous blood capillaries course throughout the perilymphatic tissue destined to supply the metabolic needs of the labyrinthine epithelium.

SCALA VESTIBULI AND SCALA TYMPANI. The cells that line these two scalae are usually extremely attenuated squamous cells with very little obvious cellular differentiation. At times, however, especially in the vicinity of the basilar membrane, the cells do become somewhat cuboidal, although they possess few structural features of note.

The Basilar Membrane. The most elaborate specialization of perilymphatic tissue is the basilar membrane, which provides a supporting base for the cells of the organ of Corti and which by its movement presumably transmits vibrations to the hair cells. The basilar membrane is a highly organized layer of collagen-like fibers. There is some indication that the perilymphatic cells may actively secrete the basilar membrane, but this has not been clearly established. It is divided into two distinct zones: the one, running from the osseous spiral lamina approximately one third of the way to the outer cochlear wall, is termed the *pars arcuata (tecta)*; the other, comprising approximately two thirds of the width of the basilar membrane, is termed the *pars pectinata* and contains, even at the light microscope level, distinct parallel striations termed the *auditory strings.* In fact, both portions of the membrane are composed of transversely oriented filaments (80 to 100 Å thick) embedded in an amorphous matrix. In the pars pectinata the filaments are aggregated into bundles that run in two strata: one immediately beneath the organ of Corti is composed of small bundles, and another situated more deeply in the lamina is composed of larger bundles. At the outer wall of the cochlea, these two layers again merge to pass into the connective tissue of the spiral ligament. Blood vessels penetrate into the pars arcuata but not into the pars pectinata.

The term *spiral ligament* is an unfortunate designation for the lateral insertion of the basilar membrane, because this component does not have the histological structure of ligaments found elsewhere in the body (Fig. 35-12). It is merely a local differentiation of periosteal connective tissue containing numerous fibroblasts and blood vessels. A better term would be *spiral crest*.

Endolymph and Perilymph

The spaces delimited by the membranous labyrinth are filled with the viscous fluid called endolymph, and the labyrinth is surrounded by the perilymph, which occupies the perilymphatic spaces. The two fluids are amazingly different in their chemical composition. The most striking difference is in their electrolyte composition. Whereas perilymph to some degree resembles extracellular fluid in general, endolymph has the characteristics of intracellular fluid in having high K^+ and low Na^+ concentrations.

It was recognized early in this century that endolymph was a product of secretion, although the actual site or sites of its elaboration were not known. It was supposed that the stria vascularis, the spiral prominence, and the planum semilunatum were primarily responsible. Recent evidence would indicate that these areas do indeed take part in elaboration of endolymph, but the electron microscope has made it clear that many of the cells lining the membranous labyrinth have cytological characteristics compatible with synthetic and secre-

tory activity and might therefore participate in endolymph metabolism. Specifically, autoradiographic studies have implicated the planum semilunatum in elaboration of sulfated mucopolysaccharides, and measurement with microelectrodes has shown that the high DC potential of the scala media is produced in the vicinity of the stria vascularis, which would indicate that some sort of ion secretion is taking place there.

The site of absorption of endolymph has been thought to be the endolymphatic sac. Recent evidence is compatible with this interpretation. Again, however, electron micrographs of cells of the membranous labyrinth show many instances of micropinocytotic activity, which would suggest that absorption may be going on in many areas of the labyrinth.

Although it is well established that endolymph is a secretion, the genesis of perilymph is still being debated. Some feel that it is an ultrafiltrate of plasma, others that it is derived from cerebrospinal fluid. There is no doubt that the perilymphatic spaces are functionally connected to the subarachnoid space, but the exact functional significance of this relationship is not yet clear.

Nerves of the Labyrinth

The eighth cranial nerve supplies the sensory areas of the labyrinth. It consists of two parts of quite different functional nature and central connections—the *vestibular* and the *cochlear* nerves (Figs. 35-5 and 35-25). Each is composed of primary afferent fibers from the sense organs and efferent feedback fibers from the central nervous system. The cell bodies of the afferent fibers are bipolar cells and form two peripheral ganglia, the *spiral* or *cochlear ganglion* in the modiolus and the *vestibular* or *Scarpa's ganglion* in the internal auditory meatus of the temporal bone.

The vestibular nerve divides into a superior and an inferior branch. The superior branch supplies the horizontal crista ampullaris, the superior crista ampullaris, the macula utriculi, and a small part of the macula sacculi. The inferior branch supplies the posterior crista ampullaris and the major portion of the macula sacculi, and it sends a small anastomosing branch to the cochlear nerve.

The bipolar cell bodies, both in the vestibular ganglion and in the cochlear ganglion,

Electrolyte Composition of Body Fluids (mEq./l.)*

	PLASMA	C.S.F.	PERILYMPH	ENDOLYMPH
Protein	6000–8000	10–38	75–100	10
K	20	12–17	15	140
Na	140	150	148	26
Cl	600	750	120	110
Sugar	70–120	40–80		
Mg	1.0–3.0	2.0	2.0	0.9
Ca	7.0	3.0	3.0	3.0

* (From F. C. Ormerod.)

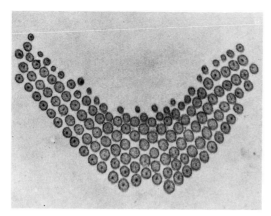

Figure 35-22. Electron micrograph of the **W** configuration of the hairs or stereocilia on the outer sensory cells of the human organ of Corti. × 10,500. (Courtesy of R. Kimura.)

are invested by a thin layer of myelin, and this continues onto the axons. The axons of the cochlear nerve lose their myelin as they run through the canals of the osseous spiral lamina on their way to the hair cells. In the vestibular nerve, myelin persists until the nerve enters the sensory area.

The cochlear nerve contains two morphological kinds of nerve fibers. The first, thin and numerous, radiate from the spiral ganglion in parallel bundles to the nearest segments of the organ of Corti. Because of their course they are called the *direct acoustic fibers*. The second category of fibers, usually thicker and fewer than the first, are also arranged radially at the outset, but after reaching the organ of Corti they turn sharply and follow a spiral course. These are the *spiral fibers* (Fig. 35-23).

The functional implications of these two patterns of distribution is not clear. Although the relationship between the peripheral receptors and acoustic neurons is not as individualized as the monosynaptic relationship of the foveal cones, they are sufficiently restricted to permit the reception of localized stimuli impinging upon small segments of the cochlea and, as in the retina, they must have a receptor surface whose different points have different functional values.

The vestibular nerve terminates centrally in the reflex centers of the medulla oblongata and cerebellum. Its cortical connections are unknown, although it mediates reflex movements of the eyes through its thalamic connections. The cochlear nerve also has reflex

centers in the medulla oblongata and the midbrain, but most of its fibers run in the lateral lemniscus to the medial geniculate body of the thalamus and thence to the temporal lobe gyri of the cortex.

Both the vestibular and cochlear divisions of the eighth cranial nerve contain appreciable numbers of efferent fibers (of Rasmussen) that originate bilaterally from the vicinity of the superior olive. Initially these fibers travel in the vestibular nerve, but within the internal auditory meatus some efferent fibers reach the cochlear nerve by way of the anastomosis between the vestibular and cochlear nerves. The peripheral terminations of the efferent component are presumably at the hair cells, but incontrovertible evidence for the position and mode of ending of these fibers is still lacking. Stimulation of the efferent bundle results in suppression of auditory nerve activity, and anatomical evidence derived from sectioning the bundle indicates that the "granulated" ending are efferent, for they apparently degenerate after sectioning (Figs. 35-10 and 35-18).

Blood Vessels of the Labyrinth

The labyrinthine artery is a branch of the inferior cerebellar artery. It enters the internal auditory meatus and divides into two branches, the *vestibular* artery and the *common cochlear* artery. The latter divides into the *vestibulocochlear* artery and the *cochlear* artery proper.

The vestibular artery supplies the upper and lateral parts of the utricle and saccule and parts of the superior and lateral semicircular ducts. It forms dense networks of capillaries in the region of the maculae; in the thin perilymphatic tissue of these structures the capillary networks are relatively loose.

The vestibulocochlear artery supplies, with its vestibular branch, the lower and medial parts of the utricle and saccule, the crus commune, and the posterior semicircular duct. Its cochlear branch supplies the lowest part of the first cochlear coil.

The cochlear artery proper penetrates the cavities of the modiolus, where its tortuous branches run spirally to the apex. This is the so-called "spiral tract." From it, branches go to the spiral ganglion and, through the periosteum of the scala vestibuli and the osseous spiral lamina, to the inner parts of the basilar membrane. Here the capillaries are arranged in arcades in the tympanic covering layer under the tunnel and the limbus; from them arise the *vas spirale*. The vascular stria and the spiral crest receive their blood through branches of the spiral arterial tract, which run in the roof of the scala vestibuli. They do not form connections with the vessels of the basilar membrane. The lower wall of the scala tympani receives its own small arteries from the same source.

The course of the veins of the labyrinth is quite different from that of the arteries. There are three main venous drainage channels. In the cochlea, veins originate in the region of the spiral prominence and run downward and inward through the periosteum of the scala tympani to the spiral vein, which is found under the spiral ganglion. Upper and lower spiral veins, belonging to the corresponding coils of the cochlea, receive branches from the osseous spiral lamina and the spiral ganglion. Above the spiral vein is the small vein of the spiral lamina, which receives a part of the blood from the spiral lamina and spiral ganglion and is connected by anastomoses with the spiral vein.

These cochlear veins form a plexus in the modiolus, which empties the blood partly into the internal auditory vein and partly into the vein of the cochlear aqueduct, which drains into the jugular vein. The veins of the vestibule empty into the veins of the vestibular and cochlear aqueducts.

This arrangement of the vessels in the internal ear seems to ensure the best possible protection of the sound receptors from the arterial pulse wave. The arteries are arranged for the most part in the wall of the scala vestibuli, while the wall of the scala tympani contains the veins. The course of the spiral arteries in the modiolus probably also contributes to the damping of pulsations. In certain mammals the coiling of these arteries is so prominent that the convoluted regions suggest glomeruli.

True lymphatics are absent from the labyrinth. Instead the fluid is drained into the perilymphatic spaces, which are connected with the subarachnoid space. A certain amount of drainage may be effected through perivascular and perineural connective tissue sheaths.

EMBRYOLOGICAL DEVELOPMENT OF THE EAR

EXTERNAL AND MIDDLE EARS. The tympanic cavity and the auditory tube are derivatives of the first branchial pouch. The external auditory meatus develops through an invagination of the integument directed toward the tympanic cavity. The tissue layer remaining between this invagination and the tympanic cavity becomes the tympanic membrane.

INTERNAL EAR. The primordium of the labyrinth develops as a shallow groove of thickened ectoderm, dorsal to the first branchial groove, on both sides of the brain, between the myelencephalon and the metencephalon (human embryo of eight somites). The groove is invaginated into the subjacent mesenchyme and becomes the *otic vesicle*. In the human embryo of 2.8 mm. it separates from the ectoderm by constriction and is surrounded by mesenchyme. The vesicle is lined by tall, pseudostratified epithelium, which secretes the endolymph filling it. From its earliest stages the otic vesicle comes into contact with the large acoustic ganglion, which later divides into vestibular and cochlear ganglia. Unequal proliferation in places in the wall of the otic vesicle transforms it into an extremely complex system of saccular

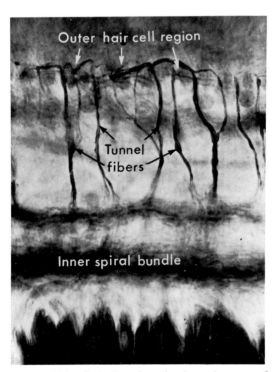

Figure 35-23. Optical section of guinea pig organ of Corti viewed from above, showing the nerve fibers traversing the tunnel to reach the region of outer hair cells. (Courtesy of H. Engström.)

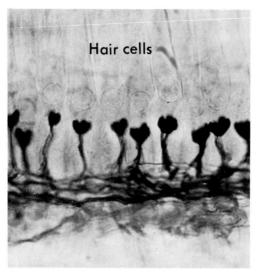

Hair cells

Figure 35-24. Silver stained longitudinal section of the organ of Corti, showing the efferent nerve fibers ending about the bases of the outer hair cells. (Courtesy of H. Engström.)

and tubular cavities. Soon after its isolation from the ectoderm, the otic vesicle sends out a dorsal evagination, which is the primordium of the endolymphatic duct. Then a larger, dorsal part of the vesicle becomes distinct from a smaller, ventral part. The first, or vestibular, portion gives rise to the semicircular ducts and the utricle. The second, the cochlear portion, forms the saccule and cochlea.

On the wall of the vestibular portion three evaginations appear and develop into the three semicircular ducts and their ampullae. What remains of the vestibular portion is now the utricle. The cochlear portion sends out a curved out-pocketing—the primordium of the cochlea. It gradually gains in length, coils as it grows, and becomes separated from the saccule by a deep constriction. In a human embryo of 22 mm. the form of the labyrinth corresponds to that in the adult.

Maculae, Cristae, and Organ of Corti. The maculae and cristae develop earlier than the organ of Corti. On its medial side, where the acoustic ganglion is located, the epithelium of the wall of the otic vesicle develops a thickened area, the *macula communis,* which later divides into an upper and a lower epithelial pad. The first gives rise to the macula of the utricle and to the upper and lateral cristae. A small part of the second thickening forms the crista of the posterior ampulla; the rest of the second

part divides into the macula sacculi and the primordium of the organ of Corti, which gradually extends into the growing cochlea.

The differentiation of the organ of Corti proceeds from the basal coil of the growing cochlea to its apex. The epithelium extends along the basal wall of the canal as a long ridge, which divides longitudinally into a large inner ridge and small outer one. In the former, connective tissue penetrates the epithelium and separates it into radial rows of flask-shaped cells embedded in the connective tissue. This region develops into the spiral limbus. In the outer part of the ridge, the tall cells gradually involute, leaving a squamous epithelium that lines the inner spiral sulcus.

The small outer ridge, the primordium of the organ of Corti, at first consists of uniform cells. Then, flask-shaped inner and outer hair cells appear among them (Fig. 35-26). The remaining elements elaborate tonofilaments and differentiate into the supporting cells.

The surface of both epithelial ridges is covered from the beginning by the future tectorial membrane.

While the otic vesicle grows and differentiates, the mesenchyme surrounding it develops into a layer of cartilage, which remains separated from the epithelium by a layer of mesenchyme. This later condenses into a fibrous layer around the membranous labyrinth to form a supporting structure for the epithelium. Between the wall and the cartilaginous capsule, the mesenchyme loosens and its meshes enlarge into the perilymphatic spaces. The mesenchymal cells which remain on the surface of the trabeculae and of the labyrinthine wall and perichondrium become mesenchymal epithelium.

In anuran tadpoles, if the otic vesicle is transplanted into another area it becomes surrounded by cartilage arising from local mesenchyme.

The cochlea receives its perilymphatic spaces through extension of the perilymphatic cisterna surrounding the saccule and utricle in the vestibule. The scala tympani appears in the region of the cochlea fenestra in embryos of 43 mm., and the scala vestibuli appears at the 50 mm. stage. They gradually grow and coil with the cochlear duct, remaining attached to its upper and lower walls. At the outer aspect of the cochlear duct, as well as at its inner edge, the wall of the duct remains connected with the cartilaginous capsule. Later, ossification occurs and gives rise to the modiolus and the bony cochlea.

FUNCTIONAL CONSIDERATIONS

Functions of the various structural components of the ear have already been mentioned briefly in the descriptions under specific headings. It is impossible, of course, to consider in detail the functioning of the ear in a textbook of histology, but there are certain physiological considerations that suggest new problems and approaches to research on this organ.

The external and middle ears lend themselves quite well to physiological research and have been intensively studied for some time. The vibrations of the tympanic membrane are transmitted through the chain of auditory ossicles to the fenestra ovalis and thence to the perilymph filling the scala tympani. The organ of Corti is the receptor for sound stimuli, but this function depends to a large degree upon the properties of the basilar membrane. This membrane may be compared to an unstressed gelatinous plate with varying resistance to displacement related to its uniformly varying width. The deformation of this membrane produced by movement of the stapes resembles a traveling wave. Regions of observed maximum displacement change with frequency, but are rather broad. As the stimulus frequency rises, the length of the basilar membrane responding

becomes shorter, and progressively more of the distal area becomes inactive. The pitch discriminating ability of the ear is only partly due to this physical separation of the responding areas along the basilar membrane.

Nerve impulses elicited by stimulation of the maculae and the cristae play an important role in the regulation and coordination of the movements of equilibrium and locomotion. The stimuli to the vestibular end organs are *angular acceleration* for the semicircular ducts and *linear acceleration* for the maculae. These impulses exert their influences upon coordinated muscular contraction, upon muscular tonus, and upon eye movement through the brainstem and cerebellum.

The ear is essentially a biological transducer. The transduction in the external and middle ears is relatively easily monitored. The extreme anatomical complexity of the internal ear, however, has hindered attempts at understanding the transducer phenomenon by which mechanical energy (the stimulus) is transferred into electrical energy (the nerve impulse). It is generally believed that the transduction process takes place in the apex of the hair cells. Indications are that the mechanism in vestibular and cochlear hair cells probably does not differ significantly, even though there are considerable anatomical differences in the cells.

It has been possible to show very clearly

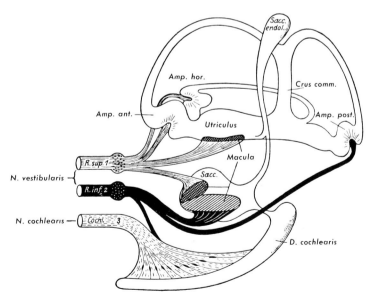

Figure 35-25. Diagram of distribution of nerves in the membranous labyrinth of the rabbit. (After deBurlet, from Kolmer.)

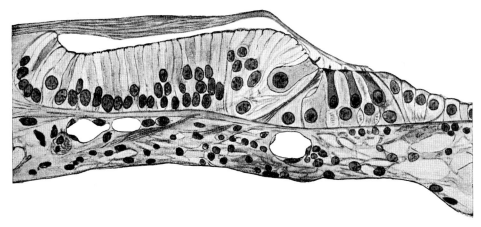

Figure 35-26. A stage in development of the organ of Corti in a human fetus of six months. The tectorial membrane has become detached from the large epithelial ridge and remains connected only at the periphery with the surface of the smaller ridge (the future organ of Corti); hair cells make their appearance. × 311. (After Kolmer.)

in the ampulla of Lorenzini in fish, where the sensory cells are in many respects anatomically similar to vestibular hair cells, that bending of the hairs toward the kinocilium results in depolarization of the cell. Bending in the opposite direction hyperpolarizes the cell, while bending normal to these directions has no appreciable ionic effect. The same probably holds true in mammals, although the structural differences between mammalian and nonmammalian hair cells would suggest that there are also some functional differences. An adequate stimulus would seem to be bending of the hairs. The stepwise lengthening of the hairs may provide a built-in biological amplifier. How the transduction process takes place remains unexplained, however, for the hairs extend into the endolymph with its highly unusual ionic composition. Thus, with equal K^+ and Na^+ inside and outside the cell, the $Na^+ = K^+$ movements that are known to be involved in excitation in other excitable cells would not take place. Nevertheless, it has been shown that a nerve cell membrane put into the same ionic conditions as the hairs responds to pressure changes by transient potential changes across the membrane, and although the mechanism for this is equally unclear, it is possible that this experimental system is analogous to the hairs. In the near future it may help to explain how hair cells function.

REFERENCES

Alexander, G.: Zur Histologie der Mittelohrschleimhaut. Monatschr. Ohrenh., *61*:446, 1927.

Alexander, G., and O. Marburg: Handbuch der Neurologie des Ohres. Vienna and Berlin, 1921–1926.

Bast, T. H.: Ossification of the otic capsule in human fetuses. Carnegie Contributions to Embryol., *21*:53, 1930.

Bast, T. H., and B. J. Anson: The Temporal Bone and the Ear. Springfield, Ill., Charles C Thomas, 1949.

von Békésy, G., Experiments in Hearing. New York, McGraw-Hill Book Co., 1960.

Bowen, R. E.: The cupula of the membranous labyrinth. J. Comp. Neurol., *58*:517, 1933.

deBurlet, H. M.: Vergleichende Anatomie des stato-akustischen Organs. *In* Bolk, et al., eds.: Handbuch der Vergleichenden Anatomie der Wirbelthiere. Berlin and Vienna, Urban und Schwarzenberg, 1934, Vol. 2, p. 1293.

Citron, L., D. Exley, and C. S. Hallpike: Formation, circulation and chemical properties of the labyrinthine fluids. Brit. M. Bull., *12*:101, 1956.

Carlström, D., H. Engström, and S. Hjorth: Electron microscopic and x-ray diffraction studies of statoconia. The Laryngoscope, *63*:1052, 1953.

Davis, H.: Biophysics and physiology of the inner ear. Physiol. Rev., *37*:1, 1957.

Davis, H.: Some principles of sensory receptor action. Physiol. Rev., *41*:391, 1961.

Engström, H., On the double innervation of the sensory epithelia of the inner ear. Acta Otolaryngol., *49*:109, 1958.

Engström, H.: The cortilymph, the third lymph of the inner ear. Acta Morph. Nederlandoscandinavica, *3*:195, 1960.

Engström, H., H. Ades, and J. Hawkins: Structure and function of the sensory hairs of the inner ear. J. Acoust. Soc. Amer., *34*:1356, 1962.

Engström, H., and J. Wersäll: Structure and innervation of the inner ear sensory epithelia. Int. Rev. Cytol., *7*:535, 1958.

Fernandez, C.: The innervation of the cochlea (guinea pig). The Laryngoscope, *51*:1152, 1951.

Fex, J.: Auditory activity in centrifugal and centripetal cochlear fibers in the cat. Acta Physiol. Scandinav., *55*(Suppl.):189, 1962.

Flock, A.: The ultrastructure of the macula utriculi with special reference to directional interplay of sensory response as revealed by morphological polarization. J. Cell Biol., *22*:413, 1964.

Flock, A.: Transducing mechanisms in lateral line canal organ receptors. Cold Spring Harbor Symposium on Quantitative Biology, Vol. 30, Sensory Receptors, 1965, p. 133.

Flock, A., and J. Wersäll: A study of the orientation of the sensory hairs of the receptor cells in the lateral line organ of fish with special reference to the function of the receptors. J. Cell Biol., *15*:19, 1962.

Foley, J. O.: The cytological processes involved in the formation of the scalae of the internal ear. Anat. Rec., *49*:1, 1931.

Granit, R.: Receptors and Sensory Perception; A Discussion of the Aims, Means and Results of Electrophysiological Research into the Process of Reception. New Haven, Conn., Yale University Press, 1955.

Graves, G. O., and L. F. Edwards: The eustachian tube. A review of its descriptive, microscopic, topographic and clinical anatomy. Arch. Otolaryngol., *39:*359, 1944.

Guild, S. R.: Observations upon the structure and normal contents of the ductus and saccus endolymphatic in the guinea pig (Cavia cobaya). Am. J. Anat., *39:*1, 1927.

Guild, S. R.: Circulation of the endolymph. Am. J. Anat., *39:*57, 1927.

Hamberger, L. A., and H. Hyden: Cytochemical changes in the cochlear ganglion caused by acoustic stimulation and trauma. Acta Otolaryngol., Suppl. 61, 1945.

Hamilton, D. W.: Perilymphatic fibrocytes in the vestibule of the inner ear. Anat. Rec., in press.

Held, H.: Die Cochlea der Säuger und der Vögel, Entwicklung und ihr Bau. Handbuch der normale und pathologische Physiologie. Berlin, Julius Springer, 1926, Vol. 11, p. 467.

Hinojosa, R., and E. L. Rodriguez-Echandia: The fine structure of the stria vascularis of the cat inner ear. Am. J. Anat., 188: 631, 1966.

Iurato, S.: Submicroscopic structure of the membranous labyrinth. 1. The tectorial membrane. 2. The epithelium of Corti's organ. 3. The supporting structure of Corti's organ (basilar membrane, limbus spiralis and spiral ligament). Zeitschr. f. Zellforsch., *52:* 105, 1960; *53:*259, 1961; *56:*40, 1962.

Kimura, R. S.: Hairs of the cochlear sensory cells and their attachment to the tectorial membrane. Acta Otolaryng., *61:*55, 1966.

Kimura, R. S., P-G. Lundquist, and J. Wersäll: Secretory epithelial linings in the ampullae of the guinea pig labyrinth. Acta Otolaryngol., *57:*517, 1964.

Kimura, R. S., H. F. Schuknecht, and I. Sundo: Fine morphology of the sensory cells in the organ of Corti in man. Acta Otolaryngol., *58:*390, 1965.

Kimura, R. S., and J. Wersäll: Termination of the olivo-cochlear bundle in relation to the outer hair cells of the organ of Corti in guinea pig. Acta Otolaryngol., *55:*1, 1962.

Kolmer, W.: Gehörorgan. *In* von Möllendorff, W., and W. Bargmann, eds.: Handbuch der mikroskopischen Anatomie des Menschen. Berlin, Julius Springer, 1927, Vol. 3, p. 250.

Ladman, A. J., and A. J. Mitchell: The topographical relations and histological characteristics of the tubuloacinar glands of the eustachian tube in mice. Anat. Rec., *121:*167, 1955.

Lorente de Nó, R.: Études sur l'anatomie et la physiologie du labyrinthe de l'oreille et du VIIIe nerf. Trabajos (Travaux) Invest. Biol. Madrid, *24:*53, 1926.

Lorente de Nó, R.: Anatomy of the eighth nerve. The Laryngoscope, *43:*3, 1933.

Lundquist, P-G.: The enodlymphatic duct and sac in the guinea pig. Acta Otolaryngol., Suppl. 201, 1965.

Lundquist, P-G., R. Kimura, and J. Wersäll: Ultrastructural organization of the epithelial lining in the endolymphatic duct and sac in the guinea pig. Acta Otolaryngol., 57: 65, 1963.

Ormerod, F. C.: The physiology of the endolymph. J. Laryngol. Otol., *74:*659, 1960.

Perry, E. T.: The Human Ear Canal. Springfield, Ill., Charles C Thomas, 1957.

Polyak, S.: Über den allgemeinen Bauplan des Gehör-systems und über seine Bedeutung für die Physiologie, für die Klinik und für die Psychologie. Zeitschr. f. d. ges. Neurtol. u. Psychiat., *110:* 1, 1927.

Polyak, S., G. McHugh, and D. K. Judd, Jr.: The Human Ear in Anatomical Transparencies. New York, T. H. McKenna, Inc., 1946.

Ramón y Cajal, S.: Histologie du Système Nerveux de l'Homme et des Vertébrés. 2 vols. Paris, A. Maloine, 1909–1911.

Rasmussen, G., and W. F. Windle, eds.: Neural Mechanisms of the Auditory and Vestibular Systems. Springfield, Ill., Charles C Thomas, 1961.

Smith, C. A.: Structure of the stria vascularis and spiral prominence. Ann. Otol., Rhin., Laryngol., *66:*521, 1957.

Smith, C. A., O. H. Lowry, and M. L. Wu: The electrolytes of the labyrinthine fluids. The Largyngoscope, *64:*141, 1954.

Smith, C. A., and F. Sjöstrand: A synaptic structure in the hair cells of the guinea pig cochlea. J. Ultrastruct. Res., *5:*184, 1961.

Smith, C. A., and F. Sjöstrand: Structure of the nerve endings on the external hair cells of the guinea pig cochlea as studied by serial sections. J. Ultrastruct. Res., *5:*523, 1961.

Sophian, L. H., and B. H. Senturia: Anatomy and histology of the external ear in relation to the histogenesis of external otitis. The Laryngoscope, *64:*772, 1954.

Spoendlin, H.: Submikroskopische Strukturen im Cortischen Organ der Katze. Acta Otolaryngol., *52:*111, 1960.

Vinnikov, Y. A., and L. K. Titova: The Organ of Corti. (English translation.) New York, Consultant's Bureau, 1964.

Wersäll, J.: Studies on the structure and innervation of the sensory epithelium of the cristae ampullares in the guinea pig. Acta Otolaryngol., Suppl. 126, 1956.

Wersäll, J., and A. Flock: Physiological aspects on the structure of vestibular end organs. Acta Otolaryngol., Suppl. 192, 1964, p. 85.

Wersäll, J., A. Flock, and P-G. Lundquist: Structural basis for directional sensitivity in cochlear and vestibular sensory receptors. Cold Spring Harbor Symposium on Quantitative Biology, Vol. 30, Sensory Receptors, 1965, p. 133.

Wislocki, G. B., and A. J. Ladman: Selective and histochemical staining of the otolithic membranes, cupulae and tectorial membrane of the inner ear. J. Anat., *89:*3, 1955.

Wolff, D., R. J. Belucci, and A. A. Eggston: Microscopic Anatomy of the Temporal Bone. Baltimore, Williams & Wilkins Co., 1957.

Index

Page numbers in *italics* refer to illustrations